WIN A WEEKEND BREAK AND A YEAR'S SUPPLY OF IAMS PETFOOD

You could win a short break at one of the AA Pet Friendly Places to Stay, which includes two nights B&B based on two people sharing. Plus the winner will also receive a year's free supply of Iams petfood. Simply fill in your details below. By telling us a bit more about you and your pets we can send you relevant information in the future, to help keep your pet healthier for longer.

Title: Mr ☐ Mrs ☐ Miss ☐ Other ☐

First name: _____ Surname: _____

Address: _____

_____

_____ Postcode: _____

Email address (if you have one): _____

How many dogs do you own? ☐ How many cats do you own? ☐

	Pet 1	Pet 2	Pet 3	Pet 4
Name of pet				
Breed of pet				
Age of pet				
Weight of pet				
Gender of Pet				

Where do you buy your pet food most often?

Supermarket ☐ Pet Superstore ☐ Local pet shop ☐ Vet ☐

☐ Please tick the box if you do not wish to receive news of products or special offers

2005
Pet Friendly
Places to stay

This 4th edition published 2004

© Automobile Association Developments Limited 2004.
The Automobile Association Limited retains the copyright
in the current edition © 2004 and in all subsequent
editions, reprints and amendments to editions.

The information contained in this directory is sourced
entirely from the AA's establishment database, Information
Research, AA Hotel Services.

Maps prepared by the Cartography Department of
The Automobile Association.
Maps © Automobile Association Developments Limited 2004.

 Ordnance This product includes mapping data
Survey™ licensed from Ordnance Survey® with the
permission of the Controller of Her Majesty's Stationery
Office. © Crown copyright 2004.
All rights reserved. Licence number 399221.

This product includes mapping based upon data
licensed from Ordnance Survey of Northern
Ireland® reproduced by permission of the Chief
Executive, acting on behalf of the Controller of Her Majesty's
Stationery Office.
© Crown copyright 2004. Permit No. 40070

Republic of Ireland mapping based on Ordnance Survey
Ireland Permit No. MP002104 © Ordnance Survey Ireland
and Government of Ireland.

Main cover photograph courtesy of Ladyridge Farm
Guest House, Brockhampton

Editorial contributions from Anne O'Rorke

Typeset/Repro by Servis, Manchester

Printed and bound in Spain by Graficas Estella S.A., Navarra

Directory compiled by the AA Hotel Services Department
and generated from the AA establishment database.

www.theAA.com

To contact us:
Advertising Sales Department:
advertisingsales@the AA.com
Editorial Department: lifestyleguides@theAA.com
AA Hotel Services: 01256 844455

Published by AA Publishing, a trading name of Automobile
Association Developments Limited, whose registered office
is Southwood East, Apollo Rise, Farnborough, Hampshire
GU14 0JW. Registered number 1878835

A CIP catalogue record for this book is available from the
British Library

ISBN 0 7495 2233

A02156

Contents

Iams Prize draw … … … … … … … … … …1

Welcome to the guide … … … … … … … …6

AA Pet Friendly Hotel and Guest
Accommodation of the Year Awards … … … …7

How to Use this Guide … … … … … … …8

Symbols and Abbreviations … … … … … …9

Star and Diamond Classifications … … … …10

County Maps … … … … … … … … … …12

Useful Information … … … … … … … …15

Hotel Groups Information … … … … … …16

Pet Patrol … … … … … … … … … … …17

The Pet Travel Scheme … … … … … … …19

Holidays are Here with Iams … … … … …20

Animal Scrapbook … … … … … … … …26

Hotel Booking Service … … … … … … …28

DIRECTORY OF ACCOMMODATION

England … … … … … … … … … … …30

Channel Islands … … … … … … … … …260

Isle of Man … … … … … … … … … … …260

Scotland … … … … … … … … … … …262

Scottish Islands … … … … … … … … …300

Wales … … … … … … … … … … … …304

Ireland … … … … … … … … … … …331

Location Atlas … … … … … … … … …336

Index … … … … … … … … … … … …354

Welcome to the guide

This guide is perfect for pet owners who are reluctant to put their animals into kennels or catteries while they go on holiday. In these pages you can find places to stay in which not just cats and dogs are welcome – there is an increasing number of establishments, bed and breakfasts in particular, that have stables available. Again this year we have added information about kennels - look for this symbol which is given where an establishment has kennels:

As this guide shows, there are a great many hotels and bed and breakfasts that offer a warm welcome and an extensive range of facilities to both pet lovers and their animal companions. Though all the establishments listed have told us they are happy to admit animals, some go out of their way to make you and your pet feel at home, offering animal welcome packs, comfortable dog baskets, water bowls, special blankets, home-made treats

and comprehensive information on local country walks. Each year we highlight two of the very best places to stay with your pet, the winners appear on the opposite page.

Do remember though, that even the pet-friendliest of proprietors appreciate advance warning if you intend to bring your animal with you. See pages 17-25 for helpful hints and tips on planning your trip.

While summer is an obvious time to book a holiday, you might like to consider taking an off-peak break when animals – dogs in particular – are more likely to enjoy cooler temperatures and crowd-free destinations.

Whatever time of year you choose to go away, *AA Pet Friendly Places to Stay* is an essential guide to planning a break, offering a wide-ranging assortment of accommodation where every member of the family will be made welcome.

AA Pet Friendly Hotel & Guest Accommodation of the Year Awards in association with

These special awards are presented to two establishments that we found especially welcoming to pets and their owners. Standards of hospitality and facilities are improving all the time with more places offering extra special treats for people taking a break with their pet.
The winners for 2004-2005 are:

AA Pet Friendly Hotel of the Year

★★★ 圏圏圏

The Devonshire Arms Hotel, Bolton Abbey, North Yorkshire

This beautiful hotel set in the Yorkshire Dales is owned by the Duke and Duchess of Devonshire and dates back to the 17th century. Here the staff certainly think ahead if you're taking your pet along with you. When booking you can ask them to get in your pets' favourite brand of food, or they can prepare something homemade for them if preferred.
This is a wonderful place for a dog with a huge estate to explore, and the hotel admits it doesn't even mind them having a bit of mud on their paws. It has been reported that on occasion Louis, the very friendly spaniel-in-residence, has been known to look a little hurt when other dogs turn up to grab all the attention! **(See entry on page 241)**

AA Pet Friendly Guest Accommodation of the Year

◆◆◆◆

The Silverdale, Seaford, East Sussex

Owners Ted and Gilly Cowdrey are very happy to accommodate guests and their pets, and Bertie and Bessie, the resident American Cocker Spaniels will offer their own welcome too. For dog owners the first-floor double is recommended as it has its own conservatory with table and chairs just so visitors 'can spread out a bit'. On arrival thoughtful extras extend to a welcome pack with treats, a bowl for use in the bedroom and a list of local pubs and restaurants that are dog-friendly. And for peace of mind in case of the unthinkable mishap, Gilly even provides a pet tag with the B&B's address and telephone number on it. For walking, the beach is just four minutes away, and of course the glorious South Downs are within striking distance. **(See entry on page 211)**

How to Use this Guide

Explanation of entries and notes on abbreviations (see also the key opposite)

Sample Entry

1 — **ANY TOWN** **Map 00 NS00**

2 — 🐕 🐈 🐇 🐦 🐴 🏠

3 — **♦♦♦♦♦ Any Place**

Any Walk XX37 6XX
☎ 09689 24444144 📠 09689 24444145
e-mail: address@test.co.uk

4 — ***Dir:*** *on A422 900 yds NW of town centre*

5 — **PETS: Bedrooms £10 Pet Food Exercise area Dog walking service** RESIDENT PETS: Felix (Cat) Jessica and Bob (Springer Spaniels)

11

This welcoming family home is conveniently situated for exploring Any Town and the surrounding area. Bedrooms are comfortable and well equipped, and public areas are cosy and inviting. Good value cuisine is served in the conservatory restaurant. Breakfast features home-made sausages and freshly made bread.

6 — **ROOMS:** 19 en suite (3 fmly) (3GF) s £35-38; d £68-76 No smoking in bedrooms 7 **FACILITIES:** Indoor swimming (H) Fishing Pool table

8 — **PARKING:** 49 9 **NOTES:** RS Xmas 10 **CARDS:** 💳 💳 💳 💳

1 **Locations** The guide is divided into countries. Each country is listed in county order, and then in alphabetical town/village order within each county. A county map appears on pages 12-13 and there is an atlas at the back of the guide. The map reference in each entry gives the map page number, then the National Grid Reference. Read the first figure horizontally and the second figure vertically within the lettered square.

2 **Pets accommodated** Five special symbols show what kinds of animals are welcome - dogs, cats small caged animals, caged birds and horses.

🏠 - places that provide kennels

3 **The establishment name** is preceded by the star (hotels) or diamond (guest accommodation) rating and followed by the address, phone/fax numbers and e-mail address where applicable. (Please note that e-mail addresses are believed correct at the time of printing but may change during the currency of the guide.) Hotels also show a Quality Percentage Score to offer a comparison of quality within their star rating. The AA's Top 200 hotels are awarded Red Stars. These hotels stand out as the very best in the country, regardless of size or type of operation. The very best ten per cent of AA guest accommodation within the three, four and five Diamond rating levels are awarded Red Diamonds. Hotels and B&Bs may also have an AA Rosette award for food. Within each location, hotels are listed first, in descending order of stars and Quality Percentage Score, followed by B&Bs in descending order of diamonds. A company or consortium name or logo may appear.

4 **Dir:** Directions to the establishment are given where supplied to us.

5 **PET FACILITIES** are highlighted in a yellow box. **Charged** Some establishments charge a fee for accommodating your pet: if a price is shown, this represents the charge per animal per night. **Bedrooms** Most establishments allow pets to sleep in the same room as their owner, although they may not necessarily be left unattended. In some establishments, pets are housed in separate accommodation, such as kennels. If **Sep accom** (separate accommodation) appears, do ask for more information when booking to check that this will be suitable for your pet. **Public areas** Some establishments are happy to let your pet accompany you in public areas. Please note that animals are not usually allowed in dining rooms or restaurants. Any special facilities for pets are as stated. **Exercise area** The approximate distance from the nearest exercise area is shown. **Resident Pets** indicates the names and breeds of the proprietors' own pets.

⑥ ROOMS The first figure shows the number of en suite letting bedrooms, or total number of bedrooms, then the number with en suite facilities, and number of ground floor rooms. **Prices** (per room per night) are provided by proprietors in good faith and are indications not firm quotations. Breakfast is included in the price unless otherwise indicated. Some establishments only accept cheques if notice is given and a cheque card produced. Not all establishments take travellers cheques. (B&Bs only -* indicates 2004 prices)

⑦ FACILITIES Leisure facilities are as stated. **Child facilities** may include: baby intercom, babysitting service, playroom, playground, laundry, drying/ironing facilities, cots, high chairs, special meals. In some establishments children can sleep in parents' rooms at no extra cost; check all details when booking. Hotels only: Colour TV is provided in all bedrooms unless otherwise indicated.

⑧ PARKING Shows numbers of spaces available for guests' use. May include covered, charged spaces.

⑨ NOTES No children A minimum age may be given, e.g. 'No children 4 years'. If neither 'ch fac' (see FACILITIES) or 'no children' appears, the establishment accepts children but may not offer special facilities such as high chairs. Check before booking if you have very young children. **RS** Some establishments have a restricted service during quieter months, when some of the listed facilities are not available; ask when booking.
B&Bs only: Dinner indicates that dinner is available. Guests may have to order this in advance - please check when booking. **Licensed** indicates that the establishment is licensed to serve alcohol.

⑩ CARDS Credit cards may be subject to a surcharge; check when booking if this is how you intend to pay.

⑪ Photographs Establishments may choose to include a photograph with their entry.

Symbols and Abbreviations

PETS ACCOMMODATED

🐾	Dogs
🐱	Cats
🐹	Small caged animals, e.g. rabbits, hamsters
🐦	Caged birds
🐴	Stabling available
🐕	Kennels

AA AWARDS, RATINGS & OTHER ACCOMMODATION CATEGORIES

Hotels only

★	Star Classification (see page 10)
%	Quality Percentage score (see opposite page)
★	Red Stars indicate the AA's Top 200 hotels in Britain and Ireland (see opposite page)
U	Star rating not yet confirmed
⚘	Country House Hotel
🏠	Town House Hotel
🏠	Restaurant with Rooms
⇧	Travel Accommodation

B&Bs only

♦	Diamond Classification (see page 10)
♦	Red Diamond Award (see opposite page)
🐓	Farmhouse
🍺	Inn

Hotels and B&Bs

❀	AA Rosette Award for quality of food

ROOMS

s	Single room
d	Double room
LB	Special leisure breaks available

Bedroom restrictions are as stated, e.g. No smoking in 15 bedrooms

FACILITIES

TV	Television in bedrooms (B&Bs only)

Colour television is provided in all hotel bedrooms unless otherwise stated

STV	Satellite television
Indoor swimming (H)	Heated indoor swimming pool
Outdoor swimming (H)	Heated outdoor swimming pool
ch fac	Special facilities for children
Xmas	Special programme for Christmas/ New Year

Leisure facilities are as stated, e.g. Gym Fishing Croquet

NOTES

No children	Indicates that children cannot be accommodated
RS	Restricted service, e.g. RS Jan-Mar, Closed Xmas/ New Year

Other restrictions are as stated, e.g. No smoking in restaurant

CARDS

Cards accepted where symbols are shown

Star and Diamond Classifications

An important part of planning a holiday is knowing what amenities to expect of the hotel or bed and breakfast that you have booked. This is especially true when you are taking your pet along too. From the definitions listed below, you can be very sure of what to expect and make your choice accordingly.

All of the hotels and bed and breakfasts in this guide are inspected and rated by the AA Hotel Inspectors according to the Star and Diamond Classification schemes. These ratings ensure that your accommodation meets the AA's highest standards of cleanliness, with the emphasis on professionalism, proper booking procedures and a prompt and efficient service.

AA Star Classification

If you stay in a **one-star** hotel, you should expect a relatively informal yet competent style of service and an adequate range of facilities, including a television in the lounge or bedroom and a reasonable choice of hot and cold dishes. The majority of bedrooms are en suite, with a bath or shower room always available. A **two-star** hotel is run by smartly and professionally presented management and offers at least one restaurant or dining room for breakfast and dinner, while a **three-star** hotel includes direct-dial telephones, a wide selection of drinks in the bar and last orders for dinner no earlier than 8pm. A **four-star** hotel is characterised by uniformed, well-trained staff, with additional services, a night porter and a serious approach to cuisine. Finally, and most luxurious of all, is the **five-star** hotel, offering many extra facilities, attentive staff, top-quality rooms and a full concierge service. A wide selection of drinks, including cocktails, is available in the bar, and the impressive menu reflects and complements the hotel's own style of cooking.

AA Diamond Awards

The AA's Diamond Awards cover bed and breakfast establishments only, reflecting guest accommodation at five grades of quality, with one Diamond indicating the simplest, and five Diamonds at the upper end of the scale. The criteria for eligibility is guest care and quality rather than the choice of extra facilities. Establishments are vetted by a team of qualified inspectors to ensure that the accommodation, food and hospitality meets the AA's own exacting standards.

Guests should receive a prompt, professional check in and check out, comfortable accommodation equipped to modern standards, regularly changed bedding and towels, sufficient hot water supply at all times, good, well-prepared meals, and a full English or continental breakfast.

There's a better way to care for his heart.
And help keep it healthy for life.

County Maps

The county map shown here will help you identify the counties within each country. You can look up each county in the guide using the county names at the top of each page. To find towns featured in the guide use the atlas and the index.

England

1 Bedfordshire
2 Berkshire
3 Bristol
4 Buckinghamshire
5 Cambridgeshire
6 Greater Manchester
7 Herefordshire
8 Hertfordshire
9 Leicestershire
10 Northamptonshire
11 Nottinghamshire
12 Rutland
13 Staffordshire
14 Warwickshire
15 West Midlands
16 Worcestershire

Scotland

17 City of Glasgow
18 Clackmannanshire
19 East Ayrshire
20 East Dunbartonshire
21 East Renfrewshire
22 Perth & Kinross
23 Renfrewshire
24 South Lanarkshire
25 West Dunbartonshire

Wales

26 Blaenau Gwent
27 Bridgend
28 Caerphilly
29 Denbighshire
30 Flintshire
31 Merthyr Tydfil
32 Monmouthshire
33 Neath Port Talbot
34 Newport
35 Rhondda Cynon Taff
36 Torfaen
37 Vale of Glamorgan
38 Wrexham

Western Isles

Orkney Islands

Shetland Islands

Highland

Moray

Aberdeen City

Aberdeenshire

SCOTLAND

Angus

Perth & Kinross

Dundee City

Argyll & Bute

Stirling

Fife

East Lothian

Argyll & Bute

Stirling

18

22

Fife

25

20

Falkirk

Inverclyde

North Ayrshire

23

17

North Lanarkshire

West Lothian

City of Edinburgh

North Ayrshire

19

24

21

19

South Lanarkshire

Midlothian

Borders (Scottish)

Borders (Scottish)

South Ayrshire

Dumfries & Galloway

Northumberland

Tyne & Wear

Isle of Man

Cumbria

Durham

North Yorkshire

East Riding of Yorkshire

Lancashire

West Yorkshire

South Yorkshire

Isle of Anglesey

Merseyside

6

Derbyshire

Lincolnshire

Conwy

30

Cheshire

11

ENGLAND

29

38

Gwynedd

13

Norfolk

WALES

Shropshire

9

12

Ceredigion

Powys

15

14

10

5

Suffolk

Pembrokeshire

7

16

1

Carmarthenshire

4

8

Essex

Swansea

Gloucestershire

Oxfordshire

Greater London

33

26

32

31

36

2

Surrey

Kent

35

28

34

3

Wiltshire

Hampshire

27

Cardiff

Somerset

West Sussex

East Sussex

37

Devon

Dorset

Isle of Wight

Cornwall

Isles of Scilly

Guernsey

Jersey

0   20   40   60   80   100 miles

0   20 40 60 80 100 120 140 160 kilometres

Before you go anywhere, take a trip to Pets at Home.

Whatever your pet needs, cruise down to Pets at Home. With a comprehensive range of quality food, treats, toys and bedding, we've everything a pet could ask for every day of the year. And when it's holiday time, there's even a fantastic choice of accessories for pets on the move, including pet carriers, H20 'to go' water bottles, portable travel bowls, toothbrushes, travel blankets and more. Plus, if it's travel tips you're looking for, we can offer all the expert advice you need to ensure a smooth journey. Wherever you're heading, head for Pets at Home first.

Useful Information

BRITAIN

The Fire Precautions Act does not apply to the Channel Islands, Republic of Ireland, or the Isle of Man, which have their own rules. As far as we are aware, all establishments listed in Great Britain have applied for and not been refused a fire certificate.

Licensing laws differ in England, Wales, Scotland, the Republic of Ireland, the Isle of Man, the Isles of Scilly and the Channel Islands. Public houses are generally open from mid morning to early afternoon, and from about 6 or 7pm until 11pm, although closing times may be earlier or later and some pubs are open all afternoon. Unless otherwise stated, hotels listed in this guide are licensed. (For guest accommodation, please refer to the individual gazetteer entry. Note that licensed premises are not obliged to remain open throughout the permitted hours.) Hotel residents can obtain alcoholic drinks at all times, if the licensee is prepared to serve them. Non-residents eating at the hotel restaurant can have drinks with meals. Children under 14 (or 18 in Scotland) may be excluded from bars where no food is served. Those under 18 may not purchase or consume alcoholic drinks. A club licence means that drinks are served to club members only. 48 hours must elapse between joining and ordering.

Prices The AA encourages the use of the Hotel Industry Voluntary Code of Booking Practice, which aims to ensure that guests know how much they will have to pay and what services and facilities that includes, before entering a financially binding agreement. If the price has not previously been confirmed in writing, guests should be given a card stipulating the total obligatory charge when they register at reception.

The Tourism (Sleeping Accommodation Price Display) **Order of 1977** compels hotels, travel accommodation, guest houses, farmhouses, inns and self-catering accommodation with four or more letting bedrooms, to display in entrance halls the minimum and maximum prices charged for each category of room. Tariffs shown are the minimum and maximum for one or two persons but they may vary without warning.

NORTHERN IRELAND & REPUBLIC OF IRELAND

The Euro In 2002, Euro banknotes and coins came into circulation throughout the Republic of Ireland. Prices in the guide for accommodation in the Republic of Ireland are therefore shown in Euros.

The Fire Services (NI) Order 1984 covers establishments accommodating more than six people, which must have a certificate from the Northern Ireland Fire Authority. Places accommodating fewer than six persons need adequate exits. AA officials inspect emergency notices, fire-fighting equipment and fire exits here. Republic of Ireland safety regulations are a matter for local authority regulations. For your own and others' safety, read the emergency notices and be sure you understand them.

Licensing Regulations

Northern Ireland: public houses open Mon-Sat 11.30-23.00 and Sun 12.30-14.30 and 19.00-22.00. Hotels can serve residents without restriction. Non-residents can be served from 12.30-22.00 on Christmas Day. Children under 18 are not allowed in the bar area and may neither buy nor consume liquor in hotels.

Republic of Ireland: General licensing hours are Mon-Sat 10.30-23.00 (23.30 in summer). Sun and St Patrick's Day (17 March), 12.30-14.00 and 16.00-23.00. Hotels can serve residents without restriction. There is no service on Christmas Day (except for hotel residents) or Good Friday.

Telephone numbers: Area codes for numbers in the Republic of Ireland apply only within the Republic. If dialling from outside, check the telephone directory. Area codes for numbers in Britain and Northern Ireland cannot be used directly from the Republic.

Aku, Thatch Close, Ross on Wye

Hotel Groups Information

 Best Western **08457 73 73 73**

 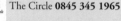 Campanile UK **0208 326 1500**
Campanile offers modern accommodation for the budget market

 The Circle **0845 345 1965**

 Classic British **0845 0 70 70 90**

 Copthorne **0800 414741**

CRERAR Crerar Hotels **08700 507 711**

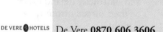 Courtyard By Marriott **0800 221 222**
or 0800 699 996

 Days Inn **0800 02 80 400**
Good quality modern budget accommodation at motorway services.
www.welcomebreak.co.uk

DE VERE HOTELS De Vere **0870 606 3606**

 Exclusive Hotels **01276 471774**

Forestdale Hotels Forestdale **0808 1449494**

 Handpicked Hotels **0800 9 177 877**

  Hanover International **01455 630000**

 Hotel Ibis UK **0870 6090963**
Ibis is a growing chain of modern travel accommodation with properties across the UK

THE INDEPENDENTS The Independents **0800 88 55 44**

 MACDONALD HOTELS Macdonald Hotels **0870 400 90 90**

 Malmaison **0207 479 9512 (Head Office)**

 Manor House Hotels **08705 300 200**
00 353 1 295 8900

 Marriott Hotels **0800 221 222**
0800 699 996

 Millennium **0800 41 47 41**

 Novotel **020 8283 4500**

 Old English Inns & Hotels **0800 917 3085**

  Peel Hotels **0800 1696128**

 Pride of Britain **01666 824666 (Head Office)**

 Red Carnation **020 7514 5633 (Head Office)**

 Relais et Chateaux **00 33 1 457 296 50**

 Scotland Hotels of Distinction
01333 360 888

 Small Luxury Hotels of the World
00800 525 48000
00 49 69 664 19601

 Tulip Inn

 Von Essen Hotel **01761 241631**

 Welcome Break **0800 731 4466**
Good-quality, modern, budget accommodation at motorway services.
www.welcomebreak.co.uk

 WREN'S HOTELS Wren's Hotel Group **01753 442 455**
(Head Office)

Pet Patrol

Some tips on taking your pet on holiday

At first, the prospect of taking your pet to a hotel or bed and breakfast may seem a little daunting - even if it is animal friendly. There is their welfare to think of and the responsibility of trying to ensure they fit comfortably into their new surroundings. Many proprietors have cats and dogs of their own and will quickly build up a good rapport with your pet. This can play a vital role in the success of your holiday, and if all goes well, owners who are genuine animal lovers will be welcoming you back year after year. On the whole, proprietors report favourably on their pet guests, often commenting that their behaviour is at least as good as their owners!

We all love our pets and want to give them the care they deserve, but holidays can mean a certain amount of stress for us and also for our pets. Changes in routine can upset an animal as much as its owner. This is why we ask our pet owners to take special care of their animals when staying away. Keep them to their regular mealtimes if possible and take plenty of water for them on your journey, especially when the weather is hot.

Remember that an animal shut in a strange hotel room for long periods may become distressed. We have stories from our hotels and B&Bs of dogs chewing up furniture or howling mournfully while their owners are out and these are symptoms of boredom and separation anxiety, particularly if your pet is a rescue animal.

On arrival, give your pet time to adjust to his new surroundings and if you think he will be upset and bark or howl, don't leave him alone in your room. You should keep your pet quiet at all times.

Watching our pets let off steam in a different environment is one of the pleasures of a good holiday, but it is important to remember that although they are cherished members of the family who provide many hours of fun and enjoyment, owners have a duty to ensure that their pet is kept under proper control at all times.

Always remember to advise the proprietor when booking that you intend bringing your pet with you. This gives you both the opportunity to establish whether the accommodation really is suitable for your pet's needs. Some hotels and B&Bs impose restrictions on the type, size or number of animals permitted; those that accept dogs may not accommodate larger breeds.

Not all rooms will necessarily be available to guests with animals and some rooms may be set aside for people with allergies.

When booking, you should also check the establishment's supervision policy. Some may require your pet to be caged when unattended, or may ask you not to leave your pet alone at all.

The gazetteer entry indicates whether you should expect to pay an additional charge or deposit for your pet, but we recommend that you confirm the amount when booking.

In the case of dogs, allowing them to socialise with people and other animals from an early age means that, under your supervision, they will be at ease with other residents and their pets during your stay. It's not uncommon to end up

Jessica, Wrangham House Hotel, North Yorkshire

swapping dog stories with guests or even members of staff. Lasting friendships are sometimes formed this way!

Unless otherwise indicated by the management, please don't allow your pet on the furniture, or *in* the bed. If he or she likes to sleep on the bed, remember to bring a sheet, a blanket or a bedspread of your own, unless the proprietor provides one. Remember also to take an old towel to dry your pet after a walk in the rain and don't use the bath or shower for washing your animal in.

Clean up after your pet immediately - inside the room and out - and leave no trace of them on departure. Take a supply of supermarket carrier bags with you and poop scoop anywhere in the hotel or grounds.Management will advise on disposal of the bags - some hotels/B&Bs have an animal toilet area and provide

Lucy & Tara, Tymawr Hotel, Gwynedd

bags. If something has been damaged by your pet, notify the management immediately.

It's really a case of simple common sense.

If the hotel/B&B allows you to take animals into public areas, be sure that you keep your pet under control at all times. Keep dogs on leads, especially when around small children. Your dog may be easily distracted by the sights and smells of unfamiliar surroundings, and may not respond to your commands as well as at home.

For your family holiday to be a complete success, you'll need to do a little research and planning. As well as finding somewhere suitable to stay, you might like to contact the tourist board for leaflets and brochures on pet-friendly places of interest. Remember to keep your dog under tight control when visiting local attractions.

Bear in mind that dogs need to be exercised regularly - even on holiday - and time should be set aside for this as often as possible, especially if they have

been travelling with you in the car for most of the day. Most country hotels and bed and breakfasts will have plenty of good walks on the doorstep, which makes the chore of exercising your dog that much more enjoyable. This is where old towels are essential for drying off wet, muddy feet and coats.

One final tip is to check your insurance for the level of cover it offers before taking your pet away. Pet insurance may not cover personal liability but your house insurance might. Should your pet chew the furniture or take a nip at a passing ankle, you would be well advised to have covered this eventuality by having the appropriate, up-to-date insurance policy.

Willow, Collaven Manor Hotel, Devon

Archie, Stoneycroft Hotel, Leicester

The Pet Travel Scheme

Pets are on the move. They now travel more often with their owners in the United Kingdom and, because of changes in quarantine regulations, pets can now be taken abroad and then return to the UK, subject to certain conditions.

This guide includes over 1,500 pet-friendly hotels and guest houses throughout the UK, solving the problem of what to do with your pet while you want to go on holiday. But what happens if you plan to go further afield - abroad perhaps? What are the regulations?

The Pet Travel Scheme (PETS), which only applies to cats, dogs and ferrets and certain other pets, enables pets resident in the UK to enter, without quarantine, certain countries throughout the world and then return to Britain. Thanks to the relaxation of quarantine controls in this country, they can go straight home on their arrival. However, in order to do so the scheme requires that your pet is fitted with a microchip, vaccinated against rabies and given a blood test. Before returning to the UK, your animal will also need to be treated against tapeworm and ticks.

For information on how to prepare your animal for the Pet Travel Scheme please contact the PETS Helpline (see below).

You should also think carefully about the welfare of your pet and whether a holiday abroad is appropriate. A leaflet on how to protect their welfare is available from the PETS Helpline and website.

Amongst those countries included in PETS are Austria, Belgium, Finland, Gibraltar, Spain, Portugal, Italy, Switzerland, New Zealand, Bermuda and Japan. Routes change, so check with the PETS Helpline. Pets resident anywhere in the UK can travel unrestricted within Britain and are not subject to quarantine regulations or the PETS rules unless they are entering the country from overseas.

PETS gives information about the microchip identity tag; guidance for pet owners and also for ferry/train and airlines on looking after pets during transport; routes you can travel on; help finding a vet; bringing your pet from a Long Haul country (pets travelling by air to the UK must travel in a container bearing an official seal); charges and lots more. Contact details below.

Remember, whether in the UK or abroad, animals can die if left in vehicles in direct sunshine or high temperatures.

For more information about PETS and travelling abroad with your pet, call the PETS Helpline on 0870 241 1710 between 8.30am and 5pm Monday to Friday; e-mail pets.helpline@dfra.gsi.gov.uk, or visit the PETS website at http://www.defra.gov.uk/animalh/quarantine/pets/contacts.htm.

HOLIDAYS ARE HERE!

Going away with your family is one of life's great pleasures. But one of the most treasured members of the family often gets left behind. With this guide, there is no longer any reason why you shouldn't take your faithful friend on holiday with you! And you can even take your cat, rabbit or feathered friend to some of these wonderful pet friendly locations.

We've 'sniffed out' some of the best places for you and your pet to stay throughout England, Scotland, Wales, Ireland and the Channel Islands. So wherever your travels take you, you're bound to end up in a comfy bed with your pet at your feet at the end of the day.

TRAVELLING INFO & TIPS

Preparations are the key for a happy and successful holiday....

Getting ready to go:
When packing a suitcase for your dog, stick to the essentials.
Things to take include:

- Pet bed; if it's too bulky, pack a familiar-smelling blanket to help him settle in his new environment
- Basic first aid kit
- A few toys to help your dog relax
- One or two towels to dry off muddy paws and a cloth just in case your dog has an accident
- A corkscrew stake so he doesn't wander off during any picnics
- An old sheet or blanket to throw over sofas or beds just in case your pet climbs on for a quick snooze
- Food and water bowls. Take a collapsible water bowl and water bottle with you as well so you can give your dog a drink during the journey
- For safety and comfort your cat should travel in a travel basket. And don't forget that your feline friend will also enjoy a few familiar toys and blankets too.
- Dried foods such as Iams are ideal to take away from home as they are easy to prepare, lighter to carry and less messy to dispose of than canned foods.

Before you set off:
Every animal is different, but many dogs are happier travelling after having eaten a small amount of food. Having eaten, don't forget to give your pet the opportunity to go to the toilet before you put him in the car.

Top tip:
Wherever you decide to go with your four-legged friend, remember to take his favourite toys with you. It will help him to relax and prevent him from getting frustrated.

Top tip:
Spoiling yourself and over-indulging is an intrinsic part of a holiday. However, changing your dog's feeding patterns could lead to an upset stomach, so don't treat him to unfamiliar foods, keep him on what he loves best - Iams. Keeping to your dog's regular feeding routine will also help him to enjoy himself.

Top tip:
In strange surroundings and places, there is always the small chance that your dog may become under the weather, and you may need to contact a vet. There is a register of all vets on www.findavet.org.uk, which means you are never far from emergency care and professional advice.

IAMS

Travelling by car

Long journeys may mean that your dog will spend more time in the car than he's used to. Travel boxes are one of the safest ways for your dog to travel and allows him to have his own space in the car.

Think about breaking up the journey if your dog isn't used to spending long periods of time in the car. Plan rest stops every couple of hours where you and your pet can stretch your legs. Keep your dog on a lead when near traffic though – even in car parks.

Make sure that your pet has enough ventilation at all times. Dogs find it difficult to regulate their own body temperature so never leave your dog in a car in hot weather, even with the windows open.

Travelling by train

Dogs are welcome on most mainline trains provided that they do not cause inconvenience to other customers or to staff. You should keep your dog on a lead at all times and you may be charged for the use of a seat if your dog travels in a carrier. Do try to avoid travelling during the rush hour though as your fellow passengers might not be as dog friendly as you'd like them to be!

ENJOYING THE GREAT OUTDOORS

There's nothing better than going for a long walk with your dog whilst on holiday with long lazy days stretching ahead of you. Extensive research has shown that walking regularly can not only improve your general health, but also reduce the risk of cardiovascular disease, so get out there and enjoy some of the most beautiful countryside in the world.

Although you might feel that you are in the middle of nowhere, there might still be restrictions on where you can walk your dog, so make sure that you check.

Important Countryside Rules:

Don't drop litter
Leave gates as you find them (either open or closed)
Don't let your dog worry livestock

HELP KEEP YOUR PET ACTIVE FOR LONGER

Combined with exercise, the correct diet can make all the difference to your pet's overall health. Iams is a complete food and contains all the goodness that your pet will ever need, no matter what his lifestage or lifestyle.

And Iams can also help your dog and cat to remain healthy for longer. Just like middle-age in humans, changes start to occur in the metabolism and physiology of your pet from 7 years of age.

One of these changes will be a reduction in joint function and mobility, because your pet's limbs will have reduced shock absorption, lubrication and resistance to joint compression. This may result in your pet being less willing or able to run, jump and play.

So making sure your dog's or cat's joints are healthy is critical as they start to mature. And with healthy flexible joints, 'walkies' will still be the word that sends your dog trembling with excitement.

Iams Active Maturity 7+ has been specifically designed to provide essential nutrition for pets aged between 7 and 11 years old, helping to support healthy joints to keep them active for longer.

They now say that in humans life begins at fifty – and with Active Maturity 7+ your dog or cat can enjoy the same privilege!

Before travelling with your dog you should check his overall health and fitness. There's nothing worse than being ill away from home! You can use this Iams MOT Health Check as a guide on what you should be looking out for in your pet's health. We have marked with an asterisk the areas where you should see a difference after feeding Iams for three weeks. If this check alerts you to any health issues please do contact your vet for a more thorough examination. Even if your pet seems healthy we strongly recommend you schedule regular check ups with your vet. You can also check your cat using the same criteria.

EYES* – Should be clear and sparkling without any discharge or redness as this could be a sign of infection. The eyelids should also be checked for warts or cysts.

EARS – The inside of your dog's ears should be clean with no odour. If they do smell this could be a sign that they are infected. A dog's ears should be cleaned regularly – ask your vet to recommend a cleaning product and just as importantly, the best way to clean them without damage.

MUZZLE – The nose should be free of discharge

TEETH & GUMS* – Gently lift your dog's lips – the gums should be salmon pink, (some dogs have naturally black pigmented gums). Teeth should be clean and white with no yellow plaque or tartar and there should not be a bad smell! Iams with DentalCare doesn't just work on the chewing teeth, but all teeth. Minerals are released when your pet chews, which help reduce tartar build-up, helping to keep every tooth clean, every day. Your vet might recommend dental cleaning or dog toothpaste. A vet should also take care of any loose teeth or bleeding gums.

COAT & SKIN* – The coat should look glossy and feel tangle free, not dull. The skin should not feel greasy or look flaky (no dandruff).

BODY CHECKS – Check for any lumps or wounds by running your hands over your dog's body. Part the hair to check for signs of fleas or ticks. Check a dog's testicles and a bitch's mammary glands for any unusual swellings.

WEIGHT – Be aware of what weight your dog should be and monitor it carefully – overfeeding can be just as damaging as underfeeding. As a general rule run your hands down the sides of your dog's belly and you should be able to feel the rib cage. By feeling your dog's rib cage you should be able to tell if he is under, over or just right! If your dog does seem overweight, check with your vet who may recommend a Light food.

PAWS – Check the pads for open cuts, splinters or seeds which can become embedded. Nails should be short and healthy looking without any splitting.

UNDER THE TAIL* – Hold up the tail and see if there are any signs of soreness or discharge. Also check your dog's stools, they should be firm and fairly small – this is a good sign of healthy digestion.

ENERGY* – Dependent on his age, your dog should be alert and energetic without any signs of stiffness or breathlessness. Any reluctance to exercise should be looked into.

HAPPY HOLIDAYS

The United Kingdom boasts some of the most spectacular places to visit, so there are lots of exciting times ahead for you and your dog. From the Highlands of Scotland to the beaches of Cornwall, there are miles of beautiful countryside to explore.

Always be aware of your pet's capabilities – you may be determined to conquer England's highest peak, however, your dog may just not be up to it, due to age, health or size.

Also be aware that some walks and sights have restrictions on dogs, so always look out for signs and carry a lead. Even better – do your homework and check that your chosen place to visit is as dog-friendly as you are.

And if you are the city type, then your pooper-scooper is a vital piece of equipment. Although the less glamorous side of caring for your pet, it is vital to ensure the area remains as clean as you would like to find it!

Most importantly, have fun with your four-legged friend. Playing games is fun for both of you, and can involve all your friends and family too. So get out that Frisbee or ball and have a throw around.

There's nothing better than going on holiday with your pet. Not only will you discover amazing new places together, you will also bring home some treasured memories.

Our team of dedicated nutrition advisors are always on hand to help you with any queries that you might have about your pet and Iams. If you would like any advice please call the **Iams Careline on 0808 100 70 10** and speak to our team of experts, Monday to Friday between 9am and 5pm.

With all these fantastic places to stay, you are sure to have a few happy tales to tell. If you have any recommendations or would like to tell us about a particularly enjoyable holiday with your pet, write to us at Iams, Good Relations, Holborn Gate, 26 Southampton Buildings, London, WC2A 1PQ.

For more general information please visit our web site at **www.iams.com** where you can find feeding guidelines, top tips and all the latest news from Iams.

Animal Scrapbook

Well, it's time to think about holidays again and, where you can take your pet. As usual there are a surprising number of hotels and bed and breakfasts in these pages that open their doors to visitors and their animals. Whether you have a horse or donkey, dog or cat, hamster or goldfish, you and your pet can find welcoming places to stay, most of which have animals of their own on the premises.

We also give you a taste of some interesting menus available for hungry animals, and some pet stories.

Munchy Menus

At St Fillans, Perthshire, the canine à la carte includes: Bugs Bunny and Carrots, Rooster and Rice, and Hairy Hamish's Highland Haggis.

Down in Newquay, at the Headland Hotel, a visiting dog had scrambled egg ordered for him for breakfast, and at Dryburgh Abbey Hotel, St Boswells, the owner of two visiting Wolfhounds ordered them full, cooked English breakfasts.

Perhaps the grandest menu comes from Cliveden in Taplow. Their K9 guests are offered: Noisettes of meat with Sauce Aromatique, followed by a Trio of Lights, Spleen and Lungs

Delicious!

Crackers about each other

Love birds (the feathered variety) Sticky and Fluffy dance together - stamping and rushing backwards at full speed and singing with heads held high. Both watch television and sing loudly to the Eastenders signature tune.

Hungry hound

Trixie, called small by her owner when booking in, turned out to be the size of a Shetland pony. After a series of mishaps, Trixie shot into the kitchen, snatched an apple pie, grabbed the cooling roast pork from the table and made off. 'She's only a puppy' her adoring owner volunteered.

At their farm at Cardington, Church Stretton, Chris and George Brandon-Lodge breed Gordon Setters and English Springer Spaniels and have a Crufts entry for 2005. Pictured here under the plum tree are setters Clover and Saffron. They've been labelled plum thieves, but seem to be taking a rest for a few minutes.
North Hill Farm, Church Stretton

Clover and Saffron, North Hill Farm

Willow, a young, short-haired tortoiseshell cat, is thoroughly modern, microchipped and ready for a bit of travel. People-friendly and playful, she enjoys indulging her main personality trait - curiosity.
Collaven Manor Hotel, Sourton (see her picture on p.18).

Resident 'pub dog' Ben is half Whippet and half Labrador and is getting on a bit. In his time he's seen off burglars and also, has kindly given up his garden for visiting dogs to enjoy. In his younger days his escapades included one where he jumped over a wall, crashed through a Perspex window and landed on a kitchen table, giving his owner a £600 bill to pay!
The Black Cock Inn, Broughton-in-Furness

This is Amber, the Bassett Hound, who lives with Alfie, also a Bassett, and Sindy, a Black Labrador – they are the best of friends and love all the attention from the staff and guests alike. They're a docile bunch but at breakfast time they really show lots of enthusiasm at the hotel's kitchen door, when the chef or the waitress serves them their own special sausages!
Tyacks Hotel, Camborne, Cornwall

Teddy & Harry, Ees Wyke Country House

Amber, Tyacks Hotel

Two Old English Sheepdogs, Teddy and Harry, live at Ees Wyke, but look as if they would be at home on the polar ice cap.
Ees Wyke Country House, Near Sawrey

Meet the real McCoy - a soft-coated Wheaten terrier who is known for his skill at hoovering up crumbs after service. He's particularly keen on the homemade shortbread biscuits, treats that are made every day for visitors.
Knife and Cleaver Inn, Bedford

Elma, The Old Rectory

McCoy, Knife and Cleaver Inn

Elma, a Golden Labrador aged six, has been a proud mum no less than 3 times! She is very much loved by the family and is a favourite with the guests too.
The Old Rectory, Lacock, Wiltshire

There are facilities for horses at the stables at Farley Farm, and 1,100 acres of woodland nearby for riding, or walking dogs. The owners breed Border terriers, the youngest of which is called Hunny and teams up for a game with resident pony Tigger.
Farley Farm, Matlock

ENGLAND

The Ridgeway, Berkshire

England

ENGLAND

BEDFORDSHIRE

ASPLEY GUISE
Map 04 SP93

★★★ 69% **Moore Place**

The Square MK17 8DW

☎ 01908 282000 📠 01908 281888

e-mail: manager@mooreplace.com

Dir: M1 junct 13, take A507 signed Aspley Guise & Woburn Sands. Hotel on left side of village square

PETS: Bedrooms

This impressive Georgian house, set in delightful gardens in the village centre, is very conveniently located for the M1. Bedrooms do vary in size, but consideration has been given to guest comfort, with many thoughtful extras provided. There is a wide range of meeting rooms and private dining options.

ROOMS: 39 en suite 27 annexe en suite (16 GF) No smoking in 45 bedrooms s £55-£105; d £75-£200 (incl. bkfst) **LB**

FACILITIES: Xmas **PARKING:** 70 **NOTES:** No smoking in restaurant

CARDS: 💳

BEDFORD
Map 04 TL04

◆◆◆◆ ⊛ ⊜ ▇ **Knife & Cleaver**

The Grove, Houghton Conquest MK45 3LA

☎ 01234 740387 📠 01234 740900

e-mail: info@knifeandcleaver.com

Dir: turn off A6 signed Houghton Conquest, 5m S of Bedford. Inn opposite church in village

PETS: Bedrooms (unattended) Exercise area

RESIDENT PETS: McCoy (Wheaten Terrier)

In a pleasant village setting, this relaxing restaurant-with-rooms consists of a cosy bar and an elegant conservatory restaurant. Interesting dishes are offered, complemented by a good wine list. Bedrooms come in a variety of styles, located in a garden annexe, all comfortably appointed and well-equipped; deluxe rooms are particularly good.

FACILITIES: 9 annexe en suite (1 fmly) (9 GF) No smoking in 2 bedrooms No smoking in dining room STV TVB tea/coffee Direct dial from bedrooms Cen ht No coaches Dinner Last d 9.30pm

PRICES: s £53-£63; d £68-£78✳ **PARKING:** 35

NOTES: Closed 27-30 Dec rs Sun evening

CARDS: 💳

DUNSTABLE
Map 04 TL02

★★★ 65%

Hanover International Hotel

Church St LU5 4RT

☎ 01582 662201 📠 01582 696422

e-mail: gerard.virlombier@hanover-international.com

Dir: M1 junct 11 and take A505. Hotel 2m on right opp Priory church

PETS: Pets accepted by prior arrangement Bedrooms £10

Meeting the needs of a regular business trade, this hotel is ideally located close to the town centre and has ample private parking. Public areas include a comfortably furnished bar lounge and an

continued

attractive air-conditioned restaurant. Bedrooms are available in a variety of styles, club and executive rooms being the most plush.

ROOMS: 68 en suite (7 fmly) (21 GF) No smoking in 36 bedrooms s £60-£109; d £119-£149 (incl. bkfst) **LB FACILITIES:** STV Xmas **SERVICES:** Lift **PARKING:** 70 **NOTES:** No dogs (ex guide dogs) No smoking in restaurant **CARDS:** 💳

WOBURN
Map 04 SP93

★★★ 73% ⊛ **The Inn at Woburn**

George St MK17 9PX

☎ 01525 290441 📠 01525 290432

e-mail: enquiries@theinnatwoburn.com

Dir: M1 junct 13, left to Woburn, at Woburn left at T-junct, hotel in village

PETS: Bedrooms (unattended) Exercise area (50 yards)

This inn has been substantially refurbished and provides a high standard of accommodation. Bedrooms are divided between the original house, a modern extension and some stunning cottage suites. Public areas include the beamed, club-style Tavistock Bar, a range of meeting rooms and an attractive restaurant with interesting dishes on offer.

ROOMS: 50 en suite 7 annexe en suite (4 fmly) (21 GF) No smoking in 19 bedrooms s £105-£125; d £120-£180 **LB FACILITIES:** STV Golf 54 Access to Woburn Safari Park and Woburn Abbey Xmas **PARKING:** 80 **NOTES:** No children No smoking in restaurant

CARDS: 💳

BERKSHIRE

ASCOT
Map 04 SU96

★★★★ 66% ⊛ **The Berystede**

Bagshot Rd, Sunninghill SL5 9JH

☎ 0870 400 8111 📠 01344 872301

e-mail: berystede@macdonald-hotels.co.uk

MACDONALD HOTELS

Dir: A30/B3020 (Windmill Pub). Continue 1.25m to hotel on left just before junct with A330

PETS: Bedrooms (unattended) £10 Public areas (lounge only) Exercise area (on site)

This impressive Victorian mansion, close to Ascot Racecourse, is set in nine acres of wooded grounds. Spacious bedrooms have comfortable armchairs and internet facilities for guest use. There is a cosy bar and fine traditional restaurant, which overlooks the heated outdoor swimming pool and gardens. An excellent range of modern meeting rooms is available.

ROOMS: 90 en suite (26 fmly) (20 GF) No smoking in 58 bedrooms s £55-£170; d £108-£200 (incl. bkfst) **LB FACILITIES:** STV Outdoor swimming (H) Croquet lawn Putting green Full leisure complex from July 2005 Xmas **SERVICES:** Lift **PARKING:** 240 **NOTES:** No smoking in restaurant **CARDS:** 💳

> **All information was correct at the time of going to press; we recommend you confirm details on booking**

COOKHAM DEAN Map 04 SU88

🐕

The Inn on the Green Garry Hollihead

The Old Cricket Common SL6 9NZ

☎ 01628 482638 📠 01628 487474

e-mail: reception@theinnonthegreen.com

Dir: *A404 towards Marlow High St. Cross suspension bridge towards Bisham. 1st left into Quarry Wood Rd, right Hills Lane, right at Memorial Cross*

PETS: **Bedrooms (unattended)**

This charming English country inn enjoys a peaceful location in a beautiful rural Berkshire village. Individually designed stylish bedrooms, some located round a delightful courtyard, retain many original features and are equipped with lots of thoughtful extras. Imaginative, noteworthy food is served in the attractive wood panelled dining room.

ROOMS: 9 en suite (4 GF) s £120-£185; d £130-£195 (incl. bkfst) **LB**
FACILITIES: Spa STV Jacuzzi Xmas **PARKING:** 50
CARDS:

HUNGERFORD Map 04 SU36

🐕 🐈 🐇 🐦

♦♦♦♦ Crown & Garter

Great Common, Inkpen RG17 9QR

☎ 01488 668325

e-mail: gill.hern@btopenworld.com

Dir: *turn off A4 into Kintbury, turn opposite corner stores onto Inkpen Road, straight ahead for 2m, do not turn off this road*

PETS: **Bedrooms Public areas (except dining room) Exercise area (surrounding countryside)** RESIDENT PETS: Amber & Tabitha - black cats, fish pond

Peacefully located in the attractive village of Inkpen, this 17th-century inn maintains its charm particularly in the hop draped bar where an interesting range of well-prepared dishes are offered. The bedrooms, which are located around a pretty garden, offer a more contemporary style and are well equipped and comfortable.

FACILITIES: 8 annexe en suite (8 GF) No smoking in bedrooms No smoking in dining room TVB tea/coffee Cen ht No coaches Dinner Last d 9.30pm **PRICES:** s fr £50; d fr £70✱ **LB** **PARKING:** 40
CARDS:

Please mention AA Pet Friendly Places to Stay when booking

Don't forget to let proprietors know when you book that you're bringing your pet

All AA listed accommodation, restaurants and pubs can be found on the AA's website www.theAA.com

🐕 🐈 🐇 🐦

♦♦♦ Beacon House

Bell Ln, Upper Green, Inkpen RG17 9QJ

☎ 01488 668640 📠 01488 668640

e-mail: l.g.cave@classicfm.net

Dir: *A4 Newbury-Hungerford, S turn to Kintbury/Inkpen. At Kintbury, left (Inkpen Rd), 1m to x-rds, straight ahead, bear right to common, 3rd left after Crown & Garter pub*

PETS: **Bedrooms (unattended) Exercise area (adjacent)**
RESIDENT PETS: Shadow & Bilbo - spaniels, Joby & Jennie - donkeys

This large house has been owned by the same family for many years and is set in peaceful countryside. Bedrooms, comfortably furnished, overlook the fields and there is a spacious lounge for guests to relax in. Fresh produce from the garden is a feature of the carefully prepared meals, whilst hospitality is warm and genuine.

FACILITIES: 3 rms No smoking TVB Cen ht TVL No coaches Art Studio & Gallery Dinner Last d 4pm **PRICES:** s £25; d £50✱ **LB** **PARKING:** 6

MAIDENHEAD Map 04 SU88

🐕 🐈

★★ 69% Elva Lodge

Castle Hill SL6 4AD

☎ 01628 622948 📠 01628 778954

e-mail: reservations@elvalodgehotel.co.uk

Dir: *A4 out of Maidenhead towards Reading. Hotel at top of hill on left*

PETS: **Bedrooms £5 Public areas (except restaurant) Exercise area (0.5m) Pet Food** RESIDENT PETS: Buster (Terrier)

Within easy reach of the town centre, this family-run hotel offers a warm welcome and friendly service. Bedrooms are pleasantly decorated and equipped with thoughtful extras. Spacious public areas include a smart, stylish lounge, a bar and the Lion's Brasserie, which offers a wide range of popular dishes.

ROOMS: 26 rms (23 en suite) (1 fmly) (5 GF) No smoking in 6 bedrooms s £55-£95; d £70-£108 (incl. bkfst) **FACILITIES:** Reduced rates at local Leisure Centre **PARKING:** 32 **NOTES:** No smoking in restaurant Closed 24-30 Dec **CARDS:**

England

MEMBURY MOTORWAY SERVICE AREA (M4) Map 04 SU37

🏠 **Days Inn**
Membury Service Area RG17 7TZ
☎ 01488 72336 📠 01488 72336
e-mail: membury.hotel@welcomebreak.co.uk
Dir: M4 between junct 14&15

PETS: Bedrooms Public areas (Only to get to rooms) Exercise area (adjacent)

This modern building offers accommodation in smart, spacious and well-equipped bedrooms, suitable for families and business travellers, and all with en suite bathrooms. Continental breakfast is available and other refreshments may be taken at the nearby family restaurant. For further details see the Hotel Groups page.
ROOMS: 38 en suite s £40-£60; d £40-£60

PANGBOURNE   Map 04 SU67

★★★ 75% ◉◉
The Copper Inn Hotel and Restaurant
RG8 7AR
☎ 0118 984 2244 📠 0118 984 5542
e-mail: reservations@copper-inn.co.uk
Dir: M4 junct 12 take A4 W then A340 to Pangbourne. Hotel next to church at junct of A329 & A340

Best Western

PETS: Bedrooms

This 19th-century coaching inn is well known for its high standards of hotel keeping. Public rooms include a popular and lively bar, a quiet lounge and lovely restaurant where service is friendly and efficient. Well-equipped bedrooms, many of which overlook the secluded rear gardens, are comfortably appointed and individually decorated.
ROOMS: 14 en suite 8 annexe en suite (1 fmly) (4 GF) No smoking in all bedrooms s £50-£90; d £50-£110 LB **FACILITIES:** STV Xmas
PARKING: 20 **NOTES:** No smoking in restaurant
CARDS: 💳💳💳💳💳💳

READING   Map 04 SU77

★★★★ 74% ◉◉
Millennium Madejski Hotel Reading
Madejski Stadium RG2 0FL
☎ 0118 925 3500 📠 0118 925 3501
e-mail: sales.reading@mill-cop.com
Dir: M4 junct 11 onto A33, follow signs for Madejski Complex

MILLENNIUM
HOTELS AND RESORTS

PETS: Bedrooms Exercise area

A stylish hotel, that features an atrium lobby with specially commissioned water sculpture, is part of the Madejski stadium complex, home to both Reading Football and London Irish Rugby teams. Bedrooms are appointed with spacious workstations and plenty of amenities; there is also a choice of suites and a club floor with its own lounge. The hotel also has an award-winning, fine dining restaurant.
ROOMS: 140 en suite (4 fmly) No smoking in 92 bedrooms s £195; d £195 LB **FACILITIES:** Spa STV Indoor swimming (H) Sauna Solarium Gym Jacuzzi Stadium - home to Reading FC and London Irish RFC **SERVICES:** Lift air con **PARKING:** 150 **NOTES:** RS Xmas & New Yr
CARDS: 💳💳💳💳💳💳

★★★ 71%
Courtyard by Marriott Reading
Bath Rd, Padworth RG7 5HT
☎ 0870 400 7234 📠 0870 400 7334
Dir: M4 junct 12 onto A4 towards Newbury. Hotel 3.5m on left, after petrol station

COURTYARD

PETS: Bedrooms Public areas Exercise area

This purpose-built hotel combines the benefits of a peaceful rural location with the accessibility afforded by good road links. Modern comforts include air-conditioned bedrooms and rooms with easy access for less mobile guests. A feature of the hotel is its pretty courtyard garden, which can be seen from the restaurant.
ROOMS: 50 en suite (25 GF) No smoking in 45 bedrooms s £50-£110; d £50-£110 LB **FACILITIES:** STV Gym Fitness room Xmas
SERVICES: air con **PARKING:** 200 **NOTES:** No smoking in restaurant
CARDS: 💳💳💳💳💳💳

SONNING   Map 04 SU77

★★★ 69% **The Great House at Sonning**
Thames St RG4 6UT
☎ 0118 969 2277 📠 0118 944 1296
e-mail: greathouse@btconnect.com
Dir: exit A4 at rdbt with Texaco Garage & take B478 into Sonning (signed). Through village, over mini rdbt, down steep hill and bear right. Hotel on right, before bridge

PETS: Bedrooms (unattended) Exercise area (adjacent) Pet Food

This characteristic property enjoys a riverside location with a mile and a half of private mooring and attractive terraces and lawns, making it a popular wedding venue. Comfortable, well-equipped bedrooms are situated either in the main house or set in various buildings located round an attractive courtyard. A choice of bars and restaurants are available as well as al fresco dining on the terrace.
ROOMS: 12 en suite 37 annexe en suite (11 GF) s £129-£169; d £149-£199 (incl. bkfst) LB **FACILITIES:** STV entertainment ch fac
PARKING: 120 **NOTES:** RS 27 Dec-9 Jan
CARDS: 💳💳💳💳💳💳

STREATLEY   Map 04 SU58

★★★★ 69% ◉◉ **The Swan at Streatley**
High St, Streatley on Thames RG8 9HR
☎ 01491 878800 📠 01491 872554
e-mail: sales@swan-at-streatley.co.uk
Dir: from S right at lights in Streatley, Swan on left before bridge

PETS: Bedrooms (unattended) £15 Public areas (except restaurant) Exercise area

A stunning location set beside the Thames, ideal on an English summer's day. Many bedrooms enjoy the views and rooms are well appointed. The hotel offers a range of facilities including meeting rooms, plus there's the 'Streatley Belle', moored beside the hotel, which makes an unusual venue. Cuisine is accomplished and dining here is not to be missed.
ROOMS: 46 en suite (13 GF) No smoking in 9 bedrooms s fr £99; d £138-£218 (incl. bkfst) **FACILITIES:** STV Indoor swimming (H) Fishing Sauna Solarium Gym Croquet lawn Jacuzzi Electric motor launches for hire Xmas **PARKING:** 170 **NOTES:** No smoking in restaurant
CARDS: 💳💳💳💳💳💳

England

WINDSOR
Map 04 SU97

★★★ 74% ◉◉ **The Castle**
18 High St SL4 1LJ
☎ 0870 400 8300 📠 01753 830244
e-mail: castle@macdonald-hotels.co.uk
Dir: M4 junct 6/M25 junct 15 - follow signs to Windsor town centre and castle. Hotel at top of hill by castle opp Guildhall

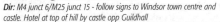
MACDONALD HOTELS

PETS: Bedrooms £15 Exercise area (adjacent)

The Castle Hotel is one of the oldest hotels in Windsor, beginning life as a coaching inn in the middle of the 16th century. Located opposite the Castle, it is an ideal base from which to explore the town. Bedrooms are traditional in style and include four-poster and executive rooms. Guests have a choice of formal and informal dining options and an all-day lounge menu.
ROOMS: 41 en suite 70 annexe en suite (18 fmly) No smoking in 50 bedrooms s fr £175; d fr £175 (incl. bkfst) **LB FACILITIES:** STV Xmas **SERVICES:** Lift air con **PARKING:** 100 **NOTES:** No smoking in restaurant **CARDS:** 💳💳💳💳💳💳

★★★ 69% **Royal Adelaide**
46 Kings Rd SL4 2AG
☎ 01753 863916 📠 01753 830682
e-mail: royaladelaide@meridianleisure.com
Dir: M4 junct 6, A322 to Windsor. 1st left off rdbt into Clarence Rd. At 4th lights right into Sheet St and into Kings Rd. Hotel on right

PETS: Bedrooms (unattended) £10 Exercise area
RESIDENT PETS: Misha & Zara (Toy Poodles)

This attractive Georgian-style hotel has seen much renovation and enhancement. Close to the town centre and with parking, it offers tastefully furnished and well-equipped bedrooms. Public areas include a range of meeting rooms, a bar and an elegant restaurant.
ROOMS: 38 en suite 4 annexe en suite (5 fmly) No smoking in 12 bedrooms s £60-£99; d £79-£119 (incl. bkfst) **LB FACILITIES:** STV Xmas **SERVICES:** air con **PARKING:** 22 **NOTES:** No smoking in restaurant **CARDS:** 💳💳💳💳💳💳

◆◆◆ **Clarence Hotel**
9 Clarence Rd SL4 5AE
☎ 01753 864436 📠 01753 857060
Dir: M4 junct 6 follow dual-carriageway to Windsor, turn left at 1st rdbt into Clarence Rd

PETS: Bedrooms Exercise area (100yds)

This Grade II listed Victorian townhouse is situated in the heart of Windsor. Space in some rooms is limited, but all are well maintained and offer excellent value for money. Added facilities include a lounge with well stocked bar and steam room. Breakfast is served in the dining room overlooking attractive gardens.
FACILITIES: 20 en suite (6 fmly) (2 GF) No smoking in dining room TVB tea/coffee Licensed Cen ht TVL Sauna Steam room
PRICES: s £40-£62; d £49-£72✱ **PARKING:** 4
CARDS: 💳💳💳💳💳

All abbreviations are explained on page 9

BRISTOL
Map 03 ST57

★★★ 70% ◉ **Arno's Manor**
470 Bath Rd, Arno's Vale BS4 3HQ
☎ 0117 971 1461 📠 0117 971 5507
e-mail: arnos.manor@forestdale.com

Forestdale Hotels

PETS: Bedrooms (unattended) £7.50 Public areas (not in restaurant/bar) Pet Food

Once the home of a wealthy merchant, this historical 18th-century building is now a comfortable hotel and offers spacious, well-appointed bedrooms with plenty of workspace. The lounge was once the chapel and has many original features, while meals are taken in the atmospheric, conservatory-style restaurant.
ROOMS: 73 en suite (1 fmly) (7 GF) s fr £95; d fr £120 (incl. bkfst) **LB FACILITIES:** STV Xmas **SERVICES:** Lift **PARKING:** 200 **NOTES:** No smoking in restaurant
CARDS: 💳💳💳💳💳💳

★★★ 68% **Berkeley Square**
15 Berkeley Square, Clifton BS8 1HB
☎ 0117 925 4000 📠 0117 925 2970
e-mail: berkeleysquare@bestwestern.co.uk
Dir: M32 follow Clifton signs. 1st left at traffic lights by Wills Memorial Tower (University) into Berkeley Sq

Best Western

PETS: Bedrooms (unattended) Public areas (not in restaurant/bar) Exercise area (in front of hotel) Pet Food

Set in a peaceful square close to the university, art gallery and Clifton village, this smart, elegant Georgian hotel has tastefully decorated bedrooms that include many welcome extras. There is a busy bar in the basement, and the restaurant features interesting dishes from a choice of menus.
ROOMS: 42 en suite (1 fmly) No smoking in 17 bedrooms s £54-£116; d £90-£127 (incl. bkfst) **LB FACILITIES:** STV complimentry use of local gym and swimming pool **SERVICES:** Lift **PARKING:** 20
NOTES: No smoking in restaurant
CARDS: 💳💳💳💳💳💳

★★★ 66% **The Avon Gorge**
Sion Hill, Clifton BS8 4LD
☎ 0117 973 8955 📠 0117 923 8125
e-mail: info@avongorge-hotel-bristol.com
Dir: M5 junct 19, follow signs for Clifton Toll, over suspension bridge, 1st right into Sion Hill

PEEL HOTELS

PETS: Bedrooms Exercise area Pet bowls provided but no food

Overlooking Avon Gorge and Brunel's famous suspension bridge, this popular hotel offers rooms with glorious views. Bedrooms are very well equipped and have extras such as ceiling fans. Public areas include a traditional restaurant and a popular modern bar and brasserie, both overlooking a large outdoor terraced area.
ROOMS: 76 en suite (6 fmly) No smoking in 30 bedrooms s £120; d £130 (incl. bkfst) **LB FACILITIES:** STV Childrens activity play area Xmas **SERVICES:** Lift **PARKING:** 20 **NOTES:** No smoking in restaurant
CARDS: 💳💳💳💳💳💳

BRISTOL continued

★★★ 65% **Henbury Lodge**
Station Rd, Henbury BS10 7QQ
☎ 0117 950 2615 ▤ 0117 950 9532
e-mail: jonathan.pearce@btconnect.co.uk
Dir: M5 junct 17/A4018 towards city centre, 3rd rdbt right into Crow Ln. At end turn right & hotel 200mtrs on right

PETS: Bedrooms (unattended) Exercise area (2 minutes)

This comfortable 18th-century country house has a delightful home from home atmosphere and is conveniently situated with easy access to the M5 and the city centre. Bedrooms are available both within the main house and in the adjacent converted stables; all are attractively decorated and well-equipped. The pleasant dining room offers a selection of carefully prepared dishes using fresh ingredients.
ROOMS: 12 en suite 9 annexe en suite (4 fmly) (3 GF) No smoking in 8 bedrooms s £57-£96; d £94-£112 (incl. bkfst) **LB FACILITIES:** STV Sauna Solarium Xmas **PARKING:** 24 **NOTES:** No smoking in restaurant **CARDS:** 🖿🖿🖿🖿🖿🖿

★★ 68% **The Bowl Inn**
16 Church Rd, Lower Almondsbury BS32 4DT
☎ 01454 612757 ▤ 01454 619910
e-mail: reception@thebowlinn.co.uk
Dir: M5 junct 16 onto Gloucester road, N for 500yds. Turn left into Over Lane, turn right by Garden Centre. Hotel next to church on right

PETS: Bedrooms £5 Public areas (not in restaurant) Exercise area (500yds)

With easy access to the motorway network, this popular village inn offers all the comforts of modern life in a charming 16th-century hostelry. Each bedroom has been individually furnished to complement the many original features. Dining options include an extensive bar menu with cask ales, or a more intimate restaurant.
ROOMS: 11 en suite 2 annexe en suite (1 GF) No smoking in 4 bedrooms s £44.50-£95.45; d £71-£113.40 (incl. bkfst) **LB**
FACILITIES: STV **PARKING:** 30 **NOTES:** RS 25 Dec
CARDS: 🖿🖿🖿🖿🖿🖿

◆◆◆ **Washington Hotel**
11-15 St Pauls Rd, Clifton BS8 1LX
☎ 0117 973 3980 ▤ 0117 9734740
e-mail: washington@cliftonhotels.com
Dir: follow A4018 into city, turn right at lights opp BBC buildings, hotel is 200yds on left

PETS: Bedrooms Exercise area (200 yards)

This large terraced guesthouse is located within walking distance of the city centre and Clifton Village. Bedrooms, many of which have been refurbished, are ideally equipped for business guests. Public areas include a modern reception lounge and bright basement breakfast room. The property benefits from secure parking and a rear patio garden.
FACILITIES: 46 rms (40 en suite) (4 fmly) No smoking in 13 bedrooms No smoking in dining room STV TVB tea/coffee Direct dial from bedrooms Licensed Cen ht Hon. membership of nearby fitness centre Last d 11pm **PRICES:** s £35-£49; d £59-£64✹ **PARKING:** 20 **NOTES:** Closed 23 Dec-3 Jan **CARDS:** 🖿🖿🖿🖿🖿🖿

BUCKINGHAMSHIRE

AMERSHAM
Map 04 SU99

★★★ 69% **The Crown**
High St HP7 0DH
☎ 0870 400 8103 ▤ 01494 431283
e-mail: crown@macdonald-hotels.co.uk

MACDONALD HOTELS

PETS: Bedrooms (unattended) £10 Public areas (Not in restaurant)

Combining the charm of a bygone era with the modern conveniences expected by today's traveller, this 16th-century coaching inn is a great base for antique shopping and walks in the Chilterns. One claim to fame is that the hotel was featured in the film 'Four Weddings and a Funeral'. Bedrooms are a strength, all are individually styled and some feature original hand-painted murals.
ROOMS: 19 en suite 18 annexe en suite (10 GF) No smoking in 21 bedrooms s £65-£170; d £130-£190 (incl. bkfst) **LB FACILITIES:** STV Xmas **PARKING:** 30 **NOTES:** No smoking in restaurant **CARDS:** 🖿🖿🖿🖿🖿🖿

BUCKINGHAM
Map 04 SP63

★★★ 64% **Buckingham Beales**
Buckingham Ring Rd MK18 1RY
☎ 01280 822622 ▤ 01280 823074
e-mail: buckingham@bealeshotels.co.uk
Dir: M1 junct 13/14 follow signs to Buckingham-A422/A421. M40 exit junct 9/10 follow signs Buckingham. Hotel on ring road

Best Western

PETS: Bedrooms (unattended) £10 per night

A purpose-built hotel which offers spacious rooms with well-designed working spaces for business travellers. There are also extensive conference facilities. The open-plan restaurant and bar offers a good range of dishes, and the well-equipped leisure suite is popular with guests.
ROOMS: 70 en suite (6 fmly) No smoking in 24 bedrooms s £80-£95; d £92-£115 (incl. bkfst) **LB FACILITIES:** STV Indoor swimming (H) Sauna Solarium Gym Jacuzzi entertainment Xmas **PARKING:** 120 **NOTES:** No smoking in restaurant **CARDS:** 🖿🖿🖿🖿🖿🖿

GAYHURST
Map 04 SP84

◆◆◆ ⍩ **Mill Farm**
MK16 8LT
☎ 01908 611489 ▤ 01908 611489
e-mail: adamsmillfarm@aol.com
Dir: take B526 from Newport Pagnell, after 2.5m turn left into Haversham Rd, Mill Farm is 1m on left

PETS: Bedrooms Sep Accom Exercise area (adjacent)

Within easy reach of Newport Pagnell and the M1, this period farmhouse enjoys a peaceful setting and wonderful views over local farmland. Cosy bedrooms are decorated in a homely style and have a host of thoughtful extras. A sumptuously furnished lounge/dining room, enhanced with fine antiques, is available for guest use.
FACILITIES: 3 rms (2 en suite) 1 annexe en suite (1 fmly) (1 GF) No smoking in 2 bedrooms No smoking in dining room No smoking in 1 lounge TVB tea/coffee Cen ht TVL Tennis (hard) Fishing Riding Croquet lawn Rough shooting Trout & Coarse fishing 550 acres mixed **PRICES:** s £20-£25; d £40-£50✹ **PARKING:** 13

England

MILTON KEYNES — Map 04 SP83

★★★ 70% Novotel Milton Keynes
Saxon St, Layburn Court, Heelands MK13 7RA
☎ 01908 322212 ◎ 01908 322235
e-mail: H3272@accor-hotels.com

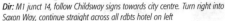 NOVOTEL

Dir: M1 junct 14, follow Childsway signs towards city centre. Turn right into Saxon Way, continue straight across all rdbts hotel on left

PETS: Bedrooms £5 Exercise area

Contemporary in style, this purpose-built hotel is situated on the outskirts of the town, just a few minutes' drive from the centre and mainline railway station. Bedrooms provide ample workspace and a good range of facilities for the modern traveller, and public rooms include a children's play area and indoor leisure centre.
ROOMS: 124 en suite (40 fmly) (40 GF) No smoking in 105 bedrooms
s £119; d £119 **LB FACILITIES:** STV Indoor swimming (H) Sauna Gym Steam bath **SERVICES:** Lift air con **PARKING:** 130
CARDS:

★★★ 70% Parkside
Newport Rd, Woughton on the Green MK6 3LR
☎ 01908 661919 ◎ 01908 676186
e-mail: parkside@macdonald-hotels.co.uk

MACDONALD HOTELS

PETS: Bedrooms Exercise area (Adjacent)

Situated in five acres of landscaped grounds in a peaceful village setting, the Parkside hotel is only five minutes' drive from the centre of Milton Keynes. Bedrooms are divided between executive rooms in the main house and standard rooms in the adjacent coach house. Public rooms include a range of meeting rooms, Lanes restaurant and Strollers bar.
ROOMS: 49 rms (38 en suite) (1 fmly) (19 GF) No smoking in 15 bedrooms s £65-£135; d £80-£155 **FACILITIES:** STV Discounted entry to local health & fitness club Xmas **PARKING:** 75 **NOTES:** No smoking in restaurant **CARDS:**

★★ 68% Swan Revived
High St, Newport Pagnell MK16 8AR
☎ 01908 610565 ◎ 01908 210995
e-mail: swanrevived@btinternet.com

THE INDEPENDENTS

Dir: M1 junct 14 onto A509 then B526 into Newport Pagnell for 2m. Hotel on High St

PETS: Bedrooms (unattended) Exercise area

Once a coaching inn, this hotel dates from the 17th century, occupying a prime location in the centre of town. Well-appointed bedrooms are spacious, individually styled and have good levels of comfort. Public areas include a popular bar and a restaurant offering a variety of freshly prepared dishes.
ROOMS: 42 en suite (2 fmly) s £49-£83.95; d £60-£90 (incl. bkfst) **LB**
FACILITIES: STV **SERVICES:** Lift **PARKING:** 18 **NOTES:** No smoking in restaurant RS 25 Dec-1 Jan **CARDS:**

Don't forget to let proprietors know when you book that you're bringing your pet

⌂ Campanile
40 Penn Rd, Fenny Stratford, Bletchley MK2 2AU
☎ 01908 649819 ◎ 01908 649818
e-mail: mk@envergure.co.uk

 Campanile

Dir: M1 junct 14, follow A4146 to A5. Southbound on A5. 4th exit at 1st rdbt to Fenny Stratford. Hotel 500yds on left

PETS: Bedrooms (not bar and restaurant)

This modern building offers accommodation in smart, well-equipped bedrooms, all with en suite bathrooms. Refreshments may be taken at the informal Bistro. For further details consult the Hotel Groups page.
ROOMS: 80 en suite s fr £45.95; d fr £45.95

⌂ Welcome Lodge
Newport Pagnell MK16 8DS
☎ 01908 610878 ◎ 01908 216539
e-mail: newport.hotel@welcomebreak.co.uk

Welcome Break

Dir: M1 junct 14-15. In service area - follow signs to Barrier Lodge

PETS: Bedrooms (unattended) Exercise area (adjacent)

This modern building offers accommodation in smart, spacious and well-equipped bedrooms, suitable for families and business travellers, and all with en suite bathrooms. Refreshments may be taken at the nearby family restaurant. For further details consult the Hotel Groups page.
ROOMS: 90 en suite

TAPLOW — Map 04 SU98

★★★★★ ◎◎◎ ⚓ Cliveden
SL6 0JF
☎ 01628 668561 ◎ 01628 661837
e-mail: reservations@clivedenhouse.co.uk

Dir: M4 junct 7, follow A4 towards Maidenhead for 1.5 miles, turn onto B476 towards Taplow, 2.5 miles, hotel on left

PETS: Bedrooms (unattended) Exercise area (in grounds)
Pet Food dog menu, dog sitting

This wonderful stately home stands at the top of a gravelled boulevard. Visitors are treated as house-guests and staff recapture the tradition of fine hospitality. Bedrooms have individual quality and style, and reception rooms retain a timeless elegance. Both restaurants here are awarded AA rosettes - The Terrace with its delightful views has two rosettes, and Waldo's, offering innovative menus in discreet, luxurious surroundings, has three. Exceptional leisure facilities include cruises along Cliveden Reach and massages in the Pavilion.
ROOMS: 39 en suite (8 GF) No smoking in 12 bedrooms d £225-£950 (incl. bkfst) **LB FACILITIES:** STV Indoor swimming (H) Outdoor swimming (H) Tennis (hard) Squash Snooker Sauna Solarium Gym Croquet lawn Jacuzzi Full range of beauty treatments at the Pavilion Spa, 3 vintage launches entertainment Xmas **SERVICES:** Lift **PARKING:** 60
NOTES: No smoking in restaurant
CARDS:

 Places with this symbol are farms

CAMBRIDGESHIRE

CAMBRIDGE Map 05 TL45

★★★★ 76% ◉◉ Hotel Felix
Whitehouse Ln CB3 0LX
☎ 01223 277977 📠 01223 277973
e-mail: help@hotelfelix.co.uk
Dir: Travelling N on A1307 (Huntingdon Rd) turn R at The Travellers Rest into Whitehouse Lane.

PETS: Bedrooms (unattended) Exercise area (200yds)

A beautiful Victorian mansion set amidst three acres of landscaped gardens, this property was originally built in 1852 for a surgeon from the famous Addenbrookes Hospital. The contemporary-style bedrooms have carefully chosen furniture and many thoughtful touches, whilst public rooms feature a large open-plan bar, the adjacent Graffiti restaurant and a small quiet lounge.
ROOMS: 52 en suite (5 fmly) (26 GF) No smoking in 22 bedrooms s £128-£178; d £158-£265 (incl. cont bkfst) **LB FACILITIES:** STV Xmas **SERVICES:** Lift **PARKING:** 90 **NOTES:** No smoking in restaurant **CARDS:** 💳💳💳💳💳💳

★★★★ 68%
De Vere University Arms
Regent St CB2 1AD
☎ 01223 351241 📠 01223 273037
e-mail: dua.sales@devere-hotels.com

DE VERE ● HOTELS

Dir: M11 junct 11, follow city centre signs for 3m. Right at 2nd mini rdbt, left at lights into Regent St. Hotel 600yds on right

PETS: Bedrooms (unattended) £5 per animal Exercise area (2 min walk)

Built as a post house in 1834, the University Arms has an enviable position in the very heart of the city, overlooking Parker's Piece. Public rooms include an elegant domed lounge, a smart restaurant on the High St, a bar and lounge overlooking the park. Conference and banqueting rooms are extensive, many with Oak panelling. Car parking is a bonus given the hotel's central location.
ROOMS: 120 en suite (2 fmly) No smoking in 83 bedrooms **FACILITIES:** STV Reduced rate at local fitness centre Play Stations and pay movies in all rooms **SERVICES:** Lift **PARKING:** 88 **NOTES:** No smoking in restaurant **CARDS:** 💳💳💳💳💳💳

★★★ 71% Gonville
Gonville Place CB1 1LY
☎ 01223 366611 & 221111 📠 01223 315470
e-mail: all@gonvillehotel.co.uk

Best Western

Dir: M11 junct 11, on A1309 follow city centre signs. At 2nd mini rdbt right into Lensfield Rd, over junct with traffic lights. Hotel 25yds on right

PETS: Bedrooms Exercise area

This hotel is situated on the inner ring road, a short walk across the green from the city centre. Well-established, with regular guests and very experienced staff, the Gonville is popular for its relaxing, informal atmosphere. The air-conditioned public areas are cheerfully furnished, recently enhanced by the creation of a new lounge bar and brasserie; bedrooms are well-appointed and appealing.
ROOMS: 78 en suite (1 fmly) (5 GF) No smoking in 38 bedrooms s £89-£120; d £99-£150 (incl. bkfst) **LB FACILITIES:** Arrangement with gym/swimming pool **SERVICES:** Lift **PARKING:** 80 **NOTES:** No smoking in restaurant **CARDS:** 💳💳💳💳💳💳

★★★ 68% Royal Cambridge
Trumpington St CB2 1PY

Forestdale Hotels

☎ 01223 351631 📠 01223 352972
e-mail: royal.cambridge@forestdale.com
Dir: M11 junct 11, signed city centre. 1st mini rdbt left into Fen Causeway. Hotel 1st right

PETS: Bedrooms (unattended) £7.50 Public areas (except restaurant) Pet Food

This impressive Georgian hotel enjoys a central location. Bedrooms are well-equipped and comfortable and include new superior bedrooms/apartments. Public areas are traditionally decorated to a good standard: the elegant restaurant is a popular choice and the lounge/bar serves evening snacks. Parking and conferencing are added benefits.
ROOMS: 57 en suite (9 fmly) No smoking in 28 bedrooms s fr £120; d fr £155 (incl. bkfst) **LB FACILITIES:** STV Xmas **SERVICES:** Lift **PARKING:** 80 **NOTES:** No smoking in restaurant **CARDS:** 💳💳💳💳💳💳

🌲 **Places with this symbol are country house hotels**

All abbreviations are explained on page 9

Please mention AA Pet Friendly Places to Stay when booking

All AA listed accommodation, restaurants and pubs can be found on the AA's website www.theAA.com

England

◆◆◆ Lynwood House
217 Chesterton Rd CB4 1AN
☎ 01223 500776 ▤ 01223 300552
e-mail: lynwood.house@ntlworld.com
Dir: M11 North exit junct 13. Follow A1303 to Cambridge. At mini rdbt turn left, at traffic lights go straight on, at ring road follow signs for Haverhill. Lynwood House on left.

> **PETS:** Bedrooms (By arrangement) Exercise area (100yds)

Located close to the river and central attractions, this well-maintained guest house provides a range of practically equipped bedrooms, some of which have the benefit of modern en suite shower rooms. Wholesome breakfasts are taken in a cosy dining room and a warm welcome is assured.
FACILITIES: 8 rms (5 en suite) (2 fmly) (3 GF) No smoking TVB tea/coffee Cen ht No children No coaches **PRICES:** s £25-£50; d £50-£60✱ **PARKING:** 3 **CARDS:** ▭ ▭ ▭ ⑤

DUXFORD   Map 05 TL44

★★★ 74% ◉◉ Duxford Lodge
Ickleton Rd CB2 4RT
☎ 01223 836444 ▤ 01223 832271
e-mail: admin@duxfordlodgehotel.co.uk
Dir: M11 junct 10, onto A505 to Duxford. 1st right at T-junct. Hotel on left

> **PETS:** Bedrooms Exercise area (500 metres)

A warm welcome is assured at this attractive red-brick hotel in the heart of a delightful village. Public areas include a cosy relaxing bar, separate lounge, and an attractive restaurant, where an excellent and imaginative menu is offered. The bedrooms are well-appointed, comfortable and smartly furnished.
ROOMS: 11 en suite 4 annexe en suite (2 fmly) d £60-£85; d £105-£115 (ind. bkfst) **LB FACILITIES:** entertainment Xmas **PARKING:** 34
NOTES: No smoking in restaurant Closed 26-30 Dec
CARDS: ▭ ▭ ▭ ▭ ⑤

ELY   Map 05 TL58

★★★ 66% Lamb
2 Lynn Rd CB7 4EJ
☎ 01353 663574 ▤ 01353 662023
e-mail: lamb.ely@oldenglishinns.co.uk
Dir: from A10 into Ely, hotel in town centre on corner of Lynn Road & High Street

> **PETS:** Bedrooms Public areas Exercise area (200 metres) Pet bowls available but no food

Centrally located, this 15th-century former coaching inn is a focal point of this market town. Recently fully refurbished, the hotel offers a combination of light, modern and traditional public rooms, whilst the bedrooms have all been upgraded to a good modern standard. Food is available throughout the hotel, the same menu provided within the bar and restaurant areas.
ROOMS: 31 en suite (6 fmly) No smoking in 24 bedrooms s £50-£70; d £75-£95 (ind. bkfst) **LB FACILITIES:** STV Xmas **PARKING:** 20
NOTES: No smoking in restaurant
CARDS: ▭ ▭ ▭ ▭ ▭ ▭ ⑤

◆◆◆ Castle Lodge Hotel
50 New Barns Rd CB7 4PW
☎ 01353 662276 ▤ 01353 666606
e-mail: castlelodgehotel@supanet.com
Dir: turn off A10 at 1st rdbt on Ely bypass, at lights turn left, over next lights and take next right. At top of rd turn left. Hotel on right

> **PETS:** Bedrooms Exercise area (0.25 miles)
> **RESIDENT PETS:** Charlie (dog), Joey & Lucy (African grey parrots)

Located within easy walking distance of the cathedral, this extended Victorian house offers well-equipped bedrooms which come in a variety of sizes. Public areas include a traditionally furnished dining room and an air-conditioned comfortable bar lounge; informal service is both friendly and helpful.
FACILITIES: 11 rms (6 en suite) (2 fmly) No smoking in dining room TVB tea/coffee Direct dial from bedrooms No dogs (ex guide dogs) Licensed Cen ht TVL No coaches Dinner Last d 9pm
PRICES: s £25-£45; d £55-£65✱ **PARKING:** 6
CARDS: ▭ ▭ ▭ ⑤

◆◆ Chapel Cottage
11 Chapel St CB6 1AD
☎ 01353 668768
e-mail: daffmort@talk21.com
Dir: leave A10 at Ely by-pass rdbt taking 2nd exit, continue into City centre at T-junct, left at traffic lights (Lamb Hotel facing), 1st left into Chapel Street

> **PETS:** Bedrooms Public areas Exercise area (0.25 mile - park) Food and bowls provided by prior arrangement
> **RESIDENT PETS:** Otis - Lhasa Apso (dog)

Located in a residential area of this historic town, not far from the famous cathedral, this is a modest and homely establishment. Bedrooms vary in size but are practical and comfortable. There is a pleasant conservatory lounge looking out over a small terrace, which is also available to guests in sunny weather.
FACILITIES: 2 rms No smoking in bedrooms No smoking in dining room No smoking in 1 lounge TVB tea/coffee Cen ht TVL No children 5yrs No coaches **PRICES:** s £25; d £50✱

HUNTINGDON   Map 04 TL27

★★★★ 71%
Huntingdon Marriott Hotel
Kingfisher Way, Hinchingbrooke Business Park
PE29 6FL   **Marriott**
☎ 01480 446000 ▤ 01480 451111   HOTELS · RESORTS · SUITES
e-mail: reservations.huntingdon@whitbread.com
Dir: 1m from Huntington centre on A14, close to Brampton racecourse

> **PETS:** Bedrooms Exercise area

With its excellent road links, this modern, purpose-built hotel is a popular venue for conferences and business meetings, and is convenient for Huntingdon, Cambridge and racing at Newmarket. Bedrooms are spacious and offer every modern comfort, including air conditioning. Leisure facilities are also impressive.
ROOMS: 150 en suite (45 GF) No smoking in 60 bedrooms s £72-£200; d £104-£250 (incl. bkfst) **LB FACILITIES:** Spa STV Indoor swimming (H) Sauna Solarium Gym Jacuzzi entertainment Xmas
SERVICES: Lift air con **PARKING:** 250 **NOTES:** No smoking in restaurant **CARDS:** ▭ ▭ ▭ ▭ ▭ ▭ ⑤

KIRTLING
Map 05 TL65

♦♦♦ ❦ Hill Farm Guest House
CB8 9HQ
☎ 01638 730253 📠 01638 731957

PETS: Telephone for details

Located on arable land, south of Newmarket and in the heart of horse-breeding country, this 400-year-old property retains many original features. Public areas are furnished in keeping with the period of the building. Hearty breakfasts are taken at a family table in the elegant dining room.
FACILITIES: 3 rms (2 en suite) No smoking in 1 bedroom TVB tea/coffee Direct dial from bedrooms Cen ht TVL Croquet lawn Games room 500 acres arable **PARKING:** 15

MADINGLEY
Map 05 TL36

♦♦♦♦ ❦ Beck Brook Farm
The Avenue CB3 8AD
☎ 01954 211620 📠 01954 211620
Dir: Turn off M11 junct 14. In 0.5m turn left into The Avenue (signposted Madingley). Farmhouse 0.5m on right behind a wood

PETS: Bedrooms Exercise area (Woodland on site)
RESIDENT PETS: Blondie - Labrador, Fluffy - cat, chickens, guinea fowl, bantams, peacock/peahen, pheasants & muntjac deer in woods

Conveniently located for the M11/A14 and Cambridge 'Park & Ride', this charming period farmhouse sits in a quiet and secluded location on the outskirts of the village. Sitting in 17-acre grounds where the woods and lake are being further developed to encourage wildlife. Guests are welcome to use the 11-meter heated swimming pool and tennis court. Breakfast is taken in the conservatory, or in winter, the pleasant dining room; service is both helpful and friendly.
FACILITIES: 4 rms (2 en suite) (1 fmly) No smoking TVB tea/coffee Cen ht Indoor swimming pool (heated) Tennis (hard) Woodland walks in 17 acre grounds Woodland / wildlife area Dinner Last d order day before **PRICES:** s £30-£32; d £50-£52✳ **PARKING:** 4

PETERBOROUGH
Map 04 TL19

★★★ 71% Bull
Westgate PE1 1RB

PEEL HOTELS

☎ 01733 561364 📠 01733 557304
e-mail: info@bull-hotel-peterborough.com
Dir: off A1, follow city centre signs. Hotel opp Queensgate shopping centre. Car park on Broadway next to Library

PETS: Bedrooms (by arrangement) £25 Exercise area (on site)

This pleasant city-centre hotel offers well-equipped, modern accommodation, which includes several new wings of deluxe bedrooms. Public rooms include a popular bar and a brasserie-style restaurant serving a flexible range of dishes, with further informal dining available in the lounge. There is a good range of meeting rooms and conference facilities.
ROOMS: 118 en suite (3 fmly) No smoking in 40 bedrooms **FACILITIES:** STV Xmas **PARKING:** 100 **NOTES:** No smoking in restaurant CARDS: 🔲 🔲 🔲 🔲 🔲 🔲 🔲

KIRTLING — ORTON HALL (top right)

★★★ 67% ⚜ Orton Hall
Orton Longueville PE2 7DN

Best Western

☎ 01733 391111 📠 01733 231912
e-mail: reception@ortonhall.co.uk
Dir: off A605 E opposite Orton Mere

PETS: Bedrooms (unattended) £5 Public areas (not in restaurants) Exercise area (On site)

Set in 20 acres of woodland, this impressive country house has spacious and relaxing public areas. Original features include oak panelling in the Huntly Restaurant, in the Grand Hall, which is a popular banqueting venue, and some 16th-century terracotta floors. The Ramblewood Inn, across the courtyard from the main hotel, offers an alternative, informal dining and bar option.
ROOMS: 65 en suite (2 fmly) (15 GF) No smoking in 42 bedrooms **FACILITIES:** STV Three quarter size snooker table **PARKING:** 200 **NOTES:** No smoking in restaurant CARDS: 🔲 🔲 🔲 🔲 🔲 🔲 🔲

ST IVES
Map 04 TL37

★★★ 70% Slepe Hall
Ramsey Rd PE27 5RB
☎ 01480 463122 📠 01480 300706
e-mail: mail@slepehall.co.uk
Dir: from A14 on A1096 & follow by-pass signed Huntingdon towards St Ives, left into Ramsey Rd at lights by Toyota garage, hotel on left

PETS: Bedrooms £5 Exercise area (adjacent) Pet Food any request accommodated with prior notice RESIDENT PETS: Mollie & Mayhem - Bernese Mountain dogs

A welcoming and friendly atmosphere exists within Slepe Hall, which is located close to the town centre. Bedroom types vary, with traditional and modern styles both available. A choice of dining options is provided within the refurbished public rooms, with light meals served in the lounge and bar or more formal dining options in the restaurant.
ROOMS: 16 en suite (1 fmly) s £50-£80; d £75-£99 (incl. bkfst) LB **FACILITIES:** STV Guests have free access to local private leisure club **PARKING:** 70 **NOTES:** No smoking in restaurant Closed 24-26 Dec & 1 Jan CARDS: 🔲 🔲 🔲 🔲 🔲 🔲 🔲

ST NEOTS
Map 04 TL16

★★ 63% Abbotsley Golf Hotel
Potton Rd, Eynesbury Hardwicke PE19 6XN
☎ 01480 474000 📠 01480 471018
e-mail: abbotsley@americangolf.uk.com
Dir: A1(M) onto A428 towards Cambridge, left at Tesco rdbt, 3rd exit at 4th rdbt then 1st right & follow signs

PETS: Bedrooms £3 Exercise area (100yds)
RESIDENT PETS: 3 cats & 2 dogs

This purpose-built hotel caters well for its many avid golfing guests, with a 250-acre estate encompassing two courses, a golf school and leisure complex. The bedrooms are generally spacious and surround a pleasing courtyard garden with a putting green. Public rooms overlook the adjacent greens.
ROOMS: 42 annexe en suite (2 fmly) (13 GF) No smoking in 10 bedrooms s £54-£56; d £78-£85 (incl. bkfst) LB **FACILITIES:** Golf 36 Squash Solarium Gym Putting green Holistic Health & Beauty Salon, pool tables **PARKING:** 80 **NOTES:** No smoking in restaurant RS Closed Xmas Day CARDS: 🔲 🔲 🔲 🔲 🔲 🔲 🔲

SIX MILE BOTTOM
Map 05 TL55

★★★ 72% ⊛ Swynford Paddocks
CB8 0UE
☎ 01638 570234 🗎 01638 570283
e-mail: info@swynfordpaddocks.com
Dir: M11 junct 9, take A11 towards Newmarket, turn onto A1304 to Newmarket, hotel 0.75m on left in Six Mile Bottom Village

PETS: Bedrooms Exercise area (4 miles)

This smart country house is set in attractive grounds, within easy reach of Newmarket. Bedrooms are comfortably appointed, thoughtfully equipped and include some delightful four-poster rooms. Imaginative, carefully prepared food is served in the elegant restaurant, and meeting and conference facilities are available. Service is friendly and attentive.
ROOMS: 15 en suite (1 fmly) s £110-£140; d £135-£195 (incl. bkfst) **LB**
FACILITIES: STV Tennis (hard) Croquet lawn Putting green
PARKING: 180 **NOTES:** No smoking in restaurant
CARDS:

WISBECH
Map 05 TF40

★★★ 68% Elme Hall
Elm High Rd PE14 0DQ
☎ 01945 475566 🗎 01945 475666
e-mail: elme@paktel.co.uk
Dir: off A47 onto A1101 towards Wisbech. Hotel on right

PETS: Bedrooms Exercise area

An imposing, Georgian-style property conveniently situated on the outskirts of the town centre just off the A47. The spacious, individually decorated bedrooms are tastefully furnished with quality reproduction pieces and equipped to a high standard. Public rooms include a choice of attractive lounges, as well as two bars, meeting rooms and a banqueting suite.
ROOMS: 7 en suite (3 fmly) No smoking in all bedrooms d £68-£210 (incl. bkfst) **PARKING:** 200 **NOTES:** No smoking in restaurant
CARDS: ▦

CHESHIRE

AUDLEM
Map 07 SJ64

◆◆◆◆ ❦ Little Heath Farm
CW3 0HE
☎ 01270 811324
e-mail: hilaryandbob@ukonline.co.uk
Dir: 6m from Nantwich on A529. At 30mph sign in Audlem, farm on right

PETS: Bedrooms (unattended) £5 Public areas (except lounge or dining room) Exercise area (side of garden)
RESIDENT PETS: Rosie - collie/springer spaniel cross, Ruby - Jack Russell

This 200-year-old brick-built farmhouse retains much of its original character, with low beamed ceilings and traditionally furnished public areas. These include a cosy sitting room and a separate dining room where guests dine family-style. Bedrooms have been
continued

refurbished to a stylish, comfortable standard, and the friendly proprietors create a relaxing atmosphere for their guests.
FACILITIES: 3 en suite (1 fmly) No smoking TVB tea/coffee Cen ht TVL 50 acres beef dairy mixed. Dinner Last d 10am **PRICES:** s £25-£30; d fr £48✱ **LB PARKING:** 3 **NOTES:** Closed Xmas & New Year

CHESTER
Map 07 SJ46

★★★ 72% Grosvenor Pulford
Wrexham Rd, Pulford CH4 9DG
☎ 01244 570560 🗎 01244 570809
e-mail: enquiries@grosvenorpulfordhotel.co.uk
Dir: Leave M53/A55 at junct signposted A483 Chester, Wrexham and North Wales. Turn on to B5445, hotel is 2 miles on the right.

PETS: Bedrooms (unattended) Exercise area (on site)

Set in rural surroundings, this modern, stylish hotel features a magnificent leisure club with a large Roman-style swimming pool. Among the bedrooms available are several executive suites and others containing spiral staircases leading to the bedroom sections. A new brasserie restaurant and bar provide a wide range of imaginative dishes in a relaxed atmosphere.
ROOMS: 73 en suite (6 fmly) (21 GF) No smoking in 10 bedrooms s £75-£105; d £100-£160 (incl. bkfst) **LB FACILITIES:** Spa STV Indoor swimming (H) Tennis (hard) Snooker Sauna Solarium Gym Jacuzzi Hairdressing & Beauty salon, coffee bar Xmas **PARKING:** 200
NOTES: No smoking in restaurant
CARDS:

★★★ 66% Blossoms
St John St CH1 1HL
☎ 0870 400 8108 🗎 01244 346433
e-mail: general.blossoms@macdonald-hotels.co.uk
Dir: in city centre, follow signs for Eastgate and City Centre Hotels, continue through pedestrianised zone, hotel on the left

PETS: Bedrooms (unattended) £20 Public areas Exercise area (300 metres) Pet Food

For those seeking to explore this charming, medieval walled city, the central location of this elegant hotel is ideal. The public areas retain much of their Victorian charm. Occasionally, piano music at dinner adds to the intimate atmosphere.
ROOMS: 64 en suite (3 fmly) No smoking in 43 bedrooms s £65-£98; d £75-£118 (incl. bkfst) **LB FACILITIES:** STV Free use of local health club entertainment Xmas **SERVICES:** Lift **NOTES:** No smoking in restaurant
CARDS: ▦

◆◆◆◆ The Mount
Lesters Ln, Higher Kinnerton CH4 9BQ
☎ 01244 660275 🗎 01244 660275
e-mail: major@mountkinnerton.freeserve.co.uk
Dir: turn off A55 onto A5104, left at 2nd rbt, through Broughton then 1st left signed Kinnerton. Follow lane for 0.75m, house on right

PETS: Sep Accom (pantry & kennel) Exercise area (adjacent) **RESIDENT PETS:** 3 dogs (Jack Russell, cocker spaniel & long haired dachshund)

This elegant Victorian house enjoys an idyllic location, set in extensive grounds and gardens. Bedrooms and public areas are furnished with fine period pieces and are thoughtfully equipped
continued on p40

CHESTER continued

with a host of extras. Warm hospitality is provided by the friendly hosts and a relaxing atmosphere is created for guests. The house is a convenient base for exploring Chester and North Wales.
FACILITIES: 3 en suite No smoking TVB tea/coffee No dogs (ex guide dogs) Cen ht No children 12yrs No coaches Tennis (hard) Croquet lawn **PRICES:** s £35; d £55✱ **PARKING:** 10
NOTES: Closed 22 Dec-6 Jan

FRODSHAM
Map 07 SJ57

★★★ 70% **Forest Hill Hotel & Leisure Complex**
Overton Hill WA6 6HH
☎ 01928 735255 📠 01928 735517
e-mail: info@foresthillshotel.com
Dir: at Frodsham turn onto B5151. After 1m right into Manley Rd, right into Simons Ln after 0.5m. Hotel 0.5m past Frodsham golf course

> **PETS:** Bedrooms (unattended) £5 Exercise area (on site)

This modern, purpose-built hotel is set high up on Overton Hill, offering panoramic views. There is a range of spacious, well-equipped bedrooms, including executive rooms. Guests have a choice of bars and there is a tasteful split-level restaurant, as well as conference facilities and a very well equipped leisure suite and gymnasium.
ROOMS: 58 en suite (4 fmly) No smoking in 5 bedrooms s £65-£90; d £65-£90 (incl. bkfst) **LB** **FACILITIES:** STV Indoor swimming (H) Snooker Sauna Solarium Gym Jacuzzi Nightclub entertainment Xmas **PARKING:** 350 **NOTES:** No smoking in restaurant
CARDS: 🗖🗖🗖🗖🗖🗖🗖

KNUTSFORD
Map 07 SJ77

★★ 75% **The Longview Hotel & Restaurant**
55 Manchester Rd WA16 0LX
☎ 01565 632119 📠 01565 652402
e-mail: enquiries@longviewhotel.com
Dir: M6 junct 19 take A556 W towards Chester. Left at lights onto A5033, 1.5m to rdbt then left. Hotel 200yds on right

> **PETS:** Telephone for details

This friendly Victorian hotel offers high standards of hospitality and service. Attractive public areas include a cellar bar and foyer lounge area. The restaurant has a traditional feel and offers an imaginative selection of dishes. Bedrooms are individually styled and offer a good range of thoughtful amenities, including broadband internet access.
ROOMS: 13 en suite 13 annexe en suite (1 fmly) (4 GF) s £52-£115; d £72-£137 (incl. bkfst) **LB** **FACILITIES:** ch fac **PARKING:** 20
CARDS: 🗖🗖🗖🗖🗖🗖🗖

> 🍺 **Places with this symbol are pubs**

> 🌲 **Places with this symbol are country house hotels**

LYMM
Map 07 SJ68

★★★ 68% **Lymm Hotel**
Whitbarrow Rd WA13 9AQ
☎ 01925 752233 📠 01925 756035
e-mail: lymm@macdonald-hotels.co.uk
Dir: take M6 to B5158 to Lymm. Left at junct, right at mini rdbt, left into Brookfield Rd and 3rd left into Whitbarrow Rd

MACDONALD HOTELS

> **PETS:** Bedrooms (unattended) £10 Public areas (except food areas) Exercise area (50yds)

In a peaceful residential setting, this hotel benefits from both its quiet setting and its convenient access to local motorway networks. The hotel offers comfortable bedrooms equipped for both the business and leisure guest. Public areas include an attractive bar and an elegant restaurant. There is also extensive car parking.
ROOMS: 18 rms (15 en suite) 48 annexe en suite (5 fmly) (4 GF) No smoking in 34 bedrooms **FACILITIES:** STV Xmas **PARKING:** 120
NOTES: No smoking in restaurant
CARDS: 🗖🗖🗖🗖🗖🗖🗖

MALPAS
Map 07 SJ44

◆◆◆◆ 💚 **Millmoor Farm**
Nomansheath SY14 8DY
☎ 01948 820304
e-mail: dave-sal@millmoor-farm.fsnet.co.uk
Dir: A41 S towards Whitchurch, right towards Nomansheath, 1m after Hampton Heath rdbt. Left at mini rdbt in village, Millmoor Farm signed after 0.5m

> **PETS:** Bedrooms Sep Accom (shed) £2-£4 Exercise area (surrounding) **RESIDENT PETS:** Pippa - Jack Russell, Alice - pig, 2 cats, cows, calves, chickens

Quietly located in attractive gardens on a beef and dairy farm near Nomansheath, parts of this tastefully modernised farmhouse date back to the late 17th century. Bedrooms include one with a four-poster bed and some within a quality cottage, also used for self-catering. An attractive combined lounge and dining room features a welcoming log fire for those cooler months.
FACILITIES: 3 rms (2 en suite) No smoking TVB tea/coffee Cen ht Fishing 270 acres dairy & beef Dinner Last d midday **PRICES:** s £18-£24; d £36-£48✱ **LB** **BB** **PARKING:** 11

NANTWICH
Map 07 SJ65

★★★ ◎◎ 🌲🌲 **Rookery Hall**
Main Rd, Worleston CW5 6DQ
☎ 01270 610016 📠 01270 626027
e-mail: rookeryhall-cro@handpicked.co.uk
Dir: B5074 off 4th rdbt, on Nantwich by-pass. Hotel 1.5m on right

Hand PICKED

> **PETS:** Bedrooms (unattended)

This fine 19th-century mansion is set in 38 acres of gardens, pasture and parkland. Bedrooms, some in an adjacent coach house, are spacious and luxuriously appointed. The public areas are particularly stylish and include a salon with enormous sofas and a mahogany-panelled dining room. Many of the refurbished bedrooms provide a dazzling array of extras that include wide

continued

screen plasma TVs and DVD players. The staff are notable for their professionalism and hospitality. Hand Picked Hotels – AA Hotel Group of the Year 2004-5.
ROOMS: 30 en suite 16 annexe en suite (6 GF) s £115-£130; d £150 (incl. bkfst) **LB FACILITIES:** STV Fishing Croquet lawn Xmas
SERVICES: Lift **PARKING:** 100 **NOTES:** No smoking in restaurant
CARDS:

★★ 70% **Crown**
High St CW5 5AS
☎ 01270 625283 📠 01270 628047
e-mail: info@crown-hotel.net
Dir: A52 to Nantwich, hotel in centre of town

Best Western

PETS: Bedrooms Public areas

Ideally set in the heart of this historic and delightful market town, The Crown has been offering hospitality for centuries. It has an abundance of original features and the well-equipped bedrooms retain an old world charm. There is also a bar with live entertainment throughout the week and diners can enjoy Italian food in the atmospheric brasserie.
ROOMS: 18 en suite (2 fmly) No smoking in 2 bedrooms s £60-£70; d £74-£80 **LB FACILITIES:** Putting green entertainment **PARKING:** 18
CARDS: ▭ ▨ ▨ ▨ ▨

NORTHWICH   Map 07 SJ67

★★★ 65% **The Floatel, Northwich**
London Rd CW9 5HD
☎ 01606 44443 📠 01606 42596
e-mail: enquiries@hotels-northwich.com
Dir: M6 junct 19, follow A556 for 4m, take right turn & follow signs town centre

COTSWOLD

PETS: Bedrooms (unattended) Exercise area (on site)

A first in the UK - this floating hotel has been built over the river and a very successful concept has been created. The bedrooms are modern and well equipped, and there is a carvery style restaurant which overlooks the river.
ROOMS: 60 en suite (2 fmly) No smoking in 30 bedrooms s £35-£75; d £45-£85 **LB FACILITIES:** STV Xmas **SERVICES:** Lift **PARKING:** 110
NOTES: No smoking in restaurant
CARDS: ▭ ▨ ▨ ▨ ▨

PUDDINGTON   Map 07 SJ37

★★★★ 67% ⊛ ♨ **Craxton Wood**
Parkgate Rd, Ledsham CH66 9PB
☎ 0151 347 4000 📠 0151 347 4040
e-mail: craxtonwood@macdonald-hotels.co.uk
Dir: from M6 take M56 towards N Wales, then A5117 then A540 to Hoylake. Hotel 200yds past lights

MACDONALD HOTELS

PETS: Bedrooms (unattended) £10 per dog Public areas (only lounge area)

Set in extensive grounds, this hotel offers a variety of bedroom styles; the modern rooms are particularly comfortable. The nicely furnished restaurant overlooks the grounds and offers a wide

continued

choice of dishes, whilst full leisure facilities and a choice of function suites completes the package.
ROOMS: 72 en suite (8 fmly) (30 GF) No smoking in all bedrooms s fr £60; d fr £100 (incl. bkfst) **LB FACILITIES:** STV Indoor swimming (H) Sauna Solarium Gym Beauty spa Xmas **SERVICES:** Lift
PARKING: 220 **NOTES:** No smoking in restaurant
CARDS: ▭ ▨ ▨ ▨ ▨

RUNCORN   Map 07 SJ58

⌂ **Campanile**
Lowlands Rd WA7 5TP
☎ 01928 581771 📠 01928 581730
e-mail: runcorn@envergure.co.uk
Dir: M56 junct 12, take A557, then follow signs for Runcorn rail station

Campanile

PETS: Bedrooms

This modern building offers accommodation in smart, well-equipped bedrooms, all with en suite bathrooms. Refreshments may be taken at the informal Bistro. For further details consult the Hotel Groups page.
ROOMS: 53 en suite s fr £41.95; d fr £41.95

TARPORLEY   Map 07 SJ56

★★★ 67% **Willington Hall**
Willington CW6 0NB
☎ 01829 752321 📠 01829 752596
e-mail: enquiries@willingtonhall.co.uk
Dir: 3m NW off unclass road linking A51 & A54, at Clotton turn off A51 at Bulls Head, then follow signs

PETS: Bedrooms (unattended) Exercise area Pet Food

Situated in 17 acres of parkland and built in 1829, this attractively furnished country house hotel offers spacious bedrooms, many with views over open countryside. Service is courteous and friendly, and freshly prepared meals are offered in the dining room or adjacent bar and drawing room. A smart new function suite confirms the popularity of this hotel as a premier venue for weddings and conferences.
ROOMS: 10 en suite s fr £70; d £110-£120 (incl. bkfst) **LB**
FACILITIES: STV Fishing Riding Croquet lawn **PARKING:** 60
NOTES: Closed 25 & 26 Dec **CARDS:** ▭ ▨ ▨ ▨ ▨

◆◆◆◆ **Hill House Farm**
Rushton CW6 9AU
☎ 01829 732238 📠 01829 733929
e-mail: rayner@hillhousefarm.fsnet.co.uk
Dir: A51/A49 lights at Tilstone Fearnall take Eaton turning in 1m. Turn right at war memorial into Lower Lane, take 3rd road right into The Hall Lane. Farm in 0.5m

PETS: Bedrooms Sep Accom (kennels) Public areas (if well behaved) Exercise area (surrounding)
RESIDENT PETS: 2 Springer Spaniels, 2 Labradors, Patterdale Terrier

This impressive, brick built farmhouse is set in very attractive gardens and nestles quietly within 14 acres of rolling pastureland. The three stylish bedrooms have either en suite or private facilities.

continued on p42

England

TARPORLEY continued

There is a spacious and comfortable lounge and a traditionally furnished breakfast room. The proprietors are especially friendly.
FACILITIES: 3 rms (2 en suite) (1 fmly) No smoking TVB tea/coffee Cen ht No coaches **PRICES:** s £35-£40; d £60✱ **LB PARKING:** 6
NOTES: Closed Xmas & New Year **CARDS:** 🔲 💳 🔲 🔲 🔲

WARRINGTON
Map 07 SJ68

★★★★ 75%
De Vere Daresbury Park

DE VERE ● HOTELS

Chester Rd, Daresbury WA4 4BB
☎ 01925 267331 📠 01925 265615
e-mail: reservations.daresbury@devere-hotels.com
Dir: M56 junct 11, take 'Daresbury Park' exit at rdbt. Hotel is 100m along.

PETS: Bedrooms (unattended) £7.50 per night
Exercise area (1 mile)

Close to the local motorway networks and many tourist attractions, this modern hotel is a very popular venue for both business and leisure travellers. Public areas are themed around 'Alice in Wonderland' in tribute to local author Lewis Carroll. These include a range of eating and drinking options, leisure facilities and extensive conference facilities.
ROOMS: 181 en suite (14 fmly) (62 GF) No smoking in 128 bedrooms s £70-£129; d £80-£139 **LB FACILITIES:** Spa STV Indoor swimming (H) Squash Snooker Sauna Solarium Gym Jacuzzi Steam Room, Beauty salon ch fac Xmas **SERVICES:** Lift **PARKING:** 400
CARDS: 🔲 💳 🔲 🔲 🔲

★★★ 72% **Fir Grove**

Best Western

Knutsford Old Rd WA4 2LD
☎ 01925 267471 📠 01925 601092
e-mail: firgrove@bestwestern.co.uk
Dir: M6 junct 20, follow signs for A50 to Warrington for 2.4m, before swing bridge over canal, turn right, and right again

PETS: Bedrooms (unattended)

Situated in a quiet residential area, this hotel is convenient for both the town centre and the motorway network. Comfortable, smart bedrooms, including new spacious executive rooms, offer some excellent extra facilities such as Playstations and CD players. Public areas include a smart lounge/bar, a neatly appointed restaurant and excellent function and meeting facilities.
ROOMS: 52 en suite (3 fmly) (20 GF) No smoking in 20 bedrooms s £70-£94; d £70-£104 (incl. bkfst) **FACILITIES:** STV Xmas
PARKING: 100 **NOTES:** No smoking in restaurant
CARDS: 🔲 💳 🔲 🔲 🔲

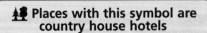
⚜ Places with this symbol are country house hotels

☙ Places with this symbol are farms

★★ 68% **Paddington House**

THE INDEPENDENTS

514 Old Manchester Rd WA1 3TZ
☎ 01925 816767 📠 01925 816651
e-mail: hotel@paddingtonhouse.co.uk
Dir: 1m from M6 junct 21, off A57, 2m from town centre

PETS: Bedrooms (unattended) Exercise area

This busy, friendly hotel is conveniently situated just over a mile from the M6. Bedrooms are attractively furnished, and include four-poster and ground-floor rooms. Guests can dine in the wood-panelled Padgate restaurant or in the cosy bar. Conference and function facilities are also available.
ROOMS: 37 en suite (9 fmly) (6 GF) No smoking in 17 bedrooms s £57.50; d £63 (incl. bkfst) **LB SERVICES:** Lift **PARKING:** 50
NOTES: No smoking in restaurant
CARDS: 🔲 💳 🔲 🔲 🔲

WYBUNBURY
Map 07 SJ64

◆◆◆ ☙ **Lea Farm**

Wrinehill Rd CW5 7NS
☎ 01270 841429 📠 01270 841429
e-mail: contactus@leafarm.co.uk
Dir: M6 junct 16, take A1550, at 1st rdbt Keele, 2nd rdbt Nantwich. Over railway bridge, 1st left to T-junct, turn left, 2nd farm on right

PETS: Bedrooms Sep Accom £2 Exercise area (surrounding fields) RESIDENT PETS: Lucy (Collie)

This working dairy farm is located in an idyllic setting surrounded by delightful gardens in the beautiful Cheshire countryside. Spacious bedrooms are equipped with modern facilities and the cosy lounge features a small snooker table. Hearty breakfasts are served in the attractive dining room, which looks out over the garden, with its resident peacocks.
FACILITIES: 3 rms (2 en suite) (1 fmly) No smoking TVB tea/coffee Cen ht TVL Fishing Pool Table Bird watching 150 acres dairy & beef
PRICES: s £26-£29; d £44-£50✱ **PARKING:** 24

CORNWALL & ISLES OF SCILLY

BOSCASTLE
Map 02 SX09

◆◆◆◆ **Old Coach House**

Tintagel Rd PL35 0AS
☎ 01840 250398 📠 01840 250346
e-mail: parsons@old-coach.demon.co.uk
Dir: at junct of B3266 and B3263

PETS: Bedrooms

Over 300 years old, The Old Coach House enjoys lovely views over the village and the rolling countryside. The pleasantly decorated bedrooms are well equipped and include two rooms on the ground floor, which provide for the less mobile. A hearty breakfast is served in the conservatory, which overlooks the well-kept garden.
FACILITIES: 8 en suite (3 fmly) (2 GF) No smoking TVB tea/coffee Cen ht TVL No coaches **PRICES:** s £38-£44; d £42-£44✱ **LB**
PARKING: 9 **NOTES:** Closed Xmas **CARDS:** 🔲 🔲 🔲 🔲 🔲

◆◆◆◆ Tolcarne House Hotel

Tintagel Rd PL35 0AS
☎ 01840 250654 ▤ 01840 250654
e-mail: crowntolhouse@eclipse.co.uk
Dir: at junct of B3266/B3263 in Boscastle, 5m from A39 'Atlantic Highway'

PETS: Bedrooms Public areas Exercise area (400yds)

Guests are assured of a warm welcome at this substantial Victorian residence, set in delightful grounds and gardens. The well-equipped bedrooms are stylishly decorated and well equipped with many extras. There is a lounge with an open fire and a separate cosy bar. Evening meals are also available by arrangement and are served in the elegant dining room.
FACILITIES: 8 en suite (1 fmly) No smoking in 6 bedrooms No smoking in dining room No smoking in 1 lounge TVB tea/coffee Licensed No children 10yrs No coaches Croquet lawn large garden Dinner Last d 5pm **PRICES:** s £36-£38; d £60-£72✳ **LB PARKING:** 15
NOTES: Closed Nov-Feb **CARDS:** ▤ ▤ ▤ ▤ ▤

BUDE
Map 02 SS20

★★ 68% Penarvor

Crooklets Beach EX23 8NE
☎ 01288 352036 ▤ 01288 355027
e-mail: hotel.penarvor@boltblue.com
Dir: From A39 towards Bude for 1.5m. At 2nd rdbt right, pass shops. Top of hill left signed Crooklets Beach

PETS: Bedrooms £2 Public areas (not in restaurant)
Exercise area (adjacent, close to the beach)
RESIDENT PETS: Bonnie - Old English/Border Collie cross, Charlie - Cocker Spaniel

Adjacent to the golf course and overlooking Crooklets Beach, this family owned hotel benefits from a relaxed and friendly atmosphere. Bedrooms vary in size and are all equipped to a similar standard. An interesting selection of dishes, using fresh local produce, is available in the restaurant; bar meals are also provided.
ROOMS: 16 en suite (6 fmly) No smoking in all bedrooms s £27-£45; d £54-£68 (incl. bkfst) **LB PARKING:** 20 **NOTES:** No smoking in restaurant **CARDS:** ▤ ▤ ▤ ▤ ▤

◆◆◆◆ Cliff Hotel

Maer Down, Crooklets Beach EX23 8NG
☎ 01288 353110 & 356833 ▤ 01288 353110
Dir: A39 through Bude. Left at top of High Street and past Somerfields. 1st right between golf course, straight over x-roads, hotel at end of road

PETS: Bedrooms (unattended) £1.50 Exercise area (nearby) RESIDENT PETS: Merlin & Lady (Boxers), 13 rabbits

Enjoying a cliff top location, overlooking the sea, this friendly and efficiently run hotel provides spacious, well-equipped bedroom. Public areas are numerous and include a bar and lounge as well as an impressive range of leisure facilities. Delicious dinners and tasty breakfasts are available in the attractive dining room.
FACILITIES: 15 en suite (15 fmly) No smoking in 1 bedroom No smoking in dining room TVB tea/coffee Direct dial from bedrooms Licensed Cen ht TVL No coaches Indoor swimming pool (heated) Tennis (hard) Gymnasium Pool Table Putting green Bowling green, canal fishing. Dinner Last d 6pm **PRICES:** s £49.80-£54.60; d £83-£91✳ **LB PARKING:** 18 **NOTES:** Closed Nov-Mar **CARDS:** ▤ ▤ ▤ ▤

◆◆◆◆ Fairway House

8 Downs View EX23 8RF
☎ 01288 355059
e-mail: enquiries@fairwayguesthouse.co.uk
Dir: Through town, past post office at top of main street. Follow brown tourist signs to Downs View from golf course.

PETS: Bedrooms £2.50 Exercise area (100yds)
RESIDENT PETS: Harvey (dog)

Genuine hospitality and attentive service awaits at this delightful Victorian terraced property, which overlooks the golf course and is close to the beach and town centre. Bedrooms are of a high standard, comfortable and with many thoughtful extra facilities. A hearty breakfast, using local produce, is served at separate tables.
FACILITIES: 7 rms (5 en suite) (1 fmly) No smoking TVB tea/coffee Cen ht TVL **PRICES:** s £20-£32; d £38-£50✳ **LB BB**
NOTES: Closed Dec-Jan

CAMBORNE
Map 02 SW64

★★★ 66% Tyacks

27 Commercial St TR14 8LD
☎ 01209 612424 ▤ 01209 612435
e-mail: tyacks@westcountryhotelrooms.co.uk
Dir: W on A30 past A3047 junct & turn off at Camborne West junct. Left & left again at rdbt, follow town centre signs. Hotel on left

PETS: Bedrooms (unattended) Public areas (On a lead)
Exercise area RESIDENT PETS: Sindy - Basset/Labrador cross, Alfie & Amber - Basset Hounds

This 18th-century former coaching inn has spacious, well-furnished public areas which include a smart lounge and bar, a popular public bar and a restaurant serving fixed-price and carte menus. The comfortable bedrooms are attractively decorated and well equipped; two have separate sitting areas.
ROOMS: 15 en suite (2 fmly) No smoking in 4 bedrooms s fr £49.50; d fr £75 (incl. bkfst) **LB FACILITIES:** STV 6x6 sports entertainment screen entertainment ch fac Xmas **PARKING:** 27 **NOTES:** No smoking in restaurant **CARDS:** ▤ ▤ ▤ ▤ ▤ ▤

CONSTANTINE
Map 02 SW72

★★ 70% ● Trengilly Wartha Inn

Nancenoy TR11 5RP
☎ 01326 340332 ▤ 01326 341121
e-mail: reception@trengilly.co.uk
Dir: A39 to Falmouth. At rdbt by Asda in Penryn, signed to Constantine then Gweek. Hotel signed on left in 1m

THE CIRCLE
Selected Individual Hotels
GREAT BRITAIN

PETS: Telephone for details

The charm and tranquillity of this character inn, which is located close to the Helford River, provides a welcoming environment. Interesting cuisine using local produce, fine wines, hand pulled ales and an impressive selection of malts are offered along with comfortable bedrooms and pleasant public rooms.
ROOMS: 6 en suite 2 annexe en suite (2 fmly) No smoking in 2 bedrooms s fr £49; d £78-£96 (incl. bkfst) **LB PARKING:** 50
NOTES: No smoking in restaurant RS 25 Dec (b'fast only) 31 Dec
CARDS: ▤ ▤ ▤ ▤ ▤ ▤

CRANTOCK — Map 02 SW76

★★★ 71% Crantock Bay
West Pentire TR8 5SE
☎ 01637 830229 ▤ 01637 831111
e-mail: stay@crantockbayhotel.co.uk
Dir: at Newquay A3075 to Redruth. After 500yds rt towards Crantock, follow signs to West Pentire

PETS: Bedrooms (unattended) £3 Exercise area Pet Food

This family-run hotel has spectacular sea views and a tradition of friendly and attentive service. With direct access to the beach from its four acres of grounds, and its extensive leisure facilities, the hotel is a great place for family guests. There are separate lounges, a spacious bar and enjoyable cuisine is served in the dining room.
ROOMS: 33 en suite (3 fmly) (10 GF) s £60-£90; d £120-£180 (incl. bkfst & dinner) **LB FACILITIES:** Indoor swimming (H) Tennis (hard) Sauna Gym Croquet lawn Putting green Jacuzzi Hotel leads on to sandy beach ch fac Xmas **PARKING:** 40
NOTES: No smoking in restaurant Closed 2 wks Nov & Jan RS Dec & Feb
CARDS: 🌑 💳 🌑 💳 🌑 💳

FALMOUTH — Map 02 SW83

★★★ 73% Green Lawns
THE INDEPENDENTS
Western Ter TR11 4QJ
☎ 01326 312734 ▤ 01326 211427
e-mail: info@greenlawnshotel.com
Dir: on A39

PETS: Bedrooms (unattended) Exercise area (0.25 miles)

This attractive property enjoys a convenient location close to the town centre and within easy reach of the sea. Spacious public areas include inviting lounges, an elegant restaurant, conference and meeting facilities and a leisure centre. Bedrooms vary in size and style and all are well equipped and comfortable. Friendly service is a highlight.
ROOMS: 39 en suite (8 fmly) (11 GF) No smoking in 24 bedrooms s £60-£110; d £110-£170 (incl. bkfst) **LB FACILITIES:** Indoor swimming (H) Tennis (hard & grass) Squash Sauna Solarium Gym Jacuzzi Swimming pool (cameras) **PARKING:** 69 **NOTES:** No smoking in restaurant Closed 24-30 Dec **CARDS:** 🌑 💳 🌑 💳 🌑 💳

All AA listed accommodation, restaurants and pubs can be found on the AA's website www.theAA.com

All information was correct at the time of going to press; we recommend you confirm details on booking

★★★ 72%
Falmouth Beach Resort Hotel
Gyllyngvase Beach, Seafront TR11 4NA
☎ 01326 310500 ▤ 01326 319147
e-mail: info@falmouthbeachhotel.co.uk
Dir: A39 to Falmouth, follow seafront signs.

Best Western

PETS: Bedrooms £5 Public areas (except restaurant) Exercise area (adjacent)

Enjoying wonderful views, this popular hotel is situated opposite the beach and within easy walking distance of Falmouth's attractions and port. A friendly atmosphere is maintained and guests have a good choice of leisure and fitness, entertainment and dining options. Bedrooms, many with balconies and sea views, are well equipped and comfortable.
ROOMS: 116 en suite 7 annexe en suite (20 fmly) (4 GF) No smoking in 94 bedrooms s £51-£61; d £102-£122 (incl. bkfst) **LB FACILITIES:** Spa STV Indoor swimming (H) Tennis (hard) Sauna Solarium Gym Jacuzzi Steam room entertainment Xmas **SERVICES:** Lift **PARKING:** 88
NOTES: No smoking in restaurant **CARDS:** 🌑 💳 🌑 💳 🌑 💳

★★★ 69% Falmouth
Castle Beach TR11 4NZ
☎ 01326 312671 & 0800 0193121 ▤ 01326 319533
e-mail: info@falmouthhotel.com
Dir: take A30 to Truro then A390 to Falmouth. Follow signs for beaches, hotel on seafront near Pendennis Castle

PETS: Bedrooms £7.50 Public areas Exercise area (50 metres) RESIDENT PETS: Luke (Black Labrador)

This spectacular beachfront Victorian property affords wonderful sea views from many of its comfortable bedrooms, some of which boast their own balconies. Spacious public areas include a number of inviting lounges, beautiful leafy grounds, a choice of dining options and an impressive range of leisure facilities.
ROOMS: 69 en suite 34 annexe en suite (13 fmly) No smoking in 18 bedrooms s £45-£50; d £65-£135 **LB FACILITIES:** STV Indoor swimming (H) Snooker Sauna Solarium Gym Putting green Jacuzzi Beauty Salon **SERVICES:** Lift **PARKING:** 175 **NOTES:** No smoking in restaurant Closed 24 Dec-2 Jan **CARDS:** 🌑 💳 🌑 💳

★★★ 66% Penmorvah Manor
Budock Water TR11 5ED
☎ 01326 250277 ▤ 01326 250509
e-mail: reception@penmorvah.co.uk
Dir: A39 to Hillhead rdbt, take 2nd exit. Right at Falmouth Football Club, through Budock and hotel opposite Penjerrick Gardens

PETS: Bedrooms £5 Public areas Exercise area Pet Food Large woodland area available for walking
RESIDENT PETS: Millie (Cocker Spaniel)

Situated within two miles of central Falmouth, this extended Victorian manor house is a peaceful hideaway, set in six acres of private woodland and gardens. Penmorvah is well positioned to visit the local gardens, and offers many garden tour breaks. Dinner features locally sourced quality ingredients such as Cornish cheeses, meat, fish and game.
ROOMS: 27 en suite (1 fmly) (10 GF) No smoking in all bedrooms s £50-£60; d £90-£130 (incl. bkfst) **LB FACILITIES:** Pool table Xmas
PARKING: 150 **NOTES:** No smoking in restaurant Closed 31 Dec-31 Jan
CARDS: 🌑 💳 🌑 💳 🌑 💳

♦♦♦♦ Prospect House

1 Church Rd, Penryn TR10 8DA
☎ 01326 373198 ▤ 01326 373198
e-mail: stay@prospecthouse.co.uk
Dir: turn off A39 at Treluswell rdbt onto B3292, past pub & through lights, after 50mtrs turn right through white gates next to phone box

> **PETS:** Bedrooms £2.50 Exercise area (150 metres)
> **RESIDENT PETS:** Jerry (black & white cat)

Situated close to the waterside, Prospect House is an attractive building, which was built for a ship's captain around 1820. The original style and charm of the house have been carefully maintained. The bedrooms are attractively decorated and well-equipped. A comfortable lounge is available and freshly cooked breakfasts are served in the elegant dining room.
FACILITIES: 4 rms (3 en suite) No smoking TVB tea/coffee Cen ht TVL No coaches Dinner Last d 9.30pm **PRICES:** s £30-£40; d £60-£70✱ **LB**
PARKING: 4 **CARDS:** ▭ ▭ ▭

♦♦♦♦ Rosemary Private Hotel

22 Gyllyngvase Ter TR11 4DL
☎ 01326 314669
e-mail: rosemaryhotel@lineone.net
Dir: A39 Melvill Rd signed to beaches & seafront, right into Gyllyngvase Rd, then 1st left into Gyllyngvase Terrace

> **PETS:** Bedrooms Public areas (except dining room) Exercise area (0.25 miles)

In a pleasant location with splendid views over Falmouth Bay, this is a friendly and comfortable place to stay. Bedrooms, some with sea views, are thoughtfully equipped and attractively decorated. There is a pleasant lounge where guests can relax and take a drink from the well-stocked bar. Dinner, by arrangement, offers a selection of tempting dishes.
FACILITIES: 10 en suite (2 fmly) No smoking in bedrooms No smoking in dining room TVB tea/coffee Licensed Cen ht TVL No coaches garden with sundeck & sea views **PRICES:** s £29-£32; d £58-£64✱
PARKING: 3 **NOTES:** Closed Nov-Jan **CARDS:** ▭ ▭ ▭ ▭ ▭

FOWEY   Map 02 SX15

★★★ 78% ◉◉ Fowey Hall

Hanson Dr PL23 1ET
☎ 01726 833866 ▤ 01726 834100
e-mail: info@foweyhall.com
Dir: in Fowey, cross mini rdbt into town centre. Pass school on right, after 400mtrs right into Hanson Dr

> **PETS:** Bedrooms £7 Public areas (on lead) Pet Food
> **RESIDENT PETS:** Millie (Collie/Spaniel cross)

Built in 1899, this listed mansion looks out on to the English Channel. The imaginatively designed bedrooms offer charm, individuality and sumptuous comfort, while beautifully appointed public rooms include the wood-panelled dining room where accomplished cuisine is served. Enjoying glorious views, the well-kept grounds have a covered pool and sunbathing area.
ROOMS: 16 en suite 8 annexe en suite (18 fmly) s £144-£200; d £160-£395 (incl. bkfst & dinner) **LB FACILITIES:** STV Indoor swimming (H) Croquet lawn Childrens play area, Table tennis, Bicycle hire ch fac Xmas **PARKING:** 40 **NOTES:** No smoking in restaurant
CARDS: ▭ ▭ ▭ ▭ ▭ ▭

★★ ◉◉ Marina

Esplanade PL23 1HY
☎ 01726 833315 ▤ 01726 832779
e-mail: marina.hotel@dial.pipex.com
Dir: into town down Lostwithiel St, near bottom of hill, right into Esplanade

> **PETS:** Bedrooms (unattended) Public areas Exercise area

Built in 1815 as a seaside retreat, the Marina has much style, and from its setting on the water's edge has glorious views of the river and the sea. Bedrooms, some with balconies, are spacious and comfortable - not forgetting the addition of a host of thoughtful touches provided. Skilled cuisine, using the freshest local produce, including fish landed nearby, is the hallmark of the waterside restaurant.
ROOMS: 13 en suite (1 fmly) No smoking in all bedrooms s £90; d £130 (incl. bkfst) **LB FACILITIES:** Fishing Sailing Xmas **PARKING:** 13
NOTES: No smoking in restaurant **CARDS:** ▭ ▭ ▭ ▭ ▭

♦♦♦♦ Carnethic House

Polvillion Rd PL23 1HQ
☎ 01726 833336 ▤ 01726 833296
e-mail: allisonpaul@btconnect.com
Dir: off A3082, directly opposite 'Welcome to Fowey' sign

> **PETS:** Bedrooms Public areas Exercise area (adjacent)
> **RESIDENT PETS:** Cocker Spaniel, Persian cat

A warm and friendly atmosphere awaits at this charming Regency house, situated in delightful gardens. Bedrooms are comfortable and well presented, the superior rooms offering extra space. The lounge benefits from a well-stocked bar, whilst the adjacent dining room is the venue for scrumptious breakfasts featuring local produce.
FACILITIES: 11 en suite (3 fmly) (2 GF) No smoking in bedrooms No smoking in dining room TVB tea/coffee Licensed Cen ht TVL Outdoor swimming pool (heated) Tennis (grass) Croquet lawn Putting green Badminton, golf practice net, lawn tennis **PRICES:** s £42.50-£52.50; d £70-£105✱ **LB PARKING:** 20
NOTES: Closed mid Nov-mid Feb **CARDS:** ▭ ▭ ▭ ▭ ▭

♦♦♦♦ Trevanion

70 Lostwithiel St PL23 1BQ
☎ 01726 832602 ▤ 01726 832602
e-mail: alisteve@trevanionguesthouse.co.uk
Dir: A3082 into Fowey, down hill turn left (Lostwithiel Street), continue down hill. Trevanion next on left

> **PETS:** Bedrooms (unattended) Public areas Exercise area (adjacent) food and bowls provided with prior notice
> **RESIDENT PETS:** Poppy (Hans Macaw)

A warm welcome is extended to all guests here at Trevanion. An ideal base for visiting The Eden Project and within easy walking distance of the historic town of Fowey, this 16th-century merchant's house provides comfortable accommodation. A hearty farmhouse style cooked breakfast, using many local ingredients, is served in the attractive dining room and a number of other menu options are available.
FACILITIES: 4 rms (3 en suite) (2 fmly) No smoking TVB tea/coffee Cen ht No coaches Garden Dinner Last d morning **PRICES:** s £30-£35; d £50-£60✱ **LB PARKING:** 4

England

GILLAN
Map 02 SW72

★★ Tregildry
TR12 6HG
☎ 01326 231378 ▤ 01326 231561
e-mail: trgildry@globalnet.co.uk
Dir: From Helston take A3083 Lizard Rd. 1st left turn for St Keverne and follow signs for Manaccan & Gillan

PETS: Bedrooms Exercise area (on site)

From its unspoilt and peaceful location Tregildry is blessed with both sea and river views. The tastefully furnished bedrooms and lounges are designed with comfort in mind and make the most of the wonderful views. Imaginative and innovative menus are served in the stylish dining room. There is direct access to the beach and adjacent coastal footpath.
ROOMS: 10 en suite No smoking in all bedrooms s £80-£99; d £140-£198 (incl. bkfst & dinner) **LB FACILITIES:** Boat hire Windsurfing **PARKING:** 15 **NOTES:** No children 8yrs No smoking in restaurant Closed Nov-Feb **CARDS:** ▭ ▭ ▭ ▭

LAND'S END
Map 02 SW32

★★★ 65% *The Land's End Hotel*
TR19 7AA
☎ 01736 871844 ▤ 01736 871599
e-mail: landsendhotel@madasafish.co.uk
Dir: from Penzance take A30 and follow Land's End signs. After Sennen 1m to Land's End

PETS: Telephone for details

This famous location provides a most impressive setting for this attractive hotel. Bedrooms, many with stunning views of the Atlantic, are pleasantly decorated and comfortable. A relaxing lounge and attractive bar are provided and in the 'Longships' restaurant, fresh local produce and fish dishes are a speciality.
ROOMS: 33 en suite (2 fmly) **FACILITIES:** Free entry Lands End visitor centre ch fac **PARKING:** 1000 **NOTES:** No smoking in restaurant **CARDS:** ▭ ▭ ▭ ▭ ▭

> **Don't forget to let proprietors know when you book that you're bringing your pet**

LAUNCESTON
Map 02 SX38

★★ 65% Eagle House
Castle St PL15 8BA
☎ 01566 772036 ▤ 01566 772036
e-mail: eaglehousehotel@aol.com
Dir: from Launceston on Holsworthy Rd follow brown signs for hotel

PETS: Bedrooms Exercise area

Next to the castle, this elegant Georgian house dates back to 1767 and is within walking distance of all local amenities. Many of the bedrooms have wonderful views over the Cornish countryside. A fixed-price menu is served in the restaurant, and on Sunday evenings a more modest menu is available.
ROOMS: 14 en suite (1 fmly) **FACILITIES:** STV **PARKING:** 100 **CARDS:** ▭ ▭ ▭ ▭ ▭

LISKEARD
Map 02 SX26

★★ ◉◉◉ ▲▲ Well House
St Keyne PL14 4RN
☎ 01579 342001 ▤ 01579 343891
e-mail: enquiries@wellhouse.co.uk
Dir: from Liskeard on A38 take B3254 to St Keyne (3 miles). At church fork left and hotel 0.5m

PETS: Bedrooms (unattended) Exercise area

Tucked away in an attractive valley and set in impressive grounds, Well House enjoys a tranquil setting. Friendly staff provide attentive yet relaxed service and add to the elegant atmosphere of the house. The comfortable lounge offers deep cushioned sofas and an open fire and in the intimate bar an extensive choice of wines and drinks is available. The accomplished cuisine features carefully sourced ingredients from local suppliers resulting in enjoyable dining.
ROOMS: 9 en suite (1 fmly) **FACILITIES:** Outdoor swimming (H) Tennis (hard) Croquet lawn Xmas **PARKING:** 30 **NOTES:** No smoking in restaurant Closed 2 weeks in Jan **CARDS:** ▭ ▭ ▭ ▭

LOOE
Map 02 SX25

★★★ 66% Hannafore Point
THE INDEPENDENTS
Marine Dr, West Looe PL13 2DG
☎ 01503 263273 ▤ 01503 263272
e-mail: stay@hannaforepointhotel.com
Dir: A38, left onto A385 to Looe. Over bridge left. Hotel 0.5m on left

PETS: Bedrooms £8 Public areas (except food service areas) Exercise area Pet Food

With panoramic coastal views embracing St George's Island around to Rame Head, this popular hotel provides a warm welcome. The wonderful view is also a feature of the spacious restaurant and bar, a scenic backdrop for dinners and breakfasts. Additional facilities include a heated indoor pool, squash court and gymnasium.
ROOMS: 37 en suite (5 fmly) s fr £48; d fr £96 (incl. bkfst) **LB FACILITIES:** Spa Indoor swimming (H) Squash Sauna Solarium Gym Jacuzzi Tennis/bowls 200yds away entertainment ch fac Xmas **SERVICES:** Lift **PARKING:** 32 **NOTES:** No smoking in restaurant **CARDS:** ▭ ▭ ▭ ▭ ▭

★★ 76% **Fieldhead**

 THE INDEPENDENTS

Portuan Rd, Hannafore PL13 2DR
☎ 01503 262689 📠 01503 264114
e-mail: enquiries@fieldheadhotel.co.uk
Dir: in Looe go over bridge & turn left, signposted 'Hannafore'. Past waterside church, up hill to seafront. 1st right then right again into Portuan Rd

PETS: Bedrooms (2 ground floor rooms only) Exercise area (200yds) Beach nearby that dogs can use RESIDENT PETS: Bones (Airedale)

Overlooking the bay, this engaging hotel has a relaxing atmosphere. Bedrooms are furnished with care and many have sea views. Smartly presented public areas include a convivial bar and restaurant, and outside there is a palm-filled garden with a secluded patio and swimming pool. The fixed-price menu changes daily and features quality local produce.
ROOMS: 15 en suite (2 fmly) (2 GF) s £30-£45; d £60-£80 (incl. bkfst)
LB FACILITIES: Outdoor swimming (H) ch fac **PARKING:** 15
NOTES: No smoking in restaurant Closed Xmas
CARDS: 〇〇〇〇〇

♦♦♦ **Gulls Hotel**

Hannafore Rd PL13 2DE
☎ 01503 262531
Dir: A38 from Plymouth, A387 to Looe, cross bridge from East Looe to West Looe, left by river to seafront, turn right by pub & right again

PETS: Bedrooms Public areas (not in dining room) Exercise area (200 yards) RESIDENT PETS: Lady (Poodle), Amber & Ginty (cats)

This friendly, family-run establishment enjoys an elevated position with spectacular views of both East and West Looe. The bedrooms are neat and attractive and guests have use of a comfortable lounge and cosy bar. In warmer weather guests can relax on the terrace.
FACILITIES: 10 rms (4 en suite) (1 fmly) No smoking TVB tea/coffee Licensed Cen ht TVL No coaches **PRICES:** s £18-£21; d £36-£50✳ **LB BB PARKING:** 3 **NOTES:** Closed Nov-Etr

> **All information was correct at the time of going to press; we recommend you confirm details on booking**

★★★ 69% **Restormel Hotel**

Best Western

Castle Hill PL22 0DD
☎ 01208 872223 📠 01208 873568
e-mail: restlodge@aol.com
Dir: on A390 in Lostwithiel

PETS: Bedrooms (unattended) £10 Exercise area (200mtrs)

A short drive from the Eden Project, this popular hotel offers a friendly welcome to all visitors and is ideally situated for exploring the area. The original building houses the bar, restaurant and lounges, with some original features adding to the character. Bedrooms are comfortably furnished, with a number overlooking the secluded outdoor pool.
ROOMS: 24 en suite 12 annexe en suite (2 fmly) No smoking in 30 bedrooms s fr £75; d £100-£120 (incl. bkfst) **LB FACILITIES:** STV Outdoor swimming (H) Xmas **PARKING:** 40 **NOTES:** No smoking in restaurant **CARDS:**

★★ 70% **Godolphin Arms**

TR17 0EN
☎ 01736 710202 📠 01736 710171
e-mail: enquiries@godolphinarms.co.uk
Dir: from A30 follow Marazion signs for 1m to hotel. At end of the causeway to St Michael's Mount

PETS: Bedrooms (unattended) Public areas (except restaurant) Exercise area (100yds)

This 170-year-old waterside hotel is in a prime location. Stunning views of St Michael's Mount provide a backdrop for the restaurant and lounge bar. Bedrooms are colourful, comfortable and spacious. A choice of menu is offered in the main restaurant and the Gig Bar, all with an emphasis on local seafood.
ROOMS: 10 en suite (2 fmly) (2 GF) s £45-£69.50; d £70-£119 (incl. bkfst) **LB FACILITIES:** STV Direct access to large beach
PARKING: 48 **NOTES:** No smoking in restaurant Closed 24 & 25 Dec
CARDS: 〇〇〇〇〇

> 🐓 **Places with this symbol are farms**

> **All abbreviations are explained on page 9**

> 🍺 **Places with this symbol are pubs**

> 🌲 **Places with this symbol are country house hotels**

MAWNAN SMITH
Map 02 SW72

★★★ 78% ♨ Meudon
TR11 5HT
☎ 01326 250541 📠 01326 250543
e-mail: wecare@meudon.co.uk
Dir: from Truro A39 towards Falmouth at Hillhead rdbt, follow signs to Maenporth Beach. Hotel on left 1m after beach

PETS: Bedrooms (unattended) £7.50 Exercise area (adjacent) 8.5 acres of subtropical gardens & private beach
RESIDENT PETS: Jerry & Felix (cats)

This charming late Victorian mansion, with its friendly hospitality, attentive service and impressive nine acres of gardens leading down to a private beach, provides a relaxing place to stay. Bedrooms are comfortable and spacious and cuisine features the best of local Cornish produce served in the conservatory restaurant. Meudon Hotel has been Highly Commended in the AA Accessible Hotel of the Year Award 2004-5.
ROOMS: 29 en suite (2 fmly) (15 GF) s £69-£125; d £138-£250 (incl. bkfst & dinner) **LB FACILITIES:** Fishing Riding Private beach, Hair salon, Yacht for skippered charter, sub-tropical gardens ch fac Xmas
SERVICES: Lift **PARKING:** 52 **NOTES:** No smoking in restaurant Closed 3-31 Jan **CARDS:** 💳

MEVAGISSEY
Map 02 SX04

★★ 65% Spa Hotel
Polkirt Hill PL26 6UY
☎ 01726 842244 📠 01726 842244
e-mail: Alan@the-spa-hotel.fsnet.co.uk
Dir: from St Austell follow Mevagissey then Portmellon signs. Sign for hotel on right

PETS: Bedrooms Public areas (except lounge) Exercise area (300yds) Pet Food

Quietly situated in an elevated position, this family-run hotel offers a friendly welcome with wonderful coastal and countryside views. A wide choice of bedrooms is available; all are light, airy and attractively decorated, and some have patio areas leading on to well-tended gardens. There is a comfortable, cane-furnished lounge and a cosy bar.
ROOMS: 11 en suite (5 fmly) No smoking in 7 bedrooms s £40-£50; d £64-£70 (incl. bkfst) **LB FACILITIES:** Putting green **PARKING:** 12
NOTES: No smoking in restaurant **CARDS:** 💳

MULLION
Map 02 SW61

★★★ 71% Polurrian
TR12 7EN
☎ 01326 240421 📠 01326 240083
e-mail: polurotel@aol.com
Dir: A30 onto A3076 to Truro. Follow signs for Helston on A39 then A394 to The Lizard and Mullion

PETS: Bedrooms (unattended) £8 Exercise area

This long-established hotel is set in 12 acres of landscaped gardens, 300 feet above the sea. The spectacular views over Polurrian Cove will remain long in the memory, along with the wonderful sunsets. Public areas are spacious and comfortable, and the bedrooms are individually styled. There is a well-equipped leisure centre.
ROOMS: 39 en suite (22 fmly) s £55-£120 (incl. bkfst & dinner) **LB FACILITIES:** STV Indoor swimming (H) Outdoor swimming (H) Tennis (hard) Squash Snooker Sauna Solarium Gym Croquet lawn Putting green Jacuzzi Cricket net Whirlpool Mountain bikes Surfing Body boarding entertainment ch fac Xmas **PARKING:** 80
NOTES: No smoking in restaurant
CARDS: 💳

NEWQUAY
Map 02 SW86

★★★★ 68% Headland
Fistral Beach TR7 1EW
☎ 01637 872211 📠 01637 872212
e-mail: office@headlandhotel.co.uk
Dir: off A30 onto A392 at Indian Queens, approaching Newquay follow signs for Fistral Beach, hotel adjacent

PETS: Bedrooms (unattended) Dogs £8-10, others by negotiation Public areas (except restaurant) Exercise area (in grounds) Pet Food tinned & dried food available, plus any kitchen scraps **RESIDENT PETS:** Milly - Airedale terrier

This Victorian hotel enjoys a stunning location overlooking the sea on three sides - views can be enjoyed from most of the windows. Bedrooms are comfortable and spacious, with a number having now been refurbished. Grand public areas, with impressive floral displays, include various lounges and dining options.
ROOMS: 104 en suite (40 fmly) s £70-£123; d £110-£197 (incl. bkfst)
LB FACILITIES: Spa STV Indoor swimming (H) Outdoor swimming (H) Golf 9 Tennis (hard) Snooker Sauna Gym Croquet lawn Putting green Jacuzzi Children's outdoor play area, Harry Potter playroom entertainment ch fac Xmas **SERVICES:** Lift **PARKING:** 400 **NOTES:** No smoking in restaurant Closed 23-27 Dec **CARDS:** 💳

★★★ 70% **Hotel Bristol**

Narrowcliff TR7 2PQ
☎ 01637 875181 📠 01637 879347
e-mail: info@hotelbristol.co.uk
Dir: off A30 onto A392, then onto A3058. Hotel 2.5m on left

PETS: Bedrooms (unattended) £5 **Exercise area**
(50 metres)

This hotel is conveniently situated and many of the bedrooms
enjoy fine sea views. Staff are friendly and provide a professional
and attentive service. There is a range of comfortable lounges,
ideal for relaxing prior to eating in the elegant dining room. There
are also leisure and conference facilities.
ROOMS: 74 en suite (23 fmly) s £55-£80; d £90-£130 LB
FACILITIES: STV Indoor swimming (H) Snooker Sauna Solarium Table
tennis ch fac Xmas **SERVICES:** Lift **PARKING:** 105
NOTES: No smoking in restaurant
CARDS: 💳

★★★ 69% **Esplanade Hotel**

Esplanade Rd, Pentire TR7 1PS
☎ 01637 873333 📠 01637 851413
e-mail: info@newquay-hotels.co.uk
*Dir: from A30 take A392 at Indian Queens towards Newquay, follow to
rdbt and take left to Pentire, then right fork to beach*

PETS: Bedrooms (unattended) £4 **Exercise area (Grass**
area across from hotel)

Overlooking the rolling breakers at Fistral Beach, this family-
owned hotel offers a friendly welcome. There is a choice of
bedroom sizes; all have modern facilities and the most popular
rooms benefit from stunning sea views. There are a number of
bars, a continental-style coffee shop and the more formal Ocean
View Restaurant.
ROOMS: 93 en suite (44 fmly) No smoking in 5 bedrooms s £28-£55;
d £56-£110 (incl. bkfst & dinner) LB **FACILITIES:** Spa STV Indoor
swimming (H) Outdoor swimming (H) Sauna Solarium Jacuzzi Table
tennis entertainment ch fac Xmas **SERVICES:** Lift **PARKING:** 40
NOTES: No smoking in restaurant
CARDS: 💳

★★★ 67% **Barrowfield**

Hilgrove Rd TR7 2QY
☎ 01637 878878 📠 01637 879490
e-mail: booking@barrowfield.demon.co.uk
*Dir: A3058 to Newquay towards Quintrell Downs. Right at rdbt into town,
left at Texaco garage*

PETS: Bedrooms £4 **Exercise area (200yds)**

Offering a pleasant range of facilities and spacious public rooms,
this popular hotel is ideally situated and offers friendly and
attentive service. Bedrooms, some with sea views and balconies,
are well appointed and comfortable. Public areas include an
elegant restaurant, spacious foyer lounge, attractive coffee shop
and an intimate piano bar.
ROOMS: 81 en suite 2 annexe en suite (18 fmly) s £35-£42; d £70-£84
(incl. bkfst & dinner) LB **FACILITIES:** Spa STV Indoor swimming (H)
Outdoor swimming (H) Snooker Sauna Solarium Gym Jacuzzi Table
tennis, Coffee shop, pool room, snooker room, trimnasium entertainment
Xmas **SERVICES:** Lift **PARKING:** 70 **NOTES:** No smoking in restaurant
CARDS: 💳

★★ 72% **Whipsiderry**

Trevelgue Rd, Porth TR7 3LY
☎ 01637 874777 📠 01637 874777
e-mail: info@whipsiderry.co.uk
*Dir: right onto Padstow road (B3276) out of Newquay, in 0.5m right at
Trevelgue Rd*

PETS: Bedrooms (unattended) **Public areas (some areas)**
Exercise area

Quietly located, overlooking Porth Beach, this friendly hotel offers
bedrooms in a variety of sizes and styles, many with superb views.
A daily-changing menu offers interesting and well-cooked dishes
with the emphasis on fresh, local produce. An outdoor pool is
available, and at dusk guests can enjoy badger-watching in the
attractive grounds.
ROOMS: 20 rms (19 en suite) (5 fmly) (3 GF) No smoking in
8 bedrooms s £45-£54; d £90-£108 (incl. bkfst & dinner) LB
FACILITIES: Outdoor swimming (H) Sauna American pool entertainment
ch fac Xmas **PARKING:** 30 **NOTES:** No smoking in restaurant
Closed Nov-Etr (ex Xmas) **CARDS:** 💳

★★ 69% **Philema**

1 Esplanade Rd, Pentire TR7 1PY
☎ 01637 872571 📠 01637 873188
e-mail: info@philema.co.uk
*Dir: from A30 follow A392 then signs for Fistral Beach. Hotel on junction
Esplanade Rd & Pentire Ave*

PETS: Bedrooms (unattended) £5 **Exercise area (250yds)**
RESIDENT PETS: Peckham - budgie

With excellent views over Fistral beach, the Philema provides a
relaxed and friendly family environment. Extensive leisure facilities
are available, including the heated indoor pool, which overlooks
the garden. Many rooms have wonderful views and all are
comfortably furnished. The attractive dining room offers a range
of home-cooked dishes.
ROOMS: 32 en suite (27 fmly) **FACILITIES:** Spa STV Indoor
swimming (H) Snooker Sauna Solarium Jacuzzi pool table, games
machine entertainment ch fac Xmas **PARKING:** 40
NOTES: No smoking in restaurant Closed 2 Jan-2 Feb
CARDS: 💳

◆◆◆◆◆ ◉ 🚫 **Corisande Manor Hotel**

Riverside Av, Pentire TR7 1PL
☎ 01637 872042 📠 01637 874557
e-mail: relax@corisande.com

PETS: Bedrooms

Tucked away in a delightful location on the side of an estuary, this
attractive manor house has a tranquil and impressive setting.
Friendly proprietors provide attentive and skilled service.
Bedrooms, many with superb views, are tastefully decorated and
furnished with great care, imagination and individuality. Freshly
prepared dishes are served from a daily-changing menu and
supported by a lovingly compiled wine list of considerable merit.
FACILITIES: 12 en suite No smoking in dining room TVB tea/coffee
Direct dial from bedrooms Licensed No coaches Dinner Last d 6pm
PRICES: d £150-£210✳ LB **PARKING:** 19 **CARDS:** 💳

England

NEWQUAY continued

✦✦✦✦ Kellsboro Hotel
12 Henver Rd TR7 3BJ
☎ 01637 874620
e-mail: kellsborohotel@btconnect.com
Dir: From A30 follow A392 to Quintrell Downs, turn right at rdbt (A3058) follow road approx 2m, sign on right for "Lusty Glaze Beach". Hotel on left

PETS: Bedrooms £3 (reception area only) Exercise area (100yds) RESIDENT PETS: 2 Bearded Collies & 1 Beagle

Conveniently located for the town and beaches, this popular hotel is spacious and comfortable, and offers friendly hospitality. A large bar and games area is provided for guests' use and the indoor pool is also popular. Traditional well-cooked dinners are served in the attractive dining room.
FACILITIES: 14 en suite (5 fmly) No smoking in bedrooms No smoking in dining room No smoking in 1 lounge TVB tea/coffee Licensed Cen ht TVL No children 2 yrs Indoor swimming pool (heated) Pool Table Dinner Last d at breakfast **PRICES:** d £52-£72✱ **LB PARKING:** 12 **NOTES:** Closed Nov & Feb **CARDS:** 💳 💳 💳 💳 💳

PADSTOW   Map 02 SW97

★★★ 70% 🏵 The Metropole
Station Rd PL28 8DB
☎ 01841 532486 📠 01841 532867
e-mail: info@the-metropole.co.uk
Dir: M5/A30 pass Launceston, turn off & follow signs for Wadebridge & N Cornwall. Take A39 & follow signs for Padstow

Best Western

PETS: Bedrooms (unattended) £5 Public areas (except restaurant)

This long-established hotel first opened its doors to guests back in 1904 and there is still an air of the sophistication and elegance of a bygone age. Bedrooms are soundly appointed and well-equipped and dining options include the informal Met Café Bar and the main restaurant, with enjoyable cuisine and wonderful views over the Camel estuary.
ROOMS: 50 en suite (3 fmly) (2 GF) No smoking in 10 bedrooms s £69-£105; d £138-£170 (incl. bkfst & dinner) **LB FACILITIES:** Outdoor swimming (H) Swimming pool open Jul & Aug only Xmas **SERVICES:** Lift **PARKING:** 36 **NOTES:** No smoking in restaurant
CARDS: 💳 💳 💳 💳 💳

★★ 67% The Old Ship Hotel
Mill Square PL28 8AE
☎ 01841 532357 📠 01841 533211
e-mail: stay@oldshiphotel-padstow.co.uk
Dir: from M5 take A30 to Bodmin then A389 to Padstow, follow brown tourist signs to car park

PETS: Bedrooms £2 Public areas Exercise area (100yds)

This attractive inn is situated in the heart of the old town's quaint and winding streets, just a short walk from the harbour. A warm welcome is assured, accommodation is pleasant and comfortable, and public areas offer plenty of character. Freshly caught fish features on both the bar and restaurant menus.
ROOMS: 14 en suite (4 fmly) s £35-£45; d £70-£100 (incl. bkfst) **LB**
FACILITIES: STV entertainment Xmas **PARKING:** 20
NOTES: No smoking in restaurant **CARDS:** 💳 💳 💳 💳 💳

◉◉◉ 🏨 The Seafood Restaurant
Riverside PL28 8BY
☎ 01841 532700 📠 01841 532942
e-mail: reservations@rickstein.com
Dir: A38 towards Newquay, then A389 towards Padstow. After 3m, right at T-junct, follow signs for Padstow town centre. Restaurant on left

PETS: Bedrooms (unattended) Exercise area (500yds)

Rick Stein's Seafood Restaurant enjoys an enviable reputation for the freshness and quality of its cuisine, and it is no surprise to discover that such high standards are repeated in the accommodation here. Each of the bedrooms is spacious and comfortable, complete with fine quality fixtures and fittings. Additional rooms are housed close by in St.Edmunds, where refurbishment has resulted in luxurious standards with much style.
ROOMS: 13 en suite 19 annexe en suite (7 fmly) (3 GF)
FACILITIES: STV **PARKING:** 22 **NOTES:** Closed 1 May & 24-26 Dec
CARDS: 💳 💳 💳 💳 💳

✦✦✦✦✦ ◉ 🛏 🍴 🚪
St Petroc's Hotel and Bistro
4 New St PL28 8EA
☎ 01841 532700 📠 01841 532942
e-mail: reservations@rickstein.com
Dir: A30-A38-A389 towards Padstow, continue 3m, right at T-junct, follow signs to Padstow town centre

PETS: Bedrooms (unattended) Exercise area (200yds)

One of the oldest buildings in town, this charming establishment is located just up the hill from the picturesque harbourside. Style, comfort and individuality are all great strengths here, particularly so in the smartly appointed and impressively equipped bedrooms. Lunch, dinner and breakfast all reflect a serious approach to cuisine and the restaurant has a relaxed, bistro style, which is particularly popular. Lounges, a reading room and lovely gardens complete the picture.
FACILITIES: 10 en suite No smoking in dining room TVB tea/coffee Direct dial from bedrooms Licensed Cen ht No coaches Dinner Last d 10pm **PRICES:** d £110-£180✱ **LB PARKING:** 10
NOTES: Closed 1 May & 24-26 Dec **CARDS:** 💳 💳 💳 💳 💳

✦✦✦✦ The Newlands Hotel
PL28 8QX
☎ 01841 520469
e-mail: enquiries@newlandshoteltrevone.co.uk
Dir: turn off B3276 Padstow to Newquay road at Windmill. Follow road towards beach and Hotel on left just before beach car park

PETS: Bedrooms (unattended) Public areas (except dining room) Exercise area (20yds) Dogs are put in rooms with independent access to car park RESIDENT PETS: Mac - cat

This friendly hotel is just a short walk from the beautiful sandy beach at Trevone Bay. Bedrooms, some of which are on the ground floor, are light, airy and well equipped. Two comfortable lounges and a cosy bar are available to guests, and imaginative, home-cooked meals can be enjoyed in the dining room.
FACILITIES: 11 en suite (3 fmly) (5 GF) No smoking TVB tea/coffee Licensed Cen ht TVL Dinner Last d 4pm **PRICES:** s £28-£35; d £56-£70✱ **LB PARKING:** 14 **NOTES:** rs Nov-Mar
CARDS: 💳 💳 💳 💳 💳

◆◆◆◆ 🍴 Rick Stein's Cafe
10 Middle St PL28 8AP
☎ 01841 532700 📠 01841 532942
e-mail: reservations@rickstein.com
Dir: off B3276 at junct signposted St Petrocs Church, follow road past church on right, 3rd turning right is Middle Street, house halfway on right

PETS: Bedrooms (unattended) Exercise area

Another Rick Stein success story, this lively café by day, restaurant by night, offers good food, quality accommodation and is conveniently located just a short walk from the harbourside. Three rooms are available, all quite different but sharing similarly high standards of cosseting comfort. Friendly and personable staff complete the picture.
FACILITIES: 3 en suite (1 fmly) No smoking in dining room TVB tea/coffee Direct dial from bedrooms Licensed Cen ht Dinner Last d 9.30pm **NOTES:** Closed 1 May & 22-27 Dec
CARDS: 🖭 🖭 💳 🖭 🖭

PENSILVA   Map 02 SX27

★★ 66% 🌑 Wheal Tor Country Hotel
Caradon Hill PL14 5PJ
☎ 01579 362281 📠 01579 363401
e-mail: enquiries@whealtorhotel.co.uk

PETS: Bedrooms (One only) £10 Exercise area (adjacent)

Wheal Tor has splendid views over Bodmin Moor and is set well away from the road. The proprietors provide friendly hospitality. The hotel and its 'Restaurant des Hauteurs' are proving increasingly popular with locals, offering attractive and accomplished cuisine.
ROOMS: 7 en suite (1 fmly) No smoking in all bedrooms s £55-£72; d £65-£95 (incl. bkfst) **LB FACILITIES:** Xmas **PARKING:** 50
NOTES: No smoking in restaurant **CARDS:** 🖭 🖭 💳 🖭 🖭

PENZANCE   Map 02 SW43

★★★ 76% 🌑🌑 Mount Prospect
Britons Hill TR18 3AE
☎ 01736 363117 📠 01736 350970
e-mail: enquiries@hotelpenzance.com
Dir: from A30 pass heliport on right, left at next rdbt for town centre. 3rd right and hotel on right

THE CIRCLE
Selected Individual Hotels
GREAT BRITAIN

PETS: Bedrooms £5 Public areas (Not in restaurant)
Exercise area (300mtrs) **RESIDENT PETS:** Thomas & Gerry (Birman cats)

This Edwardian house has been tastefully redesigned, focusing on the contemporary Bay Restaurant. Style is not limited to the rooms, but is also apparent in the cuisine based upon fresh Cornish produce. Bedrooms have also been appointed to modern standards and are particularly well-equipped; many rooms have views across Mounts Bay.
ROOMS: 24 en suite (2 fmly) (2 GF) No smoking in 20 bedrooms s £58-£87.50; d £90-£125 (incl. bkfst) **LB FACILITIES:** STV Outdoor swimming (H) ch fac Xmas **PARKING:** 14 **NOTES:** No smoking in restaurant RS Nov-Apr **CARDS:** 🖭 🖭 💳 🖭 🖭

★★★ 68% Queen's
The Promenade TR18 4HG
☎ 01736 362371 📠 01736 350033
e-mail: enquiries@queens-hotel.com
Dir: A30 to Penzance, follow signs for seafront, pass harbour and into promenade, hotel 0.5m on right

PETS: Bedrooms Public areas Exercise area

With views across Mounts Bay towards Newlyn, this impressive Victorian hotel has a long and distinguished history. Comfortable public areas are filled with interesting pictures and artefacts, and in the dining room guests can choose from the daily-changing menu. Bedrooms, many with sea views, vary in style and size.
ROOMS: 70 en suite (10 fmly) s £49-£69; d £94-£148 (incl. bkfst) **LB**
FACILITIES: STV Xmas **SERVICES:** Lift **PARKING:** 50
NOTES: No smoking in restaurant
CARDS: 🖭 🖭 💳 🖭 🖭 🖭

◆◆◆ Woodstock
29 Morrab Rd TR18 4EZ
☎ 01736 369049 📠 01736 369049
e-mail: info@woodstockguesthouse.co.uk
Dir: from railway station, along seafront 1km, right at approach to Queens Hotel. Woodstock 200mtrs on right

PETS: Bedrooms (unattended) £2 Exercise area
(200 metres) **RESIDENT PETS:** Molly (Collie), Milly (cat)

This smart Victorian terraced house sits in well-tended gardens in a quiet residential area convenient for both the town and seafront. The proprietors are friendly and provide attentive service. Bedrooms are smartly decorated and well-equipped and beds are particularly comfortable. Hearty breakfasts are served in the dining room.
FACILITIES: 8 rms (5 en suite) (1 fmly) (1 GF) No smoking TVB tea/coffee No children 5yrs No coaches **PRICES:** s £20-£30; d £40-£60❋
NOTES: Closed Jan **CARDS:** 🖭 🖭 💳 🖭 🖭

All AA listed accommodation, restaurants and pubs can be found on the AA's website www.theAA.com

England

PENZANCE continued

◆◆◆ Penmorvah Hotel
61 Alexandra Rd TR18 4LZ
☎ 01736 363711
Dir: from A30 follow Penzance town centre signs past Rail station. Follow coast road to mini-rdbt. Right into Alexandra Rd. Penmorvah is on right with blue sign

PETS: Bedrooms Public areas (except dining room) Exercise area RESIDENT PETS: Paddy - Lhasa Apso, Max - Jack Russell

Situated in a quiet, tree-lined road only a short walk from the seafront and town centre and convenient for the ferry port, the Penmorvah provides a friendly and relaxing atmosphere. Bedrooms are well-appointed, comfortable and equipped with many thoughtful extras. Well-cooked breakfast is served in the attractive dining room. **FACILITIES:** 8 en suite (2 fmly) (1 GF) No smoking TVB tea/coffee Cen ht TVL **PRICES:** s £20-£25; d £40-£50✳ **CARDS:** 🃏

POLPERRO   Map 02 SX25

★★★ 76% ◉◉ ♨ Talland Bay
PL13 2JB
☎ 01503 272667 📠 01503 272940
e-mail: reception@tallandbayhotel.co.uk
Dir: signed from x-rds on A387 Looe to Polperro road

PETS: Bedrooms (Some rooms) £7.50 Exercise area

The hotel has the benefit of being sited in its own extensive gardens which run down almost to the cliff edge. The atmosphere is warm and friendly. Bedrooms have a number of styles, some are with sea views and balconies. New talent in the kitchen is attracting very good reviews. **ROOMS:** 20 en suite 3 annexe en suite (4 fmly) (6 GF) No smoking in 3 bedrooms s £80-£170; d £90-£180 (incl. bkfst) **LB FACILITIES:** STV Outdoor swimming (H) Croquet lawn Putting green Xmas **PARKING:** 23 **NOTES:** No smoking in restaurant **CARDS:** 🃏

◆◆◆◆ Higher Polgassic
Lansallos PL13 2PY
☎ 01503 272454 📠 01503 272454
e-mail: info@higherpolgassic.co.uk
Dir: from A390 turn left onto B3359, after 5.5m turn right (signposted Lansallos

PETS: Bedrooms £2 Exercise area RESIDENT PETS: Chas - Cavalier King Charles spaniel, Lowey - budgie

This light and airy, family-run establishment provides a peaceful setting for a stress-free break. Just 1.5 miles from the beach, this is an excellent base for exploring south-east Cornwall. Being a bungalow, there is level access throughout. Bedrooms are neatly presented and offer good levels of comfort and quality. Evening meals, by prior arrangement, come highly recommended. A self-catering holiday cottage is also available. **FACILITIES:** 3 en suite (3 GF) No smoking TVB tea/coffee Cen ht No coaches 2 acre grounds, miniature passenger steam railway Dinner Last d 5pm **PRICES:** s £30-£35; d £46-£54✳ **LB PARKING:** 10

◆◆◆◆ Penryn House Hotel
The Coombes PL13 2RQ
☎ 01503 272157 📠 01503 273055
e-mail: chrispidcock@aol.com
Dir: follow A387 to Polperro, at mini-rdbt bear left down hill into village, ignoring restricted access sign. Hotel 200yds on left

PETS: Bedrooms Sep Accom (Office) (unattended) £5 per stay Public areas (except restaurant) Exercise area (200yds) food by prior request RESIDENT PETS: Yogi - Weimaraner

Penryn House offers a relaxed atmosphere and warm welcome with every effort made to ensure a memorable stay. Bedrooms are neatly presented and reflect the age and character of the building. After a day's exploration, a drink at the bar followed by enjoyable and accomplished cuisine should prove a satisfying end to the day. **FACILITIES:** 11 rms (11 en suite) No smoking in bedrooms No smoking in dining room TVB tea/coffee Direct dial from bedrooms Licensed No coaches Dinner Last d 9.30pm **PRICES:** s £25-£31; d £50-£68✳ **LB PARKING:** 13 **NOTES:** rs Nov-Etr **CARDS:** 🃏

PORTHCURNO   Map 02 SW32

◆◆◆◆ The Porthcurno Hotel
The Valley TR19 6JX
☎ 01736 810119 📠 01736 810711
e-mail: mail@porthcurnohotel.co.uk
Dir: off A30 onto B3283, through St Buryan and after 3m turn left for Porthcurno, hotel is on right as you go down the valley

PETS: Bedrooms (in one room only) £5 Exercise area (25yds)

Situated in the dramatic Cornish cove of Porthcurno, the drama also continues in the nearby Minack Theatre. This hotel provides convenient and comfortable accommodation and guests are assured of a friendly welcome and attentive service. Food is an important feature, with fresh local ingredients on the daily-changing menu served in the stylish dining room, which enjoys spectacular views. Guests may enjoy the sub-tropical gardens and perhaps take a drink on the balcony. **FACILITIES:** 12 rms (8 en suite) (1 fmly) (1 GF) No smoking in 2 bedrooms No smoking in dining room TV8B tea/coffee Licensed Cen ht TVL No coaches Dinner Last d 8pm **PRICES:** d £55-£90✳ **LB PARKING:** 18 **NOTES:** rs Oct-May **CARDS:** 🃏

PORT ISAAC   Map 02 SW98

◆◆◆◆ The Corn Mill
Port Isaac Rd, Trelill PL30 3HZ
☎ 01208 851079
Dir: between villages of Pendoggett and Trelill

PETS: Bedrooms £2 RESIDENT PETS: Digger (Jack Russell), Mugsy (cat), Millie (cat), Rosie (retriever), geese, guinea fowl & ducks

Dating from the 18th century, this former mill has been lovingly restored to provide a charming home, packed full of character. The bedrooms are individually styled and personal touches

continued

contribute to a wonderfully relaxed and homely atmosphere. The farmhouse kitchen is the venue for a delicious breakfast.
FACILITIES: 3 rms (2 en suite) (1 fmly) No smoking in bedrooms No smoking in dining room TV1B tea/coffee Cen ht No coaches
PRICES: d £60✱ **PARKING:** 3 **NOTES:** Closed 24 Dec-5 Jan

PORTSCATHO — Map 02 SW83

🐕 🐈

★★★ 🏵🏵 Rosevine

TR2 5EW
☎ 01872 580206 📠 01872 580230
e-mail: info@rosevinehotels.co.uk
Dir: from St Austell take A390 for Truro. Left onto B3287 to Tregony.Take A3078 through Ruan High Lanes. Hotel 3rd left

PETS: **Bedrooms Public areas (with prior arrangement only) Exercise area (100yds) Pet Food**

Set in secluded splendour, with views over beautifully tended gardens towards the sea, this Georgian country house has its own beach at the head of the Roseland peninsula. The proprietors and staff are attentive and friendly and create a relaxed atmosphere. Bedrooms are impressively equipped, with fresh fruit, flowers and up-to-date reading material - most enjoy the views and some have balconies. Cuisine features the local harvest of fresh fish and shellfish and the best of Cornish produce.
ROOMS: 11 en suite 6 annexe en suite (7 fmly) (3 GF) s £126-£178; d £168-£224 (incl. bkfst) **LB** **FACILITIES:** Indoor swimming (H) Table tennis Childrens playroom entertainment ch fac **PARKING:** 20
NOTES: No smoking in restaurant Closed Dec-8 Feb
CARDS:

REDRUTH — Map 02 SW64

🐕 🐈 🐇 🐦

★★ 65% Crossroads Lodge

THE INDEPENDENTS

Scorrier TR16 5BP
☎ 01209 820551 📠 01209 820392
e-mail: crossroads@hotelstruro.com
Dir: turn off A30 onto A3047 towards Scorrier

PETS: **Bedrooms (unattended) £4.50 Exercise area (surrounding area)**

Situated on an historic stanary site and conveniently located just off the A30, the Crossroads Lodge has a smart appearance with attractive flower baskets. Bedrooms are soundly furnished and include executive and family rooms. Public areas include an attractive dining room, a quiet lounge and a lively bar. Conference, banqueting and business facilities are also available.
ROOMS: 36 en suite (2 fmly) (8 GF) No smoking in 8 bedrooms s £44-£54; d £60-£67.50 (incl. bkfst) **LB** **FACILITIES:** ch fac
SERVICES: Lift **PARKING:** 140 **NOTES:** No smoking in restaurant
CARDS:

★ Red stars indicate the AA's Top 200 Hotels in Britain & Ireland

Please mention AA Pet Friendly Places to Stay when booking

ST AGNES — Map 02 SW75

🐕 🐇 🐦 🐎

★★★ 72% Rose in Vale Country House

Mithian TR5 OQD
☎ 01872 552202 📠 01872 552700
e-mail: reception@rose-in-vale-hotel.co.uk
Dir: A30 through Cornwall, right onto B3277 signed St Agnes. Pick up Rose-in-Vale directions within 500yds

PETS: **Bedrooms (unattended) £5 Exercise area (on site)**
RESIDENT PETS: Jake & Katy - Labradors, ducks

Peacefully located in a wooded valley this Georgian manor house has a wonderfully relaxed atmosphere and abundant charm and where guests are assured of a warm welcome. Accommodation varies in size and style; several rooms are situated on the ground floor. An imaginative fixed-price menu featuring local produce is served in the spacious restaurant.
ROOMS: 18 en suite (3 fmly) (3 GF) No smoking in all bedrooms s £71-£80; d £126-£204 (incl. bkfst & dinner) **LB** **FACILITIES:** Outdoor swimming (H) Sauna Croquet lawn games room, table tennis, garden badminton Xmas **PARKING:** 40 **NOTES:** No smoking in restaurant Closed Jan-Feb **CARDS:**

🐕 🐈 🐇 🐦

★★ 70% The Beacon Country House Hotel

Goonvrea Rd TR5 0NW
☎ 01872 552318 📠 01872 552318
e-mail: info@beaconhotel.co.uk
Dir: From A30 take B3277 to St Agnes. At rdbt left onto Goonvrea Rd. Hotel 0.75 miles on right.

PETS: **Bedrooms (unattended) Exercise area**
RESIDENT PETS: Hercules (Chocolate Labrador), Piglet & Wellington (cats), Betty & Gus (rabbits)

Set in a quiet and attractive area away from the busy village, this relaxed, family-run hotel has splendid views over the countryside towards the sea. Guests are assured of a friendly welcome, and many return for another stay. Bedrooms are comfortable and well equipped and many benefit from the good views.
ROOMS: 11 en suite (2 fmly) (2 GF) No smoking in all bedrooms s £28-£56; d £56-£82 (incl. bkfst) **LB** **PARKING:** 14
NOTES: No smoking in restaurant **CARDS:**

Don't forget to let proprietors know when you book that you're bringing your pet

♦♦♦♦ 🍺 Driftwood Spars Hotel

Trevaunance Cove TR5 0RT
☎ 01872 552428 & 553323 📠 01872 553701
e-mail: driftwoodspars@hotmail.com
Dir: off A30 at rdbt signed St Agnes, through village bear right past church, left at bottom of hill, hotel on right

PETS: Telephone for details

This historic inn was built from wrecked timbers - hence the name. Bedrooms are attractively decorated in a bright seaside style, with comfortable furnishings and many interesting features. A good range of local produce is offered, from hand-pulled beers to a selection of delicious smoked fish.

FACILITIES: 9 en suite 6 annexe en suite (5 fmly) (5 GF) No smoking in dining room No smoking in 1 lounge TVB tea/coffee Direct dial from bedrooms Cen ht TVL Snooker Pool Table Sea fishing, surfing Dinner Last d 9.30pm **PRICES:** s £37-£55; d £74-£84✱ **PARKING:** 81
NOTES: Closed 24-25 Dec **CARDS:** 〰️ 🔲 🔲 📇 🔲 🔲 💲

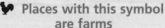

🌲 Places with this symbol are country house hotels

🐓 Places with this symbol are farms

★★ 71% White Hart

Church St PL25 4AT
☎ 01726 72100 📠 01726 74705

PETS: Bedrooms £5 small dogs, £10 large dogs Public areas (except restaurant) (10 mins by car)

Situated in the town centre, this 18th-century, stone-built inn has been completely refurbished with impressive results. Bedrooms offer high standards of comfort and public areas are stylish and contemporary. The light and airy restaurant is the venue for a modern menu that makes good use of local produce.
ROOMS: 17 en suite (2 fmly) No smoking in all bedrooms s £55; d £80 (incl. bkfst) **LB** **FACILITIES:** entertainment Xmas **PARKING:** 13
NOTES: No smoking in restaurant
CARDS: 〰️ 🔲 🔲 📇 🔲 🔲 💲

♦♦♦♦ The Lodge at Carlyon Bay

91 Sea Rd, Carlyon Bay PL25 3SH
☎ 01726 815543 📠 01726 810070
e-mail: thelodge@carlyonbay.demon.co.uk
Dir: A390 Liskeard/St Austell at St Blazey Gate turn left at 1st rdbt to Par Moor Rd, after 0.25m right onto Sea Rd. At sign to Carlyon Bay golf course, continue on this road, under railway bridge straight on at x-rds, Lodge first turn right

PETS: Bedrooms £5 Public areas (except sitting room) Exercise area (opposite) food provided by prior arrangement
RESIDENT PETS: Retriever - Robo, Labrador cross - Ben

Hospitality and service are major strengths at this charming guest house, which stands in its own gardens close to Carlyon Bay. All of the spacious well-equipped bedrooms are on the ground floor and overlook the delightful grounds. Facilities include a well-appointed residents' lounge, bar and dining room.
FACILITIES: 6 en suite (2 fmly) (6 GF) No smoking TVB tea/coffee Licensed Cen ht TVL No coaches Carlyon Bay golf club is opposite Dinner Last d at breakfast **PRICES:** s £60; d £90✱ **PARKING:** 12
CARDS: 〰️ 🔲 🔲 📇 🔲 💲

♦♦♦♦ Sunnycroft

28 Penwinnick Rd PL25 5DS
☎ 01726 73351 📠 01726 879409
e-mail: info@sunnycroft.net
Dir: heading towards Truro from St.Austell on the A390, pass MacDonalds on left, straight across double rdbt, Sunnycroft is 400yds on right

PETS: Bedrooms Exercise area (100yds)

Just a few minutes' walk from the town-centre, this 1930s house is conveniently located for the Eden Project. Bedrooms are light and bright, all of which offer good levels of comfort with two ground-floor rooms available. Breakfast is taken in the smart dining room, providing a tasty and substantial start to the day!
FACILITIES: 5 en suite 2 annexe en suite (1 fmly) (3 GF) No smoking TVB tea/coffee Cen ht No coaches Cycle hire **PRICES:** s £25-£35; d £50-£60✱ **LB** **PARKING:** 7 **CARDS:** 〰️ 🔲 🔲 📇 🔲 🔲 💲

ST IVES
Map 02 SW54

◆◆◆◆ 🏵 Chy Roma
2 Seaview Ter TR26 2DH
☎ 01736 797539 ▧ 01736 797539
e-mail: jenny@omshanti.demon.co.uk
Dir: on entering St Ives on A3074 fork left at Porthminster Hotel, then 1st left, 1st right, down slope 2nd guest house on left

PETS: Bedrooms Exercise area **RESIDENT PETS:** Saorisa - Golden Retriever, Tigger - cat

This friendly home is quietly tucked away and its attentive proprietors offer genuine hospitality. Bedrooms are smartly decorated and comfortably appointed. Some have pleasant views over the harbour and St Ives Bay. Freshly prepared, substantial breakfasts are served in the lounge/dining room. Some car parking is available.
FACILITIES: 6 en suite (2 fmly) No smoking TVB tea/coffee Cen ht TVL No children 5yrs No coaches Dinner **PRICES:** s £26-£35; d £52-£90✳ **LB PARKING:** 5

◆◆◆◆ The Old Vicarage Hotel
Parc-an-Creet TR26 2ES
☎ 01736 796124 ▧ 01736 796343
e-mail: holidays@oldvicaragehotel.com
Dir: as 1st hill with shops in St Ives levels out, turn left at Nat West bank on B3306 to Land's End. 0.5m turn right into Parc-an-Creet

PETS: Bedrooms Public areas (must be well behaved) Exercise area

This former Victorian rectory is set in its own secluded gardens, in a quiet part of St Ives and is convenient for the seaside and other attractions. Bedrooms are comfortable and enhanced by modern facilities. A good choice of local produce is offered at breakfast and home-made yoghurt and preserves are a speciality.
FACILITIES: 7 en suite (4 fmly) No smoking in bedrooms No smoking in dining room No smoking in 1 lounge TVB tea/coffee Licensed Cen ht TVL No coaches Putting green **PRICES:** s £45-£50; d £60-£70✳ **PARKING:** 12 **NOTES:** Closed Oct-Etr **CARDS:** 🔲 💳 💳 🔲 🟡

ST JUST (NEAR LAND'S END)
Map 02 SW33

◆◆◆ 🍺 Wellington Hotel
Market Square TR19 7HD
☎ 01736 787319 ▧ 01736 787906
e-mail: wellingtonhotel@msn.com
Dir: take A30 to W of Penzance then take A3071. St Just is 6m W of Penzance. Hotel overlooks Main Square

PETS: Bedrooms (unattended) £10 per visit Public areas Exercise area (20mtrs) Area ideal for long walks

This friendly inn, situated in the busy Market Square, offers comfortable accommodation and is popular with locals and visitors alike. Bedrooms are spacious and well equipped, and home-cooked food and local ales along with a well stocked bar all make for a pleasant stay at the Wellington.
FACILITIES: 5 en suite 6 annexe en suite (4 fmly) (3 GF) No smoking in 1 bedroom No smoking in dining room TVB tea/coffee Cen ht TVL Pool Table Dinner Last d 9pm **PRICES:** s £30-£35; d £50-£65✳ **LB CARDS:** 🔲 💳 💳 💳 🔲 🟡

ST KEVERNE
Map 02 SW72

◆◆◆ 🍺 🍺 White Hart Hotel
The Square TR12 6ND
☎ 01326 280325 ▧ 01326 280325
e-mail: whitehart@easynet.co.uk
Dir: from Helston, towards the Lizard, follow signs to St Keverne

PETS: Bedrooms Public areas (on a lead) Exercise area (300yds)

This establishment has now changed ownership. Located in the village square of this charming Cornish village, The White Hart offers spacious bedrooms equipped with modern comforts and many extra features. The restaurant and bar are traditional, with inglenook fireplaces, and serve an exciting range of food, including local seafood specials. A relaxed atmosphere prevails.
FACILITIES: 2 en suite No smoking in area of dining room TVB tea/coffee No coaches Riding Pool Table Dinner Last d 9pm **PRICES:** s £35; d £50✳ **PARKING:** 10 **NOTES:** rs 25 Dec & 1 Jan **CARDS:** 🔲 💳 💳 🔲 🟡

◆◆◆ Gallen-Treath Guest House
Porthallow TR12 6PL
☎ 01326 280400 ▧ 01326 280400
e-mail: gallentreath@btclick.com
Dir: A3083 from Helston. At rdbt left onto B3293 and right at next rdbt in Rosevear. Proceed past Goonhilly to St Keverne. Continue down road to Porthallow and round other side of valley, house on left

PETS: Bedrooms (unattended) £1 Public areas (on a lead and not in dining room) Exercise area (nearby) food and blankets by prior request

Gallen Treath enjoys super views over the sea and the countryside from its elevated position above Porthallow. Bedrooms are individually decorated and feature many personal touches. Guests can relax in the large, comfortable lounge complete with balcony. Hearty breakfasts and dinners (by arrangement) can be enjoyed in the bright dining room.
FACILITIES: 5 rms (4 en suite) (1 fmly) (1 GF) No smoking in bedrooms No smoking in dining room TVB tea/coffee Licensed Cen ht TVL No children 6yrs Dinner Last d 6pm **PRICES:** s £21-£26; d £42-£52✳ **LB PARKING:** 6

ST MAWES
Map 02 SW83

★★★ 77% 🏵🏵 Idle Rocks
Harbour Side TR2 5AN
☎ 01326 270771 ▧ 01326 270062
e-mail: reception@idlerocks.co.uk
Dir: off A390 onto A3078, 14m to St Mawes. Hotel on left

PETS: Bedrooms (unattended) £5 Public areas (except restaurant) Exercise area (0.25 mile)

The Idle Rocks has splendid sea views overlooking the attractive fishing port. The lounge and bar also benefit from the views and in warmer months service is available on the terrace. Bedrooms are individually styled and tastefully furnished to a high standard. The daily-changing menu served in the new restaurant features fresh local produce and imaginative cooking.
ROOMS: 23 en suite 10 annexe en suite (1 GF) s £59-£179; d £118-£298 (incl. bkfst & dinner) **LB FACILITIES:** Xmas **PARKING:** 5 **NOTES:** No smoking in restaurant **CARDS:** 🔲 💳 💳 💳 🔲 🟡

England

ST MAWGAN
Map 02 SW86

◆◆◆◆ 🍺 🔥 The Falcon
TR8 4EP
☎ 01637 860225 📠 01637 860884
e-mail: enquiries@falconinn.net
Dir: from A30 follow signs to Newquay Airport, then St Mawgan village. Pub at bottom of hill in village centre

PETS: Bedrooms Sep Accom (bedding for pets) Public areas Exercise area

This delightful 16th-century inn is opposite the village church in a quiet wooded valley. A warm and friendly atmosphere prevails, with log fires blazing in the open hearth. Bedrooms vary in size and are comfortable and pleasantly furnished. A good choice is available at lunch and dinner, with the menus featuring local fish and cheeses.
FACILITIES: 3 rms (2 en suite) No smoking in dining room TVB tea/coffee Direct dial from bedrooms Cen ht Dinner Last d 10pm
PRICES: s £26-£27; d £54-£74✱ **PARKING:** 20
CARDS: 💳

ST TEATH
Map 02 SX08

◆◆◆◆◆ Tregarthen Bed & Breakfast
PL30 3JX
☎ 01208 850603
e-mail: wendy@tregarthen.net
Dir: 3m S of Camelford turn off A39

PETS: Bedrooms £3 Exercise area (footpaths 100mtrs) **RESIDENT PETS:** 3 cats, 2 dogs

Tregarthen, which is ideally situated for The Eden Project, local golf courses and the beach, offers a very high standard of accommodation. A warm welcome and tray of tea and biscuits await all guests. Bedrooms are delightfully decorated and equipped with a thoughtful range of extras and many personal touches. An enjoyable breakfast, featuring local ingredients, is taken in the cosy kitchen around the communal table.
FACILITIES: 3 en suite No smoking in bedrooms No smoking in dining room No smoking in lounges TVB tea/coffee Cen ht No coaches
PRICES: s £35-£40; d £50-£60✱ **PARKING:** 3

SALTASH
Map 02 SX45

◆◆◆◆ 🔥 The Crooked Inn
Stoketon Cross, Trematon PL12 4RZ
☎ 01752 848177 📠 01752 843203
e-mail: crooked.inn@virgin.net
Dir: A38 to Tamar Bridge, cross bridge & through tunnel. Straight over rdbt towards Liskeard. 2nd left (Trematon), immediate right to Inn

PETS: Bedrooms (unattended) Public areas Exercise area (on site) **RESIDENT PETS:** 2 dogs, pig, sheep, 2 horses, 5 cats, geese, rabbits, ducks

The numerous friendly animals that freely roam the inn's courtyard add to the relaxed country style of this delightful inn. Bedrooms are comfortable, spacious and well equipped. A good selection of freshly-cooked dinners is available in either the bar or

continued

conservatory, and breakfast is served in the cottage-style dining room.

FACILITIES: 18 annexe rms (15 en suite) (5 fmly) (7 GF) No smoking in 7 bedrooms No smoking in area of dining room No smoking in 1 lounge TVB tea/coffee Cen ht Outdoor swimming pool Childrens play area Dinner Last d 9.30pm & 10pm Fri/Sat **PARKING:** 45
CARDS: 💳

See advert on opposite page

TINTAGEL
Map 02 SX08

★★ 64% Bossiney House
Bossiney PL34 OAX
☎ 01840 770240 📠 01840 770501
e-mail: bossineyhh@eclipse.co.uk
Dir: from A39 take B3263 into Tintagel, then Boscastle Rd, 0.5m to hotel on left

PETS: Bedrooms (2 rooms only) (unattended) £10 per stay for dogs Exercise area (100 yards)

This personally-run, friendly hotel is located on the outskirts of the picturesque coastal village. Set in the grounds, an attractive Scandinavian-style log cabin houses the majority of the leisure facilities, including a swimming pool. Public areas include a comfortable lounge and the convivial bar, which is a popular venue for pre-dinner drinks and chat.
ROOMS: 19 en suite (1 fmly) s £24-£35 (incl. bkfst) **LB**
FACILITIES: Indoor swimming (H) Sauna Solarium Putting green
PARKING: 17 **NOTES:** No smoking in restaurant Closed 25/26 Dec, 2-31 Jan **CARDS:** 💳

> **All abbreviations are explained on page 9**

> 🔥 **Places with this symbol are pubs**

> ★ **Red stars indicate the AA's Top 200 Hotels in Britain & Ireland**

♦♦♦♦ Port William

Trebarwith Strand PL34 0HB
☎ 01840 770230 🖹 01840 770936
e-mail: theportwilliam@btinternet.com
Dir: off B3263 from Camelford to Tintagel

PETS: Bedrooms £2.50 Public areas (not in restaurant)
Exercise area (nearby) on coast path RESIDENT PETS: Sasha &
Holly (black Labradors), William (parrot), Molly (cat)

Just a short distance from Tintagel, this inn is splendidly situated
on the side of a cliff, and enjoys spectacular views. Bedrooms are
attractive and benefit from sea views. The nautically themed bar is
furnished with old church pews and large wooden tables. A wide
range of creative dishes is available, including locally caught fish.

FACILITIES: 8 en suite (1 fmly) No smoking in bedrooms No smoking in
area of dining room No smoking in 1 lounge TVB tea/coffee Direct dial
from bedrooms Cen ht TVL Dinner Last d 9.30pm **PRICES:** s £57-£64;
d £75-£89✳ **LB PARKING:** 50 **CARDS:**

TRURO   Map 02 SW84

★★★ 73% ◉◉ Alverton Manor

Tregolls Rd TR1 1ZQ
☎ 01872 276633 🖹 01872 222989
e-mail: reception@alvertonmanor.co.uk
Dir: at Carland Cross take A39 to Truro

PETS: Bedrooms (unattended) £3 Exercise area
(10 minutes' walk) Pet Food

Formerly a convent, this impressive sandstone property stands in
six acres of grounds, within walking distance of the city centre. It
has a wide range of smart bedrooms, combining comfort with
character. Stylish public areas include the library and the former
chapel, now a striking function room. An interesting range of
dishes is offered in the elegant restaurant.

ROOMS: 32 en suite (3 GF) No smoking in 10 bedrooms s £90-£130;
d £115-£150 (incl. bkfst) **LB FACILITIES:** STV Golf 18 Xmas
SERVICES: Lift **PARKING:** 120 **NOTES:** No smoking in restaurant
CARDS:

WADEBRIDGE   Map 02 SW97

★★ 63% Molesworth Arms

Molesworth St PL27 7DP
☎ 01208 812055 🖹 01208 814254
e-mail: info@moleswortharms.co.uk
*Dir: A30 to Bodmin, then take A389 into Wadebridge. Over old bridge,
turn right at rdbt, then 1st left*

PETS: Bedrooms (unattended) Public areas Exercise area
(400yds) Pet bowls available, but not food
RESIDENT PETS: Ruby & Lola - black Labradors

Situated in a pedestrian area of the town, this 16th-century former
coaching inn is a popular base for exploring the area. The
comfortable bedrooms retain their original character and charm.
In addition to the wide range of snacks and meals served in the
lively bar, the Courtyard Restaurant offers a comprehensive carte
with daily specials.

ROOMS: 16 rms (14 en suite) (2 fmly) s £57.50; d £90 (incl. bkfst &
dinner) **LB FACILITIES:** STV **PARKING:** 16 **NOTES:** No smoking in
restaurant **CARDS:**

England

CUMBRIA

AMLESIDE Map 07 NY30

★★★ 75% ● **Regent**
Waterhead Bay LA22 0ES
☎ 015394 32254 📠 015394 31474
e-mail: info@regentlakes.co.uk
Dir: 1m S on A591

PETS: Bedrooms (unattended) £4.50 Exercise area
(Immediate area) Pet Food

This attractive holiday hotel, situated close to Waterhead Bay,
offers a warm welcome. Bedrooms come in a variety of styles,
including three suites and five bedrooms in the garden wing.
There is a modern swimming pool and the restaurant offers a fine
dining experience in a contemporary setting.
ROOMS: 30 en suite (7 fmly) No smoking in 4 bedrooms s £60-£80;
d £90-£120 (incl. bkfst) **LB FACILITIES:** Indoor swimming (H) Xmas
PARKING: 39 **NOTES:** No smoking in restaurant
CARDS: 💳

★★★ 68% **Skelwith Bridge**
Skelwith Bridge LA22 9NJ
☎ 015394 32115 📠 015394 34254
e-mail: skelwithbr@aol.com
Dir: 2.5m W on A593 at junct with B5343 to Langdale

PETS: Bedrooms £5 Public areas (not restaurant)
Exercise area (100 metres)

This delightful 17th-century inn is peacefully located at the heart of
the Lake District National Park. It offers high standards of comfort
and friendly service. Bedrooms include rooms with four-poster
beds, and are tastefully appointed and thoughtfully equipped.
Spacious public areas include a choice of lounges and bars and
the elegant Bridge restaurant overlooks the stunning Lakeland
fells.
ROOMS: 21 en suite 6 annexe en suite (2 fmly) No smoking in
21 bedrooms s £40-£60; d £68-£150 (incl. bkfst) **LB FACILITIES:** Xmas
PARKING: 60 **NOTES:** No smoking in restaurant
CARDS: 💳

◆◆◆◆ **Brathay Lodge**
Rothay Rd LA22 0EE
☎ 015394 32000
e-mail: brathay@globalnet.co.uk
*Dir: M6 J36. Follow A591 to Ambleside. One-way system into town centre.
Lodge on R opp church.*

PETS: Bedrooms £5 Exercise area (50mtrs)

Brathay Lodge is a bright contemporary refurbishment of a
traditional property, and functions as a high-amenity, limited
service B&B. The pine-furnished bedrooms are mainly very
spacious. Some share a communal balcony and some of the
ground floor rooms have their own outside entrance; all rooms
have spa baths. Breakfast is available, self-service style, in the
informal lounge or can be taken in the bedrooms.
FACILITIES: 17 en suite 4 annexe en suite (3 fmly) (6 GF) No smoking
TVB tea/coffee Cen ht TVL use of Langdale Country Club
PRICES: d £70-£95✱ **PARKING:** 23 **CARDS:** 💳

◆◆◆◆ **Wanslea**
Low Fold, Lake Rd LA22 0DN
☎ 015394 33884
e-mail: information@wanslea.co.uk
*Dir: approaching Ambleside from S on A591, fork right at Waterhead,
continue 700yds, Wanslea on right opposite garden centre*

PETS: Bedrooms £5 Public areas Exercise area (200yds)
Splash mat, bowls and biscuits on arrival, sausage at breakfast,
towels for dogs **RESIDENT PETS:** Barney (Collie) & Strand (cat)

Guests are assured of a warm and friendly welcome at this family-
run guest house, situated within easy walking distance of the lake
and central amenities. Bedrooms are well equipped and
comfortably proportioned, and many are suitable for families.
There is a spacious dining room and a relaxing lounge, which is
well stocked with games and toys.
FACILITIES: 6 en suite (2 fmly) No smoking TVB tea/coffee Licensed
Cen ht TVL No coaches **PRICES:** d fr £56✱ **LB**
NOTES: Closed 23-26 Dec & 2-31 Jan **CARDS:** 💳

APPLEBY-IN-WESTMORLAND Map 12 NY62

★★★ 78% ●●
Appleby Manor Country House
Roman Rd CA16 6JB
☎ 01768 351571 📠 01768 352888
e-mail: reception@applebymanor.co.uk
*Dir: M6 junct 40/A66 towards Brough. Take Appleby turn, then
immediately right. Continue 0.5m*

PETS: Bedrooms (Annexe only) (unattended) £10
Exercise area (adjacent)

This imposing country mansion is set in extensive grounds amid
fabulous Cumbrian scenery. The Dunbobbin family and their

continued

experienced staff ensure a warm welcome and attentive service. Bedrooms, including a number with patios, vary in style, with the garden rooms now refurbished. The bar offers a wide range of malt whiskies and the restaurant serves carefully prepared meals.
ROOMS: 23 en suite 7 annexe en suite (9 fmly) No smoking in 23 bedrooms s £84-£94; d £128-£148 (incl. bkfst) **LB FACILITIES:** STV Indoor swimming (H) Sauna Solarium Putting green Jacuzzi Steam room, Table tennis, Pool table **PARKING:** 53 **NOTES:** No smoking in restaurant Closed 24-26 Dec **CARDS:**

BARROW-IN-FURNESS — Map 07 SD26

★★ 64% **Lisdoonie**
307/309 Abbey Rd LA14 5LF
☎ 01229 827312 ▤ 01229 820944
e-mail: lisdoonie@aol.com
Dir: on A590, at 1st set of lights in town (Strawberry pub on left) continue for 100yds, hotel on right

PETS: Bedrooms **RESIDENT PETS:** Peggy - German Wirehaired Pointer

This friendly hotel is conveniently located for access to the centre of the town and is popular with commercial visitors. The comfortable bedrooms are well equipped, and vary in size and style. There are two comfortable lounges, one with a bar and restaurant adjacent. There is also a large function suite.
ROOMS: 12 en suite (2 fmly) s fr £49.50; d fr £60 (incl. bkfst) **LB PARKING:** 30 **NOTES:** Closed Xmas & New Year **CARDS:**

BASSENTHWAITE — Map 11 NY23

★★★★ 72% ● **Armathwaite Hall**
CA12 4RE
☎ 017687 76551 ▤ 017687 76220
e-mail: reservations@armathwaite-hall.com
Dir: M6 junct 40/A66 to Keswick rdbt then A591 signed Carlisle. 8m to Castle Inn junct, turn left. Hotel 300yds

PETS: Bedrooms (unattended) £10 (Pets allowed in garden if on a lead) Exercise area Pet Food

Enjoying fine views over Bassenthwaite Lake, this impressive mansion, dating from the 17th century, is peacefully situated amid 400 acres of deer park. Comfortably furnished bedrooms are complemented by a choice of public rooms featuring splendid wood panelling and roaring log fires in the cooler months. The indoor and outdoor leisure facilities are also an added attraction.
ROOMS: 43 en suite (4 fmly) (8 GF) s £119-£155; d £150-£290 (incl. bkfst) **LB FACILITIES:** Spa STV Indoor swimming (H) Tennis (hard) Fishing Snooker Sauna Solarium Gym Croquet lawn Putting green Jacuzzi Archery, Beauty salon, Clayshooting, Quad bikes, Falconry, Mountain Bikes ch fac Xmas **SERVICES:** Lift **PARKING:** 100 **NOTES:** No smoking in restaurant **CARDS:**

Please mention AA Pet Friendly Places to Stay when booking

★★★ 75% ● **The Pheasant**
CA13 9YE
☎ 017687 76234 ▤ 017687 76002
e-mail: info@the-pheasant.co.uk
Dir: Midway between Keswick & Cockermouth, signed from A66

PETS: Bedrooms (In annexe only) Sep Accom (kennels available) £5 Public areas (Except dining room) Exercise area (20yds) Pet Food **RESIDENT PETS:** 2 Golden Retrievers - Scotch & Soda

Enjoying a rural setting on the western side of Bassenthwaite Lake, this 500-year-old, friendly, inn is steeped in tradition. The attractive oak panelled bar has seen few changes in recent years and features log fires and a great selection of malt whisky. The individually decorated bedrooms are stylish and thoughtfully equipped.
ROOMS: 13 en suite 2 annexe en suite (2 GF) No smoking in 2 bedrooms s £80-£100; d £150-£200 (incl. bkfst) **LB PARKING:** 40 **NOTES:** No children 8yrs No smoking in restaurant Closed 25 Dec **CARDS:**

BORROWDALE — Map 11 NY21

★★★ 70% **Borrowdale**
CA12 5UY
☎ 01768 777224 ▤ 01768 777338
e-mail: theborrowdalehotel@yahoo.com
Dir: 3 miles from Keswick, on B5289 at S end of Lake Derwentwater

PETS: Bedrooms Sep Accom (Kennels) (unattended) Public areas (not in restaurant and bar at lunch) Exercise area (50 metres) Pet Food

Situated in the beautiful Borrowdale Valley overlooking Derwent Water, this traditional hotel has been family-run for over 30 years. Extensive public areas include a choice of lounges, a stylish dining room, and a lounge bar, plus a conservatory. There are a wide variety of bedroom sizes and styles; some rooms are rather spacious, including two at the rear that are particularly suitable for the less able.
ROOMS: 34 en suite 2 annexe en suite (9 fmly) (2 GF) s £70-£90; d £130-£190 (incl. bkfst & dinner) **LB FACILITIES:** Free use of nearby Health Club ch fac Xmas **PARKING:** 100 **NOTES:** No smoking in restaurant **CARDS:**

★ 69% **Royal Oak**
CA12 5XB
☎ 017687 77214 ▤ 017687 77214
e-mail: info@royaloakhotel.co.uk
Dir: 6m S of Keswick on B5289 in centre of Rosthwaite

PETS: Telephone for details

Set in a village in one of Lakeland's most picturesque valleys, this family-run hotel offers friendly and obliging service. There is a variety of accommodation styles, with particularly impressive rooms being located in a converted barn across the courtyard and backed by a stream. Family rooms are available. The cosy bar is

continued on p60

England

BORROWDALE continued

for residents and diners only. A set home-cooked dinner is served at 7pm.

Royal Oak

ROOMS: 11 rms (8 en suite) 4 annexe en suite (6 fmly) s £30-£34; d £60-£80 (incl. bkfst) **LB FACILITIES:** no TV in bdrms **PARKING:** 15 **NOTES:** No smoking in restaurant Closed 5-19 Jan & 7-27 Dec **CARDS:**

BRAMPTON
Map 12 NY56

★★★ ◎◎ ♨ **Farlam Hall**
CA8 2NG
☎ 016977 46234 ▤ 016977 46683
e-mail: farlamhall@dial.pipex.com
Dir: On A689 from Brampton to Alston. Hotel 2m on left, not in Farlam village

RELAIS & CHATEAUX

PETS: Bedrooms Public areas (except restaurant) Exercise area Pet Food Bowls provided, fresh food can be provided if required **RESIDENT PETS:** 4 llamas, 3 rare breed sheep, border collie

This delightful family-run country house dates back to 1428. Steeped in history, the hotel is set in beautifully landscaped Victorian gardens complete with an ornamental lake and stream. Lovingly restored over many years, it now provides the highest standards of comfort and hospitality. Gracious public rooms invite
continued

relaxation, whilst every thought has gone into the beautiful bedrooms, many of which are simply stunning.

ROOMS: 11 en suite 1 annexe en suite (2 GF) No smoking in all bedrooms s £135-£160; d £270-£300 (incl. bkfst & dinner) **LB FACILITIES:** Croquet lawn **PARKING:** 35 **NOTES:** No children 5yrs No smoking in restaurant Closed 25-30 Dec **CARDS:**

BROUGHTON-IN-FURNESS
Map 07 SD28

♦♦♦♦ 🍴 🍷 **The Black Cock Inn**
Princes St LA20 6HQ
☎ 01229 716529
e-mail: blackcockinn@yahoo.co.uk
Dir: M6 J36, take A590 until Greenodd, turn right onto A5092 and follow directly to Broughton-In-Furness.

PETS: Bedrooms (unattended) Public areas (not in restaurant) Exercise area (50 metres) dog bed available **RESIDENT PETS:** Ben (Whippet/Labrador cross)

Set in a quiet street just south of the main square, this white painted inn enjoys a good reputation for its locally sourced food and selection of cask ales. Guests may enjoy sitting outside in the rear beer garden or at the picnic tables at the front on fine days. The four bedrooms on the first floor are all individually styled and have all the expected facilities.
FACILITIES: 4 en suite (1 fmly) (1 GF) No smoking in bedrooms No smoking in dining room No smoking in lounges TVB tea/coffee Cen ht Dinner Last d 9pm **PRICES:** s £35; d £70✱ **NOTES:** Closed 25 Dec **CARDS:**

BUTTERMERE
Map 11 NY11

★★★ 70% **Bridge**
CA13 9UZ
☎ 017687 70252 ▤ 017687 70215
e-mail: enquiries@bridge-hotel.com
Dir: A66 around town centre, off at Braithwaite. Over Newlands Pass. Follow Buttermere signs. Hotel in village

PETS: Bedrooms (unattended) Exercise area

Enjoying a tranquil setting in a dramatic valley close to Buttermere, this long-established hotel has undergone impressive refurbishment. The bedrooms are tastefully appointed and have stylish bathrooms and the comfortable public areas include a delightful lounge, attractive dining room and lively bar popular with walkers.
ROOMS: 21 en suite No smoking in 15 bedrooms s £55-£79; d £110-£158 (incl. bkfst & dinner) **LB FACILITIES:** no TV in bdrms ch fac Xmas **PARKING:** 40 **NOTES:** No smoking in restaurant **CARDS:**

England

CARLISLE
Map 11 NY45

★★★ 66% Lakes Court
Court Square CA1 1QY
☎ 01228 531951 📠 01228 547799
e-mail: reservations@lakescourthotel.co.uk
Dir: M6 junct 43, to city centre, then follow road to left & railway station

PETS: Bedrooms £10 Public areas (except dining room)
Exercise area (100 metres)

This Victorian building is located in the heart of the city centre, adjacent to the railway station. The bedrooms, including a four-poster room, are modern in style and mostly spacious. There are extensive conference facilities and a secure car park. A comfortable bar serves light meals and a wide range of drinks.
ROOMS: 70 en suite (3 fmly) No smoking in 19 bedrooms s £55-£70; d £65-£90 (incl. bkfst) **LB FACILITIES:** STV entertainment Xmas **SERVICES:** Lift **PARKING:** 20 **NOTES:** No smoking in restaurant **CARDS:** 🖩🖩🖩🖩🖩🖩

★★★ 61% The Crown & Mitre
4 English St CA3 8HZ

PEEL HOTELS

☎ 01228 525491 📠 01228 514553
e-mail: info@crownandmitre-hotel-carlisle.com
Dir: A6 to city centre, pass station & Woolworths on left. Right into Blackfriars St. Rear entrance at end

PETS: Bedrooms Public areas (except restaurant)

Located in the heart of the city, this Edwardian hotel is close to the cathedral and a few minutes' walk from the castle. Hotel bedrooms vary in size and style from smart executive rooms to more functional standard rooms. Public rooms include the lovely bar with its feature stained glass windows and a comfortable lounge area.
ROOMS: 74 en suite 20 annexe en suite (4 fmly) No smoking in 10 bedrooms s £85-£95; d £95-£110 (incl. bkfst) **FACILITIES:** STV Indoor swimming (H) Jacuzzi Xmas **SERVICES:** Lift **PARKING:** 42 **CARDS:** 🖩🖩🖩🖩🖩🖩

♦♦♦♦ Angus Hotel & Almonds Bistro
14 Scotland Rd CA3 9DG
☎ 01228 523546 📠 01228 531895
e-mail: angus@hadrians-wall.fsnet.co.uk
Dir: exit M6 at junct 44, on A7 at lights. Approx 2m from junct 44 on left

PETS: Bedrooms £4 Public areas (except restaurant)
Exercise area (400 metres)

Just north of the city, this family-run hotel is ideal for both the business and leisure guest. A warm welcome is assured and accommodation is comfortable and well-equipped. Almonds Bistro provides enjoyable food and home-baking, and there is also a lounge and large meeting room.
FACILITIES: 11 en suite (4 fmly) No smoking in 8 bedrooms No smoking in area of dining room TVB tea/coffee Direct dial from bedrooms Licensed Cen ht No coaches Laptop points in bedrooms, internet cafe Dinner Last d 9pm **PRICES:** s £38-£48; d £50-£60✱ **LB PARKING:** 6 **CARDS:** 🖩🖩🖩🖩🖩🖩

♦♦♦♦ Cherry Grove
87 Petteril St CA1 2AW
☎ 01228 541942 📠 01228 541942
e-mail: petteril87@aol.com
Dir: M6 junct 43, 4th set of traffic lights, Cherry Grove is on left towards M6

PETS: Bedrooms £5 Exercise area (500 metres)
RESIDENT PETS: Tess (German Shepherd)

Attractively decorated and meticulously maintained, this friendly family-run guest house lies within walking distance to the city centre. Attractively decorated and comfortably furnished, bedrooms include one situated on the ground floor. There is a cosy lounge and a smart dining room where hearty breakfasts are served at individual polished pine tables.
FACILITIES: 4 en suite (2 fmly) (1 GF) No smoking in bedrooms No smoking in dining room STV TVB tea/coffee Cen ht No coaches **PRICES:** s £25-£30; d £40-£45✱ **PARKING:** 3 **CARDS:** 🖩🖩🖩🖩🖩

CARTMEL
Map 07 SD37

♦♦♦♦♦ ◉◉ 🛏 🍽 Uplands Hotel
Haggs Ln LA11 6HD
☎ 015395 36248 📠 015395 36848
e-mail: uplands@kencomp.net
Dir: road signed to Grange opposite Pig & Whistle in Cartmel 0.75m on left

PETS: Bedrooms Exercise area RESIDENT PETS: Mabel (Jack Russell), Basil and Teddy (cats)

On the outskirts of Cartmel village, this pleasant country house enjoys super views towards the Duddon Estuary. The lounge is bright and comfortable, and ambitious cooking is served in the spacious restaurant. Bedrooms are comfortable and traditional in style, and staff are thoughtful and attentive.
FACILITIES: 5 en suite No smoking in bedrooms No smoking in dining room TVB Direct dial from bedrooms Licensed Cen ht No children 8yrs No coaches Dinner Last d 7.30pm **PRICES:** (incl. dinner) s £84-£94; d £148-£168✱ **LB PARKING:** 18 **NOTES:** Closed Jan-Feb **CARDS:** 🖩🖩🖩🖩🖩🖩

COCKERMOUTH
Map 11 NY13

★★★ 76% ◉ The Trout
Crown St CA13 0EJ
☎ 01900 823591 📠 01900 827514
e-mail: enquiries@trouthotel.co.uk
Dir: next to Wordsworth House

PETS: Bedrooms (unattended) £10

Dating back to 1670, this privately owned hotel has an enviable setting on the banks of the River Derwent. The well-equipped bedrooms, some contained in a new wing overlooking the river, are mostly spacious and comfortable. The new Terrace bar and bistro, serving food all day, has a sheltered patio area. There also is a cosy bar, a choice of lounge areas and an attractive, traditional style dining room offering a good choice of table d'hôte and carte dishes.
ROOMS: 43 en suite (4 fmly) (15 GF) No smoking in 12 bedrooms s £59.95-£129; d £109-£149 (incl. bkfst) **LB FACILITIES:** STV Fishing ch fac Xmas **PARKING:** 40 **NOTES:** No smoking in restaurant **CARDS:** 🖩🖩🖩🖩

England

COCKERMOUTH continued

⌂ Shepherds Hotel
Lakeland Sheep & Wool Centre, Egremont Rd CA13 0QX
☎ 01900 822673 ▤ 01900 822673
e-mail: reception@shepherdshotel.co.uk
Dir: At junct of A66 and A5086 S of Cockermouth, entrance off A5086 200mtrs off rdbt

PETS: Bedrooms (unattended) Exercise area (on site) RESIDENT PETS: dogs, sheep, geese, Jersey cow

This hotel is modern in style and offers thoughtfully equipped accommodation. The property also houses the Lakeland Sheep and Wool Centre, with live sheep shows from Easter to mid November. A restaurant serving a wide variety of meals and snacks is open all day.
ROOMS: 13 en suite **FACILITIES:** STV **PRICES:** s&d £45-£60
PARKING: 100 **CARDS:** ▨▨▨▨▨ 🔳

◆◆◆◆ 🎄 ♥ Highside Farmhouse
Embleton CA13 9TN
☎ 01768 776893 ▤ 01768 776893
e-mail: highside@winstanley38.freeserve.co.uk
Dir: A66 Keswick-Cockermouth, left at sign to Lorton/Buttermere, left at T-junct. After 300 mtrs turn right opp church, Farm at top of hill

PETS: Bedrooms £2 Public areas (must be controlled) Exercise area (adjacent) RESIDENT PETS: Jaz (Border Collie), two cats

True to its name, this 17th-century farmhouse sits over 600 feet up Ling Fell and commands breathtaking panoramic views right across to the Solway Firth and Scotland. Add to that warm hospitality, great breakfasts, an inviting lounge/dining room with open fire in season and nice pine furnished bedrooms, and the trip up the narrow winding road to Highside is well worth it.
FACILITIES: 2 en suite No smoking TVB tea/coffee Cen ht
No children 10yrs 2 acres non working **PRICES:** s £36-£38; d £52-£56✱
PARKING: 2

All abbreviations are explained on page 9

◆◆◆◆ 🍴 Rose Cottage
Lorton Rd CA13 9DX
☎ 01900 822189 ▤ 01900 822189
e-mail: bookings@rosecottageguest.co.uk
Dir: leave A66 at Cockermouth, follow signs to Lorton/Buttermere. Rose Cottage on R.

PETS: Bedrooms Public areas (not in dining room) Exercise area (200 metres) RESIDENT PETS: Flynn (Irish Wolfhound)

This former inn is situated on the edge of town and has been carefully and thoughtfully refurbished to provide attractive, modern accommodation. Smart, well-equipped bedrooms have en suite facilities and are brightly appointed, including a self-contained studio room with external access. There is a cosy, intimate guest lounge and a smart dining room, where delicious home cooked dinners are a highlight.
FACILITIES: 7 en suite 1 annexe en suite (3 fmly) (3 GF) No smoking TVB tea/coffee Licensed Cen ht Dinner Last d 8.30pm
PRICES: s £35-£45; d £50-£75✱ **LB PARKING:** 12
NOTES: Closed 24-27 Dec **CARDS:** ▨▨▨▨▨ 🔳

CROSTHWAITE   Map 07 SD49

★★★ 61% Damson Dene
LA8 8JE
☎ 015395 68676 ▤ 015395 68227
e-mail: info@damsondene.co.uk
Dir: M6 junct 36, follow A590 signed Barrow in Furness, after 5m turn right onto A5074 . Hotel on right after 5m

PETS: Bedrooms (unattended) Public areas (except restaurant/leisure club) Exercise area

A short drive from Lake Windermere, this hotel enjoys a tranquil and scenic setting. Bedrooms, many of which have been recently refurbished, include a number with four-poster beds and jacuzzi baths. The spacious restaurant serves a daily-changing menu, with much of the produce coming from the hotel's own kitchen garden. Real fires warm the lounge and there is a games room and cosy bar.
ROOMS: 37 en suite (4 fmly) (9 GF) s £59-£79; d £78-£118 (incl. bkfst)
LB FACILITIES: Spa Indoor swimming (H) Squash Sauna Solarium Gym Jacuzzi Beauty salon Xmas **PARKING:** 45 **NOTES:** No smoking in restaurant **CARDS:** ▨▨▨▨▨ 🔳

England

♦♦♦♦ Crosthwaite House
LA8 8BP
☎ 015395 68264 ▤ 015395 68264
e-mail: bookings@crosthwaitehouse.co.uk
Dir: M6 J36, A591 (Kendal), A590 (Barrow), right onto A5074, 4m take small through-road for Crosthwaite, 0.5m turn left

PETS: Bedrooms (unattended) Exercise area (on site)
RESIDENT PETS: Pepper (Labrador), Fidge(Labrador/Collie cross) & Bertie (cat)

Commanding stunning views across the Lyth Valley, this delightful Georgian house is a haven for peace and tranquillity. Bedrooms are spacious and offer a host of thoughtful extras. The reception rooms include a comfortable lounge and a pleasant dining room with polished floorboards and individual tables. Hospitality is warm and friendly.
FACILITIES: 6 en suite No smoking TVB tea/coffee Licensed Cen ht TVL No coaches Dinner Last d 5pm **PRICES:** s £22.50-£25; d £45-£50✱
PARKING: 10 **NOTES:** Closed mid Nov-Dec rs Feb-Mar

GLENRIDDING   Map 11 NY31

★★★ 72% The Inn on the Lake
Lake Ullswater, Glenridding CA11 0PE
☎ 01768 482444 ▤ 01768 482303
e-mail: info@innonthelakeullswater.co.uk
Dir: M6 junct 40, then A66 to Keswick. At rdbt take A592 to Ullswater Lake. Along lake to Glenridding. Hotel on left on entering village

PETS: Bedrooms (unattended) £5 Public areas (except reception & bar area) Exercise area RESIDENT PETS: Chrissy (Black Labrador)

In a picturesque lakeside setting, this restored Victorian hotel is a popular destination for weddings and conferences. Superb Lakeland views may be enjoyed from the bedrooms which face the open lake or towering fells, and afternoon teas are served on the garden terrace during warmer months. Moorings for yachts are available to guests and sailing tuition can be provided.
ROOMS: 46 en suite (6 fmly) (2 GF) No smoking in 15 bedrooms
FACILITIES: STV Golf 9 Tennis (grass) Fishing Sauna Solarium Gym Croquet lawn Putting green Jacuzzi Sailing, 9 hole pitch and putt, Bowls
SERVICES: Lift **PARKING:** 200 **NOTES:** No smoking in restaurant
CARDS:

★★★ 70% Glenridding
CA11 0PB
☎ 01768 482228 ▤ 01768 482555
e-mail: glenridding@bestwestern.co.uk
Dir: Northbound M6 exit 36, A591 Windermere then A592 14 miles. Southbound M6 exit 40, A592 for 13 miles

Best Western

PETS: Bedrooms (unattended) Public areas (except dining areas) Exercise area

This friendly hotel benefits from a picturesque location in the centre of the village. Bedrooms, many with fine views of the lake and fells, include a number of newly upgraded rooms. Public

continued

areas are extensive and include a choice of restaurants and bars, a coffee shop including a cyber café, and smart leisure facilities.
ROOMS: 36 en suite (9 fmly) No smoking in all bedrooms s £70-£83; d £77-£145 (incl. bkfst) **LB FACILITIES:** STV Indoor swimming (H) Tennis (hard) Sauna Jacuzzi Billiards 3/4 Snooker table Table tennis Xmas **SERVICES:** Lift **PARKING:** 38 **NOTES:** No smoking in restaurant
CARDS:

GRANGE-OVER-SANDS   Map 07 SD47

★★★ 73% Netherwood
Lindale Rd LA11 6ET
☎ 015395 32552 ▤ 015395 34121
e-mail: blawith@aol.com
Dir: on B5277 before station

PETS: Bedrooms £3.50 Public areas Exercise area (200 metres)

This imposing hotel stands in terraced grounds and enjoys fine views of Morecambe Bay. Though a popular conference and wedding venue, good levels of hospitality and service ensure all guests are well looked after. Bedrooms vary in size but all are well furnished and decorated, and have smart modern bathrooms. Magnificent woodwork is a feature of the public areas.
ROOMS: 32 en suite (5 fmly) No smoking in 18 bedrooms s fr £65; d £140-£170 (incl. bkfst) **LB FACILITIES:** Spa Indoor swimming (H) Solarium Gym Croquet lawn Jacuzzi Beauty salon, Steam room
SERVICES: Lift **PARKING:** 100 **NOTES:** No smoking in restaurant
CARDS:

♦♦♦♦ Elton Hotel
Windermere Rd LA11 6EQ
☎ 015395 32838 ▤ 015395 32838
e-mail: info@eltonprivatehotel.co.uk
Dir: turn off A590 onto B5277 signed to Grange-over-Sands. Past train station to T junct. Turn right and hotel 100yds on left

PETS: Bedrooms (unattended) Public areas Exercise area (adjacent) RESIDENT PETS: CJ & Poppy (cats)

Friendly, attentive service is assured at The Elton Hotel. Just a short stroll from the town, this attractive Victorian house provides well-equipped bedrooms, two of which are on the ground floor. The spacious lounge is comfortable and boasts a stunning feature fireplace.
FACILITIES: 7 rms (5 en suite) (1 fmly) (2 GF) No smoking TVB tea/coffee Licensed Cen ht TVL No coaches **PRICES:** s £30-£32; d £42-£52✱ **LB PARKING:** 5 **NOTES:** Closed Nov-Feb

> All information was correct at the time of going to press; we recommend you confirm details on booking

England

GRASMERE
Map 11 NY30

★★★ 72% Thistle Grasmere
Keswick Rd LA22 9PR
☎ 0870 333 9135 ▤ 0870 333 9235
e-mail: grasmere@thistle.co.uk
Dir: N - A51 Grasmere. 1st hotel on left opposite Dove Cottage. S - follow signs for Ambleside. Last hotel on right opposite Dove Cottage.

PETS: Bedrooms (unattended) £5 Public areas (except food areas)

This large hotel stands in its own gardens leading to the lake, and many of the bedrooms have fine views over the surrounding fells. Bedrooms are comfortably furnished and include a stylish suite, complete with a four-poster bed. Service is friendly and the choice of meals, from a selection of restaurant and bar menus, should suit most tastes.
ROOMS: 72 en suite (8 fmly) No smoking in 58 bedrooms s £59-£132; d fr £75 (incl. bkfst) LB **FACILITIES:** STV Fishing Xmas **PARKING:** 60
NOTES: No smoking in restaurant
CARDS: ▨▨▨▨▨▨▨

★★★ 71% The Swan
LA22 9RF
☎ 0870 400 8132 ▤ 015394 35741
e-mail: swangrasmere@macdonald-hotels.co.uk
Dir: M6 junct 36, A591 towards Kendal, A590 to Keswick through Ambleside. The Swan on right on entering the village

MACDONALD HOTELS

PETS: Bedrooms (unattended) £10 per stay Public areas (except dining room)

Close to Dove Cottage and occupying a prominent position on the edge of the village, this 300-year-old inn is mentioned in Wordsworth's poem 'The Waggoner'. Attractive public areas are spacious and comfortable, and bedrooms are equally stylish and have CD players. A good range of bar meals is available, while the elegant restaurant offers more formal dining.
ROOMS: 38 en suite (1 fmly) (28 GF) No smoking in 14 bedrooms s £50-£75; d £100-£150 (incl. bkfst) LB **FACILITIES:** Xmas
PARKING: 45 **NOTES:** No smoking in restaurant
CARDS: ▨▨▨▨▨▨▨

★★ 74% Grasmere
Broadgate LA22 9TA
☎ 015394 35277 ▤ 015394 35277
e-mail: enquiries@grasmerehotel.co.uk
Dir: A591 north from Ambleside, 2nd left into Grasmere town centre. Follow road over humpback bridge, past playing field. Hotel on left

PETS: Bedrooms (unattended) £5 per pet per stay Exercise area (100 metres) Pet Food

Attentive and hospitable service contribute to the atmosphere at this family-run hotel, set in secluded gardens bordered by the River Rothay. There are two inviting lounges (one with residents' bar) and an attractive dining room looking onto the garden. The thoughtfully prepared dinner menu makes careful use of fresh

continued

ingredients. Pine furniture is featured in most bedrooms, along with some welcome personal touches.
ROOMS: 13 en suite (2 GF) No smoking in all bedrooms s £50-£70; d £90-£140 (incl. bkfst & dinner) LB **FACILITIES:** Access to full leisure facilities at nearby country club Xmas **PARKING:** 14
NOTES: No children 9yrs No smoking in restaurant Closed 3 Jan-early Feb
CARDS: ▨▨▨▨▨▨▨

★★ 72% Oak Bank
Broadgate LA22 9TA
☎ 015394 35217 ▤ 015394 35685
e-mail: info@lakedistricthotel.co.uk
Dir: on right in village centre

PETS: Bedrooms £2.50 Public areas (except front lounge) Exercise area (50 metres)

This privately owned and personally run hotel provides well-equipped accommodation, including a bedroom on ground floor level and a four-poster room. Public areas include a choice of comfortable lounges with welcoming log fires when the weather is cold. There is a pleasant bar and an attractive restaurant with a conservatory extension overlooking the garden.
ROOMS: 15 en suite (1 fmly) (1 GF) No smoking in all bedrooms s £60-£65; d £50-£65 (incl. bkfst & dinner) LB **FACILITIES:** Jacuzzi Xmas **PARKING:** 11 **NOTES:** No smoking in restaurant Closed 6-20 Jan
CARDS: ▨▨▨▨▨

GRIZEDALE
Map 07 SD39

♦♦♦♦ Grizedale Lodge The Hotel in the Forest
LA22 0QL
☎ 015394 36532 ▤ 015394 36572
e-mail: enquiries@grizedale-lodge.com
Dir: from M6 junct 36 follow signs to Windermere, Ambleside & Hawkshead. At Hawkshead follow signs to Grizedale, lodge 2m on right

PETS: Bedrooms (unattended) Exercise area (200-300yds) Breakfast doggy bag

Tranquilly situated in the heart of the Grizedale forest, this charming small hotel provides particularly well appointed bedrooms, some of which have fine four-poster beds and splendid views. There is an attractive dining room where hearty breakfasts are served, off which leads a balcony where guests can relax on summer days.
FACILITIES: 8 en suite (1 fmly) (2 GF) No smoking TVB tea/coffee Licensed Cen ht Dinner **PRICES:** d £50-£80✳ LB **PARKING:** 20
CARDS: ▨▨▨▨▨

🍺 **Places with this symbol are pubs**

🌲 **Places with this symbol are country house hotels**

HAWKSHEAD — Map 07 SD39

♦♦♦ **Kings Arms Hotel**
LA22 0NZ
☎ 015394 36372 🖷 015394 36006
e-mail: info@kingsarmshawkshead.co.uk
Dir: from Windermere take A591 to Ambleside then B5286 to Hawkshead, in main square

PETS: Bedrooms Public areas (except dining room) Exercise area

A traditional Lakeland inn right in the heart of this conservation village. The cosy, thoughtfully equipped bedrooms retain their character and are traditionally furnished. A good choice of freshly prepared food is available in both the lounge bar and the neatly presented dining room.
FACILITIES: 9 rms (8 en suite) (3 fmly) No smoking in dining room No smoking in lounges TVB tea/coffee Direct dial from bedrooms Cen ht Fishing Dinner Last d 9.30pm **PRICES:** s £34-£43; d £58-£76✳ **LB**
NOTES: Closed 25 Dec **CARDS:** 🖸🖸🖸🖸🖸🖸🖸

HELTON — Map 12 NY52

♦♦♦♦ **Beckfoot Country House**
CA10 2QB
☎ 01931 713241 🖷 01931 713391
e-mail: info@beckfoot.co.uk
Dir: from S, leave M6 at junct 39 onto A6 to Shap. Through Shap & follow signs to Bampton and Haweswater. Through Bampton Grange and Bampton, 2m further, house on left

PETS: Bedrooms Exercise area (on site)
RESIDENT PETS: 2 cats, 2 Shetland ponies

This delightful Victorian country house enjoys a peaceful location in well-tended gardens surrounded by beautiful open countryside, yet is only minutes' drive from Penrith. Bedrooms are spacious, comfortable and particularly well equipped. The stunning four-poster room is particularly impressive. Public areas include an elegant drawing room, where guitar workshops are occasionally held, an oak panelled dining room and a TV lounge.
FACILITIES: 7 en suite (1 fmly) No smoking in bedrooms No smoking in dining room STV TVB tea/coffee Licensed Cen ht TVL No coaches
PRICES: s £25-£38; d £60-£90✳ **LB PARKING:** 12
NOTES: Closed Dec-Feb **CARDS:** 🖸🖸🖸

HOWTOWN (NEAR POOLEY BRIDGE) — Map 12 NY41

★★★ ◉◉◉ ♣♣
Sharrow Bay Country House
Sharrow Bay CA10 2LZ
☎ 017684 86301 & 86483 🖷 017684 86349
e-mail: enquiries@sharrow-bay.com
Dir: at Pooley Bridge right fork by church to Howtown. At x-rds right and follow Lakeside Rd for 2m

PETS: Telephone for details

Enjoying breathtaking views and an idyllic location on the shores of Lake Ullswater, Sharrow Bay is often described as the first country house hotel. Individually styled bedrooms, all with a host of thoughtful extras, are situated either in the main house, in delightful buildings in the hotel's grounds or at Bank House - an Elizabethan farmhouse complete with lounges and breakfast room. Opulently furnished public areas include a choice of inviting lounges and two elegant dining rooms.
ROOMS: 8 en suite 14 annexe en suite (5 GF) s £150; d £160-£235 (incl. bkfst & dinner) **LB FACILITIES:** Xmas **PARKING:** 35
NOTES: No dogs No children 13yrs No smoking in restaurant
CARDS: 🖸🖸🖸🖸🖸🖸

KENDAL — Map 07 SD59

♦♦♦ **Gilpin Bridge**
Bridge End, Levens LA8 8EP
☎ 015395 52206 🖷 015395 52444
e-mail: info@gilpinbridgeinn.co.uk
Dir: on A5074, 100mtrs from junct with A590

PETS: Public areas (Not in food areas) Exercise area (Within the grounds) **RESIDENT PETS:** Border collie

Situated just outside Levens, this modern Tudor-style inn has a strong culinary theme and features an extensive bar and restaurant menu. The modern bedrooms are stylishly decorated and offer practical accommodation with all expected amenities. There is also a games room and a function suite.
FACILITIES: 10 en suite (1 fmly) No smoking in bedrooms No smoking in dining room No smoking in lounges TVB tea/coffee No dogs (ex guide dogs) Cen ht Pool Table Dinner Last d 9pm **PRICES:** s £40; d £55-£70✳ **LB PARKING:** 100
CARDS: 🖸🖸🖸🖸🖸🖸🖸

KESWICK — Map 11 NY22

★★★ 75% **Derwentwater**
Portinscale CA12 5RE
☎ 017687 72538 🖷 017687 71002
e-mail: info@derwentwater-hotel.co.uk
Dir: off A66 turn into Portinscale and through village then as road turns right take left turn as signed

PETS: Bedrooms (unattended) £5 Public areas (bar & lounge only) Exercise area (in grounds)

This is a popular and friendly holiday hotel with gardens that stretch down to the shores of Derwentwater. It offers a wide range of bedrooms, all thoughtfully equipped and some with good views

continued on p66

England

KESWICK continued

of the lake. Inviting public areas include a conservatory lounge and shop.
ROOMS: 46 en suite (1 fmly) (2 GF) s £65-£85; d £130-£190 (incl. bkfst) **LB FACILITIES:** Fishing Croquet lawn Putting green Access to local leisure facilities entertainment Xmas **SERVICES:** Lift
PARKING: 100 **NOTES:** No smoking in restaurant
CARDS:

◆◆◆◆ 🏆 Howe Keld Lakeland Hotel

5/7 The Heads CA12 5ES
☎ 017687 72417 📠 017687 72417
e-mail: david@howekeld.co.uk
Dir: from town centre take rd to Borrowdale. Turn right opp main car park, 1st on left

PETS: Bedrooms Public areas (except lounge) Exercise area

Offering modern accommodation throughout, this friendly, well-run hotel is close to the town and lakeside. Bedrooms are smartly decorated and furnished and the first floor lounge offers spectacular views of the fells. Breakfast is a particular highlight, with local and home-made produce featuring strongly on the menu. Dinner is available by prior arrangement.
FACILITIES: 15 en suite (3 fmly) (2 GF) No smoking TVB tea/coffee Licensed Cen ht No coaches Dinner Last d Breakfast time
PRICES: s £33-£35; d £60-£70✱ **LB PARKING:** 9 **NOTES:** Closed Xmas & Jan **CARDS:** ▬▬ 💳 ▬▬ 🔜 ⑤

◆◆◆◆ Craglands

Penrith Rd CA12 4LJ
☎ 017687 74406
e-mail: craglands@msn.com
Dir: from A66, 1st exit signed Keswick and Windermere. 1m on right, 50yds past road junct

PETS: Bedrooms £5 Exercise area (Adjacent)
RESIDENT PETS: Jaffa & Jerry - cats

Situated in an elevated location on the edge of, but within walking distance of the town centre, this stylish Victorian house offers good value, comfortable accommodation. Bedrooms are attractively decorated and well equipped with many thoughtful extras. The ground floor dining room is an appropriate setting for delicious hearty breakfasts.
FACILITIES: 7 rms (5 en suite) No smoking TVB tea/coffee Cen ht No children 8yrs No coaches **PRICES:** s £20-£30; d £50-£70✱
PARKING: 6 **CARDS:** ▬▬ 💳 ⑤

◆◆◆◆ Hall Garth

37 Blencathra St CA12 4HX
☎ 017687 72627 📠 017687 72627
e-mail: tracyhallgarth@aol.com
Dir: off A591, turning left by Millfield Nursing Home

PETS: Bedrooms (unattended) Exercise area (500yds)

This friendly and welcoming family-run guest house is situated in a peaceful residential area, within walking distance of the town centre. Bedrooms, all attractively decorated and well equipped, are stylish and modern. The pretty breakfast room is on the
continued

ground floor and is an appropriate setting for hearty Cumbrian breakfasts.
FACILITIES: 4 en suite No smoking TVB tea/coffee Cen ht
PRICES: d £40-£44✱ **CARDS:** ▬▬ ▬▬ ⑤

◆◆◆◆ Hazeldene Hotel

The Heads CA12 5ER
☎ 017687 72106 📠 017687 75435
e-mail: info@hazeldene-hotel.co.uk
Dir: from A66 follow signs for Borrowdale and lake. Turn right into The Heads opposite central car park

PETS: Bedrooms £5 Public areas Exercise area (50yds)

Situated overlooking Hope Park, and enjoying views of Catbells, Causey Pike and Walla Crag, this friendly family-run hotel is within walking distance of the town centre. Bedrooms are comfortably proportioned, brightly decorated and well equipped. There are two lounges, one of which has a bar, a games room and a spacious dining room where hearty breakfasts are served.
FACILITIES: 17 en suite (4 fmly) No smoking in bedrooms No smoking in dining room TVB tea/coffee Direct dial from bedrooms Licensed Cen ht TVL No coaches Pool Table **PRICES:** s £25-£35; d £50-£100✱
LB PARKING: 12 **NOTES:** Closed Dec-Jan
CARDS: ▬▬ 💳 ▬▬ 🔜 ⑤

◆◆◆◆ Hazelmere

Crosthwaite Rd CA12 5PG
☎ 017687 72445 📠 017687 74075
e-mail: info@hazelmerekeswick.co.uk
Dir: leave A66 at Crosthwaite rdbt (A591 junct). Follow signs toward Keswick and Hazelmere is 400yds on right

PETS: Bedrooms Exercise area (100yds)

This large Victorian house is situated only a short walk from Keswick's Market Square and within walking distance of Derwentwater and the local fells. Attractive bedrooms are comfortably furnished and well equipped. The ground floor dining room, which enjoys delightful views, is an appropriate setting for hearty Cumbrian breakfasts, served at individual tables.
FACILITIES: 5 rms (4 en suite) (1 fmly) No smoking TVB tea/coffee Cen ht No children 8yrs No coaches **PRICES:** s £22-£25; d £54-£60✱
LB PARKING: 7 **CARDS:** ▬▬ 💳 ▬▬ ⑤

◆◆◆◆ Keswick Park Hotel

33 Station Rd CA12 4NA
☎ 017687 72072 📠 017687 72648
e-mail: reservations@keswickparkhotel.com
Dir: M6 junct 40 take A66 westbound for 17m, 1st exit for Keswick, down slip road and turn left. Proceed 0.5m to T-junct A591, turn right 0.75m, park and river on right, traffic lights ahead, Keswick Park Hotel on right

PETS: Bedrooms £10 flat rate Public areas (except dining area) Exercise area (10 yards) **RESIDENT PETS:** Henri - Springer Spaniel

A warm and friendly welcome awaits at this comfortable guest house, situated within walking distance of the town centre. The Victorian house has been sympathetically renovated to provide attractive, well-equipped accommodation. Bedrooms are of a good size, and feature both practical and homely extras. Dinner,
continued

including a good range of vegetarian options, is available in the modern Conrad's restaurant.
FACILITIES: 16 en suite (2 fmly) No smoking TVB tea/coffee Direct dial from bedrooms Licensed Cen ht No coaches **PRICES:** s £27-£45; d £54-£84✱ **LB PARKING:** 8 **CARDS:** 🖃 💳 💳 🔲 📱

◆◆◆◆ Rickerby Grange Hotel
Portinscale CA12 5RH
☎ 017687 72344 📠 017687 75588
e-mail: joe@ricor.co.uk
Dir: bypass Keswick on A66 Cockermouth Rd, left at Portinscale sign, pass Farmer Arms Inn on left, 2nd lane to right

PETS: Bedrooms

Built at the turn of the last century by a local farmer, this small friendly family hotel is peacefully situated in the village of Portinscale. Bedrooms are brightly decorated, comfortably proportioned and include one on the ground floor. There is a spacious, bright dining room with an adjoining bar and lounge area. Evening meals by prior arrangement and traditional breakfasts are served at individual tables. There is a large private car park.
FACILITIES: 11 rms (9 en suite) (3 fmly) (1 GF) No smoking TVB tea/coffee Direct dial from bedrooms Licensed Cen ht No children 5yrs No coaches Dinner Last d 6pm **PRICES:** s £34-£39; d £68-£78✱ **LB PARKING:** 20 **CARDS:** 🖃 💳 🔲 📱

◆◆◆ Cragside
39 Blencathra St CA12 4HX
☎ 017687 73344
e-mail: wayne-alison@cragside39blencathra.fsnet.co.uk
Dir: from A66 take turning onto A591 (Penrith Road) into Keswick. Pass the BP garage and under railway bridge. Turn left at the Millfield Hotel onto Blencathra Street

PETS: Bedrooms (unattended) Public areas Exercise area

Expect warm hospitality at this friendly guest house, located within easy walking distance of the town centre. Bedrooms are attractive and well equipped with many enjoying fine views of the fells. Hearty Cumbrian breakfasts are served in the breakfast room, overlooking the small front garden. Visually or hearing impaired guests are well catered for, with braille information, TVs with teletext and a loop system installed in the dining room.
FACILITIES: 4 en suite (2 fmly) No smoking TVB tea/coffee Cen ht No coaches **PRICES:** d £40-£50✱ **NOTES:** Closed 24-26 Dec
CARDS: 🖃 💳 💳 💳 🔲 📱

◆◆◆ Heatherlea
26 Blencathra St CA12 4HP
☎ 017687 72430
e-mail: david@heatherleagh.fsnet.co.uk
Dir: exit M6 onto A66 to Keswick, follow signs to Keswick, after petrol station take 2nd left

PETS: Bedrooms Exercise area (200yds)
RESIDENT PETS: 2 Border Collies

Situated a short stroll from the town centre, this end-of-terrace Victorian house provides well equipped, tastefully decorated bedrooms. Guests can be assured of a warm and friendly welcome from proprietors and substantial breakfasts are served in the dining room, which has lovely views of the surrounding fells.
FACILITIES: 4 en suite (2 fmly) No smoking TVB tea/coffee Cen ht No children 5yrs No coaches **PRICES:** d £43✱
NOTES: Closed 24/25 Dec

KIRKBY STEPHEN   Map 12 NY70

◆◆◆◆◆ Brownber Hall Country House
Newbiggin-on-Lune CA17 4NX
☎ 015396 23208
e-mail: enquiries@brownberhall.co.uk
Dir: turn off M6 junct 38 onto A685 towards Kirkby Stephen. After 5.5m turn left at sign for Great Asby. After 60yds turn right through gate house entrance and follow lane for 0.25m. Then turn sharp left onto drive

PETS: Bedrooms Public areas (Under supervision)
Exercise area RESIDENT PETS: Sooty & Polar Bear - cats

Enjoying an elevated location with superb views of the surrounding countryside, Brownber Hall, built in 1860, has been lovingly and sympathetically restored to its former glory. Bedrooms, all of which enjoy en suite facilities, are comfortably proportioned, attractively decorated and well equipped. The ground floor boasts two lovely reception rooms, which have retained many period features and a charming dining room where delicious evening meals and traditional breakfasts are served. There is also a lift and other facilities for guests with disabilities.
FACILITIES: 6 en suite (1 GF) No smoking TVB tea/coffee Lift Cen ht Dinner Last d 24hrs in advance **PRICES:** s £30-£36; d fr £60✱
PARKING: 12 **CARDS:** 🖃 💳 🔲 🔲 📱

◆◆◆ ❦ Southview Farm
Winton CA17 4HS
☎ 017683 71120 📠 017683 71120
e-mail: southviewwinton@hotmail.com
Dir: M6 junct 38, take A685 to Brough for approx 10m. Signed Winton

PETS: Bedrooms (unattended) Exercise area (300yds)

A friendly house, South View lies in the centre of the village of Winton, in a terraced row with the working farm to the rear. Two well-proportioned bedrooms are available and there is a cosy lounge where breakfast is also served around one table.
FACILITIES: 2 rms (2 fmly) No smoking tea/coffee TVL 280 acres beef, dairy Dinner Last d 8am **PRICES:** s £18; d £34-£36✱ **BB PARKING:** 2

LOWESWATER
Map 11 NY12

★★ 69% **Grange Country House**
CA13 0SU
☎ 01946 861211 & 861570
e-mail: gchloweswater@hotmail.com
Dir: left off A5086 for Mockerkin, through village. After 2m left for Loweswater Lake. Hotel at bottom of hill on left

PETS: Bedrooms (unattended) £3-£5 Pet Food Dog meat and dry meal provided at an extra cost

This delightful country hotel is set in a quiet valley at the north-western end of Loweswater and continues to prove popular with guests seeking 'peace and quiet'. It has a friendly and relaxed atmosphere, and the cosy public areas include a small bar, a residents' lounge, and an attractive dining room. The bedrooms are well equipped and comfortable.
ROOMS: 8 en suite (2 fmly) (1 GF) s £35-£45; d £66-£80 (incl. bkfst)
FACILITIES: National Trust boats & fishing ch fac Xmas **PARKING:** 22
NOTES: No smoking in restaurant RS Jan-Feb

MUNGRISDALE
Map 11 NY33

★ 77% ● **The Mill**
CA11 0XR
☎ 01768 779659 🖷 01768 779155
e-mail: quinlan@evemail.net
Dir: M6 junct 40, 2m N of A66

PETS: Bedrooms (unattended) Exercise area Pet Food

Formerly a mill cottage dating from 1651 and set in magnificent rural scenery, this charming hotel and restaurant lies beside the old millstream. Inside there are cosy lounges, low ceilings, books, antiques, paintings and period pieces. Excellent five-course dinners will satisfy the heartiest of appetites.
ROOMS: 7 rms (5 en suite) s £35-£50; d £60-£90 (incl. bkfst)
FACILITIES: Fishing Games room **PARKING:** 15 **NOTES:** No smoking in restaurant Closed Nov-Feb

NEAR SAWREY
Map 07 SD39

♦♦♦♦♦ 🏛 🍽 **Ees Wyke Country House**
LA22 0JZ
☎ 015394 36393 🖷 015394 36393
e-mail: mail@eeswyke.co.uk
Dir: 2m outside Hawkshead on B5285 on road to ferry across Windermere

PETS: Bedrooms Exercise area (Adjacent)
RESIDENT PETS: Old English Sheepdogs - Teddy & Harry

A warm welcome awaits at this elegant Georgian country house with panoramic views over Lake Esthwaite and the surrounding countryside. The comfortable, thoughtfully equipped bedrooms have been decorated and furnished with care. There is a charming lounge, complete with a real fire, and a splendid dining room where a carefully prepared five-course dinner is served. Breakfasts enjoy a fine reputation thanks to the skilful use of local produce.
FACILITIES: 8 en suite (1 GF) No smoking TVB tea/coffee Licensed Cen ht No children 12yrs No coaches Dinner Last d noon
PRICES: d £130-£144✳ **LB PARKING:** 12
CARDS: 〰 VISA 〰 〰 §

NEWBY BRIDGE
Map 07 SD38

♦♦♦♦ **Lakes End**
LA12 8ND
☎ 015395 31260 🖷 015395 31260
e-mail: vjf.lakesend@virgin.net
Dir: on A590 in Newby Bridge, premises 100mtrs from rdbt on left just before Newby Bridge hotel

PETS: Bedrooms Public areas Exercise area

In a sheltered, wooded setting away from the road, Lakes End is convenient for the coast, lakes and other holiday attractions. Each of the comfortable bedrooms has been thoughtfully furnished and equipped, and one is located on the ground floor. Traditional English breakfasts are served and delicious home-cooked evening meals can be provided by prior arrangement.
FACILITIES: 4 en suite (2 fmly) (1 GF) No smoking TVB tea/coffee Licensed Cen ht TVL No coaches Free use of local leisure club Dinner Last d 8pm **PRICES:** s £22-£25; d £44-£52✳ **LB PARKING:** 8
CARDS: 〰 VISA 〰 §

PENRITH
Map 12 NY53

♦♦♦♦ **Glendale**
4 Portland Place CA11 7QN
☎ 01768 862579 🖷 01768 867934
e-mail: glendale@lineone.net
Dir: M6 junct 40, follow signs for 'Tourist Information'. Follow road over mini-rdbts past railway station and ruined castle. Proceed downhill past supermarket, turn left at bottom onto one-way system and head into town. Take 1st left at Royal Pub/Town Hall, house on left

PETS: Bedrooms Public areas (not in dining room) Exercise area (across the road)

Built in the Victorian era, this friendly family-run guesthouse forms part of a terraced row only a short stroll from the town centre and is convenient for the Lakes and Eden Valley; drying facilities are available. Bedrooms vary in size, but all are attractive, and well equipped and presented. Hearty breakfasts are served at individual tables in the charming ground floor dining room.
FACILITIES: 7 rms (6 en suite) (4 fmly) No smoking TVB tea/coffee Cen ht **PRICES:** s £30-£36; d £45-£55✳ **CARDS:** 〰 VISA §

♦♦♦♦ 🍽 🍺 **Queen's Head Inn**
Tirril CA10 2JF
☎ 01768 863219 🖷 01768 863243
e-mail: bookings@queensheadinn.co.uk
Dir: M6 junct 40 take A66 towards Appleby, at rdbt take A6 S towards Shap, at mini rdbt turn right just after Crown Hotel. Tirril is 1.5m along road on the left

PETS: Bedrooms £5 Public areas (except restaurant) Exercise area (200yds)

This privately owned traditional inn, dating back to 1719, has been sympathetically extended and restored, appealing to the modern traveller in many respects. Set in a peaceful village and home to The Tirril Brewery, real ale fans will be well satisfied. Good home-
continued

cooked food is served in all of the public areas and bedrooms are bright, comfortable and well-appointed.

FACILITIES: 7 en suite No smoking in dining room No smoking in lounges TVB tea/coffee Cen ht No children 3-13yrs No coaches Pool Table Dinner Last d 9.25pm **PRICES:** s £35-£40; d £65-£70✱ **LB**
PARKING: 40 **CARDS:** ▆▆ ▆▆ ▆▆ ▆▆ ▆

RAVENSTONEDALE Map 07 SD09

★★ 66% **The Fat Lamb**
Crossbank CA17 4LL
☎ 015396 23242 🖹 015396 23285
e-mail: fatlamb@cumbria.com
Dir: on A683, between Kirkby Stephen and Sedbergh

> **PETS:** Bedrooms Public areas Exercise area

Open fires and solid stone walls are a feature of this 17th-century inn, set in its own nature reserve. There is a choice of dining options with an extensive menu available in the traditional bar or a more formal dining experience in the restaurant. Bedrooms are bright and cheerful and include family rooms and easily accessible rooms for guests with limited mobility.

ROOMS: 12 en suite (4 fmly) No smoking in all bedrooms s £48-£50; d £76-£80 (incl. bkfst) **LB FACILITIES:** Fishing Private 5 acre nature reserve ch fac Xmas **PARKING:** 60 **NOTES:** No smoking in restaurant **CARDS:** ▆▆ ▆▆ ▆▆ ▆

SILLOTH Map 11 NY15

★★★ 59% **The Skinburness**
CA7 4QY
☎ 016973 32332 🖹 016973 32549
Dir: M6 junct 41, take B5305 to Wigton, then B5302 to Silloth. M74 junct 44, take A595 to Carlisle then on to Wigton, B5302 to Silloth

> **PETS:** Bedrooms (unattended) Exercise area (200 yards)

Enviably located on the peaceful Solway Estuary, close to sandy beaches and coastal walks, this popular hotel provides traditionally furnished bedrooms with a host of modern facilities. There is also a small leisure complex with a small pool, sauna and spa. Good meals are available in the popular bar and the pleasant hotel restaurant.

ROOMS: 33 en suite (3 fmly) (1 GF) No smoking in 6 bedrooms **FACILITIES:** Indoor swimming (H) Sauna Solarium Gym Jacuzzi entertainment ch fac Xmas **PARKING:** 120 **NOTES:** No smoking in restaurant Closed 4-23 Jan **CARDS:** ▆▆ ▆▆ ▆▆ ▆▆ ▆

TEBAY Map 07 NY60

★★★ 72% ⊛ **Westmorland Hotel & Bretherdale Restaurant**
Westmorland Place, Orton CA10 3SB
☎ 015396 24351 🖹 015396 24354
e-mail: sales@westmorlandhotel.com
Dir: located at the northbound service area between junctions 38 & 39 on the M6. Accessible from southbound service area

> **PETS:** Bedrooms (unattended) £2 Exercise area (200 metres)

This modern, friendly hotel has breathtaking views over the beautiful Cumbrian countryside. Bedrooms, varying in style, are all
continued

---

comfortably appointed and particularly well-equipped. Spacious, open-plan public areas are visually appealing and include a split-level restaurant where local produce features highly. Meetings and conferences are well-catered for.

ROOMS: 50 en suite (18 fmly) (13 GF) No smoking in 30 bedrooms s £65-£89; d £83-£105 (incl. bkfst) **LB FACILITIES:** STV ch fac Xmas **SERVICES:** Lift **PARKING:** 100 **NOTES:** No smoking in restaurant **CARDS:** ▆▆ ▆▆ ▆▆ ▆▆ ▆

♦♦♦ ☖ **Cross Keys**
CA10 3UY
☎ 015396 24240 🖹 015396 24240
e-mail: stay@crosskeys-tebay.co.uk
Dir: from M6 junct 38 right at rdbt onto A685 to Kendal. Inn 0.25m

> **PETS:** Bedrooms Public areas (except dining times) Exercise area

Situated in the centre of the village, only a few minutes from the motorway, this traditional coaching inn boasts a host of original features such as low beamed ceilings and open fires. A wide selection of popular dishes is served in either the bar or the smart dining room. The bedrooms are comfortably proportioned and traditionally furnished.

FACILITIES: 9 rms (6 en suite) (1 fmly) (6 GF) No smoking in 3 bedrooms No smoking in dining room TVB tea/coffee Cen ht TVL Tennis (hard) Fishing Pool Table Pool Darts Dinner Last d 9pm **PRICES:** s £25-£45; d £40-£65✱ **LB PARKING:** 30
CARDS: ▆▆ ▆▆ ▆▆ ▆

TROUTBECK (NEAR WINDERMERE) Map 07 NY40

★★ 72% **Mortal Man**
LA23 1PL
☎ 015394 33193 🖹 015394 31261
e-mail: enquiries@themortalman.co.uk
Dir: 2.5m N from junct of A591/A592, turn left before church into village, right at t-junct, hotel 800mtrs on right

> **PETS:** Bedrooms (unattended) £5 per stay Public areas (not in dining room) Exercise area

Dating from 1689, this traditional Lakeland inn enjoys a superb setting with stunning views towards Windermere. New owners are considerably improving the hotel, though the public areas, which include two bar areas and a cosy lounge, will retain their original features. A range of enjoyable meals can be served in either the bars, with real fires, outside on fine days, or in the formal restaurant. Bedrooms are particularly well equipped and include a four-poster room.

ROOMS: 12 en suite No smoking in all bedrooms s £60-£65; d £100-£130 (incl. bkfst & dinner) **LB FACILITIES:** Fishing, Horse Riding, Sailing, Guided Walks, Watersports Xmas **PARKING:** 20
NOTES: No smoking in restaurant **CARDS:** ▆▆ ▆▆ ▆▆ ▆

England

ULVERSTON — Map 07 SD27

★★ 70% Lonsdale House Hotel
11 Daltongate LA12 7BD
☎ 01229 582598 ▤ 01229 581260
e-mail: info@lonsdalehousehotel.co.uk
Dir: In Ulverston take right at 2nd rdbt, follow one way system until mini-rdbt. Turn left pass zebra crossing then right & 1st right.

PETS: Bedrooms £3 Public areas (except bar or restaurant) Exercise area (200yds)

Enjoying a town centre location, this family-run hotel was once a coaching inn. Bedrooms vary in style and size but all are extremely well equipped, and refurbished rooms benefit from stylish furniture and soft furnishings. Public areas include an attractive bar and restaurant, an inviting lounge and a delightful rear garden.
ROOMS: 20 en suite (2 fmly) No smoking in 16 bedrooms s £55-£72.50; d £75-£110 (incl. bkfst) LB **FACILITIES:** STV Xmas **NOTES:** No smoking in restaurant **CARDS:** ▤▤▤▤▤

See advert on opposite page

◆◆◆◆ Church Walk House
Church Walk LA12 7EW
☎ 01229 582211
e-mail: churchwalk@mchadderton.freeserve.co.uk
Dir: follow 'Town Centre' at main rdbt, turn sharp R at junct opp Kings Arms, house is opp Stables furniture shop

PETS: Bedrooms Public areas Exercise area (Adjacent) Bowls provided if necessary, owners to bring food

Located in the heart of this historic market town, this Grade II listed building is a carefully converted 18th-century gentleman's residence. Stylishly decorated, elegant accommodation includes attractive bedrooms with a mix of both antique and contemporary pieces. A peaceful atmosphere prevails with attentive service provided.
FACILITIES: 3 rms (2 en suite) No smoking tea/coffee Cen ht TVL No coaches **PRICES:** s £25-£40; d £50-£60✱ LB

WATERMILLOCK — Map 12 NY42

★★★★ 72% ⊛ ♨ Leeming House
CA11 0JJ
☎ 0870 400 8131 ▤ 017684 86443
MACDONALD HOTELS
e-mail: leeminghouse@macdonald-hotels.co.uk
Dir: M6 junct 40, take A66 to Keswick. Turn left after 1m onto A592 (to Ullswater). Continue for 5m until T-junct and turn right. Hotel on left (3m)

PETS: Bedrooms (unattended) £10 (except lounges or restaurant)

This hotel enjoys a superb location - it is set in 20 acres of mature wooded gardens in the Lake District National Park, overlooking Ullswater. Many rooms offer views of the lake and the rugged fells beyond, with more than half having their own balcony. Public rooms include three sumptuous lounges, a cosy bar and library.
ROOMS: 41 en suite No smoking in 11 bedrooms **FACILITIES:** STV Fishing Croquet lawn **PARKING:** 50 **NOTES:** No smoking in restaurant **CARDS:** ▤▤▤▤▤

◆◆◆◆ ⊜ ◧ Brackenrigg
CA11 0LP
☎ 017684 86206 ▤ 017684 86945
e-mail: enquiries@brackenrigginn.co.uk
Dir: 6m from M6. Take A66 towards Keswick and A592 to Ullswater. Turn right at lake & continue about 3m

PETS: Bedrooms £5 per stay Public areas (allowed in the bar only) Exercise area (surrounding) RESIDENT PETS: Collie

This 18th-century former coaching inn enjoys superb views of Ullswater and the surrounding countryside. A selection of freshly prepared dishes and daily specials are served by friendly staff in the traditional bar and restaurant. Tastefully furnished bedrooms include six attractive rooms in the stable cottages, which are suitable for guests with limited mobility.
FACILITIES: 11 en suite 6 annexe en suite (8 fmly) (3 GF) No smoking in bedrooms No smoking in dining room No smoking in lounges TVB tea/coffee Cen ht small field out the back Dinner Last d 9pm
PRICES: s £32-£37; d £54-£69✱ LB **PARKING:** 40
CARDS: ▤▤▤▤▤

WINDERMERE — Map 07 SD49

★★★★ 66% Low Wood
LA23 1LP
☎ 015394 33338 ▤ 015394 34072
e-mail: lowwood@elhmail.co.uk
Dir: M6 junct 36, follow A590 then A591 to Windermere, then 3m towards Ambleside, hotel on right

PETS: Bedrooms £10

Benefiting from a lakeside location, this hotel offers an excellent range of leisure and conference facilities. Bedrooms, many with panoramic lake views, are attractively furnished, and include a number of larger executive rooms and suites. There is a choice of bars, a spacious restaurant and the more informal Café del Lago. The Poolside bar offers internet and e-mail access.
ROOMS: 110 en suite (13 fmly) No smoking in 55 bedrooms s £103-£120; d £150-£190 (incl. bkfst) LB **FACILITIES:** Spa STV Indoor swimming (H) Fishing Squash Snooker Sauna Solarium Gym Croquet lawn Jacuzzi Water skiing Sub aqua diving Windsurfing Canoeing Laser clay pigeon shooting entertainment ch fac Xmas **SERVICES:** Lift **PARKING:** 200 **NOTES:** No smoking in restaurant
CARDS: ▤▤▤▤▤

★★★ ⊛⊛⊛ Holbeck Ghyll Country House
Holbeck Ln LA23 1LU
☎ 015394 32375 ▤ 015394 34743
e-mail: stay@holbeckghyll.com
Dir: 3m N on A591, right into Holbeck Lane (signed Troutbeck), hotel 0.5m on left

PETS: Bedrooms (unattended) £4.50 Public areas (only allowed in front hall) Exercise area (on site) Pet Food range of pet foods & biscuits, bowls, blankets etc available
RESIDENT PETS: Solie & Brook - Black Labradors

With a peaceful setting in extensive grounds, this beautifully maintained hotel enjoys breathtaking views over Lake Windermere and the Langdale Fells. Public rooms include

continued

luxurious, comfortable lounges and two elegant dining rooms, where memorable meals are served. Bedrooms are individually styled, beautifully furnished and many have balconies or patios. Some in an adjacent, more private lodge are less traditional in design and have superb views. The professionalism and attentiveness of the staff is exemplary.

ROOMS: 14 en suite 6 annexe en suite (3 fmly) (3 GF) No smoking in 6 bedrooms s £125-£280; d £190-£340 (incl. bkfst & dinner) **LB FACILITIES:** **Spa** STV Tennis (hard) Sauna Gym Croquet lawn Putting green Jacuzzi Beautician Steam room ch fac Xmas **PARKING:** 28 **NOTES:** No smoking in restaurant **CARDS:** 🔲🔲🔲🔲🔲

★★★ ◎◎ ♣♠
Linthwaite House Hotel
Crook Rd LA23 3JA
☎ 015394 88600 📠 015394 88601
e-mail: admin@linthwaite.com
Dir: *A591 towards The Lakes for 8m to large rdbt, take 1st exit (B5284), 6m, hotel on left , 1m past Windermere golf club*

PETS: Sep Accom (kennel) Exercise area (14 acre grounds) Pet Food Bowls and food available by request

Linthwaite House is set in 14 acres of hilltop grounds and enjoys stunning views over Lake Windermere. Inviting public rooms include an attractive conservatory and adjoining lounge, a smokers' bar and an elegant restaurant serving cutting-edge

continued

cuisine. Bedrooms, which are individually decorated, combine contemporary furnishings with classical styles. All are thoughtfully equipped and include CD players. Service and hospitality at this delightful hotel are first class.

ROOMS: 26 en suite (1 fmly) (7 GF) No smoking in all bedrooms s £99-£149; d £170-£270 (incl. bkfst & dinner) **LB FACILITIES:** STV Fishing Croquet lawn Putting green Free use of nearby leisure spa, Practice golf hole Xmas **PARKING:** 40 **NOTES:** Guide dogs only in hotel No smoking in restaurant **CARDS:** 🔲🔲🔲🔲🔲🔲

★★★ 79% ◎◎ Storrs Hall
Storrs Park LA23 3LG
☎ 015394 47111 📠 015394 47555
e-mail: storrshall@ELHmail.co.uk
Dir: *on A592 2m S of Bowness, on Newby Bridge road*

PETS: Bedrooms £10

Set in 17 acres of landscaped grounds by the lakeside, this imposing Georgian mansion is a delight. There are numerous lounges to relax in, furnished with fine art and antiques. Bedrooms are mostly well-proportioned and boast impressive bathrooms. The restaurant enjoys fine views across the lawn to the lake and fells beyond.

ROOMS: 29 en suite No smoking in 10 bedrooms s fr £125; d fr £185 (incl. bkfst) **LB FACILITIES:** Fishing Sailing Water skiing Water sports Xmas **PARKING:** 50 **NOTES:** No children 12yrs No smoking in restaurant **CARDS:** 🔲🔲🔲🔲🔲🔲

England

WINDERMERE continued

★★★ 72% ® Langdale Chase
Langdale Chase LA23 1LW
☎ 015394 32201 📄 015394 32604
e-mail: sales@langdalechase.co.uk
Dir: 2m S of Ambleside and 3m N of Windermere, on A591

PETS: Bedrooms Public areas (hotel gardens) Pet Food As required, pre-arranged RESIDENT PETS: Nobby - Boxer

Enjoying unrivalled views of Lake Windermere, this imposing country manor has been trading as a hotel for over 70 years. Public areas feature carved fireplaces, oak panelling and a galleried staircase. Bedrooms, many now refurbished, have stylish, spacious bathrooms and outstanding views.
ROOMS: 20 en suite 7 annexe en suite (2 fmly) (1 GF) s £65-£99 (incl. bkfst) LB **FACILITIES:** Fishing Croquet lawn Putting green Sailing boats ch fac Xmas **PARKING:** 50 **NOTES:** No smoking in restaurant **CARDS:** 💳

★★★ 62% The Old England
Church St, Bowness LA23 3DF
☎ 0870 400 8130 📄 015394 43432
e-mail: oldengland@macdonald-hotels.co.uk
Dir: Through Windermere to Bowness. Hotel behind church

MACDONALD
HOTELS

PETS: Bedrooms (unattended) £10 Exercise area (in grounds)

Occupying arguably one of the best positions on Lake Windermere, this elegant Victorian mansion is tastefully furnished with period and antique pieces. Many of the stylish bedrooms have wonderful lake views, as do the restaurant, bar and lounge. The hotel benefits from an outdoor heated swimming pool and a private jetty. Stylish conference facilities are impressive.
ROOMS: 76 en suite (8 fmly) (6 GF) No smoking in 26 bedrooms s £55-£80; d £120-£160 (incl. bkfst) LB **FACILITIES:** Outdoor swimming (H) Snooker Xmas **SERVICES:** Lift **PARKING:** 82
NOTES: No smoking in restaurant
CARDS: 💳

★★ 70% Hideaway
Phoenix Way LA23 1DB
☎ 015394 43070 📄 015394 48664
e-mail: enquiries@hideaway-hotel.co.uk
Dir: off A591 at Ravensworth Hotel. Hotel 100yds on right

PETS: Bedrooms (unattended) £5 (except dining room) Exercise area (Adjacent)

Enjoying a secluded location, yet only a few minutes from the centre of town, hospitality is a real feature at this family-run hotel. Bedrooms, some housed in a separate building across the courtyard, are smartly appointed and individually furnished. Four-
continued

poster and family rooms are available. Dinner features tasty, home-made food and breakfasts are hearty.

ROOMS: 10 en suite 5 annexe en suite (3 fmly) s £40-£60; d £70-£130 (incl. bkfst) LB **FACILITIES:** Free use of nearby leisure facilities Xmas **PARKING:** 16 **NOTES:** No smoking in restaurant Closed 3-31 Jan **CARDS:** 💳

🐓 **Places with this symbol are farms**

♦♦♦♦♦ Cedar Manor Country Lodge
Ambleside Rd LA23 1AX
☎ 015394 43192 📄 015394 45970
e-mail: cedarmanor@fsbdial.co.uk
Dir: M6 J36, take A591 to Windermere, stay on A591 past Windermere/Bowness turning. Hotel is on the left just past St Mary's Church.

PETS: Bedrooms (Some rooms) Sep Accom (Dog pound if customer prefers) £5 Exercise area (adjacent)
RESIDENT PETS: Barnaby & Rudge - cocker spaniels

Warm hospitality and attentive service feature highly at this neatly maintained hotel, set in its own well-tended gardens on the edge of town. Bedrooms are thoughtfully equipped and smartly appointed; one having a four-poster and two having spa baths.
continued

Public areas include a delightful lounge and an elegant split-level breakfast room.

FACILITIES: 9 en suite 2 annexe en suite (4 fmly) (2 GF) No smoking in bedrooms No smoking in dining room STV TVB tea/coffee Direct dial from bedrooms Licensed Cen ht No coaches Use of leisure facilities at Windermere Marina **PRICES:** s £37-£70; d £74-£150✱ **LB** **PARKING:** 15 **CARDS:**

◆◆◆ 🚐 The Coppice
Brook Rd LA23 2ED
☎ 01534 88501 🖷 01534 42148
e-mail: chris@thecoppice.co.uk
Dir: 0.25m S of village centre on A5074

PETS: Bedrooms Sep Accom (Kennels) £5 Exercise area (50 yards) Kennels for overnight use only - not daytime.

The exterior of this detached bed and breakfast house between Windermere and Bowness is attractively painted. This is continued inside, with colourful public rooms and bedrooms. There is a restaurant serving freshly prepared local produce, though it would be best to check at time of booking that it is open. Bedrooms vary in size and style, and have all the expected facilities.
FACILITIES: 8 en suite (2 fmly) No smoking TVB tea/coffee Licensed Cen ht No coaches Private leisure club membership Dinner Last d 10am **PRICES:** s £30-£45; d £60-£75✱ **LB** **PARKING:** 10 **CARDS:**

WORKINGTON   Map 07 NY02

★★★ 67% Hunday Manor Country House
Hunday, Winscales CA14 4JF
☎ 01900 61798 🖷 01900 601202
e-mail: info@hunday-manor-hotel.co.uk
Dir: off A66 onto A595 towards Whitehaven, hotel is 3m on right, signed

PETS: Bedrooms

Delightfully situated and enjoying distant views of the Solway Firth, this charming hotel has comfortable, well-furnished rooms. The open-plan bar and foyer lounge boast welcoming open fires, and the attractive restaurant overlooks the woodland gardens. The function suite has ensured that the hotel makes an excellent wedding venue and there are 10 new bedrooms.
ROOMS: 24 en suite s £55-£69; d £69-£89 (incl. bkfst) **LB**
FACILITIES: Xmas **PARKING:** 50 **NOTES:** No smoking in restaurant **CARDS:**

ASHBOURNE   Map 07 SK14

★★ 64% The Dog & Partridge
Swinscoe DE6 2HS   THE INDEPENDENTS
☎ 01335 343183 🖷 01335 342742
e-mail: info@dogandpartridge.co.uk
Dir: A52 towards Leek, hotel 4m on left

PETS: Bedrooms (unattended) Public areas (not in restaurant) Exercise area (on site) Pet Food Dog walking service if required

This 17th-century inn is situated in the hamlet of Swinscoe, within easy reach of Alton Towers. Bedrooms have direct access and are sited within the hotel's grounds. Well-presented self-catering family suites are also available. Meals are served every evening until late and can be enjoyed either in the bar, the conservatory or on outdoor terrace weather permitting.
ROOMS: 25 en suite (15 fmly) s £45-£90; d £75-£100 (incl. bkfst) **LB**
FACILITIES: Fishing ch fac Xmas **PARKING:** 115 **NOTES:** No smoking in restaurant **CARDS:**

◆◆◆◆ 🐦 Mercaston Hall
Mercaston DE6 3BL
☎ 01335 360263
e-mail: mercastonhall@btinternet.com
Dir: A52 Ashbourne/Derby road, in Brailsford left along Luke Lane, after 1m at 1st x-roads turn right. After Mugginton turn on left, house on right

PETS: Bedrooms Sep Accom (stables) £1 dog Public areas Exercise area Field, woodland, and stream nearby

Located in a pretty rural hamlet, this historic property dates from the 11th century and retains many original features. Bedrooms are practical and homely, and additional facilities include an all-weather tennis court and a livery service. This is an ideal location for visiting the many stately homes, the Derwent Valley Mills and nearby Dovedale.
FACILITIES: 3 en suite No smoking TVB tea/coffee Cen ht No children 8yrs Tennis (hard) 60 acres mixed **PRICES:** s £30-£35; d £50-£55✱ **PARKING:** 3 **NOTES:** Closed Xmas

◆◆◆ Stone Cottage
Green Ln, Clifton DE6 2BL
☎ 01335 343377 🖷 01335 347117
e-mail: info@stone-cottagesnet.co.uk
Dir: 1m out of Ashbourne on A52 Leek-Uttoxeter. Left at sign for Clifton, 2nd house on right

PETS: Bedrooms £2 Exercise area

An ideal base for touring the area and only a few minutes' drive from the town centre, this well maintained stone-built house stands in pretty gardens and provides homely bedrooms. Freshly cooked breakfasts are served in an attractive conservatory, and a good selection of tourist information is available.
FACILITIES: 3 en suite (1 fmly) No smoking STV TVB tea/coffee No dogs (ex guide dogs) Cen ht TVL No coaches Dinner Last d 9.30am **PRICES:** s £28-£38; d £48-£56✱ **PARKING:** 4 **NOTES:** Closed 25 Dec **CARDS:**

England

BAKEWELL

Map 08 SK26

★★★ 67% **Rutland Arms**

The Square DE45 1BT
☎ 01629 812812 📠 01629 812309
e-mail: rutland@bakewell.demon.co.uk
Dir: M1 junct 28 to Matlock, A6 to Bakewell. Hotel in town centre

PETS: Bedrooms (Annexe) (unattended) Exercise area (100 yards)

This 19th-century hotel lies at the very centre of Bakewell and offers a wide range of quality accommodation. The friendly staff are attentive and welcoming, and The Four Seasons candlelit restaurant offers interesting fine dining in elegant surroundings.
ROOMS: 18 en suite 17 annexe en suite (2 fmly) No smoking in 12 bedrooms s £51-£69; d £81-£115 (incl. bkfst) **LB FACILITIES:** Xmas
PARKING: 25 **NOTES:** No smoking in restaurant
CARDS: 🔲🔲🔲🔲🔲🔲🔲

★★ 70% **Monsal Head Hotel**

Monsal Head DE45 1NL
☎ 01629 640250 📠 01629 640815
e-mail: christine@monsalhead.com
Dir: A6 from Bakewell to Buxton. After 2m turn into Ashford-in-the-Water, take B6465 for 1m

PETS: Bedrooms (unattended) £5 Public areas (Not in restaurant) Exercise area

Popular with walkers, this friendly hotel commands one of the most splendid views in the Peak Park, overlooking Monsal Dale and the walking path along the disused railway line. Bedrooms are well equipped, and four have superb views down the valley. There is a comfortable lounge with an open fire and a wide selection of games. The hotel specialises in local foods, real ales and rarer wines.
ROOMS: 7 en suite (1 fmly) s £45-£70; d £45-£100 (incl. bkfst) **LB**
PARKING: 20 **NOTES:** No smoking in restaurant Closed 25 Dec
RS Nov-Mar **CARDS:** 🔲🔲🔲🔲🔲

◆◆◆◆ **Croft Cottages**

Coombs Rd DE45 1AQ
☎ 01629 814101
e-mail: croftco@btopenworld.com
Dir: from town centre A619 towards Chesterfield. Turn sharp right immediately over Bakewell Bridge into Coombs Rd then 1st house on left

PETS: Bedrooms (unattended) Exercise area (50yds)
RESIDENT PETS: Steffi (Belgian Shepherd)

This Derbyshire-stone Grade II listed building lies adjacent to the River Wye and the town centre. Thoughtfully equipped bedrooms are available in the main house or in the adjoining sympathetically renovated barn suite. Breakfast is taken in a spacious and attractive dining room containing a lounge area.
FACILITIES: 3 en suite 1 annexe en suite (1 fmly) TVB tea/coffee Cen ht No coaches **PRICES:** d £52-£70✱ **LB PARKING:** 2

BAMFORD

Map 08 SK28

★★ 72% **Yorkshire Bridge Inn**

Ashopton Rd, Hope Valley S33 0AZ
☎ 01433 651361 📠 01433 651361
e-mail: mr@ybridge.force9.co.uk
Dir: A57 Sheffield/Glossop road, at Ladybower Reservoir take A6013 Bamford road, inn 1m on right

PETS: Bedrooms Public areas (not during meals) Exercise area Pet Food **RESIDENT PETS:** Scribble - Border Terrier

A well-established country inn, ideally located beside Ladybower Dam and within reach of the Peak District's many beauty spots. The hotel offers a wide range of excellent dishes in both the bar and dining area, along with a good selection of real ales. Bedrooms are attractively furnished, comfortable and well-equipped.
ROOMS: 14 en suite (3 fmly) (4 GF) No smoking in 10 bedrooms s £47; d £64-£90 (incl. bkfst) **LB FACILITIES:** Xmas **PARKING:** 40
NOTES: No smoking in restaurant **CARDS:** 🔲🔲🔲🔲🔲

BARLBOROUGH

Map 08 SK47

⛱ **Hotel Ibis Sheffield South**

Tallys End, Chesterfield Rd S43 4TX
☎ 01246 813222 📠 01246 813444
e-mail: H3157@accor-hotels.com
Dir: M1 junct 30. Towards A619, right at rdbt towards Chesterfield. Hotel immediately left

PETS: Bedrooms Exercise area

Modern, budget hotel offering comfortable accommodation in bright and practical bedrooms. Breakfast is self-service and dinner is available in the restaurant. For further details, consult the Hotel Groups page.
ROOMS: 86 en suite s £31.95-£41.95; d £31.95-£41.95

BUXTON

Map 07 SK07

★★★ 77% @@
Best Western Lee Wood
The Park SK17 6TQ
☎ 01298 23002 ▤ 01298 23228
e-mail: leewoodhotel@btinternet.com
Dir: NE on A5004, 300mtrs beyond Devonshire Royal Hospital

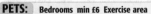

> **PETS:** Bedrooms min £6 Exercise area

This elegant Georgian hotel offers high standards of comfort and hospitality. Individually furnished bedrooms are generally spacious, with all of the expected modern conveniences. There is a choice of two comfortable lounges and a conservatory restaurant. Quality cooking is a feature of the hotel, as is good service and fine hospitality.
ROOMS: 35 en suite 5 annexe en suite (4 fmly) No smoking in 25 bedrooms s £65-£90; d £95-£140 **LB FACILITIES:** STV Xmas
SERVICES: Lift **PARKING:** 50 **NOTES:** No smoking in restaurant
CARDS: ▢▤▤▤▤▢▢

★★★ 68% **Buckingham Hotel**
1 Burlington Rd SK17 9AS
☎ 01298 70481 ▤ 01298 72186
e-mail: frontdesk@buckinghamhotel.co.uk
Dir: follow tourist signs for Pavilion Gardens Car Park. Hotel opposite car park at junct of St Johns (A53) & Burlington Rd

> **PETS:** Bedrooms (unattended) Public areas (not in restaurant) Exercise area (100 yards)

The Buckingham is close to the Pavilion Gardens and offers pleasant, modern public areas. These include Ramsay's Bar, serving bar meals and real ales, and the popular carvery, serving grills and other dishes. Bedrooms, many of which have been recently refurbished, are spacious and comfortable; many overlook the Pavilion Gardens. Walls throughout the hotel are adorned with photographs of film stars.
ROOMS: 37 en suite (13 fmly) No smoking in 27 bedrooms s £50-£75; d £60-£99 (incl. bkfst) **LB FACILITIES:** STV **SERVICES:** Lift
PARKING: 35 **NOTES:** No smoking in restaurant Closed Christmas
CARDS: ▢▤▤▤▤▢▢

♦♦♦ **Wellhead Farm**
Wormhill SK17 8SL
☎ 01298 871023 ▤ 0871 236 0267
e-mail: wellhead4bunkntrough@cbits.net
Dir: between Bakewell and Buxton. Take A6 to B6049 signed Millers Dale/Tideswell then left to Wormhill.

> **PETS:** Bedrooms Public areas (except dining room)
> Exercise area (250yds) RESIDENT PETS: Zoro & Phoebe - cats, Zack - Retriever, Murphy - Border Terrier

This 16th-century farmhouse is in a peaceful location, and boasts low beams and two comfortable lounges. The bedrooms, some with four poster beds, are all equipped with radios, beverage trays

continued

and many thoughtful extras. The proprietors provide friendly and attentive hospitality in their delightful home.

FACILITIES: 4 en suite (1 fmly) No smoking in bedrooms No smoking in dining room No smoking in 1 lounge tea/coffee Cen ht TVL No coaches Dinner Last d 9am **PRICES:** d £54-£62✱ **LB PARKING:** 4

♦♦♦ **Hawthorn Farm**
Fairfield Rd SK17 7ED
☎ 01298 23230 ▤ 01298 71322
e-mail: alan.pimblett@virgin.net
Dir: on A6 Manchester/Stockport rd opposite St Peter's church

> **PETS:** Bedrooms Exercise area RESIDENT PETS: 2 Springer Spaniels - Holly & Ben; 1 German Shepherd - Flash

A delightful Tudor farmhouse, set back from the Manchester road in attractive gardens. The lounge boasts a feature stone fireplace and many rooms display original beams. Some of the bedrooms are in converted farm buildings.
FACILITIES: 3 en suite 6 annexe rms (4 en suite) (1 fmly) (4 GF) No smoking TVB tea/coffee Cen ht TVL No coaches
PRICES: s £30-£50; d £55-£65✱ **PARKING:** 12
CARDS: ▤▤▤▤▤▤▤

CALVER

Map 08 SK27

♦♦♦♦ **Valley View**
Smithy Knoll Rd S32 3XW
☎ 01433 631407 ▤ 01433 631407
e-mail: sue@a-place-2-stay.co.uk
Dir: junct 29 M1, follow brown signs for Chatsworth House through Chesterfield on A619. From Baslow, take A623 towards Chapel-en-le-Frith for 2m into Calver, take 3rd left onto Donkey Lane

> **PETS:** Bedrooms Exercise area Adjacent to open fields where dogs can be let off the lead

This detached stone house is situated in the heart of the village close to every amenity. It is very well-furnished throughout and delightfully friendly service is provided. A hearty breakfast is served in the cosy dining room, which is also well-stocked with many local guide books.
FACILITIES: 3 en suite (1 fmly) No smoking TVB tea/coffee Cen ht No children 5yrs No coaches **PRICES:** s £40-£56; d £50-£56✱ **LB**
PARKING: 6

England

CASTLETON
Map 07 SK18

◆◆◆◆ 🖂 The Rising Sun Hotel
Thornhill Moor, Bamford S33 0AL
☎ 01433 651323 📠 01433 651601
e-mail: info@the-rising-sun.org
Dir: on A625 from Sheffield to Castleton

PETS: Bedrooms (unattended) £5 Public areas
RESIDENT PETS: Fizz (springer spaniel)

Located at Thornhill Moor within the Hope Valley, this 18th-century inn has been sympathetically renovated to provide high standards of comfort and facilities. Spacious luxury bedrooms offer quality furnishings and efficient modern bathrooms and some have stunning views of the surrounding countryside. The staff is friendly and capable and the comfortable public areas are an ideal setting to enjoy the imaginative food on offer.
FACILITIES: 12 en suite (2 fmly) No smoking in bedrooms No smoking in area of dining room No smoking in 1 lounge TVB tea/coffee Cen ht Dinner Last d 10pm LB **PARKING:** 120 **CARDS:** 🖃 💳 ⬛ 📇 💰

DERBY
Map 08 SK33

★★★ 68% Aston Court Hotel & Conference Centre
Midland Rd DE1 2SL
☎ 01332 342716 📠 01332 293503
e-mail: astoncourtderby@hotelres.co.uk
Dir: Midland Road opposite entrance of the Derby Railway Station

PETS: Bedrooms Exercise area (0.5 mile)

Situated just a few minutes from the city centre and opposite the station, this hotel has recently undergone a massive refit programme which was completed at the end of 2004. All bedrooms and public areas have been refurbished, offering comfort and more contemporary surroundings.
ROOMS: 55 en suite (5 fmly) (6 GF) No smoking in 36 bedrooms s £30-£85; d £50-£125 LB **FACILITIES:** STV More facilities available at a nearby health club Xmas **SERVICES:** Lift **PARKING:** 70
NOTES: No smoking in restaurant
CARDS: 🖃 💳 ⬛ 📇 💰

★★★ 63% International
288 Burton Rd DE23 6AD
☎ 01332 369321 📠 01332 294430
e-mail: internationalhotel.derby@virgin.net
Dir: 0.5m from city centre on A5250

PETS: Bedrooms (unattended) £5

Within easy reach of the city centre, this hotel offers comfortable, modern public rooms. An extensive range of dishes is served in the pleasant restaurant. There is a wide range of bedroom sizes and styles, and each room is very well equipped; some suites are also available, and parking is a bonus.
ROOMS: 41 en suite 21 annexe en suite (4 fmly) No smoking in 28 bedrooms s £47.50-£81; d £54-£89.50 (incl. bkfst) LB
FACILITIES: STV entertainment Xmas **SERVICES:** Lift **PARKING:** 100
CARDS: 🖃 💳 ⬛ 📇 💰

⬆ Days Hotel Derby
Derbyshire C C Ground, Pentagon Roundabout, Nottingham Rd DE21 6DA
☎ 01332 363600 📠 01332 200630
e-mail: derby@kewgreen.co.uk
Dir: M1 junct 25, take A52 towards Derby. At Pentagon rdbt take 4th exit and turn into cricket club

PETS: Bedrooms (unattended) Public areas Exercise area

This modern building offers accommodation in smart, spacious and well-equipped bedrooms, suitable for families and business travellers, and all with en suite bathrooms. Continental breakfast is available and other refreshments may be taken at the nearby family restaurant. For further details see the Hotel Groups page.
ROOMS: 100 en suite s £52.50-£74.95; d £52.50-£74.95

DERBY SERVICE AREA (A50)
Map 08 SK42

⬆ Days Inn
Welcome Break Services DE72 2WW
☎ 01332 799666 📠 01332 794166
e-mail: donnington.hotel@welcomebreak.co.uk
Dir: M1 J24/24a, onto the A50 towards Stoke/Derby. Hotel is situated btw J1 & 2

PETS: Bedrooms Public areas (must be kept on lead/in carrier)

This modern building offers accommodation in smart, spacious and well-equipped bedrooms, suitable for families and business travellers, and all with en suite bathrooms. Continental breakfast is available and other refreshments may be taken at the nearby family restaurant. For further details see the Hotel Groups page.
ROOMS: 47 en suite s £49-£69; d £49-£69

EYAM
Map 08 SK27

◆◆◆◆ 🖂 Miners Arms
Water Ln S32 5RG
☎ 01433 630853 📠 01433 639050
e-mail: minersarms@plaguevillage.fsnet.co.uk
Dir: M1 J29, take A619 to Chesterfield then A623 to Baslow and follow signs to Calver. Through Stoney Middleton turn right for Eyam.

PETS: Bedrooms (unattended) Public areas (bar area only) Exercise area (20 metres) cat and dog food provided

Located within this historic village, this 17th century inn is very much the focal point of local life, and has a strong following for both its imaginative food and well-stocked bars. Bedrooms are brightly decorated and comfortable, and public areas include an attractive restaurant, a cosy separate breakfast room and bars with polished brasses and ornaments.
FACILITIES: 7 en suite (1 fmly) (1 GF) No smoking in bedrooms No smoking in dining room No smoking in 1 lounge TVB tea/coffee Cen ht Dinner Last d 9pm **PRICES:** s £25-£40; d £50-£80✱ LB
PARKING: 75 **CARDS:** 🖃 💳 ⬛ 📇 💰

FENNY BENTLEY   Map 07 SK14

★★ 68% Bentley Brook Inn
DE6 1LF
☎ 01335 350278 ▤ 01335 350422
e-mail: all@bentleybrookinn.co.uk
Dir: 2m N of Ashbourne at junct of A515 & B5056, entrance off B5056

PETS: Bedrooms Public areas Exercise area 5 acres on site with woodlands

This popular family-owned inn is located within the Peak District National Park, just north of Ashbourne. It is a charming building with an attractive terrace, sweeping lawns, and nursery gardens. A well-appointed family restaurant dominates the ground floor, where a wide range of dishes is available all day. The characterful bar serves beer from its own micro-brewery. Bedrooms vary in styles and sizes, but all are well equipped.
ROOMS: 9 en suite 1 annexe rms No smoking in 1 bedroom s £50; d £72.50 (incl. bkfst) **LB FACILITIES:** Fishing Boules Skittles Brewery tour Xmas **PARKING:** 100 **NOTES:** No smoking in restaurant
CARDS:

FOOLOW   Map 07 SK17

◆◆◆◆ Bulls Head
S32 5QR
☎ 01433 630873 ▤ 01433 631738
Dir: M1 junct 29 follow signs to Bakewell. At Baslow take A623 Foolow (3m after Stoney Middleton)

PETS: Bedrooms (by arrangement) £5 Public areas (except dining room)

Located centrally in the village this popular inn retains many original features and offers comfortable, well-equipped bedrooms. Extensive and imaginative bar meals are served in both the traditionally furnished dining room or in the cosy bar areas. The inn welcomes well behaved dogs in the bar, and doesn't even mind muddy boots on the stone flagged areas.
FACILITIES: 3 en suite (1 fmly) No smoking in bedrooms No smoking in dining room TVB tea/coffee Cen ht Dinner Last d 8.45pm
PRICES: s fr £50; d fr £70✶ **PARKING:** 20
CARDS:

GLOSSOP   Map 07 SK09

◆◆◆◆ Brentwood
120 Glossop Rd, Charlesworth SK13 5HB
☎ 01457 869001
Dir: on A626, 1m from A57 on road to Marple, next door but one to rugby field and garden centre

PETS: Telephone for details

This spacious family home is located on the edge of Charlesworth village and offers good accommodation and fine hospitality. The bedrooms are well equipped and pleasantly furnished, and a comfortable lounge is provided for guests. Substantial breakfasts are served in the attractive dining room, which overlooks the large garden complete with a pond.
FACILITIES: 3 en suite (1 GF) No smoking TVB tea/coffee Cen ht TVL No coaches Golf 9 **PRICES:** s fr £25; d fr £50✶ **PARKING:** 6
NOTES: Closed Xmas & New Year

◆◆◆ Kings Clough Head Farm
Back Rowarth SK13 6ED
☎ 01457 862668
e-mail: kingscloughheadfarm@hotmail.com
Dir: Monks Road off A624 near Grouse Inn

PETS: Bedrooms Sep Accom (barn) Exercise area

Situated in the mountains with stunning countryside views, this 18th-century mellow-stone house provides a range of thoughtfully furnished bedrooms and a modern, efficiently designed bathroom. Breakfast is taken at one table in an antique-furnished dining room, and a warm welcome is assured.
FACILITIES: 3 rms No smoking TVB tea/coffee Cen ht TVL No coaches **PRICES:** s £20; d £38✶ **BB PARKING:** 4

GREAT HUCKLOW   Map 07 SK17

◆◆◆ The Queen Anne
SK17 8RF
☎ 01298 871246
e-mail: mal@thequeenanne.net
Dir: on A623, turn off at Anchor pub junct towards Bradwell, 2nd right to Great Hucklow

PETS: Bedrooms (unattended) up to £3 Public areas Exercise area (on site)

Located in the heart of this pretty hamlet, the Queen Anne has been a licensed inn for over three hundred years and public areas retain many original features. The cosy bedrooms are situated in a separate building and benefit from modern en suite shower rooms.
FACILITIES: 2 en suite (2 GF) No smoking in bedrooms No smoking in area of dining room No smoking in 1 lounge TVB tea/coffee Cen ht Darts, Shove Ha'penny, cards & other pub games Dinner Last d 8.30pm
PRICES: d £55-£65✶ **PARKING:** 30 **CARDS:**

HOPE   Map 07 SK18

◆◆◆◆◆ Underleigh House
Off Edale Rd S33 6RF
☎ 01433 621372 ▤ 01433 621324
e-mail: underleigh.house@btinternet.com
Dir: from village church on A6187 (formerly A625) take Edale Road for 1m then left into lane

PETS: Exercise area (nearby public footpath)
RESIDENT PETS: Tessa - Border Terrier

Situated at the end of a private lane, surrounded by glorious scenery, Underleigh House was converted from a barn and cottage which dated back to 1873, and now offers tastefully furnished and attractively decorated bedrooms with modern facilities. One room has a private lounge and others have access to the gardens. There is a very spacious guest lounge with comfortable chairs and a welcoming log fire. Memorable breakfasts are served at one large table in the dining room.
FACILITIES: 6 en suite (2 GF) No smoking TVB tea/coffee Direct dial from bedrooms No dogs (ex guide dogs) Licensed Cen ht No children 12yrs No coaches **PRICES:** s £46-£49; d £64-£85✶ **LB PARKING:** 6 **NOTES:** Closed Xmas & New Year
CARDS:

HOPE continued

◆◆◆◆ Stoney Ridge
Granby Rd, Bradwell S33 9HU
☎ 01433 620538 📠 01433 623154
e-mail: toneyridge@aol.com
Dir: from N end of Bradwell turn up Town Lane, left uphill for 300yds. Sharp left (Granby Rd), house 4th on right

PETS: Bedrooms (unattended) Public areas (except dining area) **RESIDENT PETS:** Donald and Felicity (ducks), Paddy and Sybil (cockatiels), Colin & Samson (cockerels) & many chickens

This large, split-level bungalow sits in attractive mature gardens at the highest part of the village commanding extensive views. Hens and ducks roam freely in the landscaped garden, and their fresh eggs contribute towards the hearty breakfasts. Bedrooms are attractively furnished and thoughtfully equipped and guests have sole use of a spacious comfortable lounge and a superb indoor swimming pool.
FACILITIES: 4 en suite No smoking in dining room No smoking in 1 lounge STV TVB tea/coffee Cen ht TVL No children 10yrs No coaches Indoor swimming pool (heated) **PRICES:** s £40; d £60✱ **LB**
PARKING: 3 **CARDS:** 💳💳💳💳💳

◆◆◆ 🐾 Round Meadow Barn
Parsons Ln S33 6RB
☎ 01433 621347 📠 01433 621347
e-mail: rmbarn@bigfoot.com
Dir: 0.5m from Hope, N at staggered x-rds, 200yds over rail bridge. 200yds right into Hay barn-yard, through gates, across 3 fields, house on left

PETS: Bedrooms Sep Accom (stable) £2.50 Exercise area (on site) **RESIDENT PETS:** Puzzle (Jack Russell), Paws (cat)

This converted barn, with original stone walls and exposed timbers, is situated in open fields in the picturesque Hope Valley. The bedrooms are large enough for families and there are two modern bathrooms for guests' use. Breakfast is served at one large table adjoining the family kitchen.
FACILITIES: 4 rms (1 en suite) (3 fmly) No smoking TVB tea/coffee Golf Riding 4 acres non-working **PRICES:** s £25-£35✱ **LB PARKING:** 8

🌲 **Places with this symbol are country house hotels**

LONGFORD　　　　　　　　Map 07 SK23

◆◆◆◆ Russets
Off Main St DE6 3DR
☎ 01335 330874 📠 01335 330874
e-mail: geoffrey.nolan@virgin.net
Dir: from A516 turn into Sutton Lane in Hatton. Follow this until 'T' junction, R onto Long Lane. Next R into Longford & R before telephone box on main st.

PETS: Telephone for details

An indoor swimming pool is available at this beautifully maintained bungalow, which is peacefully located near Alton Towers. Bedrooms are well equipped and have smart modern bathrooms. Comprehensive breakfasts are taken at one family table in a homely dining room, and a comfortable guest lounge is also available.
FACILITIES: 2 en suite (1 fmly) (2 GF) No smoking STV TVB tea/coffee Cen ht TVL No coaches Indoor swimming pool (heated) Gymnasium **PRICES:** s £30; d £50✱ **PARKING:** 4 **NOTES:** Closed 3rd wk Dec-1st wk Jan

MATLOCK　　　　　　　　Map 08 SK36

★★★ 77% ◉◉ 🌲 Riber Hall
DE4 5JU
☎ 01629 582795 📠 01629 580475
e-mail: info@riber-hall.co.uk
Dir: 1m off A615 at Tansley

PETS: Bedrooms (unattended) Exercise area (adjacent fields)

This beautiful Elizabethan manor house enjoys an idyllic location in charming grounds overlooking Matlock. Beautifully furnished, thoughtfully equipped bedrooms, many with oak four-poster beds, are situated round a delightful courtyard with its own fountain. Tastefully appointed public rooms are furnished with period and antique pieces and an impressive wine list complements the imaginative and award-winning cuisine.
ROOMS: 3 en suite 11 annexe en suite No smoking in 4 bedrooms s £97-£112; d £136-£182 (incl. cont bkfst) **LB FACILITIES:** STV Tennis (hard) Croquet lawn **PARKING:** 50 **NOTES:** No children 10yrs No smoking in restaurant RS 25 Dec
CARDS: 💳💳💳💳💳

★★★ 69% New Bath

New Bath Rd DE4 3PX
☎ 0870 400 8119 ▤ 01629 580268

MACDONALD
HOTELS

e-mail: general.newbath@macdonaldhotels.co.uk
Dir: M1 junct 28 to Alfreton, follow Matlock then Matlock Bath signs. Hotel on A6 just after Matlock Bath on right

PETS: Bedrooms (unattended) £10 Public areas (except restaurant)

Set in five acres of grounds in the beautiful Derwent Gorge, the hotel has indoor and outdoor pools fed by natural thermal springs, the medicinal properties of which were first recognised in Regency times. Bedrooms are tastefully furnished and decorated, two rooms have four-poster beds, and some have balconies.
ROOMS: 55 en suite (5 fmly) No smoking in 45 bedrooms s £70-£100; d £90-£120 **LB FACILITIES:** STV Indoor swimming (H) Outdoor swimming (hard) Sauna Solarium Xmas **PARKING:** 200
NOTES: No smoking in restaurant
CARDS: 〓〓〓〓〓〓〓〓

♦♦♦♦ ❦ Hearthstone Farm

Hearthstone Ln, Riber DE4 5JW
☎ 01629 534304 ▤ 01629 534372
e-mail: bed_and_breakfast@hearthstonefarm.fsbusiness.co.uk
Dir: A615 at Tansley 2m E of Matlock, turn opp Royal Oak towards Riber, at gates to Riber Hall left into Riber Road and 1st left into Hearthstone Lane, farmhouse on left

PETS: Bedrooms Exercise area (Adjacent)

Situated in a stunning, elevated location, this period stone farmhouse retains many original features and is stylishly decorated throughout. Bedrooms are equipped with a wealth of homely extras and comprehensive breakfasts feature the farm's own organic produce. Adjacent, there is a very comfortable guests' lounge, and many farm animals in the grounds are an attraction.
FACILITIES: 3 en suite No smoking TVB tea/coffee Cen ht 150 acres organic beef lamb pigs Dinner Last d 10am **PRICES:** s £30-£40; d £55-£60✳ **LB PARKING:** 6 **NOTES:** Closed Xmas & New Year

♦♦♦♦ 🏨 Hodgkinsons Hotel

150 South Pde, Matlock Bath DE4 3NR
☎ 01629 582170 ▤ 01629 584891
e-mail: enquiries@hodgkinsons-hotel.co.uk
Dir: on A6 in centre of village

PETS: Bedrooms (unattended) Public areas (Not restaurant) Exercise area (100 yards) Bowls provided

This fine Georgian hotel was renovated in Victorian times and has many interesting and unusual features. Bedrooms are equipped with fine antique furniture and a wealth of thoughtful extras to enhance guest comfort. An elegant dining room is the setting for imaginative dinners and a comfortable lounge is also available.
FACILITIES: 7 en suite (1 fmly) No smoking in 2 bedrooms No smoking in dining room TVB tea/coffee Direct dial from bedrooms Licensed Cen ht No coaches garden Dinner Last d 8.30pm **PRICES:** s fr £38; d fr £75✳ **LB PARKING:** 5 **NOTES:** Closed 24-26 Dec
CARDS: 〓〓〓〓〓〓〓

♦♦♦ ❦ Farley

Farley DE4 5LR
☎ 01629 582533 & 07801 756409 ▤ 01629 584856
e-mail: eric.b@ukgateway.net
Dir: A6 Buxton/Bakewell 1st R after rdbt in Matlock. Turn R at top of hill, then L up Farley Hill, 2nd farm on L

PETS: Bedrooms Sep Accom (kennels, stables & pens) Public areas (except dining room) Exercise area (15yds) mats, bowls, buckets, hay/straw/feed (if forgotten), milk for cats/dogs, horse riding menage, woodland nearby
RESIDENT PETS: 3 Border Terriers, 1 Labrador, 1 pony - Tigger

Guests can expect a warm welcome at this traditional stone-built farmhouse dating back to the 12th century. In addition to farming, the proprietors also breed dogs and horses. The bedrooms are pleasantly decorated and equipped with many useful extras. Breakfast is served communally around one large table and dinner is available by prior arrangement.
FACILITIES: 2 en suite (2 fmly) No smoking in bedrooms No smoking in area of dining room TVB tea/coffee Cen ht TVL Riding 165 acres arable beef dairy Dinner Last d 5pm **PRICES:** s fr £25; d £40-£45✳ **LB PARKING:** 8

ROWSLEY   Map 08 SK26

★★★ 76% ◉◉ The Peacock at Rowsley

Bakewell Rd DE4 2EB
☎ 01629 733518 ▤ 01629 732671
e-mail: reception@thepeacockatrowsley.com
Dir: A6, 3m before Bakewell, 6m from Matlock towards Bakewell

PETS: Bedrooms (unattended) Exercise area (500yds) **Pet Food** will provide dog dinners

Now owned once again by the estate of Haddon Hall this hotel has undergone a massive transformation. It is now a smart contemporary destination, which still retains many original features and period pieces of furniture. Dry fly fishing is a great attraction here as the hotel owns fishing rights in the area.
ROOMS: 16 en suite (5 fmly) No smoking in 2 bedrooms s £65-£79; d £100 (incl. cont bkfst) **FACILITIES:** STV Fishing Croquet lawn Woodlands Fitness Centre with concessions Xmas **PARKING:** 27
NOTES: No smoking in restaurant **CARDS:** 〓〓〓〓〓〓

SWADLINCOTE   Map 08 SK21

♦♦♦♦ Overseale House

Acresford Rd, Overseal DE12 6HX
☎ 01283 763741 ▤ 01283 760015
e-mail: oversealehouse@hotmail.com
Dir: in the village of Overseal on the A444 between Burton-on-Trent and M42 J11

PETS: Bedrooms Exercise area

Located in the village of Overseal, this well-proportioned Georgian mansion, built for a renowned industrialist, retains many original features including a magnificent dining room ornately decorated with fine mouldings. The period-furnished ground floor areas include a cosy sitting room, and bedrooms contain many thoughtful extras.
FACILITIES: 4 en suite 1 annexe rms (3 fmly) (2 GF) No smoking TVB tea/coffee Cen ht No coaches 3 acre garden **PRICES:** s £25-£30; d £50-£60✳ **PARKING:** 6

England

THORPE (DOVEDALE)

Map 07 SK15

★★★ 76% Izaak Walton

Dovedale DE6 2AY
☎ 01335 350555 📠 01335 350539
e-mail: reception@izaakwaltonhotel.com
Dir: A515 on B5054, follow road to Thorpe village, continue straight over cattle grid & 2 small bridges, take 1st right & sharp left

PETS: Bedrooms (unattended) Public areas

This hotel is peacefully situated, with magnificent views over the valley of Dovedale to Thorpe Cloud. Many of the bedrooms have lovely views, and 'executive' rooms are particularly spacious. Meals are served in the bar area, with more formal dining in the Haddon restaurant. Staff are friendly and efficient. Fishing on the River Dove can be arranged.
ROOMS: 37 en suite (6 fmly) (7 GF) No smoking in 31 bedrooms s £100-£110; d £130-£170 **LB FACILITIES:** STV Fly fishing on nearby River Dove Xmas **PARKING:** 80 **NOTES:** No smoking in restaurant
CARDS:

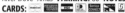

★★★ 67% The Peveril of the Peak

DE6 2AW
☎ 01335 350396 📠 01335 350507
e-mail: frontdesk@peverilofthepeak.co.uk
Dir: Ashbourne A515 towards Buxton, after 1m turn left to Thorpe, approx. 4m on right just before Thorpe Village.

PETS: Bedrooms (unattended) Public areas (not at food service times)

Situated in Dovedale's picture-book scenery, this hotel is named after one of Sir Walter Scott's heroic novels. Most bedrooms open on to the gardens, while the rest have individual patios. Some rooms have been adapted for less able guests. There is a cosy cocktail bar, a comfortable lounge and an attractive restaurant overlooking the extensive gardens. Conference and meeting rooms are also available.
ROOMS: 46 en suite (16 fmly) (6 GF) No smoking in 30 bedrooms s £65-£75; d £95-£105 (incl. bkfst) **FACILITIES:** STV ch fac Xmas **PARKING:** 80 **NOTES:** No smoking in restaurant
CARDS:

TIDESWELL

Map 07 SK17

♦♦♦ Greystones

Sunny Bank Ln SK17 8JY
☎ 01298 871591
Dir: turn off A623 onto B6049 signposted Tideswell, turn right into Cherry Tree Square. Sunny Bank Lane runs up from the square

PETS: Bedrooms (unattended) Public areas Exercise area (20 metres) RESIDENT PETS: Bess & Nell (Border Collies)

A small, attractive private house built of Derbyshire stone, situated in an elevated position in a quiet lane close to the centre of the village. There are two bedrooms, both very tastefully decorated and comfortably furnished. Substantial breakfasts can be enjoyed in the downstairs dining room, which looks out over a pretty garden and patio.
FACILITIES: 2 rms No smoking TVB tea/coffee Cen ht No children 5yrs No coaches **PRICES:** s £25-£27; d £45-£47✱ **NOTES:** Closed Dec-Jan

♦♦♦ Jaret House

Queen St SK17 8JZ
☎ 01298 872470
e-mail: jarethouse@tesco.net
Dir: A6/A623-B6049, Jaret House in centre of village opposite Hills and Dales Tearooms

PETS: Bedrooms Exercise area (5 minutes)
RESIDENT PETS: Pipsqueak (cat)

This typical Derbyshire cottage offers traditionally furnished bedrooms, all with en suite shower rooms. Friendly and attentive service is provided. A comfortable sitting room is warmed by a log fire during the colder months and substantial freshly-prepared breakfasts are served in a cosy dining room.
FACILITIES: 3 en suite (1 fmly) No smoking TVB tea/coffee No dogs (ex guide dogs) Cen ht No coaches **PRICES:** s £25; d £45-£50✱ **LB**

♦♦♦ Poppies

Bank Square SK17 8LA
☎ 01298 871083
e-mail: poptidza@dialstart.net
Dir: Leave A623 onto B6049, Poppies 0.5m on right in centre of village opposite Natwest bank

PETS: Bedrooms Public areas Exercise area (200yds)

A friendly welcome is assured at this non-smoking house, located in the heart of a former lead mining and textile community, a few minutes' walk from the 14th-century parish church. Bedrooms are homely and comfortable and the excellent breakfast features good vegetarian options.
FACILITIES: 3 rms (1 en suite) (1 fmly) No smoking TVB tea/coffee Cen ht Dinner Last d previous day **PRICES:** s £20-£22; d £40-£44✱

All AA listed accommodation, restaurants and pubs can be found on the AA's website www.theAA.com

---

ASHBURTON

Map 03 SX77

★★★ 74% ◉◉ Holne Chase

Two Bridges Rd TQ13 7NS
☎ 01364 631471 📠 01364 631453
e-mail: info@holne-chase.co.uk
Dir: 3m N on unclass Two Bridges/Tavistock road

PETS: Bedrooms £7.50 (dogs). £25 (horses) Public areas (not restaurant) Exercise area (outside hotel) Pet Food Dog grooming parlour RESIDENT PETS: Batty - Basset Hound and Brulee - Labrador

This former hunting lodge is peacefully situated in a secluded position, with sweeping lawns leading to the river and panoramic views of the moor. Bedrooms are attractively and individually

continued

furnished, and there are a number of split-level suites available. Good quality local produce features on the daily-changing menu.

ROOMS: 10 en suite 7 annexe en suite (9 fmly) (1 GF) s £95-£125; d £140-£230 (incl. bkfst) **LB** **FACILITIES:** Fishing Riding Croquet lawn Putting green Fly fishing, Riding, Beauty treatments for people and dogs ch fac Xmas **PARKING:** 40 **NOTES:** No smoking in restaurant **CARDS:** ⬛⬛⬛⬛⬛

◆◆◆◆ 🚏 🍺 **The Rising Sun**
Woodland TQ13 7JT
☎ 01364 652544 📠 01364 654202
e-mail: mail@risingsunwoodland.co.uk
Dir: turn off A38 Exeter/Plymouth at sign for Woodland and Denbury (after sign Plymouth 26m), continue down lane 1.5m, Rising Sun is on left

PETS: **Bedrooms (unattended) Public areas Exercise area (50 yards) RESIDENT PETS:** Rosie and Bella - Labradors, 3 peacocks, 2 horses

Peacefully situated in the scenic South Devon countryside and an excellent base for touring the area, this inn is just a short drive from the A38. A friendly welcome is extended to all guests: business, leisure and families alike. Bedrooms are comfortable and well equipped. Dinner and breakfast feature much local and organic produce. A good selection of homemade puddings, West Country cheeses, local wines and quality real ales is available.
FACILITIES: 6 en suite (2 fmly) (2 GF) No smoking in bedrooms No smoking in dining room TVB tea/coffee Cen ht Dinner Last d 9.15pm **PRICES:** s £38-£45; d £60-£70✹ **PARKING:** 30
CARDS: ⬛⬛⬛⬛⬛

ASHWATER Map 03 SX39

★★ ◉◉
Blagdon Manor Hotel & Restaurant
EX21 5DF
☎ 01409 211224 📠 01409 211634
e-mail: stay@blagdon.com
Dir: Take A388 N of Launceston towards Holsworthy. Approx 2m N of Chapman's Well take 2nd right for Ashwater. Next right beside Blagdon Lodge, hotel 0.25m

PETS: **Bedrooms £5 Public areas (except restaurant) Exercise area (20 acres of grounds) 3 acres of gardens and 17 acres of fields RESIDENT PETS:** Nutmeg & Cassia (Labradors)

Located on the borders of Devon and Cornwall, this small and friendly hotel offers a charming home-from-home atmosphere. The tranquillity of the secluded setting, the character and charm of the

continued

house and its unhurried pace ensures calm and relaxation. High levels of service, personal touches and thoughtful extras are all part of a stay here. Steve Morey cooks with passion and his dependence on only the finest of local ingredients speaks volumes.

ROOMS: 7 en suite No smoking in all bedrooms s fr £72; d fr £100 (incl. bkfst) **FACILITIES:** Croquet lawn Boules, giant chess/draughts **PARKING:** 10 **NOTES:** No children 12yrs No smoking in restaurant Closed 2wks Jan/Feb & 2wks Oct/Nov **CARDS:** ⬛⬛⬛⬛⬛

AXMINSTER Map 03 SY29

★★★ 72% ◉ 🐎 **Fairwater Head**
Hawkchurch EX13 5TX
☎ 01297 678349 📠 01297 678459
e-mail: reception@fairwater.demon.co.uk
Dir: off B3165, Crewkerne to Lyme Regis road. Hotel signposted to Hawkchurch

Best Western

PETS: **Bedrooms (unattended) £5 Public areas (Not dining room) Exercise area (adjacent) Pet Food RESIDENT PETS:** Hector - Boxer

Under new ownership, this well-managed hotel is peacefully located in the countryside in attractive gardens. The proprietors and staff provide a friendly and attentive service in a relaxing environment. Bedrooms are individually decorated, spacious and comfortable, and guests can enjoy well-cooked dishes in the dining room.
ROOMS: 14 en suite 7 annexe en suite (9 GF) No smoking in all bedrooms s £93-£98; d £166-£196 (incl. bkfst) **LB**
FACILITIES: Croquet lawn Pianist twice weekly entertainment Xmas **PARKING:** 25 **NOTES:** No children 6 yrs No smoking in restaurant **CARDS:** ⬛⬛⬛⬛⬛

◆◆◆◆◆ **Lea Hill**
Membury EX13 7AQ
☎ 01404 881881 📠 01404 881890
e-mail: reception@leahill.co.uk
Dir: from Chard take A30 W for 1m, turn left signed Stockland/Wambrook, continue to x-rds signed right to Membury, drive through village, pass Church and Trout Farm, Lea Hill is signed on right

PETS: **Bedrooms (unattended) Public areas (As long as the other guests are happy) Exercise area Bowls/dried meal for dogs, 2 fields, 2 footpaths RESIDENT PETS:** Florrie - Collie/Labrador cross, Tiger - tabby cat

Set in eight acres of stunning grounds and gardens, Lea Hill is the epitome of tranquillity. The annexes to the main house - a thatched Devon long house, which dates back to the 14th century

continued on p82

England

- provide the accommodation. Bedrooms are furnished to a high standard and offer a thoughtful range of extras. Take tea on the terrace, or enjoy a game of golf on the nine-hole course. Breakfast is a highlight, with many ingredients sourced locally.
FACILITIES: 1 en suite 3 annexe en suite (2 GF) No smoking TVB tea/coffee Cen ht No children 5yrs No coaches Golf 6 Dinner Last d 4.30pm **PRICES:** d £50-£90✳ **LB PARKING:** 20

✿✿✿ ❧ Sellers Wood Farmhouse
Combpyne Rd, Musbury EX13 8SR
☎ 01297 552944 ▤ 01297 552944
e-mail: sellerswood@hotmail.com
Dir: A358 Axminster/Seaton road, left at Jet garage in Musbury. At Musbury stores/post office right along Combpyne Road for 0.75m heading out of village; at end of long Devon-stone wall, left into driveway

PETS: Bedrooms £4 per animal Public areas (not in kitchen or dining room) Exercise area (100 yards)
RESIDENT PETS: 3 dogs - Barley (Yellow Labrador), Laird (Black Labrador) and Scruffy (Jack Russell)

Situated on the edge of the village of Musbury between Axminster and Seaton, this delightful 16th-century farmhouse has a wealth of beams and flagstone floors and enjoys an elevated position with sweeping views over the Axe Valley to the cliffs of Beer. Tasty farmhouse dinners using homegrown vegetables are available by prior arrangement.
FACILITIES: 4 rms (1 en suite) (1 fmly) No smoking tea/coffee Cen ht TVL Croquet lawn 3 acres working (small holding) Dinner Last d before 9am **PRICES:** s £28-£30; d £50-£54✳ **LB PARKING:** 6

✿✿✿ 🏰 Exeter Inn
Tiverton Rd EX16 9DY
☎ 01398 331345 ▤ 01398 331460
e-mail: innbampton@msn.com
Dir: on A396 between Bampton & Tiverton

PETS: Bedrooms Sep Accom (5 kennels available) Public areas Exercise area (100 yards)

This ancient, charming country inn stands beside the A396, one mile from Bampton in the Exmoor National Park. The bedrooms, while not large, are well equipped, with private bathrooms and several welcome extra facilities. A range of home-cooked fare is served in a friendly manner, either in the bar or the restaurant.
FACILITIES: 12 rms (11 en suite) No smoking in dining room TVB tea/coffee Direct dial from bedrooms No dogs (ex guide dogs) Cen ht Riding local fly fishing, clay pigeon & game shooting Dinner Last d 9.30pm **PRICES:** s fr £39.75; d fr £69.50✳ **LB PARKING:** 70 **CARDS:** 💳

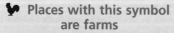

❧ Places with this symbol are farms

★ Red stars indicate the AA's Top 200 Hotels in Britain & Ireland

✿✿✿✿✿ ◉◉ ♨ Halmpstone Manor
Bishop's Tawton EX32 0EA
☎ 01271 830321 ▤ 01271 830826
e-mail: jane@halmpstonemanor.co.uk
Dir: 2m SE of Bishop's Tawton off unclassified road

PETS: Bedrooms (unattended) Public areas Exercise area (100yds) RESIDENT PETS: Barley (Cocker Spaniel)

Parts of the 12th and 13th-century structure still remain of a house mentioned in the Doomsday Book. Today, Halmpstone Manor provides comfortable, quality accommodation, personal service, and fine cuisine. Delightful day rooms include a spacious lounge complete with deep sofas and a roaring fire, whilst the elegant restaurant is an idyllic venue in which to enjoy the creative daily changing menu. Superb hospitality and excellent value make this hotel popular with those looking for a restful, peaceful break.
FACILITIES: 5 en suite No smoking in bedrooms No smoking in dining room TVB tea/coffee Licensed No coaches Dinner Last d 8pm **PRICES:** s £70; d £100-£140✳ **PARKING:** 12 **NOTES:** Closed Xmas & New Year **CARDS:** 💳

✿✿✿ Cresta
26 Sticklepath Hill EX31 2BU
☎ 01271 374022 ▤ 01271 374022
Dir: M5/A361, then B3233 towards Bideford, cross long bridge up Sticklepath Hill (main road) railway station on L, top of hill on R

PETS: Bedrooms Exercise area

Warm and friendly standards of hospitality are provided at this detached property on the outskirts of the town. The well-equipped bedrooms are comfortable; two are available on the ground floor. A hearty breakfast is served in the recently redecorated dining room.
FACILITIES: 6 rms (4 en suite) (2 fmly) (2 GF) No smoking in dining room No smoking in lounges TVB tea/coffee Cen ht No coaches **PRICES:** s £19; d £39✳ **BB PARKING:** 6 **CARDS:** 💳

★★ 74% ◉ Yeoldon Country House
Durrant Ln, Northam EX39 2RL
☎ 01237 474400 ▤ 01237 476618
e-mail: yeoldonhouse@aol.com
Dir: A39 from Barnstaple over River Torridge Bridge. At rdbt turn right onto A386 towards Northam, then 3rd right into Durrant Ln

PETS: Bedrooms (unattended) Public areas (Lounge only) Exercise area (100yds) Pet Food Dog food provided and, on occasion, beef & gravy RESIDENT PETS: Muttley & Shaz (Collie cross)

In a tranquil location with superb views over the River Torridge and attractive grounds, the Yeoldon is a charming Victorian house. Bedrooms are individually decorated, some have balconies with breathtaking views and all are well equipped. The public rooms are full of character with many interesting features and artefacts. Dinner offers a daily changing menu with fresh local produce and imaginative dishes.
ROOMS: 10 en suite No smoking in all bedrooms s £65-£70; d £100-£115 (incl. bkfst) **LB PARKING:** 20 **NOTES:** No smoking in restaurant Closed 24-27 Dec **CARDS:** 💳

◆◆◆◆ Pines at Eastleigh
The Pines, Eastleigh EX39 4PA
☎ 01271 860561
e-mail: pirrie@thepinesateastleigh.co.uk
Dir: turn off A39 Barnstaple/Bideford rd onto A386 signed Torrington. Take first left signed Eastleigh, 500yds, 1st left also signed Eastleigh, 1.5m to village, house on right

PETS: Bedrooms (unattended) Exercise area (on site) Spare bowls available, cat/dog food available on request, gardens, orchards & fields

Friendly hospitality is assured at this Georgian farmhouse, set in seven acres of gardens. Two of the comfortable bedrooms are located in the main house, the remainder in converted barns around a charming courtyard, with a pretty pond and well. A delicious breakfast featuring local and home-made produce is served in the dining room and a guest lounge and honesty bar is also available.
FACILITIES: 6 en suite (3 fmly) (4 GF) No smoking TVB tea/coffee Direct dial from bedrooms Licensed Cen ht No coaches Croquet lawn Badminton, Link with outdoor activity centre **PRICES:** s £25-£45; d £60-£100✱ **LB PARKING:** 20 **CARDS:** 〰️ 🟦 💳 ➖ 🦳 🟢

BISHOPSTEIGNTON   Map 03 SX97

★★ 65% Cockhaven Manor Hotel   THE INDEPENDENTS
Cockhaven Rd TQ14 9RF
☎ 01626 775252 📠 01626 775572
e-mail: cockhaven.manor@virgin.net
Dir: M5/A380 towards Torquay, then A381 towards Teignmouth. Turn left at Metro Motors. Hotel 500yds on left

PETS: Bedrooms (unattended) Public areas (Not in restaurant) Exercise area (20yds) Pet Food
RESIDENT PETS: Dog - Bitsy

A friendly, family run inn, the Cockhaven Manor dates back to the 16th century. Bedrooms are well equipped and many enjoy views across the beautiful Teign estuary. A choice of dining options is offered, and traditional and interesting dishes along with locally caught fish are popular with visitors and locals alike.
ROOMS: 12 en suite (2 fmly) No smoking in 10 bedrooms s fr £35; d £55-£65 (incl. bkfst) **LB FACILITIES:** Petanque **PARKING:** 50
NOTES: No smoking in restaurant RS 26 Dec
CARDS: 〰️ 🟦 💳 ➖ 🦳 🟢

BOVEY TRACEY   Map 03 SX87

★★ 70% Coombe Cross
Coombe Ln TQ13 9EY
☎ 01626 832476 📠 01626 835298
e-mail: info@coombecross.co.uk
Dir: A38 signed Bovey Tracey & town centre, along High St, up hill 400yds beyond Parish Church. Hotel on left

PETS: Bedrooms £4.50 Exercise area (100 yards)

With delightful views over Dartmoor, this peaceful hotel is set in well-tended gardens on the edge of the town. There are comfortable public areas and bedrooms and a range of leisure

continued

and fitness facilities is available. At dinner, carefully prepared dishes are served in the spacious dining room.
ROOMS: 22 en suite (1 fmly) (2 GF) No smoking in all bedrooms s £39-£44; d £58-£74 (incl. bkfst) **LB FACILITIES:** Spa Indoor swimming (H) Sauna Solarium Gym Table tennis **PARKING:** 20
NOTES: No smoking in restaurant Closed 24 Dec-31 Jan
CARDS: 〰️ 🟦 💳 ➖ 🦳 🟢

BRANSCOMBE   Map 03 SY18

★★ 68% 🏵 The Masons Arms
EX12 3DJ
☎ 01297 680300 📠 01297 680500
e-mail: reception@masonsarms.co.uk
Dir: off A3052 towards Branscombe, hotel in valley at bottom of hill

PETS: Bedrooms (unattended) £5 Public areas (except restaurant) Exercise area - coastal path good for walks

This delightful 14th-century village inn is just half a mile from the sea. Bedrooms in the thatched annexed cottages tend to be more spacious and most have their own patio area with seating, whilst those in the inn enjoy the character and charm of the period, as do the bars and public areas. An extensive selection of dishes, which includes many local specialities, is offered. The Waterfall Restaurant offers a more formal dining option.
ROOMS: 6 rms (4 en suite) 16 annexe en suite (2 fmly) (1 GF) s £25-£130; d £50-£150 (incl. bkfst) **LB FACILITIES:** Xmas **PARKING:** 43 **NOTES:** No smoking in restaurant
CARDS: 〰️ 🟦 💳 ➖ 🦳 🟢

BRENDON   Map 03 SS74

◆◆◆◆ Leeford Cottage
EX35 6PS
☎ 01598 741279 📠 01598 741392
e-mail: g.linley@virgin.net
Dir: approx. 4.5m E of Lynton. Off A39 at Brendon sign, cross packhorse bridges and village green, straight over x-rds Leeford Cottage is on left

PETS: Bedrooms Public areas (except dining room) Exercise area (Adjacent) **RESIDENT PETS:** Benny & Bramble (goats), Meggy (Labrador), Toby & Claude (cats), chickens & Marcus - cockerel

Situated in the quiet hamlet of Brendon, this 400-year-old cottage is steeped in character. The welcoming proprietors grow their own vegetables and rear hens, which provide the eggs for breakfasts. Bedrooms are cosy and comfortable and dinner features good home cooking.
FACILITIES: 3 rms (1 en suite) No smoking tea/coffee Cen ht TVL No coaches Dinner Last d 5pm **PRICES:** s £27-£28; d £45-£47✱ **LB PARKING:** 10

All information was correct at the time of going to press; we recommend you confirm details on booking

BRIXHAM — Map 03 SX95

★★★ 68% **Berryhead**

THE INDEPENDENTS

Berryhead Rd TQ5 9AJ
☎ 01803 853225 📠 01803 882084
e-mail: stay@berryheadhotel.com
Dir: Turn left at town hall to harbour. Right past statue, sharp left leave marina, 1m, hotel on left

PETS: Bedrooms £8 Public areas (lounge only) Exercise area (20yds) Pet Food

From its stunning cliff-top location, this imposing property dating back to 1809 has spectacular views across Torbay. Public areas include two comfortable lounges, an outdoor terrace, a swimming pool, together with a bar serving a range of popular dishes. Many of the bedrooms have the benefit of the splendid sea views.
ROOMS: 13 en suite (7 fmly) s £48-£80; d £96-£160 (incl. bkfst & dinner) LB **FACILITIES:** Spa Indoor swimming (H) Croquet lawn Jacuzzi Petanque Sailing Deep sea fishing entertainment ch fac Xmas **PARKING:** 200 **NOTES:** No smoking in restaurant
CARDS: 🟦

BURRINGTON (NEAR PORTSMOUTH ARMS STATION) — Map 03 SS61

★★★ ⚜⚜ **Northcote Manor**

EX37 9LZ
☎ 01769 560501 📠 01769 560770
e-mail: rest@northcotemanor.co.uk
Dir: off A377 opp Portsmouth Arms, into hotel drive. Do not enter Burrington village

PETS: Bedrooms (unattended) £5 Public areas (bar and drawing room only) Exercise area (on site) Pet Food

A warm and friendly welcome is assured at this beautiful country house hotel. Built in 1716, the house sits in 20 acres of grounds and woodlands. Guests can enjoy wonderful views over the Taw River Valley whilst relaxing in the environment created by the attentive staff. An elegant restaurant is a highlight with the finest of local produce used in well-prepared dishes. Bedrooms, including some suites, are individually styled, spacious and well appointed.
ROOMS: 11 en suite s £99-£165; d £140-£240 (incl. bkfst) LB **FACILITIES:** STV Tennis (hard) Croquet lawn Xmas **PARKING:** 30 **NOTES:** No smoking in restaurant **CARDS:** 🟦

CHAGFORD — Map 03 SX78

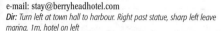

★★★ ⚜⚜⚜⚜ 🐾 **Gidleigh Park**

TQ13 8HH
☎ 01647 432367 📠 01647 432574
e-mail: gidleighpark@gidleigh.co.uk
Dir: from Chagford, right at Lloyds Bank into Mill St. After 150yds fork right, follow lane 2m to end

PETS: Bedrooms (unattended) Pet Food

This delightful, globally acclaimed establishment, set in 45 acres of lovingly tended grounds and gardens, boasts its own putting course, along with bowling, croquet and tennis courts. Individually styled bedrooms are beautifully furnished, some with separate
continued

seating areas and many enjoying views across the gardens and valley beyond. Public rooms are spacious and inviting, featuring antique pieces and beautiful flower arrangements. Dinner is a highlight of any stay and the accompanying wine list reflects the proprietors' own enthusiasm for the subject.
ROOMS: 12 en suite 3 annexe en suite s £275-£500; d £440-£575 (incl. bkfst & dinner) LB **FACILITIES:** STV Tennis (hard) Fishing Croquet lawn Putting green Bowls **PARKING:** 25 **NOTES:** No smoking in restaurant Closed 12 days Jan
CARDS: 🟦

★★★ 76% ⚜⚜ **Mill End**

Dartmoor National Park, Sandy Park TQ13 8JN
☎ 01647 432282 📠 01647 433106
e-mail: info@millendhotel.com
Dir: from A30 at Whiddon Down follow A382 to Moretonhampstead. After 3.5m hump back bridge at Sandy Park, hotel on right by river

PETS: Bedrooms (unattended) £10 Exercise area 2/3 acre dog paddock on site, dog room & dog towels available
RESIDENT PETS: Harry & Orvis (Labradors), 2 cats

In a peaceful and attractive location, Mill End is set on the riverside and offers six miles of angling on the River Teign. Bedrooms are available in a range of sizes and all are stylishly decorated and thoughtfully equipped. Cuisine is a feature here and menus offer exciting dishes featuring local produce.
ROOMS: 15 en suite (3 GF) s £70-£100; d £100-£140 (incl. bkfst) LB **FACILITIES:** Fishing Croquet lawn Xmas **PARKING:** 21 **NOTES:** No smoking in restaurant **CARDS:** 🟦

★★ 68% **Three Crowns Hotel**

High St TQ13 8AJ
☎ 01647 433444 📠 01647 433117
e-mail: threecrowns@msn.com
Dir: left off A30 at Whiddon Down, in Chagford town centre opposite church

PETS: Bedrooms (unattended) Public areas (except restaurant) Exercise area (200 metres) Pet Food

This 13th-century inn is located in the heart of the village. Exposed beams, mullioned windows and open fires are all part of the charm which is evident throughout. There is a range of bedrooms; several with four-poster beds, all are comfortable and now upgraded. A choice of bars is available along with a pleasant lounge and separate dining room.
ROOMS: 17 en suite (1 fmly) No smoking in 8 bedrooms s £55-£70; d £74 (incl. bkfst) LB **FACILITIES:** STV Xmas **PARKING:** 20 **NOTES:** No smoking in restaurant **CARDS:** 🟦

◆◆◆◆ 🏛 The Barn-Rodgemonts
Rodgemonts EX18 7ET
☎ 01769 580200
e-mail: pyerodgemonts@btinternet.com
Dir: from Exeter take A377. At Eggesford Stn (level crossing on left), right B3042 to Chawleigh, 1.5m. At T- junct left onto B3096 towards Chulmleigh, 0.5m signed Chawleigh Week, fork left. After 250mtrs Rodgemonts drive on right

PETS: Bedrooms Public areas (Not in main house)
RESIDENT PETS: Leo (German Shepherd cross)

Set amid peaceful countryside, this attractive house offers friendly hospitality. Bedrooms are located in the thatched, converted former hay barn, each with views of the orchard from which the proprietors produce their own apple juice which features in the delightful breakfasts. By prior arrangement, Aga cooked dinners are served in the farmhouse kitchen, overlooking the well-tended gardens.
FACILITIES: 2 en suite (1 fmly) No smoking TVB tea/coffee Cen ht No coaches Dinner **PRICES:** d £42-£52✳ **LB PARKING:** 3

◆◆◆◆ Lower Orchard
Swan Hill Rd EX24 6QQ
☎ 01297 553615
Dir: on A3052 in Colyford, between Lyme Regis & Sidmouth

PETS: Bedrooms (unattended) Public areas Exercise area
(300 metres) RESIDENT PETS: Biene & Sasha (Tibetan Terriers)

This modern ranch-style family home enjoys views over the Axe Valley. The spacious ground floor bedrooms are very well equipped. Breakfast is served in the lounge/dining room, which has patio doors leading to a private sun terrace and splash pool. The owners are creating a 'motoring memories' museum and a classic car showroom.
FACILITIES: 2 en suite (1 fmly) (2 GF) No smoking TVB tea/coffee Cen ht TVL No coaches Outdoor swimming pool **PRICES:** s £35-£40; d £45-£50✳ **PARKING:** 3

> 🌲 **Places with this symbol are country house hotels**

> **All abbreviations are explained on page 9**

> 🍺 **Places with this symbol are pubs**

> ★ **Red stars indicate the AA's Top 200 Hotels in Britain & Ireland**

◆◆◆ 🌿 Brimpts Farm
PL20 6SG
☎ 01364 631450 📠 01364 631179
e-mail: info@brimptsfarm.co.uk
Dir: off A38 onto B3357. Follow signs to Dartmeet. Establishment signposted on R at top of hill

PETS: Bedrooms Public areas Exercise area (adjacent)

A popular venue for walkers and lovers of the great outdoors, Brimpts is peacefully situated in idyllic surroundings and has been a Duchy of Cornwall farm since 1307. Bedrooms are all simply furnished, and many enjoy lovely views across Dartmoor. Dinner, served by prior arrangement, makes use of fresh, local produce. The sauna and spa are welcome facilities after a long day.
FACILITIES: 10 en suite (2 fmly) (7 GF) No smoking in bedrooms No smoking in area of dining room No smoking in 1 lounge TV1B tea/coffee Licensed Cen ht TVL Sauna Pool Table Abseiling, Climbing, Canoeing, Riding, Hot tub 700 acres beef Dinner **PRICES:** s £24; d £40-£50✳ **LB PARKING:** 50 **CARDS:** 💳💳💳💳💳

◆◆◆◆ Cherub's Nest
15 Higher St TQ6 9RB
☎ 01803 832482
e-mail: geofcherubnest@aol.com
Dir: from Lower Dartmouth ferry proceed along Lower St, take 2nd left into Smith Street, left again into Higher Street. Cherubs Nest 50yds on left

PETS: Bedrooms Exercise area (0.25 miles)

Dating back to 1710, this former merchant's house is ideally located in the very heart of historic Dartmouth. Full of character, the individually decorated bedrooms vary in size, but all are attractive and well-equipped. A choice of breakfasts is served in the cosy dining room.
FACILITIES: 3 en suite No smoking TVB tea/coffee Cen ht No children 10yrs No coaches **PRICES:** s £35-£70; d £60-£70✳ **LB**

◆◆◆◆ Warfleet Lodge
Warfleet TQ6 9BZ
☎ 01803 834352
Dir: from Dartmouth riverfront and hospital take Hauley Rd to Newcomen Rd-Southtown-Warfleet (in all same road) in 0.5m driveway on right

PETS: Telephone for details RESIDENT PETS: 3 cats

Just ten minutes' stroll from the centre of historic Dartmouth, Warfleet Lodge, built in 1870 and frequented by Edward VII, is a relaxing retreat from everyday life. With fine views over Warfleet creek and the River Dart, accommodation is elegant and comfortable. Breakfast is a highlight, parking is a bonus and pets are welcome.
FACILITIES: 3 en suite TVB tea/coffee Cen ht No coaches **PRICES:** d £65-£80✳ **PARKING:** 4

England

DAWLISH — Map 03 SX97

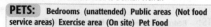

★★★ 70% Langstone Cliff

THE INDEPENDENTS

Dawlish Warren EX7 0NA
☎ 01626 868000 📠 01626 868006
e-mail: reception@langstone-hotel.co.uk
Dir: 1.5m NE off A379 Exeter road to Dawlish Warren

PETS: Bedrooms (unattended) Public areas (Not food service areas) Exercise area (On site) Pet Food

A family owned and run hotel, the Langstone Cliff offers a range of leisure, conference and function facilities. Bedrooms, many with sea views and balconies, are spacious, comfortable and well equipped. There are a number of attractive lounges and a well stocked bar. Dinner is served, often carvery style, in the restaurant.
ROOMS: 62 en suite 4 annexe en suite (52 fmly) (10 GF) s £62-£71; d £106-£154 (incl. bkfst) **LB FACILITIES:** STV Indoor swimming (H) Outdoor swimming (H) Tennis (hard) Snooker Gym Table tennis, Golf practice area, Hair and beauty salon entertainment ch fac Xmas
SERVICES: Lift **PARKING:** 200
CARDS: 〰 🖼 〰 🖼 🖼 🖼

EXETER — Map 03 SX99

★★★★ ◉ 🏠 Hotel Barcelona

Magdalen St EX2 4HY
☎ 01392 281000 📠 01392 281001
e-mail: info@aliasbarcelona.com
Dir: from A30 Okehampton follow city centre signs. At Exe Bridges rdbt right for city centre, up hill, straight on at lights. Hotel on right

PETS: Bedrooms £15 per stay Exercise area (adjacent)

Situated within walking distance of the city centre, Hotel Barcelona was formerly an eye hospital and has been totally transformed to provide stylish accommodation with a glamorous atmosphere. Public areas include Café Paradiso, an informal eatery with a varied menu, a night club, a range of meeting rooms and a delightful garden terrace ideal for al fresco dining.
ROOMS: 46 en suite No smoking in 3 bedrooms s £85-£90; d £95-£120 **LB FACILITIES:** STV entertainment **SERVICES:** Lift **PARKING:** 35
NOTES: No smoking in restaurant
CARDS: 〰 🖼 〰 🖼 🖼 🖼

★★★ 73% ◉◉ Lord Haldon Country House

THE INDEPENDENTS

Dunchideock EX6 7YF
☎ 01392 832483 📠 01392 833765
e-mail: enquiries@lordhaldonhotel.co.uk
Dir: M5 junct 31 or A30 signed to Ide, 2.5m through village. Left after phone box. 0.5m left after stone bridge

PETS: Telephone for details

Set amidst rural tranquillity, this attractive country house goes from strength to strength. Guests are assured of a warm welcome from the resident owners and the well-equipped bedrooms are comfortable, many with stunning views. Skilful cookery features

continued

on the daily-changing menu, with most of the produce sourced locally.
ROOMS: 19 en suite (3 fmly) No smoking in 10 bedrooms s £48.50-£60; d £85-£105 (incl. bkfst) **LB FACILITIES:** Xmas **PARKING:** 90
NOTES: No smoking in restaurant **CARDS:** 〰 🖼 🖼 🖼 🖼

★★★ 72% ◉◉ St Olaves Hotel & Restaurant

Mary Arches St EX4 3AZ
☎ 01392 217736 📠 01392 413054
e-mail: info@olaves.co.uk
Dir: city centre, signed to Mary Arches Parking. Hotel entrance opposite car park entrance

PETS: Bedrooms (unattended) £5 Public areas (except restaurant) Pet Food food and bowls provided with prior warning

Only a short stroll from the cathedral and city centre and set in an attractive walled garden, St Olaves seems to be a country house in its almost hidden location. Bedrooms are comfortably furnished and full of character along with thoughtful extra touches. The daily-changing menus offer imaginative cuisine and feature West Country produce.
ROOMS: 15 en suite (2 fmly) (1 GF) No smoking in all bedrooms s £105-£145; d £115-£155 (incl. cont bkfst) **LB FACILITIES:** STV Xmas
PARKING: 15 **NOTES:** No smoking in restaurant
CARDS: 〰 🖼 🖼 🖼

★★★ 68% ◉ Queens Court

Bystock Ter EX4 4HY
☎ 01392 272709 📠 01392 491390
e-mail: sales@queenscourt-hotel.co.uk
Dir: M5 junct 30 to Middlemoor, follow sign for A377 Crediton. At clock tower rdbt exit to Crediton, 1st left, 1st left.

PETS: Bedrooms Pet Food

Quietly located within walking distance of the city centre, this refurbished, privately owned hotel occupies listed early-Victorian premises and provides friendly hospitality. The smart public areas and bedrooms are tastefully furnished in contemporary style. Rooms are available for conferences, meetings and other functions. The bright and attractive Olive Tree restaurant offers an interesting selection of predominantly fish dishes.
ROOMS: 18 en suite (1 fmly) No smoking in 9 bedrooms s £59-£59; d £66-£76 **LB FACILITIES:** Xmas **SERVICES:** Lift **NOTES:** No smoking in restaurant Closed Christmas & Boxing Day RS Restaurant closed Sunday lunch **CARDS:** 〰 🖼 🖼 🖼 🖼

◆◆◆◆ The Edwardian

30/32 Heavitree Rd EX1 2LQ

☎ 01392 276102 & 254699 📠 01392 253393

e-mail: michael@edwardianexeter.co.uk

Dir: M5 J29. R at lights signed city centre. On Heavitree Rd after Exeter University, School of Education on L

PETS: Bedrooms Exercise area

Tastefully decorated in period style, this attractive Edwardian terraced property is situated within walking distance of the city centre. All of the bedrooms feature personal touches and a number have four-poster beds. Books and local tourist information are provided in the comfortable lounge, and the resident proprietors are on hand to help guests plan their stay.
FACILITIES: 12 en suite (4 fmly) (3 GF) No smoking in bedrooms No smoking in dining room TVB tea/coffee Direct dial from bedrooms Cen ht TVL No coaches **PARKING:** 3 **NOTES:** Closed Xmas
CARDS: 📇

◆◆◆◆ 🍴 Gissons Arms

Kennford EX6 7UD

☎ 01392 832444

Dir: A38 towards Torquay, before fork in road, up slip road on left

PETS: Bedrooms

With parts dating back to the 15th century, this delightful inn offers comfortable, well-equipped bedrooms, some boasting four-poster beds. The bars retain the original character and charm of the building and have a relaxed atmosphere. In addition to the extensive choice of dishes from the carvery, a range of daily special dishes and a tempting selection of desserts are available.
FACILITIES: 14 en suite No smoking in area of dining room TVB tea/coffee Direct dial from bedrooms Cen ht Dinner Last d 10pm **PRICES:** s £40; d £60✱ **PARKING:** 100 **NOTES:** rs Xmas night and Boxing Day night **CARDS:** 📇

◆◆◆◆ 🐾 Rydon

Woodbury EX5 1LB

☎ 01395 232341 📠 01395 232341

e-mail: sallyglanvill@aol.com

Dir: from Exeter A376, B3179 (Woodbury). In village turn right 10yds before 30mph sign

PETS: Bedrooms Exercise area (adjacent)

Dating back to the 16th century, this Devon longhouse has been owned by the same family for eight generations. The farmhouse provides spacious bedrooms, which are equipped with many useful extra facilities and one has a four-poster bed. There is a guests' TV lounge and a delightful garden in which to relax. Breakfast is served in front of an inglenook fireplace.
FACILITIES: 3 rms (2 en suite) (1 fmly) No smoking in bedrooms No smoking in dining room tea/coffee Cen ht TVL 400 acres dairy **PRICES:** s £30-£38; d £56-£64✱ **LB PARKING:** 3
CARDS: 📇

Please mention AA Pet Friendly Places to Stay when booking

◆◆◆ Culm Vale Country House

Culm Vale, Stoke Canon EX5 4EG

☎ 01392 841615 📠 01392 841615

Dir: From Exeter follow all Tiverton signs (A396). After 'Stoke Canon' sign, Culm Vale is the 5th property on right (white entrance)

PETS: Bedrooms £2.50 Exercise area (adjacent)
RESIDENT PETS: Blacks (cat), Rhoda & Bianca (English Bull Terriers) Justin & Golly (horses), Lucy & Amber (ponies), 2 canaries, chickens

A warm welcome is extended to guests at this impressive house situated on the edge of a pretty village. Culm Vale is family run, full of character and it offers very spacious, comfortable accommodation. Breakfast, featuring eggs laid by the family's own hens, can be enjoyed in the grand dining room.
FACILITIES: 3 rms (1 en suite) No smoking TVB tea/coffee Cen ht No coaches **PRICES:** s £20-£35; d £35-£45✱ **BB PARKING:** 3
CARDS: 📇

★★★ 71% Royal Beacon

The Beacon EX8 2AF

☎ 01395 264886 📠 01395 268890

e-mail: reception@royalbeaconhotel.co.uk

Dir: From M5 take A376 and Marine Way. Follow seafront signs. On Imperial Rd turn left at T-junct then 1st left. Hotel 100yds on left

PETS: Bedrooms (unattended) Public areas (except restaurant) Exercise area (adjacent) Pet Food
RESIDENT PETS: Riffles & Raffles (Bichon Frise)

This elegant Georgian property sits in an elevated position overlooking the town and has fine views of the estuary towards the sea. Bedrooms are individually styled and many have sea views. Public areas include a well stocked bar, a cosy lounge, an impressive function suite and a restaurant where freshly prepared and enjoyable cuisine is offered.
ROOMS: 30 en suite (2 fmly) No smoking in 10 bedrooms s £48-£80; d £85-£110 (incl. bkfst) **LB FACILITIES:** STV entertainment Xmas
SERVICES: Lift **PARKING:** 16 **NOTES:** No smoking in restaurant
CARDS: 📇

★★★ 77% @@@ Horn of Plenty

PL19 8JD

☎ 01822 832528 📠 01822 832528

e-mail: enquiries@thehornofplenty.co.uk

Dir: from Tavistock take A390 W for 3m. Right at Gulworthy Cross. After 400yds turn left and after 400yds hotel on right

PETS: Bedrooms 1 dog free, 2 or more £10

With memorable and stunning views over the Tamar Valley, The Horn of Plenty maintains its reputation as one of Britain's impressive country houses. The bedrooms are well equipped and have many thoughtful extras; some, more simply decorated, are in adjacent converted cottages. Cuisine here is also impressive and local produce provides interesting and memorable dining.
ROOMS: 4 en suite 6 annexe en suite (3 fmly) (4 GF) No smoking in all bedrooms s £105-£190; d £115-£200 (incl. bkfst) **LB**
FACILITIES: Xmas **PARKING:** 25 **NOTES:** No smoking in restaurant Closed 24-26 Dec **CARDS:** 📇

England

HARTLAND

Map 02 SS22

♦♦♦ Fosfelle
EX39 6EF
☎ 01237 441273 📠 01237 441273
Dir: off A39 onto B3248 for 2m, entrance on right

PETS: Sep Accom (Kennels) £2 Exercise area (Adjacent)

Dating back to the 17th century, this delightful manor house offers comfortable accommodation close to the village of Hartland. It is set in six acres of gardens with two fishing lakes. Guests can enjoy pool or darts in the welcoming bar, and the restaurant offers a range of freshly prepared dishes.
FACILITIES: 7 rms (4 en suite) (2 fmly) No smoking in bedrooms TV6B tea/coffee No dogs (ex guide dogs) Licensed Cen ht TVL Fishing Pool Table Dinner Last d 9pm **PRICES:** s £26-£32; d £52-£60✱ **LB**
PARKING: 20 **CARDS:** 💳💳

HAYTOR VALE

Map 03 SX77

★★ 75% 🏵 Rock Inn
TQ13 9XP
☎ 01364 661305 & 661465 📠 01364 661242
e-mail: inn@rock-inn.co.uk
Dir: off A38 onto A382 to Bovey Tracey, after 0.5m turn left onto B3387 to Haytor

PETS: Bedrooms £5

Dating back to the 1750s, this former coaching inn is in a pretty hamlet on the edge of Dartmoor. Each named after a Grand National winner, the individually decorated bedrooms have some nice extra touches. Bars are full of character, with flagstone floors and old beams and offer a wide range of dishes, cooked with imagination and flair.
ROOMS: 9 en suite (2 fmly) No smoking in 2 bedrooms s £65.50; d £75.95-£85.95 (incl. bkfst) **LB FACILITIES:** STV **PARKING:** 20
NOTES: No dogs (ex guide dogs)
CARDS: 💳💳💳

★ **Red stars indicate the AA's**
Top 200 Hotels in Britain & Ireland

HONITON

Map 03 ST10

★★★ 🏵🏵 ♣♣ Combe House Hotel & Restaurant
Gittisham EX14 3AD
☎ 01404 540400 📠 01404 46004
e-mail: stay@thishotel.com
Dir: off A30 1m S of Honiton, follow Gittisham Heathpark signs

PETS: Bedrooms (unattended) £5 Public areas (except restaurant) Exercise area (adjacent) Pet Food Bowl and food provided if ordered in advance **RESIDENT PETS:** Tabby - cat

Standing proud in an elevated position, this Elizabethan mansion enjoys uninterrupted views over acres of its own woodland, meadow and pasture. Bedrooms are a blend of comfort and quality with relaxation being the ultimate objective. A range of atmospheric public rooms retain all the charm and history of the old house. Dining is equally impressive, a skilled kitchen brigade maximising the best of local and home-grown produce, augmented by excellent wines. Private dining is available in the magnificently restored old kitchen.
ROOMS: 15 en suite s £125-£165; d £140-£148 (incl. bkfst) **LB**
FACILITIES: Fishing Croquet lawn Jacuzzi ch fac Xmas **PARKING:** 51
NOTES: No smoking in restaurant **CARDS:** 💳💳💳💳💳

★★ 69% Home Farm
Wilmington EX14 9JR
☎ 01404 831278 📠 01404 831411
e-mail: homefarmhotel@breathemail.net
Dir: 3m E of Honiton on A35

PETS: Bedrooms (unattended) £3 Exercise area
RESIDENT PETS: Chester & Harvey - Golden Retrievers, Skippy & Tigs - cats

Set in well-tended gardens, this thatched former farmhouse is now a comfortable hotel. Many of the original features have been retained with the cobbled courtyard and farm implements attractively displayed. A range of interesting dishes is offered either in the bar or in the more intimate restaurant. Bedrooms, some with private gardens, are well equipped and comfortably furnished.
ROOMS: 8 en suite 5 annexe en suite (4 fmly) (6 GF) No smoking in all bedrooms s £48-£70; d £70-£100 (incl. bkfst) **LB FACILITIES:** Xmas
PARKING: 20 **NOTES:** No smoking in restaurant
CARDS: 💳💳💳

◆◆◆◆ Atwell's at Wellington Farm
Wilmington EX14 9JR
☎ 01404 831885
e-mail: wilmington@btinternet.com
Dir: 3m from Honiton, take A35 towards Dorchester, approx 500yds through Wilmington on left

PETS: **Bedrooms (unattended) Public areas Exercise area (100mtrs)** RESIDENT PETS: Horses, ponies, chickens, a sheep, a goat, Shetland pony - star of children's books!

Convenient for Honiton and the coast, this delightful Grade II listed 16th-century farmhouse is set in five acres, which also accommodates a rescue centre for animals including hens, a goat, sheep and horses of varying sizes - from Shire to Shetland. This friendly house offers comfortable accommodation, hearty breakfasts using fresh local produce and cream teas.
FACILITIES: 3 rms (2 en suite) (1 GF) No smoking TVB Cen ht TVL No coaches **PRICES:** s fr £20; d £44-£50✳ **PARKING:** 10

◆◆◆◆ The Crest
Moorcox Ln, Wilmington EX14 9JU
☎ 01404 831419
Dir: 3m E of Honiton on A35 at eastern end of village; after river bridge turn left, guest house 100 metres on right

PETS: **Bedrooms (unattended) Exercise area Large field** RESIDENT PETS: Penny & Molly - collies

Guests are assured of a warm welcome at The Crest, which enjoys delightful views across the Umborne Valley and its own gardens. Each room is equipped with modern comforts and two are located on the ground floor. Breakfast is served around one large table in the dining room and guests can also relax in the bright conservatory. By special arrangement, evening meals are served.
FACILITIES: 3 en suite (1 fmly) (2 GF) No smoking in bedrooms No smoking in dining room TVB tea/coffee Cen ht No coaches Dinner Last d previous day **PARKING:** 6

◆◆◆◆ Ridgeway Farm
Awliscombe EX14 3PY
☎ 01404 841331 📠 01404 841119
e-mail: jessica@ridgewayfarm.co.uk
Dir: Off A30, onto A373 towards Cullompton, through village of Awliscombe, just before leaving the 40mph section turn right opposite Godford Farm, up a very small lane. Ridgeway farm 500m ahead

PETS: **Bedrooms Public areas Exercise area (surrounding farmland)** RESIDENT PETS: Blossom - Black Labrador, Crumble - Terrier, Puzzle - Border Terrier, 2 horses

This 18th-century farmhouse is in a peaceful, elevated setting and enjoys country views. It is ideally located for exploring nearby Honiton and the east Devon coast. Recent renovations have brought the cosy accommodation to a high standard and the atmosphere is relaxed and homely. The proprietors and their family pets assure a warm welcome.
FACILITIES: 2 en suite No smoking in bedrooms No smoking in dining room TVB tea/coffee No dogs (ex guide dogs) Cen ht TVL No coaches Dinner Last d morning **PRICES:** s £27.50-£32.50; d £48-£54✳ **LB** **PARKING:** 4

ILFRACOMBE Map 02 SS54

◆◆◆◆ Strathmore Hotel
57 St Brannock's Rd EX34 8EQ
☎ 01271 862248
e-mail: peter@small6374.fsnet.co.uk
Dir: take A361 from Barnstaple to Ilfracombe, Strathmore is approx 1.5m from Mullacot Cross entering Ilfracombe

PETS: **Bedrooms £4.50 (dogs/cats) Public areas (Allowed in bar and lounge only) Exercise area (0.25 mile) Bowls of water and biscuits provided and welcome letter for dogs** RESIDENT PETS: Sasha - Sheltie

Situated within walking distance of the town centre and beach, this charming Victorian hotel offers guests a very warm welcome. Bedrooms are attractively decorated and comfortably furnished. Public areas include a well-stocked bar, an attractive terraced garden, and an elegant breakfast room.
FACILITIES: 8 en suite (3 fmly) No smoking TVB tea/coffee Licensed Cen ht No coaches **PRICES:** s £30-£40; d £48-£70✳ **LB PARKING:** 5
NOTES: Closed 16 Dec-31 Jan **CARDS:** 🖥 💳 💳 🔲 💲

◆◆◆◆ Norbury House Hotel
Torrs Park EX34 8AZ
☎ 01271 863888
e-mail: info@norburyhousehotel.co.uk
Dir: A361 from Barnstaple, 1st set of traffic lights turn left. At 2nd set, turn left & left again into Torrs Park, Norbury House on right

PETS: **Bedrooms (unattended) £1 Public areas (not in dining room; on a lead) Exercise area (200 mtrs) Bowls, mats, food, dog bins on request** RESIDENT PETS: Spot - Jack Russell

This establishment is quietly located in an elevated position, with views over the town and the sea in the distance. Norbury House was built as a gentleman's residence in 1870. The well-equipped bedrooms are comfortable. In addition to the inviting lounge, there is also a cosy bar. Breakfast is served in the pleasant dining room and dinners are available by prior arrangement.
FACILITIES: 8 rms (6 en suite) (3 fmly) No smoking TVB tea/coffee Licensed Cen ht TVL No coaches Dinner Last d 10am
PRICES: s £25-£27; d £50-£54✳ **LB PARKING:** 6 **NOTES:** Closed Jan
CARDS: 🖥 💳 💳 🔲 💲

England

England

ILSINGTON

Map 03 SX77

★★★ 72%

The Ilsington Country House

Ilsington Village TQ13 9RR

☎ 01364 661452 ▧ 01364 661307

e-mail: hotel@ilsington.co.uk

Best Western

Dir: M5 onto A38 to Plymouth. Exit at Bovey Tracey. 3rd exit from rdbt to 'Ilsington', then 1st right. Hotel 5m by Post Office

PETS: Bedrooms (unattended) £7 Exercise area (5 mins walk)

Peacefully situated with far-reaching views, this friendly hotel occupies an elevated position on the southern slopes of Dartmoor. Bedrooms, some of which are on the ground floor, are individually furnished. Local fish, meat and game feature on the daily-changing, innovative menus. On-site leisure facilities are available for hotel residents.

ROOMS: 25 en suite (2 fmly) (8 GF) No smoking in 5 bedrooms s £76-£82; d £116-£120 (incl. bkfst) **LB FACILITIES:** Spa Indoor swimming (H) Tennis (hard) Sauna Gym Jacuzzi Xmas **SERVICES:** Lift **PARKING:** 100 **NOTES:** No smoking in restaurant **CARDS:** ▧▧▧▧▧▧▧

JACOBSTOWE

Map 02 SS50

◆◆◆◆ ◗ ❦ Higher Cadham

EX20 3RB

☎ 01837 851647 ▧ 01837 851410

e-mail: kingscadham@btopenworld.com

Dir: from A30 turn off to Okehampton. By White Hart Hotel traffic lights take A386 signed Hatherleigh. Travel through Folly Gate then turn right onto A3072 for Jacobstowe, at junct turn left, take sharp right immediately after church then continue for 0.5m.

PETS: Bedrooms (unattended) £2 Public areas (On a lead) Exercise area (footpaths from farm)

Guests return here for the excellent standards of hospitality and enjoyable food. The location is perfect for either cycling or walking breaks. Visiting children will enjoy the animals and the large play area. Ground floor bedrooms are available, two especially for the disabled. There is a comfortable lounge and bar.

FACILITIES: 8 en suite (2 fmly) (4 GF) No smoking TVB tea/coffee Licensed Cen ht TVL Nature Trail, Pets corner, Play area 120 acres beef & sheep Dinner Last d 5pm **PRICES:** s £27.50-£30; d fr £55✳ **LB PARKING:** 30 **NOTES:** Closed 3-10 Oct & 21 Dec-10 Jan rs Sunday **CARDS:** ▧▧▧▧▧▧

KINGSBRIDGE

Map 03 SX74

★★★ Buckland-Tout-Saints

Goveton TQ7 2DS

☎ 01548 853055 ▧ 01548 856261

e-mail: buckland@tout-saints.co.uk

Dir: off A381 Totnes/Kingsbridge road to Goveton. Left into Goveton, up hill to St Peter's Church. Hotel 2nd right after church

PETS: Bedrooms (unattended) £3 Public areas (except restaurant) Pet Food food provided by prior arrangement, large garden RESIDENT PETS: Charlie - West Highland terrier

It's well worth navigating the winding country lanes to find this delightful Queen Anne manor house that has been host to many famous guests over the years. Set in seven acres of gardens and grounds the hotel is a peaceful retreat. Bedrooms are tastefully furnished and attractively decorated, most of them enjoying views of the gardens. Local produce is used with care and imagination in the restaurant. The large function room opens on to the terrace and is a popular choice for weddings.

ROOMS: 12 en suite (1 fmly) No smoking in 1 bedroom s £75-£140; d £150-£300 (incl. bkfst) **LB FACILITIES:** Croquet lawn Putting green Petanque pitch Xmas **PARKING:** 42 **NOTES:** No smoking in restaurant Closed 3 wks Jan **CARDS:** ▧▧▧▧▧

LEWDOWN

Map 02 SX48

★★★ Lewtrenchard Manor

EX20 4PN

☎ 01566 783256 & 783222 ▧ 01566 783332

e-mail: info@lewtrenchard.co.uk

Dir: A30 from Exeter to Plymouth/Tavistock road. At T-junct turn right, then left onto old A30 Lewdown road. After 6m left signed Lewtrenchard

PETS: Bedrooms £10 Exercise area (adjacent)

This Jacobean mansion was built in the 1600s, with many interesting architectural features, and is surrounded by its own idyllic grounds in a quiet valley close to the northern edge of Dartmoor. Public rooms include a fine gallery, as well as magnificent carvings and oak panelling. Meals can be taken in the dining room where imaginative and carefully prepared dishes are served using the best of Devon produce. Bedrooms are comfortably furnished and spacious.

ROOMS: 9 en suite s £95-£120; d £135-£200 (incl. bkfst) **LB FACILITIES:** Fishing Croquet lawn Clay pigeon shooting Xmas **PARKING:** 50 **NOTES:** No children 8yrs No smoking in restaurant **CARDS:** ▧▧▧▧▧▧

★ Red stars indicate the AA's Top 200 Hotels in Britain & Ireland

All AA listed accommodation, restaurants and pubs can be found on the AA's website www.theAA.com

🏕 Places with this symbol are country house hotels

❦ Places with this symbol are farms

LIFTON
Map 02 SX38

★★★ 75% ◎◎◎ Arundell Arms
PL16 0AA
☎ 01566 784666 🖹 01566 784494
e-mail: reservations@arundellarms.com
Dir: 1m off A30 in Lifton

PETS: Bedrooms (unattended) £4 plus food Public areas (Not restaurant, or on river bank) Exercise area (0.5 mile) Pet Food

This creeper clad, former coaching inn sits in the heart of a quiet Devon village. Internationally famous for its sporting facilities, the inn boasts a long history and continues to offer style, comfort and a relaxed atmosphere. Food is a major aspect here and the cuisine is a celebration of the best of Devon's produce. Angling as well as winter shooting, golf and other country pursuits are offered.
ROOMS: 22 en suite 5 annexe en suite (4 GF) No smoking in all bedrooms s £68-£89; d £104-£136 (incl. bkfst) **LB FACILITIES:** STV Fishing Skittle alley, 3 acre lake, Shooting in Winter **PARKING:** 70
NOTES: No smoking in restaurant Closed 3 days Xmas
CARDS: ▱▱▱▱▱▱ ⑤

LYDFORD
Map 02 SX58

♦♦♦♦♦ 🍽 Moor View House
Vale Down EX20 4BB
☎ 01822 820220 🖹 01822 820220
Dir: turn off A30 at Sourton Cross onto A386 Tavistock road, hotel drive approx 4m on right

PETS: Bedrooms £5 Exercise area

Built around 1870, this charming house once changed hands over a game of cards. Retaining many original features, the bedrooms are elegant and beautifully decorated, furnished with an interesting collection of pieces. The two acres of moorland gardens have access to Dartmoor. Breakfast, and dinner by prior arrangement, are served house-party style at a large oak table.
FACILITIES: 4 en suite No smoking TVB tea/coffee Licensed Cen ht TVL No children 12yrs No coaches Bowls Croquet Dinner Last d 24 hrs prior **PRICES:** s £47.50-£52.50; d £65-£80✱ **LB PARKING:** 15

LYMPSTONE
Map 03 SX98

♦♦♦♦ Varnes
Church Rd EX8 5JT
☎ 01395 276999 🖹 01395 271787
e-mail: chris@varnes16.freeserve.co.uk
Dir: from Lympstone Railway Station, left under bridge and continue uphill for 300mtrs, opposite public house

PETS: Sep Accom (Downstairs - dogs sleep with resident dogs) Public areas Exercise area (Adjacent)
RESIDENT PETS: 2 Black Labradors

Guests are assured a warm welcome at this establishment set in the heart of the pretty village and ideally located for touring the Devonshire coast. Bedrooms are spacious, comfortably furnished and well equipped. Breakfast, featuring home-made preserves, is
continued

served in the conservatory dining room. There is a pleasant garden to be enjoyed during good weather.
FACILITIES: 2 rms (1 en suite) (1 fmly) No smoking TV1B tea/coffee Cen ht TVL No children 10yrs No coaches **PRICES:** s £30; d £50✱
PARKING: 5 **NOTES:** Closed 3 days Xmas & Etr

LYNMOUTH
Map 03 SS74

★★★ 64% Tors
EX35 6NA
☎ 01598 753236 🖹 01598 752544
e-mail: torshotel@torslynmouth.co.uk
Dir: adjacent to A39 on Countisbury Hill just before entering Lynmouth from Minehead

PETS: Bedrooms (unattended) £1.50 Public areas (except restaurant and luxury suite) Exercise area (Woodland around hotel) Pet Food Bowls provided

In an elevated position overlooking Lynmouth Bay, this friendly hotel is set in five acres of woodland. The majority of the bedrooms benefit from the superb views, as do the public areas which are generous and well-presented. Both fixed-price and short carte menus are offered in the restaurant.
ROOMS: 31 en suite (6 fmly) s £68-£170; d £96-£200 (incl. bkfst) **LB**
FACILITIES: Outdoor swimming (H) Table tennis Pool table ch fac Xmas
SERVICES: Lift **PARKING:** 40 **NOTES:** No smoking in restaurant Closed 4-31 Jan RS Feb (wknds only)
CARDS: ▱▱▱▱▱▱ ⑤

★★ 68% Bath
Sea Front EX35 6EL
☎ 01598 752238 🖹 01598 753894
e-mail: bathhotel@torslynmouth.co.uk
Dir: M5 junct 25, follow A39 to Minehead then Porlock and Lynmouth

PETS: Bedrooms (unattended) Public areas (not in restaurant) Exercise area (200yds) **RESIDENT PETS:** Boadecia & Polyanna (Persian cats)

This well-established, friendly hotel is situated near the harbour and offers lovely views from the attractive, sea-facing bedrooms and an excellent starting point for scenic walks. There are two lounges and a sun lounge and the restaurant menu makes good use of fresh produce and local fish.
ROOMS: 22 en suite (9 fmly) No smoking in 1 bedroom s £40-£53; d £66-£116 (incl. bkfst) **LB FACILITIES:** ch fac **PARKING:** 12
NOTES: No smoking in restaurant Closed Jan & Dec RS Feb-Mar and Nov
CARDS: ▱▱▱▱▱▱ ⑤

England

LYNMOUTH continued

♦♦♦♦♦ The Heatherville

Tors Park EX35 6NB
☎ 01598 752327 📠 01598 752634
Dir: off A39 into Tors Rd, 1st left fork into Tors Park

PETS: **Bedrooms Public areas (except dining room) Exercise area (adjacent)**

From a secluded and elevated south facing position, the Heatherville enjoys splendid views over Lynmouth and surrounding woodland. The recently redecorated bedrooms are comfortable and well appointed. By prior arrangement, enjoyable evening meals are provided in the dining room and feature organic and free-range produce wherever possible. In addition, a cosy bar and an attractive lounge with a fireplace are available.
FACILITIES: 6 en suite No smoking TVB tea/coffee Licensed Cen ht No children 16yrs No coaches Dinner Last d breakfast
PRICES: d £58-£76* **LB** **PARKING:** 7 **NOTES:** Closed Nov-Feb
CARDS:

♦♦♦♦ Countisbury Lodge Hotel

6 Tors Park, Countisbury Hill EX35 6NB
☎ 01598 752388
e-mail: paulpat@countisburylodge.co.uk
Dir: travelling W on A39, turn left at sign for Countisbury Lodge on Countisbury Hill, just before entering Lynmouth

PETS: **Bedrooms (unattended) Exercise area (10 mins walk) Dog food by prior arrangement** RESIDENT PETS: Golden Retrievers - Jessica & Magic, cat - Eric

From its peaceful elevated position high above the town, this former Victorian vicarage enjoys spectacular views of the harbour and countryside. The atmosphere is friendly and informal but with attentive service. The comfortable bedrooms are attractively decorated and breakfast is served in the pleasant dining room; in addition a cosy honesty bar is available for guests.
FACILITIES: 4 en suite (1 fmly) No smoking TVB tea/coffee Licensed Cen ht No coaches **PRICES:** s £27-£30; d £54-£60* **PARKING:** 6
CARDS:

LYNTON Map 03 SS74

★★★ 68% Lynton Cottage

North Walk EX35 6ED
☎ 01598 752342 📠 01598 752597
e-mail: enquiries@lynton-cottage.co.uk
Dir: M25 junct 23, A39 to Lynmouth then Lynton, hotel 100mtrs on right

PETS: **Bedrooms (unattended) Public areas (except restaurant) Exercise area (in hotel grounds) Pet Food Dog and cat food available** RESIDENT PETS: Ivor - Golden Labrador

Magnificent views can be enjoyed from this peaceful hideaway, which stands some 500 feet above the sea. Bedrooms vary in size and most have scenic views, whilst public areas, such as the cosy Victorian-style bar, provide a relaxing environment. In Sanford's Restaurant, a short carte offers a balanced selection of tempting dishes.
ROOMS: 15 en suite (2 fmly) (1 GF) No smoking in 3 bedrooms s £54-£105; d £78-£150 (incl. bkfst) **LB** **PARKING:** 17
NOTES: No smoking in restaurant Closed Dec-Jan
CARDS:

★★ 72% Seawood

North Walk EX35 6HJ
☎ 01598 752272 📠 01598 752272
e-mail: GIInJnK@aol.com
Dir: turn right at St. Mary's Church in Lynton High St for hotel, 2nd on left

PETS: **Bedrooms £3 Exercise area (10 yards)**

Tucked away in a quiet area and spectacularly situated 400 feet above the seashore, the Seawood enjoys magnificent views, and is set in delightfully planted grounds. This is a friendly place where many guests return on a regular basis. Bedrooms, many with sea views and some with four-poster beds, are comfortable and well equipped. At dinner, the daily changing menu provides freshly prepared and appetising cuisine.
ROOMS: 12 en suite s £30-£34; d £60-£76 (incl. bkfst) **PARKING:** 12
NOTES: No children 10yrs No smoking in restaurant Closed Dec-Feb
CARDS:

MORETONHAMPSTEAD
Map 03 SX78

U Bovey Castle
TQ13 8RE
☎ 01647 445000 🖷 01647 440961
e-mail: reception@boveycastle.com
Dir: 2m from Moretonhampstead towards Princetown on B3212

PETS: Sep Accom (Kennels) Pet Food

At the time of going to press, the star classification for this hotel was not confirmed. Please refer to the AA internet site www.theAA.com for current information.
ROOMS: 60 en suite 5 annexe en suite (5 fmly) (2 GF) No smoking in all bedrooms s £145-£550; d £145-£550 **FACILITIES:** Spa STV Indoor swimming (H) Outdoor swimming (H) Golf 18 Tennis (hard & grass) Fishing Snooker Sauna Solarium Gym Croquet lawn Putting green Jacuzzi clay pigeon shooting, archery, fly-fishing entertainment ch fac Xmas **SERVICES:** Lift **PARKING:** 100 **NOTES:** No dogs No smoking in restaurant **CARDS:** 💳💳💳💳💳

MORTEHOE
Map 02 SS44

★★ 66% *Lundy House Hotel*
Chapel Hill EX34 7DZ
☎ 01271 870372 🖷 01271 871001
e-mail: info@lundyhousehotel.co.uk
Dir: A361 to Braunton and Ilfracombe. Woolacombe exit at rdbt. In village right along esplanade, up hill to Mortehoe, hotel on left

PETS: Telephone for details

Facing south across the rugged North Devon coastline to Lundy Island in the distance, this personally run hotel offers a warm, friendly welcome. In the dining room, honest home cooking is served; vegetarians are particularly well catered for. It is very much a dog-friendly hotel, and there is direct access to the coastal path from the hotel's terraced gardens.
ROOMS: 9 en suite (4 fmly) No smoking in all bedrooms **PARKING:** 9
NOTES: No smoking in restaurant Closed Nov-Mar
CARDS: 💳💳💳💳

> **All information was correct at the time of going to press; we recommend you confirm details on booking**

NEWTON ABBOT
Map 03 SX87

◆◆◆◆ 🏠 ❦ Bulleigh Park
Ipplepen TQ12 5UA
☎ 01803 872254 🖷 01803 872254
e-mail: bulleigh@lineone.net
Dir: turn off A381 for Compton at Jet garage, follow for approx 1m. Signposted

PETS: Public areas

With mesmerising views across the glorious Devon countryside, Bulleigh Park is a working farm that produces award-winning Aberdeen Angus beef. A friendly welcome is offered and guests will find it easy to relax in this family home. Breakfasts, notable for their wealth of fresh, local and home-made produce, are taken in the pleasant dining room.
FACILITIES: 2 en suite 1 annexe en suite No smoking in bedrooms No smoking in dining room No smoking in 1 lounge TVB tea/coffee No dogs (ex guide dogs) Cen ht TVL Stabling available for own horse 60 acres beef, sheep **PRICES:** s £30-£35; d £52-£60✳ **LB PARKING:** 6
NOTES: Closed Xmas **CARDS:** 💳💳💳

OTTERY ST MARY
Map 03 SY19

◆◆ Fluxton Farm
Fluxton EX11 1RJ
☎ 01404 812818 🖷 01404 814843
Dir: from Exeter/Honiton, off A30 at Daisymount junct for Ottery St Mary (B3174). Right at 1st set of x-rds at 30mph sign. Continue for 1m

PETS: Bedrooms Sep Accom (Pens for cats only) (unattended) Exercise area (next door) Can provide whatever is required RESIDENT PETS: 18 cats, farm is also a cat rescue sanctuary; geese, chickens

A haven for cat lovers, Fluxton Farm offers comfortable accommodation with a choice of lounges, a bar and a large garden, complete with pond and ducks. Located just four miles from the coast in a peaceful farmland setting, this interesting 16th-century longhouse has a wealth of beams and open fireplaces.
FACILITIES: 11 rms (10 en suite) (1 fmly) No smoking in dining room No smoking in 1 lounge TVB tea/coffee Licensed Cen ht TVL No children 8yrs No coaches **PRICES:** s £25-£27.50; d £50-£55✳ **LB PARKING:** 15

> **All abbreviations are explained on page 9**

England

◆◆◆ Park Hotel
Esplanade Rd TQ4 6BQ
☎ 01803 557856 ▤ 01803 555626
e-mail: stay@parkhotel.me.uk
Dir: turn off A380 onto B3060, located on Paignton seafront, nearly opposite the pier

PETS: Bedrooms Exercise area (15yds)

This large hotel enjoys a prominent and imposing position on the seafront and has excellent views of Torbay. Bedrooms, many recently refurbished and many having sea views, are all pleasantly spacious and are available in a number of sizes. Entertainment is provided on some evenings in the lounge. Dinner and breakfast are served in the spacious dining room, which overlooks the attractive front lawn.
FACILITIES: 47 rms (31 en suite) (5 fmly) (3 GF) No smoking in bedrooms No smoking in dining room No smoking in 1 lounge TVB tea/coffee Licensed Lift Cen ht ch fac games room with 3/4 snooker table & table tennis Dinner Last d 6pm **PARKING:** 35
CARDS: 〰 🔲🔲 🔲 🔲 🔳 ⑤

◆◆◆ Bay Cottage Hotel
4 Beach Rd TQ4 6AY
☎ 01803 525729
e-mail: info@baycottagehotel.co.uk
Dir: travel along B3201 (Esplanade Rd) past Paignton Pier, Beach Rd is 2nd on the right. Bay Cottage is the 4th Hotel

PETS: Bedrooms £1.50 Public areas Exercise area (100yds)

With easy level access to the beach, theatre and the shops, Bay Cottage offers friendly accommodation. In the bedrooms, the best possible use has been made of available space. Dinner, by prior arrangement, offers home-cooked food served in the pleasant surroundings of the pine-furnished dining room, and a comfortable lounge is provided for guests' use.
FACILITIES: 8 en suite (3 fmly) No smoking in bedrooms No smoking in dining room TVB tea/coffee Cen ht TVL No coaches Dinner Last d 9.30am **LB NOTES:** Closed 20 Dec-3 Jan

★★★ 72% ⓦ Penhaven Country House
Rectory Ln EX39 5PL
☎ 01237 451388 & 451711 ▤ 01237 451878
e-mail: reservations@penhaven.co.uk
Dir: off A39 at Horns Cross, follow signs to Parkham, 2nd left after church into Rectory Ln

PETS: Bedrooms £3 Exercise area

The countryside is very much at the heart of this establishment and lucky guests can spot tame badgers most evenings in the lovely grounds. The tranquillity of the location and the friendliness of the staff combine to create a truly relaxing place to stay. Bedrooms are spacious and well equipped; some are located in the cottage annexe and two are on the ground floor. Dinners feature fresh, local produce and vegetarians are especially welcome.
ROOMS: 12 en suite   s £90-£100;   d £180-£200 (incl. bkfst & dinner) **LB**
FACILITIES: 9 acres of woodland trail Xmas **PARKING:** 50
NOTES: No children 10yrs No smoking in restaurant
CARDS: 〰 🔲🔲 🔲 🔳 ⑤

★★★ 65% Novotel Plymouth
Marsh Mills PL6 8NH
☎ 01752 221422 ▤ 01752 223922
e-mail: H0508@accor-hotels.com
Dir: Exit A38 at Marsh Mills, follow Plympton signs, hotel on left

NOVOTEL

PETS: Bedrooms (unattended) £6 Exercise area (0.25 mile)

Conveniently located on the outskirts of the city, close to Marsh Mills roundabout, this modern hotel offers good value accommodation. All rooms are spacious and designed with flexibility for family use. Public areas are open-plan with meals available throughout the day in either the Garden Brasserie, the bar, or from room service.
ROOMS: 100 en suite (17 fmly) (18 GF) No smoking in 80 bedrooms s £50-£70; d £50-£85 **LB FACILITIES:** STV Outdoor swimming (H) Xmas **SERVICES:** Lift **PARKING:** 140 **CARDS:** 〰 🔲🔲 🔲 🔲 🔳 ⑤

★★ 63% The Moorland
Wotter, Shaugh Prior PL7 5HP
☎ 01752 839228 ▤ 01752 839153
e-mail: reservations@moorlandhotel.com
Dir: Take Lee Mill exit from A38. Through underpass turn right then left, follow road 6 miles through Cornwood and on to Wotter.

PETS: Bedrooms Sep Accom (secure field for horses) (unattended) Public areas (not in restaurants) Exercise area (adjacent) Pet Food Can provide whatever is required, if notice given RESIDENT PETS: Rottweiler - Lowen, Labrador - Gwennap, Dalmatian - Winnie , Burmese cat - Bournville, ginger moggy - Muffin

Situated on the northern slopes of the Dartmoor National Park, this family-run hotel offers a warm welcome to visitors. Bedrooms are soundly appointed and all have pleasant views. The convivial bar is popular with both visitors and locals; the atmosphere always good-natured and entertaining. A range of menus is available in either the bar or attractive restaurant.
ROOMS: 18 en suite (2 fmly) No smoking in 4 bedrooms s £32.30-£47.50; d £51-£60 (incl. bkfst) **LB FACILITIES:** Games room, secure field available for guests' horses. **PARKING:** 40
NOTES: No smoking in restaurant **CARDS:** 〰 🔲 🔳 ⑤

★★ 61% Camelot
5 Elliot St, The Hoe PL1 2PP
☎ 01752 221255 & 669667 ▤ 01752 603660
e-mail: camelot@hotelplymouth.fsnet.co.uk
Dir: from A38 follow city centre signs, then signs to The Hoe. Into Citadel Road, then on to Elliot Street

PETS: Pets accepted by prior arrangement Bedrooms Exercise area (2 mins walk) RESIDENT PETS: Rottweiler - Louis

Just a short walk from The Hoe, the Barbican and the city centre, this is a convenient choice for visitors to this historic naval city. The friendly, small hotel provides comfortable accommodation, with bedrooms varying in size and style. The convivial bar is a popular meeting point and additional facilities include a TV lounge and function room.
ROOMS: 18 en suite (5 fmly) No smoking in 3 bedrooms s £43; d £55 (incl. bkfst) **NOTES:** No smoking in restaurant
CARDS: 〰 🔲🔲 🔲 🔳 ⑤

⬆ Hotel Ibis

Marsh Mills, Longbridge Rd, Forder Valley PL6 8LD
☎ 01752 601087 📠 01752 223213
e-mail: H2093@accor-hotels.com

Dir: A38 to Plymouth, 1st exit after flyover towards Estover, Leigham and Parkway Industrial Est. At rdbt, hotel on 4th exit

PETS: Bedrooms £3 Public areas Exercise area (0.5 mile)

Modern, budget hotel offering comfortable accommodation in bright and practical bedrooms. Breakfast is self-service and dinner is available in the restaurant. For further details, consult the Hotel Groups page.
ROOMS: 52 en suite

♦♦♦♦ Cranbourne

278-282 Citadel Rd, The Hoe PL1 2PZ
☎ 01752 263858 & 224646 📠 01752 263858
e-mail: cran.hotel@virgin.net

PETS: Bedrooms Public areas (except dining room) Exercise area (100yds)

This attractive Georgian terraced house has been extensively renovated, and is located just a short walk from The Hoe, The Barbican and the city centre. Bedrooms are practically furnished and well equipped. Hearty breakfasts are served in the elegant dining room and there is also a cosy bar.
FACILITIES: 40 rms (28 en suite) (5 fmly) No smoking in dining room TVB tea/coffee Licensed Cen ht TVL **PRICES:** s £20-£35; d £40-£50✳
PARKING: 14 **CARDS:** 💳

♦♦♦ Four Seasons

207 Citadel Rd East, The Hoe PL1 2JF
☎ 01752 223591
Dir: off A38 for Plymouth and follow signs for city centre and then The Hoe

PETS: Bedrooms (unattended) Public areas Exercise area (100yds) RESIDENT PETS: West Highland terrier - Edward, black cat - Sophie

Under new ownership, this guest house is conveniently located for the Barbican, Hoe and city centre. Many personal touches, such as fresh flowers, complement the friendly and hospitable atmosphere. One bedroom is located on the ground floor. A full English breakfast, or a vegetarian option on request, is served in the cosy, smartly appointed dining room.
FACILITIES: 7 rms (5 en suite) (1 GF) No smoking TVB tea/coffee Cen ht No coaches **PRICES:** d £32-£50✳ **BB CARDS:** 💳

♦♦♦ The Lamplighter Hotel

103 Citadel Rd, The Hoe PL1 2RN
☎ 01752 663855 📠 01752 228139
e-mail: lamplighterhotel@ukonline.co.uk
Dir: exit A38, follow signs to city centre, 1st exit at rdbt, left at 3rd traffic lights, right at 5th traffic lights and take 2nd right

PETS: Bedrooms £2 Exercise area (200yds) RESIDENT PETS: 2 cats

Conveniently located with easy access to The Hoe, Barbican and city centre, this comfortable guest house provides an ideal base

continued

for those visiting for leisure or business. Bedrooms, including family rooms, are light and airy and furnished to a consistent standard. Breakfast is taken in the dining room, which also has an adjoining lounge area.
FACILITIES: 9 en suite (2 fmly) No smoking in dining room TVB tea/coffee Cen ht TVL **PRICES:** s £22-£28; d £35-£44✳ **LB BB**
PARKING: 4 **NOTES:** Closed 25 Dec **CARDS:** 💳

POSTBRIDGE   Map 03 SX67

♦♦♦♦♦ ♟ Lydgate House

PL20 6TJ
☎ 01822 880209 📠 01822 880202
e-mail: lydgatehouse@email.com
Dir: M5/A30 take B3212 to Moretonhampstead & continue to Postbridge. Left down lane before bridge. From A386 Plymouth/Tavistock to Yelverton & Princetown on B3212 & onto Postbridge, right over bridge. House 500yds

PETS: Bedrooms Public areas Exercise area (36 acre grounds) RESIDENT PETS: Donkey - Rachel; sheep - Jack & Jill; chickens; cats - MaCavity, Spike, Gus, Bo, Mungo, Teaser, Stoffers, Button Moon; Labradors - Wellie, Bootie, Barnaby

Set in a secluded valley and surrounded by 36 acres of moorland, with the East Dart River flowing through the fields below the house, this central Dartmoor location is ideal for walking the moors and exploring many places of interest. Rooms and public areas are beautifully appointed, comfortable and enhanced with many extra facilities. Lunches, afternoon cream teas and dinner are all available. Guests are invited to relax in the delightful lounge bar or on the sun terrace.
FACILITIES: 7 en suite (1 GF) No smoking TVB tea/coffee Licensed Cen ht No children 12yrs No coaches Fishing Dinner Last d 6pm
PRICES: s £67-£72; d £144-£164✳ **PARKING:** 10 **NOTES:** Closed Jan
CARDS: 💳

ROCKBEARE   Map 03 SY09

♦♦♦ 🐞 Lower Allercombe Farm

EX5 2HD
☎ 01404 822519 📠 01404 822519
e-mail: susie@allercombe.fsnet.co
Dir: exit A30 at Daisy Mount onto B3180. After 200yds turn right to Allercombe. In 1m at Allercombe x-rds turn right, farm is 50yds on right

PETS: Bedrooms Sep Accom (Loose box) Public areas Exercise area (Adjacent) RESIDENT PETS: Lizzie - Patterdale Terrier, Daisy - ginger cat

Rurally situated, Lower Allercombe dates back to the 17th century and offers comfortable accommodation. It is located close to the A30 and Exeter Airport, and makes an ideal base for visiting the many local attractions. A self-catering cottage is also available.
FACILITIES: 3 rms (1 en suite) (1 fmly) No smoking in bedrooms No smoking in dining room TVB tea/coffee Cen ht 180 acres competition horses & Stud **PRICES:** s fr £30; d fr £50✳

Don't forget to let proprietors know when you book that you're bringing your pet

SALCOMBE
Map 03 SX73

★★★★ 73% ☺☺ Soar Mill Cove
Soar Mill Cove, Malborough TQ7 3DS
☎ 01548 561566 ▤ 01548 561223
e-mail: info@soarmillcove.co.uk
Dir: 3m W of town off A381 at Malborough. Follow 'Soar' signs

PETS: Bedrooms Exercise area (adjacent)

Situated amid spectacular scenery with dramatic sea views, this hotel provides a relaxing stay. Family-run, with a committed team, keen standards of hospitality and service are apparent. Bedrooms are well equipped and many rooms have private terraces. There are different seating areas where impressive cream teas are served, or, for the more active, a choice of swimming pools. Local produce is used to good effect in the restaurant.
ROOMS: 22 en suite (5 fmly) (21 GF) No smoking in all bedrooms s £150-£180; d £180-£220 (incl. bkfst) **LB FACILITIES:** Indoor swimming (H) Outdoor swimming (H) Tennis (grass) Sauna Putting green Table tennis, Games room, 9 hole Pitch n putt, Spa treatment suite entertainment ch fac Xmas **PARKING:** 30 **NOTES:** No smoking in restaurant Closed 1 Nov-11 Feb **CARDS:** ▨ ▨ ▨ ▨ ▨

★★★ 77% ☺ Tides Reach
South Sands TQ8 8LJ
☎ 01548 843466 ▤ 01548 843954
e-mail: enquire@tidesreach.com
Dir: off A38 at Buckfastleigh to Totnes. Then take A381 to Salcombe, follow signs to South Sands

PETS: Bedrooms (unattended) £5 Public areas (in one lounge only) Exercise area (adjacent)

Superbly situated at the water's edge, this personally run, friendly hotel has splendid views of the estuary and beach. Bedrooms, many with balconies, are spacious and comfortable. In the bar and lounge attentive service can be enjoyed along with the view, and the Garden Room restaurant serves appetising and accomplished cuisine.
ROOMS: 35 en suite (7 fmly) No smoking in 2 bedrooms s £93-£128; d £158-£280 (incl. bkfst & dinner) **LB FACILITIES:** Indoor swimming (H) Squash Snooker Sauna Solarium Gym Jacuzzi Windsurfing, dinghy sailing, kayaking, scuba diving entertainment **SERVICES:** Lift **PARKING:** 100 **NOTES:** No children 8yrs No smoking in restaurant Closed Dec-early Feb **CARDS:** ▨ ▨ ▨ ▨ ▨ ▨ ▨

SAMPFORD PEVERELL
Map 03 ST01

★★ 67% Parkway House Country Hotel
EX16 7BJ
☎ 01884 820255 ▤ 01884 820780
e-mail: p-way@m-way.freeserve.co.uk
Dir: M5 junct 27, follow signs for Tiverton Parkway Station. Hotel on right, entering village of Sampford Peverell

PETS: Pets by prior arrangement Bedrooms (unattended) £5-£10 Public areas (except restaurant) Exercise area (50yds) Pet Food RESIDENT PETS: Portia, Mopsie & Cassie - Pugs

An ideal choice for both business and leisure travellers, this hotel is located within a mile of the M5 and benefits from extensive views across the Culm Valley. The well-equipped bedrooms are

continued

comfortable and smartly presented. A popular venue for conferences and day meetings.
ROOMS: 10 en suite (2 fmly) s £40-£50; d £60-£70 (incl. bkfst) **LB FACILITIES:** STV Childrens Play Area **PARKING:** 100 **NOTES:** No smoking in restaurant **CARDS:** ▨ ▨ ▨ ▨ ▨

SIDMOUTH
Map 03 SY18

★★★ 73% Sid Valley Country House
Sidbury EX10 0QJ
☎ 01395 597274 & 597587
e-mail: sidvalleyhotel@totalise.co.uk
Dir: off A375, 2.5m from Sidmouth in village of Sidbury, hotel signed

PETS: Bedrooms (Specific rooms only) Sep Accom (kennel) £7 for dogs Exercise area (on site) Pet Food Open countryside & 7 acres RESIDENT PETS: Khan - Welsh cob pony, Guss - Shetland, Ben - Black Labrador

Situated in an Area of Outstanding Natural Beauty, this family-run hotel has glorious views down the valley. Friendly, unobtrusive service is the key here. Bedrooms vary in size and are equipped with numerous thoughtful extras. Every evening an imaginative menu is served using the best of fresh, local produce. A selection of well-equipped, self-catering cottages is also available.
ROOMS: 10 en suite (2 fmly) (1 GF) No smoking in all bedrooms s £49.50-£65; d £99-£130 (incl. bkfst) **LB FACILITIES:** STV Outdoor swimming (H) Riding ch fac Xmas **PARKING:** 32 **NOTES:** No smoking in restaurant **CARDS:** ▨ ▨ ▨ ▨ ▨

★★ 76% Kingswood
The Esplanade EX10 8AX
☎ 01395 516367 ▤ 01395 513185
e-mail: enquiries@kingswood-hotel.co.uk
Dir: in centre of Esplanade

PETS: Bedrooms (unattended) £4

Super standards of hospitality are only surpassed by this hotel's prominent position on the esplanade. All bedrooms have modern facilities and some enjoy the stunning sea views. The two lounges offer comfort and space and the attractive dining room serves good traditional cooking.
ROOMS: 26 rms (25 en suite) (7 fmly) (2 GF) No smoking in all bedrooms **FACILITIES:** guests receive vouchers for local swimming pool & spectating at cricket club **SERVICES:** Lift **PARKING:** 17 **NOTES:** No smoking in restaurant Closed Dec-13 Feb **CARDS:** ▨ ▨ ▨ ▨ ▨

♦♦♦♦♦ ☺ ☕ The Salty Monk
Church St, Sidford EX10 9QP
☎ 01395 513174 ▤ 01395 513174
e-mail: saltymonk@btconnect.com
Dir: on A3052 in village of Sidford opposite church

PETS: Bedrooms £3 Public areas (on a lead) Exercise area (Adjacent) Dry food and bowls can be provided, fridge available for any meat owner brings RESIDENT PETS: Fin & Mardi - Irish Water Spaniels

Set in the village of Sidford, this attractive property dates back to the 16th century. The well-presented bedrooms are comfortable, with many thoughtful extras; several rooms feature spa baths or special showers and a ground floor courtyard room boasts a king-

continued

sized water bed. Meals are served in the recently extended restaurant. The two owners both cook, using fresh local produce, ensuring that the food is of a high standard and thoroughly enjoyable.
FACILITIES: 5 en suite (3 GF) No smoking in bedrooms No smoking in dining room TVB tea/coffee Licensed Cen ht No coaches Pool Table Dinner Last d 9pm **PRICES:** s fr £55; d £85-£115✱ **LB** **PARKING:** 20 **CARDS:**

SOURTON   Map 02 SX59

★★ 75% **Collaven Manor**
EX20 4HH
☎ 01837 861522 ▤ 01837 861614
e-mail: collavenmanor@supanet.com
Dir: off A30 onto A386 to Tavistock, hotel 2m on right

PETS: Bedrooms (unattended) £4 Exercise area (direct from grounds) Pet Food RESIDENT PETS: Willow (cat)

This delightful 15th-century manor house is quietly located in five acres of well-tended grounds. The friendly proprietors provide attentive service and ensure a relaxing environment. Charming public rooms have old oak beams and granite fireplaces, and provide a range of comfortable lounges and a well stocked bar. In the restaurant, a daily changing menu offers interesting dishes.
ROOMS: 9 en suite (1 fmly) s fr £58; d £92-£128 (incl. bkfst) **LB**
FACILITIES: Croquet lawn Bowls **PARKING:** 50 **NOTES:** No smoking in restaurant **CARDS:**

STOCKLAND   Map 03 ST20

◆◆◆◆ 🍺 🍴 **The Kings Arms Inn**
EX14 9BS
☎ 01404 881361 ▤ 01404 881732
e-mail: info@kingsarms.net
Dir: from centre of Honiton head for NE junct of A30. Just before junct Stockland is signed right, straight ahead for 3m, turn left downhill into village

PETS: Bedrooms (unattended) Public areas (bar only) Exercise area RESIDENT PETS: Lola (Doberman) & Jack (Jack Russell)

A convivial atmosphere prevails at this attractive village inn, where staff are helpful and attentive at all times. Bedrooms are spacious and comfortable, with high quality en suite facilities. Food is a highlight, with an extensive and imaginative range of tempting home-made dishes to choose from. A garden is available and ample parking is a bonus.
FACILITIES: 3 en suite No smoking in dining room TVB tea/coffee Direct dial from bedrooms Cen ht TVL Dinner Last d 9pm
PRICES: s £50; d £70✱ **PARKING:** 40 **NOTES:** Closed Xmas Day
CARDS:

★ Red stars indicate the AA's Top 200 Hotels in Britain & Ireland

Please mention AA Pet Friendly Places to Stay when booking

STOKE GABRIEL   Map 03 SX85

★★★ 73% **Gabriel Court**
Stoke Hill TQ9 6SF
☎ 01803 782206 ▤ 01803 782333
e-mail: reservations@gabrielcourthotel.co.uk
Dir: off A38 at Buckfastleigh onto A384 (Totnes) then A385 (Paignton). Turn right at Parkers Arms to Stoke Gabriel

PETS: Bedrooms (unattended) £2.50 Public areas (not in restaurant) Exercise area (300yds)

Overlooking the pretty riverside village of Stoke Gabriel, this gracious manor house stands within terraced Elizabethan gardens, surrounded by three acres of grounds. Peace and tranquillity are in abundance and there are several secluded outdoor hideaways for relaxation, or there is an elegant lounge. Bedrooms offer ample space and comfort, and many also have lovely views. The 'Churchward' restaurant serves enjoyable cuisine.
ROOMS: 19 en suite (3 fmly) s £56-£64; d fr £92 (incl. bkfst) **LB**
FACILITIES: Outdoor swimming (H) ch fac Xmas **PARKING:** 25
NOTES: No smoking in restaurant **CARDS:**

TAVISTOCK   Map 02 SX47

★★★ 70% 🌸🌸 **Bedford**   THE INDEPENDENTS
1 Plymouth Rd PL19 8BB
☎ 01822 613221 ▤ 01822 618034
e-mail: jane@bedford-hotel.co.uk
Dir: M5 junct 31 - Launceston/Okehampton A30. Take A386 to Tavistock, follow town centre signs. Hotel opp church

PETS: Bedrooms Sep Accom (unattended) Public areas Exercise area

Built on the site of a Benedictine abbey, this impressive castellated building has been welcoming visitors for over 200 years. Very much a local landmark, the hotel offers comfortable and relaxing public areas, all reflecting the charm and character throughout. Bedrooms are traditionally styled with contemporary comforts, whilst the Woburn Restaurant provides a refined setting for enjoyable cuisine.
ROOMS: 30 en suite (1 fmly) No smoking in 11 bedrooms s £55-£85; d £120-£130 (incl. bkfst) **LB** **FACILITIES:** Xmas **PARKING:** 45
NOTES: No smoking in restaurant
CARDS:

◆◆◆ **Sampford Manor**
Sampford Spiney PL20 6LH
☎ 01822 853442 ▤ 01822 855691
e-mail: manor@sampford-spiney.fsnet.co.uk
Dir: B3357 towards Princetown, at 1st x-rds, right. Next x-rds "Warren Cross" left for Sampford Spiney. Take 2nd right, at brown speed sign, past cottage on left. House is below church

PETS: Bedrooms Sep Accom (kennel) (unattended) £2 per stay Public areas (except dining room) Exercise area (adjacent) RESIDENT PETS: William & Reg - English Setters, Spin - terrier)

Pre-dating the Domesday Book and once owned by Sir Francis Drake, this manor house is tucked away in a tranquil corner of Dartmoor National Park. The family home is full of character, with

continued on p98

TAVISTOCK continued

exposed beams, slate floors and thick walls. A warm welcome is assured and freshly-cooked breakfasts feature home-laid eggs. Children, horses (stabling available) and dogs are welcome.
FACILITIES: 3 rms No smoking in bedrooms No smoking in dining room TVB tea/coffee Cen ht No coaches Riding Croquet lawn
PRICES: s £25-£35; d £45-£60✽ **PARKING:** 3

◆◆◆ Coach House
PL19 8NS
☎ 01822 617515 ▤ 01822 617515
e-mail: the-coachhouse@otterytavistock.fsnet.co.uk
Dir: from Tavistock A390 W for 2m to Gulworthy Cross, turn right to chip shop. In village turn right to Ottery, 1st building on right

PETS: Telephone for details

Dating back to 1857, this building was constructed for the Duke of Bedford and sympathetically converted by the current owners. Some bedrooms are available on the ground floor and also in an adjacent barn conversion. Dinner is available in the cosy dining room or the newly constructed restaurant, which leads onto the south-facing garden.
FACILITIES: 6 en suite 3 annexe en suite (1 fmly) (4 GF) No smoking in bedrooms No smoking in dining room TVB tea/coffee Direct dial from bedrooms Licensed Cen ht No children 5yrs Dinner Last d 9pm
PRICES: s £39; d £60✽ **LB PARKING:** 24
CARDS: ▨▨▨▨ ▨

TEIGNMOUTH

◆◆◆◆ Potters Mooring
30 The Green, Shaldon TQ14 0DN
☎ 01626 873 225 ▤ 01626 872909
e-mail: mail@pottersmooring.co.uk
Dir: off A38 onto A380 signposted to Torquay. Follow B3192 to Teignmouth, then Shaldon. After crossing river follow signs to Potters Mooring

PETS: Bedrooms (unattended) Public areas Exercise area

A former sea captain's residence dating back to 1625, Potters Mooring has been sympathetically refurbished to provide charming accommodation of a very high standard, including a four-poster room and a family-size cottage. The friendly proprietors make every effort to ensure an enjoyable stay and the Captain Potter's breakfast features tasty local produce.
FACILITIES: 6 rms (5 en suite) (2 fmly) No smoking TVB tea/coffee Cen ht No coaches **PRICES:** s £30-£40; d £60-£80✽ **LB PARKING:** 8
CARDS: ▨▨▨▨ ▨

THURLESTONE

Map 03 SX64

★★★★ 72% ❀ **Thurlestone**
TQ7 3NN
☎ 01548 560382 ▤ 01548 561069
e-mail: enquiries@thurlestone.co.uk
Dir: A38 take A384 into Totnes, A381 towards Kingsbridge, onto A379 towards Churchstow, onto B3197, turn into lane signed to Thurlestone

PETS: Bedrooms (unattended) £6

This perennially popular hotel has been in the same family-ownership since 1896. A range of indoor and outdoor leisure facilities provide something for everyone and wonderful views of the south Devon coast can be enjoyed from several vantage points, including many of the bedrooms, some of which also have balconies. Elegant public rooms are styled to ensure rest and relaxation.
ROOMS: 64 en suite (23 fmly) s £60-£125; d £120-£250 (incl. bkfst & dinner) **LB FACILITIES: Spa** STV Indoor swimming (H) Outdoor swimming (H) Golf 9 Tennis (hard) Squash Snooker Sauna Solarium Gym Croquet lawn Putting green Jacuzzi entertainment ch fac Xmas
SERVICES: Lift **PARKING:** 121 **NOTES:** No smoking in restaurant Closed Jan **CARDS:** ▨▨▨▨ ▨

TIVERTON

Map 03 SS91

★★★ 68% **Tiverton**
Blundells Rd EX16 4DB
☎ 01884 256120 ▤ 01884 258101
e-mail: sales@tivertonhotel.co.uk
Dir: M5 junct 27, onto dual carriageway A361 Devon link road, Tiverton exit 7m W. Hotel on Blundells Rd next to business park

Best Western

PETS: Bedrooms (unattended) Exercise area (200 metres) Pet Food

Conveniently situated on the outskirts of the town, with easy access to the M5, this comfortable hotel has a relaxed atmosphere. The spacious bedrooms are well-equipped and decorated in a contemporary style. A formal dining option is offered by the Gallery Restaurant, while lighter snacks are served in the bar area. Room service is extensive, as is the range of conference facilities.
ROOMS: 69 en suite (10 fmly) No smoking in 53 bedrooms s fr £65; d fr £92 (incl. bkfst) **LB FACILITIES:** STV ch fac Xmas **PARKING:** 130
NOTES: No smoking in restaurant
CARDS: ▨▨▨▨ ▨

◆◆◆◆◆ ☙ Rhode Farm House
Exeter Hill EX16 4PL
☎ 01884 242853 ▤ 01884 242853
e-mail: david@rhodefarmhouse.com
Dir: follow signs to Grand Western Canal. Take right fork signed Exeter Hill and Rhode Farm House approx 3m on left

PETS: Exercise area

Guests are assured a warm welcome at Rhode Farm House, where customer care is a priority. Set in five acres of land, with stables in the yard, Exeter city centre is approximately a 30-minute drive. Bedrooms are finished with many considerate extras and there is an inviting lounge with a log fire for those cold winter nights. A

continued

delicious breakfast, featuring local produce, is served around a communal table in the dining room. Carefully prepared and presented dinner is available by prior arrangement.

FACILITIES: 2 en suite (2 fmly) No smoking TVB tea/coffee No dogs (ex guide dogs) Cen ht TVL No children 4yrs Riding grazing for horses Dinner Last d 12pm **PRICES:** s £30; d £50-£55✱ **PARKING:** 5 **CARDS:**

TORQUAY   Map 03 SX96

★★★ ◎◎
Orestone Manor Hotel & Restaurant
Rockhouse Ln, Maidencombe TQ1 4SX
☎ 01803 328098 🖷 01803 328336
e-mail: enquiries@orestone.co.uk
Dir: off A379 coast road, Torquay-Teignmouth road (formerly B3199)

PETS: Bedrooms (unattended) £5 Public areas (not in restaurant & lounge) Exercise area (200 yards) Pet Food

This country house hotel is located on the fringe of Torbay and is set in a spectacular location overlooking Lyme Bay. There is a colonial theme throughout the public areas, which are most charming and comfortable. Bedrooms are individually styled and all are spacious; some have balconies. The hotel's cuisine is highly regarded and dishes, based on local ingredients, are skilfully prepared.

ROOMS: 12 en suite (3 fmly) (1 GF) s £89-£139; d £119-£199 (incl. bkfst) **LB FACILITIES:** STV Outdoor swimming (H) ch fac Xmas **PARKING:** 40 **NOTES:** No smoking in restaurant **CARDS:**

★★★ 67% **Belgrave**
Seafront TQ2 5HE
☎ 01803 296666 🖷 01803 211308
e-mail: info@belgrave-hotel.co.uk
Dir: from Exeter A380 to Newton Abbot & Torquay. Torquay continue to lights with Torre Station on right. Turn right into Avenue Rd, continue to Kings Drive. Turn left at seafront, hotel at lights

PETS: Bedrooms (unattended) £6 Public areas (not in restaurant or sun lounge) Exercise area

Enjoying an impressive position overlooking Torbay, the Belgrave offers a range of spacious and well-appointed public rooms, including comfortable lounges, the elegant restaurant and outdoor pool and patio areas. The Dickens bar is particularly stylish, and offers an innovative menu, featuring local produce. A variety of

continued

bedroom styles is available, many of which have the added bonus of stunning sea views.

ROOMS: 72 en suite (20 fmly) (18 GF) No smoking in 18 bedrooms s £49-£71; d £98 (incl. bkfst) **LB FACILITIES:** Outdoor swimming entertainment Xmas **SERVICES:** Lift **PARKING:** 90 **NOTES:** No smoking in restaurant **CARDS:**

★★★ 61% **Rainbow International**
Belgrave Rd TQ2 5HJ
☎ 01803 213232 🖷 01803 212925
e-mail: enquiries@rainbow-hotel.co.uk
Dir: Close to harbour and marina

PETS: Bedrooms £3 Exercise area

This large hotel is located within easy walking distance of the seafront. Bedrooms vary in size and shape; many family rooms are available and all rooms have the convenience of hairdriers and irons provided. Entertainment is provided every evening in the nightclub and the residents' ballroom.

ROOMS: 134 en suite (70 fmly) **FACILITIES:** Indoor swimming (H) Outdoor swimming Solarium Gym Table tennis Steam room entertainment ch fac **SERVICES:** Lift **PARKING:** 100 **NOTES:** No smoking in restaurant **CARDS:**

★★ 75% **Albaston House**
27 St Marychurch Rd TQ1 3JF
☎ 01803 296758 🖷 01803 211509

PETS: Bedrooms (unattended) Public areas (not restaurant) Exercise area (0.5 mile)

Many guests return time after time to this friendly, family run hotel where hospitality is genuine and welcoming. The Albaston is situated close to the town centre and is also convenient for the quieter attractions of Babbacombe. Standards of maintenance and cleanliness are high throughout with both public areas and bedrooms reflecting a combination of comfort and quality.

ROOMS: 13 en suite (4 fmly) s £38-£40; d £76-£80 (incl. bkfst) **LB PARKING:** 12 **NOTES:** No smoking in restaurant Closed Jan **CARDS:**

★★ 70% **Ansteys Lea**
Babbacombe Rd, Wellswood TQ1 2QJ
☎ 01803 294843 🖷 01803 214333
e-mail: stay@ansteys-lea.com
Dir: from Torquay harbour take Babbacombe road, hotel approx 0.75m

PETS: Bedrooms (unattended) £5 Exercise area (0.5 mile)
RESIDENT PETS: Daisy - West Highland Terrier

Taking its name from nearby Ansteys Cove, this friendly hotel is conveniently placed for both the town centre and seafront. The well-furnished bedrooms are comfortable and provide a good range of facilities. Public areas include an attractive lounge/TV room overlooking the garden with a heated outdoor pool. The fixed price, five-course dinner menu offers a choice of home-cooked dishes.

ROOMS: 24 en suite (4 fmly) No smoking in all bedrooms s £26-£32; d £52-£64 (incl. bkfst) **LB FACILITIES:** Outdoor swimming (H) Sauna ch fac Xmas **PARKING:** 20 **NOTES:** No smoking in restaurant **CARDS:**

England

TORQUAY continued

★★ 70% **Red House**
Rousdown Rd, Chelston TQ2 6PB
☎ 01803 607811 🖨 01803 200592
e-mail: stay@redhouse-hotel.co.uk
Dir: towards seafront/Chelston, turn into Avenue Rd, 1st lights turn right. Follow road past shops and church, take next left. Hotel on right

PETS: Bedrooms (unattended) £3 Exercise area (100 yards)

With views over Torbay, this pleasant and relaxing hotel enjoys a quiet location close to Cockington village. The comfortable bedrooms are well equipped and a good choice of bar meals are available in addition to the fixed price menu for residents. Many guests return here on a regular basis for the excellent range of leisure facilities.
ROOMS: 10 en suite (5 fmly) s £25-£35; d £50-£70 (incl. bkfst)
FACILITIES: Spa Indoor swimming (H) Outdoor swimming (H) Sauna Solarium Gym Games room Table tennis Beauty salon pool table Xmas
PARKING: 10 **NOTES:** No smoking in restaurant
CARDS: 💳

★★ 66% **Anchorage Hotel**
Cary Park, Aveland Rd TQ1 3PT
☎ 01803 326175 🖨 01803 316439
e-mail: enquiries@anchoragehotel.co.uk

PETS: Bedrooms Exercise area (100 metres)

The Anchorage Hotel is quietly located in a residential area. Providing a friendly welcome, this family-run establishment enjoys a great deal of repeat business. Bedrooms offer a range of sizes and all rooms are neatly presented. Evening entertainment is provided regularly in the large and comfortable lounge.
ROOMS: 56 en suite (5 fmly) No smoking in all bedrooms s £22.50-£31.50; d £45-£63 (incl. bkfst) **LB FACILITIES:** Outdoor swimming (H) entertainment Xmas **SERVICES:** Lift **PARKING:** 26
NOTES: No smoking in restaurant **CARDS:** 💳

◆◆◆◆ 🍴 **Hotel Blue Conifer**
Higher Downs Rd, The Seafront, Babbacombe TQ1 3LD
☎ 01803 327637
Dir: follow signs for Babbacombe & seafront, hotel 500yds from model village

PETS: Bedrooms (unattended) Public areas (not in dining room) Exercise area (50 metres)

Hotel Blue Conifer enjoys splendid views across the beaches to Lyme Bay, and provides a delightful place to stay. Surrounded by neatly tended gardens, this attractive hotel has a relaxing and friendly atmosphere. Bedrooms, many of which have sea views, are well-equipped and one is available on the ground floor. Dinner is highly recommended.
FACILITIES: 7 en suite (3 fmly) (1 GF) No smoking TVB tea/coffee Licensed Cen ht No coaches Dinner Last d midday **PRICES:** s £23-£32; d £46-£64✻ **LB PARKING:** 9 **NOTES:** Closed Nov-Feb

---

🏴 Places with this symbol are pubs

◆◆◆◆ **Ingoldsby Hotel**
1 Chelston Rd TQ2 6PT
☎ 01803 607497 🖨 01803 690463
e-mail: ingoldsby.hotel@virgin.net
Dir: Head to Torquay Seafront. At sea front traffic lights right & then right again by Grand Hotel, left behind Grand Hotel, after railway bridge up hill, right at next x-rds and hotel is on right

PETS: Bedrooms Public areas (not in dining room) Exercise area (200 yards) RESIDENT PETS: Poppy (cat)

Located in the residential area just a few minutes' walk from the beach, this comfortable hotel offers a friendly home-from-home atmosphere. Bedrooms are pleasantly decorated and public areas include a sun lounge and well-stocked bar. A choice of home-cooked dinners or bar meals is available and can be enjoyed in the dining room overlooking attractive gardens.
FACILITIES: 14 en suite (3 fmly) (4 GF) No smoking in bedrooms No smoking in dining room No smoking in lounges TVB tea/coffee Licensed Cen ht TVL No coaches Pool Table Croquet lawn Putting green landscaped garden, gazebo & decking Dinner Last d 6.30pm **PRICES:** s £27-£29.50; d £54-£59✻ **LB PARKING:** 14
CARDS: 💳

◆◆◆ 🍴 **Manor Farm**
Daccombe, Newton Abbot TQ12 4ST
☎ 01803 328294 🖨 01803 328294
e-mail: daccombe1@btopenworld.com
Dir: leave main Newton Abbot/Torquay road (A380) & turn into Kingskerwell road, and follow campsite brown signs.

PETS: Bedrooms Public areas (on leads) Exercise area (nearby) RESIDENT PETS: Sami (Labrador), Meg (Border collie)

Manor Farm, which also has a campsite next door, is located in a peaceful and rural setting but is just a few minutes' drive away from bustling Torquay with its sandy beaches. Bedrooms are comfortable and well equipped and a substantial breakfast can be enjoyed around the communal table in the cosy dining room.
FACILITIES: 3 rms (1 en suite) (1 fmly) No smoking TVB tea/coffee 300 acres arable, beef **PRICES:** d fr £40✻ **LB PARKING:** 6
NOTES: Closed 20 Dec-Jan

◆◆◆ **The Palms Hotel**
537 Babbacombe Rd TQ1 1HQ
☎ 01803 293970 🖨 01803 298573
e-mail: grahamaward@yahoo.co.uk
Dir: follow signs to Torquay Harbour on B3199 Babbacombe Road, 300yds from harbour opposite Torwood gardens

PETS: Bedrooms (unattended) Public areas Exercise area (10 yards) RESIDENT PETS: Barney (Persian cat)

The owners here at Palms Hotel extend a very warm welcome to their guests. Family friendly, the hotel offers comfortable accommodation, with many books, games and videos available for the children. The Cyber café, a well stocked bar and light bar meals are welcome facilities. Breakfast is taken in the dining room, which overlooks Torwood Gardens.
FACILITIES: 9 en suite (4 fmly) No smoking in bedrooms No smoking in area of dining room No smoking in 1 lounge STV TVB tea/coffee Licensed Cen ht No coaches Internet facilities in dry bar Dinner Last d 8pm **PRICES:** s £20-£25; d £40-£50✻ **LB PARKING:** 4
CARDS: 💳

♦♦♦ Stover Lodge Hotel
29 Newton Rd TQ2 5DB
☎ 01803 297287 📠 01803 297287
e-mail: stover.lodge@ntlworld.com
*Dir: Follow signs to Torquay town centre, at station/Halfords take left lane,
Stover Lodge is 2nd hotel on left after lights*

PETS: Bedrooms (unattended) Public areas (not in dining
room) Exercise area (100yds)

Conveniently located close to the town centre, this family-run
hotel has a relaxed and friendly atmosphere. Children and babies
are welcome; a cot and high chair can be provided on request.
Hearty breakfasts, with a vegetarian option, are served in the
dining room. Guests are welcome to use the garden in summer
months.
FACILITIES: 10 rms (7 en suite) (3 fmly) (2 GF) No smoking in
6 bedrooms No smoking in dining room TVB tea/coffee Cen ht
No coaches **PRICES:** s £18-£30; d £36-£46✳ **LB BB PARKING:** 10
CARDS: 🌐🌐🌐🌐 🅂

♦♦♦ Tyndale
68 Avenue Rd TQ2 5LF
☎ 01803 380888
*Dir: A380 to Ring Rd, straight on A3022 from rdbt until Torre station, follow
signs for Paignton & Harbour (Avenue Rd). At 1st traffic lights right Old
Mill Rd and directly right into car park*

PETS: Bedrooms Public areas (not in lounge) Exercise area
(100 metres) **RESIDENT PETS:** Trixie - Jack Russell

Close to the seaside attractions and the town centre, this neatly
presented house is also a short level walk from the railway station.
Bedrooms are all brightly decorated and offer a range of sizes. A
comfortable lounge is provided and freshly cooked, traditional
British breakfast is served in the dining room.
FACILITIES: 3 en suite (1 GF) No smoking in dining room TVB
tea/coffee Cen ht TVL No coaches **PRICES:** d fr £34✳ **LB BB**
PARKING: 5

TOTNES   Map 03 SX86

★★ 65% Royal Seven Stars
The Plains TQ9 5DD
☎ 01803 862125 & 863241 📠 01803 867925
e-mail: royal7starshotel@aol.com
*Dir: A38 Devon Expressway, Buckfastleigh turn off onto A384, follow the
signs to Totnes town centre*

PETS: Bedrooms (unattended) Public areas (not
restaurant) Exercise area (50yds)

In a prominent position at the foot of the town and close to the
river, this 17th-century hostelry is a popular place. Bedrooms are
comfortable and well-equipped, many retaining the original charm
of the building. A central atrium offers a pleasant area adjacent to
the busy bar, and the restaurant offers a large choice of freshly
prepared dishes.
ROOMS: 16 rms (14 en suite) (2 fmly) s £52-£65; d £68-£84 (incl. bkfst)
LB PARKING: 20 **CARDS:** 🌐🌐🌐🌐🌐 🅂

★★ 76% ⊛ Prince Hall
PL20 6SA
☎ 01822 890403 📠 01822 890676
e-mail: bookings@princehall.co.uk
Dir: on B3357 1m E of Two Bridges road junct

PETS: Bedrooms (unattended) Public areas (except kitchen
& restaurant) Exercise area (Adjacent) Bowls and food supplied
only if necessary **RESIDENT PETS:** Bosun - Black Labrador

Charm, peace and relaxed informality pervade at this small hotel,
which has a stunning location at the heart of Dartmoor. Bedrooms,
each named after a Dartmoor tor, have been equipped with
thoughtful extras. The history of the house and its location are
reflected throughout the public areas, which are most comfortable.
The accomplished cooking is a memorable aspect of a stay here.
ROOMS: 8 en suite (1 fmly) s £84-£125; d £148-£230 (incl. bkfst &
dinner) **LB FACILITIES:** Fishing Riding Croquet lawn Guided Dartmoor
Walks, Fly fishing, Garden tours **PARKING:** 13 **NOTES:** No children 10yrs
No smoking in restaurant Closed 16 Dec-10 Feb
CARDS: 🌐🌐🌐🌐🌐 🅂

★★ 72% ⊛ Two Bridges Hotel   THE INDEPENDENTS
PL20 6SW
☎ 01822 890581 📠 01822 890575
e-mail: enquiries@warm-welcome-hotels.co.uk
Dir: junct of B3212 & B3357

PETS: Bedrooms (unattended) Public areas (except
restaurant) Exercise area walks on Dartmoor nearby

This wonderfully relaxing hotel is set in the heart of the Dartmoor
National Park, in a beautiful riverside location. Three standards of
comfortable rooms provide every modern convenience. There is a
choice of lounges and fine dining is available in the restaurant,
with menus featuring local game and seasonal produce.
ROOMS: 33 en suite (2 fmly) (6 GF) No smoking in 25 bedrooms
FACILITIES: STV Fishing **PARKING:** 100 **NOTES:** No smoking in
restaurant **CARDS:** 🌐🌐🌐🌐🌐 🅂

♦♦♦♦♦ 🏠 Eastacott Barton
EX37 9AJ
☎ 01769 540545 📠 01769 540859
e-mail: stay@eastacott.com

PETS: Bedrooms Public areas Exercise area (in grounds)
RESIDENT PETS: Ben - Black Labrador, Meggie - Jack Russell

This very large, stone-built former farmhouse has been extensively
restored to provide high quality, spacious, comfortable and well
equipped accommodation, including three bedrooms in converted
former farm buildings. There is also a self-catering cottage. Guests
have a choice of sitting rooms, and access to extensive grounds
and gardens. The house enjoys a tranquil and picturesque
location, with stunning views along the Taw Valley.
FACILITIES: 2 en suite 3 annexe en suite No smoking STV TVB
tea/coffee Cen ht TVL No children 10yrs No coaches Fishing
PRICES: s £50-£95; d £70-£115✳ **LB PARKING:** 8
NOTES: Closed 23 Dec-13 Jan **CARDS:** 🌐🌐🌐 🅂

England

WESTWARD HO!   Map 02 SS42

◆◆◆◆ Culloden House Hotel
Fosketh Hill EX39 1UL
☎ 01237 479421 📠 08701 334359
e-mail: aa@culloden-house.co.uk
Dir: M5 junct 27, follow A361 to Barnstaple, then A39 to Bideford. At rdbt just over bridge turn right onto A386. Culloden House is on left under 1m from sign "Welcome to Westward Ho!"

PETS: Bedrooms Public areas (except dining room) Exercise area (300yds) **RESIDENT PETS:** Amber - Jack Russell

Originally built as a gentleman's residence, this Victorian property enjoys an elevated position on a wooded hillside and with sweeping views over the beach and along coast. Guests to this family-run house are assured a warm welcome and friendly atmosphere. A comfortable lounge, with a wood burner, is available for guests to use.
FACILITIES: 5 en suite (2 fmly) (1 GF) No smoking TVB tea/coffee Cen ht TVL No coaches **PRICES:** s £32-£45; d £54-£64✷ **PARKING:** 5 **NOTES:** Closed Xmas **CARDS:** 🖭 🔳 🟦 🔜 ⑤

WHIMPLE   Map 03 SY09

◆◆◆◆◆ Larkbeare Farmhouse
Larkbeare, Talaton EX5 2RY
☎ 01404 822069 📠 01404 823746
e-mail: stay@larkbeare.net
Dir: turn off A30 at Daisymount exit signed to Exmouth. Take signs to Whimple. After 0.25m turn right to Larkbeare. After 0.5m turn left to Larkbeare. Entrance 1m on left

PETS: Sep Accom (warm boot room) Exercise area (garden and fields)

Now restored, this period farmhouse offers extremely comfortable accommodation. Guests are assured of a warm and friendly welcome including tea in front of the sitting room fire in winter. Breakfast, served in the dining room, features local and home-produced foods; dinner is available by prior arrangement. The quiet drawing room is an ideal location for small meetings.
FACILITIES: 3 en suite No smoking TVB tea/coffee Direct dial from bedrooms No dogs Cen ht No coaches Croquet lawn Dinner **PRICES:** s £60-£75; d £75-£90✷ **PARKING:** 15 **CARDS:** 🖭 🔳 🟦 🔜 ⑤

WINKLEIGH   Map 03 SS60

◆◆◆◆ The Old Parsonage
Court Walk EX19 8JA
☎ 01837 83772 📠 01837 680074
e-mail: tonypeel@fsbdial.co.uk
Dir: from Crediton turn left off A3124 and the Old Parsonage is on left behind Winkleigh parish church

PETS: Bedrooms Exercise area (1 mile) **RESIDENT PETS:** Cinders, Max, Jessie, Boots, Cobweb - cats

A Grade II listed thatched house, some parts dating back to the 15th century, The Old Parsonage is set in two acres of walled Victorian gardens, adjacent to the church grounds. The annexe bedrooms are individually designed and well-appointed. A

continued

delicious breakfast is taken in the dining room around a grand communal table.
FACILITIES: 3 en suite (1 GF) No smoking TVB tea/coffee Cen ht No children 4yrs No coaches **PRICES:** s £25-£30; d £45-£50✷ **PARKING:** 4

YELVERTON   Map 02 SX56

★★★ 72% Moorland Links   Forestdale Hotels
PL20 6DA
☎ 01822 852245 📠 01822 855004
e-mail: moorland.links@forestdale.com
Dir: A38 from Exeter to Plymouth, then A386 towards Tavistock. 5m onto open moorland, hotel 1m on left

PETS: Bedrooms (unattended) £7.50 Public areas (not in restaurant) Exercise area Pet Food

In Dartmoor National Park, set in nine acres of well-tended grounds, Moorland Links has spectacular views from many of the rooms across open moorland and the Tamar Valley. Bedrooms are well-equipped and comfortably furnished, and some rooms have open balconies. An ideal hotel for weddings and with ample, quiet meeting room facilities.
ROOMS: 45 en suite (4 fmly) (17 GF) No smoking in 2 bedrooms s fr £95; d fr £120 (incl. bkfst) **LB FACILITIES:** STV Tennis (hard) Xmas **PARKING:** 120 **NOTES:** No smoking in restaurant **CARDS:** 🖭 🔳 🟦 🔜 ⑤

BEAMINSTER   Map 03 ST40

★★★ 71% 🍴 Bridge House
3 Prout Bridge DT8 3AY
☎ 01308 862200 📠 01308 863700
e-mail: enquiries@bridge-house.co.uk
Dir: off A3066, 100yds from Town Square

PETS: Bedrooms Exercise area **RESIDENT PETS:** Daisy - Labrador

Dating back to the 13th century, this family-owned property offers friendly and attentive service. Bedrooms are tastefully furnished and decorated; those in the main house are generally more spacious than those in the adjacent coach house. Smartly presented public areas include the Georgian dining room, cosy bar and adjacent lounge, together with a breakfast room overlooking the attractive garden.
ROOMS: 9 en suite 5 annexe en suite (1 fmly) (4 GF) No smoking in all bedrooms s £55-£99; d £104-£138 (incl. bkfst) **LB FACILITIES:** Tennis (hard) Xmas **PARKING:** 22 **NOTES:** No smoking in restaurant Closed 27-30 Dec **CARDS:** 🖭 🔳 🟦 🔜 ⑤

All abbreviations are explained on page 9

🍴 Places with this symbol are pubs

BLANDFORD FORUM — Map 03 ST80

◆◆◆◆ 🏰 The Anvil Inn
Salisbury Rd, Pimperne DT11 8UQ
☎ 01258 453431 📠 01258 480182
e-mail: info@anvilhotel.co.uk
Dir: located 1m from Blandford Forum on A354 to Salisbury

PETS: Bedrooms (unattended) £2.50 Public areas (Only in bar and gardens) Exercise area (200mtrs) Selection of pet foods available, and bowl to take away.

Located just two miles from Blandford, this 16th-century thatched property provides a traditional Country Inn welcome with plenty of character and ambience. Bedrooms have recently been refurbished to high standards. Dinner offers a varied selection of homemade dishes in addition to a variety of hand-pulled ales and tempting wines by the glass.

FACILITIES: 13 en suite (1 GF) No smoking in bedrooms No smoking in dining room No smoking in lounges STV TVB tea/coffee Direct dial from bedrooms Cen ht No coaches Dinner Last d 9.30pm
PRICES: s £60-£65; d £80-£100✳ **LB PARKING:** 18
CARDS: 💳

◆◆◆◆ 🐾 Whiteways Farm
Winterborne Houghton DT11 0PE
☎ 01258 880429 & 0771 9644474 📠 01258 880242
e-mail: whitewaysfarm@talk21.com
Dir: A338 to Blandford then onto Winterborne Stickland. 4m S of Winterborne Houghton 1m straight through village. As road turns sharp right Whiteways Farm on left

PETS: Bedrooms Sep Accom (stable) Exercise area
RESIDENT PETS: 2 terriers

Surrounded by 32 acres of pasture, this modern, stone-built farmhouse is set in its own wooded valley. Ideal walking and riding country, guests can bring their own horses for a holiday here, too! Traditional evening meals are available by prior arrangement.
FACILITIES: 2 rms No smoking Cen ht 32 acres Sheep & Horses Dinner Last d 2 days in advance **PRICES:** s £30; d £50✳

BOURNEMOUTH — Map 04 SZ09

★★★ 76% 🏵 Langtry Manor - Lovenest of a King
Derby Rd, East Cliff BH1 3QB
☎ 01202 553887 📠 01202 290115
e-mail: lillie@langtrymanor.com
Dir: A31/A338, 1st rdbt by rail station turn left. Over next rdbt, 1st left into Knyveton Rd. Hotel opposite

PETS: Bedrooms Exercise area (200yds) 2 gardens at hotel, gardens & beach nearby

Retaining a stately air, this property was originally built in 1877 by Edward VII for his mistress Lillie Langtry. The individually furnished and decorated bedrooms include several with four-poster beds. Enjoyable cuisine is served in the magnificent dining
continued

hall, complete with several large Tudor tapestries. There is an Edwardian banquet on Saturday evenings.
ROOMS: 12 en suite 8 annexe en suite (2 fmly) (3 GF) No smoking in 4 bedrooms s £89.75-£99.75; d £139.75-£239.50 (incl. bkfst) **LB**
FACILITIES: STV Free use of local health club entertainment Xmas
PARKING: 30 **NOTES:** No smoking in restaurant
CARDS: 💳

★★★ 71% Wessex
West Cliff Rd BH2 5EU
☎ 01202 551911 📠 01202 297354
e-mail: wessex@forestdale.com
Dir: Follow M27/A35 or A338 from Dorchester & A347 N. Hotel on West Cliff side of town

Forestdale Hotels

PETS: Bedrooms (unattended) £7.50 Public areas (except restaurant) Exercise area Pet Food

Centrally located and handy for the beach, the Wessex is a popular, relaxing hotel. Bedrooms vary in size and include premier rooms; all are comfortable, and equipped with a range of modern amenities. There are excellent leisure facilities, ample function rooms and an open-plan bar and lounge.
ROOMS: 109 en suite (22 fmly) No smoking in 3 bedrooms s fr £75; d fr £120 (incl. bkfst) **LB FACILITIES:** STV Indoor swimming (H) Outdoor swimming (H) Snooker Sauna Solarium Gym Table tennis Xmas **SERVICES:** Lift **PARKING:** 160 **NOTES:** No smoking in restaurant
CARDS: 💳

★★★ 70% The Connaught
West Hill Rd, West Cliff BH2 5PH
☎ 01202 298020 📠 01202 298028
e-mail: sales@theconnaught.co.uk
Dir: follow Town Centre West & BIC signs

Best Western

PETS: Bedrooms £5 Exercise area

Conveniently located on the West Cliff, close to the BIC, beaches and town centre, this attractive hotel offers well equipped, neatly decorated rooms, some with balconies. The hotel boasts a very well equipped leisure complex with a large pool and snooker table and comprehensive gym facilities. Breakfast and dinner offer imaginative dishes made with quality local ingredients.
ROOMS: 56 en suite (15 fmly) No smoking in 18 bedrooms s £43-£67; d £86-£134 (incl. bkfst) **LB FACILITIES:** Spa STV Indoor swimming (H) Outdoor swimming (H) Snooker Sauna Solarium Gym Jacuzzi Cardio-vascular suite, Table tennis, Pool table Xmas **SERVICES:** Lift **PARKING:** 45 **NOTES:** No smoking in restaurant
CARDS: 💳

★★★ 69% Carrington House
31 Knyveton Rd BH1 3QQ
☎ 01202 369988 📠 01202 292221
e-mail: carrington.house@forestdale.com
Dir: A338 at St Paul's rdbt, continue 200mtrs & turn left into Knyveton Rd. Hotel 400mtrs on right

Forestdale Hotels

PETS: Bedrooms (unattended) £7.50 Public areas (except restaurant) Pet Food

Carrington House occupies a prominent position on a tree-lined avenue and a short walk from the seafront. Bedrooms are generally spacious, comfortable and usefully equipped. In addition
continued on p104

BOURNEMOUTH continued

to the hotel's bar and restaurant there are extensive conference facilities and a leisure complex.
ROOMS: 145 en suite (42 fmly) No smoking in 40 bedrooms s fr £75; d fr £120 (incl. bkfst) **FACILITIES:** STV Indoor swimming (H) Snooker Gym Purpose built children's play area Xmas **SERVICES:** Lift **PARKING:** 100 **NOTES:** No smoking in restaurant **CARDS:**

★★★ 67% Heathlands Hotel
12 Grove Rd, East Cliff BH1 3AY
☎ 01202 553336 ▤ 01202 555937
e-mail: info@heathlandshotel.com
Dir: A338 St Pauls rdbt 1st exit to East Cliff, 3rd exit at next rdbt to Holdenhurst Rd, 2nd exit off Lansdowne rdbt into Meyrick Rd. Left into Gervis Rd. Hotel on right

PETS: Bedrooms £5 (dogs) Exercise area (25mtrs)

This is a large hotel on the East Cliff with a newly refurbished leisure centre. The Heathlands is popular with many groups and conferences and the public areas are bright and spacious. There is a coffee shop, open all day, and regular live entertainment is provided for guests.
ROOMS: 115 en suite (16 fmly) (11 GF) No smoking in 15 bedrooms s £66-£105; d £92-£190 (incl. bkfst) **LB FACILITIES:** STV Outdoor swimming (H) Sauna Gym Jacuzzi Health suite entertainment Xmas **SERVICES:** Lift **PARKING:** 100 **NOTES:** No smoking in restaurant **CARDS:**

★★★ 66% Bay View Court
35 East Overcliff Dr BH1 3AH
☎ 01202 294449 ▤ 01202 292883
e-mail: enquiry@bayviewcourt.co.uk
Dir: on A338 left at St Pauls rdbt. Over St Swithuns rdbt. Bear left onto Manor Rd, 1st right, next right

PETS: Bedrooms £20 per stay (except guide dogs) Exercise area (5 mins)

This relaxed and friendly hotel enjoys far-reaching sea views from many of the public areas and bedrooms. Bedrooms vary in size and are attractively furnished. There is a choice of south facing lounges and, for the more energetic, an indoor swimming pool. Live entertainment is provided during the evenings.
ROOMS: 64 en suite (11 fmly) (5 GF) s £56-£64; d £112-£128 (incl. bkfst & dinner) **LB FACILITIES:** Spa STV Indoor swimming (H) Snooker Sauna Gym Jacuzzi Steam room entertainment Xmas **SERVICES:** Lift **PARKING:** 58 **NOTES:** No smoking in restaurant **CARDS:**

> **All information was correct at the time of going to press; we recommend you confirm details on booking**

★★★ 63% Burley Court
Bath Rd BH1 2NP
☎ 01202 552824 & 556704 ▤ 01202 298514
e-mail: info@burleycourthotel.co.uk
Dir: leave A338 at St Pauls rdbt, take 3rd exit at next rdbt into Holdenhurst Rd. 3rd exit at next rdbt into Bath Rd, over crossing, 1st left

PETS: Bedrooms (unattended) £8 for a dog, prices for other pets on request Exercise area (0.25 mile) Pet Food Food provided, not bowls

Located on Bournemouth's West Cliff, this well-established hotel is easily located and convenient for the town and beaches. Bedrooms, many recently refurbished, are pleasantly furnished and decorated in bright colours. A daily changing menu is served in the spacious dining room.
ROOMS: 38 en suite (8 fmly) No smoking in 20 bedrooms s £33-£46; d £66-£92 (incl. bkfst) **LB FACILITIES:** Outdoor swimming (H) Solarium Xmas **SERVICES:** Lift **PARKING:** 35 **NOTES:** No smoking in restaurant Closed 30 Dec-14 Jan **CARDS:**

★★★ 63% Ocean View Hotel
East Overcliff Dr BH1 3AR
☎ 01202 558057 ▤ 01202 556285
e-mail: enquiry@oceanview.uk.com
Dir: on A338 left at St Pauls rdbt. Over St Swithuns rdbt. Bear left onto Manor Rd, 1st right, next right

PETS: Bedrooms £20 per stay (except guide dogs) Exercise area (5 mins)

Splendid sea views can be enjoyed from all of the public rooms at this popular East Cliff hotel. Bedrooms vary in size, and all are light, airy and well equipped. A comfortable bar/lounge offers an informal alternative to the drawing room, whilst the spacious restaurant offers a fixed-price menu every evening.
ROOMS: 52 rms (51 en suite) (13 fmly) s £56-£64; d £112-£128 (incl. bkfst & dinner) **LB FACILITIES:** Outdoor swimming (H) Indoor leisure suite at Bayview Court Hotel (sister hotel) entertainment ch fac Xmas **SERVICES:** Lift **PARKING:** 39 **NOTES:** No smoking in restaurant **CARDS:**

★★ 68% Whitehall
Exeter Park Rd BH2 5AX
☎ 01202 554682 ▤ 01202 292637
e-mail: reservations@thewhitehallhotel.co.uk
Dir: follow BIC signs then turn into Exeter Park Rd off Exeter Rd

PETS: Exercise area (5 min walk)

This friendly hotel enjoys an elevated position overlooking the park and is also close to the town centre and seafront. The spacious public areas include a choice of lounges, a cosy bar and a well-presented restaurant. The bedrooms are spread over three floors and are inviting and well equipped.
ROOMS: 46 en suite (5 fmly) (3 GF) No smoking in 20 bedrooms s £33-£55; d £66-£110 (incl. bkfst) **LB FACILITIES:** Xmas **SERVICES:** Lift **PARKING:** 25 **NOTES:** No smoking in restaurant **CARDS:**

★★ 65% Fircroft
4 Owls Rd BH5 1AE
☎ 01202 309771 ▨ 01202 395644
e-mail: info@fircrofthotel.co.uk
Dir: off A338 signed Boscombe Pier. Hotel 400yds from pier close to Christchurch Rd

PETS: Bedrooms (unattended) £4 Exercise area

This friendly hotel is pleasantly located close to Boscombe pier. Offering a range of comfortable lounges and meeting facilities, the hotel is popular with tour and dance groups. In addition, entertainment is provided most nights throughout the year. All of the bedrooms are comfortable and well equipped.
ROOMS: 51 en suite (20 fmly) s £30-£36; d £60-£72 (incl. bkfst) **LB**
FACILITIES: Indoor swimming (H) Sauna Solarium Gym Jacuzzi Sports at health club owned by hotel Xmas **SERVICES:** Lift **PARKING:** 50
NOTES: No smoking in restaurant
CARDS: 🖃 🖃 🖃 🖃 🖃 🖃 🖃

★★ 64% Bournemouth Sands
2 West Cliff Gardens BH2 5HR
☎ 01202 312314 ▨ 01202 312315
e-mail: reservations@bournemouthsandshotel.com
Dir: Five roads behind Bournemouth International Centre

PETS: Bedrooms (unattended) £3.50 Exercise area

Conveniently located for the Bournemouth International Centre, beaches and other attractions, this friendly hotel offers a relaxed and informal atmosphere to guests. Bedrooms are simply furnished and comfortable. A choice of bars and lounges are available and entertainment is provided most evenings throughout the year.
ROOMS: 65 en suite (17 fmly) s £20-£38; d £40-£76 (incl. bkfst) **LB**
FACILITIES: Guests have use of leisure facilities at sister hotel Xmas
SERVICES: Lift **PARKING:** 65 **NOTES:** No smoking in restaurant
CARDS: 🖃 🖃 🖃 🖃 🖃

◆◆◆ Alum Grange Hotel
1 Burnaby Rd, Alum Chine BH4 8JF
☎ 01202 761195 07971 375130 ▨ 01202 760973
Dir: M27 to A31, at Ringwood turn left onto A338, 2nd exit at Frizzel House rdbt, left at lights, right at next rdbt and left as sea comes into view

PETS: Bedrooms £5 Exercise area (150yds)
RESIDENT PETS: George - Collie, Milly - Springer Spaniel

Located between the town centres of Bournemouth and Poole, this spacious hotel is only a short stroll from the beautiful, sandy, Alum Chine Beach. All bedrooms are tastefully furnished and brightly decorated and one room has a four-poster bed. Guests can choose from the daily changing menu, served in the attractive open plan dining room/lounge bar.
FACILITIES: 14 en suite (7 fmly) (3 GF) No smoking in bedrooms No smoking in dining room No smoking in 1 lounge TVB tea/coffee Licensed Cen ht TVL No coaches Dinner Last d mid afternoon
PRICES: s £44-£48.50; d £66-£75✱ **LB PARKING:** 11
CARDS: 🖃 🖃 🖃 🖃 🖃

◆◆◆ East Cliff Cottage Hotel
57 Grove Rd BH1 3AT
☎ 01202 552788 ▨ 01202 552788
e-mail: info@otel57.freeserve.co.uk
Dir: Wessex Way into Bournemouth, left at East Cliff Rd sign, right at next rdbt, left (Meyrick Rd), left (Grove Rd).

PETS: Bedrooms (under supervision in garden) Exercise area

Situated just 300 yards from the seafront and conveniently close to the town centre and the East Cliff Lift, this charming small hotel offers comfortable accommodation. Home-cooked meals are served in the spacious dining room. Guests can relax in the cosy lounge or in the delightful garden in fine weather.
FACILITIES: 10 rms (7 en suite) (4 fmly) No smoking in dining room STV TVB tea/coffee Direct dial from bedrooms Licensed Cen ht TVL No coaches Dinner Last d 4pm **PRICES:** s £20-£65; d £50-£80✱ **LB**
PARKING: 10 **CARDS:** 🖃 🖃 🖃 🖃 🖃 🖃

BRIDPORT   Map 03 SY49

★★ 64% Bridge House

115 East St DT6 3LB
☎ 01308 423371 ▨ 01308 459573
e-mail: info@bridgehousebridport.co.uk
Dir: follow signs to town centre from A35 rdbt, hotel 200mtrs on right

PETS: Bedrooms (unattended) Public areas (except restaurant, must be well-behaved) Exercise area (adjacent)

A short stroll from the town centre, this 18th-century Grade II listed property is undergoing a major refurbishment. The well-equipped bedrooms vary in size. In addition to the main lounge, there is a small bar-lounge and a separate breakfast room. An interesting range of home-cooked meals is provided in the restaurant.
ROOMS: 10 en suite (3 fmly) No smoking in 5 bedrooms s £44-£50; d £65-£75 (incl. bkfst) **PARKING:** 13 **NOTES:** No smoking in restaurant
CARDS: 🖃 🖃 🖃 🖃 🖃

◆◆◆◆ Britmead House
West Bay Rd DT6 4EG
☎ 01308 422941
e-mail: britmead@talk21.com
Dir: approaching Bridport on A35 follow signs for West Bay, Britmead House is 800yds S of A35

PETS: Bedrooms Exercise area (adjacent)

Britmead House is located south of Bridport, within easy reach of the town centre and West Bay harbour. Family-run, the atmosphere is friendly and the accommodation well-appointed and comfortable. Suitable for both business and leisure guests; many return on a regular basis. A choice of breakfasts is served in the light and airy dining room.
FACILITIES: 8 en suite (2 fmly) (2 GF) No smoking TVB tea/coffee Cen ht No coaches **PRICES:** s £34-£48; d £50-£66✱ **LB PARKING:** 12
CARDS: 🖃 🖃 🖃 🖃

England

CASHMOOR
Map 03 ST91

◆◆◆◆ 🎋 Cashmoor House
DT11 8DN
☎ 01725 552339 📠 01725 552291
e-mail: spencer.jones@ukonline.co.uk
Dir: on A354 Salisbury-Blandford, 3m S of Sixpenny Handley rdbt just past Inn on the Chase

PETS: Bedrooms Public areas (On a lead and under control) Exercise area (Adjacent field) RESIDENT PETS: Holly & Daisy - Springer Spaniels

Situated virtually midway between Blandford and Salisbury, parts of Cashmoor House date back to the 17th century. Retaining its original character and charm, the whole property is attractively furnished and decorated, with a warm and homely farmhouse ambience. Traditional Aga cooked breakfasts, featuring home-made bread and preserves, plus eggs laid by their own hens, are served in the beamed dining room; suppers available by prior arrangement.
FACILITIES: 4 en suite (2 fmly) (2 GF) No smoking TVB tea/coffee Cen ht TVL No coaches Dinner Last d breakfast **PRICES:** s £25-£30; d fr £45✱ **PARKING:** 8

CATTISTOCK
Map 03 SY59

◆◆◆◆ 🍺 Fox & Hounds Inn
Duck St DT2 0JH
☎ 01300 320444 📠 01300 320444
e-mail: info@foxandhoundsinn.com
Dir: follow signposts from A37 Dorchester to Yeovil

PETS: Bedrooms Public areas Exercise area (50 metres) RESIDENT PETS: Shades (border collie), Bear (German shepherd)

A traditional village inn offering warm hospitality, real ales and good food. Bedrooms are spacious and very well equipped. Quietly located in a pleasant village not far from Dorchester, this is a delightful place from which to explore the varied attractions of Dorset.
FACILITIES: 3 rms (2 en suite) No smoking in bedrooms No smoking in dining room TVB tea/coffee Cen ht No children 10yrs Pool Table Dinner Last d 8.45pm **PRICES:** s £40-£60; d £50-£60✱ **LB MEALS:** Lunch £12.40-£19.85 alc Dinner £12.40-£19.85 alc✱ **PARKING:** 4
CARDS: 〓 〓 〓 〓 ⑤

CHARMOUTH
Map 03 SY39

★★ 74% White House
2 Hillside, The Street DT6 6PJ
☎ 01297 560411 📠 01297 560702
e-mail: ian@whitehousehotel.com
Dir: off A35 signed Charmouth. Hotel opposite church halfway up hill

PETS: Bedrooms (cottage rooms only) (unattended) Exercise area (0.25 miles) RESIDENT PETS: Patsy & Mog (cats)

Famed for its fossils and cliff-top walks, the interesting beach is within walking distance of this charming Regency property. Comfortable accommodation is provided at this friendly, small hotel, where individually styled bedrooms are equipped with

continued

---

modern facilities. In the evening, imaginative cuisine is served in the attractive restaurant, cooked using fresh, local produce.
ROOMS: 6 en suite 2 annexe en suite (2 GF) No smoking in all bedrooms s fr £65; d £110-£150 (incl. bkfst & dinner) **LB**
PARKING: 9 **NOTES:** No children 14yrs No smoking in restaurant Closed Jan RS Feb, Nov & Dec **CARDS:** 〓 〓 〓 〓 ⑤

CHIDEOCK
Map 03 SY49

★★ 71% 🏵 Chideock House
Main St DT6 6JN
☎ 01297 489242 📠 01297 489184
e-mail: aa@chideockhousehotel.com
Dir: on A35 between Lyme Regis and Bridport, in centre of Chideock

PETS: Bedrooms Public areas (not restaurant) Exercise area (5 mins walk)

This delightful, partly thatched house dates back to the 15th century and retains many original features, such as beams and fireplaces. Relaxed and quietly attentive, the service is genuinely friendly and welcoming. Lots of thoughtful extras are provided in the bedrooms. An interesting and innovative menu featuring local produce is served in the comfortable restaurant.
ROOMS: 9 rms (8 en suite) s £70-£85; d £75-£85 (incl. bkfst) **LB**
FACILITIES: Xmas **PARKING:** 20 **NOTES:** No children 12yrs No smoking in restaurant RS 3 Jan-5 Feb **CARDS:** 〓 〓 〓 〓 ⑤

◆◆◆◆ Rose Cottage
Main St DT6 6JQ
☎ 01297 489994
e-mail: enquiries@rosecottage-chideock.co.uk
Dir: Take A35 from Bridport signed A35 Honiton/Exeter. Follow to Chideock (approx 0.5m). Past George Inn on right, Rose Cottage is 200yds on left

PETS: Bedrooms Exercise area (2 mins walk)

Conveniently located in the centre of this charming village, this 300-year-old cottage provides very well appointed, attractive accommodation. A friendly welcome is assured. A delicious breakfast can be enjoyed in the newly renovated dining room which has many interesting features, and in finer weather guests may relax in the pretty garden.
FACILITIES: 2 en suite No smoking TVB tea/coffee Cen ht No coaches **PARKING:** 2

🌲 **Places with this symbol are country house hotels**

🐓 **Places with this symbol are farms**

★ **Red stars indicate the AA's Top 200 Hotels in Britain & Ireland**

CHRISTCHURCH   Map 04 SZ19

♦♦♦ Stour Villa
67 Stour Rd BH23 1LN
☎ 01202 483379 ⌨ 01202 483379
e-mail: stourvilla@hotmail.com
Dir: on leaving Christchurch town centre heading towards Bournemouth on A35, left at lights to Stour Road, Villa approx 150yds right.

PETS: Telephone for details

Well located for visiting the New Forest and local beaches, Stour Villa is situated just a five-minute walk from the town centre with its various attractions and restaurants. The bedrooms and bathrooms are neatly furnished and decorated. A substantial cooked breakfast is offered in the cosy dining room.
FACILITIES: 6 en suite (2 fmly) No smoking TVB tea/coffee Cen ht No children 3yrs No coaches **PRICES:** s £22.50-£28; d £45-£56✱ **LB PARKING:** 7

♦♦♦ Long Barn House
Spadger Ln, West Stafford DT2 8UB
☎ 01305 266899
e-mail: pessame@amserve.net
Dir: follow A352 from A35, follow signs to West Stafford, on entering village turn L before church, follow signs

PETS: Bedrooms Exercise area (300 metres)

Located in the heart of the picturesque village of West Stafford, this converted 19th-century granary is ideally situated for exploring the surrounding area made famous by the author Thomas Hardy. The historic towns of Dorchester and Weymouth are just a short drive away. Bedrooms are comfortable and well-equipped and breakfast, which is partly self-service, is taken in the kitchen/dining room.
FACILITIES: 2 en suite No smoking TVB tea/coffee Cen ht No children 8yrs **PRICES:** s £25-£30; d £50-£60✱ **LB PARKING:** 4 **NOTES:** Closed Dec-Feb

DORCHESTER   Map 03 SY69

EVERSHOT   Map 03 ST50

♦♦♦♦♦ ◎◎ ⌣ Yalbury Cottage
Lower Bockhampton DT2 8PZ
☎ 01305 262382 ⌨ 01305 266412
e-mail: yalburycottage@aol.com
Dir: off A35 past Thomas Hardy's cottage, straight over x-rds, 400yds on L, past red telephone box, opp village pump

PETS: Bedrooms £5 per dog Exercise area

Dating back some 300 years, this delightfully attractive, thatched property, in the rural hamlet of Lower Bockhampton, was originally the home of the local shepherd and keeper of the water meadows. The oak-beamed ceilings, inglenook fireplaces and stone walls are features in both the lounge and restaurant - the ideal venue in which to enjoy the hotel's award-winning cuisine. The well-equipped bedrooms are comfortable and overlook either the colourful gardens or adjacent fields.
FACILITIES: 8 en suite (1 fmly) (6 GF) No smoking in bedrooms No smoking in dining room TVB tea/coffee Direct dial from bedrooms Licensed Cen ht discounted golf at 6 local courses Dinner Last d 9pm **PRICES:** s £57-£59; d £90-£94✱ **LB PARKING:** 16 **CARDS:** ▨ ▨ ▨ ▨ ▨

★★★ ▲♨ Summer Lodge
DT2 0JR
☎ 01935 83424 ⌨ 01935 83005
e-mail: enquiries@summerlodgehotel.com
Dir: 1m W of A37 halfway between Dorchester and Yeovil

RELAIS & CHATEAUX

PETS: Bedrooms (unattended) £7.50 Exercise area (100 metres) Pet Food

This picturesque hotel is situated in the heart of Dorset and is the ideal retreat for getting away from it all. Try to arrive for afternoon tea or try out the new spa and swimming pool. Bedrooms have all been recently refurbished to a very high standard, are individually designed and come with a wealth of facilities. Despite recent changes in the kitchen, early indications suggest the cuisine continues to be a high point of any stay.
ROOMS: 10 en suite 14 annexe en suite (6 fmly) (4 GF) No smoking in 10 bedrooms s fr £115; d £165-£360 (incl. bkfst) **FACILITIES:** Spa Indoor swimming (H) Tennis (hard & grass) Sauna Gym Croquet lawn Jacuzzi Xmas **SERVICES:** air con **PARKING:** 40 **NOTES:** No smoking in restaurant **CARDS:** ▨ ▨ ▨ ▨ ▨ ▨ ▨

Please mention AA Pet Friendly Places to Stay when booking

Don't forget to let proprietors know when you book that you're bringing your pet

England

◆◆◆◆◆ 🏠 ⊜ Frampton House

DT2 9NH
☎ 01300 320308 & 07785 391710 📠 01300 321600
e-mail: maynardryder@aol.com
Dir: turn off A37 onto A356 Frampton, at village green left over bridge, left again onto private drive past houses, last drive entrance on left

PETS: Public areas Exercise area (adjacent)
RESIDENT PETS: Dogger & Potter (Black Labradors), Herbert (cat), 2 horses

A truly delightful property located in the quiet village of Frampton, just outside of Dorchester. The proprietors here offer a naturally friendly and welcoming approach to hospitality and guests are made to feel instantly at home. The bedrooms, guest lounge and dining room offer high standards of quality and comfort. Dinner is available by prior arrangement and comes highly recommended.
FACILITIES: 2 en suite No smoking in bedrooms No smoking in dining room TVB tea/coffee Cen ht No children 8yrs No coaches Tennis (hard) Dinner **PRICES:** d fr £95✱ **PARKING:** 8

◆◆◆◆ ⊜ ◀ The Fox Inn

DT2 7PN
☎ 01258 880328 📠 01258 881440
e-mail: enquiries@foxansty.co.uk
Dir: from Dorchester take A35 to Poole, 4m exit at Northbrook junct to Piddlehinton. Take 1st exit and follow road for 220mtrs, turn right for Cheselbourne, stay on this road for Ansty

PETS: Bedrooms (unattended) Public areas (bar only)
Exercise area (surrounding) RESIDENT PETS: French Bulldog - Milly

This delightful country inn is surrounded by pleasant Dorset countryside. The Fox started life over 250 years ago as the home of Charles Hall, founder member of Hall and Woodhouse Brewery. The present owners have restored the atmosphere of a traditional inn, with the emphasis on local ales, delicious home-cooked meals and a friendly welcome.
FACILITIES: 12 en suite (4 fmly) No smoking in bedrooms No smoking in dining room No smoking in 1 lounge TVB tea/coffee Direct dial from bedrooms Cen ht Outdoor swimming pool (heated) Pool Table pool supervised Dinner Last d 9pm **PRICES:** s £45-£60; d £60-£90✱ **LB PARKING:** 40 **CARDS:** 🖃 💳 🖃 🖃 🖸

★★★ 71% 🌐 Alexandra

Pound St DT7 3HZ
☎ 01297 442010 📠 01297 443229
e-mail: enquiries@hotelalexandra.co.uk
Dir: from A30 , A35, then onto A358, A3052 to Lyme Regis

PETS: Bedrooms £6 Exercise area
RESIDENT PETS: 2 Springer Spaniels - Midge & Tess

This welcoming, family-run hotel is Grade II listed and dates back to 1735. Public areas are spacious and comfortable, with ample seating areas to relax, unwind and enjoy the magnificent views. The elegant restaurant offers imaginative, innovative dishes. Bedrooms vary in size and shape, decorated with pretty chintz fabrics and attractive furniture.
ROOMS: 25 en suite 1 annexe en suite (8 fmly) (3 GF) s £50-£106; d £70-£136 (incl. bkfst) **LB PARKING:** 18 **NOTES:** No smoking in restaurant Closed Xmas & Jan **CARDS:** 🖃 💳 🖃 🖃 🖃 🖸

◆◆◆◆ The White House

47 Silver St DT7 3HR
☎ 01297 443420
e-mail: whitehouselyme@btopenworld.co.uk
Dir: on B3165 Axminster-Lyme Regis road approx 50mtrs from junct with A3052

PETS: Bedrooms £1 Exercise area (100yds)

This charming guest house dates back to 1770 and is conveniently located in the centre of town, just a short walk from the beach. The well-equipped, comfortable bedrooms are cheerful and bright. Guests have use of a spacious lounge and an attractive dining room where hearty breakfasts are served.
FACILITIES: 7 en suite No smoking TVB tea/coffee Cen ht TVL No children No coaches **PRICES:** d £50-£60✱ **LB PARKING:** 7 **NOTES:** Closed Xmas

◆◆◆ ◀ Victoria Hotel

Uplyme Rd DT7 3LP
☎ 01297 444801 📠 01297 442949
e-mail: info@vichotel.co.uk
Dir: turn off A35 onto B3165, travel 2m through village of Uplymes. Hotel on left as you approach mini-rdbt

PETS: Bedrooms Exercise area (5 min walk)

Dating back to 1906 and originally built as a railway hotel, this friendly establishment overlooks the picturesque town, Lyme Bay and surrounding countryside. The comfortable bedrooms are neatly presented. While the open-plan bar is ideally suited to relaxed and informal eating, the restaurant offers more imaginative and adventurous dishes.
FACILITIES: 7 en suite No smoking in dining room No smoking in lounges TVB tea/coffee Cen ht TVL Pool Table Dinner Last d 9.30pm **PRICES:** s £35-£40; d £55-£60✱ **LB PARKING:** 15 **NOTES:** Closed last 2wks Jan rs Mondays **CARDS:** 🖃 💳 🖃 🖃 🖸

PIDDLETRENTHIDE — Map 03 SY79

◆◆◆◆ ◪ The Poachers
DT2 7QX
☎ 01300 348358 🖶 01300 348153
e-mail: thepoachersinn@piddletrenthide.fsbusiness.co.uk
Dir: 8m from Dorchester on B3143, 2m into Piddletrenthide, inn on left

PETS: Bedrooms (unattended) £2 Public areas (bar area only) Exercise area (100 metres) RESIDENT PETS: Peroni & Azzura (West Highland Terriers)

A warm welcome is assured at this friendly inn. The bar and dining areas retain much of their original 16th-century character and charm with home-cooked meals a key feature. Extensions have allowed for good-sized bedrooms, the majority of which are situated around the swimming pool, garden and adjacent stream.
FACILITIES: 5 en suite 15 annexe en suite (1 fmly) (13 GF) No smoking in area of dining room TVB tea/coffee Direct dial from bedrooms Cen ht Outdoor swimming pool (heated) Skittle alley Dinner Last d 9pm
PRICES: s £35-£45; d £65-£85✷ **LB PARKING:** 40
NOTES: Closed 24-26 Dec **CARDS:** 🔲🔲🔲🔲🔲

POOLE — Map 04 SZ09

★★★ 65% Arndale Court
62/66 Wimborne Rd BH15 2BY
☎ 01202 683746 🖶 01202 668838
e-mail: info@arndalecourthotel.com
Dir: on A349 close to town centre, opp Poole Stadium

PETS: Bedrooms Exercise area (0.5 mile)

Ideally situated for the town centre and ferry terminal, this small, privately-owned hotel has now been extensively refurbished. Bedrooms are well equipped, pleasantly spacious and comfortable. Particularly well suited to business guests, the Arndale Court has a pleasant range of stylish public areas and good parking.
ROOMS: 39 en suite (7 fmly) (14 GF) No smoking in 12 bedrooms s £67; d £80-£100 (incl. bkfst) **FACILITIES:** STV **PARKING:** 40
NOTES: No smoking in restaurant **CARDS:** 🔲🔲🔲🔲🔲

> ### Please mention AA Pet Friendly Places to Stay when booking

★★★ 64% Salterns Harbourside
38 Salterns Way, Lilliput BH14 8JR
☎ 01202 707321 🖶 01202 707488
e-mail: reception@salterns.co.uk
Dir: in Poole follow B3369 Sandbanks road. After 1m at Lilliput shops turn into Salterns Way by Barclays Bank

PETS: Bedrooms (Selected rooms) (unattended) £10 Public areas (not restaurant)

Located next to the marina with superb views across to Brownsea Island, this modernised hotel used to be the headquarters for the flying boats in WWII and was later a yacht club. Bedrooms are spacious and some have private balconies, whilst the busy bar and restaurant both share harbour views.
ROOMS: 20 en suite (4 fmly) No smoking in 3 bedrooms s £70-£110; d £80-£130 (incl. bkfst) **LB FACILITIES:** Xmas **PARKING:** 80
NOTES: No smoking in restaurant
CARDS: 🔲🔲🔲🔲🔲

★★ 62% Norfolk Lodge
1 Flaghead Rd, Canford Cliffs BH13 7JL
☎ 01202 708614 🖶 01202 708661
e-mail: allnmartin@aol.com
Dir: between Poole and Bournemouth. Hotel on corner of Haven and Flaghead Rd

PETS: Bedrooms £3 Public areas (except restaurant) Exercise area

This small, family-run hotel provides friendly and comfortable accommodation. Norfolk Lodge is convenient for the town and harbour, and only a few minutes' walk from the beaches. Bedrooms are well equipped and pleasantly spacious. The public areas offer choices of dining areas, with the dining room overlooking the attractive gardens.
ROOMS: 17 en suite (4 fmly) s £45-£55; d £58-£70 (incl. bkfst) **LB**
FACILITIES: ch fac **PARKING:** 16 **NOTES:** No smoking in restaurant
CARDS: 🔲🔲🔲🔲🔲

POWERSTOCK — Map 03 SY59

◆◆◆◆ ◪ Three Horseshoes Inn
DT6 3TF
☎ 01308 485328
e-mail: info@threehorseshoesinn.com
Dir: Powerstock signed off (Bridport to Beaminster road) A3066. 3m from Bridport

PETS: Bedrooms (unattended) Public areas (except restaurant) Exercise area (surrounding countryside)

From its elevated position in the village of Powerstock, The Three Horseshoes overlooks rolling hills. The unpretentious bar and cosy dining room appeal to both locals and visitors alike. A wide range of meals is available, with the emphasis on local, and organic where possible, produce, cooked with care. The spacious bedrooms offer comfort and all the expected facilities.
FACILITIES: 1 en suite 2 annexe en suite (1 fmly) (2 GF) No smoking in bedrooms No smoking in dining room No smoking in lounges TVB tea/coffee Cen ht Dinner Last d 9pm **PRICES:** s £40-£60; d £60-£80✷
LB PARKING: 25 **CARDS:** 🔲🔲🔲🔲🔲

England

SHAFTESBURY   Map 03 ST82

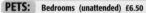

★★★ 66%  **Royal Chase**
Royal Chase Roundabout SP7 8DB
☎ 01747 853355 🖷 01747 851969
e-mail: royalchasehotel@btinternet.com
Dir: A303 to A350 signed Blandford Forum. Avoid town centre, follow road to 3rd rdbt

PETS: Bedrooms (unattended) £6.50

Equally suitable for both leisure and business guests, this well-known local landmark is situated close to the famous Gold Hill. Bedrooms come in 'standard' and 'crown' and both types offer good levels of comfort and quality. In addition to the fixed price menu in the Byzant Restaurant, guests have the option of eating more informally in the convivial bar.
ROOMS: 33 en suite (13 fmly) (6 GF) No smoking in 10 bedrooms s £95; d £110-£130 **LB FACILITIES:** Spa STV Indoor swimming (H) Turkish steam bath Xmas **PARKING:** 100 **NOTES:** No smoking in restaurant **CARDS:** ▨▨▨▨▨▨

STUDLAND   Map 04 SZ08

★★ 68% **Manor House**
BH19 3AU
☎ 01929 450288 🖷 01929 450288
e-mail: themanorhousehotel@lineone.net
Dir: A338 from Bournemouth, follow signs to Sandbanks/Sandbanks ferry, cross on ferry, then 3m to Studland

PETS: Bedrooms (unattended) £3.50 (not in bar/restaurant & lounge) Exercise area RESIDENT PETS: Fluffy (German Shepherd), Minki (Blue Burmese cat)

Set in 20 acres of attractive grounds and with delightful views overlooking Studland Bay, this elegant hotel provides an impressive range of facilities. Bedrooms, many with excellent sea views, are all well-equipped and many retain charming features of the original Gothic house. In the oak-panelled dining room, carefully prepared meals offer an interesting choice of dishes from the daily-changing menu.
ROOMS: 18 en suite 3 annexe en suite (9 fmly) (4 GF) s £85-£100; d £70-£110 (incl. bkfst & dinner) **LB FACILITIES:** Tennis (hard) Croquet lawn Xmas **PARKING:** 80 **NOTES:** No children 5yrs No smoking in restaurant Closed 3 wks Jan
CARDS: ▨▨▨▨▨▨

STURMINSTER NEWTON

★★★ 70% **Plumber Manor**
Hazelbury Bryan Rd DT10 2AF
☎ 01258 472507 🖷 01258 473370
e-mail: book@plumbermanor.com
Dir: Off A357, 1.5m SW towards Hazelbury Bryan. Follow brown tourist signs to Plumber Manor

PETS: Bedrooms Sep Accom (unattended) Exercise area (surrounding) Pet Food RESIDENT PETS: Archie & Toby (Labradors)

This 17th-century manor, set in extensive, lovingly tended grounds, is full of charm and character. Bedrooms, some set apart from the main house, are pleasantly spacious and modern in style. The public areas retain much of the style of the manor and guests can relax in the bar or lounge, or stroll in the grounds. Using fresh and local produce, the restaurant is very much the focus of the hotel.
ROOMS: 6 en suite 10 annexe en suite No smoking in all bedrooms s £90-£100; d fr £125 (incl. bkfst) **LB FACILITIES:** Tennis (hard) Croquet lawn **PARKING:** 30 **NOTES:** No smoking in restaurant Closed Feb **CARDS:** ▨▨▨▨▨

♦♦♦♦ 🍴 ♥ **Honeysuckle House**
1995 Fifehead St Quintin DT10 2AP
☎ 01258 817896
Dir: turn off A357 up Glue Hill (signed Hazelbury Bryan). Take next left, after sharp bend. Follow road for approx 2.5m

PETS: Bedrooms Sep Accom (large dog room) (unattended) £2.50 Public areas Exercise area (surrounding fields) dog sitting service available RESIDENT PETS: Trevor (Springer Spaniel), Beamish (Black Labrador)

Peace and tranquillity can be found at this 400-acre working dairy farm. The young proprietors offer a particularly friendly welcome and ensure all guests are very well looked after. Bedrooms are comfortable and include some welcome extras. Breakfasts are enormous, and be sure to book for dinner which is a real highlight of any stay.
FACILITIES: 3 en suite (1 fmly) No smoking in bedrooms TVB tea/coffee Cen ht TVL ch fac Outdoor swimming pool Fishing Riding Croquet lawn Pony rides, farm tours, childrens tractor rides 400 acres Dairy Dinner Last d Previous day **PRICES:** s £25-£35; d £45-£65✱ **LB PARKING:** 6 **NOTES:** Closed 22 Dec-2 Jan

SWANAGE Map 04 SZ07

★★★ 67% The Pines
Burlington Rd BH19 1LT
☎ 01929 425211 📠 01929 422075
e-mail: reservations@pineshotel.co.uk
Dir: A351 to seafront, left then 2nd right. Hotel at end of road

> **PETS:** Bedrooms (unattended) Public areas Exercise area (100yds) Pet Food food & bowls by prior request only
> **RESIDENT PETS:** Sid (cat)

Enjoying a peaceful location with spectacular views over the cliffs and sea, The Pines is a pleasant place to stay. Bedrooms, many with sea views, are comfortable and some have recently been refurbished. Guests can take tea in the lounge, enjoy appetising bar snacks in the attractive bar and interesting and accomplished cuisine in the restaurant.
ROOMS: 49 en suite (26 fmly) (6 GF) s £54.50-£72.50; d £109-£157 (incl. bkfst) **LB FACILITIES:** ch fac Xmas **SERVICES:** Lift **PARKING:** 60
NOTES: No smoking in restaurant **CARDS:** 〰 💳 🆚 💳 📇

SYDLING ST NICHOLAS Map 03 SY69

◆◆◆◆ 🍴 Greyhound Inn
DT2 9PD
☎ 01300 341303 📠 01300 342045
e-mail: info@thegreyhounddorset.co.uk
Dir: between Dorchester and Yeovil on A35 turn left down hill, next right at x-roads. Pub on right

> **PETS:** Bedrooms Public areas (not in restaurant) Exercise area (100 yards)

Situated in this quintessentially English village, complete with stream, the Greyhound Inn offers stylishly presented, well-equipped rooms; three on the ground floor. In the flag-floored bar an imaginative range of meals is listed on the blackboards, and are served either in the restaurant or the bar. Relaxed and friendly, this inn is ideally located as a centre from which to explore Hardy country.
FACILITIES: 6 en suite (3 fmly) (3 GF) No smoking TVB tea/coffee Cen ht Dinner Last d 10pm **PRICES:** s £65; d £75✱ **PARKING:** 30
CARDS: 〰 🆚 💳 📇

WAREHAM Map 03 SY98

★★★ 65% Worgret Manor
Worgret Rd BH20 6AB
☎ 01929 552957 📠 01929 554804
e-mail: admin@worgretmanorhotel.co.uk
Dir: on A352 from Wareham to Wool, 0.5m from Wareham rdbt

> **PETS:** Bedrooms Public areas (Bar and reception only) Exercise area (300 yards) **RESIDENT PETS:** Golden Retriever - Tammy

On the edge of Wareham, with easy access to major routes, this privately owned Georgian manor house offers a friendly, cheerful ambience. The bedrooms come in a variety of sizes. Public rooms
continued

are well presented and comprise a popular bar, a quiet lounge and an airy restaurant.
ROOMS: 12 en suite (1 fmly) (3 GF) No smoking in 8 bedrooms s £55-£60; d £80-£90 (incl. bkfst) **LB FACILITIES:** Free use of local sports centre **PARKING:** 25 **NOTES:** No smoking in restaurant
CARDS: 〰 💳 🆚 💳 📇

WEST LULWORTH Map 03 SY88

★★ 66% Cromwell House
Lulworth Cove BH20 5RJ
☎ 01929 400253 & 400332 📠 01929 400566
e-mail: catriona@lulworthcove.co.uk
Dir: 200yds beyond end of West Lulworth village, left onto high slip road, hotel 100yds on left opposite beach car park

> **PETS:** Bedrooms (unattended) Public areas (except dining room) Exercise area (adjacent) **RESIDENT PETS:** Jaldi - Springer Spaniel, Lily - cat

Built in 1881 by the Mayor of Weymouth, specifically as a guest house, this family-run hotel now provides guests with an ideal base for touring the area and for exploring the beaches and coast. Cromwell House enjoys spectacular views across the sea and countryside. Bedrooms, many with sea views, are comfortable and some have been specifically designed for family use.
ROOMS: 17 en suite (3 fmly) (17 GF) s £37.50-£55.50; d £70-£80 (incl. bkfst) **LB FACILITIES:** Outdoor swimming (H) Access to Dorset Coastal footpath & Jurassic Coast ch fac **PARKING:** 15
NOTES: No smoking in restaurant Closed 22 Dec-3 Jan
CARDS: 〰 💳 🆚 💳 📇

CO DURHAM

BARNARD CASTLE Map 12 NZ01

★★★ 73% 🏵 The Morritt Arms Hotel & Restaurant
Greta Bridge DL12 9SE
☎ 01833 627232 📠 01833 627392
e-mail: relax@themorritt.co.uk
Dir: turn off A1 at Scotch Corner onto A66 towards Penrith. Greta Bridge 9m on left

> **PETS:** Bedrooms (unattended) Public areas (Except restaurants) Exercise area (Adjacent) Pet Food

Set off the main road at Greta Bridge, this 17th-century coaching house provides comfortable public rooms full of character. The bar is focused on food and has an interesting Dickensian mural. A fine dining experience is offered in the oak-panelled restaurant. Bedrooms come in individual styles and varying sizes. The attentive service will leave a lasting impression.
ROOMS: 23 en suite (3 fmly) No smoking in 17 bedrooms s £59.50-£75; d £87.50-£126.50 (incl. bkfst) **LB FACILITIES:** ch fac Xmas **PARKING:** 40 **NOTES:** No smoking in restaurant
CARDS: 〰 💳 🆚 💳 📇

England (vertical tab)

★★★ 68% Derwent Manor
Allensford DH8 9BB
☎ 01207 592000 🖷 01207 502472
e-mail: info@derwent-manor-hotel.com
Dir: on A68 Darlington to Corbridge road. Access A68 from A1 junct 58 or A69. Hotel 11m on left

PETS: Bedrooms

This hotel, built in the style of a manor house, is set in open grounds overlooking the River Derwent. Spacious bedrooms, including a number of suites, are comfortably equipped. A popular wedding venue, there are also extensive conference facilities and a new impressive leisure suite. The 'Grouse & Claret' bar serves a wide range of drinks and light meals, and 'Guinevere's' restaurant offers fine dining.
ROOMS: 47 en suite (3 fmly) No smoking in 10 bedrooms s £99-£149; d £109-£159 (incl. bkfst) **LB FACILITIES:** STV Indoor swimming (H) Sauna Gym Jacuzzi Xmas **SERVICES:** Lift **PARKING:** 150
NOTES: No smoking in restaurant
CARDS: 💳

★★★ 67% Walworth Castle Hotel
Walworth DL2 2LY
☎ 01325 485470 🖷 01325 462257
e-mail: enquiries@walworthcastle.co.uk
Dir: A1(M) junct 58 follow signs to Corbridge. Left at rdbt, left at The Dog pub. Hotel on left after 1m

PETS: Bedrooms (some rooms only) Exercise area
Pet Food RESIDENT PETS: Holly - Golden Retriever

This 12th-century castle is privately owned and has been tastefully converted. Accommodation is offered in a range of styles, including an impressive suite and more compact rooms in an adjoining wing. Dinner can be taken in the fine dining Hansards Restaurant or the more relaxed Farmer's Bar. A popular venue for conferences and weddings.
ROOMS: 20 en suite 14 annexe en suite (4 fmly) No smoking in 6 bedrooms s £65-£80; d £80-£195 (incl. bkfst) **LB FACILITIES:** Xmas **PARKING:** 100 **NOTES:** No smoking in restaurant
CARDS: 💳

★★★ 65% Kings Head
9-12 Priestgate DL1 1NW
☎ 01325 380222 🖷 01325 382006
e-mail: admin@kingsheadhotel50.fsnet.co.uk
Dir: A1 northbound signed Darlington. 3rd exit off rdbt, 2nd off next rdbt. At 3rd rdbt 1st exit. 1st right, then 1st left. Hotel on right

PETS: Bedrooms Exercise area (0.5 mile)

Adjacent to the Cornmill Shopping Centre, this town centre hotel provides a variety of bedroom styles. Public areas include an inviting foyer lounge and upstairs a comfortable bar and restaurant. The hotel has limited secure basement car parking.
ROOMS: 85 en suite (3 fmly) No smoking in 51 bedrooms s £60-£100; d £70-£100 (incl. bkfst) **LB FACILITIES:** Free use of nearby leisure complex Xmas **SERVICES:** Lift **PARKING:** 28
CARDS: 💳

★★★★ 72% ® Durham Marriott Hotel, Royal County

Old Elvet DH1 3JN
☎ 0191 386 6821 🖷 0191 386 0704
e-mail: durhamroyal.marriott@whitbread.com
Dir: from A1(M) junct 62, then A690 to Durham, over 1st rdbt, left at 2nd rdbt, left at lights, hotel on left

PETS: Bedrooms (unattended)

In a wonderful position on the banks of the River Wear, the hotel's central location makes it ideal for visiting the attractions of this historic city. The building was developed from a series of Jacobean town houses (once owned by the Bowes-Lyon family, ancestors of the late Queen Mother). Today the hotel offers up-to-date, air-conditioned bedrooms; a choice of restaurants and lounge areas; gymnasium and swimming pool.
ROOMS: 142 en suite 8 annexe en suite (10 fmly) (15 GF) No smoking in 111 bedrooms s £130-£145; d £140-£165 (incl. bkfst) **LB**
FACILITIES: Spa STV Indoor swimming (H) Outdoor swimming Sauna Solarium Gym Jacuzzi Turkish steamroom Plungepool, sanarium, tropical fun shower **SERVICES:** Lift **PARKING:** 76 **NOTES:** No smoking in restaurant **CARDS:** 💳

★★★ 69% Kings Lodge Hotel & Restaurant
Flass Vale DH1 4BG
☎ 0191 370 9977 🖷 0191 370 9988
e-mail: manager@kingslodge.info
Dir: A1 junct 62, over 1st 3 rdbts, right at 4th. 1st left then 1st right. Hotel at end of road

PETS: Bedrooms

Benefiting from a city centre location, yet with the illusion of a secluded setting, this stylish modern hotel is popular with both business and leisure guests. Accommodation is provided in compact, well-designed rooms. Knights is a contemporary restaurant and Champagne bar; there is also a less formal bar and beer terrace and a bright and comfortable lounge.
ROOMS: 21 en suite (1 fmly) No smoking in all bedrooms s £75-£80; d £85-£120 (incl. bkfst) **FACILITIES:** STV entertainment ch fac **SERVICES:** air con **PARKING:** 35 **NOTES:** No smoking in restaurant Closed 26 Dec-1 Jan RS 25 Dec **CARDS:** 💳

★★★ 66% Bowburn Hall
Bowburn DH6 5NH
☎ 0191 377 0311 🖷 0191 377 3459
e-mail: info@bowburnhallhotel.co.uk
Dir: towards Bowburn. Right at Cooperage Pub, then 0.5m to junct signed Durham. Hotel on left

PETS: Bedrooms (unattended) Public areas Exercise area
Pet Food

A former country mansion, this hotel lies in five acres of grounds in a residential area, but within easy reach of the A1. The spacious lounge bar and conservatory overlook the gardens and are comfortable and popular venues for both bar and restaurant meals. Bedrooms are not large but are smartly presented and well equipped.
ROOMS: 19 en suite **FACILITIES:** STV **PARKING:** 100 **NOTES:** RS 24-26 Dec & 1 Jan **CARDS:** 💳

◆◆◆◆ The Gables
10 South View, Middlestone Moor DL16 7DF
☎ 01388 817544
e-mail: thegablesghouse@aol.com
Dir: from A688 follow town centre signs, then for Middlestone Moor, left at 2nd lights, then 2nd right

PETS: Bedrooms Pub areas (ex dining room) Walks nearby Pet food & blankets with prior notice **RESIDENT PETS:** Jack (Collie cross)

A warm welcome awaits at this conveniently located guest house with private parking. The house has been sympathetically renovated to provide comfortable accommodation. Bedrooms are of a good size, and feature both practical and homely extras. Light snacks are also available and are served to bedrooms.
FACILITIES: 4 en suite (1 fmly) (3 GF) No smoking in bedrooms TVB tea/coffee No children under 10yrs No coaches Last d 7.30pm
PRICES: s £35-£45; d £55-£60✳ **PARKING:** 6 **NOTES:** Closed 21 Dec-2 Jan **CARDS:** ▨▨▨▨▨

★★★ 66% Helme Park Hall Hotel
DL13 4NW
☎ 01388 730970 ▤ 01388 731799
e-mail: enquiries@helmeparkhotel.co.uk
Dir: 1m N of A689/A68 rdbt between Darlington & Corbridge

PETS: Bedrooms (unattended) Exercise area

Dating back to the 13th century, this welcoming hotel boasts superb panoramic views up the Wear Valley. The bedrooms are comfortably equipped and furnished. The cosy lounge bar is extremely popular for its comprehensive selection of bar meals, and the restaurant offers both table d'hote and carte menus.
ROOMS: 13 en suite (1 fmly) No smoking in 5 bedrooms s £52; d £85 (incl. bkfst) **LB FACILITIES:** STV Xmas **PARKING:** 70
NOTES: No smoking in restaurant **CARDS:** ▨▨▨▨▨

★★ 69% Hardwicke Hall Manor
Hesleden TS27 4PA
☎ 01429 836326 ▤ 01429 837676
Dir: NE on B1281, off A19 at sign for Durham and Blackhall

PETS: Bedrooms (unattended) Public areas (except restaurant) Exercise area

This country mansion house nestles in pleasant gardens and is full of character, providing an ideal venue for secluded weddings or meetings. Bedrooms are all individual and each one is spacious, comfortable and very well equipped. Good value meals are presented in a variety of public areas.
ROOMS: 15 en suite (2 fmly) s £55-£65; d £65-£75 (incl. bkfst) **LB PARKING:** 100 **NOTES:** No smoking in restaurant
CARDS: ▨▨▨▨▨

> 🍺 **Places with this symbol are pubs**

◆◆◆◆ The Parkwood Hotel
64-66 Darlington Rd, Hartburn TS18 5ER
☎ 01642 587933
e-mail: theparkwoodhotel@aol.com
Dir: from A19 take A66 towards Darlington. Leave at junct for A137 signed Yarm and Stockton West. Follow Stockton West and at traffic lights turn left. Hotel 0.75m on left

PETS: Bedrooms Public areas (not in dining areas) **RESIDENT PETS:** Charlie (Yorkie cross)

A very friendly welcome awaits you at this family-run hotel. The well-equipped comfortable bedrooms boast en suite facilities along with practical and homely extras. A range of well-prepared meals are professionally prepared and served in the cosy bar lounge, conservatory or the attractive non-smoking dining room.
FACILITIES: 5 en suite No smoking in bedrooms No smoking in dining room TVB tea/coffee Licensed Cen ht No coaches Dinner Last d 9.15pm
PRICES: s £38; d £50✳ **PARKING:** 36 **CARDS:** ▨▨▨▨▨

★★★ 64% The St George
Middleton St George, Darlington DL2 1RH
☎ 01325 332631 ▤ 01325 333851
e-mail: bookings@stgeorgehotel.net
Dir: turn off A67 bypass directly into Airport grounds

PETS: Bedrooms (unattended) Exercise area

This former wartime officers' mess is conveniently situated within walking distance of the airport terminal. Bedrooms, most of which are spacious, are located in two wings. Public areas include a well-stocked bar with games room, and a comfortable restaurant. Well-equipped conference and meeting rooms are also available.
ROOMS: 59 en suite No smoking in 14 bedrooms s £57; d £67 (incl. bkfst) **FACILITIES:** STV Solarium Xmas **PARKING:** 100
NOTES: No smoking in restaurant
CARDS: ▨▨▨▨▨

★★★ 70%
The Manor House Hotel & Country Club
The Green DL14 9HW
☎ 01388 834834 ▤ 01388 833566
e-mail: enquiries@manorhousehotel.net
Dir: A1(M) junct 58, then A68 to West Auckland. At T-junct turn left, hotel 150yds on right

PETS: Bedrooms (Small dogs)

This historic manor house, dating back to the 14th century, is full of character. Welcoming log fires await guests on cooler evenings. Comfortable bedrooms are individual, tastefully furnished and well equipped. The brasserie and Juniper's restaurant both offer an interesting selection of freshly prepared dishes. Well-equipped leisure facilities are also available.
ROOMS: 24 en suite 11 annexe en suite (6 fmly) (2 GF) s £36.50-£68; d £73-£99 (incl. bkfst) **LB FACILITIES:** Indoor swimming (H) Sauna Solarium Gym Jacuzzi ch fac Xmas **PARKING:** 200
NOTES: No smoking in restaurant **CARDS:** ▨▨▨▨▨

England

ESSEX

BASILDON
Map 05 TQ78

⇧ Campanile
Pipps Hill, Southend Arterial Rd SS14 3AE
☎ 01268 530810 ▤ 01268 286710
e-mail: basildon@envergure.co.uk
Dir: M25 junct 29 Basildon exit, back under A127, then left at rdbt

PETS: Bedrooms (Guide dogs only)

This modern building offers accommodation in smart, well-equipped bedrooms, all with en suite bathrooms. Refreshments may be taken at the informal Bistro. For further details consult the Hotel Groups page.
ROOMS: 97 annexe en suite s fr £44.95; d fr £44.95

BIRCHANGER GREEN MOTORWAY SERVICE AREA (M11)
Map 05 TL52

⇧ Days Inn Stansted
Birchanger Green, Bishop Stortford CM23 5QZ
☎ 01279 656477 ▤ 01279 656590
e-mail: birchanger.hotel@welcomebreak.co.uk
Dir: M11 junct 8

PETS: Bedrooms (unattended) Public areas

This modern building offers accommodation in smart, spacious and well-equipped bedrooms, suitable for families and business travellers, and all with en suite bathrooms. Continental breakfast is available and other refreshments may be taken at the nearby family restaurant. For further details see the Hotel Groups page.
ROOMS: 60 en suite s £69-£99; d £69-£99

CLACTON-ON-SEA
Map 05 TM11

◆◆◆ Sandrock Hotel
1 Penfold Rd, Marine Pde West CO15 1JN
☎ 01255 428215 ▤ 01255 428215
Dir: A12 to A120, to town/seafront, R at pier, signed Sandrock, 2nd on R

PETS: Bedrooms Exercise area (100 metres)

A warm welcome is offered at this Victorian property which is situated just off the seafront and within easy walking distance of the town centre. Bedrooms vary in size and style, and each is attractively decorated and thoughtfully equipped, some with sea views. Breakfast is served in the smart restaurant/bar and guests also have the use of a cosy residents' lounge. Dinner is available by prior arrangement.
FACILITIES: 9 en suite (3 fmly) (1 GF) No smoking in 2 bedrooms No smoking in dining room TVB tea/coffee Licensed Cen ht TVL No coaches **PRICES:** d £54-£56✳ **LB PARKING:** 6
CARDS:

All AA listed accommodation, restaurants and pubs can be found on the AA's website www.theAA.com

COGGESHALL
Map 05 TL82

★★★ 70% White Hart
Market End CO6 1NH
☎ 01376 561654 ▤ 01376 561789
e-mail: 6529@greeneking.co.uk
Dir: from A12 through Kelvedon & onto B1024 to Coggeshall

PETS: Bedrooms (unattended) £5 Public areas (except restaurant/bar) Exercise area (50 metres) Pet Food

This cosy inn, located in the centre of the town, has been completely refurbished. Bedrooms vary in size and all offer good quality and comfort with extras such as CD players, fruit and mineral water. Public areas are heavily beamed with a popular bar serving a varied menu, a large restaurant with an Italian menu and cosy residents' lounge.
ROOMS: 18 en suite (1 fmly) s £55-£75; d £75-£135 (incl. bkfst) **LB**
FACILITIES: STV entertainment ch fac Xmas **PARKING:** 47
CARDS:

DEDHAM
Map 05 TM03

◆◆◆◆ ⬤ 🍴 The Sun Inn
High St CO7 6DF
☎ 01206 323351 ▤ 01206 323964
e-mail: enquiries@thesuninndedham.com
Dir: from Colchester, follow A12 to Ipswich. Turn off A12 onto B1029 signposted Stratford St Mary. Turn right after 1m signposted Dedham. Follow road for 1m to T-junct and turn left into village. Pub opposite church on left

PETS: Public areas Exercise area

This refurbished 15th-century coaching inn sits in the centre of Dedham opposite the church. Bedrooms have been upgraded to offer quality accommodation, featuring comfortable beds including four-posters and half testers, along with effective power showers. The public rooms retain much of their original character with inglenook fires, massive oak beams and fine oak panelling in open-plan bar areas; real ales and interesting rustic Mediterranean cuisine prove a great success.
FACILITIES: 4 en suite No smoking in bedrooms No smoking in dining room TVB Cen ht Dinner Last d 10pm **LB PARKING:** 15
NOTES: Closed 25-28 Dec rs Sun evenings Oct-Mar
CARDS:

GREAT CHESTERFORD
Map 05 TL54

★★★ 67% ⊛ The Crown House
CB10 1NY
☎ 01799 530515 ▤ 01799 530683
e-mail: sales@thecrownhouse.com
Dir: From north leave M11 at junct 9, from south junct 10, follow signs for Saffron Walden & then Great Chesterford (B1383)

PETS: Bedrooms (unattended) £5 Exercise area (400 metres)

This former Georgian coaching inn, situated in a peaceful village location close to the M11, has been sympathetically restored, retaining much of its original character. The recently refurbished bedrooms are well equipped and individually decorated; some rooms have delightful four-poster beds. Public rooms include an
continued

England

attractive lounge bar, an elegant oak-panelled restaurant and an airy conservatory.
ROOMS: 8 en suite 10 annexe en suite (1 fmly) (5 GF) s £55-£69.50; d £79.50-£120 (incl. bkfst) **LB PARKING:** 30 **NOTES:** No smoking in restaurant **CARDS:** 🖃 💳 💳 💳 💳

GREAT DUNMOW
Map 05 TL62

 🏛 **Starr Restaurant with Rooms**
Market Place CM6 1AX
☎ 01371 874321 📠 01371 876337
e-mail: starrrestaurant@btinternet.com
Dir: M11 junct 8, onto A120. After 7m, left into Great Dunmow, then left into Market Place in town centre

PETS: Bedrooms Exercise area

A 15th-century, former coaching inn situated in the heart of this charming Essex village. It is well known locally for its quality food, which is served in the elegantly appointed beamed restaurant and conservatory. The spacious bedrooms are in a converted stable block adjacent to the main building, each one individually decorated and tastefully furnished.
ROOMS: 8 annexe en suite s £75-£95; d £115-£134 (incl. bkfst)
PARKING: 16 **NOTES:** No smoking in restaurant
CARDS: 🖃 💳 💳 💳 💳 💳

SOUTHEND-ON-SEA
Map 05 TQ88

  ★★ 70% **Balmoral**
34 Valkyrie Rd, Westcliff-on-Sea SS0 8BU
☎ 01702 342947 📠 01702 337828
e-mail: enq@balmoralsouthend.com
Dir: off A13

PETS: Bedrooms (unattended) Exercise area
RESIDENT PETS: Marmalade (tomcat)

A delightful hotel ideally situated just a short walk from the main shopping centre, railway station and seafront. The attractively decorated bedrooms are tastefully furnished and equipped with many thoughtful touches. Public rooms feature a smart open plan bar/restaurant and further seating is provided in the reception area.
ROOMS: 29 en suite (4 fmly) (2 GF) **FACILITIES:** STV Arrangement with nearby health club **PARKING:** 23 **NOTES:** No smoking in restaurant
Closed Xmas **CARDS:** 🖃 💳 💳 💳 💳 💳

 ♦♦♦ **Terrace Hotel**
8 Royal Ter SS1 1DY
☎ 01702 348143 📠 01702 348143
e-mail: info@theterracehotel.co.uk
Dir: Royal Terrace can only be approached from Southend seafront, via Pier Hill, opposite the pier

PETS: Bedrooms Exercise area (10 yards)

On a raised terrace above the main seafront promenade, this guest house has a comfortable, informal atmosphere. There is a cosy bar, elegant sitting room and breakfast room, and the spacious and well-planned bedrooms consist of three en suite rear-facing rooms and six front-facing rooms which share two bathrooms.
FACILITIES: 9 rms (3 en suite) (2 fmly) No smoking in 3 bedrooms
No smoking in dining room No smoking in lounges TVB tea/coffee
Cen ht TVL No coaches **PRICES:** s £28.20-£39.95; d £42.30-£54.05✳
LB NOTES: Closed 21 Dec-4 Jan **CARDS:** 🖃 💳 💳 💳

WEST THURROCK
Map 05 TQ57

 🐱
⌂ **Hotel Ibis London Thurrock**
Weston Av RM20 3JQ
☎ 01708 686000 📠 01708 680525
e-mail: H2176@accor-hotels.com
Dir: M25 junct 31 to West Thurrock Services, right at 1st and 2nd rdbts then left at 3rd rdbt. Hotel on right after 500yds

 ibis

PETS: Bedrooms Public areas (except bar/restaurant)

Modern, budget hotel offering comfortable accommodation in bright and practical bedrooms. Breakfast is self-service and dinner is available in the restaurant. For further details, consult the Hotel Groups page.
ROOMS: 102 en suite s £37.95-£48.95; d £37.95-£48.95

GLOUCESTERSHIRE

ALVESTON
Map 03 ST68

 ★★★ 75% **Alveston House**
Davids Ln BS35 2LA
☎ 01454 415050 📠 01454 415425
e-mail: info@alvestonhousehotel.co.uk
Dir: M5 junct 14 from N or junct 16 from S, on A38

PETS: Bedrooms (unattended) Exercise area

In a quiet area with easy access to the city and a short drive from both the M4 and M5, this smartly presented hotel provides an impressive combination of good service, friendly hospitality and a relaxed atmosphere. Bedrooms are well-equipped and comfortable for business or leisure use. The restaurant offers carefully prepared fresh food, and a pleasant bar and conservatory are the newest additions.
ROOMS: 30 en suite (1 fmly) (6 GF) No smoking in 24 bedrooms
s £75-£99.50; d £104.50-£109.50 (incl. bkfst) **LB FACILITIES:** STV
PARKING: 75 **NOTES:** No smoking in restaurant
CARDS: 🖃 💳 💳 💳 💳 💳

AMBERLEY
Map 03 SO80

 ★★ 71% 🌀 **The Amberley Inn**
Culver Hill GL5 5AF
☎ 01453 872565 📠 01453 872738
e-mail: theamberley@zoom.co.uk
Dir: on A46

PETS: Bedrooms (unattended) Public areas Exercise area
Pet Food **RESIDENT PETS:** Black Labrador/Collie cross - Megan

Situated on a hillside, on the edge of the common, this traditional Cotswold inn provides an equally warm welcome to both visitors and locals alike. Most bedrooms have been upgraded and offer high standards of comfort and quality, with front facing rooms boasting wonderful panoramic views over the Woodchester Valley. Public areas include a choice of bars and the attractive restaurant where excellent local produce is used in the creation of impressive and innovative dishes.
ROOMS: 14 rms (9 en suite) (1 fmly) s £49-£52.50; d £67-£84
(incl. bkfst) **LB FACILITIES:** Xmas **PARKING:** 14 **NOTES:** No smoking in restaurant **CARDS:** 🖃 💳 💳 💳 💳

England

BIBURY
Map 04 SP10

★★★ 74% ◉◉ ♣ **Bibury Court**
GL7 5NT
☎ 01285 740337 🖷 01285 740660
e-mail: info@biburycourt.com
Dir: on B4425 beside the River Coln, behind St Marys Church

PETS: Bedrooms £5 per dog Public areas (except dining areas - bar & lounge only) Exercise area (adjacent, 300 yards to footpaths/countryside)

Dating back to Tudor times, this elegant manor is the perfect antidote to the hustle and bustle of the modern world. Spacious public areas have abundant charm and character, while bedrooms offer solid quality and contemporary comforts. Seasonal produce is used to good effect in carefully prepared dishes served by a friendly team of helpful staff.
ROOMS: 18 en suite (3 fmly) (1 GF) s £115; d £135 (incl. cont bkfst)
LB FACILITIES: Fishing Croquet lawn **PARKING:** 100
NOTES: No smoking in restaurant
CARDS: ▨▨▨▨▨▨

BLAKENEY
Map 03 SO60

♦♦♦♦ **Old Nibley Farmhouse**
Nibley Hill GL15 4DB
☎ 01594 516770
e-mail: enquiries@oldnibleyfarmhouse.co.uk
Dir: on A48 to the S of Blakeney, opposite T junct, signposted to Parkend

PETS: Bedrooms (unattended) £7 a night for more than one pet Public areas (On lead in living rooms) Exercise area (Forest - 1 mile, path to fields - next door) Bowls and towels can be provided RESIDENT PETS: 3 cats - Jasper, Albert, Charlie

Dating back some 200 years, this former farmhouse has been imaginatively refurbished to provide accommodation of quality and character. Bedrooms and bathrooms are individually styled with original features cleverly incorporated with modern comforts to great effect. Guests are welcome to use the spacious, beamed lounge which features an impressive open fireplace. Breakfast and dinner (by prior arrangement) are served in the dining room with local produce used whenever possible.
FACILITIES: 4 rms (2 en suite) (1 GF) No smoking tea/coffee Cen ht TVL No children No coaches 0.75 acres of grounds Dinner Last d 8pm
PRICES: s £25-£37; d £55-£75✱ **PARKING:** 4

> ### All abbreviations are explained on page 9

> ### Places with this symbol are country house hotels

> ### 🐓 Places with this symbol are farms

CHELTENHAM
Map 03 SO92

★★★★ 69% **The Queen's**
The Promenade GL50 1NN
☎ 0870 400 8107 🖷 01242 224145
e-mail: general.queens@macdonald-hotels.co.uk
Dir: follow town centre signs. Left at Montpellier Walk rdbt. Entrance 500mtrs right

MACDONALD
HOTELS

PETS: Bedrooms £10 Public areas Exercise area Pet Food

With its spectacular position at the top of the main promenade, this landmark hotel is an ideal base from which to explore the charms of this Regency Spa town and the surrounding Cotswolds. An extensive bedroom refurbishment is being carried out, with early results being most impressive. Smart public rooms include the popular Gold Cup bar and a choice of dining options.
ROOMS: 79 en suite No smoking in 26 bedrooms s £65-£140; d £150-£210 (incl. bkfst) **LB FACILITIES:** STV Xmas **SERVICES:** Lift
PARKING: 80 **NOTES:** No smoking in restaurant
CARDS: ▨▨▨▨▨▨

★★★ ◉◉◉ **The Greenway**
Shurdington GL51 4UG
☎ 01242 862352 🖷 01242 862780
e-mail: greenway@btconnect.com
Dir: 2.5m SW on A46

PETS: Bedrooms (unattended) £5 Exercise area (on site)

This hotel, with a wealth of history, is peacefully located in a delightful setting close to the A46 and the M5. Within easy reach of the many attractions of the Cotswolds as well as the interesting town of Cheltenham, The Greenway certainly offers something special. The attractive dining room overlooks the sunken garden and is the venue for exciting food, proudly served by dedicated and attentive staff.
ROOMS: 11 en suite 10 annexe en suite (1 fmly) (4 GF) No smoking in 10 bedrooms s £109-£159; d £150-£280 (incl. bkfst) **LB**
FACILITIES: STV Croquet lawn Clay pigeon shooting, Horse riding, Mountain biking, Beauty treatment Xmas **PARKING:** 50
NOTES: No smoking in restaurant
CARDS: ▨▨▨▨▨▨

★★★ 70% **Charlton Kings**
London Rd, Charlton Kings GL52 6UU
☎ 01242 231061 🖷 01242 241900
e-mail: enquires@charltonkingshotel.co.uk
Dir: entering Cheltenham from Oxford on A40, 1st on left

THE INDEPENDENTS

PETS: Bedrooms £3 Public areas (except restaurant)

Conveniently located on the outskirts of Cheltenham, the Charlton Kings is an attractive and friendly hotel providing comfortable, modern accommodation. The neatly presented bedrooms are well-equipped with tasteful furnishings and contemporary comforts. The popular and stylish restaurant serves a variety of dishes for all tastes from a menu based on quality ingredients.
ROOMS: 13 en suite (1 fmly) (4 GF) No smoking in 12 bedrooms s £65-£85; d £95-£120 (incl. bkfst) **LB FACILITIES:** STV **PARKING:** 26
NOTES: No smoking in restaurant **CARDS:** ▨▨▨▨▨▨

★★★ 68% Carlton

Parabola Rd GL50 3AQ
☎ 01242 514453 🗎 01242 226487
e-mail: enquiries@thecarltonhotel.co.uk
Dir: Follow signs to town centre, at Town Hall straight on through 2 sets of lights, turn left, then 1st right.

PETS: Bedrooms (unattended) Exercise area

This well-presented Regency property is conveniently situated within a short walk of the town centre. Family-owned and run, it provides comfortable accommodation with a relaxed and friendly atmosphere. Bedrooms are located both in the main hotel and also within an annexe building, where rooms are larger and more luxurious. Other features include a choice of bars, lounge and conference facilities.
ROOMS: 62 en suite 13 annexe en suite (2 fmly) (4 GF) No smoking in 15 bedrooms s £45-£72.50; d £90-£97 (incl. bkfst) **LB FACILITIES:** STV Xmas **SERVICES:** Lift **PARKING:** 85 **NOTES:** No smoking in restaurant **CARDS:** 🌕 🌕 🌕 🌕 🌕 🌕

★★★ 59% White House

Gloucester Rd GL51 0ST
☎ 01452 713226 🗎 01452 857590
e-mail: stay@white-house-hotel.co.uk
Dir: M5 junct 11 onto A40 to Cheltenham. Left at rdbt, hotel 0.5m on left

PETS: Bedrooms £10 Public areas (except restaurant/bar)

The White House Hotel is situated on the edge of town, and provides comfortable and modern accommodation. The lounge bar and the restaurant are attractively presented and a number of function rooms are also available. Friendly service and helpful staff ensure a pleasant stay.
ROOMS: 49 en suite (4 fmly) No smoking in 13 bedrooms s £40-£70; d £70-£95 (incl. bkfst) **LB FACILITIES:** STV pool table bar games entertainment **PARKING:** 150 **NOTES:** No smoking in restaurant RS 12-16 Mar & 10-12 Nov **CARDS:** 🌕 🌕 🌕 🌕 🌕 🌕

★★ 68% Cotswold Grange

Pittville Circus Rd GL52 2QH
☎ 01242 515119 🗎 01242 241537
e-mail: paul@cotswoldgrange.co.uk
Dir: from town centre, follow Prestbury signs. Right at 1st rdbt, hotel 200yds on left

PETS: Bedrooms Public areas Exercise area

Built from Cotswold limestone, this attractive Georgian property retains many impressive architectural features. Situated conveniently close to the centre of Cheltenham, this long-established, family-run hotel offers well-equipped and comfortable accommodation. The convivial bar is a popular venue, and additional facilities include a spacious restaurant, cosy lounge and ample parking.
ROOMS: 25 en suite (4 fmly) s £55-£65; d £75-£85 (incl. bkfst) **FACILITIES:** ch fac **PARKING:** 20 **NOTES:** No smoking in restaurant Closed 24 Dec-5 Jan RS Sat & Sun evening (food by arrangement) **CARDS:** 🌕 🌕 🌕 🌕 🌕 🌕

♦♦♦♦ Butlers Hotel

Western Rd GL50 3RN
☎ 01242 570771 🗎 01242 528724
e-mail: info@butlers-hotel.co.uk
Dir: M5 junct 11 through 2 rdbts and 2 sets of traffic lights into Landsdown Rd, left at next lights into Christchurch Rd. Continue through next lights to end of Christchurch Rd, left at mini rdbt into Malvern Rd, Western Rd is 2nd on the right

PETS: Bedrooms (unattended) Exercise area (100 metres)
RESIDENT PETS: Max (Miniature Schnauzer)

This elegant late Regency house enjoys a quiet yet convenient location only minutes' walk from the Promenade, Montpellier and the town centre. Decor and furnishings are stylish throughout and spacious, elegant bedrooms (named after butlers from literature and history) are extremely well equipped; all have PCs. Public rooms include an inviting sitting room and a charming breakfast room that overlooks the delightful rear garden.
FACILITIES: 9 en suite (3 fmly) (1 GF) No smoking TVB tea/coffee Direct dial from bedrooms Licensed Cen ht TVL No coaches PCs in rooms, garden **PRICES:** s £45-£65; d £65-£95✳ **PARKING:** 7 **CARDS:** 🌕 🌕 🌕 🌕 🌕 🌕

♦♦♦ Hope Orchard

Gloucester Rd, Staverton GL51 0TF
☎ 01452 855556 🗎 01452 530037
e-mail: info@hopeorchard.com
Dir: turn off A40 onto B4063 at Arlecourt rdbt. After 1.25m, Hope Orchard on right

PETS: Bedrooms (unattended) Exercise area (on site) towels and shampoo for dogs on request **RESIDENT PETS:** Bertie (Staffordshire terrier), Jessie, Jasper & Louis (cats)

Situated midway between Gloucester and Cheltenham, this is an ideal base for those exploring the many attractions in the area. The comfortable bedrooms are located adjacent to the main house, all of which are on the ground floor and have their own separate entrances. There is a large garden and ample off-road parking is available.
FACILITIES: 8 en suite (2 fmly) (8 GF) No smoking TVB tea/coffee Direct dial from bedrooms Cen ht No coaches **PRICES:** s £30-£38; d £60✳ **PARKING:** 12 **CARDS:** 🌕 🌕 🌕 🌕

♦♦♦ White Lodge

Hatherley Ln GL51 6SH
☎ 01242 242347
Dir: M5 junct 11, A40 Cheltenham. 1st rdbt 4th exit Hatherley Lane, White Lodge 1st house on right

PETS: Bedrooms Public areas Exercise area (150 metres)

Built around 1900, this friendly and welcoming establishment is conveniently located for GCHQ and just a short drive from the M5. Bedrooms offer good levels of comfort and quality; a number of extra facilities are provided, including fridges. The well-appointed dining room looks out across the extensive gardens - a pleasant backdrop to the enjoyment of a tasty breakfast.
FACILITIES: 3 en suite (1 GF) No smoking TVB tea/coffee Cen ht No coaches **PRICES:** s fr £30; d fr £45✳ **PARKING:** 6

CHIPPING CAMPDEN   Map 04 SP13

★★★ 🏵🏵 Cotswold House
The Square GL55 6AN
☎ 01386 840330 ▤ 01386 840310
e-mail: reception@cotswoldhouse.com
Dir: A44 take B4081 to Chipping Campden. Right at T-junct into High St.
House in The Square

> **PETS:**   Bedrooms (unattended)   Exercise area (Chipping
> Campden Common)

Relaxation is inevitable at this mellow Cotswold stone house, set in
the centre of the town. Bedrooms, including spacious suites in the
courtyard, are impressively individual and offer a beguiling blend
of style, quality and comfort. The newly refurbished Garden
restaurant is a stunning venue to sample accomplished and
imaginative cuisine, with local produce utilised wherever possible.
Alternatively, Hicks Brasserie and Bar provides a more informal
dining experience.
ROOMS: 20 en suite   No smoking in 18 bedrooms   s fr £115;   d fr £175
(incl. bkfst)   **LB**   **FACILITIES:** STV Gym   Croquet lawn   Access to local
Sports Centre   ch fac   Xmas   **PARKING:** 20   **NOTES:** No smoking in
restaurant   **CARDS:** 🖃 🖃 🖃 🖃 🖃 Ⓢ

◆◆◆◆ 🏵 🍽 🍴 The Kings Arms Hotel
The Square GL55 6AW
☎ 01386 840256 ▤ 01386 841598
e-mail: info@thekingsarmshotel.com
Dir: turn off A44 onto B4081. Follow road for 2m and turn right at The Red
Lion Inn. The Kings Arms is 50yds on left in centre of town square

> **PETS:**   Bedrooms £5   Public areas (except restaurant)
> Exercise area (0.5 miles)

Located in the centre of historic Chipping Campden, this Grade II
listed inn is equally popular with visitors and locals alike. There's a
convivial 'buzz' with the friendly and good humoured staff
contributing to the relaxed atmosphere. Bedrooms offer ample
comfort with period features and 'mod cons' combining to stylish
effect. Food is a highlight here, the menus offering a range of
flavour-packed dishes, complemented by a particularly good range
of wines by the glass.
FACILITIES: 13 en suite   No smoking in bedrooms   No smoking in dining
room   STV   TVB   tea/coffee   Cen ht   Cycle hire arranged   Discounted green
fees   Dinner   Last d 9.30pm   **PRICES:** s £65-£120;   d £65-£140✳   **LB**
PARKING: 5   **CARDS:** 🖃 🖃 🖃 🖃 🖃 Ⓢ

◆◆◆◆ 🐾 Manor Farm
Weston-sub-Edge GL55 6QH
☎ 01386 840390 & 07889 108812 ▤ 0870 1640638
e-mail: lucy@manorfarmbnb.demon.co.uk
Dir: on B4632 Stratford to Cheltenham rd, farm on left in Weston-sub-
Edge

> **PETS:**   Bedrooms Sep Accom (Stables, hutch) £5
> Exercise area (on site)

A genuine welcome is extended to all guests at this 17th-century
mellow Cotswold stone farmhouse. This welcome is also extended
to pets, including horses, and stabling is available by prior
arrangement. Bedrooms are comfortable and homely with
thoughtful extras. Facilities include a lounge, complete with wood-

continued

---

burning stove and the elegant dining room, where mouth-
watering breakfasts are served.
FACILITIES: 3 en suite   No smoking   TVB   tea/coffee   Cen ht   TVL   Golf 18
800 acres arable cattle horses sheep   **PRICES:** s £35-£40;   d £50-£60✳
PARKING: 8   **CARDS:** 🖃 🖃 🖃 🖃 Ⓢ

CHIPPING SODBURY   Map 03 ST78

◆◆◆◆ The Moda Hotel
1 High St BS37 6BA
☎ 01454 312135 ▤ 01454 850090
e-mail: enquiries@modahotel.com
Dir: 3m from M4 junct 18

> **PETS:**   Bedrooms (unattended)   Exercise area
> **RESIDENT PETS:** Sky (Black Labrador)

In an imposing position at the top of the High Street, this Grade II*
listed Georgian House has been tastefully refurbished to provide
modern bedrooms and comfortable public areas while retaining
many original features. Among the room facilities are satellite TV
and phones.
FACILITIES: 7 en suite   3 annexe en suite (1 fmly) (3 GF)   No smoking in
9 bedrooms   No smoking in dining room   STV   TVB   tea/coffee   Direct dial
from bedrooms   Licensed   Cen ht   TVL   **PRICES:** s £55.50-£58.50;
d £66.50-£80✳   **LB**   **PARKING:**   **CARDS:** 🖃 🖃 🖃 🖃 🖃 Ⓢ

CIRENCESTER   Map 03 SP00

★★★ 70% Stratton House   Forestdale Hotels
Gloucester Rd GL7 2LE
☎ 01285 651761 ▤ 01285 640024
e-mail: stratton.house@forestdale.com
Dir: M4 junct 15, A419 to Cirencester. Hotel on left on A417 or M5 junct 11
to Cheltenham onto B4070 to A417. Hotel on right

> **PETS:**   Bedrooms (unattended) £7.50   Public areas (except
> restaurant)   Pet Food

This attractive 17th-century manor house is quietly situated about
half a mile from the town centre. Bedrooms are well presented,
and spacious premier rooms are available. The comfortable
drawing rooms and restaurant have views over well-tended
gardens: the perfect place to enjoy pre-dinner drinks on a summer
evening.
ROOMS: 41 en suite (10 GF)   No smoking in 19 bedrooms   s fr £110;
d fr £125 (incl. bkfst)   **LB**   **FACILITIES:** Xmas   **PARKING:** 100
NOTES: No smoking in restaurant
CARDS: 🖃 🖃 🖃 🖃 🖃 Ⓢ

★★★ 66% The Crown of Crucis
Ampney Crucis GL7 5RS
☎ 01285 851806 ▤ 01285 851735
e-mail: info@thecrownofcrucis.co.uk
Dir: A417 to Fairford, hotel 2.5m on left

> **PETS:**   Bedrooms £4   Public areas (bar only)   Exercise area
> (adjacent)   Pet Food

This delightful hotel consists of two buildings; one a 16th-century
coaching inn, which now houses the bar and restaurant, and a
more modern bedroom block which surrounds a courtyard.

continued

Rooms are attractively appointed and offer modern facilities; the restaurant serves a range of imaginative dishes.

ROOMS: 25 en suite (2 fmly) (13 GF) No smoking in 10 bedrooms
s fr £67; d £75-£95 (incl. bkfst) **LB FACILITIES:** Free membership of local leisure centre **PARKING:** 82 **NOTES:** No smoking in restaurant
Closed 25-26 Dec & 1 Jan **CARDS:**

★★★ 65% Fleece Hotel

THE INDEPENDENTS

Market Place GL7 2NZ
☎ 01285 658507 📠 01285 651017
e-mail: relax@fleecehotel.co.uk
Dir: A417/A419 Burford Rd junct, follow signs for town centre. Right at lights into "The Waterloo", hotel car park 250yds on left

PETS: Bedrooms (unattended) £10 Public areas (lounge only) Exercise area (100 metres)

This old town-centre coaching inn, which dates back to the Tudor period, retains many original features such as flagstone floors and oak beams. Well-equipped bedrooms vary in size and shape, all offering good levels of comfort and plenty of character. The bar lounge is a popular venue for morning coffee, and the stylish restaurant offers a range of dishes in an informal and convivial atmosphere.
ROOMS: 28 en suite (3 fmly) (4 GF) No smoking in 3 bedrooms
s £49.50-£110; d £79-£119 (incl. bkfst) **LB FACILITIES:** Xmas
PARKING: 10 **NOTES:** No smoking in restaurant
CARDS:

CLEARWELL   Map 03 SO50

★★★ 65% The Wyndham Arms

GL16 8JT
☎ 01594 833666 📠 01594 836450
e-mail: nigel@thewyndhamhotel.co.uk
Dir: off B4228, in centre of village on B4231

PETS: Bedrooms (unattended) Public areas (except when food is being served) Exercise area (on site) Pet Food
RESIDENT PETS: Ruby (Irish red setter)

The history of this charming village inn can be traced back over 600 years. It has exposed stone walls, original beams and an impressive inglenook fireplace in the friendly bar. Most bedrooms are in a modern extension, whilst rooms in the main house are more traditional in style. A range of dishes is offered in the bar or restaurant.
ROOMS: 6 en suite 12 annexe en suite (3 fmly) (6 GF) No smoking in 4 bedrooms s £35-£65; d £65-£110 (incl. bkfst) **LB FACILITIES:** ch fac
Xmas **PARKING:** 52 **NOTES:** No smoking in restaurant
CARDS:

★★ 74% 🏵 Tudor Farmhouse Hotel & Restaurant

High St GL16 8JS
☎ 01594 833046 📠 01594 837093
e-mail: info@tudorfarmhousehotel.co.uk
Dir: off A4136 onto B4228, through Coleford, turn right into Clearwell, hotel on right just before War Memorial Cross

PETS: Bedrooms (unattended) Pet Food

Dating from the 13th century, this idyllic former farmhouse retains a host of original features including exposed stonework, oak beams, wall panelling and wonderful inglenook fireplaces. Bedrooms have great individuality and style and are located either within the main house, or in converted buildings within the grounds. Creative menus offer quality cuisine, served in the intimate, candlelit restaurant.
ROOMS: 6 en suite 16 annexe en suite (2 fmly) (7 GF) No smoking in 19 bedrooms s £55; d £60-£80 (incl. bkfst) **LB FACILITIES:** STV
PARKING: 30 **NOTES:** No smoking in restaurant Closed 24-27 Dec
CARDS:

COLEFORD   Map 03 SO51

★★★ 67% The Speech House

Best
Western

GL16 7EL
☎ 01594 822607 📠 01594 823658
e-mail: relax@thespeechhouse.co.uk
Dir: on B4226 between Cinderford and Coleford

PETS: Bedrooms (unattended) £10 per stay Public areas (except dining room) Exercise area (100 metres)

Dating back to 1676, this former hunting lodge is tucked away in the Forest of Dean. Bedrooms, some with impressive four-poster beds, combine modern amenities with period charm. The beamed

continued on p120

England

COLEFORD continued

restaurant serves good, imaginative food, whilst additional features include a mini-gym, aqua spa and conference facilities.
ROOMS: 16 en suite 17 annexe rms (16 en suite) (4 fmly) (12 GF) No smoking in 6 bedrooms s £50; d £86-£120 (incl. bkfst) **LB**
FACILITIES: Golf 18 Sauna Solarium Gym Jacuzzi Beauty Salon Xmas
PARKING: 70 **NOTES:** No smoking in restaurant
CARDS:

◆◆◆ Cor Unum
Monmouth Rd, Edge-End GL16 7HB
☎ 01594 837960
e-mail: antony@jones3649.freeserve.co.uk
Dir: on main A4136 Gloucester/Monmouth road in the village of Edge End

PETS: Bedrooms Public areas Exercise area (adjacent)

A genuine welcome is assured at this comfortably appointed bungalow which is located in the heart of the Forest of Dean. Bedrooms are neatly furnished and guests also have the benefit of a lounge which provides wonderful views across the garden, to the Welsh mountains beyond. Breakfast is served in the cosy dining room, providing a tasty and fulfilling start to the day!
FACILITIES: 2 rms (2 GF) No smoking TVB tea/coffee Cen ht
No children Dinner **PRICES:** s £20-£24; d £40-£48✳ **LB PARKING:** 1

COLN ST ALDWYNS   Map 04 SP10

★★ ◎◎ The New Inn At Coln
GL7 5AN
☎ 01285 750651 01285 750657
e-mail: stay@new-inn.co.uk
Dir: 8m E of Cirencester, between Bibury and Fairford

PETS: Bedrooms £10 Public areas Exercise area

Set in the heart of the Coln Valley, this quintessential Cotswold inn has been welcoming weary travellers since the reign of Elizabeth I. The bedrooms are very cosy, while crackling log fires, flagstone floors, wooden beams and genuine hospitality make for a beguiling atmosphere. An excellent bar menu is available. Aperitifs can be savoured in the lounge, whilst perusing the flavour-packed dishes from the restaurant menu.
ROOMS: 8 en suite 6 annexe en suite (1 GF) s £120-£132; d £186-£220 (incl. bkfst & dinner) **LB FACILITIES:** Fishing Xmas **PARKING:** 22
NOTES: No children 10 yrs No smoking in restaurant
CARDS:

CORSE LAWN   Map 03 SO83

★★★ ◎◎ Corse Lawn House
GL19 4LZ
☎ 01452 780479 780771 01452 780840
e-mail: enquiries@corselawn.com
Dir: on B4211 5m SW of Tewkesbury

PETS: Bedrooms (unattended) Public areas Exercise area
Pet Food RESIDENT PETS: 2 Black Labradors, 3 ponies/horses

This gracious Grade II listed Queen Anne house has been home to the Hine family since 1978. Aided by an enthusiastic and committed team, the family still presides over all aspects, creating
continued

a relaxed and wonderfully comforting environment. Bedrooms offer a reassuring mix of comfort and quality. Impressive cuisine is based upon excellent produce, much of it locally sourced.

ROOMS: 19 en suite (2 fmly) (5 GF) s £85; d £130-£165 (incl. bkfst) **LB FACILITIES:** STV Indoor swimming (H) Tennis (hard) Croquet lawn Badminton Croquet Table tennis **PARKING:** 62 **NOTES:** No smoking in restaurant Closed 24-26 Dec **CARDS:**

EWEN   Map 04 SU09

★★ 67% ◎ Wild Duck Inn
Drakes Island GL7 6BY
☎ 01285 770310 01285 770924
e-mail: wduckinn@aol.com
Dir: from Cirencester take A429. At Kemble left to Ewen

PETS: Bedrooms (unattended) £10 per dog Public areas (except restaurant) Exercise area RESIDENT PETS: Monkey (Yorkshire Terrier)

This bustling, ever-popular inn dates back to the early 16th century and is full of character. Bedrooms vary in style and are well equipped and tastefully furnished. Open fires, old beams and rustic pine tables add to the charm in the bar and restaurant, where imaginative, robust cooking has earned a loyal following and well-deserved reputation.
ROOMS: 11 en suite s £60-£80; d £80-£130 (incl. cont bkfst)
FACILITIES: Discounted leisure facilities within 3m **PARKING:** 50
NOTES: RS 25 Dec **CARDS:**

All information was correct at the time of going to press; we recommend you confirm details on booking

GLOUCESTER
Map 03 SO81

★★★ 62% Hatherley Manor
Down Hatherley Ln GL2 9QA
☎ 01452 730217 ▤ 01452 731032
e-mail: hatherleymanor@countrytownhotels.co.uk
Dir: off A38 onto Down Hatherley Lane, signposted. Hotel 600yds on left

PETS: Bedrooms (unattended)

Within easy striking distance of the M5, Gloucester, Cheltenham and the Cotswolds, this stylish 17th-century manor remains popular with both business and leisure guests. Some bedrooms are in the original building, and some are purpose-built; all offer contemporary comforts. A range of meeting and function rooms is available.
ROOMS: 52 en suite No smoking in 20 bedrooms s £45-£85; d £50-£105 (incl. bkfst) **LB FACILITIES:** Xmas **PARKING:** 250 **NOTES:** No smoking in restaurant **CARDS:** ▨▨▨▨▨

GUITING POWER
Map 04 SP02

♦♦♦♦♦ ➾ Guiting Guest House
Post Office Ln GL54 5TZ
☎ 01451 850470 ▤ 01451 850034
e-mail: info@guitingguesthouse.com
Dir: A40, Andoversford lights proceed to Stow-on-the-Wold on A436, 4m left to Lower Swell on B4068, 1m left to Guiting Power. Left into village, house in centre.

PETS: Bedrooms Sep Accom (Kennel) Exercise area (200 yards) Dried dog food RESIDENT PETS: Two Black Labradors

In keeping with all the surrounding houses, this engaging family home is built of mellow Cotswold stone. Charming and comfortable bedrooms offer both individuality and character, as do the public rooms, which include the stylish dining room and snug lounge. Both breakfast and dinner (by prior arrangement) make use of excellent local produce as much as possible.
FACILITIES: 3 rms (2 en suite) 4 annexe en suite (2 GF) No smoking TVB tea/coffee Cen ht No coaches Dinner Last d 48hrs prior
PRICES: d £70-£75✳ **PARKING:** 4 **CARDS:** ▨▨▨▨▨

> ★ Red stars indicate the AA's
> Top 200 Hotels in Britain & Ireland

> Don't forget to let proprietors
> know when you book that
> you're bringing your pet

> All AA listed accommodation,
> restaurants and pubs can be
> found on the AA's website
> www.theAA.com

♦♦♦♦ 🍴 Hollow Bottom
Winchcombe Rd GL54 5UX
☎ 01451 850392 ▤ 01451 850945
Dir: M5 junct 11 follow A40 through Cheltenham. At Andoversford take A436 signed Stow-on-the Wold, after 4m bear left for Guitings B4068, Guiting Power signed on left after approx. 2m

PETS: Bedrooms (unattended) Public areas (Not restaurant) Exercise area (On site) RESIDENT PETS: Lassie (Collie)

Original features have been retained at this inn, located on the edge of this unspoilt Cotswold village and popular with followers of National Hunt racing. Rustic furniture and racing memorabilia all add to the atmosphere. A range of real ales and good food is complemented by warm hospitality.
FACILITIES: 4 en suite (1 fmly) (1 GF) No smoking in bedrooms TVB tea/coffee Cen ht golf & riding stables within 1m Dinner Last d 9.30pm
PRICES: s £45; d £65✳ **PARKING:** 12 **CARDS:** ▨▨▨▨▨

LAVERTON
Map 04 SP03

♦♦♦♦ Leasow House
Laverton Meadows WR12 7NA
☎ 01386 584526 ▤ 01386 584596
e-mail: leasow@clara.net
Dir: from Broadway B4632 to Winchcombe for 2m, turn R to Wormington then 1st on R

PETS: Bedrooms (unattended) donation to pet charity Public areas (not in dining room) Exercise area (on site) RESIDENT PETS: Dolly (Rottweiler), Squeak and Domino (cats)

Located to the south of the village, this 16th-century former farmhouse has been lovingly restored to provide high standards of comfort. Bedrooms are filled with a wealth of homely extras and an attractive dining room is the setting for comprehensive breakfasts. An elegant library lounge is also available and a warm welcome is assured.
FACILITIES: 7 en suite 2 annexe en suite (2 fmly) (1 GF) No smoking TVB tea/coffee Direct dial from bedrooms Cen ht No children 8yrs No coaches **PRICES:** s £37-£57; d £57-£67✳ **PARKING:** 10
NOTES: Closed Xmas & New Year **CARDS:** ▨▨▨▨▨

LOWER SLAUGHTER
Map 04 SP12

★★★ 75% ◎◎ Washbourne Court
GL54 2HS
☎ 01451 822143 ▤ 01451 821045
e-mail: info@washbournecourt.co.uk
Dir: off A429 at signpost 'The Slaughters', between Stow-on-the-Wold and Bourton-on-the-Water. Hotel in centre of village

PETS: Bedrooms (unattended) £10 Public areas Exercise area (on site)

Beamed ceilings, log fires and flagstone floors are some of the attractive features of this part 17th-century hotel, set in four acres of immaculate grounds beside the River Eye. Smartly decorated bedrooms are in the main house and self-contained cottages, many offering lovely views. The riverside terrace is popular during summer months, whilst the elegant dining room serves an interesting menu and a comprehensive wine list.
ROOMS: 15 en suite 13 annexe en suite s £80-£100; d £120-£130 (incl. bkfst) **LB FACILITIES:** Xmas **PARKING:** 40 **NOTES:** No smoking in restaurant **CARDS:** ▨▨▨▨▨

England

MICKLETON
Map 04 SP14

★★★ 72% ❀ Three Ways
Mickleton GL55 6SB
☎ 01386 438429 ▤ 01386 438118
e-mail: threeways@puddingclub.com
Dir: in centre of Mickleton on B4632 Stratford-upon-Avon to Broadway Rd

PETS: Bedrooms (unattended) Public areas (except restaurant) Exercise area (100 metres)

Built in 1870, this charming hotel has welcomed guests for over 100 years and is home to the world famous Pudding Club, formed in 1985 to promote traditional English puddings. Individuality is a hallmark here, as reflected in a number of bedrooms which have been styled according to a pudding theme. Public areas are stylish and include the air-conditioned restaurant, lounges and meeting rooms.
ROOMS: 48 en suite (7 fmly) (14 GF) s £72-£85; d £99-£140 (incl. bkfst) LB **FACILITIES:** entertainment ch fac Xmas **SERVICES:** Lift **PARKING:** 37 **NOTES:** No smoking in restaurant
CARDS: 🖃 🖃 🖃 🖃 🖃 🖃 🖃 🖃

NAILSWORTH
Map 03 ST89

◆◆◆◆ Aaron Farm
Nympsfield Rd GL6 0ET
☎ 01453 833598 ▤ 01453 833626
e-mail: aaronfarm@aol.com
Dir: off A46 at Nailsworth mini rdbt into Spring Hill, this continues into Nympsfield Rd. Farm is 1m on left at top of hill

PETS: Bedrooms Exercise area

Located in an elevated semi-rural position on the outskirts of town, this mellow stone former farmhouse has been sympathetically extended to provide spacious bedrooms filled with thoughtful extras. Breakfasts, using local produce, are taken in the cosy dining room and a comfortable lounge is also available exclusively for guests.
FACILITIES: 3 en suite No smoking TVB tea/coffee Cen ht No coaches **PRICES:** s £32-£35; d £45-£50✷ **PARKING:** 6

NAUNTON
Map 04 SP12

◆◆◆◆ Mill View
2 Mill View GL54 3AF
☎ 01451 850 586 ▤ 01451 850970
e-mail: ralph.boult@care4free.net
Dir: Naunton is 0.75m off B4068, between Stow and Andoversford. Mill View Guesthouse is in the east of the village.

PETS: Bedrooms Public areas Exercise area (adjacent)
RESIDENT PETS: Smoke (long haired cat)

Opposite an old watermill in historic Naunton village, this former family home has been extended and modernised to provide every comfort. Ideal for walkers or touring rural Gloucestershire, a warm welcome and attentive care is assured in this non-smoking house which has one bedroom equipped for less able guests.
FACILITIES: 3 en suite (1 GF) No smoking TVB tea/coffee Cen ht TVL No coaches Dinner Last d 4pm **PRICES:** s £40-£45; d £50-£60✷ LB

NEWNHAM
Map 03 SO61

◆◆◆◆ Swan House Country Guest House
Swan House, High St GL14 1BY
☎ 01594 516504 ▤ 01594 516177
e-mail: enquiries@swanhousenewnham.co.uk
Dir: on service road set back from A48 between clock tower & Ship PH.

PETS: Bedrooms (Stables in village) (unattended) £5 per stay Public areas (except dining room) Exercise area (200yds)

This Grade II listed house, parts of which date back to 1640, is centrally placed in the picturesque village. No two bedrooms are alike, but all share similarly high standards of comfort and quality. Breakfast, and dinner by prior arrangement, are served in the cosy dining room with local produce used wherever possible. A guest lounge is also available, complete with honesty bar.
FACILITIES: 6 en suite (1 GF) No smoking in dining room No smoking in lounges TVB tea/coffee Licensed Cen ht No coaches Secure storage for bicycles, surf boards & canoes Dinner Last d 6pm **PRICES:** s £28-£38; d £56-£76✷ **PARKING:** 5 **NOTES:** Closed Xmas & New Year
CARDS: 🖃 🖃 🖃 🖃 🖃

NORTHLEACH
Map 04 SP11

◆◆◆◆ ❀ 🛏 🍽 The Puesdown Inn
Compton Abdale GL54 4DN
☎ 01451 860262 ▤ 01451 861262
e-mail: inn4food@btopenworld.com
Dir: Situated on A40(Cheltenham to Oxford). 7m from Cheltenham, 3m from Northleach

PETS: Bedrooms (by arrangement) (unattended) Public areas (Dogs on leads) Exercise area (adjacent) Bowls provided RESIDENT PETS: Neffi & Portia - Chocolate Labradors, Habibe - tabby cat

A friendly welcome awaits you at this long established inn, a popular 'stop-off' for those travelling between Cheltenham and Oxford. The stylish, modern restaurant provides an enjoyable and unpretentious environment for sampling the accomplished cuisine. Individually designed bedrooms, which are accessed externally, have great appeal and offer high standards of contemporary comfort and quality.
FACILITIES: 3 en suite (1 fmly) (3 GF) No smoking in bedrooms No smoking in dining room No smoking in 1 lounge TVB tea/coffee Cen ht large garden Dinner Last d 10.30pm **PRICES:** d £70-£85✷ LB **PARKING:** 80 **CARDS:** 🖃 🖃 🖃 🖃 🖃

England

◆◆◆◆ The Wheatsheaf Inn
West End GL54 3EZ
☎ 01451 860244 ▤ 01451 861037
e-mail: caspar@wheatsheafatnorthleach.com
Dir: Take the A40 towards Cheltenham, once past Burford, Northleach is 9m along A40 on left

PETS: Public areas (except restaurant) Bowls provided

Dating back to the 16th century, this former coaching inn is situated in the heart of the Cotswolds. Popular with both locals and visitors alike, The Wheatsheaf has a great atmosphere. Wooden and stone floors give a reassuring feeling of solidity with log fires providing that extra little something. Bedrooms offer good standards of comfort, and some have king-size beds. An interesting and innovative menu is offered, using quality local produce and fresh fish.
FACILITIES: 8 en suite (1 fmly) No smoking in bedrooms No smoking in dining room TVB tea/coffee Direct dial from bedrooms Cen ht Dinner Last d 10pm **PRICES:** s £50-£60; d £60-£80✱ **PARKING:** 20
CARDS: ▤▤▤▤▤

STONEHOUSE   Map 03 SO80

★★★ 68% Stonehouse Court
GL10 3RA
☎ 0871 871 3240 ▤ 0871 871 3241
e-mail: info@stonehousecourt.co.uk
Dir: M5 junct 13, off A419. Follow signs for Stonehouse, hotel on right 0.25m after 2nd rdbt

PETS: Bedrooms Exercise area (200 metres)

This establishment has recently changed ownership. Set in six acres of secluded gardens, this fine Grade II listed manor house dates back to 1601; since then it has been extended considerably. The individually decorated bedrooms offer all modern comforts, two of which have four-poster beds. Elegant public rooms include a lounge, bar, restaurant and gymnasium. Extensive conference facilities are also available.
ROOMS: 9 en suite 27 annexe en suite (2 fmly) (2 GF) No smoking in 6 bedrooms s £85-£90; d £95-£135 (incl. bkfst) LB **FACILITIES:** STV Gym Croquet lawn Xmas **PARKING:** 200 **NOTES:** No smoking in restaurant **CARDS:** ▤▤▤▤▤

STOW-ON-THE-WOLD   Map 04 SP12

★★★★ 73% ◉◉◉ Wyck Hill House
Burford Rd GL54 1HY
☎ 01451 831936 ▤ 01451 832243
e-mail: enquiries@wyckhillhouse.com
Dir: turn off A429, Wyck Hill House is situated 1m on the right hand side

PETS: Bedrooms (unattended) £10 Public areas (Not dining room or bar) Exercise area (On site) Pet Food Canned or fresh food available

This charming 18th-century house enjoys superb views across the Windrush Valley and is ideally positioned for a relaxing weekend exploring the Cotswolds. The spacious and thoughtfully equipped bedrooms provide high standards of comfort and quality and are located both in the main house and the original coach house. Elegant public rooms include the cosy bar, library and the
continued

magnificent front hall with crackling log fire. The imaginative cuisine makes effective use of local produce.
ROOMS: 16 en suite 16 annexe en suite (1 fmly) (10 GF) s £79-£118; d £79-£170 (incl. bkfst) LB **FACILITIES:** STV Croquet lawn Archery Clay pigeon shooting Ballooning Honda pilots ch fac Xmas **SERVICES:** Lift **PARKING:** 100 **NOTES:** No smoking in restaurant
CARDS: ▤▤▤▤▤

★★★ 70% The Unicorn
Sheep St GL54 1HQ
☎ 01451 830257 ▤ 01451 831090
e-mail: reception@birchhotels.co.uk
Dir: situated at junct of A429 & A436

PETS: Bedrooms (unattended) £10 supplement Public areas (bar only) Exercise area (1 mile)

This attractive limestone hotel dates back to the 17th century. Individually designed bedrooms are stylish and include some delightful four poster rooms. Spacious public areas retain much character and include a choice of inviting lounges and a traditional bar offering a good selection of bar meals and ales, as well as an attractive restaurant.
ROOMS: 20 en suite No smoking in 8 bedrooms s £60-£65; d £78-£105 (incl. bkfst) LB **FACILITIES:** Xmas **PARKING:** 40 **NOTES:** No smoking in restaurant **CARDS:** ▤▤▤▤▤

★★ 68% Old Stocks
The Square GL54 1AF   THE INDEPENDENTS
☎ 01451 830666 ▤ 01451 870014
e-mail: aa@theoldstockshotel.co.uk
Dir: turn off A429 to town centre. Hotel is facing Village Green

PETS: Bedrooms (unattended) £5 per stay Public areas (except restaurant) Exercise area (500 metres)

Overlooking the old market square, this Grade II listed, mellow Cotswold stone building is a comfortable and friendly base from which to explore this picturesque area. There is a lot of character and atmosphere with bedrooms all offering individuality and charm. Facilities include guest lounge, restaurant and bar, whilst outside, the patio is a popular summer venue for refreshing drinks and good food.
ROOMS: 15 en suite 3 annexe en suite (5 fmly) (4 GF) No smoking in 10 bedrooms s £45-£60; d £90-£120 (incl. bkfst) LB **FACILITIES:** ch fac Xmas **PARKING:** 12 **NOTES:** No smoking in restaurant **CARDS:** ▤▤▤

◆◆◆ Limes
Evesham Rd GL54 1EJ
☎ 01451 830034 ▤ 01451 830034
e-mail: thelimes@zoom.co.uk
Dir: turn off A429 towards Evesham on A424. The Limes 800yds on left

PETS: Bedrooms (unattended) Public areas (not in breakfast room) Exercise area (5 minute walk)
RESIDENT PETS: Oscar (Doberman/Setter cross)

Just a few minutes' walk from the village centre, this Victorian house provides a comfortable base from which to explore this beautiful area. Bedroom styles vary, with both four-poster and ground-floor rooms offered. A warm and genuine welcome is extended to all guests, many of whom return on a regular basis. A
continued on p124

STOW-ON-THE-WOLD continued

spacious lounge is available and breakfast is served in the light and airy dining room.
FACILITIES: 4 en suite 1 annexe en suite (1 fmly) (1 GF) No smoking in bedrooms No smoking in dining room STV TVB tea/coffee Cen ht TVL No coaches **PRICES:** s £30-£46; d £46-£50✱ **PARKING:** 4 **NOTES:** Closed 24 Dec-2 Jan

STROUD　　　　　　　　　　　　Map 03 SO80

★★ 66% The Bell
Wallbridge GL5 3JS
☎ 01453 763556 📠 01453 758611
e-mail: sarahclose@thebellhotel.demon.co.uk
Dir: at junct of A419/A46, outside Stroud Town Centre

PETS: Bedrooms (unattended) £10 Public areas (except restaurant) Exercise area (50yds)

This former coaching inn dates back to Victorian times and is conveniently situated close to the town centre. Small and friendly, there is an informal and relaxed atmosphere here and many guests return on a regular basis. Bedrooms are well-equipped and comfortably furnished with a four-poster room available. Facilities include a meeting room, popular lounge bar, restaurant and ample parking.
ROOMS: 12 en suite (2 fmly) s £30-£45; d £62.50-£115 (incl. bkfst) **LB** **FACILITIES:** Xmas **PARKING:** 15 **NOTES:** No smoking in restaurant **CARDS:** 💳 💳 💳 💳

♦♦♦♦ Hyde Crest
Cirencester Rd GL6 8PE
☎ 01453 731631
e-mail: HydeCrest@compuserve.com
Dir: off A419, 7m (Cirencester to Stroud) at sign marked Minchinhampton and Aston Down. Hyde Crest 3rd house on right opposite Ragged Cot pub

PETS: Bedrooms (unattended) Public areas Exercise area (in garden and nearby common)

Hyde Crest sits on the edge of the picturesque village of Minchinhampton overlooking unspoilt commonland. Bedrooms are tastefully decorated and all are located on the ground floor, each with the added bonus of individual patio areas. Scrumptious breakfasts are served in the small dining room, which also doubles as a guest lounge.
FACILITIES: 3 en suite (3 GF) No smoking TVB tea/coffee Cen ht TVL No children 7yrs No coaches **PRICES:** s £30-£35; d £50-£60✱ **PARKING:** 6

TETBURY　　　　　　　　　　　　Map 03 ST89

★★★ 70% Hare & Hounds
Westonbirt GL8 8QL
☎ 01666 880233 & 881000 📠 01666 880241
e-mail: reception@hareandhoundshotel.com
Dir: 2.5m SW of Tetbury on A433

PETS: Bedrooms (unattended) £5 per pet Public areas (Not in restaurant) Exercise area (fields nearby) Excellent walks nearby

This popular hotel, set in extensive grounds, is situated close to Westonbirt Arboretum and has been run by the same family for 50 years. Staff are keen to help and public areas are charming, with polished parquet flooring, and bedrooms are traditional in style and located in both the main house and adjacent coach house. Leisure facilities include squash and tennis courts.
ROOMS: 24 en suite 7 annexe en suite (3 fmly) (5 GF) No smoking in 12 bedrooms s £75-£83; d £90-£105 (incl. bkfst) **LB** **FACILITIES:** STV Tennis (hard) Squash Croquet lawn Putting green Table tennis Half size snooker table entertainment Xmas **PARKING:** 85 **NOTES:** No smoking in restaurant **CARDS:** 💳 💳 💳 💳 💳 💳

♦♦♦♦ Tavern House
Willesley GL8 8QU
☎ 01666 880444
e-mail: robertson@tavernhouse.co.uk
Dir: From M4 take A46, at Petty France right fork to Tetbury/Didmarton, onto A433, 4m to Willesley. Tavern House is on right, set back from road

PETS: Sep Accom (stable or porch) Exercise area (adjacent)

Within easy reach of Bath and Bristol, this former staging post and inn, built of beautiful local stone dates back to the 17th century. Sympathetically restored, it provides smart, comfortable accommodation. Bedrooms, all with spacious en suites, are thoughtfully equipped and elegantly furnished. Original features include oak beams, a fine open fireplace and a delightful walled garden.
FACILITIES: 4 en suite No smoking in bedrooms No smoking in dining room No smoking in 1 lounge TVB tea/coffee Direct dial from bedrooms Licensed Cen ht TVL No coaches Dinner Last d 9pm
PRICES: s £50-£65; d £60-£85✱ **PARKING:** 12

🍺 **Places with this symbol are pubs**

England

TEWKESBURY
Map 03 SO83

★★★ 60% Royal Hop Pole
Church St GL20 5RT
☎ 01684 293236 📠 01684 296680
e-mail: info@theroyalhoppolehotel.co.uk
Dir: M5 junct 9 for Tewkesbury approx 1.5m. At War Memorial rdbt, go straight across, hotel on right

PETS: Bedrooms £10 Exercise area (200 yards)

This former coaching inn is within walking distance of historic Tewkesbury Abbey and has been offering a warm welcome to weary travellers since the 14th century. There is character in abundance here with many original features including age darkened beams and sloping floors. Bedrooms have great individuality some being in the main house, others in the more recent garden wing. Additional facilities include a popular bar, attractive restaurant and relaxing lounge.
ROOMS: 29 en suite (1 fmly) (5 GF) No smoking in 20 bedrooms s £52-£75; d £90-£150 (incl. bkfst & dinner) **FACILITIES:** All guests have use of facilities at Tewkesbury Park Hotel Golf and Country Club Xmas
PARKING: 35 **NOTES:** No smoking in restaurant
CARDS: 🌐

THORNBURY
Map 03 ST69

★★★ 75% 🏵🏵 Thornbury Castle
Castle St BS35 1HH
☎ 01454 281182 📠 01454 416188
e-mail: info@thornburycastle.co.uk
Dir: on A38 travelling N from Bristol take 1st turning to Thornbury. End High St left into Castle St, follow brown sign, entrance to Castle on left behind St Mary's church

PETS: Bedrooms £10 Exercise area (next door)
RESIDENT PETS: Princess - cat

Henry VIII beheaded the first owner of this castle. Guests today have the opportunity of sleeping in historical surroundings fitted out with all modern amenities. Most rooms have four-poster or coronet beds and real fires. Tranquil lounges enjoy views over the gardens, while elegant, wood-panelled dining rooms make a memorable setting for a leisurely meal.
ROOMS: 25 en suite (3 fmly) (2 GF) s £80-£110; d £130-£370 (incl. bkfst) **LB FACILITIES:** STV Snooker Croquet lawn Hot air ballooning, archery, helicopter ride, clay pigeon shooting Xmas
PARKING: 40 **NOTES:** No smoking in restaurant
CARDS: 🌐

TIRLEY
Map 03 SO82

◆◆◆ 🐓 Town Street Farm
GL19 4HG
☎ 01452 780442 📠 01452 780890
e-mail: townstreetfarm@hotmail.com
Dir: M5 junct 9 to Tewkesbury. Take A38 towards Gloucester, then right onto B4213 at traffic lights. 3m over River Severn, turn right at x-rds towards Chaceley, 1st farm on right

PETS: Bedrooms Sep Accom (kennels or stables) £2
Public areas (not in breakfast room) Exercise area (on farm)
RESIDENT PETS: Norfolk Terrier & Collie

Surrounded by over 500 acres of rolling farmland, this is an ideal base for exploring the Forest of Dean, the Wye Valley or the Cotswolds. Bedrooms are spacious and comfortable with rural views. Hearty breakfasts are served in the conservatory and there are a number of pubs nearby. Facilities include a guest lounge and a tennis court.
FACILITIES: 3 en suite (1 fmly) No smoking in dining room No smoking in lounges TVB tea/coffee Cen ht TVL Tennis (hard) 500 acres beef arable **PRICES:** s £28-£30; d £52-£53✱ **PARKING:** 6

TORMARTON
Map 03 ST77

★★ 71% Compass Inn
GL9 1JB
☎ 01454 218242 & 218577 📠 01454 218741
e-mail: info@compass-inn.co.uk
Dir: 0.5m from M4 junct 18

 Best Western

PETS: (unattended) £3 Public areas (except restaurant)
Exercise area **RESIDENT PETS:** Harry & Basil (Black Poodles), Nick & Chloe (cats)

Originally a coaching inn dating from the 18th century, this welcoming hostelry has grown considerably over the years. Bedrooms are spacious and well equipped, whilst public areas include a choice of bars and varied dining options. A range of conference rooms are also available, providing facilities for varied functions.
ROOMS: 26 en suite (5 fmly) (12 GF) No smoking in 8 bedrooms s £83.50-£93.50; d £93.50-£103.50 **LB FACILITIES:** ch fac
PARKING: 160 **NOTES:** Closed 24-26 Dec
CARDS: 🌐

🌲 **Places with this symbol are country house hotels**

🐓 **Places with this symbol are farms**

All abbreviations are explained on page 9

All AA listed accommodation, restaurants and pubs can be found on the AA's website www.theAA.com

All information was correct at the time of going to press; we recommend you confirm details on booking

England

GREATER LONDON

BARKING

⌂ **Hotel Ibis**
Highbridge Rd IG11 7BA
☎ 020 8477 4100 📠 020 8477 4101
e-mail: H2042@accor-hotels.com
Dir: exit Barking on A406

PETS: Bedrooms (Only caged animals to be left unattended)
Public areas Exercise area (2 min walk - Barking Park)
Pet Food

Modern, budget hotel offering comfortable accommodation in
bright and practical bedrooms. Breakfast is self-service and dinner
is available in the restaurant. For further details, consult the Hotel
Groups page.
ROOMS: 86 en suite s £50-£55; d £50-£55

HEATHROW AIRPORT (LONDON)   Map 04 TQ07

★★★ 69%
Novotel London Heathrow
Junction 4 M4, Cherry Ln UB7 9HB
☎ 01895 431431 📠 01895 431221
e-mail: H1551@accor-hotels.com
*Dir: M4 junct 4, follow Uxbridge signs on A408. Keep left and take 2nd exit
off traffic island into Cherry Ln signed West Drayton. Hotel on left*

PETS: Bedrooms (unattended) £10

Conveniently located close to Heathrow and the motorway
network, this modern hotel provides comfortable accommodation.
The large, airy indoor atrium creates a good sense of space in the
public areas, which include a bar, meeting rooms, fitness centre
and swimming pool.
ROOMS: 178 en suite (34 fmly) (10 GF) No smoking in 112 bedrooms
s £115-£125; d £115-£125 **LB FACILITIES:** STV Indoor swimming (H)
Gym **SERVICES:** Lift **PARKING:** 100
CARDS: 💳

♦♦♦♦ **Harmondsworth Hall**
Summerhouse Ln, Harmondsworth Village UB7 0BG
☎ 020 8759 1824 & 07713 104229 📠 020 8897 6385
e-mail: Elaine@harmondsworthhall.com
*Dir: M4 junct 4 left onto A3044 Holloway Lane towards Harmondsworth.
After 3rd rdbt into Harmondsworth village after Crown Pub on left, next left
into Summerhouse Lane*

PETS: Bedrooms Public areas (except breakfast room)
Exercise area (2 mins walk)

Hidden away in the old part of the village, this guest house is
ideally located for the airport and motorways. Breakfast is served
in an attractive wood-panelled dining room, which looks out on to
the gardens, and guests have the use of a spacious comfortably
appointed lounge. Each bedroom is well-equipped and
individually furnished and decorated.
FACILITIES: 10 en suite (4 fmly) (2 GF) No smoking TVB tea/coffee
Direct dial from bedrooms Licensed Cen ht TVL No coaches Dinner
Last d by arrangement **PRICES:** s £55-£65; d £70-£75✱ **LB**
PARKING: 8 **CARDS:** 💳

KINGSTON UPON THAMES

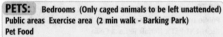

♦♦♦♦ **Chase Lodge Hotel**
10 Park Rd, Hampton Wick KT1 4AS
☎ 020 8943 1862 📠 020 8943 9363
e-mail: info@chaselodgehotel.com
*Dir: From A308, take A310 signed Twickenham. Turn 1st left into Park
Road, Chase Lodge 50yds on right.*

PETS: Bedrooms (unattended) Exercise area (2 mins walk)
RESIDENT PETS: Dibley - Jack Russell

This delightful guest house is set in a quiet residential area, a short
walk from Kingston Bridge. The individually decorated rooms vary
in size and are all well-appointed and feature a range of useful
extras. An attractive open-plan lounge/bar/restaurant is provided
where both lunch and dinner are served. On-street parking is
available.
FACILITIES: 6 en suite 5 annexe en suite (2 fmly) (4 GF) No smoking in
2 bedrooms No smoking in area of dining room No smoking in lounges
STV TVB tea/coffee Direct dial from bedrooms Licensed Cen ht
No coaches Dinner Last d 9pm **PRICES:** s £65-£98; d £71-£185✱ **LB**
PARKING: CARDS: 💳

See advert on opposite page

PINNER

★★ 69% **Tudor Lodge**
50 Field End Rd, Eastcote HA5 2QN
☎ 020 8429 0585 📠 020 8429 0117
e-mail: tudorlodge@meridianleisure.com
*Dir: off A40 at Swakeleys rdbt to Ickenham, onto A312 to Harrow. Left at
Northolt Station to Eastcote*

PETS: Bedrooms £10 Exercise area (200 metres)

This friendly hotel, set in its own grounds, is convenient for
Heathrow Airport and many local golf courses. Bedrooms vary in
style and size but all are well equipped, with some suitable for
families. A good range of bar snacks is offered as an alternative to
the main restaurant.
ROOMS: 24 en suite 22 annexe en suite (9 fmly) (17 GF) No smoking
in 6 bedrooms s £65-£89; d £75-£94 (incl. bkfst) **LB FACILITIES:** STV
Xmas **PARKING:** 30 **NOTES:** No smoking in restaurant
CARDS: 💳

★ **Red stars indicate the AA's
Top 200 Hotels in Britain & Ireland**

ALTRINCHAM   Map 07 SJ78

★★★ 67% Cresta Court

Church St WA14 4DP

☎ 0161 927 7272 📠 0161 929 6548
e-mail: stewart5738@btconnect.com

PETS: Bedrooms (unattended) Public areas Exercise area
(200 yards) Pet Food Bowls/foods provided (also by prior
arrangement)

This modern hotel enjoys a prime location on the A56, close to the
station and town centre shops and amenities. Bedrooms vary in
style from spacious four-posters to smaller, traditionally furnished
rooms. Public areas include a choice of bars, a small gym, hair
and beauty salon and extensive function and conference facilities.
ROOMS: 136 en suite (8 fmly) No smoking in 80 bedrooms s £49-£69;
d £49-£69 **LB FACILITIES:** STV Tennis (hard & grass) Solarium Gym
Putting green Beauty salon/fitness & cardiovascular training room
entertainment ch fac Xmas **SERVICES:** Lift **PARKING:** 200
NOTES: No smoking in restaurant **CARDS:** 🔲🔲🔲🔲🔲🔲

★★★ 66% Quality Hotel Altrincham

Langham Rd, Bowdon WA14 2HT
☎ 0161 928 7121 📠 0161 927 7560
e-mail: enquiries@hotels-altrincham.com
*Dir: M6 junct 19 to airport, join A556, over M56 rdbt onto A56, right at
traffic lights onto B5161. Hotel 1m on right*

PETS: Bedrooms £10 Exercise area (100 metres)
RESIDENT PETS: George (cat)

This popular hotel is located within easy reach of the motorways
and airport. It provides comfortable and well-equipped bedrooms.
The public areas consist of the modern Cafe Continental, the main
restaurant which offers modern cuisine, and a leisure club. A
range of conference rooms is also available.
ROOMS: 91 en suite (6 fmly) (13 GF) No smoking in 19 bedrooms
s £50-£99; d £75-£115 **LB FACILITIES:** STV Indoor swimming (H)
Sauna Solarium Gym Jacuzzi Beauty treatments Xmas **PARKING:** 160
CARDS: 🔲🔲🔲🔲🔲

BOLTON   Map 07 SD70

♦♦♦ Broomfield Hotel

33-35 Wigan Rd, Deane BL3 5PX
☎ 01204 61570 📠 01204 650932
e-mail: chris@broomfield.force9.net
Dir: M61 J5, take A58 to 1st set lights, straight on A676, hotel on R

PETS: Bedrooms (unattended) Public areas Exercise area
(100yds) **RESIDENT PETS:** Max & Tess - Labradors

A friendly relaxed atmosphere prevails at this hotel conveniently
located close to the motorway and west of the town centre. The
bedrooms, some suitable for families, are equipped with modern
facilities. Public areas include a bar, a lounge and a dining room,
which offers good-value dinners and hearty breakfasts.
FACILITIES: 20 en suite (2 fmly) (2 GF) No smoking in 4 bedrooms
No smoking in dining room TVB tea/coffee Licensed Cen ht TVL Pool Table
3/4 Snooker table & darts Dinner Last d 8.30pm **PRICES:** s £36-£40; d £50✻
PARKING: 12 **CARDS:** 🔲🔲🔲🔲🔲

Chase Lodge Hotel

An Award Winning Hotel

*with style & elegance, set in
tranquil surroundings at
affordable prices.*

Pets welcome

10 Park Road, Hampton Wick,
Kingston-Upon-Thames KT1 4AS

Tel: 020 8943 1862
Fax: 020 8943 9363

E-mail: info@chaselodgehotel.com
Website: www.chaselodgehotel.com

*AA*** Les Routiers*

*Quality en suite bedrooms
Close to Bushy Park
Full English Breakfast
À la carte menu
Licensed bar
Wedding Receptions
Honeymoon suite available with
jacuzzi & steam area
20 minutes from Heathrow Airport
Close to Kingston town centre &
all major transport links*

All major credit cards accepted

LITTLEBOROUGH   Map 07 SD91

♦♦♦♦♦ Hollingworth Lake Bed & Breakfast

164 Smithy Bridge Rd OL15 0DB
☎ 01706 376583
*Dir: M62 junct 21, follow brown signs to Hollingworth Lake Country Park.
At T junct onto small rdbt, turn right into Smithy Bridge Road and B&B
50yds on right before Hollingworth Lake*

PETS: Bedrooms (in annexe) Sep Accom £5 Exercise area
'pet' bedrooms have a wooden floor **RESIDENT PETS:** 2 tabby
cats - Max & Jorja

Situated within walking distance of the lake, this very well-
furnished house offers excellent hospitality and well-equipped
bedrooms, some of which are located in the lovely garden to the
rear. A good hearty breakfast is provided in the delightful dining
room.
FACILITIES: 3 rms (2 en suite) 2 annexe en suite (1 fmly) (2 GF)
No smoking in bedrooms No smoking in dining room No smoking in
lounges TVB tea/coffee Cen ht **PRICES:** s fr £25; d fr £40; (room only)
✻ **PARKING:** 7 **CARDS:** 🔲🔲🔲🔲🔲

Please mention AA Pet Friendly
Places to Stay when booking

MANCHESTER — Map 07 SJ89

★★★ 77% Malmaison

Malmaison

Piccadilly M1 3AQ
☎ 0161 278 1000 🖨 0161 278 1002
e-mail: manchester@malmaison.com
Dir: follow city centre signs, then signs to Piccadilly station. Hotel opposite station, at bottom of station approach

PETS: Bedrooms (unattended) £10 Exercise area Pet Food Bowls and bed provided, owner to provide food

Stylish and chic, the Malmaison offers the very best of contemporary hotel keeping in a relaxed and comfortable environment. The hotel offers a range of bright meeting rooms, health spa with gym and treatment rooms, as well as the ever popular bar and French-style brasserie. Air-conditioned bedrooms combine style and comfort and provide a range of extras.
ROOMS: 167 en suite s £129-£165; d £129-£165 **FACILITIES:** Spa STV Sauna Solarium Gym Jacuzzi **SERVICES:** Lift air con
CARDS: ▬▬ ▬▬ ▬ ▬ ▬ ▬ ▬

★★★ 65% Old Rectory Hotel

Meadow Ln, Haughton Green, Denton M34 7GD
☎ 0161 336 7516 🖨 0161 320 3212
e-mail: reservations@oldrectoryhotelmanchester.co.uk

PETS: Bedrooms Public areas (except restaurant) Exercise area (100 yards) Pet Food Bowls provided, 2 min walk from bridle-paths and woods

This former Victorian rectory, peacefully set around an enclosed garden, is only a short drive from Manchester city centre. Modern bedrooms are generally spacious and well appointed. Public rooms include a bar, an attractive and popular restaurant and a newly equipped mini-gym. Extensive banqueting facilities make this a popular wedding venue.
ROOMS: 30 en suite 6 annexe en suite (1 fmly) (12 GF) No smoking in 12 bedrooms s £50-£55; d £60-£70 (incl. bkfst) **LB FACILITIES:** STV Gym Xmas **PARKING:** 50 **NOTES:** No smoking in restaurant
CARDS: ▬▬ ▬▬ ▬ ▬ ▬ ▬ ▬

★★★ 63% Novotel Manchester West

Worsley Brow M28 2YA
☎ 0161 799 3535 🖨 0161 703 8207
e-mail: H0907@accor-hotels.com

PETS: Bedrooms (unattended) £5 Exercise area (garden)

(For full entry see Worsley)

⌂ Hotel Ibis Manchester City Centre

96 Portland St M1 4GY
☎ 0161 234 0600 🖨 0161 234 0610
e-mail: H3142@accor-hotels.com
Dir: In city centre, between Princess St & Oxford St. 10min walk from Picadilly

PETS: Bedrooms Public areas

Modern, budget hotel offering comfortable accommodation in bright and practical bedrooms. Breakfast is self-service and dinner is available in the restaurant. For further details, consult the Hotel Groups page.
ROOMS: 127 en suite s £45.95-£58.95; d £45.95-£58.95

OLDHAM — Map 07 SD90

★★★ 65% La Pergola

THE INDEPENDENTS

Rochdale Rd, Denshaw OL3 5UE
☎ 01457 871040 🖨 01457 873804
e-mail: reception@lapergola.freeserve.co.uk
Dir: M62 junct 21, right at rdbt onto A640, under motorway, left at Wagon & Horses public house. Hotel 500yds on left

PETS: Bedrooms Public areas (except restaurant) Exercise area

Situated in open moorland and convenient for the M62, this friendly, family-owned and run hotel offers comfortable and well-equipped bedrooms. There is a good range of food available either in the bar or restaurant, and a comfortable lounge in which to relax.
ROOMS: 26 en suite (4 fmly) No smoking in 14 bedrooms s £43-£52.50; d £60.50-£65.50 (incl. bkfst) **LB FACILITIES:** Xmas **PARKING:** 75 **NOTES:** No smoking in restaurant Closed 26 Dec & 1 Jan RS BH Mondays
CARDS: ▬▬ ▬▬ ▬ ▬ ▬ ▬ ▬

ROCHDALE — Map 07 SD91

★★★★ 62% Norton Grange

MACDONALD HOTELS

Manchester Rd, Castleton OL11 2XZ
☎ 01706 630788 🖨 01706 649313
e-mail: nortongrange@macdonald-hotels.co.uk
Dir: M62 junct 20, follow signs for A664, left after "All-in-One" Garden centre

PETS: Bedrooms £15 Exercise area (5 mins walk)

Standing in nine acres of grounds and mature gardens, this Victorian house provides comfort in elegant surroundings. The well-equipped bedrooms have been refurbished to provide a host of extras for both the business and leisure guest. Public areas include the Pickwick bistro and bar and a smart restaurant, both offering a good choice of dishes.
ROOMS: 51 en suite No smoking in 40 bedrooms s £88-£105; d £103-£120 (incl. bkfst) **LB FACILITIES:** STV Complimentary use of leisure centre Xmas **SERVICES:** Lift **PARKING:** 150
NOTES: No smoking in restaurant
CARDS: ▬▬ ▬▬ ▬ ▬ ▬ ▬ ▬

> **Don't forget to let proprietors know when you book that you're bringing your pet**

> **All abbreviations are explained on page 9**

> **All AA listed accommodation, restaurants and pubs can be found on the AA's website www.theAA.com**

England

STOCKPORT
Map 07 SJ88

◆◆◆◆ Henry's
204-206 Buxton Rd, Davenport SK2 7AE
☎ 0161 292 0202 ▦ 0161 355 6585
e-mail: enquiries@henryshotel.com

PETS: Bedrooms (unattended) £20 refundable deposit
Public areas (not in dining room) Exercise area
RESIDENT PETS: Henry & Kodey (Rottweilers)

Situated on the main road a short way from the town, this family owned and run guest house offers fine hospitality. The bedrooms are modern and well equipped and a cosy lounge and separate bar are provided for guests' comforts.
FACILITIES: 10 en suite (1 fmly) (2 GF) No smoking TVB tea/coffee Licensed Cen ht TVL Solarium **PRICES:** s £30-£35; d £40-£45; (room only) ✳ **PARKING:** 24 **CARDS:**

WORSLEY
Map 07 SD70

★★★ 63% Novotel Manchester West
Worsley Brow M28 2YA
☎ 0161 799 3535 ▦ 0161 703 8207
e-mail: H0907@accor-hotels.com
Dir: adjacent to M60 junct 13

PETS: Bedrooms (unattended) £5 Exercise area (garden)

Well-placed for access to the Peak and Lake Districts, as well as the thriving city of Manchester, this modern hotel successfully caters for both families and business guests. Spacious bedrooms all have sofa beds and a large work area, and the hotel also boasts an outdoor swimming pool and children's play area.
ROOMS: 119 en suite (4 fmly) **FACILITIES:** STV Outdoor swimming (H)
SERVICES: Lift **PARKING:** 140 **CARDS:**

HAMPSHIRE

ALTON
Map 04 SU73

★★★ 70% Alton Grange
London Rd GU34 4EG
☎ 01420 86565 ▦ 01420 541346
e-mail: info@altongrange.co.uk
Dir: from A31 right at rdbt signed Alton/Holybourne/Bordon B3004. Hotel 300yds on left

PETS: Bedrooms (unattended) £5 Public areas
Exercise area (100 yards) RESIDENT PETS: Fudge, Caramel, Barley, Smartie, Treacle, Honey, Saffron, Cracker (cats)

A friendly and family owned hotel, conveniently located on the outskirts of this market town and set in its own well-manicured grounds. The individually styled bedrooms include three suites and are thoughtfully equipped. Diners can choose between the more formal Truffles Restaurant or relaxed Muffins Brasserie. The attractive public areas also include a function suite.
ROOMS: 26 en suite 4 annexe en suite (4 fmly) (7 GF) No smoking in 6 bedrooms s £81-£99; d £99-£115 (incl. bkfst) **FACILITIES:** STV Hot air ballooning **PARKING:** 48 **NOTES:** No children 3yrs No smoking in restaurant Closed 24 Dec-2 Jan **CARDS:**

ANDOVER
Map 04 SU34

★★★ 73% ⚜⚜ Esseborne Manor
SP11 0ER
☎ 01264 736444 ▦ 01264 736725
e-mail: esseborne@aol.com
Dir: halfway between Andover & Newbury on A343, just 1 mile N of Hurstbourne Tarrant

PETS: Bedrooms (unattended) Exercise area (100yds)

Set in two acres of well-tended gardens, this attractive manor house is surrounded by the open countryside of the North Wessex Downs. Bedrooms are delightfully individual and are split between the main house, an adjoining courtyard and separate garden cottage. A wonderfully relaxed atmosphere pervades throughout, with public rooms combining elegance with comfort.
ROOMS: 6 en suite 9 annexe rms (8 en suite) (6 GF) s £95-£105; d £100-£180 (incl. bkfst) **LB FACILITIES:** STV Tennis (hard) Croquet lawn **PARKING:** 50 **NOTES:** No smoking in restaurant
CARDS:

BASINGSTOKE
Map 04 SU65

★★★★ 69%
Hanover International Hotel & Club
Scures Hill, Nately Scures, Hook RG27 9JS
☎ 01256 764161 ▦ 01256 768341
e-mail: reception.basingstoke@hanover-international.com
Dir: M3 junct 5, take A287 towards Newnham. L at lights. Hotel 200mtrs on R

PETS: Bedrooms (In bedrooms only) Exercise area (Adjacent)

This modern hotel is popular with both business and leisure guests. Comfortable bedrooms are well equipped and include a number of spacious executive rooms. Guests have a choice of dining in the formal restaurant, or for lighter meals and snacks there is a relaxing café or a smart bar. Extensive conference and leisure facilities complete the picture.
ROOMS: 100 en suite (14 fmly) (26 GF) No smoking in 45 bedrooms s £47-£192.95; d £94-£205.90 (incl. bkfst) **FACILITIES:** STV Indoor swimming (H) Sauna Solarium Gym Jacuzzi Xmas **SERVICES:** Lift air con **PARKING:** 200 **NOTES:** No smoking in restaurant **CARDS:**

◆◆◆◆ Hatchings
Woods Ln, Cliddesden RG25 2JF
☎ 01256 465279
Dir: M3 junct 6, take Alton road A339 & pass under road bridge. Immediate right signed Cliddesden B3046, after 0.75m take next right

PETS: Bedrooms Exercise area

This delightful house is situated in the pretty village of Cliddesden, convenient for both Basingstoke and the M3. Comfortable bedrooms look out onto peaceful gardens and the extra touches are excellent. A hearty full English breakfast is served in the bedrooms, with cereals, bread, jams, fruit and biscuits all freely available.
FACILITIES: 3 en suite No smoking TVB tea/coffee Direct dial from bedrooms Cen ht No children 10yrs No coaches
PRICES: s £33.50-£35; d £55-£60✳ **PARKING:** 10

England

BEAULIEU   Map 04 SU30

★★★ 63% **Beaulieu**
Beaulieu Rd SO42 7YQ
☎ 023 8029 3344 📠 023 8029 2729
e-mail: beaulieu@newforesthotels.co.uk
Dir: M27 junct I/A337 towards Lyndhurst. Left at lights in Lyndhurst, through village, turn right onto B3056, continue for 3m.

PETS: Bedrooms (unattended) £5 Public areas
Exercise area (direct access to forest)

Conveniently located in the heart of the New Forest and close to Beaulieu Road railway station, this popular, small hotel provides an ideal base for exploring the surrounding area. Facilities include an indoor swimming pool, an outdoor children's play area and an adjoining pub. A daily changing menu is offered in the restaurant.
ROOMS: 15 en suite 3 annexe en suite (2 fmly) s £75-£82.50;
d £120-£155 (incl. bkfst) **LB FACILITIES:** Indoor swimming (H) Steam room Xmas **PARKING:** 60 **NOTES:** No smoking in restaurant
CARDS: 〓〓〓〓〓

BOTLEY   Map 04 SU51

★★★★ 69%
Botley Park Hotel & Country Club
Winchester Rd, Boorley Green SO32 2UA
☎ 01489 780888 📠 01489 789242   MACDONALD
e-mail: botleypark@macdonald-hotels.co.uk   HOTELS
Dir: A334 towards Botley, left at 1st rdbt past M&S, continue over next 4 mini-rdbts, at 3rd rdbt follow hotel signs

PETS: Bedrooms (unattended) £10 Public areas
Exercise area

This modern and spacious hotel sits peacefully in the midst of its own 176 acres of parkland golf course. Bedrooms are comfortably appointed with a good range of extras and an extensive range of leisure facilities is on offer. Attractive public areas include a relaxing restaurant and the more informal Swing and Divot Bar.
ROOMS: 100 en suite (34 GF) No smoking in 52 bedrooms
FACILITIES: STV Indoor swimming (H) Golf 18 Tennis (hard) Squash Sauna Solarium Gym Jacuzzi Aerobics studio, Beauty salon, Golf driving range ch fac **PARKING:** 250 **NOTES:** No smoking in restaurant
CARDS: 〓〓〓〓〓〓

BROCKENHURST   Map 04 SU30

★★★ 73% ◉◉ **New Park Manor**
Lyndhurst Rd SO42 7QH
☎ 01590 623467 Y 📠 01590 622268
e-mail: info@newparkmanor.co.uk
Dir: M27 junct I, A337 to Lyndhurst & Brockenhurst. Hotel 1.5m on right

PETS: Bedrooms (unattended) Public areas Exercise area
Pet Food

Once the favoured hunting lodge of King Charles II, this well presented hotel enjoys a peaceful setting in extensive acreage of the New Forest and comes complete with an equestrian centre. Bedrooms have now been refurbished and are divided between

continued

the old house and a purpose-built wing, and the smart public areas include a new mezzanine lounge.
ROOMS: 24 en suite (6 fmly) No smoking in all bedrooms s £90-£130; d £120-£210 (incl. bkfst) **LB FACILITIES:** Outdoor swimming (H) Tennis (hard) Riding Croquet lawn Mountain biking Xmas
PARKING: 70 **NOTES:** No smoking in restaurant
CARDS: 〓〓〓〓〓

★★★ 67% **Forest Park**
Rhinefield Rd SO42 7ZG   Forestdale Hotels
☎ 01590 622844 📠 01590 623948
e-mail: forest.park@forestdale.com
Dir: A337 to Brockenhurst turn into Meerut Rd, follow road through Waters Green. Right at t-junct into Rhinefield Rd

PETS: Bedrooms (unattended) £7.50 Public areas (not in restaurant) Pet Food

A friendly hotel offering good facilities for both adults and children. A heated pool, riding, children's meal times and a quiet location in the forest are just a few of the advantages here. The well-equipped, comfortable bedrooms vary in size and style, and a choice of lounge and bar areas is available.
ROOMS: 38 en suite (2 fmly) (7 GF) No smoking in 2 bedrooms
s fr £90; d fr £120 (incl. bkfst) **LB FACILITIES:** Outdoor swimming (H) Tennis (hard) Riding Sauna Xmas **PARKING:** 80 **NOTES:** No smoking in restaurant **CARDS:** 〓〓〓〓〓

◆◆◆◆◆ ◉◉◉ ⌂
Thatched Cottage Hotel & Restaurant
16 Brookley Rd SO42 7RR
☎ 01590 623090 📠 01590 623479
e-mail: sales@thatchedcottage.co.uk
Dir: M27 junct I/A337 towards Brockenhurst and turn right just before crossing

PETS: Bedrooms (unattended) Exercise area (1 mile)

This 17th-century thatched, timber-framed cottage has been converted into a delightful small hotel, combining modern essentials with old-world charm. Bedrooms are individually furnished with many useful extras, and one has a four-poster bed. The stylish restaurant, with its open kitchen, offers interesting and well-prepared dishes, featuring fresh, locally sourced produce. In the summer, why not eat lunch in the garden?
FACILITIES: 5 en suite (3 GF) No smoking in dining room STV TVB tea/coffee Direct dial from bedrooms Licensed Cen ht No children 12yrs No coaches Dinner Last d 9.30pm **PRICES:** d £95-£185✳ **LB**
PARKING: 10 **NOTES:** rs Jan **CARDS:** 〓〓〓〓〓〓

◆◆◆ **Bridge House**
Lyndhurst Rd SO42 7TR
☎ 01590 623135 & 624760 📠 01590 623916
e-mail: jmvb2@aol.com
Dir: situated on A337

PETS: Bedrooms £3 one off charge Exercise area (100yds)
RESIDENT PETS: Tess and Poppy (Springer Spaniels), Tipper (cat), 6 guinea pigs

Located in the Waters Green conservation area, this 18th-century house is set just off the main Brockenhurst to Lyndhurst road. Well-positioned for easy access to the village and surrounding

continued

England

areas of the New Forest, the comfortably furnished bedrooms are equipped with thoughtful extra facilities. Breakfast is a hearty affair.

FACILITIES: 3 en suite (1 fmly) No smoking TVB tea/coffee Cen ht No coaches **PRICES:** d £50-£64✱ **LB** **PARKING:** 5 **NOTES:** Closed Xmas **CARDS:**

♦♦♦ Seraya
8 Grigg Ln SO42 7RE
☎ 01590 622426 📠 01590 622426
e-mail: edwin.ward@btinternet.com
Dir: exit Lymington-Lyndhurst road opp Careys Manor Hotel. Now on Grigg Lane. 800yds on right is Horlock Road, house on corner Horlock Rd/Grigg Lane

PETS: Bedrooms Exercise area (500 metres)

Well-placed for visiting the New Forest and situated close to the centre of town, with its multitude of eating options, this delightful guest house offers quiet, well-decorated rooms with a wide selection of extra facilities. A hearty breakfast is served around the communal dining table.
FACILITIES: 3 rms (1 en suite) No smoking TVB tea/coffee Cen ht No coaches **PRICES:** d fr £45✱ **LB** **PARKING:** 3

BURLEY Map 04 SU20

★★★ 70% Burley Manor
Ringwood Rd BH24 4BS   *Forestdale Hotels*
☎ 01425 403522 📠 01425 403227
e-mail: burley.manor@forestdale.com
Dir: leave A31 at Burley sign, hotel 3m on left

PETS: Bedrooms (unattended) £7.50 Public areas (not in restaurant) Pet Food

Set in extensive grounds, this 18th-century former mansion enjoys a relaxed ambience and a peaceful setting. Half of the well-equipped, comfortable bedrooms, including several with four-posters, are located in the main house. The remainder, many of which have balconies, are in the adjacent converted stable block. Cosy public rooms benefit from log fires in winter.
ROOMS: 21 en suite 17 annexe en suite (3 fmly) (17 GF) No smoking in 4 bedrooms s fr £115; d fr £130 (incl. bkfst) **LB** **FACILITIES:** Outdoor swimming (H) Fishing Riding Croquet lawn Xmas **PARKING:** 60 **NOTES:** No smoking in restaurant
CARDS:

DAMERHAM Map 04 SU11

♦♦♦♦ 🍴 The Compasses
Damerham SP6 3HQ
☎ 01725 518231 📠 01725 518880
e-mail: info@compassesinn.net
Dir: centre of Fordingbridge at mini rdbt take rd marked Sandleheath/Damerham, 3m to Damerham. On left after garage

PETS: Bedrooms Public areas (except dining room) Exercise area (adjacent) RESIDENT PETS: Sasha & Phoenix (Dobermans), Toggs (cat)

This friendly, 400-year-old traditional inn enjoys a peaceful village location just three miles from Fordingbridge and is an ideal base for exploring this delightful area. The comfortable bedrooms are pleasantly furnished and well-equipped. The bars feature a selection of real ales and over 100 malt whiskies. Tasty meals are available at both lunch and dinner. Two self-catering units are also available.
FACILITIES: 6 en suite (1 fmly) No smoking in dining room No smoking in 1 lounge TVB tea/coffee Direct dial from bedrooms Cen ht Pool Table Large garden & bar games Dinner Last d 9.30pm **PRICES:** s £39.50-£45; d £69-£80✱ **LB** **PARKING:** 30 **CARDS:**

FAREHAM Map 04 SU50

♦♦♦ Travelrest-Avenue House Hotel
22 The Avenue PO14 1NS
☎ 01329 232175 📠 01329 232196
Dir: on A27, 0.5m from town centre, 500mtrs from railway station

PETS: (unattended) £5 Exercise area

Conveniently situated just west of the town centre, this well-presented hotel is ideally located for the continental ferry terminals and naval heritage sites. The comfortable bedrooms are spacious, attractive and well-equipped and one has a four-poster bed. Breakfast is served in the cosy conservatory dining room. Conference rooms are also available.
FACILITIES: 19 en suite (3 fmly) (6 GF) No smoking in 10 bedrooms No smoking in dining room No smoking in lounges TVB tea/coffee Direct dial from bedrooms Cen ht Landscaped garden **PRICES:** s £45-£53; d £50-£62.50✱ **PARKING:** 27
CARDS:

England

FLEET MOTORWAY SERVICE AREA (M3)   Map 04 SU75

⭐ Days Inn

Fleet Services GU51 1AA
☎ 01252 815587 ▤ 01252 815587
e-mail: fleethotel@welcomebreak.co.uk
Dir: Welcome Break Fleet Motorway Service area between junct 4a & 5 southbound on the M3

PETS: Bedrooms (unattended) Exercise area

This modern building offers accommodation in smart, spacious and well-equipped bedrooms, suitable for families and business travellers, and all with en suite bathrooms. Continental breakfast is available and other refreshments may be taken at the nearby family restaurant. For further details see the Hotel Groups page.
ROOMS: 58 en suite s £45-£55; d £45-£65

FORDINGBRIDGE   Map 04 SU11

⭐⭐ 72% ◉ Ashburn Hotel & Restaurant

Station Rd SP6 1JP
☎ 01425 652060 ▤ 01425 652150
e-mail: ashburn@mistral.co.uk
Dir: from Fordingbridge High St, follow Damerham signs. Pass police and fire stations, hotel 400yds on left

PETS: Bedrooms £3 (Only in garden) Exercise area (0.25 mile) Pet Food By prior arrangement dog food can be purchased RESIDENT PETS: Jim (cat)

This friendly family-run hotel, situated in an elevated position on the edge of the village, is surrounded by beautiful countryside. Bedrooms, some in the original house and others in a purpose built extension, are comfortable and well equipped. There is a smart function room, a spacious bar, a cosy lounge and a wonderful garden. A good choice is offered at dinner and dishes are carefully prepared.
ROOMS: 20 en suite (3 fmly) No smoking in 10 bedrooms s £39.50-£69.50; d £80-£112 (incl. bkfst) LB **FACILITIES:** ch fac Xmas **PARKING:** 60 **NOTES:** No smoking in restaurant RS 24-29 Dec, 1-5 Jan
CARDS: 💳

HOOK   Map 04 SU75

◆◆◆ Oaklea

London Rd RG27 9LA
☎ 01256 762673 ▤ 01256 762150
e-mail: oakleaguesthouse@amserve.net
Dir: on A30, 200yds from centre of Hook, towards Basingstoke

PETS: Bedrooms Public areas Exercise area
RESIDENT PETS: Shih Tsu

Guests can be sure of a warm welcome at this Victorian house just a few minutes' drive from the M3. Bedrooms are well appointed with modern facilities. The residents' lounge is comfortably furnished and the large dining room also has a bar.
FACILITIES: 11 rms (9 en suite) (2 fmly) No smoking in bedrooms No smoking in dining room TVB tea/coffee Licensed Cen ht TVL No coaches Dinner Last d noon **PRICES:** s £39-£45; d £49-£58✴
PARKING: 11 **CARDS:** 💳

LYMINGTON   Map 04 SZ39

⭐⭐⭐ 71% ◉ Stanwell House

14-15 High St SO41 9AA
☎ 01590 677123 ▤ 01590 677756
e-mail: sales@stanwellhousehotel.co.uk
Dir: A337 to town centre, on right of High St, before descent to quay

PETS: Bedrooms £15 Public areas (except restaurant) Exercise area (500yds)

Centrally situated, this stylish hotel offers friendly and attentive service. Bedrooms are comfortable and very well equipped; some rooms in the older part of the building are particularly interesting and some have four-poster beds. The award-winning cuisine provides interesting freshly prepared dishes.
ROOMS: 29 en suite (1 fmly) No smoking in 10 bedrooms s £85-£160; d £110-£160 (incl. bkfst) LB **NOTES:** No smoking in restaurant
CARDS: 💳

◆◆◆◆ 🍴 Efford Cottage

Everton SO41 0JD
☎ 01590 642315 ▤ 01590 641030
e-mail: effordcottage@aol.com
Dir: on A337, 2m W of Lymington

PETS: Bedrooms £2 Public areas (On leads, not in dining room) Exercise area (500yds) RESIDENT PETS: Misty (Springer Spaniel)

Set in attractive gardens, this charming property offers large, comfortable bedrooms which are well furnished and feature a host of thoughtful extras. There is a spacious lounge to relax in, and by arrangement guests can enjoy a delicious evening meal using local and home-grown produce. The extensive breakfast menu features home-made bread.
FACILITIES: 3 en suite (1 fmly) No smoking in bedrooms No smoking in dining room TVB tea/coffee Direct dial from bedrooms Cen ht No children 14yrs no coaches **PARKING:** 4 **NOTES:** Closed Nov-Feb rs Nov-Feb

◆◆◆◆ Harts Lodge

242 Everton Rd, Everton SO41 0HE
☎ 01590 645902
Dir: At Everton (2.5m W of Lymington) turn off A337 into Everton Rd, Harts Lodge is 0.5m on left.

PETS: Bedrooms Exercise area (1 mile)

This attractive bungalow is peacefully situated in three acres of gardens and paddocks. The bedrooms are furnished to a high standard and feature many thoughtful touches; one room has outside access. Public areas include a lounge and a pleasant breakfast room, with views of the garden and small Wildlife Lake.
FACILITIES: 3 en suite (1 fmly) (3 GF) No smoking TVB tea/coffee Cen ht TVL No coaches **PRICES:** s £35-£55; d fr £55✴ LB **PARKING:** 6

★ **Red stars indicate the AA's Top 200 Hotels in Britain & Ireland**

◆◆◆◆ Jevington
47 Waterford Ln SO41 3PT
☎ 01590 672148 ▦ 01590 672148
e-mail: jevingtonbb@lineone.net
Dir: from High St, turn R at St Thomas Church into Church Lane. Take L fork into Waterford Lane

PETS: Bedrooms Exercise area (100yds)
RESIDENT PETS: terrier cross

Situated within walking distance of the town centre and marinas, Jevington offers attractively decorated bedrooms, furnished to a high standard and well co-ordinated soft furnishings. An appetising breakfast is served at two tables in the open-plan dining room whilst the friendly proprietors are happy to suggest places for dinner.
FACILITIES: 3 en suite (1 fmly) No smoking TVB tea/coffee Cen ht No children 5 yrs No coaches **PRICES:** d £50-£60✱ **PARKING:** 3

◆◆◆◆ 1 Honeysuckle Gardens
Everton SO41 0EH
☎ 01590 641282
Dir: from A337 Lymington/Christchurch road turn N into Everton Rd. Honeysuckle Gardens 3rd left approx. 300mtrs from A337

PETS: Bedrooms Exercise area (Adjacent)

Located in a new residential development in the village of Everton, this charming modern house offers an ideal base to visit Lymington, New Milton or the New Forest. Bedrooms are well furnished and decorated with a useful range of extra facilities provided. Full English breakfasts are served around one large table.
FACILITIES: 3 rms (2 en suite) No smoking TVB tea/coffee Cen ht No children 3yrs No coaches **PRICES:** s fr £27; d £54✱ **LB**
PARKING: 3 **NOTES:** Closed Xmas & New Year

◆◆◆ Gorse Meadow
Sway Rd SO41 8LR
☎ 01590 673354 ▦ 673336
e-mail: gorse.meadow.guesthouse@wildmushrooms.co.uk
Dir: turn off A337 from Brockenhurst right into Sway Road before Toll House Pub, continue for 1.5m and Gorse Meadow is on the right.

PETS: Bedrooms Exercise area Dog food, leftovers of meat, vegetables, pen for exercise

This imposing Edwardian house is situated within 14 acres of grounds and most bedrooms enjoy views across the gardens and paddocks. Situated just a mile from Lymington, this is an excellent base to enjoy the many leisure pursuits that the New Forest has to offer. Meals are also available here, and Mrs Tee often uses the local wild mushrooms in her dishes.
FACILITIES: 5 en suite (2 fmly) (2 GF) No smoking in dining room No smoking in lounges TVB tea/coffee Licensed Cen ht No coaches Dinner Last d 6pm **PRICES:** s £50; d £80-£90✱ **PARKING:** 20
CARDS: ▦ ▦ ▦ ▦ ▦

> **Don't forget to let proprietors know when you book that you're bringing your pet**

◆◆◆ Passford Farm
Southampton Rd SO41 8ND
☎ 01590 674103
Dir: opposite the Welcome to Lymington sign

PETS: Exercise area (10yds)

Set in five acres with delightful gardens and a pond, parts of this charming thatched cottage date back 700 years. With its wealth of beams and fireplaces, Passford Farm is full of character. The proprietors adopt a relaxed and friendly approach, ensuring guests are comfortable enjoying the facilities.
FACILITIES: 3 en suite (1 fmly) No smoking in bedrooms No smoking in dining room TVB tea/coffee No dogs (ex guide dogs) Cen ht No coaches half size snooker table **PRICES:** d £56✱ **PARKING:** 30

LYNDHURST   Map 04 SU30

★★★ 69% Lyndhurst Park
High St SO43 7NL   *Forestdale Hotels*
☎ 023 8028 3923 ▦ 023 8028 3019
e-mail: lyndhurst.park@forestdale.com
Dir: M27 junct 1-3 to A35 to Lyndhurst. Hotel at bottom of High St

PETS: Bedrooms (unattended) £7.50 Public areas (except restaurant) Pet Food

Although it is only a short walk from the High Street, the hotel is offered some seclusion from the town by its five acres of mature grounds. The comfortable bedrooms have home-from-home touches such as ducks in the bath! There are two bars and an oak-panelled restaurant with a sunny conservatory.
ROOMS: 59 en suite (3 fmly) No smoking in 10 bedrooms s fr £90; d fr £115 (incl. bkfst) **LB FACILITIES:** STV Outdoor swimming (H) Tennis (hard) Snooker Sauna Table tennis Xmas **SERVICES:** Lift
PARKING: 100 **NOTES:** No smoking in restaurant
CARDS: ▦ ▦ ▦ ▦ ▦ ▦ ▦

★ 71% Knightwood Lodge
Southampton Rd SO43 7BU   *THE INDEPENDENTS*
☎ 023 8028 2502 ▦ 023 8028 3730
e-mail: jackie4r@aol.com
Dir: exit M27 junct 1 follow A337 to Lyndhurst. Left at traffic lights in village onto A35 towards Southampton. Hotel 0.25m on left

PETS: Bedrooms (Annexe rooms only) (unattended) Exercise area (Across road)

This friendly, family-run hotel is situated on the outskirts of

continued on p134

England

LYNDHURST continued

Lyndhurst. Comfortable bedrooms are modern in style and well-equipped with many useful extras. The hotel offers an excellent range of facilities including a swimming pool, a Jacuzzi and a small gym area.

ROOMS: 15 en suite 4 annexe en suite (2 fmly) s £45-£55; d £40-£55 (incl. bkfst) **LB FACILITIES:** STV Indoor swimming (H) Sauna Gym Jacuzzi Steam room **PARKING:** 15 **NOTES:** No smoking in restaurant **CARDS:**

MILFORD ON SEA — Map 04 SZ29

★★★ ◉◉ **Westover Hall**

Park Ln SO41 0PT
☎ 01590 643044 📠 01590 644490
e-mail: info@westoverhallhotel.com
Dir: M3 & M27 W onto A337 to Lymington. Follow signs to Milford-on-Sea onto B3058. Hotel outside village centre towards cliff

> **PETS:** Bedrooms (unattended) £10 Public areas (except restaurant/bar) Exercise area RESIDENT PETS: Arthur (cat)

Just a few moments' walk from the beach and boasting uninterrupted views across Christchurch Bay to the Isle of Wight in the distance, this late-Victorian mansion offers a relaxed, informal and friendly atmosphere together with efficient standards of hospitality and service. Each of the bedrooms has been decorated with flair and style. Architectural delights include dramatic stained-glass windows, extensive oak panelling and a galleried entrance hall. The cuisine is prepared with much care and attention to detail.

ROOMS: 12 en suite (1 fmly) No smoking in all bedrooms s £100-£150; d £165-£230 (incl. bkfst) **LB FACILITIES:** Beach Hut Xmas **PARKING:** 50 **NOTES:** No children 5 yrs No smoking in restaurant **CARDS:**

PETERSFIELD — Map 04 SU72

★★ 69% **Langrish House**

Langrish GU32 1RN
☎ 01730 266941 📠 01730 260543
e-mail: frontdesk@langrishhouse.co.uk
Dir: off A3 onto A272 towards Winchester. Hotel signed, 3m on left

> **PETS:** Bedrooms (unattended) £10 Public areas (Not the restaurant) Exercise area (All around the hotel) Pet pack for dogs - blanket, poop scoop, biscuits, welcome letter & a towel RESIDENT PETS: Tonga (Black Labrador)

Located in a secluded spot just outside Petersfield, this family home dates back to the 17th century. Rooms offer good levels of comfort with beautiful views over the countryside. The public areas consist of a small cosy restaurant, a bar in the vaults, and conference and banqueting rooms that are popular for weddings.

ROOMS: 13 en suite (1 fmly) (3 GF) No smoking in all bedrooms s £65.70-£73; d £104.40-£140 (incl. bkfst) **LB FACILITIES:** Fishing Xmas **PARKING:** 80 **NOTES:** No smoking in restaurant **CARDS:**

PORTSMOUTH — Map 04 SU60

★★★★ 65%
Portsmouth Marriott Hotel

Southampton Rd PO6 4SH
☎ 0870 400 7285 📠 0870 400 7385
e-mail: reservations.portsmouth@marriotthotels.com
Dir: M27 junct 12 keep left and hotel on left

> **PETS:** Bedrooms

Close to the motorway and ferry port, this hotel is well suited to business trade. The comfortable and well laid-out bedrooms provide a comprehensive range of facilities including up-to-date workstations. The leisure club offers a pool, a gym, and a health and beauty salon.

ROOMS: 174 en suite (77 fmly) No smoking in 130 bedrooms s £67-£155; d £84-£185 **FACILITIES:** STV Indoor swimming (H) Sauna Solarium Gym Jacuzzi Exercise studio, Beauty salon Xmas **SERVICES:** Lift air con **PARKING:** 250 **CARDS:**

★★★ 70% **Royal Beach**

South Pde, Southsea PO4 0RN
☎ 023 9273 1281 📠 023 9281 7572
e-mail: enquiries@royalbeachhotel.co.uk
Dir: M27 to M275, follow signs to seafront. Hotel on seafront

> **PETS:** Bedrooms Public areas (except restaurant) Exercise area (100yds)

A recent and ongoing refurbishment has transformed this former Victorian seafront hotel into a smart and comfortable venue suitable for leisure and business guests alike. Bedrooms are well-presented and generally spacious and there is an indoor golf simulator for those wishing to take some exercise after dinner!

ROOMS: 124 en suite (18 fmly) No smoking in 72 bedrooms s £75-£95; d £90-£105 (incl. bkfst) **LB FACILITIES:** STV Xmas **SERVICES:** Lift **PARKING:** 50 **NOTES:** No smoking in restaurant **CARDS:**

★★ 72% **Seacrest**

11/12 South Pde, Southsea PO5 2JB
☎ 023 9273 3192 📠 023 9283 2523
e-mail: seacrest@boltblue.com
Dir: from M27/M275 follow signs for seafront, Pyramids and Sea Life Centre. Hotel opposite Rock Gardens and Pyramids

> **PETS:** Bedrooms £5 Public areas (except dining room) Exercise area (25yds)

In a premier seafront location, this smart hotel provides the ideal base for exploring the town. Bedrooms, many benefiting from sea views, are decorated to a high standard with good facilities. Guests can relax in either the south-facing lounge, furnished with large leather sofas, or the adjacent bar; there is also a cosy dining room popular with residents.

ROOMS: 28 en suite (3 fmly) No smoking in 20 bedrooms s £45-£55; d £60-£89 (incl. bkfst) **LB FACILITIES:** STV **SERVICES:** Lift **PARKING:** 12 **NOTES:** No smoking in restaurant **CARDS:**

RINGWOOD Map 04 SU10

♦♦♦♦♦ Little Forest Lodge
Poulner Hill BH24 3HS
☎ 01425 478848 📠 01425 473564
Dir: 1.5m E of Ringwood on A31

PETS: Bedrooms £3 Public areas (not in dining room)
Exercise area (on site) RESIDENT PETS: Millie - dog; Harry &
Spike - cats, 8 ducks & 12 chickens

A warm welcome is assured at this charming Edwardian house set
in two acres of gardens and woodland. Bedrooms are pleasantly
decorated and equipped with many thoughtful extras. By prior
arrangement, guests may enjoy home-cooked meals, which make
good use of fresh local produce. Both the attractive wood-panelled
dining room and the delightful lounge, with its cosy bar and
wood-burning fire, overlook the gardens.
FACILITIES: 6 en suite (3 fmly) (1 GF) No smoking TVB tea/coffee
Licensed Cen ht No coaches Croquet lawn clock golf, badminton Dinner
Last d 7.30pm **PRICES:** s £40-£45; d £60-£70✱ **PARKING:** 10
CARDS: 🟦 🟦 🟦 🟦

♦♦♦ Lochend
Hurst Rd BH24 1AX
☎ 01425 473836 📠 01425 475624
e-mail: kenburnsbrown@btopenworld.com
*Dir: turn off A31 onto A338 towards Fordingbridge. After approx 500mtrs,
take 2nd right into Hurst Rd. Lochend is first house on right*

PETS: Bedrooms RESIDENT PETS: Tabby cat - Libby

Located on the north side of town with easy access to the shops,
the New Forest and various places of interest, this delightful
property has both of its spacious, comfortable bedrooms on the
ground floor. A charming garden is also available to guests, and
English breakfasts are served at one large table.
FACILITIES: 2 rms (1 en suite) (1 fmly) (2 GF) No smoking TVB
tea/coffee Cen ht No coaches **PRICES:** s £25-£30; d £44-£46✱ **LB**
PARKING: 4 **NOTES:** Closed Xmas & New Year

> 🛢 **Places with this
> symbol are pubs**

> 🌲 **Places with this symbol are
> country house hotels**

ROMSEY Map 04 SU32

★★★ 64% The White Horse
Market Place SO51 8ZJ
☎ 0870 400 8123 📠 01794 517485
e-mail: whitehorseromsey@macdonald-hotels.co.uk

MACDONALD
HOTELS

*Dir: M27 junct 3, follow A3057 to Romsey, signs to town centre. Past hotel,
take 1st left into Latimer St, then left again into car park.*

PETS: Bedrooms (unattended) £10 Exercise area

It is thought that the hotel was originally a guesthouse for Romsey
Abbey in the 12th century, although the present structure dates back
to the time of Henry VIII. Bedrooms vary in size; the majority have
now been refurbished and all are equipped with a range of modern
facilities. Public rooms include a cosy lounge, bar and restaurant.
ROOMS: 26 en suite 7 annexe en suite (7 fmly) (7 GF) No smoking in
10 bedrooms s £70-£90; d £95-£130 **LB** **FACILITIES:** STV Xmas
PARKING: 40 **NOTES:** No smoking in restaurant
CARDS: 🟦 🟦 🟦 🟦 🟦

ROWLANDS CASTLE Map 04 SU71

♦♦♦♦ 🛢 The Fountain Inn
34 The Green PO9 6AB
☎ 023 9241 2291 📠 023 9241 2291
e-mail: Fountaininn@amserve.com
*Dir: A3(M) junct 2, follow B2149 for 2m, turn left at rdbt down Redhill Rd.
Inn overlooks village green*

PETS: Bedrooms (unattended) If large, and if more than
one Public areas (well-behaved dogs allowed in the bar only)
Exercise area (Village green outside) RESIDENT PETS: Bertie -
English Pointer, Millie - Jack Russell & Joe - three-legged black cat

A charming coaching inn set back from the road and overlooking
the village green. The well-equipped bedrooms have been
tastefully refurbished and have many thoughtful touches; one
room has a lovely four-poster bed. Public areas consist of a
popular local bar and cosy restaurant.
FACILITIES: 4 en suite (1 fmly) No smoking TVB tea/coffee Cen ht
Dinner Last d 9.30pm **LB** **PARKING:** **CARDS:** 🟦 🟦 🟦 🟦 🟦

SOUTHAMPTON Map 04 SU41

★★★ 69% 🌲 The Woodlands Lodge
Bartley Rd, Woodlands SO40 7GN
☎ 023 8029 2257 📠 023 8029 3090
e-mail: reception@woodlands-lodge.co.uk
*Dir: A326 towards Fawley. 2nd rdbt turn right, left after 0.25m by White
Horse PH. In 1.5m cross cattle grid, hotel is 70yds on left*

PETS: Bedrooms (unattended) Exercise area (50 yards)
RESIDENT PETS: Bentley (Dalmatian)

An 18th-century former hunting lodge, this hotel is set in four
acres of impressive and well-tended grounds on the edge of the
New Forest. Well-equipped bedrooms come in varying sizes and
styles and all bathrooms have a jacuzzi bath. Public areas provide
a pleasant lounge and intimate cocktail bar. The dining room, with
its hand-painted ceiling, serves delicious award-winning cuisine.
ROOMS: 16 en suite (1 fmly) (3 GF) No smoking in 2 bedrooms
s £72-£95; d £98-£142 (incl. bkfst) **LB** **FACILITIES:** STV Jacuzzi ch fac
Xmas **PARKING:** 31 **NOTES:** No smoking in restaurant
CARDS: 🟦 🟦 🟦 🟦 🟦

England

SOUTHAMPTON continued

★★★ 66% Southampton Park

Forestdale Hotels

Cumberland Place SO15 2WY
☎ 023 8034 3343 ▥ 023 8033 2538
e-mail: southampton.park@forestdale.com
Dir: hotel at northern end of the Inner Ring Rd opposite Watts Park & Civic Centre

PETS: Bedrooms (unattended) £7.50 Public areas (not in restaurant) Pet Food

Located in the heart of the city opposite Watts Park, this modern hotel provides well-equipped, smartly appointed bedrooms with comfortable furnishings. The public areas include a good leisure centre, a spacious bar and lounge and the lively MJ's Brasserie. Parking is available in the multi-storey car park behind the hotel.
ROOMS: 72 en suite (10 fmly) No smoking in 20 bedrooms s fr £90; d fr £120 (incl. bkfst) LB **FACILITIES:** Spa STV Indoor swimming (H) Sauna Solarium Gym Jacuzzi **SERVICES:** Lift **NOTES:** No smoking in restaurant Closed 25 & 26 Dec nights
CARDS: 💳

★★ 68% Elizabeth House

42-44 The Avenue SO17 1XP
☎ 023 8022 4327 ▥ 023 8022 4327
e-mail: enquiries@elizabethhousehotel.com
Dir: on A33, on left towards city centre, after Southampton Common, before main lights

PETS: Bedrooms (unattended) Exercise area

The Elizabeth House is conveniently situated on The Avenue, and as such provides an ideal base for both business and leisure guests. The bedrooms are well equipped and are attractively furnished with comfort in mind. There is also a relaxing and attractive restaurant and a cosy cellar bar.
ROOMS: 20 en suite 7 annexe en suite (8 fmly) (8 GF) s £52; d £62 (incl. bkfst) **PARKING:** 30 **NOTES:** No smoking in restaurant
CARDS: 💳

⌂ Hotel Ibis

ibis

West Quay Rd, Western Esplanade SO15 1RA
☎ 023 8063 4463 ▥ 023 8022 3273
e-mail: H1039@accor-hotels.com
Dir: M27 junct 3/M271. Left to city centre (A35), follow Old Town Waterfront until 4th lights, left, then left again, hotel opposite station

PETS: Bedrooms (unattended) Exercise area

Modern, budget hotel offering comfortable accommodation in bright and practical bedrooms. Breakfast is self-service and dinner is available in the restaurant. For further details, consult the Hotel Groups page.
ROOMS: 93 en suite s £58.95

> All information was correct at
> the time of going to press; we
> recommend you confirm
> details on booking

◆◆◆◆ Hunters Lodge Hotel

25 Landguard Rd, Shirley SO15 5DL
☎ 023 8022 7919 ▥ 023 8023 0913
e-mail: hunterslodge.hotel@virgin.net
Dir: From Southampton Central, turn right into Hill Lane. Landguard Road is the fourth turning on your left

PETS: Bedrooms (unattended) Public areas (not in dining room) Exercise area (1 mile)

Located in a leafy residential area close to the city centre and conveniently situated for the docks, ferry terminal, university and hospital, this double fronted Victorian house provides business and leisure guests with comfortable, well-equipped bedrooms. Full English breakfast is served at shared tables in the elegant dining room. There is also a TV lounge and a well-stocked bar.
FACILITIES: 14 en suite (1 fmly) (1 GF) No smoking in bedrooms No smoking in dining room No smoking in 1 lounge TVB tea/coffee Direct dial from bedrooms Licensed Cen ht TVL **PRICES:** s £37-£50; d £60-£65✱ **PARKING:** 16 **CARDS:** 💳

STOCKBRIDGE   Map 04 SU33

◆◆◆◆ York Lodge

Five Bells Ln, Nether Wallop SO20 8HE
☎ 01264 781313
e-mail: bradley@yorklodge.fslife.co.uk
Dir: Leave A343 (Andover/Salisbury Rd) onto B3084 signed Romsey. Take 2nd left (Hocketts Ln) & fork left into Five Bells Ln. York Lodge 1st house on right with large wooden automatic gates

PETS: Bedrooms (unattended) Public areas Exercise area
RESIDENT PETS: Polly (Black Labrador)

Located in the picturesque village famous for Agatha Christie's *Miss Marple* series, this charming house has comfortable accommodation in a self-contained wing. Bedrooms are stylishly presented with many thoughtful extra facilities. The dining room overlooks peaceful gardens. Delicious dinners are available by prior arrangement.
FACILITIES: 2 en suite (2 GF) No smoking TVB tea/coffee Cen ht No children 8yrs No coaches Dinner Last d 24hrs prior
PRICES: s £30-£35; d £50-£70✱ **PARKING:** 4

STRATFIELD TURGIS   Map 04 SU65

★★★ 67% Wellington Arms

RG27 0AS
☎ 01256 882214 ▥ 01256 882934
e-mail: Wellington.Arms@virgin.net
Dir: A33 between Basingstoke & Reading

PETS: Bedrooms (unattended) £10 Exercise area

Situated at one of the entrances to the ancestral home of the Duke of Wellington, the white Georgian façade is a familiar landmark on the A33. The majority of bedrooms are located in the Garden Wing and have now benefited from refurbishment, whereas rooms in the original building are more individual and have a period feel. Public rooms include a comfortable lounge bar with a log fire and a pleasant, formal restaurant; informal dining is available in the bar.
ROOMS: 35 en suite (2 fmly) No smoking in 3 bedrooms
PARKING: 150 **CARDS:** 💳

England

SWAY   Map 04 SZ29

★★ 68% Sway Manor Restaurant & Hotel
Station Rd SO41 6BA
☎ 01590 682754 ▤ 01590 682955
e-mail: info@swaymanor.com
Dir: turn off B3055 Brockenhurst/New Milton road into Sway village centre

PETS: Bedrooms (unattended) £5 Public areas (not in restaurant) Exercise area (in grounds)

Built at the turn of the 20th century, this attractive mansion is set in its own grounds, which include an outdoor swimming pool, and is also conveniently located in the centre of the village. Bedrooms are well appointed and generously equipped whilst the bar and restaurant, which both have views over the gardens, are popular with locals.
ROOMS: 15 en suite (3 fmly) No smoking in 12 bedrooms s £43–£51; d £70–£102 (incl. bkfst) LB **FACILITIES:** Outdoor swimming (H) entertainment Xmas **SERVICES:** Lift **PARKING:** 40 **NOTES:** No smoking in restaurant **CARDS:**

♦♦♦♦ Acorn Shetland Pony Stud
Meadows Cottage, Arnewood Bridge Rd SO41 6DA
☎ 01590 682000 ▤ 01590 682000
e-mail: meadows.cottage@virgin.net
Dir: M27 through Lyndhurst towards Brockenhurst, take B3055 signed Sway, pass Birchy Hill Nursing Home, over x-rds, take 2nd entrance left

PETS: Bedrooms £3 for dog Public areas Exercise area (on site) towels for muddy dogs **RESIDENT PETS:** 9 Shetland ponies

Peacefully located on the outskirts of Sway this comfortable establishment is set in over six acres of pony paddocks and a landscaped water garden. The ground-floor bedrooms are well furnished and have direct access onto patios. The enjoyable breakfasts use a good range of freshly-cooked produce including delicious home-made bread.
FACILITIES: 2 en suite (1 fmly) (2 GF) No smoking TVB tea/coffee Cen ht No coaches Carriage driving **PRICES:** d fr £48✱ LB **PARKING:** 3

WINCHESTER   Map 04 SU42

★★★★ ⑳⑳ ♨ Lainston House
Sparsholt SO21 2LT
☎ 01962 863588 ▤ 01962 776672
e-mail: enquiries@lainstonhouse.com
Dir: 2m NW off B3049 towards Stockbridge

ExclusivE
HOTELS & GOLF CLUBS

PETS: Bedrooms (unattended) £10 Public areas

This graceful example of a William and Mary house enjoys a countryside location amidst mature grounds and gardens. Staff provide good levels of courtesy and care with a polished, professional service. Bedrooms are tastefully appointed and include some spectacular spacious rooms with stylish handmade beds and stunning bathrooms. Public rooms include a cocktail bar built entirely from a single cedar and stocked with an impressive range of rare drinks and cigars.
ROOMS: 50 en suite (6 fmly) (18 GF) s £80–£120; d £95–£175 LB **FACILITIES:** STV Tennis (hard) Fishing Gym Croquet lawn Putting green Archery, Clay pigeon shooting, cycling entertainment Xmas **PARKING:** 150 **NOTES:** No smoking in restaurant **CARDS:**

★★★★ 63% The Wessex
Paternoster Row SO23 9LQ
☎ 0870 400 8126 ▤ 01962 841503
e-mail: wessex@macdonald-hotels.co.uk
Dir: M3, follow signs for town centre, at rdbt by King Alfred's statue past Guildhall, next left, hotel on right

MACDONALD
HOTELS

PETS: Bedrooms (unattended) £20 Public areas (except dining areas) Exercise area (0.25 mile)

A modern hotel occupying an enviable location in the centre of this historic city and adjacent to the spectacular cathedral, yet quietly situated on a side street. Inside, the ambience is modern, restful and welcoming, with many public areas and bedrooms enjoying unrivalled views of the hotel's centuries-old neighbour.
ROOMS: 94 en suite (6 fmly) No smoking in 61 bedrooms s £65–£160; d £110–£250 (incl. bkfst) LB **FACILITIES:** STV Solarium Gym Free use of local leisure centre, beauty therapy Xmas **SERVICES:** Lift **PARKING:** 60 **NOTES:** No smoking in restaurant **CARDS:**

HEREFORDSHIRE

ABBEY DORE   Map 03 SO33

♦♦♦♦ ⚑ ❦ Tan House Farm
HR2 0AA
☎ 01981 240204 ▤ 01981 240204
e-mail: jppowell@ereal.net
Dir: turn right off A465 at Wormbridge and follow signs for Dore Abbey

PETS: Telephone for details

This stone-built farmhouse is close to the 12th-century Cistercian Dore Abbey in the beautiful Golden Valley. The traditionally furnished bedrooms have modern facilities. Breakfast is served family-style in the combined breakfast room and lounge, which has fine antique furnishings. Hospitality is warm and the welcome second to none.
FACILITIES: 3 en suite No smoking in bedrooms No smoking in dining room TVB tea/coffee No dogs (ex guide dogs) Cen ht TVL 350 acres arable cattle sheep horses **PRICES:** s £25; d £50✱ **PARKING:** 3

BROMYARD   Map 03 SO65

♦♦♦♦ Little Hegdon Farm House
Hegdon Hill, Pencombe HR7 4SL
☎ 01885 400263
e-mail: howardcolegrave@hotmail.com
Dir: between villages of Pencombe & Risbury, at top of Hegdon Hill turn down a farm lane, property approx 500mtrs

PETS: Sep Accom (stable) Public areas (except dining area) Exercise area (adjacent) **RESIDENT PETS:** Meg & Snuff (Border Collies), Pepsi (Lakeland Terrier), Ebony & Pippa (horses)

Located in a pretty hamlet, this fine period house has been sympathetically renovated to provide high standards of comfort. There are many original features, including exposed beams and open fires. Bedrooms are equipped with lots of thoughtful extras and enjoy stunning views of the surrounding countryside.
FACILITIES: 2 en suite No smoking in bedrooms No smoking in dining room No smoking in 1 lounge TVB tea/coffee Cen ht No coaches Riding Pool Table Croquet lawn **PRICES:** s £30; d £50✱ **PARKING:** 4

England

HEREFORD — Map 03 SO54

◆◆◆◆ 👿 Sink Green
Rotherwas HR2 6LE
☎ 01432 870223 📠 01432 870223
e-mail: enquiries@sinkgreenfarm.co.uk
Dir: on B4399 2m from junction with A49

PETS: Bedrooms Public areas Exercise area (adjoining)
RESIDENT PETS: Bob & Buzz - dogs

This charming 16th-century farmhouse is set in attractive countryside and has many original features including stone-flagged floors, ceilings with exposed beams, and open fireplaces. Bedrooms are traditionally furnished, one of which has a four-poster bed. Outside there is a pleasant garden, with a summerhouse, hot tub and barbecue. The friendly and relaxed atmosphere leaves a lasting impression.
FACILITIES: 3 en suite No smoking TVB tea/coffee Cen ht TVL jacuzzi & summer house 180 acres beef sheep **PRICES:** s £24-£30; d £46-£54✱ **LB PARKING:** 10 **NOTES:** Closed Xmas

KINGTON — Map 03 SO25

★★★ 67% Burton
Mill St HR5 3BQ
☎ 01544 230323 📠 01544 239023
e-mail: burton@hotelherefordshire.co.uk
Dir: rdbt at A44/A411 junct, take road signed Town Centre

PETS: Bedrooms Public areas (On a lead with owner) Exercise area (300yds)

Situated in the town centre, this friendly, privately-owned hotel offers spacious, pleasantly proportioned and well equipped bedrooms. Smartly presented public areas include a lounge bar, a small lounge and an attractive restaurant where carefully prepared cuisine can be enjoyed. There are also function and meeting facilities available in a purpose-built modern wing.
ROOMS: 16 en suite (5 fmly) No smoking in 2 bedrooms s £42-£52; d £69-£75 (incl. bkfst) **LB FACILITIES:** Xmas **PARKING:** 50
CARDS: 🖻🖻🖻🖻🖻

LEOMINSTER — Map 03 SO45

◆◆◆◆◆ 🛏 👿 Ford Abbey
Pudleston HR6 0RZ
☎ 01568 760700 📠 01568 760264
e-mail: info@fordabbey.co.uk
Dir: A44 Leominster towards Worcester, turn left to Pudleston

PETS: Bedrooms (unattended) £13 Exercise area (in grounds)

Excellence, attention to detail and a high level of hospitality are all hallmarks at this sympathetically converted former medieval monastery set on a working farm. Beams and original features abound and guests can relax in a choice of lounges and an atmospheric restaurant which serves dinners using farm produce. Bedrooms are spacious and there is a leisure complex in the grounds.
FACILITIES: 6 en suite (1 GF) No smoking in bedrooms No smoking in dining room STV TVB tea/coffee Direct dial from bedrooms Licensed Cen ht TVL Indoor swimming pool (heated) Solarium Gymnasium Croquet lawn 320 acres beef Dinner Last d am **PARKING:** 20
CARDS: 🖻🖻🖻🖻🖻

◆◆◆ 👿 Woonton Court Farm
Leysters HR6 0HL
☎ 01568 750232 📠 01568 750232
e-mail: thomas.woontoncourt@farmersweekly.net
Dir: take A49, 2.5m from Leominster onto A4112. Through Kimbolton, R for Woonton before Leysters. Farm 0.5m down lane

PETS: Sep Accom (Large porch with windows) Dogs/cats £2.50 Exercise area (50yds) Food & bowls by prior arrangement; surrounding area includes fields, footpaths and woods

This attractive 15th-century farmhouse is set in tranquil countryside, and displays many original features such as ancient beams, and family mementoes. Bedrooms are well equipped, with comfortable furnishings and many extra facilities. Freshly cooked breakfasts include farm-produced eggs, local sausages and home-made marmalade, served in the comfortable dining room.
FACILITIES: 2 rms (1 en suite) 1 annexe en suite No smoking TVB tea/coffee Cen ht TVL 250 acres mixed **PRICES:** s £25-£30; d £45-£55✱ **LB PARKING:** 4 **NOTES:** Closed 22-27 Dec

MUCH BIRCH — Map 03 SO53

★★★ 66% Pilgrim
Ross Rd HR2 8HJ
☎ 01981 540742 📠 01981 540620
e-mail: stay@pilgrimhotel.co.uk
Dir: on A49 6m from Ross-on-Wye, 5m from Hereford

THE INDEPENDENTS

PETS: Bedrooms £5 Exercise area (100yds)

This much-extended former rectory is set back from the A49 and has sweeping views over the surrounding countryside. The extensive grounds contain a pitch and putt course. Privately owned and personally run, it provides accommodation that includes ground floor and four-poster rooms. Public areas comprise a restful lounge, a traditionally furnished restaurant and a pleasant bar.
ROOMS: 20 en suite (3 fmly) (8 GF) No smoking in 12 bedrooms s £55-£75; d £75-£100 (incl. bkfst) **LB FACILITIES:** Golf 3 Croquet lawn Putting green Pitch & putt, Badminton Xmas **PARKING:** 42
NOTES: No smoking in restaurant
CARDS: 🖻🖻🖻🖻🖻🖻

ROSS-ON-WYE — Map 03 SO62

★★★ 74% Pengethley Manor
Pengethley Park HR9 6LL
☎ 01989 730211 📠 01989 730238
e-mail: reservations@pengethleymanor.co.uk
Dir: 4m N on A49 Hereford road, from Ross-On-Wye

Best Western

PETS: Bedrooms (unattended) Public areas (except restaurant or bar) Exercise area (adjacent parkland) Pet Food
RESIDENT PETS: Gem - Welsh Mountain pony, Dicksy - Dalmation, Sydney - cat

This fine Georgian mansion is set in extensive grounds with two vineyards and glorious views. The accommodation is tastefully appointed and there is a wide variety of bedroom styles, all

continued

similarly well equipped. The elegant public rooms are furnished in a style sympathetic to the character of the house.
ROOMS: 11 en suite 14 annexe en suite (3 fmly) (4 GF) s £75–£115; d £120–£180 (incl. bkfst) **LB FACILITIES:** Outdoor swimming (H) Golf 9 Fishing Croquet lawn Golf improvement course, walks accessible from Hotel ch fac Xmas **PARKING:** 70 **NOTES:** No smoking in restaurant
CARDS:

★★★ 68% Pencraig Court
Pencraig HR9 6HR
☎ 01989 770306 📠 01989 770040
e-mail: info@pencraig-court.co.uk
Dir: off A40, into Pencraig 4m S of Ross-on-Wye

PETS: Bedrooms £5, maximum £20 Public areas (except dining room) Exercise area (on site and adjacent) Pet Food food by arrangement RESIDENT PETS: Maisie - Sussex Spaniel, Rosie & Jan - Labrador/Collie cross

Impressive views of the River Wye and Ross-on-Wye beyond set the scene for a relaxing stay at this former Georgian mansion. The proprietors are on hand to ensure personal attention and service, while the bedrooms evoke a traditional feel and include a room with a four-poster bed. The country house ambience is completed by a choice of lounges and an elegant restaurant.
ROOMS: 10 en suite (1 fmly) No smoking in 6 bedrooms s £49–£52.50; d £80–£88 (incl. bkfst) **LB FACILITIES:** Fishing Croquet lawn
PARKING: 20 **NOTES:** No smoking in restaurant
CARDS: ▬▬

★★★ 67% The Royal
Palace Pound HR9 5HZ
☎ 01989 565105 📠 01989 768058
e-mail: 6504@greeneking.co.uk
Dir: at end of M50 take A40 'Monmouth'. At 3rd rdbt, left to Ross, over bridge and take road signed 'The Royal Hotel' after left bend

PETS: Bedrooms (unattended) Exercise area (0.25 mile)

Close to the town centre, this imposing hotel enjoys panoramic views from its prominent hilltop position. Reputedly visited by Charles Dickens in 1867, this establishment has been sympathetically furnished to create the ambience of a bygone era with the comforts of today. In addition to the lounge and elegant restaurant, there are function rooms and an attractive garden.
ROOMS: 42 en suite (1 fmly) No smoking in 18 bedrooms s £75–£100; d £100–£135 (incl. bkfst) **LB FACILITIES:** Xmas **PARKING:** 44
NOTES: No smoking in restaurant **CARDS:** ▬▬

★★ 74% 🌐 Wilton Court Hotel
Wilton Ln HR9 6AQ
☎ 01989 562569 📠 01989 768460
e-mail: info@wiltoncourthotel.com
Dir: M50 junct 4 onto A40 towards Monmouth, at 3rd rdbt turn left signed Ross then take 1st right, hotel on right facing river

PETS: Bedrooms Public areas (dogs only; not in restaurant)

Dating back to the 16th century, this engaging hotel has great charm with a wealth of character. Standing on the banks of the River Wye and just a short walk from the town centre, there is a genuinely relaxed, friendly and unhurried atmosphere here. Bedrooms are tastefully furnished and well equipped, while public
continued

areas include a comfortable lounge, traditional bar and pleasant restaurant with a conservatory extension overlooking the garden.
ROOMS: 10 en suite (1 fmly) No smoking in all bedrooms s £60–£85; d £80–£115 (incl. bkfst) **LB FACILITIES:** Fishing Boule Xmas
PARKING: 24 **NOTES:** No smoking in restaurant
CARDS: ▬▬

★★ 71% Castle Lodge Hotel
Wilton HR9 6AD
☎ 01989 562234 📠 01989 768322
e-mail: info@castlelodge.co.uk
Dir: on rdbt at junct of A40/A49, 0.5m from centre of Ross-on-Wye

PETS: Bedrooms £10 per stay Public areas Exercise area

This friendly hotel dates back to the 16th century and offers a convenient base on the outskirts of the town. Bedrooms are well equipped and comfortably furnished, while diners can choose between a good selection of bar meals and a varied restaurant menu, which features a wide range of fresh seafood.
ROOMS: 10 en suite (3 fmly) s fr £42.95; d fr £49.95 **LB**
FACILITIES: tennis courts (0.5m) **PARKING:** 40
CARDS: ▬▬

★★ 66% Chasedale
Walford Rd HR9 5PQ
☎ 01989 562423 📠 01989 567900
e-mail: chasedale@supanet.com
Dir: from Ross-on-Wye town centre, S on B4234, hotel 0.5m on left

PETS: Bedrooms (unattended) Exercise area (200yds)
RESIDENT PETS: Marmite - chocolate Labrador, Cassis - Black Labrador

This large, mid-Victorian property is situated on the south-west outskirts of the town. Privately owned and personally run, it provides spacious, well-proportioned public areas and extensive grounds. The accommodation is well equipped and includes ground floor and family rooms, whilst the restaurant offers a wide selection of wholesome food.
ROOMS: 10 en suite (2 fmly) (1 GF) No smoking in 1 bedroom s £33.50–£37.50; d £67–£75 (incl. bkfst) **LB FACILITIES:** Xmas
PARKING: 14 **NOTES:** No smoking in restaurant
CARDS: ▬▬

★★ 66% King's Head
8 High St HR9 5HL
☎ 01989 763174 📠 01989 769578
e-mail: reception@kingshead.co.uk
Dir: in town centre

THE INDEPENDENTS

PETS: Bedrooms Public areas (except food service areas) Exercise area

The King's Head dates back to the 14th century and has a wealth of charm and character. Bedrooms are well equipped and include both four-poster and family rooms. The restaurant doubles as a coffee shop during the day and is a popular venue with locals. There is also a very pleasant bar and comfortable lounge.
ROOMS: 16 en suite s fr £53.50; d fr £100 (incl. bkfst) **LB**
FACILITIES: Xmas **PARKING:** 24 **NOTES:** No smoking in restaurant
CARDS: ▬▬

England

ROSS-ON-WYE continued

✦✦✦✦ Brookfield House

Over Ross St HR9 7AT
☎ 01989 562188
e-mail: collcost@yahoo.co.uk
Dir: from Ross bypass (A40). At the rdbt with 'Focus DIY store' take the Ross-On-Wye exit onto Ledbury road (B4228), continue for about 0.5m, turn left into Brookmead and up driveway.

PETS: Bedrooms £1 (donated to charity) Public areas (except dining room) Exercise area (on site) Feeding mat in rooms, chemical dog toilet in garden RESIDENT PETS: Cat

Dating from the 18th century, this large detached house lies in well tended gardens just north of the town centre. Refurbished to a high standard throughout, the bedrooms are spacious, comfortably appointed and well equipped. Breakfast is served in the light and airy dining room, providing a tasty and satisfying start to the day. Guests are welcome to make use of the attractive gardens.
FACILITIES: 3 en suite (1 fmly) No smoking TVB tea/coffee Cen ht No coaches **PRICES:** s £29-£35; d £50-£58✳ **PARKING:** 12
CARDS: 💳💳💳

✦✦✦✦ Brynheulog

Howle Hill HR9 5SP
☎ 01989 562051 📠 01989 562051
Dir: from Ross-on-wye take B4234, after 1 mile turn left (signed Howle Hill). After 250yds 1st right (signed Howle Hill). At x-roads turn left, first house on right, past church

PETS: Bedrooms Sep Accom (Kennel, shed, fields) Public areas (unless other guests object) Exercise area (grounds)

This highly individual guest house has been lovingly designed by the owner to provide a high level of comfort and it benefits from superb views. The bedrooms are full of character and well equipped, with furniture built by a local craftsman. Two are in a self-contained wing with its own private lounge. Public areas consist of a tastefully decorated dining room and a relaxing lounge.
FACILITIES: 4 en suite (1 fmly) (2 GF) No smoking TV3B tea/coffee Cen ht TVL No coaches Dinner **PRICES:** s £20-£30; d £40-£60✳ LB **PARKING:** 7

✦✦✦✦ 🍴 Lea House

Lea HR9 7JZ
☎ 01989 750652 📠 01989 750652
e-mail: enquiries@leahousebandb.com
Dir: on A40, 4m SE of Ross-on-wye, towards Gloucester. Lea House located in middle of Lea Village

PETS: Bedrooms (unattended) £5 per stay Public areas (except dining room) Exercise area (adjacent) RESIDENT PETS: Pepper - Alsation/collie cross, Cocoa - small terrier, Custard & Cream - ginger & white cats

This former 16th-century coaching inn is conveniently situated on the A40 into Ross on Wye and provides a relaxing base from which to explore the delightful Herefordshire countryside. Bedrooms are thoughtfully equipped and individually furnished.

continued

Dinner and hearty breakfasts can be enjoyed, family style, in the charming dining room.

FACILITIES: 3 rms (2 en suite) (1 fmly) No smoking TVB tea/coffee Cen ht No coaches Dinner Last d by prior arrangement
PRICES: s £30-£40; d £50-£60✳ LB **PARKING:** 4
CARDS: 💳💳💳💳💳

✦✦✦✦ Lumleys

Kern Bridge, Bishopswood HR9 5QT
☎ 01600 890040 📠 0870 7062378
e-mail: helen@lumleys.force9.co.uk
Dir: A40 turn off at Goodrich onto B4229 over Kern Bridge. Right at Inn On The Wye, approx 400yds past inn opp picnic ground

PETS: Bedrooms (unattended) Public areas (except dining room) Exercise area (20yds) Anything required can be provided RESIDENT PETS: dog

This pleasant and friendly guest house overlooks the River Wye and has been a hostelry since Victorian times. It offers the character of a bygone era combined with modern comforts and facilities. Bedrooms are individually and carefully furnished and one has a four-poster bed and its own patio. Comfortable public areas include a choice of sitting rooms.
FACILITIES: 3 en suite No smoking TVB tea/coffee Direct dial from bedrooms Cen ht No children 10yrs No coaches Dinner Last d 7pm **PRICES:** d £50-£65✳ **PARKING:** 15

✦✦✦✦ Thatch Close

Llangrove HR9 6EL
☎ 01989 770 300
e-mail: info@thatchclose.co.uk
Dir: turn off A40 at Symonds Yat West/Whitchurch Junction, take road in front of Crown Inn into Llangrove (1.9m), turn right at x-rds just past P.O. and before school, keep on for 0.6m, Thatch Close is on left

PETS: Bedrooms Public areas (if no other guests staying) Exercise area (adjacent) RESIDENT PETS: Aku & Zippy (African grey parrots), & spaniel-collie cross

Peacefully located in 13 acres, this sturdy farmhouse dating back to 1760 is full of charm and character. There is a wonderfully warm atmosphere here with a genuine welcome from your hosts. The homely bedrooms are equipped for comfort with many thoughtful extras. Breakfast and dinner are served in the elegant dining room with a guest lounge also available. The extensive patios and gardens are popular in summer months, providing plenty of space to find a quiet corner and relax with a good book!
FACILITIES: 3 rms (2 en suite) No smoking TVB tea/coffee Cen ht TVL No coaches Dinner Last d 9am **PRICES:** s £28-£33; d £50-£55✳ LB **PARKING:** 8

England

SYMONDS YAT (WEST)   Map 03 SO51

◆◆◆◆ ♟ Norton House
Whitchurch, Symonds Yat HR9 6DJ
☎ 01600 890046 📠 01600 890045
e-mail: su@norton.wyenet.co.uk
Dir: *A40 sliproad for Whitchurch, right over A40, 1st left to T-junct, turn left, located 300yds on right past Memorial Hall*

> **PETS:** Bedrooms Public areas (when no other guests present) Exercise area (600 metres) Welcome packs for dogs RESIDENT PETS: Honi & Homer (black Poodles)

Built as a farmhouse, Norton House dates back 300 years and retains much character through features such as stone-flagged floors and beamed ceilings. The bedrooms, including a four-poster room, are individually styled and furnished for maximum comfort. Excellent local produce is used to create an imaginative range of breakfast and dinner options. The charming public areas include a snug guest lounge, complete with a wood burning stove. Self-catering cottages are also available here.
FACILITIES: 3 en suite No smoking TVB tea/coffee Cen ht TVL No children 12yrs No coaches Card games & Board Games Dinner Last d 9am **PRICES:** s £35-£40; d £50-£60✳ **PARKING:** 5 **NOTES:** Closed 25 Dec

---

YARKHILL   Map 03 SO64

◆◆◆◆ ♥ Garford Farm
HR1 3ST
☎ 01432 890226 📠 01432 890707
e-mail: garfordfarm@lineone.net
Dir: *from Newtown x-rds where A417 crosses A4103, take A4103 towards Hereford, farm 1.5m on the left*

> **PETS:** Bedrooms Sep Accom (kennels if required) £4 (dogs) Exercise area (25 yards) RESIDENT PETS: Bertie & Sloe (Black Labradors), Cokie & Soda (cats)

This black and white timber-framed farmhouse dates back to the 17th century. Set on a large arable holding, it has a wealth of character enhanced by period furnishings and real fires which burn in the comfortable lounge during cold weather. The traditionally furnished bedrooms, which include a family room, have modern equipment.
FACILITIES: 2 en suite (1 fmly) No smoking in dining room No smoking in lounges TVB tea/coffee Cen ht No children 2yrs Fishing Croquet lawn 200 acres arable **PRICES:** s fr £25; d fr £50✳ **PARKING:** 6 **NOTES:** Closed 25-26 Dec

> **♥ Places with this symbol are farms**

> **All AA listed accommodation, restaurants and pubs can be found on the AA's website www.theAA.com**

BISHOP'S STORTFORD   Map 05 TL42

◆◆◆◆◆ Harewood
Snakes Ln, Ugley CM22 6HW
☎ 01279 813907 📠 01279 647493
e-mail: susie-elmes@lineone.net
Dir: *M11 junct 8, A120 W for 1m then at rbt B1383 N thro Stansted Mountfitchet. In 1m turn right to Ugley Green & Elsenham, right into Snakes Lane for Harewood on left*

> **PETS:** Bedrooms Public areas Exercise area (footpaths and bridleway adjoining garden) RESIDENT PETS: Murphy and Paddy (Labradors), Twitch (cat) & Daley (pony)

Expect a warm welcome at this delightful property situated in a peaceful rural setting about 15 minutes' drive from the M11 and Stansted Airport. The house is surrounded by attractive landscaped gardens, featuring a summerhouse and a lovely pond. The individually decorated bedrooms are tastefully furnished with well-chosen pieces and have many thoughtful touches. A wide choice of locally sourced items is available for breakfast, which is served in the elegant dining room.
FACILITIES: 2 rms (1 en suite) (2 GF) No smoking TVB tea/coffee Cen ht TVL No coaches Croquet lawn **PRICES:** s £40-£45; d £70✳ **PARKING:** 4 **NOTES:** Closed 21 Dec-1 Jan

◆◆◆ Broadleaf Guest House
38 Broadleaf Av CM23 4JY
☎ 01279 835467
e-mail: paula@broadleaf63freeserve.co.uk
Dir: *from M11 follow signs for Hertford (A120), straight over 6 rdbts, at 7th left signed Bishop's Stortford, over next rdbt, right at next rdbt, & right at next rdbt into Friedburge Ave. Broadleaf Ave 5th turning on right*

> **PETS:** Bedrooms (permitted inside only to access bedrooms)

A delightful detached house situated in a peaceful residential area close to the town centre, and within easy striking distance of the M11 and Stansted Airport. The pleasantly decorated bedrooms are tastefully furnished and equipped with many thoughtful touches. Breakfast is served in the smart dining room, which overlooks the pretty garden.
FACILITIES: 1 rms (1 fmly) No smoking TVB tea/coffee Cen ht No coaches **PRICES:** s £28-£35; d £50-£70✳ **PARKING:** 2

CHIPPERFIELD   Map 04 TL00

★★ 72% The Two Brewers
The Common WD4 9BS
☎ 01923 265266 📠 01923 261884
e-mail: twobrewers.hotel@spiritgroup.com
Dir: *left in centre of village overlooking common*

> **PETS:** Bedrooms £5 Exercise area (Over the road - common and woods) Open spaces and woodland provide wonderful walks RESIDENT PETS: Golden labrador - Bonzo

This 16th-century inn retains much of its old-world charm while providing modern comforts and amenities. The spacious bedrooms are tastefully furnished and decorated, offering a comprehensive range of in-room facilities. The bar, popular with

continued on p142

CHIPPERFIELD continued

locals, is the focal point of the hotel, which serves enjoyable pub-style meals.
ROOMS: 20 en suite No smoking in 10 bedrooms s £70-£100;
d £70-£100 (incl. bkfst) **LB FACILITIES:** STV **PARKING:** 25
CARDS: 💳💳💳💳💳💳💳💳

HATFIELD
Map 04 TL20

★★★ 65% **Quality Hotel Hatfield**
Roehyde Way AL10 9AF
☎ 01707 275701 📠 01707 266033
e-mail: enquiries@hotels-hatfield.com
Dir: M25 junct 23 take A1(M) northbound to junct 2. At rdbt take exit left, hotel 0.5m on right

> **PETS:** Exercise area (adjacent) Pet Food

The well-equipped rooms at this hotel feature extras such as trouser presses and modem access. Executive rooms are very spacious. Room service is 24 hour, or guests may dine in the bar or main restaurant, where service is informal and friendly.
ROOMS: 76 en suite (14 fmly) (39 GF) No smoking in 39 bedrooms
s £105-£130; d £115-£140 **LB FACILITIES:** STV Xmas **PARKING:** 120
NOTES: No smoking in restaurant
CARDS: 💳💳💳💳💳💳💳💳

ST ALBANS
Map 04 TL10

★★★★ 72% ◉◉ **Sopwell House Hotel, Country Club & Spa**
Cottonmill Ln, Sopwell AL1 2HQ
☎ 01727 864477 📠 01727 844741/845636
e-mail: enquiries@sopwellhouse.co.uk
Dir: M25 junct 22, follow A1081 St Albans. At traffic lights, turn left into Mile House Lane, over mini-rdbt into Cottonmill Lane

> **PETS:** Bedrooms (small dogs only)

This imposing Georgian house retains an exclusive ambience. Bedrooms vary in style and include a number of self-contained cottages within the Sopwell Mews. Meeting and function rooms are housed in a separate section and leisure and spa facilities are particularly impressive. Dining options include the brasserie and the fine-dining Magnolia restaurant.
ROOMS: 113 en suite 16 annexe en suite (12 fmly) No smoking in 20 bedrooms s £129; d £169 **LB FACILITIES:** Spa STV Indoor swimming (H) Sauna Solarium Gym Health & Beauty Spa, Hairdressing salon, 11 spa treatment rooms entertainment Xmas **SERVICES:** Lift
PARKING: 350 **NOTES:** No smoking in restaurant
CARDS: 💳💳💳💳💳💳💳💳

> All information was correct at the time of going to press; we recommend you confirm details on booking

◆◆◆◆ **Apples Hotel**
133 London Rd AL1 1TA
☎ 01727 844111 📠 01727 861100
e-mail: app133@aol.com
Dir: situated on A1081 within 0.5 mile of city centre.

> **PETS:** Bedrooms (unattended) Public areas Exercise area
> (0.25 mile) RESIDENT PETS: Boxer - Tillie

Located in a mainly residential avenue within easy walking distance of the historic town centre, this attractive detached house stands in pretty mature grounds which include an outdoor heated swimming pool (available in summer months). Bedrooms are equipped with both practical and homely extras and a warm welcome is assured.
FACILITIES: 6 en suite (2 fmly) (2 GF) No smoking in 2 bedrooms
No smoking in dining room TVB tea/coffee Direct dial from bedrooms
Licensed Cen ht No coaches Outdoor swimming pool (heated)
PRICES: s £49.50-£57.50; d £70.50-£82.90✳ **PARKING:** 6
CARDS: 💳💳💳💳💳

STEVENAGE
Map 04 TL22

★★★ 66% **Novotel Stevenage**
Knebworth Park SG1 2AX
☎ 01438 346100 📠 01438 723872
e-mail: H0992@accor-hotels.com
Dir: A1(M) junct 7, at entrance to Knebworth Park

> **PETS:** Bedrooms (unattended) £10 Exercise area (in
> grounds) Pet Food

With an accessible location just off the A1(M) and a range of meeting rooms, this hotel is a popular business and conference venue. There's plenty for leisure guests too: Knebworth Park is a noteworthy neighbour and the hotel's outdoor pool and children's play area add to the appeal for families.
ROOMS: 100 en suite (20 fmly) (30 GF) No smoking in 85 bedrooms
s £55-£95; d £55-£95 **LB FACILITIES:** STV Outdoor swimming (H)
Special rates at local health club entertainment ch fac Xmas
SERVICES: Lift **PARKING:** 100 **CARDS:** 💳💳💳💳💳💳💳💳

TRING
Map 04 SP91

★★★★ 66% ◉ **Pendley Manor**
Cow Ln HP23 5QY
☎ 01442 891891 📠 01442 890687
e-mail: info@pendley-manor.co.uk
Dir: M25 junct 20. Take A41 Tring exit. At rdbt take exit for Berkhamsted/London. 1st left signed Tring Station & Pendley Manor

> **PETS:** Bedrooms (unattended) Public areas Pet Food

This impressive Victorian mansion is set in extensive and mature landscaped grounds complete with peacocks. Bedrooms, situated in the manor house or in the new wing, offer a useful range of facilities and many have four-poster beds. Public areas include a cosy bar, a conservatory lounge and a leisure centre.
ROOMS: 74 en suite (6 fmly) No smoking in 3 bedrooms
FACILITIES: Spa STV Indoor swimming (H) Tennis (hard) Snooker
Sauna Gym Croquet lawn Jacuzzi Steam room, Dance Studio, Internet coffee shop **SERVICES:** Lift **PARKING:** 250 **NOTES:** No smoking in restaurant **CARDS:** 💳💳💳💳

England

WARE
Map 05 TL31

★★★ 68% Roebuck

Forestdale Hotels

Baldock St SG12 9DR
☎ 01920 409955 ▤ 01920 468016
e-mail: roebuck@forestdale.com
Dir: turn off A10 onto B1001, turn left at rdbt, first left behind Fire Station

PETS: Bedrooms (unattended) £7.50 Public areas (not in restaurant) Pet Food

Formerly a mansion, this conveniently located hotel has been extended and modernised over the years to produce a popular venue for business guests in particular. Bedrooms are mostly spacious and a few are suitable for less mobile guests, whilst the smart public areas include a range of conference rooms, a bar and an airy restaurant.
ROOMS: 50 en suite (1 fmly) (16 GF) No smoking in 16 bedrooms s fr £95; d fr £120 (incl. bkfst) **LB FACILITIES:** STV **SERVICES:** Lift **PARKING:** 64 **NOTES:** No smoking in restaurant
CARDS: ▨▨▨▨▨▨

KENT

ASHFORD
Map 05 TR04

★★★★ ◉◉ ♨ Eastwell Manor
Eastwell Park, Boughton Lees TN25 4HR
☎ 01233 213000 ▤ 01233 635530
e-mail: enquiries@eastwellmanor.co.uk
Dir: on A251, 200yds on left when entering Boughton Aluph

PETS: Telephone for details

Set in 62 acres of beautifully kept grounds, this lovely hotel dates back to the Norman conquest and boasts a number of interesting features, including carved wood panelled rooms and huge baronial stone fireplaces. Accommodation is divided between the manor house bedrooms and the courtyard apartments in the mews cottages.
ROOMS: 23 en suite 39 annexe en suite (2 fmly) No smoking in 4 bedrooms **FACILITIES:** Spa STV Indoor swimming (H) Outdoor swimming (H) Tennis (hard) Sauna Solarium Gym Croquet lawn Putting green Jacuzzi Boules, Hairdressing salon & Beauty spa
SERVICES: Lift **PARKING:** 200 **NOTES:** No smoking in restaurant
CARDS: ▨▨▨▨▨▨

★★★★ 65% Ashford International
CLASSIC BRITISH

Simone Weil Av TN24 8UX
☎ 01233 219988 ▤ 01233 647743
e-mail: info@ashfordinthotel.com
Dir: off M20 junct 9, 3rd exit for Ashford/Canterbury. Take L at 1st rdbt, hotel 200m on L.

PETS: Bedrooms (unattended) Exercise area

Ideally situated just off the M20 and its links to the channel tunnel and ferry terminal. Public areas feature a superb mall housing a range of boutiques and eating-places, including a popular brasserie, the Alhambra Restaurant and Florentine Bar. The spacious bedrooms are pleasantly furnished and equipped with modern facilities.
ROOMS: 200 en suite (4 fmly) No smoking in 57 bedrooms s £85-£110; d £95-£115 **LB FACILITIES:** Indoor swimming (H) Sauna Solarium Gym Jacuzzi **SERVICES:** Lift **PARKING:** 400 **NOTES:** No smoking in restaurant Closed 24-27 Dec **CARDS:** ▨▨▨▨▨▨

◆◆◆◆ Croft Hotel
Canterbury Rd, Kennington TN25 4DU
☎ 01233 622140 ▤ 01233 635271
e-mail: crofthotel@btconnect.com
Dir: approx 1.5m from M20 junct 9 or 10. Take A28 towards Canterbury

PETS: Bedrooms (unattended) £20 (Not in main hotel building) Exercise area (heath across road)

An attractive redbrick house situated in two acres of smart, landscaped grounds just a short drive from Ashford railway station. The generously proportioned bedrooms are located in the main house and in pretty cottages; all are pleasantly decorated and thoughtfully equipped. Public rooms include a smart new restaurant, a bar and a cosy residents' lounge.
FACILITIES: 15 en suite 13 annexe en suite (6 fmly) (13 GF) No smoking in 6 bedrooms No smoking in dining room No smoking in 1 lounge STV TVB tea/coffee Direct dial from bedrooms Licensed Cen ht TVL ch fac Dinner Last d 9.30pm **PRICES:** s £50-£70; d £68-£83✱ **LB PARKING:** 30 **CARDS:** ▨▨▨▨▨▨

BIDDENDEN
Map 05 TQ83

◆◆◆◆ Heron Cottage
TN27 8HH
☎ 01580 291358 ▤ 01580 291358
Dir: from Biddenden take A262 from Sissinghurst. After leaving village take 1st right and after 0.25m there is a sharp left bend. Cross the bend and proceed through stone pillars opposite, then take left unmade road

PETS: Bedrooms Exercise area (Adjacent)
RESIDENT PETS: 2 donkeys - Kelly & Damson, 1 cat - Maisie, 6 geese, 9 chickens

Expect a warm welcome at this charming detached cottage situated in a peaceful rural location in the Kent countryside. The tastefully furnished bedrooms are thoughtfully equipped and have co-ordinated soft furnishings. Breakfast is served in the smart dining room and guests have the use of a cosy sitting room with an open fireplace.
FACILITIES: 7 rms (5 en suite) (1 fmly) No smoking in bedrooms No smoking in dining room TVB tea/coffee Cen ht TVL No coaches Fishing Croquet lawn Dinner Last d 9am **PRICES:** s £35-£45; d £45-£55 **PARKING:** 8 **NOTES:** Closed Dec-Feb

England

BRANDS HATCH · Map 05 TQ56

★★★★ 74% ◎◎ Brandshatch Place

Brands Hatch Rd, Fawkham DA3 8NQ
☎ 01474 875000 📠 01474 879652
e-mail: brandshatchplace@handpicked.co.uk
Dir: M25 junct 3/A20 West Kingsdown. Left at paddock entrance/Fawkham Green sign. 3rd left signed Fawkham Rd. Hotel 500mtrs on right

PETS: Bedrooms (unattended) Public areas (Not restaurant) Exercise area (20 metres)

This charming 18th-century Georgian country house close to the famous racing circuit has undergone an extensive refurbishment programme. Public areas have been completely transformed and include a range of stylish and elegant rooms. Bedrooms have also been upgraded to a very high standard, offering impressive facilities and levels of comfort and quality. The hotel also features a comprehensive leisure club with substantial creche facilities. Handpicked Hotels – AA Hotel Group of the Year 2004-5.
ROOMS: 26 en suite 12 annexe en suite (1 fmly) No smoking in 10 bedrooms **FACILITIES:** Spa STV Indoor swimming (H) Tennis (hard) Squash Snooker Sauna Solarium Gym Croquet lawn Jacuzzi Use of health/leisure club Xmas **PARKING:** 100 **NOTES:** No smoking in restaurant **CARDS:**

CANTERBURY · Map 05 TR15

★★★★ 66% The County

High St CT1 2RX
☎ 01227 766266 📠 01227 451512
e-mail: county@macdonald-hotels.co.uk
Dir: M2, junct 7. Follow Canterbury signs onto ringroad. At Wincheap rdbt turn into city. Left into Rosemary Ln, into Stour St. Hotel at end

MACDONALD HOTELS

PETS: Bedrooms (unattended) £10 Exercise area

This historic hotel has cellars dating back to the 12th century. It offers warm hospitality and comfortable accommodation in the heart of the city. Bedrooms are individually decorated and tastefully furnished, while public areas include tea rooms offering traditional cream teas and Sully's Restaurant for fine dining.
ROOMS: 74 en suite (9 fmly) No smoking in 33 bedrooms s £80-£120; d £85-£130 (incl. bkfst) **LB FACILITIES:** STV Xmas **SERVICES:** Lift **PARKING:** 62 **NOTES:** No smoking in restaurant
CARDS:

★★ 75% Ebury

65/67 New Dover Rd CT1 3DX
☎ 01227 768433 📠 01227 459187
e-mail: info@ebury-hotel.co.uk
Dir: A2 at Canterbury take ring road. Follow Dover signs, after 5th rdbt hotel 1m on left

PETS: Bedrooms (unattended) Exercise area (on site)

This Victorian former residence is set in two acres of attractive gardens and is only a short walk from the city centre. The elegant and spacious public rooms include a restaurant and lounge where the proprietor's collection of rare and unusual clocks tick away

continued

peacefully. Bedrooms are maintained to a high standard and contain a good range of useful facilities.
ROOMS: 15 en suite (2 fmly) s £60-£65; d £80-£95 (incl. bkfst) **LB**
FACILITIES: Indoor swimming (H) Jacuzzi **PARKING:** 30
NOTES: No smoking in restaurant Closed 21 Dec-13 Jan
CARDS:

◆◆◆◆ Yorke Lodge Hotel

50 London Rd CT2 8LF
☎ 01227 451243 📠 01227 462006
e-mail: enquiries@yorkelodge.com
Dir: turn off A2 onto A2050, left at 1st rdbt into London Rd, hotel on left

PETS: Bedrooms (unattended) Exercise area (200yds)
RESIDENT PETS: Fleur - Dalmatian/collie cross

This charming 18th-century property is situated in a tree-lined road about 10 minutes' walk from the town centre and railway station. The spacious bedrooms are thoughtfully equipped and tastefully decorated; some rooms have four-poster beds. Public rooms include a stylish dining room and a small reception area with a library.
FACILITIES: 8 en suite (1 fmly) No smoking in bedrooms No smoking in dining room TVB tea/coffee Cen ht TVL No coaches
PRICES: s £38-£45; d £65-£88✱ **LB PARKING:** 5
CARDS:

◆◆◆ Cathedral Gate Hotel

36 Burgate CT1 2HA
☎ 01227 464381 📠 01227 462800
e-mail: cgate@cgate.demon.co.uk
Dir: next to main gateway into cathedral precincts

PETS: Bedrooms (unattended) Public areas (not in dining room) Exercise area (0.5 mile) **RESIDENT PETS:** 2 cats (brother & sister) - Dexter & Cody

Dating back to 1438, this hotel enjoys an enviable central location adjacent to the cathedral. Old beams and winding corridors add to the character of the property and bedrooms are traditionally furnished and equipped to modern standards. Breakfasts are served in bedrooms or in a cosy breakfast room. Luggage may be unloaded at reception before parking in a local car park.
FACILITIES: 15 rms (4 en suite) 12 annexe rms (10 en suite) (5 fmly) No smoking in dining room No smoking in 1 lounge TVB tea/coffee Direct dial from bedrooms Licensed Cen ht Dinner Last d 8pm
PRICES: s £26-£60; d £50-£90✱ **LB**
CARDS:

◆◆◆ 🐾 Upper Ansdore
Duckpit Ln, Petham CT4 5QB
☎ 01227 700672 🖷 01227 700840
e-mail: upperansdore@hotels.activebooking.com
Dir: B2068 from Canterbury, through village, left by telephone, after 1.5m right signed Ansdore

PETS: Bedrooms £7.50 Public areas (not in dining room) Exercise area (50 metres) RESIDENT PETS: Rex (Jack Russell), Penny (cat)

This beautiful farmhouse once owned by a former Lord Mayor of London dates back to the 14th century. It is set in a peaceful rural location only 15 minutes drive from Canterbury and within easy reach of a number of pubs and restaurants. Bedrooms have en suite shower rooms and are comfortably furnished.
FACILITIES: 3 en suite (1 fmly) (2 GF) No smoking tea/coffee Cen ht No children 5yrs Riding 4 acres mixed small holding **PARKING:** 5
NOTES: Closed Xmas **CARDS:** 🖿🖿🖿🖿🖿🖿🖿

DARTFORD   Map 05 TQ57

⌂ Campanile
1 Clipper Boulevard West, Crossways
Business Park DA2 6QN
☎ 01322 278925 🖷 01322 278948
e-mail: dartford@envergure.co.uk
Dir: follow signs for Ferry Terminal from Dartford Bridge

Campanile

PETS: Bedrooms Pet Food

This modern building offers accommodation in smart, well-equipped bedrooms, all with en suite bathrooms. Refreshments may be taken at the informal Bistro. For further details consult the Hotel Groups page.
ROOMS: 125 en suite s fr £48.95; d fr £48.95

DEAL   Map 05 TR35

◆◆◆◆◆ 🛏 Sutherland House Hotel
186 London Rd CT14 9PT
☎ 01304 362853 🖷 01304 381146
e-mail: info@sutherlandhouse.fsnet.co.uk
Dir: on A258 Deal to Sandwich road, 200yds from Deal Hospital

PETS: Bedrooms Public areas (with consideration for other guests' comfort) Exercise area (200 metres)

This stylish hotel offers charming bedrooms, which are decorated and furnished with great style and taste. The elegant dining room provides a charming venue for home-cooked dinners and breakfasts, and guests have the use of a comfortable lounge that is extremely well stocked with books and magazines.
FACILITIES: 4 en suite (1 GF) No smoking in bedrooms No smoking in area of dining room TVB tea/coffee Direct dial from bedrooms Licensed Cen ht No children 5yrs No coaches Dinner Last d 7.00pm
PRICES: s £47-£50; d £57-£60✶ **LB PARKING:** 7
CARDS: 🖿🖿🖿🖿🖿🖿

DOVER   Map 05 TR34

◆◆◆◆ Hubert House
9 Castle Hill Rd CT16 1QW
☎ 01304 202253 🖷 01304 210142
e-mail: huberthouse@btinternet.com
Dir: at bottom of Castle Hill Rd leading to Dover Castle on A258

PETS: Bedrooms £10 Exercise area (300 metres)
RESIDENT PETS: Rollie (Italian Spinone)

Charming Georgian house within walking distance of the ferry port and town centre. Bedrooms are pleasantly decorated, furnished in a modern style and have many thoughtful touches. Breakfast, which includes both full English and healthy options, is served in the smart dining room. Families are especially welcome.
FACILITIES: 8 en suite (3 fmly) No smoking in 3 bedrooms No smoking in dining room No smoking in lounges TVB tea/coffee Cen ht
PRICES: s £30-£40; d £44-£60✶ **LB PARKING:** 6 **CARDS:** 🖿🖿🖿🖿

◆◆◆ Castle House
10 Castle Hill Rd CT16 1QW
☎ 01304 201656 🖷 01304 210197
e-mail: dimechr@aol.com
Dir: A20 for Dover; over 4 rdbts, turn left at lights past BP petrol station, 1st right into Castle Hill Rd, house just below Dover Castle

PETS: Bedrooms (unattended) Public areas Exercise area (20 metres)

Conveniently located for the ferry port and just a short walk from the town centre. Bedrooms are brightly decorated with co-ordinated soft furnishings and many thoughtful touches. Breakfast is available from 6am, which can be ideal for early morning departures and is served at individual tables in the garden room.
FACILITIES: 6 en suite (2 fmly) No smoking TVB tea/coffee Licensed Cen ht No coaches **PRICES:** s £28-£35; d £45-£55✶ **LB PARKING:** 7
CARDS: 🖿🖿🖿🖿🖿🖿

FAVERSHAM   Map 05 TR06

◆◆◆◆ Eastling Holiday Centre
Churchfields Farm, The Street, Eastling ME13 0BG
☎ 01795 890746, 07940 875196
e-mail: info@holidayhorse.com
Dir: Exit M2 at junct 6 and follow signs for Faversham. Take a left and then a left again into Brogdale road, continue along this road to Eastling. Churchfields farm is about 200yds past Carpenters Arms on left.

PETS: Bedrooms Public areas Exercise area (on site)
RESIDENT PETS: horses & ponies, cats, dog

Specialising in holidays for people with their horses this unique venue boasts superb stable facilities, paddock and tracks. Situated in a peaceful location overlooking the North Downs, this attractive and recently renovated property is close to Canterbury and the motorway network. Self-catering for longer stays is available.
FACILITIES: 2 en suite (2 fmly) (1 GF) No smoking TVB tea/coffee Cen ht No coaches Riding **PRICES:** s £55; d £55✶ **LB PARKING:** 5

England

KINGSGATE

Map 05 TR37

★★★ 70% The Fayreness
Marine Dr CT10 3LG
☎ 01843 868641 📠 01843 608750
e-mail: fayreness@thorleytaverns.com
Dir: A28 onto B2051 which becomes B2052. Pass Holy Trinity Church on right, and '19th Hole' public house. Next left, down Kingsgate Ave, hotel at end on left

PETS: Bedrooms (4 rooms only) Public areas (Dogs must be on leads) Exercise area (50yds)

Situated on the cliff tops overlooking the English Channel, just a few steps from a sandy beach and adjacent to the North Foreland Golf Club. The spacious bedrooms are tastefully furnished with many thoughtful touches; some rooms have stunning sea views. Public rooms include a large open-plan lounge/bar, a function room, dining room and conservatory restaurant.
ROOMS: 29 en suite No smoking in 17 bedrooms s £50-£140; d £65-£150 (incl. bkfst) **LB FACILITIES:** STV **PARKING:** 70 **NOTES:** No smoking in restaurant **CARDS:** 💳

MAIDSTONE

Map 05 TQ75

◆◆◆◆ Wits End
78 Bower Mount Rd ME16 8AT
☎ 01622 752684 📠 01622 752684
e-mail: mail@thewitsend.co.uk
Dir: from M20 junct 5, follow signs to Maidstone (A20). Pass 5 sets of traffic lights. After 5th set turn right into Bower Mount Road and guest house last house on right

PETS: Bedrooms Exercise area (2 mins)

Imposing Edwardian property situated in a quiet side road just a short walk from the town centre and railway station. The spacious bedrooms are tastefully decorated, thoughtfully equipped and have views over the pretty landscaped garden. Public rooms feature a panelled entrance hall with seating and a smart dining room.
FACILITIES: 8 en suite (2 fmly) (1 GF) No smoking in dining room TVB tea/coffee Cen ht **PRICES:** s fr £39; d fr £55✱ **PARKING:** 9
NOTES: Closed 25-26 Dec **CARDS:** 💳

MARGATE

Map 05 TR37

◆◆◆◆ The Greswolde Hotel
20 Surrey Rd, Cliftonville CT9 2LA
☎ 01843 223956 📠 01843 223956

PETS: Bedrooms (unattended) Public areas Exercise area

An attractive Victorian house, in a peaceful area, close to the seafront. The property has a lovely period atmosphere with interesting memorabilia and spacious bedrooms. These are pleasantly decorated, comfortably appointed and equipped with many useful extras. Breakfast is served in the elegant dining room, and guests can relax in the cosy lounge.
FACILITIES: 5 en suite (2 fmly) No smoking in bedrooms No smoking in dining room TVB tea/coffee Licensed Cen ht No coaches
PRICES: s £30-£40; d £43-£47✱ **LB CARDS:** 💳

◆◆◆ Elonville Hotel
70-72 Harold Rd, Cliftonville CT9 2HS
☎ 01843 298635 📠 01843 298635
e-mail: enquiries@elonville-hotel.demon.co.uk
Dir: from Margate clock tower stay on coastal road for 1m, Harold Rd is turn off on the right

PETS: Bedrooms (unattended) Public areas (not in dining room, except guide dogs) Exercise area (purpose built dog area on site)

Expect a warm welcome at this privately owned hotel situated just a short walk from the shops and beach. Bedrooms come in a variety of sizes and styles; each one is pleasantly decorated and thoughtfully equipped. Public rooms include a lounge bar and a dining room, which overlooks the garden.
FACILITIES: 16 rms (10 en suite) (2 fmly) (1 GF) No smoking in dining room TVB tea/coffee Licensed TVL Garden Chess & Jenga, darts, table football Dinner Last d 4.30pm **PRICES:** s £26; d £52✱ **LB CARDS:** 💳

SITTINGBOURNE

Map 05 TQ96

★★★ 71% 🏵 Hempstead House Country Hotel
London Rd, Bapchild ME9 9PP
☎ 01795 428020 📠 01795 436362
e-mail: info@hempsteadhouse.co.uk
Dir: 1.5m from Sittingbourne town centre on A2 towards Canterbury

PETS: Bedrooms (unattended) Public areas Exercise area (on site) Pet Food **RESIDENT PETS:** Jade (Staffordshire Bull Terrier), cats

Expect a warm welcome at this charming detached Victorian property, which is situated amidst three acres of mature landscaped gardens. Bedrooms are attractively decorated with lovely co-ordinated fabrics, tastefully furnished and equipped with many thoughtful touches. Public rooms feature a choice of beautifully furnished lounges as well as a superb conservatory dining room.
ROOMS: 27 en suite (7 fmly) (1 GF) No smoking in all bedrooms s £75-£95; d £85-£105 (incl. bkfst) **LB FACILITIES:** STV Outdoor swimming (H) ch fac Xmas **PARKING:** 100 **NOTES:** No smoking in restaurant **CARDS:** 💳

TENTERDEN

Map 05 TQ83

◆◆◆◆ 🍴 White Lion
The High St TN30 6BD
☎ 01580 765077 📠 01580 764157
e-mail: whitelion@lionheartinns.co.uk
Dir: in centre of Tenterden High Street on A28 Ashford/Hastings road

PETS: Bedrooms (unattended) Public areas (not in restaurant) Exercise area (0.25 mile)

A delightful 15th-century coaching inn situated on the high street of this historic town. Bedrooms are well appointed, thoughtfully equipped and some boast four-poster beds. Public rooms feature a popular bar, a separate lounge and an oak panelled restaurant serving an extensive range of dishes. There is also a small function and meeting room.
FACILITIES: 15 en suite (2 fmly) No smoking in dining room TVB tea/coffee Direct dial from bedrooms Cen ht Dinner Last d 10pm **PRICES:** s £49-£59; d £60-£74✱ **LB PARKING:** 35
CARDS: 💳

TONBRIDGE Map 05 TQ54

★★★ 66% The Langley
18-20 London Rd TN10 3DA
☎ 01732 353311 🖹 01732 771471
e-mail: thelangley@btconnect.com
Dir: leave Tonbridge in direction of Hildenborough N, hotel on Tonbridge/Hildenborough border

PETS: Bedrooms (unattended) Public areas (not in bar or restaurant) Exercise area (10 yards) Pet Food

Privately owned hotel located just a short drive from the centre of Tonbridge and ideally situated for business and leisure guests alike. Bedrooms are generally quite spacious; each one is pleasantly decorated and equipped with modern facilities. The restaurant offers a varied menu of carefully prepared fresh produce and there is a popular bar.
ROOMS: 37 en suite (3 fmly) (10 GF) No smoking in 27 bedrooms s £45-£85; d £55-£105 **LB FACILITIES:** STV Xmas **SERVICES:** Lift **PARKING:** 40 **NOTES:** No smoking in restaurant
CARDS: 🖩 🖃 💳 🖭 💳 🖳 🅂

LANCASHIRE

ACCRINGTON Map 07 SD72

★★★ 66% Sparth House Hotel
Whalley Rd, Clayton Le Moors BB5 5RP
☎ 01254 872263 🖹 01254 872263
e-mail: mail.sparth@btinternet.com
Dir: A6185 to Clitheroe along Dunkenhalgh Way, right at lights onto A678, left at next lights, A680 to Whalley. Hotel on left after 2 sets of lights

PETS: Bedrooms (unattended) £5 Exercise area

This 18th-century listed building nestles in three acres of well-tended gardens close to the motorway. Bedrooms are individually styled and those in the original house are particularly spacious, including one with original furnishings from one of the great cruise liners. The panelled restaurant is a peaceful setting in which to enjoy a wide range of dishes.
ROOMS: 16 en suite (3 fmly) No smoking in 2 bedrooms s £62.50-£85; d £70-£99 (incl. bkfst) **LB FACILITIES:** ch fac **PARKING:** 50 **NOTES:** No smoking in restaurant
CARDS: 🖩 🖃 💳 🖭 💳 🖳 🅂

BLACKPOOL Map 07 SD33

◆◆◆◆ Brabyns
1-3 Shaftesbury Av, North Shore FY2 9QQ
☎ 01253 354263 🖹 01253 352915
e-mail: brabyns@emurkin.freeserve.co.uk
Dir: M55 junct 4 turn off A583 N, head for seafront, at seafront turn right for Fleetwood. Hotel at end of promenade

PETS: Bedrooms Exercise area (50yds)

Lying just off the North Shore promenade, this friendly hotel provides comfortable, well-equipped accommodation, an attractive

continued

lounge bar and good value meals. It is a popular venue for local functions.
FACILITIES: 22 en suite No smoking in 10 bedrooms No smoking in dining room No smoking in 1 lounge STV TVB tea/coffee Direct dial from bedrooms Licensed Cen ht TVL Dinner Last d breakfast
PARKING: 5 **CARDS:** 🖩 🖃 💳 🅂

◆◆◆◆ 🖫 Briar Dene Hotel
56 Kelso Av, Thornton, Cleveleys FY5 3JG
☎ 01253 852312 🖹 01253 851190
e-mail: brairdene@aol.com
Dir: Exit M55 at junct 32 onto A585, at 3rd rdbt take 2nd left. At 2nd set of traffic lights turn left onto dual carriageway, the hotel is 400yds on the left

PETS: Bedrooms Public areas (except restaurant) Exercise area (200yds to beach and open park)

This friendly, long-established family-run hotel is situated near the centre of Cleveleys, one block away from the promenade and a short tram ride from Blackpool's many attractions. Bedrooms are equipped with modern facilities and all are en suite. Public areas are comfortably furnished and include a very relaxing lounge and a popular restaurant decorated in contemporary style.
FACILITIES: 17 en suite (4 fmly) No smoking in 6 bedrooms No smoking in dining room TVB tea/coffee Direct dial from bedrooms Licensed Cen ht TVL Dinner Last d 9.15pm **PRICES:** s £42.50; d £65-£80✱ **LB PARKING:** 12 **NOTES:** Closed 23-30 Dec
CARDS: 🖩 🖃 💳 🖭 💳 🖳 🅂

◆◆◆◆ Burlees Hotel
40 Knowle Av FY2 9TQ
☎ 01253 354535 🖹 01253 354535
e-mail: marrasimpson@aol.com
Dir: from Queens Promenade right at Uncle Tom's Cabin into Knowle Ave

PETS: Bedrooms Public areas (Bar only) Exercise area (500yds) RESIDENT PETS: 2 Amazon parrots - Barny & Parry, Collie - Fudge

A genuine welcome awaits guests at this well-maintained house, just a short stroll from the promenade. Smartly decorated bedrooms are thoughtfully equipped and there is a comfortable lounge and a cosy bar. Hearty breakfasts and evening meals by prior arrangement are served in the pine-furnished dining room.
FACILITIES: 9 en suite (2 fmly) (1 GF) No smoking in bedrooms No smoking in dining room No smoking in lounges TVB tea/coffee Licensed Cen ht TVL No coaches Dinner Last d prev evening **PRICES:** s £25-£28; d £50-£56✱ **LB PARKING:** 4 **NOTES:** Closed Dec 16-7 Jan **CARDS:** 🖩 🖃 💳 🖳 🅂

◆◆◆ Windsor Park Hotel
96 Queens Promenade FY2 9NS
☎ 01253 357025 🖹 01253 357076
e-mail: info@windsorparkhotel.net
Dir: Queens Promenade, main road North shore

PETS: Small dogs accepted Bedrooms (unattended) Public areas Exercise area

Benefiting from stunning views, this friendly, family run hotel is situated on the peaceful North Shore, just a tram's ride away from the town's main attractions. Home-cooked meals and substantial breakfasts are served in the elegant dining room and there is also

continued on p148

BLACKPOOL continued

a pleasant bar area and a sun lounge. Bedrooms offer modern amenities.

FACILITIES: 9 en suite (1 fmly) No smoking in bedrooms No smoking in dining room No smoking in 1 lounge TVB tea/coffee Licensed Cen ht TVL No coaches Stair lift Dinner Last d 4pm **PRICES:** s £17.50-£25; d £35-£50✱ **LB BB PARKING:** 6 **NOTES:** Closed 8 Nov-Etr (ex Xmas/New Year) **CARDS:**

CARNFORTH — Map 07 SD47

★★ 65% Royal Station
Market St LA5 9BT
☎ 01524 732033 & 733636 ▤ 01524 720267
e-mail: royalstation@mitchellshotels.co.uk
Dir: M6 junct 35 onto A6 signed Carnforth. After 1m at x-rds in town centre right into Market St. Hotel opposite railway station

PETS: Bedrooms Public areas (bar only) Exercise area RESIDENT PETS: Sally (Whippet), Sweep (cat)

This commercial hotel enjoys a town centre location close to the railway station. Bedrooms are well equipped and comfortably furnished. A good range of tasty good value meals can be taken in either the bright attractive lounge bar or the restaurant.
ROOMS: 13 en suite (1 fmly) s £36-£41.50; d £44-£58 **LB**
FACILITIES: Xmas **PARKING:** 4 **NOTES:** No smoking in restaurant
CARDS:

◆◆◆◆◆ 🖳 🍽 New Capernwray Farm
Capernwray LA6 1AD
☎ 01524 734284 ▤ 01524 734284
e-mail: newcapfarm@aol.com
Dir: M6 J35, follow signs for Over Kellet. Left at village green in Over Kellett, house on left after 1.7m

PETS: Bedrooms Public areas (provided other guests do not mind) Exercise area (on site) RESIDENT PETS: Heidi (Long Haired Dachshund)

A warm welcome is assured at this 17th-century, white-walled farmhouse. Bedrooms feature beamed ceilings and are all sumptuously furnished and equipped with thoughtful extras. Well prepared two course dinners and breakfast are taken in the dining room, formerly the dairy. The drawing room has views of the well-tended garden and peaceful countryside.
FACILITIES: 3 rms (2 en suite) No smoking TVB tea/coffee Cen ht No children 9yrs No coaches Dinner Last d 2pm **PRICES:** s £52-£57; d £74-£84✱ **PARKING:** 4 **NOTES:** Closed Nov-Feb
CARDS:

CHARNOCK RICHARD MOTORWAY SERVICE AREA (M6) — Map 15 SD51

⌂ Welcome Lodge
Welcome Break Service Area PR7 5LR
☎ 01257 791746 ▤ 01257 793596
e-mail: charnockhotel@welcomebreak.co.uk
Dir: on northbound side between junct 27 & 28 of M6. 500yds from Camelot Theme Park via Mill Lane

PETS: Bedrooms (unattended) Public areas (must be kept on lead) Exercise area (adjacent) welcome snack pack on arrival

This modern building offers accommodation in smart, spacious and well-equipped bedrooms, suitable for families and business travellers, and all with en suite bathrooms. Refreshments may be taken at the nearby family restaurant. For further details consult the Hotel Groups page.
ROOMS: 100 en suite s £35-£50; d £35-£50

CLITHEROE — Map 07 SD74

★★ 69% Shireburn Arms
Whalley Rd, Hurst Green BB7 9QJ
☎ 01254 826518 ▤ 01254 826208
e-mail: sales@shireburnarmshotel.com
Dir: A59 to Clitheroe, left at lights to Ribchester, follow Hurst Green signs. Hotel on B6243 at entrance to Hurst Green village

PETS: Bedrooms £5 Public areas (except dining areas) Exercise area

This long established, family-owned hotel dates back to the 17th century and enjoys panoramic views over the Ribble Valley. Rooms are individually designed and thoughtfully equipped. The lounge bar offers a selection of real ales, and the spacious restaurant, opening onto an attractive patio and garden offers home-cooked food.
ROOMS: 18 en suite (3 fmly) No smoking in 3 bedrooms s £48-£70; d £70-£90 (incl. bkfst) **LB FACILITIES:** ch fac Xmas **PARKING:** 71
NOTES: No smoking in restaurant **CARDS:**

LANCASTER — Map 07 SD46

★★★★ 71% ⊛ Lancaster House
Green Ln, Ellel LA1 4GJ
☎ 01524 844822 ▤ 01524 844766
e-mail: lancaster@elhmail.co.uk
Dir: M6 junct 33 N towards Lancaster. Through Galgate and into Green Ln. Hotel before university on right

PETS: Bedrooms £10 - dogs (0.5 mile)

This modern hotel enjoys a rural setting south of the city and close to the university. The attractive open-plan, balconied reception and lounge boasts traditional flagstone floors and a roaring log fire in season. Bedrooms are spacious and especially well equipped for business guests. The excellent business and leisure facilities make this hotel a popular conference venue. Staff are friendly and keen to please.
ROOMS: 80 en suite (10 fmly) (36 GF) No smoking in 60 bedrooms s £89-£129; d £89-£129 **LB FACILITIES:** STV Indoor swimming (H) Sauna Solarium Gym Jacuzzi Beauty salon entertainment ch fac Xmas **PARKING:** 100 **NOTES:** No smoking in restaurant
CARDS:

LYTHAM ST ANNES — Map 07 SD32

★★ 69% Lindum
63-67 South Promenade FY8 1LZ
☎ 01253 721534 & 722516 ☒ 01253 721364
e-mail: info@lindumhotel.co.uk
Dir: from M55 follow A5230 & signs for Blackpool Airport. After airport, left at lights to St Annes, right at lights in town centre. 1st left onto seafront. Hotel 250yds on left

PETS: Bedrooms (unattended) from £3 Exercise area (100yds)

The same family has run this friendly and popular seafront hotel for over 40 years. Well-equipped bedrooms are generally spacious and some enjoy superb coastal views. Extensive public areas include a games room, a choice of lounges and a popular health suite. The open-plan restaurant offers a good choice of well-cooked dishes at breakfast and dinner.
ROOMS: 76 en suite (25 fmly) No smoking in all bedrooms s £30-£45; d £50-£79 (incl. bkfst) LB **FACILITIES:** Sauna Solarium Jacuzzi entertainment ch fac Xmas **SERVICES:** Lift air con **PARKING:** 20 **NOTES:** No smoking in restaurant **CARDS:** 🖬🖬🖬🖬

MORECAMBE — Map 07 SD46

★★★ 65% Clarendon
76 Marine Rd West, West End Promenade LA4 4EP
☎ 01524 410180 ☒ 01524 421616
e-mail: clarendon@mitchellshotels.co.uk
Dir: M6 junct 34 follow Morecambe signs. At rdbt with 'The Shrimp' on corner 1st exit to Westgate, follow to seafront. Right at traffic lights, hotel 3rd block along

PETS: Bedrooms Exercise area

This seafront hotel was completely refurbished a few years ago. Well maintained throughout, it offers bright cheerful public areas and smartly appointed bedrooms all with fully tiled bathrooms.
ROOMS: 29 en suite (4 fmly) No smoking in 10 bedrooms s £60; d £90 (incl. bkfst) LB **FACILITIES:** Xmas **SERVICES:** Lift **PARKING:** 22 **NOTES:** No smoking in restaurant **CARDS:** 🖬🖬🖬🖬

★★★ 63% Elms
Bare Village LA4 6DD
☎ 01524 411501 ☒ 01524 831979
Dir: Exit M6 at J34. Follow signs to Morecambe to large rdbt. Take 4th exit into Hall Drive which becomes Bare Lane. Follow over railway crossing. Hotel is 200yds on R.

PETS: Bedrooms (unattended) Exercise area (5 mins walk)

This long-established hotel lies just off the North Promenade and is popular with business and leisure guests. Public rooms include a spacious lounge bar, a classical style restaurant, function facilities and a pub in the grounds. Many bedrooms have been upgraded.
ROOMS: 39 en suite (3 fmly) No smoking in 18 bedrooms s fr £65; d fr £90 (incl. bkfst) LB **FACILITIES:** Xmas **SERVICES:** Lift **PARKING:** 80 **NOTES:** No smoking in restaurant **CARDS:** 🖬🖬🖬🖬

◆◆◆ Hotel Prospect
363 Marine Rd East LA4 5AQ
☎ 01524 417819 ☒ 01524 417819
e-mail: peter@hotel-prospect.fsnet.co.uk
Dir: exit M6 at junct 34/35, follow Morecambe Promenade, premises just before Gala Bingo

PETS: Bedrooms Public areas (except dining area)

Situated on Morecambe Promenade, this friendly family-run hotel enjoys panoramic views over the bay to the Lakeland Hills beyond. Bedrooms are comfortably proportioned, thoughtfully furnished and carefully decorated. The bright airy dining room extends into a small lounge area, which has its own well stocked bar and overlooks the sea. There is an enclosed car park, offering off road parking.
FACILITIES: 14 rms (13 en suite) (4 fmly) (2 GF) No smoking in 2 bedrooms No smoking in dining room TVB tea/coffee Licensed Cen ht Dinner Last d 3pm **PRICES:** s £17-£19; d £34-£38✱ LB BB **PARKING:** 14 **CARDS:** 🖬🖬🖬🖬

PRESTON — Map 07 SD52

★★★ 65% Novotel Preston
Reedfield Place, Walton Summit PR5 8AA
☎ 01772 313331 ☒ 01772 627868
e-mail: H0838@accor-hotels.com
Dir: M6 junct 29, M61 junct 9, then A6 Chorley Road. Hotel next to Bamber Bridge rdbt

PETS: Bedrooms £6 Public areas (except restaurant)

The hotel is ideally located just off main motorway networks. Bedrooms are spacious and feature ample desk space and additional bed space making them ideal for families or business travellers. Flexible dining is a feature with the Garden Brasserie, open throughout the day until midnight. The hotel also boasts an outdoor pool and children's play area.
ROOMS: 96 en suite (22 fmly) No smoking in 49 bedrooms s fr £60; d fr £60 LB **FACILITIES:** STV Outdoor swimming (H) **SERVICES:** Lift **PARKING:** 140 **NOTES:** No smoking in restaurant **CARDS:** 🖬🖬🖬🖬

◆◆◆ Withy Trees
175-177 Garstang Rd, Fulwood PR2 8JQ
☎ 01772 717693 ☒ 01772 511087
e-mail: info@withytrees.co.uk
Dir: from M6 junct 32 turn left on A6 direction of Preston. Guest House approx 1.5m on right

PETS: Bedrooms £2 Exercise area (0.25 mile) Bowls provided

Conveniently located on the A6 Garstang road, this friendly, relaxed private hotel is only minutes from the town centre and from the M55 and M6 motorways. Bedrooms are well equipped and offer modern facilities. A comfortably furnished lounge is provided and substantial breakfasts served in the airy dining room.
FACILITIES: 9 en suite (3 fmly) (1 GF) No smoking in 5 bedrooms No smoking in dining room TVB tea/coffee Cen ht TVL No coaches Dinner Last d by arrangement **PRICES:** s £30-£37; d £47✱ **PARKING:** 7

England

LEICESTER Map 04 SK50

♦♦♦ Stoneycroft Hotel
5-7 Elmfield Av LE2 1RB
☎ 0116 270 7605 ☳ 0116 270 6067
e-mail: reception@stoneycrofthotel.co.uk
Dir: near city centre on A6 to Market Harborough

PETS: Bedrooms (unattended) Exercise area (250yds)
RESIDENT PETS: German Shepherd - Archie

This large hotel provides comfortable accommodation and helpful service. Public rooms include a foyer lounge area, breakfast room and conference facilities. There is also a large restaurant/bar area, which serves a good selection of freshly cooked dishes. Bedrooms have modern appointments, including desks and suitable chairs.
FACILITIES: 41 en suite (4 fmly) (6 GF) No smoking in bedrooms No smoking in dining room TVB tea/coffee Direct dial from bedrooms Licensed Cen ht TVL Pool Table Dinner Last d 9.30pm **PRICES:** s £44; d £55✱ **PARKING:** 20 **CARDS:**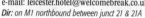

LEICESTER FOREST MOTORWAY SERVICE AREA (M1) Map 04 SK50

⌂ Days Inn
Leicester Forest East, Junction 21 M1 LE3 3GB
☎ 0116 239 0534 ☳ 0116 239 0546
e-mail: leicester.hotel@welcomebreak.co.uk
Dir: on M1 northbound between junct 21 & 21A

PETS: Bedrooms (unattended) Public areas (only dogs) Exercise area (within 1 mile)

This modern building offers accommodation in smart, spacious and well-equipped bedrooms, suitable for families and business travellers, and all with en suite bathrooms. Continental breakfast is available and other refreshments may be taken at the nearby family restaurant. For further details see the Hotel Groups page.
ROOMS: 92 en suite s fr £45; d fr £45

LOUGHBOROUGH Map 08 SK51

★★★ 65% The Quality Hotel & Suites Loughborough
New Ashby Rd LE11 4EX
☎ 01509 211800 ☳ 01509 211868
e-mail: enquiries@hotels-loughborough.com
Dir: M1 junct 23 take A512 towards Loughborough. Hotel 1m on left

PETS: Bedrooms Exercise area (200 metres)

Close to the motorway network, this popular, modern hotel offers comfortable, well-equipped accommodation. All of the bedrooms have a spacious work area, and some rooms have small lounges and kitchenettes. It is an ideal hotel for a long stay or for families. Open-plan public rooms include a lounge area, bar and carvery restaurant.
ROOMS: 94 en suite (12 fmly) (47 GF) No smoking in 47 bedrooms s £54-£100; d £84-£120 **LB FACILITIES:** STV Indoor swimming (H) Sauna Solarium Gym Jacuzzi Xmas **PARKING:** 160
NOTES: No smoking in restaurant
CARDS:

♦♦♦ Garendon Park Hotel
92 Leicester Rd LE11 2AQ
☎ 01509 236557 ☳ 01509 265559
e-mail: info@garendonparkhotel.co.uk
Dir: M1 junct 23/A512 to Loughborough, at 2nd island turn right, at 5th island turn left, at lights turn left. Hotel on right just before next lights

PETS: Bedrooms £5 for dogs Public areas Exercise area (50 yards) Dog food provided RESIDENT PETS: Molly - Yorkshire Terrier, Terra - Collie

This late Victorian house is conveniently situated just a short walk from the high street. Bedrooms are individually decorated and feature co-ordinated fabrics and thoughtful touches. Breakfast and dinner are served at individual tables in the smart dining room and guests have the use of a lounge as well as a cosy bar.
FACILITIES: 9 en suite (4 fmly) No smoking in bedrooms No smoking in dining room STV TVB tea/coffee Licensed Cen ht TVL Dinner Last d 6pm **PRICES:** s £37-£45; d £47-£60✱
CARDS: ▭

MARKET HARBOROUGH Map 04 SP78

★★★ 70% Three Swans
21 High St LE16 7NJ
☎ 01858 466644 ☳ 01858 433101
e-mail: sales@threeswans.co.uk
Dir: M1 junct 20 take A4304 to Market Harborough. Through town centre on A6 from Leicester, hotel on right

Best Western

PETS: Bedrooms (unattended) £5 incl. food Public areas (except restaurants or food service areas) Exercise area (200yds) Pet Food blankets provided

Public areas in this former coaching inn include an elegant fine dining restaurant and cocktail bar, a smart foyer lounge and popular public bar areas. Bedroom styles and sizes vary, all are very well appointed and equipped and the most recently created wing of bedrooms is particularly impressive, offering high quality spacious accommodation.
ROOMS: 18 en suite 43 annexe en suite (8 fmly) (12 GF) No smoking in 44 bedrooms s £55-£85; d £75-£135 (incl. bkfst) **LB FACILITIES:** STV ch fac Xmas **SERVICES:** Lift **PARKING:** 100 **NOTES:** No smoking in restaurant **CARDS:** ▭

MELTON MOWBRAY Map 08 SK71

★★★★ ◉◉ Stapleford Park
Stapleford LE14 2EF
☎ 01572 787522 ☳ 01572 787651
e-mail: reservations@stapleford.co.uk
Dir: 1m SW of B676, 4m E of Melton Mowbray and 9m W of Colsterworth

PETS: Bedrooms (unattended) £5 Public areas Exercise area (adjacent) Pet Food

This stunning mansion, dating back to the 14th century, sits in over 500 acres of beautiful grounds. Spacious, sumptuous public rooms include a choice of lounges and an elegant dining room; an additional brasserie-style restaurant is located in the new golf complex. The hotel also boasts a wonderful new spa with health and beauty treatments and gymnasium, a golf course, horse-riding and many other country pursuits. Bedrooms are individually

continued

styled and furnished to a high standard. Attentive service is delivered with a relaxed yet professional style, well-suited to the house. Changes in the kitchen brigade, with Chef Wayne Vickerage at the helm, have introduced quality cuisine through an interesting, fixed-priced menu.

ROOMS: 44 en suite 8 annexe en suite No smoking in 44 bedrooms s £175-£681; d £158-£681 (incl. bkfst) **LB FACILITIES:** STV Indoor swimming (H) Golf 18 Tennis (hard) Fishing Riding Sauna Solarium Gym Croquet lawn Putting green Jacuzzi Archery, Croquet, Falconry, Horse Riding, Petanque, Shooting entertainment Xmas **SERVICES:** Lift **PARKING:** 120 **NOTES:** No smoking in restaurant
CARDS:

★★★ 73% Sysonby Knoll
Asfordby Rd LE13 0HP
☎ 01664 563563 🖷 01664 410364
e-mail: reception@sysonby.com
Dir: 0.5m from town centre beside A6006

PETS: Bedrooms (by arrangement) (unattended) Public areas (except restaurant) Exercise area (5 acres on site) RESIDENT PETS: Stalky (Miniature Dachshund)

This well-established hotel is located towards the edge of town and is set within attractive gardens. A friendly and relaxed atmosphere prevails with the many return guests treated like old friends. Bedrooms, including superior rooms in an annexe, are generally spacious and thoughtfully equipped. Public areas include a cosy bar, choice of lounges and a smart and newly extended restaurant.
ROOMS: 23 en suite 7 annexe en suite (1 fmly) (7 GF) No smoking in 6 bedrooms s £58.50-£75; d £71-£94 (incl. bkfst) **LB FACILITIES:** STV Fishing Croquet lawn **PARKING:** 48 **NOTES:** No smoking in restaurant Closed 25 Dec-1 Jan **CARDS:**

◆◆◆◆ Bryn Barn
38 High St, Waltham-on-the-Wolds LE14 4AH
☎ 01664 464783 & 07791 215614 🖷 01664 464138
e-mail: glenarowlands@onetel.net.uk
Dir: off A607 onto High St between Marquis of Granby pub and church, Bryn Barn 200mtrs on right

PETS: Bedrooms (unattended) Exercise area (50yds)

A warm welcome awaits guests at this attractive, peacefully located cottage within easy reach of Melton Mowbray, Grantham, Rutland Water and Belvoir Castle. Bedrooms are smartly appointed and comfortably furnished, whilst public rooms include an inviting lounge overlooking a wonderful courtyard garden. Dinner can be taken at one of the nearby village pubs.
FACILITIES: 4 en suite (2 fmly) (1 GF) No smoking TV5B tea/coffee Cen ht TVL No coaches **PRICES:** s £28-£30; d £45-£48✱ **LB** **PARKING:** 4 **NOTES:** Closed 21 Dec-4 Jan

> **Don't forget to let proprietors know when you book that you're bringing your pet**

◆◆◆ 🍴 Noels Arms
31 Burton St LE13 1AE
☎ 01664 562363
Dir: follow signs for Oakham & railway station. Noels Arms on corner of Burton Street & Mill Lane

PETS: Sep Accom Public areas Exercise area (Park across road)

This traditional inn sits close to the town centre. The bar is the focal point of the inn and a relaxed and friendly atmosphere is generated by staff and locals; breakfast is taken within the open-plan bar area. Bedrooms come in a variety of styles and sizes, each decoratively co-ordinated and furnished in pine.
FACILITIES: 6 rms (4 en suite) (2 fmly) TVB tea/coffee Cen ht Pool Table **PRICES:** s fr £28; d fr £46✱

NOTTINGHAM EAST MIDLANDS AIRPORT Map 08 SK42

★★★ 75% ☺
Best Western Yew Lodge Hotel
Packington Hill, Kegworth DE74 2DF
☎ 01509 672518 🖷 01509 674730
e-mail: info@yewlodgehotel.co.uk
Dir: M1 junct 24. Follow signs to Loughborough & Kegworth on A6. At bottom of hill, 1st right, after 400yds lodge on right

PETS: Bedrooms (unattended) £5 Exercise area (0.5 mile)

This smart, family-owned hotel is close to both the motorway and airport, yet peacefully located. Modern bedrooms and public areas are thoughtfully appointed offering all modern comfort and facilities. The restaurant serves interesting dishes, while lounge service and extensive conference facilities are available.
ROOMS: 98 en suite (18 fmly) No smoking in 65 bedrooms s £50-£80; d £70-£100 (incl. bkfst) **FACILITIES:** Spa STV Indoor swimming (H) Sauna Solarium Gym Jacuzzi Beauty therapy suite, foot spas Xmas **SERVICES:** Lift **PARKING:** 180 **NOTES:** No smoking in restaurant **CARDS:**

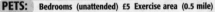

LINCOLNSHIRE

ASWARBY Map 08 TF03

◆◆◆ 🍴 Tally Ho
NG34 8SA
☎ 01529 455205 🖷 01529 455773
Dir: take A15 from Sleaford towards Bourne. Tally Ho approx 6m on left

PETS: Bedrooms (unattended) £5 Public areas (Not in restaurant) Exercise area (20 metres)

Bedrooms at this delightful inn are in an adjacent building, and all are comfortable and well equipped. Guests can enjoy a wide range of meals available at lunch and dinner in the bar or the restaurant, where service is very friendly and attentive.
FACILITIES: 6 en suite (4 GF) No smoking in bedrooms No smoking in dining room TVB tea/coffee Cen ht No coaches Dinner Last d 9.30pm **PRICES:** s £40; d £60✱ **PARKING:** 40 **CARDS:**

BELTON
Map 08 SK93

★★★★ 75% **De Vere Belton Woods**
NG32 2LN
☎ 01476 593200 ▨ 01476 574547
e-mail: belton.woods@devere-hotels.com
Dir: Follow A1 to Gonerby Moor services. Take B1174 towards Great Gonerby. At top of hill turn left towards Manthorpe/Belton. At T-junct turn left onto A607. Hotel is 0.25miles on left.

PETS: Bedrooms (unattended) Exercise area (On site)

Beautifully located amidst 475 acres of picturesque countryside, this is a destination venue for lovers of golf and sports, as well as a relaxing executive retreat for seminars. Comfortable and well-equipped accommodation complements the elegant and spacious public areas, which provide a good choice of drinking and dining options. An onsite outdoor activity company is available.
ROOMS: 136 en suite (136 fmly) (68 GF) No smoking in 117 bedrooms s £109-£135; d £125-£155 (incl. bkfst) **LB FACILITIES:** Spa STV Indoor swimming (H) Golf 45 Tennis (hard) Fishing Squash Snooker Sauna Solarium Gym Croquet lawn Putting green Jacuzzi Outdoor activity centre - quad biking, laser shooting etc entertainment ch fac Xmas
SERVICES: Lift **PARKING:** 350 **NOTES:** No smoking in restaurant
CARDS: 〓〓〓〓〓 🄯

BOSTON
Map 08 TF34

♦♦♦♦ **Boston Lodge**
Browns Drove, Swineshead Bridge PE20 3PX
☎ 01205 820983 ▨ 01205 820512
e-mail: info@bostonlodge.co.uk
Dir: adjacent to A1121, 300yds from junct with A17

PETS: Bedrooms £2 RESIDENT PETS: Trudie - Collie cross, Ellie - cat

This attractive property enjoys a convenient location close to Boston. There is an open-plan lounge/dining room complete with TV and comfortable seating, where guests can enjoy breakfast at individual tables; dinner can be taken at the local pub which is conveniently located a very short walk away. Bedrooms are pleasantly furnished and thoughtfully equipped. Ample private car parking is provided.
FACILITIES: 9 en suite (2 fmly) (3 GF) No smoking STV TVB tea/coffee Cen ht TVL No children 1yr No coaches **PRICES:** s fr £27; d fr £44✳ **LB PARKING:** 16 **CARDS:** 〓〓〓〓 🄯

BRIGG
Map 08 TA00

★★ 66% **The Red Lion Hotel**
Main Rd, Redbourne DN21 4QR
☎ 01652 648302 ▨ 01652 648900
e-mail: enquiries@redlion.org
Dir: from M180 junct 4 take A15. After 4m left at mini-rdbt, take signs left to Redbourne. Hotel 1st building on left in village

PETS: Bedrooms (unattended) £5 Public areas (not during food service) Exercise area (200 yards) RESIDENT PETS: Teasel & Higgins (Jack Russells)

Dating back to the 17th century, this former coaching inn overlooks the village green and holds a key to the historic fire station that is adjacent. Recently restored, the inn has pleasantly

continued

furnished bedrooms and a wholesome range of food is available either in the modern bar or air conditioned dining room. There is a warm and friendly atmosphere.
ROOMS: 11 en suite (2 fmly) No smoking in 2 bedrooms s £40-£45; d £55-£60 (incl. bkfst) **LB PARKING:** 30 **NOTES:** No smoking in restaurant **CARDS:** 〓〓〓〓 🄯

CLEETHORPES
Map 08 TA30

♦♦♦♦ **Tudor Terrace**
11 Bradford Av DN35 0BB
☎ 01472 600800 ▨ 01472 501395
e-mail: tudor.terrace@ntlworld.com
Dir: from sea front, turn into Bradford Ave, 1st property on left

PETS: Bedrooms Public areas (except dining room) Exercise area

This guest house offers attractive bedrooms which are thoughtfully designed and furnished to a high standard. Guests can relax in the lounge, or outside on the pleasant patio in a well-maintained garden. Very caring and friendly service is provided and the house is strictly non-smoking, except in the garden.
FACILITIES: 6 en suite (1 GF) No smoking TVB tea/coffee Cen ht TVL No children No coaches Dinner Last d 2pm **PRICES:** s £24-£29; d £45-£49.50✳ **LB PARKING:** 3 **CARDS:** 〓〓〓〓 🄯

DONINGTON ON BAIN
Map 08 TF28

♦♦♦ 🍺 **The Black Horse Inn**
Main Rd LN11 9TJ
☎ 01507 343640 ▨ 01507 343640
e-mail: barrett@blackhorse1125.freeserve.co.uk
Dir: turn off A157 Lincoln to Louth road, signed Donington on Bain. In centre of village

PETS: Bedrooms (unattended) £1.50 per stay Exercise area (0.25 mile) RESIDENT PETS: Fern (Chocolate Labrador)

An ideal touring base either for The Viking Way, nearby Cadwell Park, Market Rasen or the market town of Louth. A wide range of food and beers is available in this popular inn, and the spacious bedrooms are comfortable and all en-suite.
FACILITIES: 8 en suite (4 GF) No smoking in bedrooms No smoking in dining room No smoking in 1 lounge TVB tea/coffee Cen ht Pool Table Dinner Last d 9pm **PRICES:** s fr £26; d fr £44✳ **LB PARKING:** 60 **CARDS:** 〓〓〓〓 🄯

GRANTHAM
Map 08 SK93

★★★ 71% **Kings**
North Pde NG31 8AU
☎ 01476 590800 ▨ 01476 577072
e-mail: kings@bestwestern.co.uk
Dir: off A1 at rdbt N end of Grantham onto B1174, follow road for 2m. Hotel on left by bridge

PETS: Bedrooms Public areas (except restaurant) Exercise area (500 metres)

A friendly atmosphere exists within this extended Georgian house. Bedrooms are attractively decorated and furnished in modern light oak. Dining options include the formal Victorian restaurant and

continued

the popular Orangery, which also operates as a coffee shop and breakfast room; a lounge bar and a smart open-plan foyer lounge are also available.

ROOMS: 21 en suite (3 fmly) s £56-£66; d £66-£76 (incl. bkfst) LB
FACILITIES: STV **PARKING:** 36 **NOTES:** No smoking in restaurant
CARDS:

GRIMSBY — Map 08 TA21

★★★ 66% Elizabeth
Littlecoates Rd DN34 4LX
☎ 01472 240024 ▤ 01472 241354
e-mail: elizabeth.grimsby@elizabethhotels.co.uk
Dir: A1136 signed Greatcoates, 1st rdbt left, 2nd rdbt right. Hotel on right in 200mtrs

PETS: Bedrooms £5 Exercise area (200yds)

Bedrooms at this pleasantly situated hotel are equipped with modern comforts and many have large windows and balconies overlooking the adjoining golf course. The popular restaurant shares the same tranquil view. There is a large banqueting suite, smaller meeting and conference rooms, and extensive parking which makes this an ideal business centre.

ROOMS: 52 en suite (4 fmly) No smoking in 27 bedrooms s £60-£79; d £70-£89 (incl. bkfst) LB **FACILITIES:** STV Xmas **SERVICES:** Lift
PARKING: 200 **NOTES:** No smoking in restaurant
CARDS:

LINCOLN — Map 08 SK97

★★ 73% Hillcrest
15 Lindum Ter LN2 5RT
☎ 01522 510182 ▤ 01522 538009
e-mail: reservations@hillcrest-hotel.com
Dir: from A15 Wragby Rd and Lindum Rd, turn into Upper Lindum St at sign. Left at bottom for hotel 200mtrs on right

THE CIRCLE
Selected Individual Hotels
GREAT BRITAIN

PETS: Bedrooms Public areas Exercise area (100yds)

The hospitality offered by Jenny Bennett and her staff is one of the strengths of Hillcrest, which sits in a quiet residential location. Thoughtfully equipped bedrooms come in a variety of sizes and all are well presented and maintained. The cosy dining room and pleasant conservatory offer a good range of freshly prepared food with views out over the adjacent park. A computer room is available for residents.

ROOMS: 14 en suite (5 fmly) (6 GF) No smoking in 6 bedrooms s £65; d £85-£95 (incl. bkfst) LB **FACILITIES:** ch fac **PARKING:** 8
NOTES: No smoking in restaurant Closed 23 Dec-3 Jan
CARDS:

★★ 72% Castle
Westgate LN1 3AS
☎ 01522 538801 ▤ 01522 575457
e-mail: aa@castlehotel.net
Dir: follow signs for Historic Lincoln. Hotel at NE corner of castle

PETS: Bedrooms (Restricted) (unattended) £5
(10 minute walk) Pet Food

Located in the heart of historic Lincoln, this privately owned and run hotel has been carefully restored to offer comfortable,

continued

---

attractive, well-appointed accommodation. Bedrooms are all thoughtfully equipped, particularly the deluxe rooms and the spacious Lincoln suite. Specialising in traditional fayre, Knights Restaurant has an interesting medieval theme.

ROOMS: 16 en suite 3 annexe en suite (5 GF) No smoking in 12 bedrooms s £67-£150; d £89-£160 (incl. bkfst) LB **PARKING:** 20
NOTES: No children 8yrs No smoking in restaurant RS Evening of Dec 25
CARDS:

★★ 66% Tower Hotel
38 Westgate LN1 3BD
☎ 01522 529999 ▤ 01522 560596
e-mail: tower.hotel@btclick.com
Dir: from A46 follow signs to Lincoln N then to Bailgate area. Through arch and 2nd left

PETS: Bedrooms (unattended) Public areas (except dining areas) Exercise area (50-100yds)

The Tower Hotel stands facing the Norman castle wall and is in a very convenient location for the city. The relaxed and friendly atmosphere is one of the strengths of this hotel. Public rooms are smartly appointed following a refurbishment programme which has seen the development of a modern lounge bar, a separate, quieter lounge and a cosy brasserie dining area; food is also readily available in the bar.

ROOMS: 14 en suite (1 fmly) No smoking in 2 bedrooms s £55-£67; d £80-£85 (incl. bkfst) LB **PARKING:** 9 **NOTES:** No smoking in restaurant Closed 24-26 Dec **CARDS:**

◆◆◆◆ Eagles
552A Newark Rd, North Hykeham LN6 9NG
☎ 01522 686346
e-mail: pauline.skevington1@ntlworld.com
Dir: turn off A46 onto A1434, 0.5m on right

PETS: (Small dogs only) Bedrooms Exercise area (300yds)

This large detached house is very convenient for the bypass and has been well furnished and thoughtfully equipped. The bedrooms are bright and fresh, and a conservatory has been added for guests' use. Substantial breakfasts are served in the pleasant dining room and the resident owners provide genuine hospitality.

FACILITIES: 5 rms (4 en suite) (2 fmly) (1 GF) No smoking TVB tea/coffee Cen ht No children 10yrs No coaches **PRICES:** s £28; d £45✱
PARKING: 6

◆◆◆ Newport
26-28 Newport Rd LN1 3DF
☎ 01522 528590 ▤ 01522 542868
e-mail: info@newportguesthouse.co.uk
Dir: on A15 going N, 200mtrs on right past Radio Lincs. Or S, 0.5m from ring rd just before Newport Arch

PETS: Bedrooms Exercise area (200 metres)

Situated in the quieter upper part of the city and just a few minutes' walk from the cathedral, this double fronted terraced house offers well-equipped and comfortable bedrooms. The pleasing public areas include a very comfortable sitting room and a bright and attractive breakfast room.

FACILITIES: 9 en suite (2 GF) No smoking TVB tea/coffee Cen ht TVL No coaches **PRICES:** s £28-£35; d £50-£60✱ **PARKING:** 4
CARDS:

England

LINCOLN continued

♦♦ Edward King House
The Old Palace, Minster Yard LN2 1PU
☎ 01522 528778 🗏 01522 527308
e-mail: enjoy@ekhs.org.uk
Dir: follow directions to cathedral, then signs to Medieval Bishop's Palace. Entrance through archway in SE corner of Minster Yard.

PETS: Bedrooms (unattended) Exercise area (on site)
RESIDENT PETS: Billy - cat

Once the residence of the Bishops of Lincoln, this historic house lies in the lea of the cathedral and next to the old palace. Public areas include a television lounge and a spacious dining room where a hearty breakfast is served. The practical bedrooms are pleasantly furnished and suitably equipped.
FACILITIES: 17 rms (1 fmly) No smoking tea/coffee Licensed Cen ht TVL Dinner Last d 48 hours **PRICES:** s £21-£23; d £41-£45✱
PARKING: 12 **NOTES:** Closed Xmas/New Year
CARDS: 💳💳💳💳💳💳💳

♦♦ Jaymar
31 Newland St West LN1 1QQ
☎ 01522 532934 🗏 01522 820182
e-mail: ward.jaymar4@ntlworld.com
Dir: turn off A1 onto A46, proceed to junct with A57, turn right to Lincoln Central. At 1st set of T-lights turn left into Gresham Street, then take 2nd right by off licence, Jaymar approx 500mtrs on left

PETS: Bedrooms (unattended) Public areas Exercise area (50yds) Food bowl, drinking bowl and mat provided
RESIDENT PETS: Trixie - Manchester Terrier cross

Situated within easy walking distance of the city, this small, friendly guest house offers two well-equipped bedrooms. A full English breakfast, with vegetarian options, is served in the cosy dining room, and an early breakfast, from 5am onwards, is available on request. Children and pets are welcome, and guests can be collected from the bus or railway stations if required.
FACILITIES: 2 rms (1 fmly) No smoking TVB tea/coffee No coaches
PRICES: s £17-£20; d £32-£40✱ **LB** **BB**

LOUTH
Map 08 TF38

★★★ 70% Kenwick Park
Kenwick Park Estate LN11 8NR
☎ 01507 608806 🗏 01507 608027
e-mail: enquiries@kenwick-park.co.uk
Dir: A16 from Grimsby, then A157 Mablethorpe/Manby Rd. Hotel 400mtrs down hill on right

CLASSIC BRITISH

PETS: Bedrooms (unattended) £20 Exercise area (On site)

This elegant Georgian house is situated on the 320-acre Kenwick Park estate, overlooking its own golf course. Bedrooms are spacious, comfortable and provide modern facilities. Public areas include a restaurant and a conservatory bar, which overlook the
continued

grounds. There is also an extensive leisure centre and state-of-the-art conference and banqueting facilities.
ROOMS: 29 en suite 5 annexe en suite (10 fmly) No smoking in 11 bedrooms s £75-£105; d £100-£120 (incl. bkfst) **LB** **FACILITIES:** Spa STV Indoor swimming (H) Golf 18 Tennis (hard) Squash Sauna Solarium Gym Putting green Jacuzzi Health & Beauty Centre ch fac Xmas **PARKING:** 100 **NOTES:** No smoking in restaurant
CARDS: 💳💳💳💳💳💳💳

★★★ 69% Beaumont
66 Victoria Rd LN11 0BX
☎ 01507 605005 🗏 01507 607768
e-mail: beaumonthotel@aol.com

PETS: Bedrooms (unattended) £8.50 Exercise area (0.25 mile) Pet Food Bowls and beds provided if necessary

This smart, family-run hotel enjoys a quiet location, within easy reach of the town centre. Bedrooms are spacious and individually designed. Public areas include a smart restaurant with a strong Italian influence and an inviting lounge bar with comfortable deep sofas and open fires. Weddings and functions are also catered for.
ROOMS: 16 en suite (2 fmly) (6 GF) s £55-£65; d £80-£120 (incl. bkfst)
FACILITIES: ch fac **SERVICES:** Lift **PARKING:** 70 **NOTES:** RS Sun
CARDS: 💳💳💳💳💳

MARTON (VILLAGE)
Map 08 SK88

♦♦♦♦ Black Swan Guest House
21 High St DN21 5AH
☎ 01427 718878 🗏 01427 718878
e-mail: reservations@blackswan-marton.co.uk
Dir: on A156, at junct with A1500, 12m from Lincoln, 5m from Gainsborough

PETS: Bedrooms Exercise area (200yds)
RESIDENT PETS: TC & Scooby - black cats

Centrally located in the village of Marton, this 18th-century, former coaching inn retains many original features and offers homely bedrooms all with modern facilities. Tasty breakfasts are taken in the cosy dining room and a comfortable lounge is also available for guest use. Good hospitality is provided and transport to nearby pubs and restaurants can be provided.
FACILITIES: 6 en suite 2 annexe en suite (3 fmly) (2 GF) No smoking TVB tea/coffee Licensed Cen ht TVL No coaches Dinner
PRICES: s £30-£40; d £55-£70✱ **LB** **PARKING:** 10
CARDS: 💳💳💳💳

SCUNTHORPE
Map 08 SE81

★★★ 67% Wortley House
Rowland Rd DN16 1SU
☎ 01724 842223 🗏 01724 280646
Dir: M180 junct 3 take A18. Follow signs for Grimsby/Humberside airport, 2nd left into Brumby Wood Ln, over rdbt into Rowland Rd. Hotel 200yds on right

PETS: Bedrooms £10 deposit Exercise area (2 mins walk)

A friendly hotel with good facilities for conferences, meetings, banquets and other functions. Bedrooms offer modern comfort
continued

and facilities. Popular bar meals are served in the cocktail lounge, while more formal meals are served in the pleasant restaurant.
ROOMS: 38 en suite (3 fmly) No smoking in 28 bedrooms s £63-£84; d £67.50-£90 (incl. bkfst) **FACILITIES:** STV ch fac Xmas **PARKING:** 100
NOTES: No smoking in restaurant **CARDS:**

SKEGNESS
Map 09 TF56

★★★ 66% Vine
Vine Rd, Seacroft PE25 3DB
☎ 01754 763018 & 610611 ▤ 01754 769845
e-mail: info@thevinehotel.com
Dir: A52 to Skegness, S towards Gibraltar Point, turn right on to Drummond Rd, after 0.5m turn right into Vine Rd

Best Western

PETS: Bedrooms £6 for a dog Public areas Exercise area

Reputedly the second oldest building in Skegness, this traditional style hotel offers two character bars that serve excellent local beers. Freshly prepared dishes are served in both the bar and the restaurant; service is both friendly and helpful. The smartly refurbished bedrooms are well equipped and comfortably appointed.
ROOMS: 24 en suite (3 fmly) No smoking in 6 bedrooms s £60-£70; d £80-£90 (incl. bkfst) **LB FACILITIES:** STV Golf 18 Putting green Xmas
PARKING: 50 **NOTES:** No smoking in restaurant
CARDS:

SPALDING
Map 08 TF22

★★ 70% ® Cley Hall
22 High St PE11 1TX
☎ 01775 725157 ▤ 01775 710785
e-mail: cleyhall@enterprise.net
Dir: on A16/A151 towards Spalding, keep river on right, hotel 1.5m on left

PETS: Bedrooms Exercise area (river bank opposite)

This Georgian house overlooks the River Welland, with landscaped gardens to the rear. Most bedrooms are in an adjacent building; all are smart and include modern amenities. Dining options are popular with residents and locals alike, particularly the fine dining menu offered within the smartly refurbished Garden Restaurant. A reception-based internet/PC workstation with language translation facility is available.
ROOMS: 4 en suite 8 annexe en suite (4 fmly) (1 GF) s £55-£85; d £80-£105 (incl. bkfst) **FACILITIES:** STV competition river fishing
PARKING: 20 **NOTES:** No smoking in restaurant
CARDS:

Please mention AA Pet Friendly Places to Stay when booking

🍺 Places with this symbol are pubs

🏡 Places with this symbol are country house hotels

STAMFORD
Map 04 TF00

★★★ 69% Garden House
High St, St Martin's PE9 2LP
☎ 01780 763359 ▤ 01780 763339
e-mail: enquiries@gardenhousehotel.com
Dir: A1 to South Stamford, B1081, signed Stamford and Burghley House. Hotel on left on entering town

PETS: Bedrooms £5 Public areas Exercise area (0.5 mile) Pet Food **RESIDENT PETS:** Oliver (Golden Retriever)

Situated within a few minutes' walk of the town centre, this sympathetically transformed 18th-century town house provides pleasant accommodation. Bedroom styles vary; all are well equipped and comfortably furnished. Public rooms include a charming lounge bar, conservatory restaurant and a smart breakfast room. Service is attentive and friendly throughout.
ROOMS: 20 en suite (2 fmly) (4 GF) No smoking in 16 bedrooms s £65; d £89-£95 (incl. bkfst) **LB FACILITIES:** STV ch fac Xmas
PARKING: 22 **NOTES:** No smoking in restaurant RS 1-12 Jan
CARDS:

SUTTON-ON-SEA
Map 09 TF58

◆◆◆ Athelstone Lodge Hotel
25 Trusthorpe Rd LN12 2LR
☎ 01507 441521
Dir: on A52 N of village

PETS: Bedrooms Exercise area (300 yards)

Situated between Mablethorpe and Skegness and close to the promenade, this is an ideal touring base. Bedrooms are pleasantly decorated, soundly maintained and equipped with many useful extras. Breakfast is served in the dining room and guests also have the use of both a bar and a lounge. A variety of enjoyable home-cooked dinners are available.
FACILITIES: 6 rms (5 en suite) (2 fmly) No smoking in dining room TVB tea/coffee Licensed Cen ht TVL No coaches Dinner Last d 4.30pm
PRICES: s £22-£24; d £44-£48✱ **LB PARKING:** 6
NOTES: Closed Nov-Feb **CARDS:**

WINTERINGHAM
Map 08 SE92

◉◉◉◉◉ 🍴 Winteringham Fields
DN15 9PF
☎ 01724 733096 ▤ 01724 733898
e-mail: wintfields@aol.com
Dir: in the centre of the village at the crossroads

PETS: Bedrooms Exercise area (500yds)
RESIDENT PETS: William - Boxer, Bolly - Great Dane

This highly regarded restaurant with rooms, located deep in the countryside in Winteringham village, is six miles west of the Humber Bridge. Chef Germain Schwab has a hand in every skilfully crafted dish that leaves his kitchen, whilst Anne Schwab admirably leads a superb front of house team. Public rooms and bedrooms, some of which are housed in renovated barns and cottages, are delightfully cosseting, but it is the inspired cooking that remains the main draw.
ROOMS: 4 en suite 6 annexe en suite No smoking in all bedrooms s £95-£135; d £125-£195 (incl. cont bkfst) **PARKING:** 17
NOTES: No smoking in restaurant Closed Sun, Mon & BH/2wks Xmas/ 1wk Aug/1wk Mar **CARDS:**

England

WOODHALL SPA — Map 08 TF16

★★★ 68% Petwood
Stixwould Rd LN10 6QF
☎ 01526 352411 ▤ 01526 353473
e-mail: reception@petwood.co.uk
Dir: from Sleaford take A153 (signed Skegness). At Tattershall turn left on B1192. Hotel is signed from village

PETS: Bedrooms (unattended) £5 Exercise area (20 yards)

This lovely Edwardian house, set in 30 acres of gardens and woodlands, is steeped in history. Built in 1905, the house was used by the famous 'Dambusters' as an officers' mess during World War II. Bedrooms and public areas are spacious, comfortable and retain many original period features. Weddings and conferences are well catered for with brand new facilities.
ROOMS: 53 en suite (3 GF) No smoking in 17 bedrooms s £90–£110; d £130–£180 (incl. bkfst) **LB FACILITIES:** Snooker Croquet lawn Putting green Complimentary pass to leisure centre entertainment Xmas **SERVICES:** Lift **PARKING:** 140 **NOTES:** No smoking in restaurant
CARDS:

★★★ 63% Golf Hotel
The Broadway LN10 6SG
☎ 01526 353535 ▤ 01526 353096
Dir: from Lincoln take B1189 to Metheringham onto B1191 towards Woodhall Spa. Hotel on left approx 500yds along from rdbt

PETS: Bedrooms (some) (unattended) Exercise area (gardens)

Located near the centre of the village, this traditional hotel is ideally situated to explore the Lincolnshire countryside and coast. The adjacent golf course makes this a popular venue for golfers and gives rise to the hotel's name and much of its decorative theme. Bedrooms vary in size and include several recently refurbished rooms.
ROOMS: 50 en suite (4 fmly) (8 GF) No smoking in 21 bedrooms s £70–£84; d £90–£118 (incl. bkfst & dinner) **LB FACILITIES:** STV Croquet lawn Guests have use of private leisure centre 1m from hotel Xmas **PARKING:** 100 **NOTES:** No smoking in restaurant
CARDS:

◆◆ Claremont
9/11 Witham Rd LN10 6RW
☎ 01526 352000
Dir: on B1191 Horncastle/Kirkstead Bridge Rd, at the centre of Woodhall Spa close to mini rdbt

PETS: Bedrooms Sep Accom (exterior building) Public areas (under supervision) Exercise area (50 yards)
RESIDENT PETS: Monty & Pudding (cats)

This large guest house is located close to the town centre, and has been owned and run by Mrs Brennan for a number of years. The bedrooms are generally quite spacious, traditionally furnished and well equipped. The public areas are pleasant and include the breakfast room.
FACILITIES: 11 rms (5 en suite) (5 fmly) (2 GF) No smoking TVB tea/coffee No coaches **PRICES:** s £15–£25; d £30–£45✳ **LB BB PARKING:** 5

LONDON

E14

⌂ Hotel Ibis London Docklands
1 Baffin Way E14 9PE
☎ 020 7517 1100 ▤ 020 7987 5916
e-mail: H2177@accor-hotels.com
Dir: from Tower Bridge follow City Airport and Royal Docks signs, exit for 'Isle of Dogs'. Hotel on 1st left opposite McDonalds

PETS: Bedrooms £3 Public areas

Modern, budget hotel offering comfortable accommodation in bright and practical bedrooms. Breakfast is self-service and dinner is available in the restaurant. For further details, consult the Hotel Groups page.
ROOMS: 87 en suite s fr £56.95; d fr £56.95

EC1

★★★ 74% ⍟
Malmaison Charterhouse Square
18-21 Charterhouse Square, Clerkenwell EC1M 6AH
☎ 020 7012 3700 ▤ 020 7012 3702
e-mail: london@malmaison.com
Dir: Exit Barbican Station turn left, take 1st left. Hotel on the far left corner of Charterhouse Square.

PETS: Telephone for details

Malmaison Charterhouse represents the new face of Malmaison, with the same focus on quality of service and food, but coupled with the peace of this area of London, and the age of the building. The brasserie and bar form the centre of the hotel with a buzzing atmosphere and tradtional French cuisine.
ROOMS: 97 en suite (5 GF) No smoking in 79 bedrooms s £99–£176.25; d £99–£193.88 **FACILITIES:** STV Gym **SERVICES:** Lift air con
CARDS:

EC3

★★★ 72%
Novotel London Tower Bridge
10 Pepys St EC3N 2NR
☎ 020 7265 6000 ▤ 020 7265 6060
e-mail: H3107@accor-hotels.com

PETS: Bedrooms (unattended) £6 Public areas

Located near the Tower of London, this smart hotel is convenient for Docklands, the City, Heathrow and London City airports. Bedrooms are spacious, modern, and offer a great range of facilities, including air conditioning. There is a smart bar and restaurant, a small gym and extensive meeting and conference facilities.
ROOMS: 203 en suite (77 fmly) No smoking in 145 bedrooms s £160–£270; d £180–£240 **LB FACILITIES:** STV Sauna Gym Steam Room **SERVICES:** Lift air con **CARDS:**

N4

◆◆◆ Parkside Hotel
384 Seven Sisters Rd N4 2PL
☎ 020 8800 8888 ▤ 020 8800 8888
e-mail: reservations@parksidehotel.com
Dir: turn off A1 Holloway Rd at Nags Head into Seven Sisters Rd, hotel approx. 1m on right opposite park

PETS: Bedrooms Public areas Exercise area

Located opposite Finsbury Park, the hotel is within walking distance of the tube and convenient for both northern and central London. Comfortably furnished bedrooms are mostly en-suite and are well equipped. Facilities include a bar and lounge, a small and well-equipped gym, conference facilities and a large, free car park.
FACILITIES: 50 rms (41 en suite) (14 fmly) (12 GF) No smoking in dining room TVB tea/coffee Direct dial from bedrooms Licensed Cen ht TVL Snooker Gymnasium Pool Table Dinner Last d 8.30pm
PRICES: s £40-£52; d £55-£63✱ LB **PARKING:** 40
CARDS: 🖃 🔤 🔤 🔤 🔤 ⑤

NW3

◆◆◆ Quality Hotel Hampstead
5 Frognal, Hampstead NW3 6AL
☎ 020 7794 0101 ▤ 020 7794 0100
e-mail: quality-h@lth-hotels.com
Dir: turn off Finchley Rd into Frognal, hotel on left

PETS: Bedrooms £10 Public areas Exercise area (Hampstead Heath park 0.5 mile)

Well located off the Finchley Road, this modern purpose-built hotel is only minutes' walk from the tube and just three stops from the West End. Smartly appointed bedrooms are well equipped for both business and leisure guests. Public areas include an open-plan bar/lounge and airy basement breakfast room.
FACILITIES: 57 en suite (10 fmly) (1 GF) No smoking in 27 bedrooms STV TVB tea/coffee Direct dial from bedrooms Licensed Lift Cen ht TVL
PRICES: s £50-£79; d £50-£89✱ LB **PARKING:** 20
CARDS: 🖃 🔤 🔤 🔤 🔤 ⑤

SE1

★★★★ 68%
Novotel London City South
Southwark Bridge Rd SE1 9HH
☎ 020 7089 0400 ▤ 020 7089 0410
e-mail: H3269@accor-hotels.com
Dir: junct at Thrale St

NOVOTEL

PETS: Bedrooms £8 Public areas (Lobby only - not in food service areas)

The first of a new generation of Novotels, this newly-built hotel is contemporary in design with smart, modern bedrooms and spacious public rooms. There are a number of options for guests wanting to unwind, including treatments such as reflexology and immersion therapy, while a gymnasium is available for the more energetic.
ROOMS: 182 en suite (139 fmly) No smoking in 158 bedrooms s £150; d £170 **FACILITIES:** STV Gym **SERVICES:** Lift air con **PARKING:** 80
CARDS: 🖃 🔤 🔤 🔤 🔤 ⑤

★★★ 71%
Mercure London City Bankside
71-79 Southwark St SE1 0JA
☎ 020 7902 0800 ▤ 020 7902 0810
e-mail: H2814@accor-hotels.com
Dir: A200 to London Bridge. Left into Southwark St. Hotel 2 mins by car from station

Mercure
ACCOR HOTELS

PETS: Bedrooms £8 Public areas Exercise area (100yds) Pet Food

This smart, contemporary hotel forms part of the rejuvenation of the South Bank. With the City of London just over the river and a number of tourist attractions within easy reach, the hotel is well located for business and leisure visitors alike. Facilities include spacious air-cooled bedrooms, a modern bar and the stylish Loft Restaurant.
ROOMS: 144 en suite (24 fmly) (5 GF) No smoking in 88 bedrooms
FACILITIES: STV Gym **SERVICES:** Lift air con **PARKING:** 3
CARDS: 🖃 🔤 🔤 🔤 🔤 ⑤

SE3

★★ 68% Clarendon
8-16 Montpelier Row, Blackheath SE3 0RW
☎ 020 8318 4321 ▤ 020 8318 4378
e-mail: relax@clarendonhotel.com
Dir: off A2 at Blackheath junct. Hotel on left before village

THE INDEPENDENTS

PETS: Bedrooms Public areas Exercise area (in grounds, and Blackheath Park adjacent) **RESIDENT PETS:** Lady (cat)

Overlooking the heath, this impressive Georgian hotel offers well-equipped, attractive accommodation. A number of suites are also available. Spacious public areas include a choice of bars, a restaurant and meeting and conference facilities. The hotel has its own car park and guests have use of local leisure facilities.
ROOMS: 181 en suite (3 fmly) (5 GF) No smoking in 22 bedrooms s £80-£95; d £90-£100 (incl. bkfst) LB **FACILITIES:** STV entertainment Xmas **SERVICES:** Lift **PARKING:** 80 **NOTES:** No smoking in restaurant
CARDS: 🖃 🔤 🔤 🔤 🔤 ⑤

💊 **Places with this symbol are farms**

★ **Red stars indicate the AA's Top 200 Hotels in Britain & Ireland**

All information was correct at the time of going to press; we recommend you confirm details on booking

England

SE10

★★ 70% Hamilton House

14 West Grove, Greenwich SE10 8QT
☎ 020 8694 9899 ▤ 020 8694 2370
e-mail: reception@hamiltonhousehotel.co.uk
Dir: from Blackheath common on A2 towards Central London, 2nd right after Blackheath Tea Hut into Hyde Vale. West Grove next left

PETS: Bedrooms (unattended) Public areas (Except bar and restaurant) Exercise area (Adjacent) Large bedrooms - large dogs can be left in rooms RESIDENT PETS: Bobby - dog

This small Georgian hotel boasts true style and character and some impressive views of the Docklands. Elegant bedrooms are individually designed and equipped with a host of thoughtful extras, including CD players. The restaurant is bright and offers creative cooking. The bar area opens out to an attractive garden with seating. This hotel is very popular as a wedding venue.
ROOMS: 9 en suite (8 fmly) (1 GF) No smoking in 4 bedrooms s £100; d £120-£150 (incl. bkfst) **LB FACILITIES:** STV Xmas **PARKING:** 8
NOTES: No smoking in restaurant
CARDS: ▨▨▨▨▨▨▨

SW1

★★★★★ 🏠 No 41

41 Buckingham Palace Rd SW1W 0PS
☎ 020 7300 0041 ▤ 020 7300 0141
e-mail: manager41@rchmail.com
Dir: opp Buckingham Palace Mews entrance.

PETS: Pets accepted by prior arrangement Bedrooms pet menus & bowls available

Small, intimate and very private, this stunning town house is located opposite the Royal Mews and ideally positioned for London's theatres, shops and tourist attractions. Decorated in stylish black and white, bedrooms successfully combine comfort with state-of-the-art technology. Attentive personal service and a host of thoughtful extra touches make this town house really special.
ROOMS: 18 en suite d £220-£745 (incl. bkfst) **FACILITIES:** STV use of 2 health clubs **SERVICES:** Lift air con **CARDS:** ▨▨▨▨▨▨▨

★★★★★ 71% 🟢🟢 Sofitel St James London

6 Waterloo Place SW1Y 4AN
☎ 020 7747 2222 ▤ 020 7747 2210
e-mail: H3144@accor-hotels.com
Dir: On corner of Pall Mall & Waterloo Place

SOFITEL ACCOR HOTELS & RESORTS

PETS: Bedrooms £20 Exercise area (2 mins walk) Dog walking £40 p/h

Located in the exclusive area of St James, this Grade II listed former bank is convenient for most of the city's attractions, theatres and the financial district. The design of the hotel is a happy marriage of modern and classical styles. The bedrooms are equipped to a high standard. Public areas include the Brasserie Roux, a small fitness room and the Rose Lounge.
ROOMS: 186 en suite No smoking in 97 bedrooms s £160-£320; d £160-£320 **LB FACILITIES:** STV Gym Steam rooms, Treatment rooms entertainment Xmas **SERVICES:** Lift air con
CARDS: ▨▨▨▨▨▨▨

★★★★★ 🏠 22 Jermyn Street

St James's SW1Y 6HL
☎ 020 7734 2353 ▤ 020 7734 0750
e-mail: office@22jermyn.com
Dir: A4 into Piccadilly, right into Duke St and left into King St. Through St James's Sq to Charles II St. Left into Regent St and left again

PETS: Bedrooms (unattended) Exercise area (5 mins walk) Pet Food dog walking service

This attractive townhouse enjoys an enviable location close to Piccadilly, Regent Street and the fashionable St James's area. Smartly appointed accommodation mainly consists of spacious suites with a few smaller studios. All are thoughtfully equipped with mini-bar, satellite TV, video recorder and fax/modem lines. 24-hour room service is available and breakfast is served in guest bedrooms.
ROOMS: 18 en suite (13 fmly) s £246.75; d £246.75 **FACILITIES:** STV Membership of nearby Health Club ch fac **SERVICES:** Lift air con **PARKING:** **NOTES:** No smoking in restaurant
CARDS: ▨▨▨▨▨▨▨

★★★★ 75% 🟢 The Rubens at the Palace

39 Buckingham Palace Rd SW1W 0PS
☎ 020 7834 6600 ▤ 020 7233 6037
e-mail: bookrb@rchmail.com
Dir: opposite Royal Mews, 100mtrs away from Buckingham Palace

Red Carnation HOTELS

PETS: Bedrooms Pet Food cat & dog menus & bowls available

This hotel enjoys an enviable location next to Buckingham Palace. Stylish, air-conditioned bedrooms include the pinstripe-walled Savile Row rooms, which follow a tailoring theme, and the opulent Royal rooms, named after different monarchs. Public rooms include the Library fine dining restaurant and a comfortable stylish cocktail bar and lounge. The team here pride themselves on their warmth and friendliness.
ROOMS: 173 en suite No smoking in 80 bedrooms s £180; d £245
FACILITIES: STV Health clubs locally entertainment ch fac Xmas
SERVICES: Lift air con **NOTES:** No smoking in restaurant
CARDS: ▨▨▨▨▨▨▨

SW3

★★★★★ 🏠 The Draycott

26 Cadogan Gardens SW3 2RP
☎ 020 7730 6466 ▤ 020 7730 0236
e-mail: reservations@draycotthotel.com
Dir: From Sloane Sq station towards Peter Jones, keep to left. At Kings Rd take first right Cadogan Gdns, 2nd right, hotel on left.

PETS: Bedrooms (unattended) Public areas (not in breakfast room) Exercise area (1 mile) Pet Food Will provide whatever is required

Enjoying a prime location just yards from Sloane Square, this town house provides an ideal base in one of the most fashionable areas of London. Many regular guests regard this as their London residence and staff pride themselves on their hospitality. Beautifully appointed bedrooms include a number of very spacious suites and all are equipped to a high standard. Attractive

continued

day rooms, furnished with antique and period pieces, include a choice of lounges, one with access to a lovely sheltered garden.

ROOMS: 35 en suite (9 fmly) (2 GF) No smoking in 30 bedrooms s £141-£158; d £188-£425 **FACILITIES:** STV Beauty treatment, Massage **SERVICES:** Lift air con **CARDS:** 💳 💳 💳 💳 💳 💳

SW5

♦♦♦ Maranton House Hotel
14 Barkston Gardens, Earls Court SW5 0EN
☎ 020 7373 5782 📠 020 7244 9543
e-mail: themarantonhouse@aol.com
Dir: Round corner from Earls Court tube station

PETS: Bedrooms (unattended) Exercise area (15 minute walk)

Expect a warm welcome at this friendly guesthouse, owned and run by the same family for over twenty years. Ideally situated overlooking an attractive garden square just a short walk from Earls Court, with stylish, tastefully decorated bedrooms. Public areas include a spacious reception, modern bar and a dining room, where substantial continental breakfasts are offered. **FACILITIES:** 16 en suite (1 GF) No smoking in 6 bedrooms No smoking in area of dining room No smoking in lounges TVB tea/coffee Direct dial from bedrooms Cen ht TVL **PRICES:** s £65-£75; d £80-£95✱ **NOTES:** Closed 23-26 Dec **CARDS:** 💳 💳 💳 💳 💳 💳

SW7

★★★★★ 75% The Bentley
27-33 Harrington Gardens SW7 4JX
☎ 020 7244 5555 📠 020 7244 5566
e-mail: info@thebentley-hotel.com
Dir: directly S of A4 leading into Knightsbridge at the junct with Gloucester Rd, turn right, then right again. At 2nd turn, hotel on left just after mini rdbt

PETS: Bedrooms (unattended) Public areas (Except restaurant) Exercise area

One of London's newest hotels, The Bentley is discreetly located in the heart of Kensington. The interior throughout is one of lavish opulence. Spacious air-conditioned bedrooms are equally luxurious featuring marble bathrooms with jacuzzi baths and walk-in showers. Public areas include the Perdiot where breakfast and lunch are served, a cosy cigar den and the cocktail bar Malachite. The fine dining restaurant, 1880, which is open for dinner provides excellent contemporary cuisine and highly professional service.
ROOMS: 64 en suite No smoking in 11 bedrooms s £293.75-£2937.50; d £293.75-£2937.50 **FACILITIES:** Spa STV Sauna Gym Jacuzzi traditional Turkish Hamam entertainment Xmas **SERVICES:** Lift air con **PARKING: CARDS:** 💳 💳 💳 💳 💳 💳

SW10

★★★★★ 69% Conrad London
Chelsea Harbour SW10 0XG
☎ 020 7823 3000 📠 020 7351 6525
e-mail: londoninfo@conradhotels.com
Dir: A4 to Earls Court Rd S towards river. Right into Kings Rd, left down Lots Rd. Chelsea Harbour in front

PETS: Bedrooms £15 + VAT Public areas Exercise area (Outside hotel) Pet Food

Against the picturesque backdrop of Chelsea Harbour's small marina, this modern hotel offers spacious, comfortable accommodation. All rooms are suites and all are superbly equipped, many enjoy splendid views of the marina. In addition, there are also several luxurious penthouse suites. Public areas include a modern bar and restaurant, excellent leisure facilities and extensive meeting and function rooms.
ROOMS: 160 en suite (39 fmly) No smoking in 110 bedrooms s £180-£330; d £200-£360 LB **FACILITIES:** STV Indoor swimming (H) Sauna Solarium Gym Conrad Health Club with beauty treatments entertainment Xmas **SERVICES:** Lift air con **PARKING:** 17 **CARDS:** 💳 💳 💳 💳 💳 💳

England

SW15

◆◆◆◆ The Lodge Hotel
52-54 Upper Richmond Rd, Putney SW15 2RN
☎ 020 8874 1598 📠 020 8874 0910
e-mail: res@thelodgehotellondon.com
Dir: A3, A219 down Putney Hill, right at lights onto Upper Richmond Rd, 0.5mile on left, under railway bridge with East Putney Station on right

PETS: Bedrooms (unattended) Exercise area (0.5 mile) dog food available **RESIDENT PETS:** George - Golden Labrador

This friendly hotel is conveniently located close to east Putney tube station. Attractive public areas include a choice of lounges, a smart bar with satellite TV and conference and banqueting facilities. An impressive buffet breakfast is served in the garden conservatory. Thoughtfully equipped, comfortable bedrooms include a selection of executive rooms and suites.
FACILITIES: 62 en suite (10 fmly) (21 GF) No smoking in 35 bedrooms STV TVB tea/coffee Direct dial from bedrooms Licensed Cen ht TVL
PRICES: s £69-£109; d £75-£146✱ LB **PARKING:** 30
CARDS: ▨▨▨▨▨▨▨

W1

★★★★★ ☺ 🏠 Athenaeum
116 Piccadilly W1J 7BJ
☎ 020 7499 3464 📠 020 7493 1860
e-mail: info@athenaeumhotel.com
Dir: on Piccadilly, overlooking Green Park

PETS: Bedrooms (in apartments only) Exercise area Green Park nearby

A discreet address in the heart of Mayfair, this well-loved hotel has become a favourite with many guests over the years for its efficient service and excellent hospitality. Bedrooms are decorated to the highest standard and some have views over Green Park. A row of Edwardian town houses immediately adjacent to the hotel offer a range of spacious and well-appointed apartments. Public rooms include Bullochs Restaurant, the Windsor Lounge and a cosy cocktail bar specialising in malt whiskies.
ROOMS: 157 en suite No smoking in 58 bedrooms s £265; d £285 LB
FACILITIES: Spa STV Sauna Gym Jacuzzi Steam rooms, spa treatments ch fac Xmas **SERVICES:** Lift air con
CARDS: ▨▨▨▨▨▨▨

★★★★★ ☺ Four Seasons Hotel London
Hamilton Place, Park Ln W1A 1AZ
☎ 020 7499 0888 📠 020 7493 1895
e-mail: fsh.london@fourseasons.com
Dir: from Piccadilly into Old Park Ln. Then Hamilton Place

PETS: Bedrooms Exercise area (200yds) Pet Food Will assist with any requirements

This long-established popular hotel is discreetly located near Hyde Park Corner, in the heart of Mayfair. It successfully combines modern efficiencies with traditional luxury. Guest care is consistently of the highest order, even down to the smallest detail of the personalised wake-up call. The bedrooms are elegant and spacious, and the unique conservatory rooms are particularly

continued

special. Spacious public areas include extensive conference and banqueting facilities, Lane's bar and fine-dining restaurant and an elegant lounge where wonderful afternoon teas are served.
ROOMS: 220 en suite No smoking in 96 bedrooms s £358.38-£1762.50; d £423-£2585 LB **FACILITIES:** STV Gym Fitness club entertainment ch fac Xmas **SERVICES:** Lift air con **PARKING:** 72
CARDS: ▨▨▨▨▨▨▨

★★★★ 74% ☺ The Chesterfield
35 Charles St, Mayfair W1J 5EB
☎ 020 7491 2622 📠 020 7491 4793
e-mail: bookch@rchmail.com
Dir: From Hyde Park corner along Piccadilly, left into Half Moon St. At end left and 1st right into Queens St, then right into Charles St

Red Carnation HOTELS

PETS: Bedrooms Exercise area (3 mins walk) Pet Food

Quiet elegance and an atmosphere of exclusivity characterise this stylish Mayfair hotel where attentive, friendly service is a highlight. Bedrooms have been decorated in a variety of contemporary styles, some with fabric walls; all are extremely thoughtfully equipped and boast marble-clad bathrooms with heated floors and mirrors. Bedrooms and public areas are all air-conditioned.
ROOMS: 110 en suite (7 fmly) No smoking in 52 bedrooms s fr £160; d fr £175 LB **FACILITIES:** STV entertainment Xmas **SERVICES:** Lift air con **CARDS:** ▨▨▨▨▨▨▨

★★★★ 74% The Washington Mayfair Hotel
5-7 Curzon St, Mayfair W1J 5HE
☎ 020 7499 7000 📠 020 7495 6172
e-mail: sales@washington-mayfair.co.uk
Dir: Green Park station take Piccadilly exit and turn right. Take 4th street on right into Curzon St.

PETS: Small dogs accepted by prior arrangement Bedrooms Exercise area

Situated in the heart of Mayfair, this stylish independently owned hotel offers a very high standard of accommodation. Personalised, friendly service is a highlight. Bedrooms are attractively furnished and provide high levels of comfort. The hotel is also a popular venue for afternoon tea and refreshments, served in the marbled and wood-panelled public areas.
ROOMS: 171 en suite No smoking in 94 bedrooms **FACILITIES:** STV Gym entertainment ch fac Xmas **SERVICES:** Lift air con
CARDS: ▨▨▨▨▨▨▨

W2

★★★★ 🏠 Pembridge Court
34 Pembridge Gardens W2 4DX
☎ 020 7229 9977 📠 020 7727 4982
e-mail: reservations@pemct.co.uk
Dir: off Bayswater Rd at Notting Hill Gate by underground station

PETS: Bedrooms Exercise area (5 mins walk) Pet Food Cat food can be provided **RESIDENT PETS:** Churchill - cat

This attractive Victorian townhouse is in a residential street near the Portobello Market and Notting Hill Gate tube. Individually styled bedrooms are generally spacious and most are air-conditioned. The hotel features a collection of antique clothing

continued

and fans. Public areas include two spacious lounges, a small conference room and an airy breakfast room.

ROOMS: 20 en suite (4 fmly) (5 GF) s £125-£165; d £160-£195 (incl. bkfst) **FACILITIES:** STV Membership of local Health Club **SERVICES:** Lift air con **PARKING:** 2 **NOTES:** No smoking in restaurant RS 24 Dec-1 Jan **CARDS:**

◆◆◆ Comfort Inn Bayswater
5-7 Princes Square, Bayswater W2 4NP
☎ 0207 792 1414 🖷 0207 792 0099
e-mail: cib@lth-hotels.com
Dir: from Shepherds Bush follow signs to West End through Notting Hill Gate. Left into Queens Way, 2nd left into Porchester Gdns to Princes Sq

PETS: Bedrooms £10 Public areas Exercise area (Hyde Park 300yds)

The hotel is located in a quiet square and on-street parking is easily available. Bedrooms, all with en suite, are compact but comfortable. Public areas include two breakfast rooms and a bar. **FACILITIES:** 67 en suite (5 fmly) (7 GF) No smoking in 22 bedrooms No smoking in dining room No smoking in 1 lounge TVB tea/coffee Direct dial from bedrooms Licensed Lift Cen ht TVL **PRICES:** s £45-£81; d £50-£91; (room only) ✱ **LB PARKING:**
CARDS:

W6

★★★ 64% Vencourt
255 King St, Hammersmith W6 9LU
☎ 020 8563 8855 🖷 020 8563 9988
Dir: Central London on A4 to Hammersmith, follow A315 towards Chiswick

PETS: Bedrooms Public areas (must be supervised) Exercise area (100yds) RESIDENT PETS: Box & Marina - German Shepherds

This modern hotel provides good-value accommodation with city views from the higher floors. The hotel has open-plan public areas, including a lounge bar, where snacks are served all day, and an airy restaurant for more substantial meals. Smart, well-equipped conference and meeting facilities are also available. **ROOMS:** 120 en suite (25 fmly) No smoking in 18 bedrooms s £89-£109; d £99-£109 **LB FACILITIES:** STV Xmas **SERVICES:** Lift **PARKING:** 27 **CARDS:**

W8

★★★★★ ◎ Milestone Hotel & Apartments
1 Kensington Court W8 5DL
☎ 020 7917 1000 🖷 020 7917 1010
e-mail: guestservicesms@rchmail.com
Dir: M4 into Central London. Into Warwick Rd, then right into Kensington High St. Hotel 400yds past Kensington underground

PETS: Bedrooms Exercise area (opposite hotel) Pet Food Pet menu for cats and dogs, Kensington Gardens across the road

Red Carnation HOTELS

This delightful, stylish town house enjoys a wonderful location opposite Kensington Palace; just minutes' walk from the elegant shops on Kensington High Street and Knightsbridge. Individually themed bedrooms include a selection of stunning suites and are equipped with every conceivable extra including DVDs and videos. Public areas include a luxurious lounge, where afternoon tea is served, a delightful panelled bar, a sumptuous restaurant and a small gym. **ROOMS:** 57 en suite (3 fmly) (2 GF) No smoking in 22 bedrooms s £305.50-£951.75; d £305.50-£951.75 **LB FACILITIES:** STV Indoor swimming (H) Sauna Gym Jacuzzi Health Club entertainment Xmas **SERVICES:** Lift air con **CARDS:**

WC1

★★★★ 72% ◎ The Montague on the Gardens
15 Montague St, Bloomsbury WC1B 5BJ
☎ 020 7637 1001 🖷 020 7637 2516
e-mail: bookmt@rchmail.com
Dir: Located in Montague St, just off Russell Square. Next to British Museum

Red Carnation HOTELS

PETS: Bedrooms Public areas (except food service areas) Exercise area (2 mins walk) Pet Food Dog walking by prior arrangement, pet friendly gardens in Russell Square, pet menu, pet towels & blankets on request

This stylish hotel is situated right next to the British Museum. A special feature is the alfresco terrace overlooking a delightful garden. Other public rooms include the Blue Door Bistro and Chef's Table, a bar, a lounge and a conservatory where traditional afternoon teas are served. The bedrooms are beautifully appointed and range from split-level suites to more compact rooms. **ROOMS:** 104 en suite (18 GF) No smoking in 47 bedrooms s £165-£220; d £195-£265 **LB FACILITIES:** STV Sauna Gym Jacuzzi entertainment ch fac Xmas **SERVICES:** Lift air con **NOTES:** No smoking in restaurant **CARDS:**

All abbreviations are explained on page 9

LONDON GATEWAY MOTORWAY SERVICE AREA (M1)

★★★ 68% Days Hotel

Welcome Break Service Area NW7 3HB
☎ 020 8906 7000 ▧ 020 8906 7011
e-mail: lgw.hotel@welcomebreak.co.uk
Dir: on M1 between junct 2/4 northbound & southbound

PETS: Bedrooms (unattended) Public areas (except restaurant or bar area) Exercise area (adjacent) welcome snack pack on arrival

This modern hotel is the flagship of the Days Inn brand and occupies a prime location on the outskirts of London at London Gateway Services. Bedrooms have a contemporary feel, are spacious and well equipped. Public rooms are airy and include an open plan restaurant and bar/lounge and a range of meeting rooms. Ample parking is a bonus.
ROOMS: 200 en suite (190 fmly) (80 GF) No smoking in 162 bedrooms s £54-£85; d £54-£85 **LB FACILITIES:** STV **SERVICES:** Lift air con **PARKING:** 160 **NOTES:** No smoking in restaurant
CARDS:

MERSEYSIDE

SOUTHPORT   Map 07 SD31

★★ 65% Metropole

Portland St PR8 1LL
☎ 01704 536836 ▧ 01704 549041
e-mail: metropole.southport@btinternet.com
Dir: left off Lord St after Prince of Wales Hotel, Metropole is directly behind Prince of Wales

PETS: Bedrooms (unattended) £5 Public areas Exercise area (0.25 mile)

This family-run hotel of long standing, popular with golfers, is ideally situated just 50 yards from the famous Lord Street. Accommodation is bright and modern with family rooms available. In addition to the restaurant that offers a selection of freshly prepared dishes, there is a choice of lounges including a popular bar-lounge.
ROOMS: 23 en suite (4 fmly) No smoking in 6 bedrooms s £39; d £70 (incl. bkfst) **LB FACILITIES:** Snooker Golf can be arranged at 8 local courses Xmas **PARKING:** 12 **NOTES:** No smoking in restaurant
CARDS:

◆◆◆◆ Whitworth Falls Hotel

16 Lathom Rd PR9 0JH
☎ 01704 530074
e-mail: whitworthfalls@rapid.co.uk
Dir: from Southport town centre take Lord St towards Preston, straight over rdbt, 2nd left Alexandra Rd, 4th right Lathom Rd

PETS: Bedrooms Public areas Exercise area
RESIDENT PETS: Sherbert (African Grey Parrot), Minnie & Midge (cats)

Located on a mainly residential avenue within easy walking distance of seafront and Lord Street shops, this late Victorian house has been sympathetically renovated to provide a range of bedrooms offering a good balance between practicality and homeliness. Pre-theatre dinner and breakfasts are served in an attractive dining room and a choice of comfortable sitting room and lounge bar is also available.
FACILITIES: 12 en suite (2 fmly) (1 GF) No smoking in 7 bedrooms No smoking in dining room No smoking in lounges TVB tea/coffee Direct dial from bedrooms Licensed Cen ht TVL Dinner Last d 12noon **PRICES:** s £22-£30; d £44-£60✱ **LB PARKING:** 8
CARDS:

◆◆◆ Edendale Hotel

83 Avondale Rd North PR9 0NE
☎ 01704 530718 ▧ 01704 547299
e-mail: info@edendale-hotel.co.uk
Dir: at end of A570 right at lights follow to rdbt straight over, then 3rd road on left (Leyland Rd), then 2nd on left (Avondale Rd North), hotel on corner on left

PETS: Bedrooms Exercise area (2 minutes)

This smart Victorian house enjoys a peaceful location in a leafy residential road, a few minutes' walk from the promenade and the town centre. Bedrooms are individually styled and all benefit from a host of thoughtful facilities. There is a comfortable bar lounge adjacent to the smart dining room where imaginative evening meals and freshly cooked breakfasts are served.
FACILITIES: 8 en suite (2 fmly) No smoking TVB tea/coffee Direct dial from bedrooms Licensed Cen ht Dinner Last d 4pm **PRICES:** s £25-£35; d £40-£60✱ **LB PARKING:** 8 **CARDS:**

🌲 **Places with this symbol are country house hotels**

🐓 **Places with this symbol are farms**

★ **Red stars indicate the AA's Top 200 Hotels in Britain & Ireland**

All abbreviations are explained on page 9

England

NORFOLK

BLAKENEY
Map 09 TG04

★★ ◎◎◎ **Morston Hall**
Morston, Holt NR25 7AA
☎ 01263 741041 📠 01263 740419
e-mail: reception@morstonhall.com
Dir: 1m W of Blakeney on A149 Kings Lynn/Cromer Rd coastal road

PETS: Bedrooms Sep Accom (Kennels) (unattended) £5
Exercise area (300 yards to beach) **2 outside dog kennels**

This delightful 17th-century country house hotel enjoys a tranquil
setting amid well-tended gardens. The comfortable public rooms
offer a choice of attractive lounges and a sunny conservatory,
while the elegant dining room is a perfect setting to enjoy Galton
Blackiston's award-winning cuisine. The spacious bedrooms are
individually decorated and stylishly furnished with modern
opulence.
ROOMS: 7 en suite (1 GF) s £130-£145; d £230-£240 (incl. bkfst &
dinner) LB **FACILITIES:** ch fac **PARKING:** 40 **NOTES:** No smoking in
restaurant Closed 1 Jan-2 Feb **CARDS:** 🌑 💳 💳 📇 🌑 🌑

★★ 73% **The Pheasant**
Coast Rd, Kelling NR25 7EG
☎ 01263 588382 📠 01263 588101
e-mail: enquiries@pheasanthotelnorfolk.co.uk
Dir: on A419 coast road, mid-way between Sheringham & Blakeney

PETS: Bedrooms (unattended) £3 Public areas (Allowed in
bar area only) **Exercise area** (50yds)

Popular hotel ideally situated on the main road amidst landscaped
grounds. Bedrooms are split between the main house and a
modern wing of spacious rooms to the rear of the property. Public
rooms include a busy lounge bar, a residents' lounge and a large
restaurant where a wide selection of appetising dishes is served.
ROOMS: 30 rms (27 en suite) No smoking in all bedrooms s £53;
d £86-£96 (incl. bkfst) LB **FACILITIES:** Xmas **PARKING:** 80
NOTES: No smoking in restaurant **CARDS:** 🌑 💳 📇 🌑 🌑

BRANCASTER STAITHE
Map 09 TF74

★★ 75% ◎ **White Horse**
PE31 8BY
☎ 01485 210262 📠 01485 210930
e-mail: reception@whitehorsebrancaster.co.uk
Dir: on A149 coast road midway between Hunstanton & Wells-next-the-Sea

PETS: Bedrooms £4 Public areas (except restaurant)
Exercise area (adjoining coastal paths and beach)

A charming hotel on the north Norfolk coast with stunning views
over the tidal marshes to Scolt Head Island. The contemporary
bedrooms, in two wings, are attractively decorated, some featuring
an interesting cobbled fascia, and thoughtfully equipped. One even
has a viewing telescope. There is a large bar and lounge area leading
to the conservatory restaurant which has wide-sweeping views.
ROOMS: 7 en suite 8 annexe en suite (5 fmly) (8 GF) s £72-£90;
d £104-£140 (incl. bkfst) LB **FACILITIES:** Bar billiards Xmas
PARKING: 60 **NOTES:** No dogs No smoking in restaurant
CARDS: 🌑 💳 📇 🌑 🌑

BURNHAM MARKET
Map 09 TF84

★★ 77% ◎◎ **Hoste Arms**
The Green PE31 8HD
☎ 01328 738777 📠 01328 730103
e-mail: reception@hostearms.co.uk
Dir: signed on B1155, 5m W of Wells-next-the-Sea

PETS: Bedrooms £7.50 Public areas Pet Food
RESIDENT PETS: Augustus & Sweep - Black Labradors

Stylish, privately owned inn situated in the heart of this bustling
village close to the north Norfolk coast. The extensive public
rooms feature a range of dining areas that include a conservatory
with plush furniture, a sunny patio and a traditional pub. The
tastefully furnished, thoughtfully equipped bedrooms are generally
very spacious and offer a high degree of comfort.
ROOMS: 36 en suite (1 fmly) (7 GF) s £78-£168; d £108-£268
(incl. bkfst) LB **FACILITIES:** Xmas **PARKING:** 45
CARDS: 🌑 💳 📇 🌑 🌑

CASTLE ACRE
Map 09 TF81

◆◆◆◆ 🐾 **Lodge Farm**
Castle Acre PE32 2BS
☎ 01760 755506 📠 01760 755103
e-mail: marigoldthompson@webmail.co.za
*Dir: turn off A1065, towards Castle Acre opposite the George & Dragon
Pub. In village take 1st right, then take road to Rougham. Farm driveway is
on right after 1.5m*

PETS: Bedrooms **Exercise area** (adjacent)
RESIDENT PETS: Tina & Rosie (Black Labradors), Hazel (Cocker
Spaniel), Stumpy (Jack Russell), fowl

This large 1850's farmhouse is located in peaceful rural
surroundings within 35 acres of paddock and grounds beside the
Peddars Way and is ideal for walkers and riding - stabling
available. Bedrooms are spacious, individually furnished and
equipped with thoughtful extras. A freshly cooked breakfast is
served around the large table in the elegant dining room.
FACILITIES: 3 rms (2 en suite) (2 fmly) No smoking TVB tea/coffee
No dogs (ex guide dogs) Cen ht Croquet lawn 25 acres Non working
PRICES: s £30; d £55✳ **PARKING:** 6

📕 **Places with this
symbol are pubs**

England

CLEY NEXT THE SEA Map 09 TG04

♦♦♦♦ The George Hotel
THe High St NR25 7RN
☎ 01263 740652 📠 01263 741275
e-mail: thegeorge@cleynextthesea.com
Dir: located on A148 coastal road in the centre of Cley next the Sea

PETS: Bedrooms (unattended) Public areas Exercise area
RESIDENT PETS: Bumpy, Hovis (dogs)

Delightful inn situated in the centre of this pretty Norfolk village close to the seal colonies and the famous marshes with its abundance of bird life. Bedrooms are pleasantly decorated and furnished with pine pieces and have many useful extras. Public rooms include a smart lounge area, a restaurant and a choice of bars which feature artwork for sale by a local artist.
FACILITIES: 9 en suite 3 annexe en suite (2 fmly) (3 GF) No smoking in bedrooms No smoking in area of dining room No smoking in lounges TVB tea/coffee Cen ht Dinner Last d 9.30pm **PRICES:** s £35-£90; d £40-£120* **LB PARKING:** 20 **CARDS:**

CROMER Map 09 TG24

★★★ 63% The Cliftonville
NR27 9AS
☎ 01263 512543 📠 01263 515700
e-mail: reservations@cliftonvillehotel.co.uk
Dir: From A149 main coastal rd, 500yds from town centre northbound

PETS: Bedrooms (unattended) £4 Public areas (except restaurants) Exercise area (50 metres) Pet Food

An imposing Edwardian hotel situated on the main coast road with stunning views of the sea. Public rooms feature a magnificent staircase, Minstrels gallery, a coffee shop, a lounge bar, a further residents' lounge, Boltons Bistro and an additional restaurant. The bedrooms, for the most part spacious, are pleasantly decorated and have lovely sea views.
ROOMS: 30 en suite (5 fmly) No smoking in 14 bedrooms s £40-£52; d £80-£104 (incl. bkfst) **LB FACILITIES:** ch fac Xmas **SERVICES:** Lift **PARKING:** 20 **NOTES:** No smoking in restaurant
CARDS:

♦♦♦ Sandcliff Private Hotel
Runton Rd NR27 9AS
☎ 01263 512888 📠 01263 512888
e-mail: sandcliff@btclick.com
Dir: five minutes from town centre on Sheringham coast road

PETS: Bedrooms (unattended) £5 per stay Exercise area (100 metres)

Large family-run hotel situated on the seafront overlooking the promenade and beach, yet just a short walk from the town centre. Bedrooms are pleasantly decorated, well maintained and thoughtfully equipped; some have superb sea views. The spacious public rooms include a large lounge bar and a smartly appointed restaurant serving home-cooked food.
FACILITIES: 22 rms (16 en suite) (10 fmly) (3 GF) No smoking in dining room TVB tea/coffee Licensed Dinner Last d 6pm **PRICES:** s £28; d £56-£61* **LB PARKING:** 10 **NOTES:** Closed 21 Dec-4 Jan

FAKENHAM Map 09 TF92

♦♦♦ Abbott Farm
Walsingham Rd, Binham NR21 0AW
☎ 01328 830519 & 07986 041715 📠 01328 830519
e-mail: abbot.farm@btinternet.com
Dir: leave A148 at Thursford (Crawfish Thai Restaurant) towards Hindringham, then 4m to Binham, in village L on B1388 to Walsingham, farm 1m on L

PETS: Bedrooms Public areas Exercise area Stainless steel bowls and dried pet food available RESIDENT PETS: Buster - retriever/labrador, Fudge - cat

A detached red-brick dormer house situated in a peaceful rural location amid 150 acres of arable farmland. The spacious bedrooms are pleasantly decorated and thoughtfully equipped, the ground-floor room features a very spacious en suite shower. Breakfast is taken in the attractive conservatory, which has superb views across the countryside.
FACILITIES: 3 en suite (2 GF) No smoking TVB tea/coffee Cen ht 190 acres arable **PRICES:** s £22-£24; d £44-£48* **PARKING:** 20

GORLESTON ON SEA Map 05 TG50

♦♦♦♦ Avalon Private Hotel
54 Clarence Rd NR31 6DR
☎ 01493 662114 📠 01493 661521
e-mail: info@avalon.go-plus.net
Dir: from A12 follow seafront signs, Clarence Rd off Marine Parade

PETS: Bedrooms (unattended) Public areas (not in dining room) Exercise area (50 metres)

An Edwardian terraced house ideally situated just a short walk from the promenade and beach. The pleasantly decorated bedrooms are thoughtfully equipped and well furnished. Breakfast and dinner are served at individual tables in the smart dining room and guests have the use of a cosy lounge bar.
FACILITIES: 11 rms (10 en suite) (5 fmly) (1 GF) No smoking in 4 bedrooms No smoking in dining room TVB tea/coffee Licensed Cen ht TVL Pool Table Darts and games room Dinner Last d 2pm
PRICES: s £18-£30; d £36-£60* **LB BB**
CARDS:

Places with this symbol are country house hotels

GREAT YARMOUTH — Map 05 TG50

★★★ 71% ◉ Imperial

THE INDEPENDENTS

North Dr NR30 1EQ
☎ 01493 842000 ⊟ 01493 852229
e-mail: imperial@scs-datacom.co.uk
Dir: follow signs to seafront and turn left. Hotel opposite tennis courts

PETS: Bedrooms Public areas Exercise area (50 yards) Pet Food Food supplied, but not bowls

Friendly, family-run hotel situated at the quieter end of the seafront within easy walking distance of the town. Bedrooms are attractively decorated with co-ordinated soft furnishings and equipped with modern facilities; many rooms have superb sea views. Public areas offer a good level of comfort and include the smart Savoie Lounge Bar and the Rambouillet Restaurant.
ROOMS: 39 en suite (4 fmly) No smoking in 21 bedrooms s £50-£80; d £67-£90 (incl. bkfst) **LB FACILITIES:** STV Xmas **SERVICES:** Lift
PARKING: 50 **CARDS:** 🃏

★★★ 68% Regency Dolphin

Albert Square NR30 3JH
☎ 01493 855070 ⊟ 01493 853798
e-mail: regencydolphin@countrytown-hotels.co.uk
Dir: along seafront and right at Wellington Pier. Right into Kimberley Ter then left into Albert Sq, hotel on left

PETS: Bedrooms (unattended) Public areas (Not during meal times) Exercise area (5-10 minute walk)

Large privately owned hotel situated in the quieter end of town, just off the seafront and within easy walking distance of the town centre. The pleasantly decorated bedrooms are generally quite spacious and well equipped. Public rooms include a comfortable lounge, a bar and intimate restaurant. The hotel also has an outdoor swimming pool.
ROOMS: 47 en suite (5 fmly) (2 GF) No smoking in 9 bedrooms s £50-£70; d £60-£80 (incl. bkfst) **LB FACILITIES:** Outdoor swimming (H) Xmas **PARKING:** 19 **NOTES:** No smoking in restaurant
CARDS: 🃏

♦♦♦♦ Barnard House

2 Barnard Crescent NR30 4DR
☎ 01493 855139 ⊟ 01493 843143
e-mail: barnardhouse@btinternet.com
Dir: follow signs to Caister, through 3 sets of lights, house on right after last set of lights

PETS: Bedrooms Public areas (at other guests' discretion) Exercise area (20yds) RESIDENT PETS: Fergus & Flora (black Spaniels)

Expect a warm welcome at this friendly, family-run guest house, set in mature landscaped gardens in a residential area of town. The tastefully furnished, pleasantly decorated bedrooms are filled with many thoughtful touches. Breakfast is served at a large table in the elegant dining room and guests have the use of a cosy lounge.
FACILITIES: 3 rms (2 en suite) No smoking TVB tea/coffee Cen ht TVL No coaches Dinner Last d 4pm **PRICES:** s £30-£35; d £50-£60✱ **LB**
PARKING: 3 **CARDS:** 🃏

HORNING — Map 09 TG31

★★★ 68% Petersfield House

Lower St NR12 8PF
☎ 01692 630741 ⊟ 01692 630745
e-mail: reception@petersfieldhotel.co.uk
Dir: from Wroxham take A1062 for 2.5m then right into Horning. Hotel in centre of village on left

PETS: Bedrooms Exercise area (10 minutes)

Charming property dating back to the 1920s situated amid pretty landscaped grounds in the heart of this delightful riverside village. Bedrooms vary in size and style, each one is comfortably furnished and thoughtfully equipped; many of the rooms have lovely views of the garden. Public areas include a large lounge, a bar and a restaurant.
ROOMS: 17 en suite (1 fmly) (3 GF) s £65-£75; d £90-£105 (incl. bkfst)
LB FACILITIES: Fishing Putting green Private moorings Boating entertainment Xmas **PARKING:** 70 **NOTES:** No smoking in restaurant Closed Jan **CARDS:** 🃏

HUNSTANTON — Map 09 TF64

★★ 72% The Lodge Hotel & Restaurant

Old Hunstanton Rd PE36 6HX
☎ 01485 532896 ⊟ 01485 535007
e-mail: reception@thelodge-hotel.co.uk
Dir: 1m E of Hunstanton on A149

PETS: Bedrooms Exercise area Pet Food

Expect a friendly welcome at this family-run hotel, situated in a large landscaped garden and within easy reach of the beach and town centre. The spacious bedrooms are smartly decorated, well maintained and offer a good range of facilities. Public areas include a large lounge bar and an attractive restaurant with a cosy seating area.
ROOMS: 16 en suite 6 annexe en suite (3 fmly) (4 GF) No smoking in 6 bedrooms s £36-£59; d £72-£114 (incl. bkfst) **LB FACILITIES:** STV Darts room Pool table Xmas **PARKING:** 70 **NOTES:** No smoking in restaurant **CARDS:** 🃏

♦♦♦♦ Claremont

35 Greevegate PE36 6AF
☎ 01485 533171
e-mail: claremont@amserve.com
Dir: off A149, turn left at Greevegate, opposite recreation ground. House is 300mtrs on right before St Edmunds Church

PETS: Bedrooms Exercise area (100yds)

Spacious, family-run Victorian guest house situated in a central position close to the shops, beach and gardens. The individually decorated bedrooms are tastefully furnished and have a good range of useful extras. There is a ground floor room with access for less able guests, as well as two feature rooms, one with a four-poster, and another has a canopied bed.
FACILITIES: 7 en suite (1 fmly) (1 GF) No smoking TVB tea/coffee Cen ht TVL No children 5yrs No coaches **PRICES:** s £24-£26; d £48-£52✱ **LB PARKING:** 4 **NOTES:** Closed 15 Nov-10 Feb

England

KING'S LYNN
Map 09 TF62

◆◆◆ Maranatha Guest House
115/117 Gaywood Rd PE30 2PU
☎ 01553 774596 📠 01553 763747
e-mail: maranathaguesthouse@yahoo.co.uk
Dir: follow signs to College of West Anglia. At junct in front of college turn right into Gaywood Rd. Guest house immediately on left, opp school.

PETS: Bedrooms Exercise area (100 yards)
RESIDENT PETS: Goldie (Sheltie), Kim (Border Collie)

Formerly two separate dwellings, this Victorian house is situated opposite King Edward School and close to the hospital, a few minutes' walk from the town centre. Bedrooms are attractively decorated and practically equipped. Breakfasts are taken in the pleasant open plan lounge/dining room, which also has a pool table for guests' use.
FACILITIES: 10 rms (6 en suite) (2 fmly) No smoking in 5 bedrooms No smoking in dining room No smoking in lounges TVB tea/coffee Cen ht TVL Pool Table Dinner **PRICES:** s £25-£35; d £40-£60✱
PARKING: 12 **CARDS:** 🌑 ▭▭ 🌑 ⑤

NEATISHEAD
Map 09 TG32

◆◆◆◆ Regency
The Street NR12 8AD
☎ 01692 630233 📠 01692 630233
e-mail: regencywrigley@btopenworld.com
Dir: Neatishead is 1m off A1151, between Wroxham & Stalham

PETS: Bedrooms £4 Exercise area (adjacent)

A warm welcome is to be expected at this charming 17th-century property which is situated in the heart of this picturesque village close to the Norfolk Broads. Bedrooms are attractively decorated with co-ordinated soft furnishings and many thoughtful touches. Breakfast is served in the smart dining room and guests also have the use of two comfortable lounges.
FACILITIES: 3 rms (2 en suite) (1 fmly) No smoking in dining room No smoking in lounges TVB tea/coffee No coaches
PRICES: d £48-£52✱ **LB PARKING:** 6

NORTH WALSHAM
Map 09 TG23

★★ ◎◎ Beechwood
Cromer Rd NR28 0HD
☎ 01692 403231 📠 01692 407284
e-mail: enquiries@beechwood-hotel.co.uk
Dir: B1150 from Norwich. At North Walsham left at 1st traffic lights, then right at next

PETS: Bedrooms (unattended) £7 Public areas (except restaurant) Exercise area (400yds) Pet Food
RESIDENT PETS: Emily & Harry - Airedale terriers

Expect a warm welcome at this elegant 18th-century house, situated just a short walk from the town centre. The individually styled bedrooms are tastefully furnished with well-chosen antique pieces, attractive co-ordinated soft fabrics and many thoughtful touches. The spacious public areas include a lounge bar with

continued

plush furnishings, a further lounge and a smartly appointed restaurant.

ROOMS: 15 en suite (4 GF) No smoking in 12 bedrooms **PARKING:** 20
NOTES: No children 10yrs No smoking in restaurant
CARDS: 🌑 ▭▭ 🌑 ⑤

◆◆◆◆ Green Ridges
104 Cromer Rd NR28 0HE
☎ 01692 402448 📠 01692 402448
e-mail: admin@greenridges.com
Dir: on A149 Cromer road out of North Walsham, directly opposite left to B1145/Aylsham

PETS: Bedrooms min £5 Public areas Exercise area (100yds) Bowls, tinned/dry food available on request
RESIDENT PETS: Bruno - Weimaraner & Chester - Great Dane/Black Labrador cross, Teddy - cat

A warm welcome is offered at this attractive detached property, situated on the edge of this busy market town. The individually decorated bedrooms are pleasantly furnished and equipped with many thoughtful touches. Breakfast is served at individual tables in the smart dining room, which overlooks the mature gardens. Imaginative home-cooked dinners are available by prior arrangement.
FACILITIES: 3 en suite (1 fmly) (1 GF) No smoking STV TVB tea/coffee Cen ht No coaches Dinner Last d Previous day **PRICES:** s £30; d £45-£50✱ **PARKING:** 6

NORTHWOLD
Map 05 TL79

★★ 66% Comfort Inn Thetford
Thetford Rd IP26 5LQ
☎ 01366 728888 📠 01366 727121
e-mail: enquiries@hotels-thetford.com
Dir: W of Mundford on A134

PETS: Bedrooms (unattended) Public areas (except restaurant/bar) Exercise area (on site)

A modern purpose-built hotel in a rural setting just off the main road. The generously proportioned bedrooms are situated in courtyard style wings; each room is pleasantly decorated and well equipped. Dinner and breakfast are served in the beamed Woodland Inn, which combines the roles of country pub and hotel restaurant.
ROOMS: 34 en suite (12 fmly) (18 GF) No smoking in 17 bedrooms s £45-£85; d £55-£95 (incl. bkfst) **LB FACILITIES:** STV Xmas
PARKING: 250 **NOTES:** No smoking in restaurant
CARDS: 🌑 ▭▭ 🌑 ⑤

NORWICH   Map 05 TG20

★★★ 70% ◎ The Georgian House   THE INDEPENDENTS
32-34 Unthank Rd NR2 2RB
☎ 01603 615655 ▪ 01603 765689
e-mail: reception@georgian-hotel.co.uk
Dir: follow Roman Catholic Cathedral signs from city centre, hotel off inner ring road

PETS: Bedrooms (unattended) £5 Exercise area

This pair of Victorian houses has been carefully converted to create a comfortable hotel, which is situated just a short walk from the city centre. Public areas include a cosy bar, a TV lounge and an elegant restaurant offering a daily changing carte menu. The smartly refurbished bedrooms are well maintained and thoughtfully equipped.
ROOMS: 28 en suite (2 fmly) (10 GF) No smoking in 20 bedrooms s £64-£81.50; d £90-£120 (incl. bkfst) **LB FACILITIES:** STV
PARKING: 40 **NOTES:** No smoking in restaurant Closed 24 Dec-2 Jan
CARDS: ▨▨▨▨▨

★★ ◎ The Old Rectory
103 Yarmouth Rd, Thorpe St Andrew NR7 0HF
☎ 01603 700772 ▪ 01603 300772
e-mail: enquiries@oldrectorynorwich.com
Dir: from A47 southern bypass onto A1042 towards Norwich N and E. Left at mini rdbt onto A1242. After 0.3m over traffic lights and hotel 100mtrs on right

PETS: Bedrooms (One room only) Exercise area (200yds)
RESIDENT PETS: Rolo & Milly - Birman cats

This delightful Grade II listed Georgian property is ideally located in a peaceful area overlooking the River Yare, just a few minutes' drive from the city centre. Spacious bedrooms are individually designed with carefully chosen soft fabrics, plush furniture and many thoughtful touches; many of the rooms overlook the swimming pool and landscaped gardens. An interesting daily-changing menu features skilfully prepared local produce served in the panelled dining room.
ROOMS: 5 en suite 3 annexe en suite No smoking in all bedrooms s £68; d £88-£105 (incl. bkfst) **LB FACILITIES:** STV Outdoor swimming (H) **PARKING:** 15 **NOTES:** No smoking in restaurant Closed 21 Dec-4 Jan **CARDS:** ▨▨▨▨

★★ 73% ◎ Stower Grange
School Rd, Drayton NR8 6EF
☎ 01603 860210 ▪ 01603 860464
e-mail: enquiries@stowergrange.co.uk
Dir: Norwich ring road N to Asda supermarket. Take A1067 Fakenham Rd at Drayton village, right at traffic lights along School Rd. Hotel 150yds on right

PETS: Bedrooms (unattended) Public areas (except restaurant) Exercise area (800 metres) Pet Food
RESIDENT PETS: Ellie (Labrador)

A 17th-century ivy-clad property situated in a peaceful residential area just a short drive from the city centre and airport. The individually decorated bedrooms are generally quite spacious; each one is individually decorated, tastefully furnished and

continued

equipped with many thoughtful touches. Public rooms include a smart open-plan lounge bar and an elegant restaurant.

ROOMS: 11 en suite (1 fmly) s £67.50; d £89 (incl. bkfst)
FACILITIES: Croquet lawn **PARKING:** 40 **NOTES:** No smoking in restaurant **CARDS:** ▨▨▨▨▨

♦♦♦ Edmar Lodge
64 Earlham Rd NR2 3DF
☎ 01603 615599 ▪ 01603 495599
e-mail: mail@edmarlodge.co.uk
Dir: located on B1108 into city from A47 Southern bypass or from the inner and outer ring roads. Follow university and hospital signs

PETS: Bedrooms Exercise area (200yds)

Located just a ten minute walk from the city centre, this friendly family-run guest house offers a convenient location and ample private parking. Individually decorated bedrooms are smartly appointed and well equipped. Freshly prepared breakfasts are served within the cosy dining room; a microwave and refrigerator are also available for guests' use. Please note that this establishment is strictly non-smoking.
FACILITIES: 5 en suite (1 fmly) No smoking TVB tea/coffee Cen ht No coaches **PRICES:** s £30-£40; d £40-£44✱ **PARKING:** 6
CARDS: ▨▨▨▨▨

♦♦♦ The Larches
345 Aylsham Rd NR3 2RU
☎ 01603 415420 ▪ 01603 465340
Dir: on A140 500yds past ring road, on left adjacent to Lloyds Bank

PETS: Bedrooms Exercise area (50yds)

Modern, detached property situated only a short drive from the city centre and airport. The spacious, well-equipped bedrooms are brightly decorated, pleasantly furnished and have co-ordinated soft fabrics. Breakfast is served at individual tables in the smart open plan lounge/dining room. Dinner is available by prior arrangement.
FACILITIES: 7 en suite (2 fmly) (1 GF) No smoking in area of dining room No smoking in 1 lounge STV TVB tea/coffee Cen ht TVL No coaches Dinner Last d 3pm **PRICES:** s fr £30; d fr £40✱
PARKING: 10 **CARDS:** ▨▨▨▨

 Places with this symbol are farms

SHERINGHAM
Map 09 TG14

◆◆◆◆ Highfield
5 Montague Rd NR26 8LN
☎ 01263 825524
e-mail: gmcaldwell@aol.com
Dir: leave A148, left at mini r/about, then first right. Turn left at the church, then left into South St, which becomes Montague Rd. House is on left

PETS: Sep Accom (Conservatory) (unattended) Exercise area

Warm hospitality and a friendly welcome are offered at this delightful guesthouse, which is situated in a peaceful side road within easy walking distance of the shops and beach. This pleasantly furnished house offers smartly decorated and thoughtfully equipped bedrooms. Breakfast is served at individual tables in the attractive dining room.
FACILITIES: 7 rms (6 en suite) (3 fmly) No smoking TVB tea/coffee No dogs (ex guide dogs) Cen ht TVL No children 7yrs **PARKING:** 4
NOTES: Closed 3 wks in Oct/Nov

SHIPDHAM
Map 05 TF90

◆◆◆ ◎ 🍽 Pound Green Hotel
Pound Green Ln IP25 7LS
☎ 01362 820940 📠 01362 820940
e-mail: poundgreen@aol.com
Dir: A1075 into village, follow signs for community centre and hotel is approx 0.25m on right

PETS: Bedrooms (unattended) Public areas (except restaurant) Large garden & grounds **RESIDENT PETS:** Black cat - Ebony Ostle (or Baggybum)

Situated in a quiet residential area in the village of Shipdham between Dereham and Watton, this small privately owned hotel offers spacious, soundly maintained and well equipped bedrooms throughout. Public areas include a popular lounge bar and a large restaurant offering an interesting choice of home made dishes. There is also a function room available.
FACILITIES: 11 rms (7 en suite) (2 fmly) (4 GF) No smoking in 6 bedrooms No smoking in dining room TVB tea/coffee Licensed Cen ht wooded garden with large lawn, swing, slide Dinner Last d 9pm
PRICES: s £20-£30; d £40-£60✲ **LB PARKING:** 40
NOTES: Closed 2-17 Jan **CARDS:** 💳 💳 💳 💳

SWAFFHAM
Map 05 TF80

★★★ 67% George
Station Rd PE37 7LJ
☎ 01760 721238 📠 01760 725333
e-mail: georgehotel@bestwestern.co.uk
Dir: off A47 signposted Swaffham, hotel opp St Peter & St Paul church

Best Western

PETS: Bedrooms £10 Public areas Exercise area (800 metres)

Georgian hotel situated in the heart of this bustling market town, which is ideally placed for touring north Norfolk. Bedrooms vary in size and style; each one is pleasantly decorated and well-equipped. Public rooms include a cosy restaurant, a lounge and a busy bar where a range of drinks and snacks are available.
ROOMS: 29 en suite (1 fmly) **FACILITIES:** STV **PARKING:** 100
NOTES: No smoking in restaurant **CARDS:** 💳 💳 💳 💳 💳

THETFORD
Map 05 TL88

★★ 65% The Thomas Paine Hotel
White Hart St IP24 1AA
☎ 01842 755631 📠 01842 766505
e-mail: bookings@thomaspainehotel.com
Dir: N on A11, at rdbt immediately before Thetford take A1075, hotel on right

THE INDEPENDENTS

PETS: Bedrooms (unattended) £2 dogs/cats Exercise area (on site)

This Grade II listed building is situated close to the town centre and Thetford Forest Park is just a short drive away. Public rooms include a large lounge bar and a pleasantly appointed restaurant. Bedrooms vary in size and style; each one is pleasantly decorated and thoughtfully equipped.
ROOMS: 13 en suite (2 fmly) No smoking in 5 bedrooms s £50-£55; d £60-£66 (incl. bkfst) **LB FACILITIES:** Xmas **PARKING:** 30
NOTES: No smoking in restaurant **CARDS:** 💳 💳 💳 💳 💳 💳

THORNHAM
Map 09 TF74

★★ 69% ◎ Lifeboat Inn
Ship Ln PE36 6LT
☎ 01485 512236 📠 01485 512323
e-mail: reception@lifeboatinn.co.uk
Dir: follow coast road from Hunstanton A149 for approx 6m and take 1st left after Thornham sign

PETS: Bedrooms (unattended) Public areas (except restaurant) Exercise area (100 metres) Pet Food bowls provided but no food

This 16th-century smugglers' alehouse enjoys superb views across open meadows to Thornham Harbour. The attractive bedrooms
continued

are furnished with pine pieces and have many thoughtful touches. The public rooms have a wealth of character and feature open fireplaces and oak beams. A range of bar meals is available or guests can choose from the carte menu in the smart restaurant.
ROOMS: 13 en suite (3 fmly) (1 GF) No smoking in all bedrooms s £59-£75; d £78-£110 (incl. bkfst) **LB** **FACILITIES:** Xmas
PARKING: 120 **NOTES:** No smoking in restaurant
CARDS: ▭▭

THORPE MARKET
Map 09 TG23

★★ 74% ◉ Elderton Lodge Hotel & Langtry Restaurant
Gunton Park NR11 8TZ
☎ 01263 833547 🖷 01263 834673
e-mail: enquiries@eldertonlodge.co.uk
Dir: at N Walsham take A149 towards Cromer, hotel is 3m out of North Walsham on left, just prior to entering Thorpe Market village

PETS: Bedrooms £5 Public areas (Not in restaurant or conservatory) Exercise area (on site)

Ideally placed for touring the north Norfolk coastline, this delightful former shooting lodge is set amidst six acres of mature gardens adjacent to Gunton Hall estate. The individually decorated bedrooms are tastefully furnished and thoughtfully equipped. Public rooms include a smart lounge bar, an elegant restaurant and a sunny conservatory breakfast room.
ROOMS: 11 en suite (2 fmly) (2 GF) No smoking in all bedrooms s fr £60; d fr £95 (incl. bkfst) **LB** **FACILITIES:** Xmas **PARKING:** 50
NOTES: No children 6yrs No smoking in restaurant
CARDS: ▭▭

★★ 64% Green Farm Restaurant & Hotel
North Walsham Rd NR11 8TH
☎ 01263 833602 🖷 01263 833163
e-mail: grfarmh@aol.com
Dir: Turn right off A140 Norwich to Cromer road at Roughton, beside fish and chip shop. Continue for 1.5m to 'Give Way' sign, turn right, hotel 200yds on left in centre, on village green

PETS: Bedrooms (unattended) £7.50 Exercise area (25 metres)

Attractive flint-faced 16th-century inn situated just a short drive from Cromer. Bedrooms are located in two courtyard style wings adjacent to the main building; each one is tastefully furnished with pine pieces and has co-ordinated fabrics. Public rooms include a popular restaurant, a comfortable lounge bar, an informal dining area and a function suite.
ROOMS: 5 en suite 9 annexe en suite (1 fmly) s £55-£80; d £80-£120 (incl. bkfst) **LB** **FACILITIES:** Xmas **PARKING:** 50 **NOTES:** No smoking in restaurant **CARDS:** ▭▭

★ Red stars indicate the AA's Top 200 Hotels in Britain & Ireland

All abbreviations are explained on page 9

TITCHWELL
Map 09 TF74

★★ 78% ◉◉ Titchwell Manor
PE31 8BB
☎ 01485 210221 🖷 01485 210104
e-mail: margaret@titchwellmanor.com
Dir: on A149 coast road between Brancaster and Thornham

PETS: Bedrooms Sep Accom (kennel) (unattended) £5 Public areas Exercise area (100 yards)

A popular venue for golfers, bird watchers and walkers, this family-run hotel is ideally placed for touring the north Norfolk coastline. Bedrooms are comfortable; some in the adjacent annexe offer ground floor access. Smart public rooms include a lounge area, relaxed informal bar and a delightful conservatory restaurant, overlooking the walled garden. Imaginative menus feature quality local produce and fresh fish.
ROOMS: 8 en suite 7 annexe en suite (2 fmly) (3 GF) No smoking in 9 bedrooms s £55-£100; d £84-£130 (incl. bkfst) **LB** **FACILITIES:** ch fac Xmas **PARKING:** 50 **NOTES:** No smoking in restaurant
CARDS: ▭▭

WORSTEAD
Map 09 TG32

◆◆◆◆ The Ollands
Swanns Yard NR28 9RP
☎ 01692 535150 🖷 01692 535150
e-mail: ollands@worstead.freeserve.co.uk
Dir: turn off B1150 to Worstead. Turn right in village square keeping left. Pass post office & take next turning on left to end of lane

PETS: Bedrooms Public areas Exercise area
RESIDENT PETS: 3 black Burmese cats

Expect a warm family welcome from the caring hosts at this detached property situated in a peaceful location in the heart of the picturesque village of Worstead. The well-equipped bedrooms are pleasantly decorated and tastefully furnished. Breakfast is served in the elegant dining room and features local produce.
FACILITIES: 3 en suite (1 GF) No smoking in bedrooms No smoking in dining room TVB tea/coffee Cen ht No coaches Dinner Last d 9am
PARKING: 8

🍵 Places with this symbol are pubs

Don't forget to let proprietors know when you book that you're bringing your pet

All information was correct at the time of going to press; we recommend you confirm details on booking

NORTHAMPTONSHIRE

CRICK
Map 04 SP57

⇧ Hotel Ibis Rugby East
Parklands NN6 7EX
☎ 01788 824331 📠 01788 824332
e-mail: H3588@accor-hotels.com
Dir: M1 junct 18/A428

PETS: Bedrooms Public areas Exercise area

Modern, budget hotel offering comfortable accommodation in bright and practical bedrooms. Breakfast is self-service and dinner is available in the restaurant. For further details, consult the Hotel Groups page.
ROOMS: 111 en suite s £34.95-£44.95; d £34.95-£44.95

DAVENTRY
Map 04 SP56

★★★★ ◉◉ Fawsley Hall
Fawsley NN11 3BA
☎ 01327 892000 📠 01327 892001
e-mail: reservations@fawsleyhall.com
Dir: From A361 turn at 'Fawsley Hall' sign. Follow single track for 1.5m until reaching iron gates

PETS: Bedrooms Exercise area Pet Food

Dating back to the 15th century, this delightful hotel is peacefully located in beautiful gardens designed by 'Capability' Brown. Spacious individually designed bedrooms and stylish public areas are beautifully furnished with antique and period pieces. Afternoon tea is served in the impressive Great Hall with its sumptuous deep cushioned sofas and real fires.
ROOMS: 43 en suite (2 GF) s fr £140; d £140-£390 (incl. cont bkfst) **LB**
FACILITIES: Spa STV Tennis (hard) Sauna Gym Croquet lawn Putting green Jacuzzi Health & Beauty treatment rooms Xmas
PARKING: 100 **NOTES:** No smoking in restaurant
CARDS: ▭▭▭▭▭▭

NORTHAMPTON
Map 04 SP76

★★★★ 70%
Northampton Marriott Hotel
Eagle Dr NN4 7HW
☎ 01604 768700 📠 01604 769011
e-mail: northampton@marriotthotels.co.uk
Dir: M1 junct 15, follow signs to Delapre Golf Course, hotel on right

Marriott
HOTELS · RESORTS · SUITES

PETS: Bedrooms (unattended) Exercise area (1 min walk) Pet Food

On the outskirts of town, this modern hotel has a great deal to offer to a cross section of guests. A self-contained management centre makes this a popular conference venue, and its spacious and well-designed bedrooms cater for business travellers especially well. The hotel's proximity to a number of attractions makes this a good base to explore the area.
ROOMS: 120 en suite (12 fmly) No smoking in 82 bedrooms s £55-£120; d £70-£140 (incl. bkfst) **LB FACILITIES:** Spa STV Indoor swimming (H) Sauna Solarium Gym Jacuzzi Steam room, beauty treatment room Xmas
SERVICES: air con **PARKING:** 187 **NOTES:** No smoking in restaurant
CARDS: ▭▭▭▭▭▭

OUNDLE
Map 04 TL08

◆◆◆ 🍴 Ship
18-20 West St PE8 4EF
☎ 01832 273918 📠 01832 270232
e-mail: enquiries@theshipinn-oundle.co.uk
Dir: turn off A1 junct 17 onto A605, 9m to Oundle

PETS: Bedrooms Public areas Exercise area (100yds)

This traditional-style inn is situated in the centre of this historic town. The pleasantly appointed bedrooms are split between three converted buildings to the rear of the property; some of the newer rooms have pine furniture and bright co-ordinated fabrics. Public rooms include a busy taproom, a lounge bar and a separate dining room.
FACILITIES: 14 rms (11 en suite) (1 fmly) No smoking in dining room TV11B tea/coffee Cen ht TVL Dinner Last d 9pm **PRICES:** s £25-£50; d £50-£60✳ **PARKING:** 70 **CARDS:** ▭▭ ▭▭

WELLINGBOROUGH
Map 04 SP86

★★★ 65% The Hind
Sheep St NN8 1BY
☎ 01933 222827 📠 01933 441921
e-mail: enquiries@thehind.co.uk
Dir: on A509 in town centre

PETS: Bedrooms (unattended) Exercise area (200yds)

Dating back to Jacobean times, this centrally located hotel provides a good base for business and leisure guests visiting the town. A good choice of dishes is available in the restaurant; alternatively the all-day coffee shop offers light snacks. Bedrooms come in a variety of styles, mostly of spacious dimensions.
ROOMS: 34 en suite (2 fmly) (5 GF) No smoking in 20 bedrooms s £45-£65; d £60-£90 (incl. bkfst) **LB FACILITIES:** Pool table in public bar Xmas **PARKING:** 17 **NOTES:** No smoking in restaurant RS 24 Dec-2 Jan **CARDS:** ▭▭ ▭▭ ▭▭ ▭▭ ▭

⇧ Hotel Ibis Wellingborough
Enstone Court NN8 2DR
☎ 01933 228333 📠 01933 228444
e-mail: H3164@accor-hotels.com
Dir: on junct of A45 & A509 towards Kettering on the SW edge of Wellingborough

PETS: Bedrooms Exercise area

Modern, budget hotel offering comfortable accommodation in bright and practical bedrooms. Breakfast is self-service and dinner is available in the restaurant. For further details, consult the Hotel Groups page.
ROOMS: 78 en suite s fr £51.95; d fr £51.95

All AA listed accommodation, restaurants and pubs can be found on the AA's website www.theAA.com

England

NORTHUMBERLAND

BAMBURGH
Map 12 NU13

★★★ 71% Waren House
Waren Mill NE70 7EE
☎ 01668 214581 📠 01668 214484
e-mail: enquiries@warenhousehotel.co.uk
Dir: 2m E of A1 turn onto B1342 to Waren Mill, at t-junct turn right, hotel 100yds on right

PETS: Bedrooms Exercise area (on site)

This delightful Georgian mansion is set in six acres of woodland and offers views of the coastline. The individually designed bedrooms, including suites, are themed in differing styles, and many have large bathrooms. Good, home-cooked food is served in the elegant dining room. A comfortable lounge and library are also available.
ROOMS: 12 en suite (4 fmly) (1 GF) No smoking in all bedrooms
s £74-£110; d £90-£195 (incl. bkfst) **LB FACILITIES:** Xmas
PARKING: 20 **NOTES:** No children 14yrs No smoking in restaurant
CARDS: 🌑 💳 💳 💳 🌑 🌑

★★ 69% The Lord Crewe
Front St NE69 7BL
☎ 01668 214243 📠 01668 214273
e-mail: lordcrewebamburgh@tiscali.co.uk
Dir: just below the castle

PETS: Bedrooms £5

Located in the heart of the village in the shadow of impressive Bamburgh Castle, this hotel has been developed from an old inn. Public areas include a choice of lounges, a cosy bar and a smart modern restaurant. Bedrooms offer good levels of equipment.
ROOMS: 18 rms (17 en suite) s £47-£52; d £88-£98 (incl. bkfst)
PARKING: 20 **NOTES:** No children 5yrs No smoking in restaurant
Closed Dec/Jan **CARDS:** 🌑 💳 💳 🌑 🌑

BELFORD
Map 12 NU13

◆◆◆◆ 🏛 Market Cross
1 Church St NE70 7LS
☎ 01668 213013
e-mail: details@marketcross.net
Dir: off A1 signed Belford, establishment 0.5m on right next to post office

PETS: Bedrooms (unattended) Public areas Exercise area (200yds)

Lying in the heart of the village, this listed building offers delightful, individually styled and thoughtfully equipped bedrooms. The award-winning breakfast is a real treat - local produce features extensively and an impressive range of delicious cooked dishes is available.
FACILITIES: 3 en suite No smoking TVB tea/coffee Cen ht No coaches
Special rates at local golf courses **PARKING:** 3
CARDS: 🌑 💳 💳 💳 🌑 🌑

BERWICK-UPON-TWEED
Map 12 NT95

★★★ 70% ◉
Marshall Meadows Country House
TD15 1UT
☎ 01289 331133 📠 01289 331438
e-mail: stay@marshallmeadows.co.uk
Dir: signed off A1, 300yds from Scottish Border

PETS: Bedrooms £5 per dog Exercise area Pet Food

This stylish Georgian mansion is set in wooded grounds flanked by farmland and has convenient access from the A1. A popular venue for weddings and conferences, it offers comfortable and well-equipped bedrooms. Public rooms include a cosy bar, a relaxing lounge and a two-tier restaurant, which serves imaginative dishes.
ROOMS: 19 en suite (2 fmly) No smoking in 12 bedrooms s £80-£90;
d £105-£150 (incl. bkfst) **LB FACILITIES:** Croquet lawn Petanque Xmas
PARKING: 87 **NOTES:** No smoking in restaurant Closed 15-27 Dec
CARDS: 🌑 💳 💳 🌑 🌑

🏕 **Places with this symbol are country house hotels**

🐓 **Places with this symbol are farms**

All information was correct at the time of going to press; we recommend you confirm details on booking

England

★★★ 64% **King's Arms**
43 Hide Hill TD15 1EJ
☎ 01289 307454 ▤ 01289 308867
e-mail: kingsarms.berwick@virgin.net
Dir: follow town centre signs from A1. Hotel behind Guild Hall, on left of Hide Hill

PETS: Bedrooms (unattended) Exercise area (100 metres)

A hotel of contrasting styles, this former coaching inn boasts a bar and restaurant that are contemporary and trendy with menu to match. By contrast bedrooms are set on traditional lines but most have the benefit of being of good size.
ROOMS: 35 en suite (3 fmly) No smoking in 20 bedrooms s £35-£79; d £60-£119 (incl. bkfst) **LB NOTES:** No smoking in restaurant
Closed 24 Dec-14 Jan **CARDS:**

♦♦♦♦ **Dervaig Guest House**
1 North Rd TD15 1PW
☎ 01289 307378
e-mail: dervaig@talk21.com
Dir: turn off A1 at A1167 (North Road) to town, last house on right before railway bridge

PETS: Bedrooms Public areas (except dining room)
Exercise area (500yds) RESIDENT PETS: Bobby (Border Terrier)

Lying north of the town centre, this detached Victorian house sits in lovely sheltered gardens which guests can use. The house has a restful atmosphere and comfortable bedrooms. Breakfast is served in a bright front-facing room decorated with an interesting collection of plates. There is guests' lounge.
FACILITIES: 5 en suite (3 fmly) No smoking in bedrooms No smoking in dining room No smoking in lounges TVB tea/coffee Cen ht No coaches
PRICES: s £25-£45; d £50-£60✻ **LB PARKING:** 8
CARDS:

★ Red stars indicate the AA's Top 200 Hotels in Britain & Ireland

---

Please mention AA Pet Friendly Places to Stay when booking

🍺 Places with this symbol are pubs

All information was correct at the time of going to press; we recommend you confirm details on booking

---

★★ 69% **Lord Crewe Arms**
DH8 9SP
☎ 01434 675251 ▤ 01434 675337
e-mail: lord@crewearms.freeserve.co.uk
Dir: 10m S of Hexham via B6306

PETS: Bedrooms Public areas (Not in restaurant)
Exercise area

Adjacent to Blanchland Abbey, many rooms in this historic, monastic hotel date from medieval times. Public areas feature flagstone floors, vaulted ceilings and original inglenook fireplace. Bedrooms, some of which are housed in what was the village's second hotel, are well-equipped, and retain a period style. Bar meals are popular and there is an elegant restaurant.
ROOMS: 9 en suite 10 annexe en suite (2 fmly) **FACILITIES:** Xmas
CARDS:

★★★ 75% ◉◉ 🏊 **Tillmouth Park Country House**
TD12 4UU
☎ 01890 882255 ▤ 01890 882540
e-mail: reception@tillmouthpark.force9.co.uk
Dir: off A1(M) at East Ord rdbt at Berwick-upon-Tweed. Take A698 to Cornhill and Coldstream. Hotel 9m on left

PETS: Bedrooms (unattended) Public areas (bar only)
Exercise area (on site) Pet Food (available on request)
RESIDENT PETS: Carter & Teal (Labradors)

An imposing mansion set in landscaped grounds by the River Till. Gracious public rooms including a stunning galleried lounge with drawing room off. The quietly elegant dining room overlooks the gardens, whilst lunches and early dinners are available in the bistro. Bedrooms retain a traditional character and include several magnificent master rooms.
ROOMS: 12 en suite 2 annexe en suite (1 fmly) s £60-£140; d £140-£180 (incl. bkfst) **LB FACILITIES:** STV Fishing Croquet lawn 3/4 snooker table, Game shooting Xmas **PARKING:** 50
NOTES: No smoking in restaurant **CARDS:**

♦♦♦♦♦ 🏠 **Ivy Cottage**
1 Croft Gardens, Crookham TD12 4ST
☎ 01890 820667 ▤ 01890 820667
e-mail: ajoh540455@aol.com
Dir: A697, 10m N of Wooler, R into Crookham village, 0.5m on R past village hall.

PETS: Bedrooms Exercise area (0.25 mile)

Hospitality is second to none at this modern house set in delightful gardens in a quiet village setting. Maintained in pristine condition it offers two bedrooms each with a super private bathroom. One room is furnished in bright modern style whilst the upstairs room has antique pine. Both come with a host of thoughtful touches. Delicious Aga-cooked breakfasts are served either in the farmhouse style kitchen or cosy dining room.
FACILITIES: 2 rms (1 GF) No smoking TVB tea/coffee Cen ht No children 5yrs No coaches Dinner Last d am same day
PRICES: s £34-£38; d £58-£62✻ **LB PARKING:** 2

EMBLETON   Map 12 NU22

★★ 71% **Dunstanburgh Castle Hotel**
NE66 3UN
☎ 01665 576111 📠 01665 576203
e-mail: stay@dunstanburghcastlehotel.co.uk
*Dir: from A1, take B1340 to Denwick past Rennington & Masons Arms.
Next right signed Embleton and into village*

PETS: Bedrooms (unattended) Exercise area

The focal point of the village, this friendly family-run hotel has a
dining room and grillroom offering different menus. There is also
a cosy bar and two lounges. In addition to the main bedrooms, a
small courtyard conversion gives three stunning suites each with a
lounge and galleried bedrooom above.
ROOMS: 20 en suite (4 fmly) s £32.50-£43.50; d £65-£87 (incl. bkfst)
LB PARKING: 16 **NOTES:** No smoking in restaurant Closed Nov-Feb
CARDS: 〰️〰️

HEXHAM   Map 12 NY96

★★★★ 71% ◉ **De Vere Slaley Hall**   DE VERE ● HOTELS
Slaley NE47 0BY
☎ 01434 673350 📠 01434 673962
e-mail: slaley.hall@devere-hotels.com
Dir: A1 from S to A68 link road follow signs for Slaley Hall

PETS: Bedrooms (unattended)

One thousand acres of Northumbrian forest and parkland, two
championship golf courses and indoor leisure facilities all add up
to a range of possibilities for guests, whatever their reason for
visiting. Spacious bedrooms are fully air-conditioned and
equipped with a range of extras. Public rooms include a number
of lounges, conference and banqueting rooms, the informal Golf
Clubhouse restaurant and the impressive main restaurant.
ROOMS: 139 en suite (22 fmly) No smoking in 101 bedrooms
s £85-£140; d £120-£190 (incl. bkfst) **LB FACILITIES:** Spa STV Indoor
swimming (H) Golf 18 Sauna Solarium Gym Jacuzzi Quad bikes,
Archery, Clay pigeon shoot, 4x4 driving, Creche Xmas **SERVICES:** Lift
air con **PARKING:** 500 **NOTES:** No smoking in restaurant
CARDS: 〰️〰️

**All abbreviations are
explained on page 9**

◆◆◆◆ ❦ **Rye Hill**
Slaley NE47 0AH
☎ 01434 673259 📠 01434 673259
e-mail: info@ryehillfarm.co.uk
*Dir: 5m S of Hexham, off B6306, 1st right after Travellers Rest pub then 1st
farm road right*

PETS: Bedrooms £1-2 per dog Public areas (except dining
room) Exercise area (on site) **RESIDENT PETS:** Terrier, farm cats
& pigs

Enjoying delightful panoramic views, Rye Hill offers a real farm-
stay experience. Accommodation is contained in two converted
barns in the main courtyard. Meals are served house-party style at
two rustic pine tables overlooking the gardens. A games room and
skittles alley are also available.
FACILITIES: 6 en suite (2 fmly) No smoking in bedrooms No smoking in
dining room TVB tea/coffee Licensed Cen ht TVL Pool Table Games
room, Skittle alley 30 acres sheep Dinner Last d 4pm **PRICES:** s £30;
d £50✳ **PARKING:** 6 **CARDS:** 〰️〰️

LONGHORSLEY   Map 12 NZ19

★★★ 74% ◉◉ **Linden Hall**   MACDONALD
NE65 8XF   HOTELS
☎ 01670 500000 📠 01670 500001
e-mail: stay@lindenhall.co.uk
*Dir: Northbound A1 exit A697 towards Coldstream. 1 mile north of
Longhorsley*

PETS: Bedrooms (unattended) £10 (only 2 bedrooms)
Exercise area (on site)

This impressive Georgian mansion lies in 400 acres of parkland
and offers extensive indoor and outdoor leisure facilities including
a golf course. Elegant public rooms include an imposing entrance
hall, drawing room and cocktail bar. The Dobson restaurant
provides a fine dining experience, or guests can eat in the more
informal Linden Tree pub which is located in the grounds.
ROOMS: 50 en suite (4 fmly) (20 GF) No smoking in 21 bedrooms
s £84-£94; d fr £121 (incl. bkfst) **LB FACILITIES:** Spa STV Indoor
swimming (H) Golf Snooker Sauna Solarium Gym Croquet lawn
Putting green Jacuzzi Own golf course Hard tennis court ch fac Xmas
SERVICES: Lift **PARKING:** 260 **NOTES:** No smoking in restaurant
CARDS: 〰️〰️

OTTERBURN   Map 12 NY89

★★★ 64% **The Otterburn Tower Hotel**
NE19 1NS
☎ 01830 520620 📠 01830 521504
e-mail: sales@otterburntower.com
Dir: in Otterburn, on A696 (Newcastle to Edinburgh road)

PETS: Bedrooms Sep Accom (Kennel) £10 per visit
Public areas (except restaurant) Exercise area (on site)

Built by the cousin of William the Conqueror, this mansion is set
in its own grounds. The hotel is steeped in history - Sir Walter
Scott stayed here in 1812. Bedrooms come in a variety of sizes and
some have huge ornamental fireplaces. Though furnished in

continued on p174

England

OTTERBURN continued

period style, they are equipped with all modern amenities. The restaurant features 16th-century oak panelling.
ROOMS: 18 en suite (2 fmly) (2 GF) No smoking in all bedrooms s £75-£90; d £120-£180 (incl. bkfst) **LB FACILITIES:** STV Fishing Croquet lawn ch fac Xmas **PARKING:** 70 **NOTES:** No smoking in restaurant **CARDS:**

SEAHOUSES   Map 12 NU23

★★ 70% **Bamburgh Castle**
NE68 7SQ
☎ 01665 720283 📠 01665 720848
e-mail: bamburghcastlehotel@btinternet.com
Dir: from A1 follow signs for Seahouses, car park entrance on rbt opposite Barclays Bank, automatic barrier will rise

PETS: Bedrooms (some rooms) (unattended) £7.95 per stay Exercise area

This hotel enjoys a seafront location overlooking the harbour. Bedrooms vary in size and style, yet all are well equipped, with superior rooms being spacious and attractively appointed. Front-facing rooms, plus the main lounge and restaurant all take advantage of the views.
ROOMS: 20 en suite (3 fmly) (3 GF) No smoking in 10 bedrooms s £44.95-£56.95; d £89.90-£99.90 (incl. bkfst) **LB**
FACILITIES: Putting green ch fac **PARKING:** 30 **NOTES:** No smoking in restaurant Closed 24-26 Dec & 2wks mid Jan **CARDS:**

NOTTINGHAMSHIRE

FARNSFIELD   Map 08 SK65

♦♦♦ **Grange Cottage**
Main St NG22 8EA
☎ 01623 882259 📠 01623 883300
e-mail: bedandbreakfast@grange-cottage.co.uk
Dir: off A614 (Ollerton/Doncaster) at White Post rdbt, 3rd exit to Farnsfield. Through village to Plough Inn, house opp Plough Inn car park

PETS: Bedrooms Public areas Exercise area (Adjacent) Dried dog food available RESIDENT PETS: Ellie - Pointer & Major - Belgian Shepherd

Grange Cottage is a charming 18th-century Georgian building set in two acres of delightful gardens and grounds behind security gates. The bedrooms are comfortable and homely, each individually furnished with lots of family touches. A freshly-cooked breakfast is served at one large table in the elegant dining room.
FACILITIES: 3 rms (1 en suite) No smoking TVB tea/coffee Cen ht No coaches Croquet lawn **PRICES:** s £22.50-£30; d £45-£50✱
PARKING: 6

All AA listed accommodation, restaurants and pubs can be found on the AA's website www.theAA.com

HOLME PIERREPONT   Map 08 SK63

♦♦♦ **Holme Grange Cottage**
Adbolton Ln NG12 2LU
☎ 0115 981 0413 📠 0115 981 0174
e-mail: jean.colinwightman@talk21.com
Dir: SE of Nottingham turn off A52 onto A6011 towards Nottingham, at 2nd traffic lights right into Regatta Way, after 1.25m house on right, opposite National Watersport Centre

PETS: Bedrooms Public areas Exercise area (Adjacent) RESIDENT PETS: Peggy - King Charles Cavalier spaniel

A stone's throw from the National Water Sports Centre and boasting its own all-weather tennis court, this establishment is ideally suited to the more active guest. Indeed, when not providing warm hospitality and freshly-cooked breakfasts, the proprietor is most likely to be found on the golf course.
FACILITIES: 3 rms (1 en suite) (1 fmly) No smoking TVB tea/coffee Cen ht TVL No coaches Tennis (hard) quarter size snooker table **PRICES:** s £25-£30; d £46-£50✱ **PARKING:** 6

LANGAR   Map 08 SK73

★★★ 73% ◉◉ ♨ **Langar Hall**
NG13 9HG
☎ 01949 860559 📠 01949 861045
e-mail: langarhall-hotel@ndirect.co.uk
Dir: via Bingham from A52 or Cropwell Bishop from A46, both signed. Hotel behind church.

PETS: Bedrooms (certain rooms) Public areas (on leads only) Exercise area Fields nearby

This delightful hotel enjoys a picturesque rural location, yet is only a short drive from Nottingham. Individually styled bedrooms are furnished with fine period pieces and benefit from some thoughtful extras. There is a choice of lounges, warmed by real fires, and a snug little bar. Carefully prepared imaginative food is served in the pillared dining room.
ROOMS: 12 en suite (1 fmly) No smoking in all bedrooms s £65-£97.50; d £130-£187.50 (incl. bkfst) **LB FACILITIES:** Fishing Croquet lawn ch fac **PARKING:** 20 **NOTES:** No smoking in restaurant **CARDS:**

MANSFIELD   Map 08 SK56

★★ 65% **Portland Hall**   THE INDEPENDENTS
Carr Bank Park, Windmill Ln NG18 2AL
☎ 01623 452525 📠 01623 452550
e-mail: enquiries@portlandhallhotel.co.uk
Dir: from town centre take A60 to Worksop for 100yds then right at pelican crossing into Nursery St, Carr Bank Park 50yds on right

PETS: Bedrooms Public areas (Not in restaurant) Exercise area (50mtrs) RESIDENT PETS: Rusty & Molly (Labradors)

A former Georgian mansion, overlooking 15 acres of recently renovated parklands, the house retains some fine original features, with original plasterwork and friezes displayed in the cosy lounge bar and around the domed skylight over the spiral stairs. The attractive restaurant proves to be a popular local venue,

continued

offering a flexible choice of carvery or menu options and service is skilled and attentive.
ROOMS: 10 en suite (1 fmly) No smoking in 5 bedrooms s £47-£55; d £58.75-£65 (incl. bkfst) **FACILITIES:** Bowls Green Xmas **PARKING:** 80
NOTES: No smoking in restaurant
CARDS:

NEWARK-ON-TRENT Map 08 SK75

◆◆◆ ◀▬ Willow Tree Inn
Front St, Barnby-in-the-Willows NG24 2SA
☎ 01636 626613 ▤ 01636 626060
Dir: from A1/A17, approx 3.5m to Newark Golf Course. 300yds to Barnby sign, turn right & Inn is approx 1m

PETS: Bedrooms (unattended) Public areas (Bar only)
Exercise area (100yds) RESIDENT PETS: Golden Labrador - Lillie, black cat - Basil

The Grade II listed Willow Tree Inn dates back to the 17th century. Bedrooms of varying styles are located in the main building and the adjacent annexe; each room is well equipped. The public areas include an attractive lounge bar where real ales and bar food are served. Alternatively, freshly prepared and imaginative meals are offered in the cosy restaurant.
FACILITIES: 2 en suite 5 annexe en suite (4 fmly) (5 GF) No smoking in bedrooms No smoking in dining room TVB tea/coffee Direct dial from bedrooms Cen ht Dinner Last d 9pm **PRICES:** s £39.50-£42.50; d £49.50-£69✳ **PARKING:** 50 **CARDS:**

NOTTINGHAM Map 08 SK54

★★★★ ◎◎ 🏠 Hart's
Standard Hill, Park Row NG1 6FN
☎ 0115 988 1900 ▤ 0115 947 7600
e-mail: ask@hartshotel.co.uk
Dir: Junct of Park Row & Rope Walk, close to city centre

PETS: Bedrooms £5 Exercise area (adjacent) Pet Food

This outstanding modern building stands on the site of the ramparts of the medieval castle, overlooking the city. Many of the bedrooms enjoy splendid views. Rooms are well appointed and stylish, while the Park Bar is the focal point of the public areas; service is professional and caring. Fine dining is offered at nearby Hart's Restaurant. Secure parking and private gardens are an added bonus.
ROOMS: 32 en suite No smoking in all bedrooms s £115-£235; d £115-£235 **LB FACILITIES:** STV Gym Small, unsupervised exercise room Xmas **SERVICES:** Lift **PARKING:** 21 **NOTES:** No smoking in restaurant **CARDS:**

★★★★ ◎ 🏠 Lace Market
29-31 High Pavement NG1 1HE
☎ 0115 852 3232 ▤ 0115 852 3223
e-mail: reservations@lacemarkethotel.co.uk
Dir: follow tourist signs for Galleries of Justice which is opposite hotel

PETS: Bedrooms £20 Public areas (Allowed in bar)

This smart town house, a conversion of two Georgian houses, is located in the trendy Lace Market area of the city. Smart public areas, including the stylish and very popular Merchants Restaurant

continued

and Saints Bar, are complemented by the Cock and Hoop, a traditional pub offering real ales and fine wines. Accommodation is stylish and contemporary and bedrooms are all thoughtfully equipped.
ROOMS: 42 en suite No smoking in all bedrooms s £90; d £110-£199
LB FACILITIES: STV Complimentary use of nearby health club.
SERVICES: Lift **NOTES:** No smoking in restaurant
CARDS:

★★★ 66% Bestwood Lodge
Bestwood Country Park, Arnold NG5 8NE
☎ 0115 920 3011 ▤ 0115 964 9678
e-mail: bestwoodlodge@btconnect.com
Dir: 3m N off A60. Left at traffic lights into Oxclose Ln, right at next lights into Queens Bower Rd. 1st right and keep right at fork in road

PETS: Bedrooms (unattended) £10 Public areas
Exercise area Pet Food Food and bowls available on request

A Victorian hunting lodge in 700 acres of parkland, providing modern bedrooms of varying styles and sizes. The interior architecture includes Gothic features and high vaulted ceilings in the lounge bar and the gallery. The newly refurbished banqueting suite is a popular venue for weddings and conferences.
ROOMS: 39 en suite (5 fmly) No smoking in 5 bedrooms s £45-£90; d £90-£150 (incl. bkfst) **LB FACILITIES:** Riding Guided walks Xmas
PARKING: 120 **NOTES:** No smoking in restaurant RS 25 Dec & 1 Jan
CARDS:

◆◆◆ Fairhaven Private Hotel
19 Meadow Rd, Beeston NG9 1JP
☎ 0115 922 7509 ▤ 0115 943 6217
e-mail: bookings@fairhaven.fsnet.co.uk
Dir: from A52 take B6005 for Beeston Railway Station. Hotel 200yds after bridge

PETS: Bedrooms Exercise area (0.5 mile) Bowls provided

This well-established private hotel is situated in a quiet area of Beeston on the outskirts of Nottingham. The public rooms have been altered to offer a stylish reception lounge with bar and a new function room, while breakfast is taken in the cosy dining room. The bedrooms vary in style and size, and are comfortably equipped.
FACILITIES: 13 rms (6 en suite) (2 fmly) No smoking in 2 bedrooms No smoking in dining room No smoking in 1 lounge TVB tea/coffee Licensed Cen ht **PRICES:** s £25-£35; d £40-£45✳ **PARKING:** 13

> 🐓 **Places with this symbol are farms**

> ★ **Red stars indicate the AA's Top 200 Hotels in Britain & Ireland**

> **Please mention AA Pet Friendly Places to Stay when booking**

England

BURFORD Map 04 SP21

★★★ 74% The Lamb Inn

Sheep St OX18 4LR
☎ 01993 823155 ☐ 01993 822228
e-mail: info@lambinn-burford.co.uk
Dir: Turn off A40 into Burford, downhill, take 1st left into Sheep St, hotel last on right

PETS: Bedrooms (unattended) £5 Public areas (not in restaurant) Exercise area (Adjacent)

A stone's throw from the centre of this quintessential Cotswold town, this delightful old inn possesses an abundance of character and charm. The bedrooms retain many original features and there is a selection of comfortable lounges with flagstone floors and log fires together with an atmospheric bar in which to relax. In the elegant restaurant carefully cooked meals are served, using the best of ingredients.
ROOMS: 15 en suite (1 fmly) (3 GF) No smoking in all bedrooms s £80-£100; d £130-£200 (incl. bkfst) **LB FACILITIES:** Xmas
NOTES: No smoking in restaurant **CARDS:** 💳

★★ 67% The Inn For All Seasons

THE INDEPENDENTS

The Barringtons OX18 4TN
☎ 01451 844324 ☐ 01451 844375
e-mail: sharp@innforallseasons.com
Dir: 3m W of Burford on A40 towards Cheltenham

PETS: Bedrooms (unattended) Public areas Exercise area (Adjacent) **RESIDENT PETS:** German Shepherd - Gig, black gun dog - Bob, Springer Spaniel - Gus

This 16th-century coaching inn is conveniently near to Burford. Bedrooms are comfortable and steadily being upgraded, public areas retain a feeling of period charm with original fireplaces and oak beams. A good selection of bar meals is available at lunchtime, whilst the evening menu includes an appetising selection of fresh fish.
ROOMS: 9 en suite 1 annexe en suite (2 fmly) (1 GF) s £46-£58; d £93-£97 (incl. bkfst) **LB FACILITIES:** STV Clay pigeon shooting Xmas
PARKING: 62 **CARDS:** 💳

> Don't forget to let proprietors know when you book that you're bringing your pet

> All abbreviations are explained on page 9

> All information was correct at the time of going to press; we recommend you confirm details on booking

CHARLBURY Map 04 SP31

★★ 65% The Bell

Church St OX7 3PP
☎ 01608 810278 ☐ 01608 811447
e-mail: reservationsatthebell@msn.com
Dir: from Oxford take A34 towards Woodstock, 2nd turn off B4437 towards Charlbury. In village, 2nd on left, hotel opposite St Mary's Church

PETS: Bedrooms (unattended) Public areas Exercise area Horse tie in garden **RESIDENT PETS:** Merlin (Persian cat)

This mellow Cotswold Stone inn dates back to the 16th Century, when it was home to customs and excise, and sits close to the town centre. Popular with locals, the bar has an enjoyable and relaxed atmosphere and comes complete with flagstone floors and log fires. The well-equipped bedrooms are situated in the main building and the converted adjacent barn.
ROOMS: 7 en suite 4 annexe en suite (3 fmly) No smoking in all bedrooms s fr £69; d fr £85 (incl. bkfst) **LB FACILITIES:** Xmas
PARKING: 40 **NOTES:** No smoking in restaurant
CARDS: 💳

KINGHAM Map 04 SP22

★★★ 74% Mill House Hotel & Restaurant

OX7 6UH
☎ 01608 658188 ☐ 01608 658492
e-mail: stay@millhousehotel.co.uk
Dir: off A44 onto B4450. Hotel indicated by tourist sign

PETS: Telephone for details

This Cotswold stone former mill house has been carefully converted into a comfortable and attractive hotel, and is set in well-kept grounds bordered by their own trout stream. Bedrooms are

continued

England

comfortable and provide thoughtfully equipped accommodation. There is a peaceful lounge and bar and an atmospheric restaurant where imaginative, skilful cooking is a highlight of any stay.

ROOMS: 21 en suite 2 annexe en suite (1 fmly) (7 GF) s £85-£95; d £120-£140 (incl. bkfst) **LB FACILITIES:** STV Fishing Croquet lawn ch fac Xmas **PARKING:** 62 **NOTES:** No smoking in restaurant **CARDS:** ▨▨▨▨▨▨▨▨

KINGSTON LISLE
Map 04 SU38

U ◼ **The Blowing Stone Inn**
OX12 9QL
☎ 01367 820288

> **PETS:** Bedrooms (unattended) Public areas Exercise area (50yds)

At the time of going to press the Diamond classification for this establishment had not been confirmed. Please check the AA website www.theAA.com for up-to-date information.
FACILITIES: 5 rms (3 en suite) (1 fmly)

OXFORD
Map 04 SP50

★★★ 70% ◉
Fallowfields Country House Hotel
Faringdon Rd, Kingston Bagpuize, Southmoor OX13 5BH
☎ 01865 820416 🖷 01865 821275
e-mail: stay@fallowfields.com
Dir: from A420, take A415 towards Abingdon for 100yds. Right at mini rdbt, through Kingston Bagpuize, Southmoor and Longworth, follow signs

> **PETS:** Bedrooms (unattended) £5 Public areas (At other guests' discretion) Exercise area (Adjacent) Pet Food Bowls available **RESIDENT PETS:** Phoebe - Seal Point Mitted Ragdoll cat; Kaspar - Maine coon cat

With a history stretching back over 300 years, this spacious, comfortable hotel provides friendly, old-fashioned service. The thoughtfully equipped bedrooms are very much of this century and are decorated with skill. Public areas include an elegant drawing room and a charming conservatory restaurant in which the hotel's own seasonal produce is served.
ROOMS: 10 en suite (2 fmly) No smoking in all bedrooms s £95-£115; d £145-£170 (incl. bkfst) **LB FACILITIES:** STV Tennis (hard) Croquet lawn Falconry ch fac **PARKING:** 21 **NOTES:** No smoking in restaurant **CARDS:** ▨▨▨▨▨▨▨

TETSWORTH
Map 04 SP60

♦♦♦♦ Little Acre Bed & Breakfast
4 High St OX9 7AT
☎ 01844 281423 🖷 01844 281423
e-mail: julia@little-acre.co.uk
Dir: M40 junct 6 from S, or 8a from N. From Oxford take A40 turn off at Wheatley and follow A418 towards Thame, in 1m turn right onto A40 to Tetsworth, in 2m at 30mph sign Little Acre is on right

> **PETS:** Bedrooms Exercise area

This impressive cottage-style house is just two miles from the M40, set in twenty acres of mature grounds which also contain a neatly maintained touring caravan site. The individually themed,

continued

---

comfortable bedrooms are filled with a wealth of thoughtful extras. Separate tables are provided in the cosy breakfast room overlooking the pretty enclosed patio garden.
FACILITIES: 3 rms (2 en suite) (1 fmly) No smoking in 2 bedrooms No smoking in dining room No smoking in lounges TVB tea/coffee Cen ht No coaches **PRICES:** s £35-£40; d £40-£48✳ **LB PARKING:** 4

WALLINGFORD
Map 04 SU68

★★★ 75% ◉ **Springs Hotel & Golf Club**
Wallingford Rd, North Stoke OX10 6BE
☎ 01491 836687 🖷 01491 836877
e-mail: info@thespringshotel.com
Dir: off A4074 (Oxford-Reading road) onto B4009 - Goring. Hotel 1m on right

> **PETS:** Bedrooms (unattended) £15 Exercise area (On site)

Set on its own golf course, this Victorian mansion has a timeless and peaceful atmosphere. Bedrooms vary in size; many are spacious, and all are generously equipped. The elegant restaurant enjoys splendid views over the spring-fed lake. There is also a comfortable lounge with original features, and a cosy bar in which to relax.
ROOMS: 31 en suite (3 fmly) (8 GF) No smoking in 6 bedrooms s £95-£120; d £110-£135 (incl. bkfst) **LB FACILITIES:** STV Outdoor swimming (H) Golf 18 Fishing Sauna Croquet lawn Putting green Clay pigeon shooting entertainment ch fac Xmas **PARKING:** 150 **NOTES:** No smoking in restaurant **CARDS:** ▨▨▨▨▨▨▨

★★★ 68% Shillingford Bridge

Shillingford OX10 8LZ
☎ 01865 858567 🖷 01865 858636
e-mail: shillingford.bridge@forestdale.com
Dir: M4 junct 10 follow A329 through Wallingford towards Thame, follow B4009 through Watlington, turn right on A4074 at Benson, then left at Shillingford rdbt (unclass road) Wallingford Rd

> **PETS:** Bedrooms (unattended) £7.50 Public areas (not in restaurant) Pet Food

This hotel enjoys a superb position right on the banks of the River Thames, and benefits from private moorings and a waterside open-air swimming pool. The public areas have large picture windows making the best use of the view. Bedrooms are well equipped and furnished with comfort in mind.
ROOMS: 34 en suite 8 annexe en suite (6 fmly) No smoking in 8 bedrooms s fr £70; d fr £120 (incl. bkfst) **LB FACILITIES:** Outdoor swimming (H) Fishing Squash entertainment Xmas **PARKING:** 100 **NOTES:** No smoking in restaurant **CARDS:** ▨▨▨▨▨▨▨

WANTAGE
Map 04 SU38

U ❤ **Down Barn Farm**
Sparsholt Down OX12 9XD
☎ 01367 820272

> **PETS:** Bedrooms Sep Accom (stable) £5 Public areas Exercise area (0.25 mile) Chudleys, tinned dog & cat food **RESIDENT PETS:** Roly - Corgi/Springer Spaniel cross, Gladys - Bull Mastiff, Beatrix, Oedipus, Oliver - cats

At the time of going to press the Diamond classification for this establishment had not been confirmed. Please check the AA website www.theAA.com for up-to-date information.
FACILITIES: 3 rms (1 en suite) (3 GF)

WOODSTOCK   Map 04 SP41

★★★ 73% ◉ Feathers
Market St OX20 1SX
☎ 01993 812291 📠 01993 813158
e-mail: enquiries@feathers.co.uk
Dir: from Oxford take A44 to Woodstock, 1st left after lights. Hotel on left

PETS: Bedrooms (unattended) Public areas (not restaurant/bar) Exercise area (100yds) Pet Food food & beds
RESIDENT PETS: Johann (African Grey parrot)

This small and individual hotel enjoys a town centre location with easy access to nearby Blenheim Palace. Public areas are elegant and full of traditional character from the cosy drawing room to the atmospheric restaurant. Individually styled bedrooms are appointed to a high standard and are furnished with attractive period and reproduction furniture.
ROOMS: 20 en suite (4 fmly) (2 GF) No smoking in 1 bedroom
s £99-£185; d £135-£225 (incl. bkfst) **LB FACILITIES:** STV 1 suite has steam room Xmas **NOTES:** No smoking in restaurant
CARDS: ▨▨▨▨▨▨

✦✦✦✦ The Townhouse
15 High St OX20 1TE
☎ 01993 810843 📠 01993 810843
e-mail: info@woodstock-townhouse.com
Dir: take A44 from Oxford to Woodstock, Town House is in High Street on the right, next to card shop.

PETS: Bedrooms (unattended) Exercise area (400 yards)

Located in the heart of this historic town, close to Blenheim Palace, this 18th-century-terraced house provides cosy, attractive bedrooms filled with thoughtful and practical extras, including modern and efficient power showers. Breakfasts and afternoon teas are served in the attractive, conservatory kitchen/dining room or on the enclosed patio during the warmer months.
FACILITIES: 5 en suite (1 fmly) No smoking TVB tea/coffee Direct dial from bedrooms Cen ht **CARDS:** ▨▨▨▨▨▨

RUTLAND

EMPINGHAM   Map 04 SK90

★★ 68% The White Horse Inn
Main St LE15 8PS
☎ 01780 460221 & 460521 📠 01780 460521
e-mail: info@whitehorserutland.co.uk
Dir: on A606, Oakham to Stamford road

PETS: Bedrooms (unattended) £5 Exercise area (0.25 mile)

This attractive stone-built inn, offering bright, comfortable accommodation, is conveniently located just minutes from the A1. Bedrooms in the main building are spacious and include a number of family rooms. Public areas include a well-stocked bar, a bistro and restaurant where a wide range of meals are served.
ROOMS: 4 en suite 9 annexe en suite (3 fmly) (5 GF) No smoking in 1 bedroom s £50; d £65 (incl. bkfst) **LB FACILITIES:** Xmas
PARKING: 60 **NOTES:** No smoking in restaurant
CARDS: ▨▨▨▨▨▨

OAKHAM   Map 04 SK80

★★★ 75% ◉ Barnsdale Lodge
The Avenue, Rutland Water, North Shore LE15 8AH
☎ 01572 724678 📠 01572 724961
e-mail: enquiries@barnsdalelodge.co.uk
Dir: off A1 onto A606. Hotel 5m on right, 2m E of Oakham

PETS: Bedrooms (unattended) £10 per stay (Allowed in bar area only) Exercise area (On site) Stabling by arrangement
RESIDENT PETS: Aron - cat

A popular and interesting hotel converted from a farmstead and overlooking Rutland Water. The public areas are dominated by a
continued

very successful food operation with informal meals served in the brasserie, and a good range of appealing meals on offer in the more formal restaurant. Bedrooms are comfortably appointed with excellent beds and period furnishings, enhanced by contemporary soft furnishings and thoughtful extras.
ROOMS: 46 en suite (2 fmly) (15 GF) No smoking in 34 bedrooms s £75-£99.50; d £99.50-£120 (incl. bkfst) **LB FACILITIES:** STV Fishing Croquet lawn Shooting Archery Golf Riding arranged Xmas
PARKING: 200 **NOTES:** No smoking in restaurant
CARDS:

★★★ ◎◎◎◎ ♨ **Hambleton Hall**
Hambleton LE15 8TH
☎ 01572 756991 ▤ 01572 724721
e-mail: hotel@hambletonhall.com
Dir: 3m E off A606

RELAIS & CHATEAUX

PETS: Bedrooms £10 Public areas (except dining room) Exercise area (adjacent) Pet Food

This delightful country house hotel enjoys a tranquil location amidst landscaped gardens overlooking Rutland Water. Stylish bedrooms are individually designed, tastefully decorated and thoughtfully equipped. Luxurious public areas include a cosy bar, a sumptuous drawing room and an elegant restaurant. Imaginative, skilfully prepared, award-winning cuisine, that features locally sourced and seasonal produce, is the highlight of any stay.
ROOMS: 15 en suite 2 annexe en suite No smoking in 1 bedroom s £160-£186; d £186-£355 (incl. cont bkfst) **FACILITIES:** STV Outdoor swimming (H) Tennis (hard) Croquet lawn Outdoor pool has CCTV, private access to lake Xmas **SERVICES:** Lift **PARKING:** 40
NOTES: No smoking in restaurant
CARDS:

UPPINGHAM   Map 04 SP89

★★★ 64% **Falcon**
The Market Place LE15 9PY
☎ 01572 823535 ▤ 01572 821620
e-mail: sales@thefalconhotel.com
Dir: turn off A47 onto A6003, left at lights, hotel on right

PETS: Bedrooms (unattended) Public areas (dogs must be on leads) Exercise area Pet Food Bowls available, food on request

An attractive, 16th-century coaching inn situated in the heart of this bustling market town. Public areas feature an open-plan lounge bar, with a relaxing atmosphere and comfortable sofas.
continued

The brasserie area offers a cosmopolitan-style snack menu and more formal meals are provided in the Garden Terrace Restaurant. Conference and functions rooms are also available.
ROOMS: 25 en suite (4 fmly) (3 GF) s £60; d £90-£125 (incl. bkfst) **LB**
FACILITIES: STV Snooker entertainment ch fac Xmas **PARKING:** 33
NOTES: No smoking in restaurant **CARDS:**

SHROPSHIRE

BRIDGNORTH   Map 07 SO79

♦♦♦♦ ▦ **Oldfield Cottage**
Oldfield WV16 6AQ
☎ 01746 789257 ▤ 01746 789257
e-mail: oldfieldcottage@aol.com
Dir: B4364 from Bridgnorth, after 3m pass Down Inn, 2nd L signed Oldfield, 0.25m on R

PETS: Bedrooms Public areas (Under restraint) Exercise area (100 yards) Good walks RESIDENT PETS: Pem & Dinah - Springer Spaniels

Located within the hamlet of Oldfield and set in pretty, mature gardens, this period cottage provides homely, rustically furnished bedrooms within a sympathetic conversion of former outbuildings. Memorable breakfasts, utilising quality local or home-made produce, are served in the conservatory.
FACILITIES: 2 annexe en suite No smoking TVB tea/coffee Cen ht TVL No children 10yrs No coaches **PARKING:** 3 **NOTES:** Closed Dec-Feb

CHURCH STRETTON   Map 07 SO49

★★★ 68% ◎◎
Stretton Hall Hotel
All Stretton SY6 6HG
☎ 01694 723224 ▤ 01694 724365
e-mail: aa@strettonhall.co.uk
Dir: from Shrewsbury, on A49, right onto B4370 signed All Stretton. Hotel 1m on left opposite The Yew Tree pub

THE INDEPENDENTS

PETS: Bedrooms Public areas (except restaurant) Exercise area

This fine 18th-century country house stands in spacious gardens. Original oak panelling features throughout the lounge bar, lounge and halls. Bedrooms are traditionally furnished and have modern facilities. Family and four-poster rooms are available and the restaurant has been tastefully refurbished.
ROOMS: 12 en suite (1 fmly) s £50-£115; d £80-£130 (incl. bkfst) **LB**
FACILITIES: ch fac Xmas **PARKING:** 70 **NOTES:** No smoking in restaurant **CARDS:**

Please mention AA Pet Friendly Places to Stay when booking

 Places with this symbol are pubs

CHURCH STRETTON continued

★★ 70% Mynd House

Ludlow Rd, Little Stretton SY6 6RB
☎ 01694 722212
e-mail: info@myndhouse.co.uk
Dir: A49 onto B4370, signed Little Stretton. Hotel 0.75m on left beyond Ragleth Inn

PETS: Bedrooms (unattended) Exercise area (400 metres)

This large Edwardian house is situated in the sleepy hamlet of Little Stretton, and is reached via a steep driveway. Privately owned and personally run, it provides well-equipped bedrooms which have many thoughtful extras. Public areas include a comfortable lounge, a pleasant bar and a traditional style dining room.
ROOMS: 7 en suite (2 fmly) No smoking in all bedrooms s £45-£50; d £60-£120 (incl. bkfst) **LB PARKING:** 8 **NOTES:** No smoking in restaurant RS mid Nov-mid Feb **CARDS:** 💳

◆◆◆◆ ❦ North Hill Farm

Cardington SY6 7LL
☎ 01694 771532
e-mail: cbrandon@btinternet.com
Dir: from Cardington village take road for Church Stretton. Take turning right signed Cardington Moor, this is a No Through Road, North Hill Farm is at top of hill on the left

PETS: Bedrooms Sep Accom (kennels) £1.50 for dogs Exercise area (adjacent) RESIDENT PETS: The owners breed Gordon Setters & English Springer Spaniels

This delightful period house has been tastefully modernised to provide comfortable accommodation. It is quietly and fairly remotely located on a 20-acre sheep-rearing holding amidst the breathtaking scenery of the Shropshire hills. Facilities include a comfortable lounge with exposed beams, where welcoming log fires burn in cold weather. Guests share one large table in the breakfast room.
FACILITIES: 4 rms (1 en suite) No smoking TVB tea/coffee Cen ht No children 10yrs facilities for guests own horses 20 acres horses sheep **PRICES:** s £25; d £46-£60✱ **LB PARKING:** 6

CLEOBURY MORTIMER   Map 07 SO67

◆◆◆◆ 🍴 Old Bake House

46-47 High St DY14 8DQ
☎ 01299 270193
Dir: on A4117 from Kidderminster. 100yds past church on right with 2 bay windows

PETS: Bedrooms Public areas (with advance warning) Exercise area (250 metres) RESIDENT PETS: Holly (Bearded Collie cross)

A combination of two 18th-century townhouses, a village inn, bakery and sympathetic renovation has resulted in a homely and tastefully furnished guest house providing bedrooms filled with a wealth of thoughtful extras. Spacious ground floor areas include comfortable sitting rooms and a dining section, the setting for memorable breakfasts.
FACILITIES: 3 rms (2 en suite) No smoking in bedrooms No smoking in dining room No smoking in 1 lounge tea/coffee Cen ht TVL No coaches Dinner Last d 7pm **PRICES:** s £25-£27.50; d £50-£55✱ **PARKING:** 2

CRAVEN ARMS   Map 07 SO48

◆◆◆◆ Castle View

Stokesay SY7 9AL
☎ 01588 673712
e-mail: joyce@castleviewb-b.fsnet.co.uk
Dir: on A49 south of Craven Arms opposite turning to Stokesay Castle

PETS: Bedrooms (unattended) Exercise area (adjacent)
RESIDENT PETS: Cindy (Bearded Collie)

This mid-Victorian cottage was extended about 20 years ago. Surrounded by delightful gardens, it stands on the southern outskirts of Craven Arms and as the name would suggest, is close to historic Stokesay Castle. Bedrooms are thoughtfully furnished and breakfasts, featuring local produce, are taken in a cosy traditionally furnished dining room.
FACILITIES: 3 rms (1 en suite) No smoking TVB tea/coffee Cen ht No children 3yrs No coaches **PRICES:** s £30-£35; d £50-£55✱ **LB PARKING:** 4

IRONBRIDGE   Map 07 SJ60

◆◆◆◆ Broseley House

1 The Square, Broseley TF12 5EW
☎ 01952 882043 📠 01952 882043
e-mail: info@broseleyhouse.co.uk
Dir: from Telford take the A442 to Bridgnorth, A4169 to Ironbridge, B4373 to Broseley turn right into Church Street, in square at centre of Broseley

PETS: Bedrooms Exercise area (300yds)

This impressive early Victorian town house is located in the centre of Broseley. It retains many original features and the present owner has made many improvements. Bedrooms are well equipped and have extra thoughtful touches; one room has its own kitchen facility and is available as a self-catering unit. Hearty breakfasts are served in the elegant breakfast room.
FACILITIES: 4 en suite (1 fmly) (1 GF) No smoking TVB tea/coffee Cen ht No children 5yrs **PRICES:** s £35-£45; d £52-£75✱

◆◆◆◆ Woodlands Farm Guest House

Beech Rd TF8 7PA
☎ 01952 432741 📠 01952 432741
e-mail: woodlandsfarm@ironbridge68.fsnet.co.uk
Dir: in Ironbridge, turn into Church Hill from small rdbt with tree in middle, follow into Beech Rd, guest house approx. 0.5m on right down small private lane

PETS: Bedrooms £2 Public areas Exercise area (On site)

Located in four acres of mature grounds, which include a well-stocked fishing lake, this extended Victorian bungalow has been considerably upgraded by the present owners to provide a range of homely bedrooms filled with thoughtful extras. One room is a family suite with its own lounge and small kitchen. A comprehensive breakfast is taken in the cosy breakfast room, overlooking the pretty garden.
FACILITIES: 4 rms (3 en suite) (2 fmly) (4 GF) No smoking TVB tea/coffee Cen ht No coaches Fishing 4 acres of grounds with Lake **PRICES:** s £22.50-£48; d £48-£55✱ **LB PARKING:** 8
NOTES: Closed 24 Dec-1 Jan **CARDS:** 💳

KNOCKIN

Map 07 SJ32

◆◆◆◆ 🏠 ♥ Top Farm House

SY10 8HN
☎ 01691 682582 📠 01691 682070
e-mail: p.a.m@knockin.freeserve.co.uk
Dir: in Knockin, past Bradford Arms & shop, past turning for Kinnerley, large black & white house on left

PETS: Bedrooms Public areas (except dining room)

This impressive half-timbered Tudor house, set amid pretty gardens, retains many original features including a wealth of exposed beams and open fires. Bedrooms are equipped with many thoughtful extras, and the open-plan ground-floor area includes a comfortable sitting room and elegant dining section, where imaginative comprehensive breakfasts are served.
FACILITIES: 3 en suite (1 fmly) No smoking in dining room TVB tea/coffee Cen ht TVL **PRICES:** s £30-£40; d £50-£60✱ **LB PARKING:** 6 **CARDS:** 💳 💳 💳 💳 💳 💳

LUDLOW

Map 07 SO57

★★★ 75% ⊚⊚⊚
Overton Grange Country House

Old Hereford Rd SY8 4AD
☎ 01584 873500 📠 01584 873524
e-mail: info@overtongrangehotel.com
Dir: off A49 at B4361 to Ludlow. Hotel 200yds on left

PETS: Bedrooms £15 Exercise area (0.5 mile)

Overton Grange is a traditional country house offering superb views over the Shropshire countryside, comfortable bedrooms and a dedicated customer care team. The restaurant offers an exciting twist of good locally sourced food and a commitment to high culinary standards. Meeting and conference facilities are available.
ROOMS: 14 en suite (3 fmly) No smoking in all bedrooms s £75-£130; d £130-£190 (incl. bkfst) **LB FACILITIES:** Croquet lawn Xmas **PARKING:** 50 **NOTES:** No smoking in restaurant
CARDS: 💳 💳 💳 💳 💳

★★★ 72% ⊚⊚ Dinham Hall

By the Castle SY8 1EJ
☎ 01584 876464 📠 01584 876019
e-mail: info@dinhamhall.co.uk
Dir: opposite the castle

PETS: Bedrooms (unattended) £7 Exercise area (Adjacent) Pet Food Bowls & food on request **RESIDENT PETS:** Oscar (cat)

Built in 1792, this lovely old house stands in attractive gardens immediately opposite Ludlow Castle. It has a well-deserved reputation for warm hospitality and fine cuisine. Well-equipped bedrooms include two in a converted cottage and some with four-poster beds. The comfortable public rooms are elegantly appointed.
ROOMS: 11 en suite 2 annexe en suite (3 fmly) (1 GF) s £95-£250; d £130-£280 (incl. bkfst) **LB FACILITIES:** Xmas **PARKING:** 16 **NOTES:** No smoking in restaurant
CARDS: 💳 💳 💳 💳 💳

★★ 68% Cliffe

Dinham SY8 2JE
☎ 01584 872063 📠 01584 873991
e-mail: thecliffehotel@hotmail.com
Dir: in town centre to Castle. Left at castle gates to Dinham, follow road over bridge. Take right fork, hotel 200yds on left

PETS: Bedrooms £3 Exercise area (adjacent)

Built in the 19th century and standing in extensive grounds and gardens, this privately owned and personally run hotel is quietly located close to the castle and the river. It provides well-equipped accommodation, and facilities include a lounge bar, a pleasant restaurant and a patio overlooking the garden.
ROOMS: 9 en suite (2 fmly) No smoking in all bedrooms s £40-£50; d £60-£80 (incl. bkfst) **LB PARKING:** 22 **NOTES:** No smoking in restaurant **CARDS:** 💳 💳 💳 💳 💳

◆◆◆◆◆ Bromley Court B & B

73 Lower Broad St SY8 1PH
☎ 01584 876996 & 0854 065 6192
e-mail: phil@ludlowhotels.com
Dir: A49 fork left on B4361, through lights 100m on left.

PETS: (Guests with pets stay in a suite) Exercise area (200yds to common & river)

Located in a mainly residential area of this historic town, close to the river and central attractions, this sympathetic award-winning renovation of former Georgian cottages provides split-level suites; all are equipped with comfortable sitting areas and kitchenettes, and the tastefully furnished bedrooms are filled with a wealth of thoughtful extras. A peaceful, attractive patio garden is also available, and wholesome breakfasts are taken in an intimate cottage-style dining room in a separate house.
FACILITIES: 3 en suite No smoking TVB tea/coffee Direct dial from bedrooms No dogs Cen ht No coaches **PRICES:** d £95-£110✱
CARDS: 💳 💳 💳 💳 💳

◆◆◆◆ The Hoopits

Greete SY8 3BS
☎ 01584 879187 📠 01584 875530
e-mail: thehoopits@talk21.com
Dir: On A49 turn towards Ashford, Caynham & Clee Hill. In Caynham village turn right for Greete & Tenbury Wells, Hoopits is 1m on left

PETS: Exercise area (20yds)

Set in immaculately maintained gardens, The Hoopits occupies a peaceful location within easy distance of Ludlow and the surrounding attractions. Quality period or handcrafted furniture highlights the many original features and breakfast is taken at a superb pine table in an elegant dining room. A guest lounge with wood burner is also available.
FACILITIES: 3 rms (2 en suite) (1 fmly) (1 GF) No smoking TVB tea/coffee No dogs (ex guide dogs) Cen ht TVL No coaches Dinner Last d 10am **PRICES:** s £25; d £50✱ **LB PARKING:** 10 **NOTES:** Closed 3 Dec-1 Jan

LUDLOW continued

◆◆◆◆ Moor Hall
Cleedownton SY8 3EG
☎ 01584 823209 📠 08707 492202
e-mail: enquiries@moorhall.co.uk
Dir: A4117 Ludlow to Kidderminster, left to Bridgnorth. B4364, follow for 3.5m, Moor Hall on right

PETS: Bedrooms (unattended) Exercise area (countryside walks) RESIDENT PETS: Pike - Black Labrador, 2 cats

This impressive Georgian house, once the home of Lord Boyne, is surrounded by extensive gardens and farmland. Bedrooms are richly decorated, well equipped and one room has the benefit of its own sitting area. Public areas are spacious and comfortably furnished. There is a choice of sitting rooms and a library bar. Guests dine family-style in an elegant dining room.
FACILITIES: 3 en suite No smoking in bedrooms No smoking in dining room TVB tea/coffee Licensed Cen ht TVL No coaches Fishing Dinner Last d day before **PRICES:** s £30-£33; d £50-£56✱ **LB PARKING:** 7

◆◆◆ 🍴 Church Inn
The Buttercross SY8 1AW
☎ 01584 872174 📠 01584 877146
e-mail: Reception@thechurchinn.com
Dir: in Ludlow town centre at top of Broad St

PETS: Bedrooms (unattended) Public areas

At the heart of historic Ludlow, this Grade II listed inn has been sympathetically renovated to provide quality accommodation with smart modern bathrooms, some with spa baths. Other areas include a small guest lounge, well-equipped meeting room and cosy bar areas, the setting for imaginative food and a wide selection of real ales.
FACILITIES: 9 en suite (3 fmly) No smoking in area of dining room No smoking in 1 lounge TVB tea/coffee Direct dial from bedrooms Cen ht No coaches Dinner Last d 9pm **PRICES:** s £40-£50; d £70-£80✱
CARDS: 💳💳💳💳💳

◆◆◆ 😊 🍴 Charlton Arms
Ludford Bridge SY8 1PJ
☎ 01584 872813 📠 01584 879120
Dir: from A49 Ludlow bypass, follow signs for 'livestock market'. On approaching town centre, premises on L before bridge

PETS: Bedrooms (unattended) Public areas Bowls and food on request

Located to the south of the historic centre on the banks of the River Teme beside the 13th-century Ludford Bridge, this popular inn provides a range of practically equipped bedrooms, some with river views. Imaginative food and a wide range of real ales are taken in the open plan public areas.
FACILITIES: 6 en suite TVB tea/coffee Cen ht Fishing Pool Table Dinner Last d 8.30pm **PRICES:** s £35; d £55✱ **PARKING:** 20
CARDS: 💳💳💳💳

◆◆◆ Timberstone Bed & Breakfast
Cleestanton SY8 3EL
☎ 01584 823519
e-mail: timberstone1@hotmail.com
Dir: A4117 Ludlow to Kidderminster, left to Bridgnorth on the B4364, follow for 1.5m, right to Cleestanton, take left fork, follow for 1.5m, 1st left, cottage on left

PETS: Bedrooms Public areas Exercise area (On site, and lots of walks nearby) RESIDENT PETS: Muppet - Labrador/Collie cross; 2 cats; chickens

This ancient timber-framed, stone house is quietly located in a rural setting, north-east of Ludlow. It has been painstakingly restored without losing any of its considerable charm. The accommodation comprises one twin and one double-bedded room with their own private bath or shower room. There is a choice of lounge areas, one with log fires and television. Guests all share one table at breakfast.
FACILITIES: 2 rms (1 fmly) No smoking tea/coffee Cen ht No coaches reflexology offered **PRICES:** s £25-£35; d £50-£60✱ **PARKING:** 4

MARKET DRAYTON
Map 07 SJ63

◆◆◆◆ 🌿 Haywood Farm B & B
Haywood Ln, Cheswardine TF9 2LW
☎ 01630 661788 & 07762 139362
e-mail: haywoodfarm@hotmail.com
Dir: from Market Drayton take A529 to Hinstock, 3m out of Market Drayton, take 1st left signed for Cheswardine. Approx 1.5m take 1st left after canal bridge. This is farm lane, which is next to two cottages

PETS: Sep Accom (Stable) Exercise area (Field beside house) Where necessary food provided, dogs to stay in stables (except guide dogs) RESIDENT PETS: Max, Brandy, Annie (dogs), Maggie, Daphne (cats)

Located close to Goldstone Common, this 18th-century house has been sympathetically renovated to provide high standards of comfort and good facilities. The tastefully furnished bedrooms are filled with thoughtful extras and breakfast is taken in an elegant dining room. A guests' lounge is also available and caring hospitality is assured.
FACILITIES: 5 rms (1 en suite) (1 fmly) (1 GF) No smoking TVB tea/coffee Cen ht TVL Sauna table tennis room, football pitch 500 acres arable & beef
PRICES: s £30; d £60✱ **PARKING:** 6

MUNSLOW
Map 07 SO58

◆◆◆◆ 😊 🍴 Crown Country Inn
SY7 9ET
☎ 01584 841205 📠 01584 841255
e-mail: info@crowncountryinn.co.uk
Dir: A49, turn on to B4368 at Craven Arms, 7m on left, car park opp

PETS: Bedrooms (unattended) £5 Public areas (only after meals) Exercise area (200yds) RESIDENT PETS: Jenna (Boxer)

Located between Much Wenlock and Craven Arms, this impressive pastel coloured and half-timbered Tudor inn is full of character and charm with stone floors, exposed beams and blazing log fires during winter. Smart pine furnished bedrooms are located in a

continued

sympathetic conversion of the former stable block and spacious public areas include two dining rooms.

FACILITIES: 3 en suite (1 fmly) (1 GF) No smoking in bedrooms No smoking in dining room TVB tea/coffee Cen ht Dinner Last d 8.45pm **PRICES:** s fr £40; d £60-£65✳ **LB PARKING:** 20 **CARDS:**

OSWESTRY
Map 07 SJ22

★★★ 75% @ @ ♠♣ Pen-y-Dyffryn Hall Country Hotel
Rhydycroesau SY10 7JD
☎ 01691 653700 ▤ 01691 650066
e-mail: stay@peny.co.uk
Dir: from A5 into Oswestry town centre. Follow signs to Llansilin on B4580, hotel 3m before Rhydycroesau village

PETS: Bedrooms (unattended) Public areas (Not after 6 pm) Exercise area (On site) Pet Food

Peacefully situated in five acres of grounds, this charming old house dates back to around 1840, when it was built as a rectory. The tastefully appointed public rooms have real fires during cold weather, and accommodation includes several mini-cottages, each with their own patio. The hotel has a well deserved reputation for its food that uses local and organic ingredients.
ROOMS: 8 en suite 4 annexe en suite (1 fmly) (1 GF) No smoking in all bedrooms s £78-£79; d fr £106 (incl. bkfst) **LB FACILITIES:** Spa Jacuzzi Guided walks ch fac **PARKING:** 14 **NOTES:** No children 3yrs No smoking in restaurant Closed 24 Dec-19 Jan **CARDS:**

★★★ 70% @ Wynnstay
Church St SY11 2SZ
☎ 01691 655261 ▤ 01691 670606
e-mail: info@wynnstayhotel.com
Dir: B4083 to town, fork left at Honda Garage and right at traffic lights. Hotel opposite church

PETS: Bedrooms (unattended) Exercise area (30yds)

This Georgian property was once a posting house and surrounds a unique 200-year-old Crown Bowling Green. Public areas include a health, leisure and beauty centre. Well-equipped bedrooms are individually styled and decorated and include several suites, four-poster rooms and a self-catering apartment. There is a traditional restaurant and bar food is also on offer.
ROOMS: 29 en suite (4 fmly) No smoking in 14 bedrooms s £50-£95; d £68-£130 **LB FACILITIES:** Spa Indoor swimming (H) Sauna Solarium Gym Jacuzzi Crown green bowling Beauty suite ch fac **PARKING:** 70 **NOTES:** No smoking in restaurant **CARDS:**

SHIFNAL
Map 07 SJ70

★★★★ 68% Park House
Park St TF11 9BA
☎ 01952 460128 ▤ 01952 461658
e-mail: res.parkhouse@macdonald-hotels.co.uk
Dir: M54 junct 4 follow A464 Wolverhampton Rd for approx 2m, under railway bridge and hotel is 100yds on left

MACDONALD HOTELS

PETS: Bedrooms £20 Public areas (except restaurant or bar) Exercise area (surrounding countryside)

A major programme of expansion and redesign has created a hotel from what was originally two country homes of very different architectural styles. Located on the edge of the historic market town, the hotel offers guests easy access to motorway networks, a choice of banqueting and meeting rooms, and leisure facilities.
ROOMS: 38 en suite 16 annexe en suite (4 fmly) (8 GF) No smoking in 15 bedrooms s £55-£120; d £80-£180 (incl. bkfst) **LB FACILITIES:** STV Indoor swimming (H) Sauna Solarium Jacuzzi Xmas **SERVICES:** Lift **PARKING:** 200 **NOTES:** No smoking in restaurant **CARDS:**

SHREWSBURY
Map 07 SJ41

★★★★ 66% Albrighton Hall
Albrighton SY4 3AG
☎ 01939 291000 ▤ 01939 291123
e-mail: albrighton@macdonald-hotels.co.uk
Dir: from S M6 junct 10a to M54 to end. From N M6 junct 12 to M5 then M54. Follow signs Harlescott & Ellesmere to A528

MACDONALD HOTELS

PETS: Bedrooms £10 Public areas (Not in restaurant) Exercise area (On site)

Dating back to 1630, this former ancestral home is set within 15 acres of attractive gardens. Rooms are well-kept and generally spacious, with attic rooms popular for their sloping beams. Elegant public rooms have rich oak panelling and there is a modern, well-equipped health and fitness centre.
ROOMS: 29 en suite 42 annexe en suite (18 fmly) (11 GF) No smoking in 49 bedrooms s £50-£90; d £100-£140 (incl. bkfst) **LB FACILITIES:** Spa STV Indoor swimming (H) Squash Sauna Solarium Gym Jacuzzi Beauty treatment rooms Xmas **SERVICES:** Lift **PARKING:** 200 **NOTES:** No smoking in restaurant **CARDS:**

★★★ 77% @ ♠♣ Albright Hussey
Ellesmere Rd SY4 3AF
☎ 01939 290571 & 290523 ▤ 01939 291143
e-mail: abhhotel@aol.com
Dir: 2.5m N of Shrewsbury on A528, follow signs for Ellesmere

PETS: Bedrooms (unattended) £5 Exercise area Pet Food

First mentioned in the Domesday Book, this enchanting medieval manor house is complete with a moat. Bedrooms are situated in either the sumptuously appointed main house or in the more modern ambience of the new wing. The intimate restaurant displays an abundance of original features and there is also a comfortable cocktail bar and lounge.
ROOMS: 26 en suite (4 fmly) (8 GF) No smoking in 16 bedrooms s £79-£105; d £110-£180 (incl. bkfst) **LB FACILITIES:** Croquet lawn Jacuzzi ch fac Xmas **PARKING:** 85 **NOTES:** No smoking in restaurant **CARDS:**

England

SHREWSBURY continued

★★★ 67% Mytton & Mermaid

Atcham SY5 6QG
☎ 01743 761220 📠 01743 761292
e-mail: admin@myttonandmermaid.co.uk
Dir: from Shrewsbury cross old bridge in Atcham. Hotel beside River Severn opposite main entrance to Attingham Park

PETS: **Bedrooms (unattended) £10 Exercise area (in grounds)**

Convenient for Shrewsbury, this ivy-clad former coaching inn enjoys a pleasant location beside the River Severn. Some bedrooms, including family suites, are in a converted stable block adjacent to the hotel. The large lounge bar has been recently refurbished, and there is also a comfortable lounge and brasserie gaining a well-deserved local reputation for the quality of its food.
ROOMS: 11 en suite 7 annexe en suite (1 fmly) No smoking in 11 bedrooms s £60; d £80-£135 (incl. bkfst) **FACILITIES:** Fishing entertainment ch fac Xmas **PARKING:** 50 **NOTES:** No smoking in restaurant **CARDS:**

★★ 65% Lion & Pheasant

49-50 Wyle Cop SY1 1XJ
☎ 01743 236288 📠 01743 244475
e-mail: lionandpheasant@aol.com

PETS: **Bedrooms (unattended) Public areas (except restaurant/eating areas)**

This 16th-century coaching inn is privately owned and personally run, and is close to the town centre. The accommodation, which includes no-smoking rooms, is well equipped and the public areas are full of character, with exposed beams and wall timbers. An extensive choice of food is served in the bar/bistro.
ROOMS: 27 rms (25 en suite) (2 fmly) No smoking in 8 bedrooms s £45-£50; d £50-£60 (incl. bkfst) **LB** **PARKING:** 18
NOTES: No smoking in restaurant Closed 24-25 Dec & 1 Jan
CARDS:

♦♦♦ Lythwood Hall Bed & Breakfast

2 Lythwood Hall, Lythwood, Bayston Hill SY3 0AD
☎ 07074 874747 📠 01743 874747
e-mail: lythwoodhall@amserve.net
Dir: A49 at Bayston Hill signed Lythwood, 2nd right Lythwood Rd, through village not right but straight ahead for 100yds, then left by rd hump sign, keep right

PETS: **Bedrooms Sep Accom (kennel & run) Exercise area (adjacent)**

This friendly guest house is part of the 18th-century Lythwood Hall. Set in peaceful rural surroundings while still close to main routes to and from Shropshire. Bedrooms are well equipped, the comfortable sitting room overlooks a lovely walled garden and the attractive dining room has period furnishings.
FACILITIES: 2 rms No smoking TVB tea/coffee Cen ht TVL No coaches Dinner Last d 6pm **PRICES:** s £28; d £48✻ **LB** **PARKING:** 3

TELFORD Map 07 SJ60

★★★ 70%
Clarion Hotel Madeley Court, Telford

Castlefields Way, Madeley TF7 5DW
☎ 01952 680068 📠 01952 684275
e-mail: enquiries@hotels-telford.com
Dir: M54 junct 4, A4169 Telford, A442 at 2nd rdbt signs for Kidderminster, (ignore sign to Madeley & Kidderminster), 1st left off rdbt

PETS: **Bedrooms £15 Public areas (except restaurant/bar) Exercise area (on site)**

This beautifully restored 16th-century manor house is set in extensive grounds and gardens. Bedrooms vary between character rooms and the newer annexe rooms. There are two wood-panelled lounges and the restaurant features a mix of old stone walls and modern colour themes.
ROOMS: 29 en suite 18 annexe en suite (1 fmly) (21 GF) No smoking in 16 bedrooms s £111; d £125 (incl. bkfst) **LB** **FACILITIES:** STV Archery, Horse riding arranged Xmas **PARKING:** 180 **NOTES:** No smoking in restaurant **CARDS:**

♦♦♦♦ Avenue Farm

Uppington TF6 5HW
☎ 01952 740253 📠 01952 740401
e-mail: jones@avenuefarm.fsnet.co.uk
Dir: from M54 junct 7 take B5061 for Atcham, 2nd left signed Uppington. Pass sawmill, turn right, farm 400yds on right

PETS: **Bedrooms Sep Accom (kennel or pen) £5 Exercise area (20yds)** RESIDENT PETS: Baloo (Labrador), Spike (Lucas Terrier) & Rosie (cat)

Located within the pretty rural hamlet of Uppington, this impressive house stands in immaculate mature gardens. The many period features add to the building's charm. Bedrooms offer a balance between practicality and homeliness and a comfortable guest sitting room is also available.
FACILITIES: 3 en suite (1 fmly) No smoking in bedrooms No smoking in dining room TV1B tea/coffee Riding 430 acres arable
PRICES: s £20-£35; d £50-£55✻ **PARKING:** 4 **NOTES:** Closed Xmas

♦♦♦♦ Church Farm

Wrockwardine Village, Wellington TF6 5DG
☎ 01952 244917 📠 01952 244917
e-mail: jo@churchfarm.freeserve.co.uk
Dir: in centre of conservation village, opposite 12th century church

PETS: **Bedrooms £2 per dog Public areas (Not in dining room) Exercise area** RESIDENT PETS: Two Miniature Schnauzers Heidi and Lottie, and two cats Rosie and Ginger Bits

Located opposite the village church in the pretty rural community of Wrockwardine. With many original features such as exposed beams, flagstone floors and open fireplaces, this is an impressive Grade II listed house. Bedrooms are homely and thoughtfully furnished. A spacious guest lounge is available in addition to an elegant dining room, the setting for memorable breakfasts.
FACILITIES: 4 rms (3 en suite) 1 annexe en suite (1 fmly) (2 GF) No smoking in dining room TVB tea/coffee Cen ht TVL No children 10yrs No coaches **PRICES:** s £28-£38; d £48-£60✻ **LB**
PARKING: 10 **CARDS:**

England

TELFORD SERVICE AREA (M54) — Map 07 SJ70

⌂ Days Inn Telford

Telford Services, Priorslee Rd TF11 8TG
☎ 01952 238400 ▤ 01952 238410
e-mail: telford.hotel@welcomebreak.co.uk
Dir: M54 junct 4

PETS: Bedrooms Public areas (must be kept on lead) Exercise area (adjacent)

This modern building offers accommodation in smart, spacious and well-equipped bedrooms, suitable for families and business travellers, and all with en suite bathrooms. Continental breakfast is available and other refreshments may be taken at the nearby family restaurant. For further details see the Hotel Groups page.
ROOMS: 48 en suite d £55-£75

WORFIELD — Map 07 SO79

★★★ ◉◉◉ Old Vicarage

Worfield WV15 5JZ
☎ 01746 716497 ▤ 01746 716552
e-mail: admin@the-old-vicarage.demon.co.uk
Dir: off A454 between Bridgnorth & Wolverhampton, 5m S of Telford's southern business area

PETS: Bedrooms Sep Accom (Kennel) £5 Exercise area Pet Food Bowls and food by prior arrangement
RESIDENT PETS: Oscar - Golden Labrador (used to be Andrex puppy!)

This delightful property is set in acres of farm and woodland in a quiet and peaceful area and was originally an Edwardian vicarage. Service is friendly and helpful, and customer care is one of the many strengths of this charming small hotel. The restaurant serves award-winning modern British cuisine in elegant surroundings. The lounge and conservatory are the perfect places to enjoy a pre-dinner drink or the complimentary afternoon tea. Bedrooms are individually appointed, thoughtfully and luxuriously furnished and well equipped.
ROOMS: 10 en suite 4 annexe en suite (1 fmly) (2 GF) No smoking in all bedrooms s £80-£110; d £135-£175 (incl. bkfst) **LB FACILITIES:** Spa Croquet lawn ch fac **PARKING:** 30 **NOTES:** No smoking in restaurant **CARDS:** ▨▨▨▨▨▨

SOMERSET

BATH — Map 03 ST76

★★★★★ 67% ◉◉ The Bath Spa

Sydney Rd BA2 6JF
☎ 0870 400 8222 ▤ 01225 444006
e-mail: sales@bathspahotel.com
MACDONALD HOTELS
Dir: M4 junct 18/A46 for Bath/A4 city centre. Left onto A36 at 1st traffic lights. Right at mini rdbt then left into Sydney Place. Hotel 200yds on right

PETS: Bedrooms £25 Public areas (Lobby only) Exercise area (100 yards) Pet Food Basket and towel provided

A delightful Georgian mansion set amidst seven acres of pretty landscaped grounds, just a short walk from the many and varied
continued

---

delights of the city centre. A timeless elegance pervades the gracious public areas and bedrooms. Facilities include a popular leisure club and a choice of dining options.
ROOMS: 104 en suite (3 fmly) (17 GF) No smoking in 76 bedrooms s £250-£280; d £250-£480 **LB FACILITIES:** STV Indoor swimming (H) Tennis (hard) Sauna Gym Croquet lawn Jacuzzi Beauty treatment, Hair salon entertainment Xmas **SERVICES:** Lift **PARKING:** 156
NOTES: No smoking in restaurant **CARDS:** ▨▨▨▨▨▨

★★★ 72% Cliffe

Cliffe Dr, Crowe Hill, Limpley Stoke BA2 7FY
☎ 01225 723226 ▤ 01225 723871
e-mail: cliffe@bestwestern.co.uk
Best Western
Dir: A36 S from Bath, at A36/B3108 lights left towards Bradford on Avon, 0.5m. Turn right before bridge through village, hotel on right

PETS: Bedrooms (annexe only) £6-8 Exercise area (On site)

With stunning views of the surrounding countryside, this attractive country house is just a short drive from the city of Bath. Bedrooms vary in size and style and are well-equipped; several are particularly spacious and a number of rooms are on the ground floor. The restaurant overlooks the well-tended garden and offers a tempting selection of carefully prepared dishes.
ROOMS: 8 en suite 3 annexe en suite (2 fmly) (4 GF) No smoking in 4 bedrooms s £90-£100; d £110-£130 (incl. bkfst) **LB FACILITIES:** STV Outdoor swimming (H) peaceful gardens ch fac Xmas **PARKING:** 20
NOTES: No smoking in restaurant
CARDS: ▨▨▨▨▨▨

★★★ 70% The Francis

Queen Square BA1 2HH
☎ 0870 400 8223 ▤ 01225 319715
e-mail: francis@macdonald-hotels.co.uk
MACDONALD HOTELS
Dir: M4 junct 18/A46 to Bath junct. Take 3rd exit onto A4. Right fork into George St, sharp left into Gay St onto Queen Sq, hotel on left

PETS: Bedrooms £10 Public areas (Lobby only (except guide dogs)) Exercise area (50 yards) Pet Food

Overlooking Queen Square in the centre of the city, this elegant Georgian hotel is situated within walking distance of Bath's many attractions. Public rooms provide a variety of environments in which guests can eat, drink and relax, from the informal café-bar to the traditional lounge and more formal restaurant. Bedrooms now have air conditioning.
ROOMS: 95 en suite (16 fmly) No smoking in 41 bedrooms s £120-£180; d £120-£180 **LB FACILITIES:** Xmas **SERVICES:** Lift **PARKING:** 42
NOTES: No smoking in restaurant **CARDS:** ▨▨▨▨▨▨

> **Don't forget to let proprietors know when you book that you're bringing your pet**

> ★ **Red stars indicate the AA's Top 200 Hotels in Britain & Ireland**

England

BATH continued

★★★ 70% Pratts

South Pde BA2 4AB

Forestdale Hotels

☎ 01225 460441 📠 01225 448807

e-mail: pratts@forestdale.com

Dir: take A46 into city centre. Left at 1st lights (Curfew Pub), right at next rdbt. 2nd exit at next rdbt, right at lights & left at next rdbt, then 1st left into South Pde

PETS: Bedrooms (unattended) £7.50 Public areas (not in restaurant) Pet Food

Part of a Georgian terrace, this long-established and popular hotel stands close to the city centre. Public rooms and bedrooms have undergone a refurbishment programme and all decor has been chosen to complement the Georgian surroundings. The ground-floor day rooms include two lounges, a writing room and a very comfortable restaurant.

ROOMS: 46 en suite (2 fmly) No smoking in 8 bedrooms s fr £95; d fr £130 (incl. bkfst) **LB FACILITIES:** Xmas **SERVICES:** Lift

NOTES: No smoking in restaurant **CARDS:** 💳💳💳💳💳💳

★★★ 66% The Abbey Hotel

North Pde BA1 1LF

Best Western

☎ 01225 461603 📠 01225 447758

e-mail: ahres@compasshotels.co.uk

Dir: close to the Abbey in city centre

PETS: Bedrooms £10 per pet Public areas (Not in restaurant) Exercise area (Adjacent) Pet Food

Originally built for a wealthy merchant in the 1740s and forming part of a handsome Georgian terrace, this welcoming hotel is situated in the heart of the city. The thoughtfully equipped bedrooms vary in size and style. Public areas include a smart lounge bar and a refurbished restaurant offering a regularly changing menu.

ROOMS: 60 en suite (4 fmly) (2 GF) No smoking in 22 bedrooms s £80-£90; d £110-£120 (incl. bkfst) **LB FACILITIES:** STV **SERVICES:** Lift

NOTES: No smoking in restaurant Closed 23-27 Dec

CARDS: 💳💳💳💳💳

◆◆◆◆ Eagle House

Church St, Bathford BA1 7RS

☎ 01225 859946 📠 01225 859430

e-mail: jonap@eagleho.demon.co.uk

Dir: from A4 take A363 for 150yds towards Bradford-on-Avon, fork left into Bathford Hill, 1st right into Church Street. House 200yds on right

PETS: Bedrooms £5 Public areas Exercise area (Large garden on site)

Set in attractive gardens, this delightful Georgian house is pleasantly located on the outskirts of the city. Bedrooms are individually styled, and each is provided with a thoughtful range of extra facilities. The lounge is most impressive and is adorned with attractive pictures and the dining room has views of the grounds.

FACILITIES: 6 en suite 2 annexe en suite (2 fmly) (2 GF) No smoking in 2 bedrooms No smoking in dining room TVB tea/coffee Direct dial from bedrooms Cen ht Tennis (grass) Croquet lawn Childrens play area & treehouse **PRICES:** s £46-£58; d £56-£92✻ **LB PARKING:** 10

NOTES: Closed 12 Dec-8 Jan **CARDS:** 💳💳💳💳

◆◆◆◆ Marlborough House

1 Marlborough Ln BA1 2NQ

☎ 01225 318175 📠 01225 466127

e-mail: mars@manque.dircon.co.uk

Dir: on corner of A4 & Marlborough Lane. W of Queen Square in city centre

PETS: Bedrooms (unattended) £10 Public areas (under control) Exercise area (100yds) bowls and organic dog food available **RESIDENT PETS:** Staffordshire Terrier - Thelonious

This elegant town house, situated opposite Royal Victoria Park, is ideally placed for the city centre. American hospitality combined with antique furnishings (such as four-poster beds) and globally-inspired vegetarian cuisine using organic ingredients, make this a must for those looking for something out of the ordinary.

FACILITIES: 7 en suite (3 fmly) (1 GF) No smoking TVB tea/coffee Direct dial from bedrooms Licensed No coaches

PRICES: s £55-£85; d £65-£95✻ **LB PARKING:** 3

CARDS: 💳💳💳💳💳

BRIDGWATER   Map 03 ST33

◆◆◆◆ Model Farm

Perry Green, Wembdon TA5 2BA

☎ 01278 433999

e-mail: info@modelfarm.com

Dir: M5 J23/24, A38 into Bridgwater. A39 Minehead, proceed 1m past garage on R. Down hill, at double bend turn R (Wembdon). Turn L (Perry Green). At T-junct, follow sign No Through Road. Farm 2nd drive on L.

PETS: Bedrooms Exercise area (on site)

RESIDENT PETS: Patch & Scamp - border collies, Misty & Tigger - cats

This extensive Victorian house enjoys a peaceful rural setting and has glorious country views. Guests are assured of a warm welcome and genuine hospitality. Bedrooms are very spacious and comfortable with thoughtful touches. By arrangement, the proprietors join their guests around the large dining room table for a carefully prepared three-course dinner, which features local ingredients.

FACILITIES: 3 en suite (1 fmly) No smoking tea/coffee Licensed Cen ht TVL No children 3yrs No coaches Dinner Last d 12 noon

PRICES: s £40-£45; d £60-£70✻ **PARKING:** 6

CARDS: 💳💳💳💳

 Places with this symbol are farms

BUCKLAND ST MARY | Map 03 ST21

◆◆◆◆ Hillside
TA20 3TQ
☎ 01460 234599 & 07703 633770 📠 01460 234599
e-mail: royandmarge@hillsidebsm.freeserve.co.uk
Dir: A303, approx 4m S of Ilminster turning, right at the Eagle Tavern, next left (water tower on corner), Hillside approx 500yds on left

PETS: Bedrooms (by prior arrangement only) £2 Public areas (not dining area and kitchen) Exercise area (500yds)

A warm welcome is assured at this peaceful family home, set in large, attractive gardens and enjoying splendid far-reaching views across open countryside. Bedrooms are spacious and decorated to a high standard with many thoughtful extras. Hearty breakfasts are served hot from the Aga in the bright dining room or the conservatory, which overlooks the garden.
FACILITIES: 4 rms (2 en suite) 1 annexe rms (1 fmly) (1 GF) No smoking TV4B tea/coffee Cen ht TVL No coaches
PRICES: s £27-£35; d £47-£60✳ **LB PARKING:** 4
NOTES: Closed Xmas & New Year

BUTLEIGH | Map 03 ST53

◆◆◆ Court Lodge
Sub Rd BA6 8SA
☎ 01458 850575
Dir: from Yeovilton (Podimore) rdbt on A303. Take A37, after 1.5m 1st left through Charlton Macrell. After 1m over crossroads 3rd right signposted Butleigh. Court lodge is last house on right.

PETS: Bedrooms (unattended) Public areas Exercise area RESIDENT PETS: Judy - Labrador

Situated at the entrance to Butleigh Court and surrounded by pleasant gardens, this charming and attractive house offers comfortable accommodation. Guests are assured of a friendly welcome and made to feel relaxed. Two lounges are available, and at breakfast traditional fare is provided at the single dining table.
FACILITIES: 2 rms No smoking TVB Cen ht TVL No coaches
PRICES: s fr £18.50; d fr £37✳ **BB PARKING:**

CHARD | Map 03 ST30

★★★ 70% Lordleaze
Henderson Dr, Forton Rd TA20 2HW
☎ 01460 61066 📠 01460 66468
e-mail: lordleaze@fsbdial.co.uk
Dir: from Chard take A358, at St Mary's Church turn left to Forton & Winsham on B3162. Follow signs to hotel

PETS: Bedrooms (unattended) £5 Exercise area (adjacent)

The Lordleaze is an excellent base from which to explore the West Country. The comfortable bedrooms, some of which are on the ground floor, are well-equipped. A focal point is the relaxed and friendly lounge bar where a wood burning stove adds to the character and atmosphere. In addition to the carte menu offered in the restaurant, a tempting selection of bar meals is also available.
ROOMS: 25 en suite (2 fmly) (7 GF) No smoking in 21 bedrooms
FACILITIES: **PARKING:** 55 **NOTES:** No smoking in restaurant
CARDS: 🔲 🔲 🔲 🔲 🔲

◆◆◆ Watermead
83 High St TA20 1QT
☎ 01460 62834 📠 01460 67448
e-mail: trudy@watermeadguesthouse.co.uk
Dir: on A30 through the High St continue up the hill from shopping centre

PETS: Bedrooms £5 for dogs Public areas Exercise area (100 metres) RESIDENT PETS: Jasper (Black Labrador), Charlie (cat)

This family-run house provides smart and comfortable accommodation. Conveniently located, it is an ideal base from which to explore the area and guests are made to feel at home. Hearty breakfasts are served in the spacious dining room which overlooks the attractive garden. Bedrooms are neatly presented and a very spacious, self-contained suite proves popular with families.
FACILITIES: 9 rms (6 en suite) 1 annexe en suite (1 fmly) No smoking TVB tea/coffee Cen ht TVL No coaches **PRICES:** s £25-£37; d £49-£53✳ **LB PARKING:** 10 **CARDS:** 🔲 🔲 🔲 🔲

CLEVEDON | Map 03 ST47

★★★ 67% Walton Park
Wellington Ter BS21 7BL
☎ 01275 874253 📠 01275 343577
e-mail: waltonpark@aol.com
Dir: M5 junct 20, signs for seafront. Stay on coast road, past pier into Wellington Terrace, hotel on left

PETS: Bedrooms £7 Exercise area (20 metres) Pet Food RESIDENT PETS: Charlie (cat)

Quietly located with spectacular views across the Bristol Channel to Wales, this popular Victorian hotel offers a relaxed atmosphere. Bedrooms are well-decorated and equipped to meet the demands of both business and leisure guests. In the comfortable restaurant, a high standard of home-cooked food is served and lighter meals are available in the convivial bar at lunchtime.
ROOMS: 40 en suite (4 fmly) No smoking in 12 bedrooms s £48-£79; d £83-£99 (incl. bkfst) **LB FACILITIES:** STV **SERVICES:** Lift
PARKING: 50 **CARDS:** 🔲 🔲 🔲 🔲 🔲 🔲

CREWKERNE | Map 03 ST40

◆◆◆◆ Greenways
Boozer Pit, Merriott TA16 5PW
☎ 01460 72830 📠 01460 72919
e-mail: wardill.tim-martine@virgin.net
Dir: A303, take A356 signed Crewkerne and Merriott. Turn right on bend, 3rd house on left on entering village

PETS: Bedrooms £5 Public areas Exercise area (adjacent) RESIDENT PETS: Chancer & Diego (Labradors), Inky (cat), tropical fish, koi, goldfish & hens

Quietly located on the Somerset and Dorset borders, Greenways started life some 300 years ago as a cider house. The one bedroom with its large en suite bathroom is in a self-contained adjoining property with a private entrance. Breakfast is taken in the pleasant conservatory where guests may also enjoy delicious home-cooked dinners by prior arrangement.
FACILITIES: 1 en suite (1 GF) No smoking TVB tea/coffee Cen ht No coaches Pool Table Dinner Last d 3pm **PARKING:** 5

CREWKERNE continued

◆◆◆◆ 🌱 Manor Farm
Wayford TA18 8QL
☎ 01460 78865 & 0776 7620031 🖷 01460 78865
Dir: from Crewkerne take B3165 to Lyme Regis, after 3m in Clapton turn right into Dunsham Lane, 0.5m up hill Manor Farm on right

PETS: Sep Accom (kennel) Public areas Exercise area (adjacent)

Located off the beaten track, this fine Victorian country house has extensive views over Clapton towards the Axe Valley. The comfortably furnished bedrooms are well equipped; front-facing rooms enjoy splendid views. Breakfast is served at separate tables in the dining room, and a spacious lounge is also provided.
FACILITIES: 3 en suite 1 annexe en suite No smoking STV TVB tea/coffee Cen ht TVL Fishing Riding 20 acres breeding beef
PRICES: s £30-£35; d £50✳ **PARKING:** 14

DULVERTON   Map 03 SS92

★★ 64% Lion
Bank Square TA22 9BU
☎ 01398 323444 🖷 01398 323980
e-mail: jeffeveritt@tiscali.co.uk
Dir: from A361 at Tiverton rdbt onto A396. Left at Exbridge onto B3223. Over bridge in Dulverton, hotel in Bank Sq

PETS: Telephone for details

Old-fashioned hospitality is always on offer at this charming, traditional inn in the centre of Dulverton, an ideal base from which to explore Exmoor National Park. The bar is popular with locals and visitors alike, offering a variety of local real ales and quality meals. A pleasant dining room provides a quieter, non-smoking option.
ROOMS: 13 en suite (2 fmly) No smoking in 2 bedrooms s £38-£45; d fr £65 (incl. bkfst) **LB FACILITIES:** No coaches **PARKING:** 6
NOTES: No smoking in restaurant **CARDS:** ▨▨▨▨▨

◆◆◆◆◆ ▦ Highercombe
TA22 9PT
☎ 01398 323451 🖷 01398 323451
e-mail: highercombe@btconnect.com
Dir: from Dulverton take B3223 towards Lynton, premises are approx 2.5m on right after sharp left bend

PETS: Bedrooms Sep Accom (stables for horses) Public areas Exercise area (in grounds) Food, bowls and bedding

With delightful views over Exmoor, this charming Grade II listed former hunting lodge and farmhouse is set in eight acres of parkland and landscaped gardens. The two spacious bedrooms offer a number of welcome extra facilities. A comfortable guest
continued

lounge is available and freshly-prepared breakfast is taken in the elegant dining room.

FACILITIES: 2 en suite 1 annexe en suite (1 fmly) No smoking in bedrooms No smoking in dining room No smoking in 1 lounge TVB tea/coffee Cen ht TVL No coaches Fishing Riding Dressage and show jumping arena Dinner Last d 9pm **PARKING:** 7
CARDS:

◆◆◆◆ Threadneedle
EX16 9JH
☎ 01398 341598
e-mail: info@threadneedlecottage.co.uk
Dir: on Devon/Somerset border just off B3227 between Oldways End & East Anstey

PETS: Bedrooms Sep Accom (stable/kennel) £5 for horses Public areas Exercise area (50 yards) RESIDENT PETS: Scamp & Charlie (Shetland Sheepdogs), Jack & Bonnie (horses)

Situated on the edge of Exmoor near Dulverton, Threadneedle is built in the style of a Devon longhouse. The spacious, well-appointed family home offers guests comfortable, en suite accommodation. Traditional West Country dishes are served, by prior arrangement, in the light airy dining room, which overlooks the garden and surrounding countryside.
FACILITIES: 2 en suite (1 fmly) No smoking in bedrooms TVB tea/coffee Cen ht No coaches Dinner Last d 10am **PRICES:** s £27-£30; d £54-£60✳ **LB PARKING:** 12

DUNSTER   Map 03 SS94

★★★ 75% ⏲ The Luttrell Arms Hotel
High St TA24 6SG
☎ 01643 821555 🖷 01643 821567
e-mail: info@luttrellarms.fsnet.co.uk
Dir: A39/A396 S toward Tiverton. Hotel on left opposite Yarn Market

PETS: Bedrooms (unattended) £5 for dogs Public areas Exercise area (adjacent)

Occupying an enviable position in the high street, this 15th-century hotel looks up to the town's famous castle. Beautifully renovated and decorated in a contemporary style, high levels of comfort can
continued

be found throughout. The warm and friendly staff deliver attentive service in a relaxed atmosphere.

ROOMS: 28 en suite (3 fmly) No smoking in all bedrooms s £85-£125; d £95-£140 (incl. bkfst) **LB FACILITIES:** Exmoor safaris, Historic tours, Walking tours Xmas **NOTES:** No smoking in restaurant
CARDS:

♦♦♦♦ Higher Orchard
30 St Georges St TA24 6RS
☎ 01643 821915
e-mail: lamacraft@higherorchard.fsnet.co.uk
Dir: A39 to Minehead, left to Dunster, turn right after Exmoor National Park Visitor Centre. At T-junct, turn right hotel 75yds on right

PETS: Exercise area (75 metres)

A charming Victorian house located in the fascinating medieval village of Dunster. The impressive house has an elevated position and offers fine views over the church towards the castle. Guests are welcome to relax in the gardens surrounding the house as well as in the lounge. Breakfast offers a selection of local produce including home-made marmalade and eggs from the proprietor's own poultry.
FACILITIES: 2 rms (1 en suite) No smoking TVB tea/coffee Cen ht No children 10yrs No coaches **PRICES:** s £30; d £50✶ **PARKING:** 2
NOTES: Closed Xmas-New Year

EXFORD   Map 03 SS83

★★★ 72% ◉◉ Crown
TA24 7PP
☎ 01643 831554 ▯ 01643 831665
e-mail: info@crownhotelexmoor.co.uk
Dir: M5 junct 25, follow Taunton signs. Take A358 out of Taunton, then B3224 via Wheddon Cross into Exford

PETS: Bedrooms £5 Public areas Exercise area Pet Food
RESIDENT PETS: Samsox & PJ (Black Labradors)

Guest comfort is certainly a hallmark at the Crown Hotel. Afternoon tea is served in the lounge beside a roaring fire and tempting menus in the bar and restaurant are all part of the charm of this delightful old coaching inn specialising in breaks for shooting and other country sports. Bedrooms retain a traditional
continued

style, yet offer a range of modern comforts and facilities, many with views of the pretty moorland village.

ROOMS: 17 en suite No smoking in 3 bedrooms s £55-£65; d £95-£130 (incl. bkfst) **LB FACILITIES:** Fishing Riding Shooting, Riding Xmas **PARKING:** 30 **NOTES:** No smoking in restaurant
CARDS:

FITZHEAD   Map 03 ST12

♦♦♦ 🍽 Fitzhead Inn
TA4 3JP
☎ 01823 400667
e-mail: fitzhead@amserve.com
Dir: off A3065 Taunton to Wiveliscombe road just after Preston Bowyer

PETS: Bedrooms (unattended) Public areas Exercise area (200 metres) **RESIDENT PETS:** 2 ducks

Centrally located in the village of Fitzhead and brimming with character, this delightful old inn has a wealth of exposed beams and an inviting log fire. The charming bedrooms have been converted from an adjacent barn and are equipped with modern facilities. Delicious lunches and dinners are served in the cosy bar.
FACILITIES: 7 en suite (4 GF) No smoking in bedrooms TVB tea/coffee Cen ht Dinner Last d 9.30pm **PRICES:** s £35; d £50✶

GLASTONBURY   Map 03 ST53

♦♦ Hedgehog House B & B
3 Wells Rd BA6 9DN
☎ 01458 833067 & 07870 982323
e-mail: alan@hedgehoghouse.net
Dir: at top of Glastonbury High Street, turn left onto Wells Road (A39). Hedgehog House is 1st detached house on left

PETS: Sep Accom (cages & runs in garden) Public areas (except TV lounge & food areas) Exercise area (0.5 miles) bowls provided **RESIDENT PETS:** Marble (cat), Humbug & Liquorice (Guinea pigs), tropical fish

This vegetarian establishment is located close to the Tor and provides a friendly family atmosphere for those who wish to take in the culture of the town. Breakfast is served around one large table in the kitchen/dining room and dinner is available by prior arrangement. Shiatsu therapy is available.
FACILITIES: 3 rms (2 en suite) (1 fmly) (1 GF) No smoking Cen ht TVL No coaches yoga room/shiatsu dojo Dinner Last d at breakfast
PARKING: 2

GORDANO SERVICE AREA (M5)   Map 03 ST57

⌂ **Days Inn**
BS20 7XG
☎ 01275 373709 & 373624 🖷 01275 374104
e-mail: gordano.hotel@welcomebreak.co.uk
Dir: M5 junct 19, follow signs for Gordano services

PETS: Bedrooms

This modern building offers accommodation in smart, spacious and well-equipped bedrooms, suitable for families and business travellers, and all with en suite bathrooms. Continental breakfast is available and other refreshments may be taken at the nearby family restaurant. For further details see the Hotel Groups page.
ROOMS: 60 en suite s fr £49; d fr £49

HIGHBRIDGE   Map 03 ST34

★★ 68% **Sundowner**
74 Main Rd, West Huntspill TA9 3QU
☎ 01278 784766 🖷 01278 794133
e-mail: runnalls@msn.com
Dir: from M5 junct 23, 3m N on A38

PETS: Bedrooms Public areas Exercise area

Friendly service and an informal atmosphere are just two of the highlights of this small hotel. The open-plan lounge/bar is a comfortable area in which to relax after a busy day exploring the area or working in the locality. An extensive menu, featuring freshly cooked, imaginative dishes, is offered in the popular restaurant.
ROOMS: 8 en suite (1 fmly) s £40-£45; d £55-£60 (incl. bkfst)
PARKING: 18 **NOTES:** No smoking in restaurant Closed 26, 31 Dec & 1 Jan RS 25 Dec **CARDS:** 💳💳💳💳💳

All AA listed accommodation, restaurants and pubs can be found on the AA's website www.theAA.com

---

HOLCOMBE   Map 03 ST64

★★ 71% ⏣ *The Ring O' Roses*
Stratton Rd BA3 5EB
☎ 01761 232478 🖷 01761 233737
e-mail: ringorosesholcombe@tesco.net
Dir: A367 to Stratton on the Fosse, look for hidden left turn opposite Downside Abbey, signposted Holcombe. Next right , hotel 1.5m on left

PETS: Bedrooms (unattended) £4 Public areas (except restaurant) Exercise area (surrounding fields)
RESIDENT PETS: Sam (chocolate Labrador)

With views of Downside Abbey in the distance, this inn dates back to the 16th century. The attentive owners and pleasant staff create a friendly and relaxed atmosphere. Bedrooms are individually furnished and very comfortable. Real ales are served in the bar
continued

while in the restaurant an imaginative menu is offered, using local ingredients wherever possible.

ROOMS: 8 en suite No smoking in all bedrooms **PARKING:** 35
NOTES: No smoking in restaurant **CARDS:** 💳💳💳💳💳

HOLFORD   Map 03 ST14

★★ 76% **Combe House**
TA5 1RZ
☎ 01278 741382 🖷 01278 741322
e-mail: enquiries@combehouse.co.uk
Dir: from A39 W turn left in Holford village then left at T-junct. Left again at fork and continue 0.25m to Holford Combe

PETS: Bedrooms (unattended) £3 Public areas
Exercise area Pet Food RESIDENT PETS: Gin & Tonic - cats; Roger & Flo - springer spaniel/collie cross

Once a tannery, this 17th-century longhouse is peacefully situated in lovely grounds, and provides an ideal retreat for walking in the Quantock Hills. Bedrooms are traditional in style and the public rooms include a choice of sitting areas. There is a focus on home cooking in the dining room.
ROOMS: 17 rms (16 en suite) (3 fmly) (1 GF) No smoking in 16 bedrooms s £45-£55; d £90-£110 (incl. bkfst) **LB** **FACILITIES:** STV Indoor swimming (H) Tennis (hard) Sauna Gym Croquet lawn Xmas
PARKING: 33 **NOTES:** No smoking in restaurant
CARDS: 💳💳💳💳💳

◆◆◆◆ **Winsors Farm B & B**
TA5 1RY
☎ 01278 741435 & 741666 🖷 01278 741666
e-mail: enq@winsors-farm.co.uk
Dir: 10m W of Bridgwater on A39. On entering Holford take 1st left at Plough Inn. Winsors Farm on left, 200mtrs from A39

PETS: Bedrooms Public areas (Except kitchen)
Exercise area (Adjacent) Food and bowls provided if given notice; large garden RESIDENT PETS: Beanie, Bagheera, Whisper, Widget, Shadow - cats; George - Labrador

Reputed to be the oldest property in the village, Winsors Farm dates back to the 16th century and is located on the edge of the Quantocks. Guests are assured of a warm and friendly welcome here. The bedrooms are comfortable and well equipped and have numerous thoughtful extras. Breakfast is served around a large table in the entrance hall/dining room. Dinner is available by arrangement.
FACILITIES: 2 en suite 1 annexe en suite (1 GF) No smoking TVB tea/coffee Cen ht TVL No coaches walking, bird and deer watching
PRICES: s £30; d £45-£50✳ **PARKING:** 5

HUNSTRETE   Map 03 ST66

★★★ 79% ◉◉ ♨ Hunstrete House
BS39 4NS
☎ 01761 490490 📠 01761 490732
e-mail: user@hunstretehouse.co.uk
Dir: from Bath take A4 to Bristol. At Globe Inn rdbt 2nd left onto A368 to
Wells. 1m after Marksbury turn right for Hunstrete village. Hotel next left

PETS: Bedrooms £10 Public areas (on a lead, not in dining areas) Exercise area (100 metres) 5 stables available and four fenced paddocks

This delightful Georgian house enjoys a stunning setting in 92 acres of deer park and woodland on the edge of the Mendip Hills. Elegant bedrooms in the main building and coach house are both spacious and comfortable. Public areas feature antiques, paintings and fine china. The restaurant enjoys a well-deserved reputation for fine food and utilises much home-grown produce.
ROOMS: 25 en suite (2 fmly) (8 GF) No smoking in 14 bedrooms s £135-£145; d £170-£180 (incl. bkfst) **LB FACILITIES:** STV Outdoor swimming (H) Tennis (hard) Croquet lawn Xmas **PARKING:** 50
NOTES: No smoking in restaurant
CARDS:

ILMINSTER   Map 03 ST31

★★★ 67% Shrubbery
TA19 9AR
☎ 01460 52108 📠 01460 53660
e-mail: stuart@shrubberyhotel.com
Dir: 0.5m from A303 towards Ilminster town centre

PETS: Bedrooms (unattended) Public areas (Except restaurant) Exercise area Pet Food Food available if requested in advance - chargeable

Set in attractive terraced gardens, this Victorian hotel offers well-equipped bedrooms of various sizes, including three on the ground floor. Bar meals or full meals are available in the bar, lounges and restaurant. Additional facilities include a range of function rooms and a heated outdoor pool.
ROOMS: 16 en suite (3 fmly) s £65-£78; d £80-£98 (incl. bkfst) **LB**
FACILITIES: STV Outdoor swimming (H) Tennis (grass) **PARKING:** 100
CARDS:

KILVE   Map 03 ST14

♦♦♦♦ ◫ Hood Arms Hotel
TA5 1EA
☎ 01278 741210 📠 01278 741477
e-mail: bheason1942@aol.com
Dir: 12m W of Bridgwater on A39, midway between Bridgwater & Minehead

PETS: Telephone for details

Comfortable, well-equipped bedrooms, with a good range of facilities, are offered at this 17th-century former coaching inn,
continued

centrally located in the village of Kilve. In the beamed bars, blackboard menus offer a wide range of popular dishes.

FACILITIES: 6 en suite (1 fmly) No smoking in bedrooms No smoking in dining room TVB tea/coffee Direct dial from bedrooms Cen ht Pool Table Dinner Last d 9.30pm **PARKING:** 12
CARDS:

LOXTON   Map 03 ST35

★★★ 67% Webbington
BS26 2XA
☎ 01934 750100 📠 01934 750020
e-mail: webbington@latonahotels.co.uk

PETS: Bedrooms Public areas Exercise area (adjacent)

Despite being easily spotted from the M5 motorway, this popular hotel is nestled in the Somerset countryside with splendid views from many bedrooms and public areas. Well suited to a wide range of guests from business to leisure to families, the hotel offers a warm welcome to all. Facilities include an indoor swimming pool, tennis courts, cardio gym and varied conference rooms.
ROOMS: 59 en suite (2 fmly) No smoking in 10 bedrooms
FACILITIES: Indoor swimming (H) Sauna Solarium Gym Beauty treatments Cardiovascular suite Steam Room Xmas **PARKING:** 450
NOTES: No smoking in restaurant
CARDS:

MINEHEAD   Map 03 SS94

♦♦♦ ◫ The Old Ship Aground
Quay St TA24 5UL
☎ 01643 702087 📠 01643 709066
e-mail: enquiries@oldshipaground.co.uk
Dir: turn right towards Butlins at 1st rdbt after Dunster lights, turn left at rdbt on seafront, proceed to harbour with sea on right, on front

PETS: Bedrooms (unattended) Public areas Exercise area (200 yards)

Located at the edge of the harbour and enjoying views of the bay, the Old Ship Aground offers traditional hospitality within a laid-back atmosphere. Bedrooms are spacious and thoughtfully equipped. Bar food is available and breakfast is served in the large dining/ function room.
FACILITIES: 13 en suite (3 fmly) No smoking in 5 bedrooms No smoking in area of dining room TVB tea/coffee Cen ht Pool Table Dinner Last d 9.30pm **PRICES:** s £25-£30; d £45-£55✳ **PARKING:** 10
CARDS:

England

NETHER STOWEY
Map 03 ST13

◆◆◆◆◆ 🍴 **Castle of Comfort**

TA5 1LE

☎ 01278 741264 ▤ 01278 741144

e-mail: reception@castle-of-comfort.co.uk

Dir: on A39, approx 1.3m W of Nether Stowey on left

> **PETS:** Bedrooms **Sep Accom** (stables & kennels)
> (unattended) **Public areas** (except lounge or restaurant)
> **Exercise area** (on site)

Dating in part from the 16th century, this former inn is situated on the northern slopes of the Quantock Hills in an Area of Outstanding Natural Beauty. Bedrooms and bathrooms are well equipped whilst the public rooms are smart and comfortable. The delightful gardens and a heated swimming pool are available for guests' use in the summer months and cuisine is imaginative.

FACILITIES: 5 en suite 1 annexe en suite (1 fmly) (1 GF) No smoking TVB tea/coffee Direct dial from bedrooms Licensed Cen ht No coaches Outdoor swimming pool (heated) Stabling with access to bridle paths and hunting Dinner Last d noon **PRICES:** s £41-£91; d £103-£139✳ LB **PARKING:** 10 **NOTES:** Closed 24 Dec-2 Jan **CARDS:** 〓 〓 〓 ⑤

OAKHILL
Map 03 ST64

◆◆◆ Oakhill Lodge

Bath Rd BA3 5AQ

☎ 01749 840145 ▤ 01749 840145

Dir: A367 from Bath towards Shepton Mallet. Passing signs for Oakhill and 30mph, lodge is immediately on right. After Gurney Slade look for Oakhill sign on left.

> **PETS:** Bedrooms **Exercise area** (50yds)
> **RESIDENT PETS:** 2 cats

Between Bath and Wells, this gatehouse lodge is conveniently located for many local attractions. It provides one twin bedroom with adjacent bathroom, both of which are comfortably decorated and furnished. The village pub offers home-made food at dinner and is just a two-minute stroll away.

FACILITIES: 1 en suite (1 fmly) No smoking TVB tea/coffee No dogs (ex guide dogs) Cen ht No coaches **PARKING:** 3 **NOTES:** Closed 23 Dec-2 Jan

PORLOCK
Map 03 SS94

◎◎◎ 🏠 Andrews on the Weir

Porlock Weir TA24 8PB

☎ 01643 863300 ▤ 01643 863311

e-mail: information@andrewsontheweir.co.uk

Dir: A39 from Minehead to Porlock, through village, 1st right signed Harbour (Porlock Weir) for 1.5m

> **PETS:** Bedrooms **Exercise area** (200yds)
> **RESIDENT PETS:** Narla - Black Labrador

Enjoying a delightful location overlooking Porlock Bay, Andrews on the Weir is decorated in country house style. Bedrooms are spacious and comfortable; one has a four-poster bed. During colder months, a log fire creates a cosy atmosphere in the sitting

continued

room/bar. There is a choice of imaginative, innovative dishes available in the restaurant - Andrew Dixon is an accomplished chef. **ROOMS:** 5 en suite No smoking in all bedrooms s £65-£100; d £75-£120 (incl. bkfst) LB **FACILITIES:** Xmas **PARKING:** 6 **NOTES:** No children 12yrs No smoking in restaurant Closed Jan & Mon RS Sun night & Tue lunch **CARDS:** 〓 〓 〓 〓 ⑤

SEDGEMOOR MOTORWAY SERVICE AREA (M5)
Map 03 ST35

⌂ **Days Inn**

M5 Northbound J22-21, Sedgemoor BS24 0JL

☎ 01934 750831 ▤ 01934 750808

e-mail: sedgemoor.hotel@welcomebreak.co.uk

Dir: M5 junct 21/22

> **PETS:** Bedrooms Public areas **Exercise area** (adjacent)

This modern building offers accommodation in smart, spacious and well-equipped bedrooms, suitable for families and business travellers, and all with en suite bathrooms. Continental breakfast is available and other refreshments may be taken at the nearby family restaurant. For further details see the Hotel Groups page. **ROOMS:** 40 en suite s £45-£55; d £45-£55

SOMERTON
Map 03 ST42

◆◆◆◆ Stowford House

Charlton Adam TA11 7AT

☎ 01458 223717 ▤ 01458 223940

e-mail: harperr@totalise.co.uk

Dir: A303 Podimore Rdbt take 2nd exit A37 to Shepton Mallet, after 2m take 2nd left to Charlton Adam. Pass pub to T-junct, left at shop/post office on the left, Stowford House right

> **PETS:** Bedrooms Public areas **Exercise area**
> **RESIDENT PETS:** Shaftesbury (cat)

Stowford House is a delightful conversion of an old Victorian Methodist chapel and the village school. Centrally situated in peaceful Charlton Adam, it now offers accommodation of character and charm within a friendly atmosphere. Bedrooms are cosy and equipped with modern facilities, and the public rooms retain many stunning original features.

FACILITIES: 2 en suite (1 GF) No smoking in bedrooms TVB tea/coffee Cen ht No children 7yrs No coaches **PRICES:** s £30; d £50✳ **PARKING:** 2 **NOTES:** Closed Xmas

STANTON DREW
Map 03 ST56

◆◆◆◆ 🏠 **Greenlands**

BS39 4ES

☎ 01275 333487 ▤ 01275 331211

e-mail: greenlands@bandb.fslife.co.uk

Dir: off A37 onto B3130, establishment on right before 'Round House' and Stanton Drew Garage

> **PETS:** Telephone for details

Situated near the ancient village of Stanton Drew in the heart of the Chew Valley, Greenlands is conveniently located close to Bristol Airport and the cities of Bath, Bristol and Wells. The accommodation

continued

includes comfortable well-equipped bedrooms and a separate downstairs guest lounge. Breakfast is a highlight of any stay here.

FACILITIES: 4 en suite No smoking in bedrooms No smoking in dining room STV TVB tea/coffee Cen ht TVL No children 12yrs No coaches
PARKING: 8

STON EASTON

Map 03 ST65

★★★★ ◎◎ Ston Easton Park

BA3 4DF
☎ 01761 241631 📠 01761 241377
e-mail: info@stoneaston.co.uk
Dir: on A37

PETS: Bedrooms Sep Accom (quiet rooms) Public areas (manager's discretion) Exercise area (in grounds) Pet Food

Dating back to 1740, this stunning Palladian mansion benefits from a tranquil location amidst parkland and landscaped gardens. Individually styled, spacious bedrooms include three rooms located in the charming Gardener's Cottage. The delightful and inviting public rooms retain much of their original character and are adorned with beautiful antiques and fine paintings. The imaginative cooking provided at dinner and breakfast is a highlight of any stay here.
ROOMS: 20 en suite 3 annexe en suite (2 fmly) (2 GF) No smoking in all bedrooms s £120-£340; d £150-£395 (incl. bkfst) **LB**
FACILITIES: Tennis (hard) Fishing Snooker Croquet lawn ch fac Xmas
PARKING: 120 **NOTES:** No smoking in restaurant
CARDS: ⬛⬛⬛⬛⬛⬛

TAUNTON

Map 03 ST22

★★★ ◎◎◎ Castle

Castle Green TA1 1NF
☎ 01823 272671 📠 01823 336066
e-mail: reception@the-castle-hotel.com
Dir: from M5 junct 25/26 follow signs to town centre and to Castle Hotel

PETS: Bedrooms (unattended) £10 Exercise area (adjacent)

The wisteria covered Castle has been owned and run by the same family for over half a century and, with its Norman keep, is a landmark in the centre of the town. Much thought has gone into furnishing the bedrooms and public areas, ensuring guest comfort while retaining the character and endearing charm of the original building. Renowned for its interpretation of classic British dishes in the elegant restaurant, this hotel also offers a lively, modern brasserie for less formal dining.
ROOMS: 44 en suite s fr £115; d fr £170 (incl. bkfst) **LB**
FACILITIES: Xmas **SERVICES:** Lift **PARKING:** 50 **NOTES:** No smoking in restaurant **CARDS:** ⬛⬛⬛⬛⬛⬛

★★★ 74% Rumwell Manor

Rumwell TA4 1EL
☎ 01823 461902 📠 01823 254861
e-mail: reception@rumwellmanor.co.uk
Dir: M5 junct 26 follow signs to Wellington, turn right onto A38 to Taunton, hotel is 3m on right

Best Western

PETS: Bedrooms (Annexe rooms only) Exercise area (hotel grounds)

With easy access to Taunton and the M5, Rumwell Manor is situated in Somerset countryside and surrounded by lovingly tended gardens. A selection of freshly prepared dishes is offered each evening in the candlelit restaurant. Bedrooms vary in size and style, with those in the main house offering greater space and character. In addition to the cosy bar and adjacent lounge, several meeting/conference rooms are available.
ROOMS: 10 en suite 10 annexe en suite (3 fmly) (6 GF) No smoking in 6 bedrooms s £68-£78; d £96-£116 **LB** **FACILITIES:** Xmas
PARKING: 40 **NOTES:** No smoking in restaurant
CARDS: ⬛⬛⬛⬛⬛⬛⬛

★★ 78% ◎◎ Farthings Hotel & Restaurant

Hatch Beauchamp TA3 6SG
☎ 01823 480664 📠 01823 481118
e-mail: farthing1@aol.com
Dir: from A358, between Taunton and Ilminster turn into Hatch Beauchamp for hotel in village centre

PETS: Bedrooms (one bedroom only) (unattended) Exercise area (0.5 mile) **RESIDENT PETS:** Guinness & Murphy (Pointers)

This delightful family run hotel, set in its own extensive gardens in a peaceful village location, offers comfortable accommodation combined with all the character and charm of a building dating back over 200 years. The atmosphere is relaxed and friendly and innovative menus feature best quality local ingredients.
ROOMS: 10 en suite (2 fmly) (1 GF) No smoking in all bedrooms s £75-£90; d £105-£135 (incl. bkfst) **LB** **FACILITIES:** Xmas
PARKING: 22 **NOTES:** No smoking in restaurant
CARDS: ⬛⬛⬛⬛⬛

◆◆◆◆ Blorenge House

57 Staple Grove Rd TA1 1DG
☎ 01823 283005 📠 01823 283005
e-mail: enquiries@blorengehouse.co.uk
Dir: M5 junct 25 towards cricket ground and Safeways on left. At traffic lights turn left, at 2nd lights turn right, Blorenge House 150yds on left

PETS: Bedrooms Public areas (Not dining rooms) Exercise area (150 yards)

Conveniently situated within walking distance of the town centre, this fine old Victorian property offers spacious accommodation. The individually furnished bedrooms are well-equipped and some feature impressive four-poster beds. A bar-lounge, garden and outdoor swimming pool are available for guests, and evening meals are provided by prior arrangement.
FACILITIES: 25 rms (20 en suite) (4 fmly) (3 GF) No smoking in 23 bedrooms No smoking in dining room TVB tea/coffee Licensed Cen ht TVL Outdoor swimming pool (heated) **PRICES:** s fr £29; d fr £49✱ **LB** **PARKING:** 25 **CARDS:** ⬛⬛⬛⬛⬛

England

TAUNTON continued

◆◆◆◆ Gatchells
Angersleigh TA3 7SY
☎ 01823 421580 & 07808 164276
e-mail: info@gatchells.org.uk
Dir: from Trull just S of Taunton, turn right signed Angersleigh into Dipford Rd, follow for 2m. Gatchells marked on right, take country track to cottage at end

PETS: Bedrooms Exercise area

This delightful, thatched, early 15th-century former farmhouse nestles at the foot of the Blackdown Hills. Gatchells is surrounded by peaceful cottage gardens, which boast a super outdoor pool. The accommodation is cosy and comfortable, with many original features. Dinner, by prior arrangement, is served in the conservatory.
FACILITIES: 3 rms (2 en suite) (1 fmly) No smoking in bedrooms No smoking in dining room No smoking in lounges TVB tea/coffee TVL No coaches Outdoor swimming pool Dinner Last d 10am
PRICES: s £35-£45; d £46-£60✳ **LB PARKING:** 3 **CARDS:** 🔲 🔲

◆◆◆◆ 🍽 Meryan House Hotel
Bishop's Hull TA1 5EG
☎ 01823 337445 📠 01823 322355
e-mail: meryanhousehotel@btclick.com
Dir: from Taunton A38 to Wellington. After crematorium on left, 1st right, house approx 600yds

PETS: Bedrooms (unattended) Exercise area (300 yards)
RESIDENT PETS: Spike & Bubbles (Dandie Dinmont)

Located in a pretty village setting just over a mile from the centre of town, this 17th-century property has delightful individually furnished rooms. The comfortable bedrooms feature many antiques along with modern facilities. Interesting and varied dishes are available at dinner and there is also a cosy bar and a spacious lounge.
FACILITIES: 12 en suite (2 fmly) (2 GF) No smoking in 4 bedrooms No smoking in dining room No smoking in 1 lounge STV TVB tea/coffee Direct dial from bedrooms Licensed Cen ht TVL No coaches Dinner Last d 7.30pm **PRICES:** s £53-£58; d £60-£90✳ **LB PARKING:** 17
CARDS: 🔲 🔲 🔲 🔲 🔲

WELLINGTON
Map 03 ST12

★★★ ◎◎ ♣♠ Bindon Country House Hotel & Restaurant
Langford Budville TA21 0RU
☎ 01823 400070 📠 01823 400071
e-mail: stay@bindon.com
Dir: from Wellington B3187 to Langford Budville, through village, right towards Wiveliscombe, right at junct, pass Bindon Farm, right after 450yds

PETS: Bedrooms (stables nearby) (unattended)
Exercise area (5 mins walk 220-acre nature reserve) Pet Food

This delightful country retreat is set in seven acres of formal woodland gardens. Mentioned in the Domesday Book, it offers peace and tranquillity, the perfect antidote to stress. Bedrooms are named after battles fought by the Duke of Wellington and each is individually decorated with sumptuous fabrics and equipped with

continued

---

useful extras. Elegance, style and comfort can all be found within the public rooms, and the dining room is the venue for impressive and accomplished cuisine.
ROOMS: 12 en suite (2 fmly) (1 GF) No smoking in all bedrooms s fr £95; d £115-£215 (incl. bkfst) **FACILITIES:** Outdoor swimming (H) Tennis (hard) Croquet lawn entertainment ch fac Xmas **PARKING:** 30
NOTES: No smoking in restaurant
CARDS: 🔲 🔲 🔲 🔲 🔲 🔲

★★★ 67% The Cleve Hotel & Country Club
Mantle St TA21 8SN
☎ 01823 662033 📠 01823 660874
e-mail: reception@clevehotel.com
Dir: M5 junct 26 follow signs to Wellington, then left before Total Petrol Station upon leaving town

PETS: Bedrooms £10 **RESIDENT PETS:** George - Red Boxer

Offering comfortable bedrooms and public areas, The Cleve Hotel is quietly located in an elevated position above the town. The atmosphere is relaxed and guests can enjoy Mediterranean-influenced cuisine in the stylish restaurant. Extensive leisure facilities are available including a heated indoor pool, well-equipped gym, sauna, and snooker table.
ROOMS: 20 en suite (5 fmly) (3 GF) No smoking in all bedrooms s £55-£79.50; d £70-£95.50 (incl. bkfst) **LB FACILITIES:** Spa Indoor swimming (H) Snooker Sauna Solarium Gym **PARKING:** 60
NOTES: No smoking in restaurant **CARDS:** 🔲 🔲 🔲 🔲 🔲

WELLS
Map 03 ST54

★★ 72% White Hart
Sadler St BA5 2RR
☎ 01749 672056 📠 01749 671074
e-mail: info@whitehart-wells.co.uk
Dir: Sadler St is the start of the one-way system. Hotel opposite the cathedral

THE INDEPENDENTS

PETS: Bedrooms (unattended) Exercise area

This former coaching inn dates back to the 15th century. The bedrooms, some in an adjoining former stable block, offer comfortable, modern accommodation. Public areas include a refurbished guest lounge, together with a popular restaurant and cosy bar. The newly styled restaurant serves mainly fish, plus daily specials and meat and vegetarian dishes.
ROOMS: 15 en suite (3 fmly) (2 GF) No smoking in 5 bedrooms s £72.50-£77.50; d £92.50-£102.50 (incl. bkfst) **LB FACILITIES:** ch fac Xmas **PARKING:** 17 **NOTES:** No smoking in restaurant
CARDS: 🔲 🔲 🔲 🔲 🔲 🔲

Please mention AA Pet Friendly Places to Stay when booking

All information was correct at the time of going to press; we recommend you confirm details on booking

★★ 71% **Ancient Gate House**
20 Sadler St BA5 2SE
☎ 01749 672029 ▧ 01749 670319
e-mail: info@ancientgatehouse.co.uk
Dir: *1st hotel on left on Cathedral Green, overlooking the West Front of the Cathedral*

PETS: Bedrooms Public areas (Except restaurant) Exercise area (10 metres)

Guests are treated to good old-fashioned hospitality in a friendly informal atmosphere at this charming hotel. Bedrooms, many of which boast unrivalled cathedral views and four-poster beds, are well equipped and furnished in keeping with the age and character of the building. The hotel's Rugantino Restaurant remains popular, offering typically Italian specialities and some traditional English dishes.

ROOMS: 9 en suite No smoking in 2 bedrooms s £67.50-£72.50; d £82.50 (incl. bkfst) **LB FACILITIES:** Xmas **NOTES:** No smoking in restaurant **CARDS:** ▨▨▨▨▨▨▨

★★ 67% **Crown at Wells**
Market Place BA5 2RP
☎ 01749 673457 ▧ 01749 679792
e-mail: reception@crownatwells.co.uk
Dir: *in Market Place, follow signs for Hotels/Deliveries*

PETS: Bedrooms Public areas (allowed in lounge only) Exercise area (50 mins walk)

Retaining its original features and period charm, this historic old inn is situated in the heart of Wells, just a short stroll from the cathedral. Bedrooms vary in size and style and have modern facilities. Public areas focus around Anton's, the popular bistro, with its bold paintings and relaxed atmosphere, and the Penn Bar, an alternative eating option.

ROOMS: 15 en suite (1 fmly) No smoking in all bedrooms s £50-£80; d £80-£95 (incl. bkfst) **LB PARKING:** 15 **NOTES:** No smoking in restaurant RS 25 Dec food not available in the evening **CARDS:** ▨▨▨▨▨▨▨

♦♦♦♦ **Infield House**
36 Portway BA5 2BN
☎ 01749 670989 ▧ 01749 679093
e-mail: infield@talk21.com
Dir: *from city centre, on right of A371, driveway immediately after lights at junction with Strawberry Way*

PETS: Bedrooms Exercise area (0.5 mile) food can be provided with advance notice **RESIDENT PETS:** Poppy - Pembroke Corgi

This charming Victorian house offers comfortable, spacious rooms of elegance and style. The friendly hosts are very welcoming and provide a relaxing home from home. Guests may bring their pets, by prior arrangement. Dinners, also by prior arrangement, are

continued

served in the pleasant dining room where good home cooking ensures an enjoyable and varied range of options.

FACILITIES: 3 en suite No smoking TVB tea/coffee Cen ht TVL No children 12yrs No coaches Leisure centre nearby Dinner Last d 10.30am **PRICES:** d £46-£52✳ **PARKING:** 3 **CARDS:** ▨▨▨▨▨▨

WESTON-SUPER-MARE   Map 03 ST36

★★ 68% **Madeira Cove Hotel**
32-34 Birnbeck Rd BS23 2BX
☎ 01934 626707 ▧ 01934 624882
e-mail: madeiracove@telco4u.net
Dir: *signs to Western Seafront, follow Madeira Cove sign, north towards Kenstoke and Sand Bay, pass Grand Pier, hotel on right*

PETS: Bedrooms Public areas Exercise area water bowl provided in summer

Within easy walking distance of the town centre, this popular and friendly hotel enjoys an ideal location overlooking the sea. It provides comfortable and well-equipped accommodation. A good range of food is offered in the spacious restaurant and in addition to the bar, a separate upper floor lounge is available to guests.

ROOMS: 22 rms (21 en suite) 4 annexe en suite (2 fmly) No smoking in 3 bedrooms s £30-£45; d £60-£80 (incl. bkfst) **LB FACILITIES:** Xmas **SERVICES:** Lift **NOTES:** No smoking in restaurant **CARDS:** ▨▨▨▨▨▨

♦♦♦♦ **Braeside**
2 Victoria Park BS23 2HZ
☎ 01934 626642 ▧ 01934 626642
e-mail: braeside@tesco.net
Dir: *with sea on left, take 1st right after Winter Gardens then 1st left into Lower Church Rd. Victoria Park on right after left bend*

PETS: Bedrooms (unattended) Public areas (except dining area) Exercise area (100yds)

This small, quietly located hotel is a short stroll from the town centre and sea front. Bedrooms are comfortably furnished and well equipped, some enjoying fine views over Weston Bay. In addition to a well-laid out dining room, there is a comfortable lounge. Unrestricted on-street parking is available.

FACILITIES: 9 en suite (3 fmly) No smoking TVB tea/coffee Cen ht No coaches **PRICES:** s £30-£32; d £60-£64 **LB NOTES:** Closed Xmas & New Year

WINCANTON — Map 03 ST72

★★★ 78% ◎◎ Holbrook House
Holbrook BA9 8BS
☎ 01963 824466 ▤ 01963 32681
e-mail: reception@holbrookhouse.co.uk
Dir: from A303 at Wincanton, turn left on A371 towards Castle Cary and Shepton Mallet

PETS: Bedrooms (unattended) Exercise area Pet Food Any requirements can be met **RESIDENT PETS:** Pepsi - tabby cat

This handsome country house offers a unique blend of quality and comfort combined with a friendly atmosphere. Set in peaceful gardens and wooded grounds, Holbrook House is the perfect retreat. The restaurant provides a selection of innovative dishes prepared with enthusiasm and served by a team of caring staff.
ROOMS: 16 en suite 5 annexe en suite (2 fmly) s £135-£275; d £135-£275 (incl. bkfst) **LB FACILITIES:** STV Indoor swimming (H) Tennis (hard & grass) Sauna Solarium Gym Croquet lawn Jacuzzi Beauty treatment entertainment ch fac Xmas **PARKING:** 100
NOTES: No smoking in restaurant **CARDS:** 🌑 🌑 🌑 🌑 🌑

WINSFORD — Map 03 SS93

♦♦♦♦ ◎ ➔ Karslake House
Halse Ln TA24 7JE
☎ 01643 851242 ▤ 01643 851242
e-mail: enquiries@karslakehouse.co.uk
Dir: leave A396 (Winsford). In village turn L beyond village stores signed Karslake Hse. Around corner 50yds on R

PETS: Telephone for details

This small country hotel is situated in a peaceful Exmoor village, making it an ideal base for touring the area. Bedrooms have been thoughtfully furnished and a number of extra touches have been added. Public rooms feature original beams and fireplaces and include a dining room where interesting menus offer a selection of delicious meals.
FACILITIES: 6 rms (5 en suite) (1 GF) No smoking TVB tea/coffee Licensed Cen ht No children 12yrs No coaches Riding, shooting, fishing on request, jeep safari Dinner Last d 8.15pm **PRICES:** d £71-£106✶ **PARKING:** 15 **NOTES:** Closed Feb and Mar **CARDS:** 🌑 🌑 🌑

All abbreviations are explained on page 9

WITHYPOOL — Map 03 SS83

★★ 75% ◎ Royal Oak Inn
TA24 7QP
☎ 01643 831506 ▤ 01643 831659
e-mail: enquiries@royaloakwithypool.co.uk
Dir: 7m N of Dulverton, off B3223

PETS: Bedrooms Sep Accom (kennel) (unattended) £5 Public areas (not in restaurant) Exercise area (10 mins walk) Pet Food

For centuries this old inn has provided travellers with food, drink and shelter. Lovers of the great outdoors will find this an ideal base for exploration. Bedrooms are comfortable and each displays individuality and charm. Public areas include a choice of bars, complete with beams and crackling log fires, and the Acorn Restaurant is the venue for accomplished cuisine with an emphasis on local produce.
ROOMS: 8 rms (7 en suite) s £50-£55; d £100-£110 (incl. bkfst) **FACILITIES:** Riding Shooting Safaris arranged Xmas **PARKING:** 20
NOTES: No smoking in restaurant **CARDS:** 🌑 🌑 🌑 🌑

YEOVIL — Map 03 ST51

★★ 62% Preston
64 Preston Rd BA20 2DL
☎ 01935 474400 ▤ 01935 410142
e-mail: prestonhotelyeo@aol.co.uk
Dir: A303 onto A3088, left at 1st rdbt, over 2nd rdbt & right at 3rd rdbt

PETS: Bedrooms (unattended) Public areas Exercise area (0.5 mile) Pet Food

A relaxed and friendly atmosphere has been maintained at this popular hotel, which has undergone upgrading of the bedrooms and public areas. Well suited to both business and leisure guests, a spacious bar and cosy restaurant are available where home-cooked meals satisfy the heartiest of appetites.
ROOMS: 6 en suite 7 annexe en suite (1 fmly) (7 GF) s fr £45; d fr £55 (incl. bkfst) **PARKING:** 22 **NOTES:** No smoking in restaurant
CARDS: 🌑 🌑 🌑 🌑 🌑 🌑

YEOVILTON — Map 03 ST52

♦♦♦♦ ❤ Cary Fitzpaine Farm
BA22 8JB
☎ 01458 223250 ▤ 01458 223372
e-mail: acrang@aol.com
Dir: from junct A303/A37 at Podimore take A37 (Bristol/Shepton Mallet) for 1m. Take 1st R (Cary Fitzpaine), follow rd to farm

PETS: Bedrooms Sep Accom (downstairs utility room) (unattended) £3 - dogs, small pets free Exercise area Water bowl provided, large grounds **RESIDENT PETS:** 2 Golden Retrievers - Muffin & Toffy, 2 Jack Russells - Cookie & Tessa, guinea pigs, horses & chickens

Surrounded by 600 acres of mixed farmland, this charming farmhouse dates back to Georgian times. The comfortable bedrooms are well equipped and fitted with modern facilities.

continued

Breakfast is served at separate tables, and on sunny mornings can be enjoyed on the veranda.

FACILITIES: 3 en suite (1 fmly) No smoking TVB tea/coffee Cen ht TVL Fishing 600 acres cattle sheep horses chickens **PRICES:** s £35-£40; d £55-£65✳ **LB PARKING:** 6 **NOTES:** Closed 23-26 Dec **CARDS:**

STAFFORDSHIRE

ABBOTS BROMLEY
Map 07 SK02

◆◆◆ ❦ Marsh Farm
WS15 3EJ
☎ 01283 840323
e-mail: marshfarm@meads1967.co.uk
Dir: 1m N of Abbots Bromley on B5013

PETS: Bedrooms Exercise area (nearby)

Guests at this working farm are welcome to walk around the fields and watch the activities. The farmhouse has been sympathetically modernised and bedrooms are tastefully furnished and equipped with thoughtful extras. Comprehensive breakfasts are taken in a spacious cottage-style dining room, which also enjoys a good reputation as a tea room during the warmer months.
FACILITIES: 2 rms (1 fmly) No smoking in dining room TVB tea/coffee Cen ht 20 acres mixed **PRICES:** s £23-£25; d £44-£46✳ **PARKING:** 8 **NOTES:** Closed Dec

ALTON
Map 07 SK04

◆◆◆ Chained Oak Farm
Farley Ln ST10 4BZ
☎ 01538 702104 🖷 01538 702104
e-mail: cross@barn.fslife.co.uk
Dir: follow signs for Alton Towers theme park. Chained Oak farm is located between Alton village and Farley opposite Alton Towers.

PETS: Sep Accom (Stable) Horses - £10

This modern detached house stands in delightful grounds and affords fine all round views. It is very close to Alton Towers and offers spacious comfortable, ground-floor accommodation, together with attentive service.
FACILITIES: 2 rms (1 en suite) (1 fmly) (2 GF) No smoking TVB tea/coffee Cen ht No coaches **PRICES:** s £25-£35; d £45✳ **LB PARKING:** 10

BURTON UPON TRENT
Map 08 SK22

★★ 72% **Riverside**
Riverside Dr, Branston DE14 3EP
☎ 01283 511234 🖷 01283 511441
e-mail: riverside.branston@oldenglishinns.co.uk
Dir: follow signs for Branston on A5121 until small humped bridge, over bridge and right turn into Warren Lane. Second left into Riverside Drive

PETS: Bedrooms (unattended) Exercise area (5 yards)

With its quiet residential location and well-kept terraced garden stretching down to the River Trent, this hotel has all the ingredients for a relaxing stay. Many of the tables in the Garden Room restaurant have views over the garden. Bedrooms are tastefully furnished and decorated and provide a good range of extras.
ROOMS: 22 en suite (10 GF) No smoking in all bedrooms s £60-£80; d £80-£90 (incl. bkfst) **LB FACILITIES:** STV Fishing ch fac Xmas **PARKING:** 200 **NOTES:** No smoking in restaurant **CARDS:**

CHEDDLETON
Map 07 SJ95

◆◆◆◆ Prospect House
334 Cheadle Rd ST13 7BW
☎ 0870 756 4155 🖷 0870 756 4155
e-mail: prospect@talk21.com
Dir: 4m S of Leek on A520

PETS: Bedrooms (unattended) £4 Public areas (except dining rooms) Exercise area (20 metres)

Prospect House was built from local stone in 1838. It stands on the A520 between Cheddleton and Wetley Rocks. Bedrooms are located in a converted coach house to the rear of the house and facilities include a traditionally furnished dining room together with a cosy lounge and a pleasant garden with a conservatory which guests are welcome to use.
FACILITIES: 5 en suite (3 fmly) (2 GF) No smoking in bedrooms No smoking in dining room No smoking in 1 lounge TVB tea/coffee Direct dial from bedrooms Cen ht TVL No coaches Dinner Last d 3pm **PRICES:** s £22-£24; d £44-£48✳ **LB PARKING:** 5 **CARDS:**

LICHFIELD
Map 07 SK10

★★★ 68% **The George**
12-14 Bird St WS13 6PR
☎ 01543 414822 🖷 01543 415817
e-mail: mail@thegeorgelichfield.co.uk
Dir: from Bowling Green Island on A461 take Lichfield exit. Left at next island into Swan Road and where road bears left, turn right for George Hotel straight ahead

PETS: Bedrooms £5

Situated in the city centre, this privately owned hotel has been extensively refurbished by the new owners to provide good quality, well-equipped accommodation, which includes a room with a four-poster bed. Facilities here include a large ballroom, plus several other rooms for meetings and functions.
ROOMS: 36 en suite (6 fmly) No smoking in 24 bedrooms s £47-£106; d £74-£120 (incl. bkfst) **LB SERVICES:** Lift **PARKING:** 45 **NOTES:** No smoking in restaurant **CARDS:**

England

STAFFORD
Map 07 SJ92

◆◆◆◆ ◀ Yew Tree Inn & Restaurant
Long Compton, Ranton ST18 9JT
☎ 01785 282278 📠 01785 282278
Dir: take A518 Stafford-Newport road, on entering Haughton take right turn just before Shropshire Inn into Station Rd, after 2.5m inn on right

PETS: Bedrooms £10 Exercise area (in grounds)
RESIDENT PETS: Charlie (Mongrel Terrier)

Quietly set in lovely gardens, this delightful inn started life as a farmhouse in the 17th century and character filled bars still display many original features. Bedrooms are attractively decorated and neatly furnished. As well as a good range of bar food, there is a spacious and attractive restaurant serving a range of international dishes.
FACILITIES: 3 en suite (1 fmly) No smoking in bedrooms No smoking in dining room No smoking in 1 lounge TVB tea/coffee Cen ht Fishing Dinner Last d 9.15pm **PRICES:** s £45-£50; d £65-£70✶ **LB**
PARKING: 60 **CARDS:** 🖭 💳 💳 💳 🔽 🧾

STOKE-ON-TRENT
Map 07 SJ84

★★★ 66% ☺ Haydon House
Haydon St, Basford ST4 6JD
☎ 01782 711311 📠 01782 717470
e-mail: enquiries@haydon-house-hotel.co.uk
Dir: M6 junct 15 A500 to Stoke-on-Trent, turn onto A53 Hanley/Newcastle, at rdbt 1st exit, up hill, 2nd left at top of hill before traffic lights

PETS: Bedrooms Public areas (not in restaurant)
Exercise area (300 yards)

A Victorian property, within easy reach of Newcastle-under-Lyme. The public rooms are furnished in a style befitting the age and character of the house and bedrooms have modern furnishings; several rooms are located in a separate house across the road. The hotel has a good reputation for its food and is popular with locals.
ROOMS: 17 en suite 6 annexe en suite (4 fmly) s £65; d £85 (incl. bkfst) **PARKING:** 52 **NOTES:** No smoking in restaurant
CARDS: 🖭 💳 💳 💳 💳 🔽 🧾

TAMWORTH
Map 07 SK20

◆◆◆◆◆ ≩ ❣ Oak Tree Farm
Hints Rd, Hopwas B78 3AA
☎ 01827 56807 & 67271 📠 01827 56807
Dir: take A51 Lichfield to Tamworth road & turn into Hints Road at Tame Otter pub. Last house on left where road divides

PETS: Bedrooms (unattended) Exercise area (surrounding fields) RESIDENT PETS: Una (Greyhound)

Chickens, wild fowl and family pets provide an additional welcome at this sympathetically restored period farmhouse, located in peaceful rural surroundings. Spacious, tastefully furnished bedrooms are filled with both practical and homely extras. The elegant dining room, adorned with fine oriental artefacts, is the perfect setting for memorable breakfasts and a small conference

continued

room is also available. A convenient car journey from the NEC in Birmingham.
FACILITIES: 2 en suite 5 annexe en suite (2 GF) No smoking TVB tea/coffee Direct dial from bedrooms Cen ht No children 16yrs Indoor swimming pool (heated) Fishing Sauna Croquet lawn Steam room 4 acres non-working **PRICES:** s £57-£67; d £75-£100✶ **PARKING:** 10
NOTES: Closed Xmas & New Year **CARDS:** 🖭 💳 💳 💳 🔽 🧾

◆◆◆◆ The Old Rectory
Churchside, Harlaston B79 9HE
☎ 01827 383583 📠 01827 383583
Dir: in the centre of Harlaston, 4.5m N of Tamworth

PETS: Bedrooms £2 Public areas Exercise area (50 yards)
RESIDENT PETS: Jake - Jack Russell

This former Victorian rectory stands in the heart of this pretty, award-winning village. A range of bedrooms, furnished in quality pine with pretty co-ordinating fabrics, offer thoughtful extras, and imaginative breakfasts are taken in a spacious sunny kitchen dining room overlooking the immaculate garden.
FACILITIES: 4 rms (3 en suite) No smoking TVB tea/coffee Cen ht No coaches Croquet lawn **PARKING:** 7

UTTOXETER
Map 07 SK03

◆◆◆ Oldroyd Guest House & Motel
18-22 Bridge St ST14 8AP
☎ 01889 562763 📠 01889 568916
e-mail: enquiries@oldroyd-guesthouse.com
Dir: situated on the A518, close to Uttoxeter Race Course

PETS: Bedrooms (unattended) Exercise area (500yds)
RESIDENT PETS: Billy - canary

This privately owned and personally run guesthouse is conveniently close to the town centre and only eight miles from Alton Towers. Bedrooms are well equipped with modern facilities, and some family and ground floor rooms are available. Breakfast is served at separate tables in the bright and pleasant breakfast room.
FACILITIES: 12 rms (10 en suite) 3 annexe en suite (7 fmly) (5 GF) No smoking in bedrooms No smoking in dining room TVB tea/coffee Cen ht TVL **PRICES:** s £25-£30; d £48-£55✶ **LB PARKING:** 20
CARDS: 🖭 💳 💳 🔽 🧾

SUFFOLK

ALDEBURGH
Map 05 TM45

★★★ 77% ◎◎ **The Brudenell**
The Parade IP15 5BU
☎ 01728 452071 ▤ 01728 454082
e-mail: info@brudenellhotel.co.uk
Dir: A12/A1094, on reaching town, turn right at junct into High St. Hotel on seafront adjoining Fort Green car park

PETS: Bedrooms (unattended) £5 Public areas (Not bar, lounge or restaurant) Pet Food

Situated at the far end of the town centre just a step away from the beach. The hotel has a contemporary appearance, enhanced by subtle lighting and quality soft furnishings. Many of the bedrooms have superb sea views; they include deluxe rooms with king-sized beds and superior rooms suitable for families.
ROOMS: 42 en suite (15 fmly) No smoking in all bedrooms s £63-£94; d £98-£192 (incl. bkfst) **LB FACILITIES:** STV Xmas **SERVICES:** Lift
PARKING: 20 **NOTES:** No smoking in restaurant
CARDS: ▨▨ ▨▨ ▨▨ ▨▨ ▨▨ ▨

★★★ 77% ◎ **White Lion**
Market Cross Place IP15 5BJ
☎ 01728 452720 ▤ 01728 452986
e-mail: whitelionaldeburgh@btinternet.com
Dir: Follow signs to Aldeburgh & town centre. At x-rds left, hotel is in Market Cross Place

Best Western

PETS: Bedrooms £5 per dog Pet Food Doggie bowl and treat

A popular 15th-century hotel situated at the quiet end of town overlooking the sea. Bedrooms are pleasantly decorated and thoughtfully equipped, many rooms have lovely sea views. Public areas include two lounges and an elegant restaurant where locally caught fish and seafood are served. There is also a modern brasserie.
ROOMS: 38 en suite (1 fmly) No smoking in 19 bedrooms s £73.50-£102; d £114-£164 (incl. bkfst) **LB FACILITIES:** STV Xmas
PARKING: 15 **NOTES:** No smoking in restaurant
CARDS: ▨▨ ▨▨ ▨▨ ▨▨ ▨▨ ▨

★★★ 76% ◎ **Wentworth**
Wentworth Rd IP15 5BD
☎ 01728 452312 ▤ 01728 454343
e-mail: stay@wentworth-aldeburgh.co.uk
Dir: off A12 onto A1094, 6m to Aldeburgh, leave church on left & left at bottom of hill

PETS: Bedrooms (unattended) £2.50 Public areas (except restaurant) Exercise area (500 yards)

A delightful privately owned hotel overlooking the beach and sea beyond. The attractive, well-maintained public rooms include three stylish lounges as well as a bar and elegant restaurant. Bedrooms are smartly decorated with co-ordinated fabrics and have many thoughtful touches; some rooms have superb sea

continued

views. Several very spacious Mediterranean-style rooms are located across the road.

ROOMS: 28 en suite 7 annexe en suite (5 GF) No smoking in all bedrooms s £59-£85; d £93-£190 (incl. bkfst) **LB FACILITIES:** STV ch fac Xmas **PARKING:** 30 **NOTES:** No smoking in restaurant
CARDS: ▨▨ ▨▨ ▨▨ ▨▨ ▨▨ ▨

BARNINGHAM
Map 05 TL97

◆◆◆◆ **College House Farm**
Bardwell Rd, Barningham IP31 1DF
☎ 01359 221512 ▤ 01359 221512
e-mail: jackie.brightwell@talk21.com
Dir: A14/A143/B1111 to Garboldisham and Barningham. In village turn left at 1st crossroad by village store, immediately left again into Bardwell Rd

PETS: Bedrooms Exercise area (3 miles)
RESIDENT PETS: 5 cats - Luther, Bliss, Lenny, Jude & Seamus, 4 horses - Ocre, Cat, Ryan & Dillon

Expect a warm welcome at this charming Grade II listed Jacobean property, which is situated in a peaceful location close to Bury St Edmunds. The building has an abundance of original character and features fine period furnishings. Bedrooms are generally quite spacious and thoughtfully equipped. Public rooms include an elegant dining room and a cosy lounge.
FACILITIES: 4 rms (1 en suite) 2 annexe en suite (4 fmly) No smoking TVB tea/coffee Cen ht No children 5yrs No coaches Croquet lawn Dinner Last d by arrangement **PRICES:** s £30; d £30-£60✱ **LB BB**
PARKING: 8 **CARDS:** ▨▨

BUNGAY
Map 05 TM38

◆◆◆◆ 🛏 ❦ **Earsham Park Farm**
Old Railway Rd, Earsham NR35 2AQ
☎ 01986 892180 ▤ 01986 894796
e-mail: aa@earsham-parkfarm.co.uk
Dir: 3m SW of Bungay on A143, on right side of road in SW direction

PETS: Bedrooms £5 (dog), £10 (horse) Exercise area (20 metres) **RESIDENT PETS:** Widget (Jack Russell)

Superb detached Victorian property overlooking open countryside and forming part of a working farm. The property has been sympathetically restored by the present owners and retains many original features. Bedrooms and public areas are attractively furnished and breakfast features home-made produce including sausages and bacon from organically reared pigs.
FACILITIES: 3 en suite No smoking TVB tea/coffee Cen ht 589 acres arable / pigs **PRICES:** s £38-£58; d £58-£78✱ **PARKING:** 11
CARDS: ▨▨ ▨▨ ▨▨ ▨▨ ▨

BURY ST EDMUNDS

Map 05 TL86

★★★ 75% ◉ ♨ Ravenwood Hall

Rougham IP30 9JA

☎ 01359 270345 🖹 01359 270788

e-mail: enquiries@ravenwoodhall.co.uk

Dir: 3m E off A14

PETS: Bedrooms Public areas (except restaurant) Exercise area (directly outside rooms) Pet Food food by prior request - a charge will be made; special dog area and pet loo RESIDENT PETS: Bargain - cat, pygmy goats, geese

Delightful 15th-century property set in seven acres of woodland and landscaped gardens. The building has many original features including carved timbers and inglenook fireplaces. The spacious bedrooms are attractively decorated, tastefully furnished with well-chosen pieces and equipped with many thoughtful touches. Public rooms include an elegant restaurant and a smart lounge bar with an open fire.

ROOMS: 7 en suite 7 annexe en suite (5 GF) No smoking in all bedrooms s £81-£109; d £106-£149 (incl. bkfst) **LB**

FACILITIES: Outdoor swimming (H) Riding Croquet lawn Shooting & fishing ch fac Xmas **PARKING:** 150 **NOTES:** No smoking in restaurant **CARDS:** ▦▦▦▦▦▦ ⑤

♦♦♦♦ The Fox & Hounds

Felsham Rd, Bradfield St George IP30 0AB

☎ 01284 386379

e-mail: bradfieldfox@aol.com

Dir: turn off A134 Bury to Sudbury Rd, at Sicklesmere take turning to Little Welnetham and Bradfield St George

PETS: Bedrooms Public areas (Only in bar) Exercise area (2 acre paddock on site) Many paths and woods RESIDENT PETS: Sacha and Izzles - labradors, Dennis - Persian cat

Delightful inn set in a peaceful location amid open countryside. The spacious bedrooms are in a converted barn to the rear of the inn; each one has pine furniture and a good range of useful extras. Public areas include a smart restaurant, a cosy bar and a small conservatory.

FACILITIES: 2 annexe en suite (2 GF) No smoking in bedrooms No smoking in dining room TVB tea/coffee Licensed Cen ht Petanque pitch Dinner Last d 9pm **PRICES:** d £49.95-£79.95✳ **PARKING:** 30 **NOTES:** Closed 2-9 Jan **CARDS:** ▦▦▦▦ ⑤

ELMSWELL

Map 05 TL96

♦♦♦ Kiln Farm

Kiln Ln IP30 9QR

☎ 01359 240442 & 242604

e-mail: paul-jacky@kilnfarm.fsnet.co.uk

Dir: at junct 47 (Ixworth turnoff) of A14. Approx 1m

PETS: Bedrooms Public areas Exercise area (adjacent)

Delightful Victorian farmhouse set in a peaceful rural location amid three acres of landscaped grounds with lovely views. Bedrooms are housed in a converted barn; each is pleasantly decorated and furnished in country style. Breakfast is served in the

continued

open plan dining room/bar and guests have the use of a cosy lounge.

FACILITIES: 3 en suite 4 annexe en suite (1 fmly) (4 GF) No smoking in bedrooms No smoking in area of dining room No smoking in 1 lounge TV4B tea/coffee Cen ht No coaches Dinner Last d 9pm **PRICES:** s £25-£30; d £48-£55✳ **PARKING:** 10 **CARDS:** ▦▦▦▦▦▦ ⑤

FRAMLINGHAM

Map 05 TM26

♦♦♦ ♥ Church Farm

Church Rd, Kettleburgh IP13 7LF

☎ 01728 723532

e-mail: jbater@suffolkonline.net

Dir: from A12 northbound take 2nd left to Wickham market, follow signs to Easton Farm Park then to Kettleburgh 1.25m, house behind church

PETS: Public areas (if other guests approve) Exercise area (adjacent) RESIDENT PETS: Minnie (Jack Russell), Jessie (Labrador), Boots (Border/Jack Russell)

Charming 300-year-old farmhouse situated close to the village church amid superb grounds featuring a duck pond, mature shrubs and sweeping lawns. The property has been sympathetically converted and retains exposed beams and open fireplaces. Bedrooms are pleasantly decorated and equipped with useful extras; a ground-floor bedroom is available.

FACILITIES: 3 rms (1 en suite) (1 GF) No smoking in bedrooms No smoking in dining room tea/coffee No dogs Cen ht TVL Fishing Clay pigeon shooting 70 acres mixed Dinner Last d 7.30pm **PRICES:** s £23-£25; d £46-£50✳ **PARKING:** 10

HADLEIGH

Map 05 TM04

♦♦♦♦♦ Edgehall Hotel

2 High St IP7 5AP

☎ 01473 822458 🖹 01473 827751

e-mail: r.rolfe@edgehall-hotel.co.uk

Dir: 5m N of Colchester, left onto B1070, continue 5.5m to Hadleigh. 1st property in High St on right

PETS: Bedrooms (Annexe only) Public areas (not in the dining room) Exercise area (500 yards) RESIDENT PETS: Treacle (Poodle)

This imposing 16th-century building is situated at the quiet end of the high street and has been run by the same family for over 25 years. The spacious bedrooms are individually decorated and tastefully furnished in period style; one room has a superb four-poster bed. Breakfast is served in the elegant dining room and guests have the use of a comfortably furnished lounge.

FACILITIES: 8 rms (6 en suite) (2 fmly) (1 GF) No smoking in 6 bedrooms No smoking in dining room No smoking in lounges TVB tea/coffee Licensed Cen ht No coaches Croquet lawn **PRICES:** s £40-£55; d £55-£100✳ **LB** **PARKING:** 20

🍺 **Places with this symbol are pubs**

HINTLESHAM

Map 05 TM04

★★★★ ◎◎◎ Hintlesham Hall
George St IP8 3NS
☎ 01473 652334 ▤ 01473 652463
e-mail: reservations@hintleshamhall.com
Dir: *4m W of Ipswich on B1071 to Hadleigh and Sudbury*

> **PETS:** Bedrooms Exercise area (In the grounds) Pet Food
> Dog food provided with prior notice

Hospitality and service are key features at this imposing Grade I listed country house hotel, situated in 175 acres of grounds and landscaped gardens. Individually decorated bedrooms offer a high degree of comfort; each one is tastefully furnished and equipped with many thoughtful touches. The spacious public rooms include an elegant restaurant, which serves fine classical cuisine.
ROOMS: 33 en suite (10 GF) s £98-£195; d £120-£220 (incl. cont bkfst)
LB FACILITIES: Outdoor swimming (H) Golf 18 Tennis (hard) Sauna
Gym Croquet lawn Putting green Jacuzzi Xmas **PARKING:** 60
NOTES: No smoking in restaurant RS Sat
CARDS: ▨▨ ▨▨ ▨▨ ▨ ▨▨ ▨

HORRINGER

Map 05 TL86

★★★★ 77% ◎◎ The Ickworth
IP29 5QE
☎ 01284 735350 ▤ 01284 736300
e-mail: info@ickworthhotel.com
Dir: *Follow brown signs for Ickworth House, take 4th exit at rdbt, follow this road to staggered x-rds. Continue straight until t-junct, turn left into village & almost immediately turn right into Ickworth Estate*

> **PETS:** Bedrooms (unattended) £7 per stay Public areas
> (not in restaurant or food areas) Exercise area (1800 acres
> on estate) **RESIDENT PETS:** Truffle (Black Labrador)

This stunning property manages to combine a current National Trust property with clever retro design and still be child friendly. The combination of friendly and easygoing staff, a children's den, horses and bikes to ride, and wonderful 'Capability' Brown gardens to roam is the winning formula. Quality produce and technical skill are behind the inspiring food here.
ROOMS: 27 en suite 11 annexe en suite (35 fmly) (4 GF) No smoking in 35 bedrooms s £175.50-£486; d £195-£540 (incl. bkfst & dinner) **LB**
FACILITIES: Spa STV Indoor swimming (H) Tennis (hard) Riding
Croquet lawn Childrens creche, massage, manicures, aromatherapy ch fac
Xmas **SERVICES:** Lift **PARKING:** 40 **NOTES:** No smoking in restaurant
CARDS: ▨▨ ▨▨ ▨▨ ▨ ▨▨ ▨▨ ▨

IPSWICH

Map 05 TM14

★★★ 65% Novotel Ipswich
Greyfriars Rd IP1 1UP
☎ 01473 232400 ▤ 01473 232414
e-mail: h0995@accor-hotels.com
Dir: *from A14 towards Felixstowe. Left onto A137, follow for 2m into town centre. Hotel on double rdbt by Stoke Bridge*

> **PETS:** Bedrooms (unattended) £7.50 Public areas (Not in
> restaurant) Exercise area (0.5 mile)

Situated in the centre of town, this modern, redbrick hotel is close
continued

to shops, bars and restaurants. The open-plan public areas include a Mediterranean-style restaurant and a bar with a small games area. Bedrooms are well-designed for most needs and simply decorated; three are suitable for less mobile guests.
ROOMS: 100 en suite (6 fmly) No smoking in 76 bedrooms s £64-£98;
d £75-£109 (incl. bkfst) **LB FACILITIES:** STV Pool table, Complimentary use of gym, sauna, jacuzzi **SERVICES:** Lift air con **PARKING:** 50
CARDS: ▨▨ ▨▨ ▨▨ ▨ ▨

KEDINGTON

Map 05 TL74

◆◆◆◆◆ The White House
Silver St CB9 7QG
☎ 01440 707731 ▤ 01440 707731
e-mail: tobybarclay@natsparks.co.uk
Dir: *from A143, Haverhill to Bury St Edmunds rd, take B1061 into Kedington, then 3rd left, King's Hill. House at bottom of hill opp pub*

> **PETS:** Sep Accom (kennel & pen) Public areas (sitting room
> only by arrangement) Exercise area (20yds)
> **RESIDENT PETS:** Jura - Black Labrador, Tiska - Springer Spaniel

This Grade II listed, timber-framed 17th-century house enjoys a quiet village setting. Sympathetically extended in the Victorian era, this delightful house has been tastefully furnished and restored by enthusiastic proprietors and features exposed beams. The charming, individually furnished bedrooms offer many creature comforts, personal touches and thoughtful extras.
FACILITIES: 3 rms (2 en suite) No smoking TVB tea/coffee Licensed
Cen ht No children 12yrs No coaches Shooting tuition
PRICES: s £40-£60; d £60✳ **PARKING:** 5

LAVENHAM

Map 05 TL94

◆◆◆◆ ◎◎ ▨ ⌂ Lavenham Great House Hotel
Market Place CO10 9QZ
☎ 01787 247431 ▤ 01787 248007
e-mail: greathouse@clara.co.uk
Dir: *turn off A1141 onto Market Ln, situated just behind the cross*

> **PETS:** Bedrooms Exercise area (100yds)

Essentially, this establishment is a restaurant with rooms housed in an 18th-century Tudor building overlooking the market place. The restaurant is like a little pocket of France and offers high-quality rural cuisine served by French staff. The spacious bedrooms are individually decorated and thoughtfully equipped with many useful extras; some rooms have a separate lounge area.
FACILITIES: 5 en suite (2 fmly) No smoking in bedrooms No smoking in dining room TVB tea/coffee Direct dial from bedrooms Licensed Cen ht
No coaches Dinner Last d 9.30pm **PRICES:** s £65-£98; d £76-£150✳ **LB**
NOTES: Closed Jan rs Sun nights & Mon
CARDS: ▨▨ ▨▨ ▨▨ ▨ ▨▨ ▨

> **Don't forget to let proprietors
> know when you book that
> you're bringing your pet**

LONG MELFORD Map 05 TL84

🐕 🐈 🐹

★★★ 75% ❁ The Black Lion

Church Walk, The Green CO10 9DN
☎ 01787 312356 📠 01787 374557
e-mail: enquiries@blacklionhotel.net
Dir: at junct of A134/A1092

PETS: **Bedrooms Public areas (except restaurant) Exercise area (Adjacent) Pet Food Food by prior request - chargeable** RESIDENT PETS: Mackerson (Black Labrador)

This charming 15th-century hotel is situated on the edge of this bustling town overlooking the green. Bedrooms are generally spacious and each is attractively decorated, tastefully furnished and equipped with useful extras. An interesting range of dishes is served in the lounge bar or guests may choose to dine in the more formal restaurant.

ROOMS: 10 en suite (3 fmly) No smoking in all bedrooms s £85-£109; d £106-£146 (incl. bkfst) **LB** **FACILITIES:** Board games ch fac Xmas **PARKING:** 10 **NOTES:** No smoking in restaurant
CARDS: 💳 💳 💳 💳 💳 💳 💳

Please mention AA Pet Friendly Places to Stay when booking

LOWESTOFT Map 05 TM59

🐕 🐈 🐹 🐦

★★★ 77% ❁❁ Ivy House Country Hotel

Ivy Ln, Beccles Rd, Oulton Broad NR33 8HY
☎ 01502 501353 & 588144 📠 01502 501539
e-mail: aapets@ivyhousefarm.co.uk
Dir: on A146 SW of Oulton Broad turn into Ivy Ln beside Esso petrol station. Over railway bridge and follow private driveway

PETS: **Bedrooms (unattended) £5 per stay Public areas (except restaurant) Exercise area (50 acres of meadows) Pet Food Doggie box - bowl, chewie sticks, blanket & map of dog walks around hotel grounds** RESIDENT PETS: Patch & Tammie - dogs

A delightful, family-run hotel set in three acres of mature landscaped grounds just a short walk from Oulton Broad. Public rooms include a character 18th-century thatched barn restaurant where an interesting choice of dishes is served. Service throughout is charming and attentive. The attractively decorated bedrooms

continued

are housed in garden wings, and many have lovely views of the garden and countryside.

ROOMS: 19 annexe en suite (1 fmly) (17 GF) No smoking in 6 bedrooms s £84-£104; d £114-£149 (incl. bkfst) **LB**
FACILITIES: Reduced rates at neighbouring leisure club **PARKING:** 50
NOTES: No smoking in restaurant Closed 25 Dec-6 Jan
CARDS: 💳 💳 💳 💳 💳 💳 💳

🐕 🐹 🐦

♦♦♦♦ Albany Hotel

400 London Rd South NR33 0BQ
☎ 01502 574394 📠 01502 581198
e-mail: geoffrey.ward@btclick.com
Dir: on A12 from S. Hotel on right just into one-way system from Pakefield

PETS: **Bedrooms (unattended) Public areas Exercise area (500yds)** RESIDENT PETS: Max - Borzoi/Lurcher cross, Tuppence - cat

Expect a warm welcome at this delightful privately owned hotel, which is situated just a short walk from the beach and town centre. The attractively decorated bedrooms are tastefully furnished and have a good range of useful extras. Public rooms feature a smartly appointed lounge with a corner bar and a smart dining room.

FACILITIES: 8 rms (6 en suite) (3 fmly) No smoking in bedrooms No smoking in dining room TVB tea/coffee Licensed Cen ht TVL No coaches Dinner Last d 2pm **PRICES:** s £22.50-£29.50; d £48-£60✳ **LB** **PARKING:** 1 **CARDS:** 💳 💳 💳 💳 💳

🐕 🐈 🐹 🐦

♦♦♦♦ Somerton House

7 Kirkley Cliff NR33 0BY
☎ 01502 565665 📠 01502 501176
e-mail: hotel@somerton.screaming.net
Dir: On A12 southbound on seafront 100yds from Claremont pier

PETS: **Bedrooms Public areas Exercise area (seafront nearby)**

Victorian Grade II listed terraced house situated at the quieter end of town overlooking the sea. The smartly decorated bedrooms are tastefully furnished in a period style and some rooms have four-poster or half tester beds. Breakfast is served in the smart dining room and guests have the use of a comfortable lounge bar.

FACILITIES: 7 rms (6 en suite) (1 fmly) (1 GF) No smoking in 3 bedrooms No smoking in dining room STV TVB tea/coffee Licensed Cen ht TVL No coaches Dinner Last d 12pm **PRICES:** s £20-£33; d £50-£58✳ **LB** **NOTES:** Closed 25-26 Dec
CARDS: 💳 💳 💳 💳 💳 💳 💳

♦♦♦ Fairways
398 London Rd South NR33 0BQ
☎ 01502 572659
e-mail: amontali@netmatters.co.uk
Dir: S of town centre on A12, 1m from railway and bus station

PETS: Bedrooms Public areas (except dining room)

Expect a friendly welcome at this family-run guest house, which is located at the southern end of the town. Bedrooms come in a variety of sizes and styles; each room is pleasantly decorated and thoughtfully equipped. Breakfast is served in the smart dining room and guests also have the use of a cosy lounge.
FACILITIES: 7 rms (4 en suite) (2 fmly) No smoking in bedrooms No smoking in dining room TVB tea/coffee Licensed Cen ht TVL
PRICES: s £18-£26; d £40✳ **BB PARKING:** 2
CARDS: 〓〓〓〓〓

MILDENHALL   Map 05 TL77

★★★ 73% ◉ Riverside
Mill St IP28 7DP
☎ 01638 717274 📠 01638 715997
e-mail: bookings@riverside-hotel.net

THE CIRCLE
Selected Individual Hotels
GREAT BRITAIN

Dir: from A11 at Fiveways rdbt take A1101 in Mildenhall Town. Left at mini rdbt along High St. Hotel last building on left before bridge

PETS: Bedrooms (Cottages outside hotel) Sep Accom Exercise area (100yds)

An 18th-century red brick building situated in the heart of this charming town centre on the banks of the River Lark. Public rooms include a smart restaurant, which overlooks the river and the attractive gardens to the rear. The smartly decorated bedrooms have co-ordinated soft furnishings and many thoughtful touches.
ROOMS: 17 en suite 6 annexe en suite (4 fmly) (4 GF) s £69.50; d £95 (incl. bkfst) **LB FACILITIES:** Fishing Rowing boat hire entertainment Xmas **SERVICES:** Lift **PARKING:** 80
CARDS: 〓〓〓〓〓〓〓

NEWMARKET   Map 05 TL66

★★★ 68% Heath Court
Moulton Rd CB8 8DY
☎ 01638 667171 📠 01638 666533
e-mail: quality@heathcourthotel.com

Best Western

Dir: leave A14 at Newmarket and Ely exit on A142. Follow town centre signs over mini rdbt. At clocktower left into Moulton Rd

PETS: Bedrooms (unattended) Exercise area (100yds)

A modern redbrick hotel situated close to Newmarket Heath and perfectly placed for the town centre. Public rooms offer a choice of dining options; informal meals can be taken in the lounge bar or a modern carte is offered in the restaurant. Bedrooms are mostly spacious, each smartly presented and a number have air conditioning.
ROOMS: 41 en suite (2 fmly) No smoking in 19 bedrooms s £91-£94; d £112-£167 (incl. bkfst) **LB FACILITIES:** STV **SERVICES:** Lift
PARKING: 60 **CARDS:** 〓〓〓〓〓〓〓

ORFORD   Map 05 TM45

★★ 74% ◉◉ Crown & Castle Inn
IP12 2LJ
☎ 01394 450205
e-mail: info@crownandcastle.co.uk
Dir: turn right from B1084 on entering village, towards castle

PETS: Bedrooms (unattended) £10 (one off charge) Public areas (Bar only and table 30) Exercise area (100yds) Pet Food Doggy bag on arrival, towels & hose
RESIDENT PETS: 2 wire-haired Fox Terriers

Adjacent to a Norman castle keep, this delightful inn has been transformed in recent years. Bedrooms, light, airy and contemporary, are in the main building (some with great views) and in a purpose-built garden wing; the latter are more spacious and have patios. The restaurant, with polished tables and local artwork, has an informal atmosphere and features a high quality menu.
ROOMS: 7 en suite 11 annexe en suite (1 fmly) (11 GF) No smoking in all bedrooms s £72-£135; d £90-£135 (incl. bkfst) **LB**
FACILITIES: ch fac **PARKING:** 25 **NOTES:** No smoking in restaurant Closed 24-27 Dec, 4-8 Jan RS Nov-Etr **CARDS:** 〓〓〓〓〓

SAXMUNDHAM   Map 05 TM36

♦♦♦♦ Sandpit Farm
Bruisyard IP17 2EB
☎ 01728 663445
e-mail: susannemarshall@suffolkonline.net
Dir: E of Dennington on A1120, turn right onto B1120 and take 1st left towards Bruisyard. Follow road for approx 1.5m, house on left

PETS: Exercise area **RESIDENT PETS:** 2 Black Labradors, 23 chickens, guinea fowl

A warm welcome awaits at this delightful Grade II listed farmhouse set in 20 acres of mature grounds. Bedrooms are sympathetically decorated, equipped with many thoughtful touches and have lovely countryside views. Breakfast features quality, locally sourced produce and freshly laid free-range eggs. Guests have the use of two cosy lounges.
FACILITIES: 2 rms (1 en suite) No smoking tea/coffee No dogs Cen ht TVL No coaches Tennis (hard) Riding Croquet lawn
PRICES: d £50-£60✳ **PARKING:** 4 **NOTES:** Closed 24-26 Dec

---

SOUTHWOLD   Map 05 TM57

★★ 67% The Blyth Hotel
Station Rd IP18 6AY
☎ 01502 722632 📠 01502 724123
e-mail: accommodation@blythhotel.com
Dir: A12 onto A1045, on entering town Mights Bridge & at mini rdbt, hotel ahead

PETS: Bedrooms £5 Public areas (not in restaurant) Exercise area (100 yards) Pet Food **RESIDENT PETS:** Eric (Golden Retriever)

Situated just a short walk from the centre of this delightful seaside town, this friendly, family-run hotel offers bedrooms that are thoughtfully equipped and individually decorated with co-ordinated

continued on p204

England

England

SOUTHWOLD continued

soft furnishings and fabrics. Public rooms include a smart restaurant and two different bars serving the local Adnams ales.
ROOMS: 12 en suite (5 fmly) No smoking in all bedrooms s £65-£75; d £85-£95 (incl. bkfst) **LB FACILITIES:** Outdoor swimming Boule pitch **PARKING:** 10 **NOTES:** No smoking in restaurant
CARDS: 🏧 💳 💳 💳 💳 5️⃣

◆◆◆◆ No 21
21 North Pde IP18 6LT
☎ 01502 722573
e-mail: jackiecomie@onetel.net.uk
Dir: Over bridge into Southwold turn left at Blyth Hotel, along Pier Ave to Pier, turn right into North Pde

PETS: Bedrooms Exercise area (adjacent to beach & park)

Delightful Victorian property situated on the promenade overlooking the sea. The stylish bedrooms have co-ordinated soft furnishings and many thoughtful touches; some rooms have panoramic views of the sea. Breakfast, which includes fresh local produce, is served in the smart dining room and guests have the use of a cosy lounge.
FACILITIES: 3 en suite (1 fmly) No smoking TVB tea/coffee Cen ht No children 10yrs No coaches **NOTES:** Closed Xmas

WESTLETON
Map 05 TM46

★★ 75% ◉◉ Westleton Crown
IP17 3AD
☎ 0800 328 6001 📠 01728 648239
e-mail: reception@westletoncrown.com
Dir: N on A12, turn just beyond Yoxford, follow AA signs for 2m

PETS: Bedrooms £2.50, £10 for horses Public areas (except restaurant) Exercise area (adjacent) RESIDENT PETS: Daisy & Fleur - Bernese Mountain dogs (mother & daughter), horses

A charming coaching inn situated in a peaceful village location just a few minutes from the A12. Public rooms include a smart, award-winning restaurant, comfortable lounge, and a busy bar with exposed beams and open fireplaces. The bedrooms are individually decorated and equipped with many thoughtful little extras.
ROOMS: 10 en suite 9 annexe en suite (2 fmly) (4 GF) No smoking in all bedrooms s fr £64; d fr £79 (incl. bkfst) **LB FACILITIES:** Xmas **PARKING:** 40 **NOTES:** No smoking in restaurant RS Wknds Dinner B&B only, 24-26 Dec **CARDS:** 🏧 💳 💳 💳 💳 5️⃣

WOODBRIDGE
Map 05 TM24

★★★ 76% ◉ ♨ Seckford Hall
IP13 6NU
☎ 01394 385678 📠 01394 380610
e-mail: reception@seckford.co.uk
Dir: signed on A12. Do not follow signs for town centre

PETS: Bedrooms £7.50 Exercise area

This superb Tudor manor house is set amid lovely landscaped grounds just off the A12. The property is reputed to have been visited by Queen Elizabeth I, and retains much of its original charm and character. Public rooms include a superb panelled

continued

---

lounge, a cosy bar and an intimate restaurant. Bedrooms are spacious, attractively decorated, tastefully furnished and equipped with many thoughtful touches.
ROOMS: 22 en suite 10 annexe en suite (4 fmly) s £85-£130; d £130-£200 (incl. bkfst) **LB FACILITIES:** Spa Indoor swimming (H) Golf 18 Fishing Gym Putting green Beauty Salon **PARKING:** 200 **NOTES:** No smoking in restaurant Closed 25 Dec
CARDS: 🏧 💳 💳 💳 💳 5️⃣

★★★ 72% Best Western Ufford Park Hotel Golf & Leisure

Yarmouth Rd, Ufford IP12 1QW
☎ 01394 383555 📠 01394 383582
e-mail: mail@uffordpark.co.uk
Dir: A12 N to A1152, in Melton turn left at lights, premises 1m on right

PETS: Bedrooms (Lodge Rooms only) (unattended) £5 Exercise area

Modern, purpose-built hotel set in open countryside and boasting superb leisure facilities, including a challenging golf course. The spacious public rooms provide a wide choice of areas in which to relax and include a busy lounge bar, a carvery restaurant and the Vista restaurant. Bedrooms are pleasantly decorated and thoughtfully equipped; many rooms overlook the golf course.
ROOMS: 84 en suite 6 annexe en suite (8 fmly) (24 GF) No smoking in 30 bedrooms s £90-£120; d £110-£140 (incl. bkfst) **LB FACILITIES:** Spa Indoor swimming (H) Golf 18 Fishing Sauna Solarium Gym Putting green Jacuzzi Steam room, Golf Academy with PGA tuition, Beauty salon Xmas **SERVICES:** Lift **PARKING:** 200 **NOTES:** No smoking in restaurant **CARDS:** 🏧 💳 💳 💳 💳 5️⃣

DORKING
Map 04 TQ14

★★★ 67% The White Horse
High St RH4 1BE
☎ 0870 400 8282 📠 01306 887241
e-mail: whitehorsedorking@macdonald-hotels.co.uk
Dir: M25 junct 9 take A24 S towards Dorking. Hotel in centre of town

MACDONALD
HOTELS

PETS: Bedrooms Sep Accom £15 Public areas Exercise area (400 metres)

The hotel was first established as an inn in 1750, although parts of the building date back as far as the 15th century. Its town centre location and Dickensian charm have long made this a popular destination for travellers. Character features include beamed ceilings, open fires and four-poster beds.
ROOMS: 37 en suite 41 annexe en suite (2 fmly) (5 GF) No smoking in 59 bedrooms **FACILITIES:** STV **PARKING:** 73 **NOTES:** No smoking in restaurant **CARDS:** 🏧 💳 💳 💳 💳 5️⃣

♨ **Places with this symbol are country house hotels**

 Places with this symbol are farms

FARNHAM Map 04 SU84

◆◆◆◆ Sleepy Hollow
1 Broomleaf Corner GU9 8BG
☎ 01252 721930
Dir: from Farnham Station level crossing turn left onto B3001 into Waverley Lane. Broomleaf Corner (NOT Broomleaf Rd) 250yds on left

PETS: Bedrooms Exercise area (5 mins' walk)

This charming cottage with a home-from-home ambience is in a quiet residential area, set back from the road and only minutes' walk from the railway station and town centre. Bedrooms are comfortable and decorated individually featuring artefacts from the proprietor's travels. Breakfast is served in the dining room looking onto the attractive gardens.
FACILITIES: 3 rms No smoking TVB tea/coffee Cen ht No coaches **PRICES:** s fr £25; d fr £40✱ **PARKING:** 3 **NOTES:** Closed Xmas

HASLEMERE Map 04 SU93

◆◆◆ 🍞 🍺 Wheatsheaf
Grayswood Rd, Grayswood GU27 2DE
☎ 01428 644440 🖷 01428 641285
e-mail: thewheatsheaf@hotmail.com
Dir: A3 follow signs A286 Haslemere. 7m

PETS: Bedrooms (unattended) Public areas (Not in restaurant) Exercise area (Adjacent)

Conveniently situated just outside of Haslemere in the small village of Grayswood, this well presented inn has a warm and friendly atmosphere. A smart conservatory restaurant is a new addition, and complements the attractive dining area and informal bar, which is a popular meeting place. Bedrooms are similar in style and all furnished to a good standard.
FACILITIES: 7 en suite No smoking in bedrooms No smoking in dining room TVB tea/coffee Direct dial from bedrooms Cen ht No coaches Dinner Last d 9.45pm **PRICES:** s £55; d £75✱ **PARKING:** 21 **CARDS:** 🖃 🖃 🖃 🖃 🖃

For HORLEY see GATWICK AIRPORT, West Sussex

LEATHERHEAD Map 04 TQ15

★★ 65% Bookham Grange THE INDEPENDENTS
Little Bookham Common, Bookham KT23 3HS
☎ 01372 452742 🖷 01372 450080
e-mail: bookhamgrange@easynet.com
Dir: off A246 at Bookham High Street onto Church Rd, 1st right after Bookham railway station

PETS: Bedrooms (unattended) Exercise area

This attractive family-run hotel is situated in over two acres of landscaped grounds with extensive parking. Spacious bedrooms are individually decorated and well equipped. Public areas include extensive banqueting facilities and a beamed bar.
ROOMS: 27 en suite (5 fmly) s £75-£85; d £95-£95 (incl. bkfst) **LB** **FACILITIES:** Xmas **PARKING:** 100 **NOTES:** No smoking in restaurant **CARDS:** 🖃 🖃 🖃 🖃 🖃 🖃

PEASLAKE Map 04 TQ04

★★★ 69% ⊛ Hurtwood Inn Hotel
Walking Bottom GU5 9RR
☎ 01306 730851 🖷 01306 731390
e-mail: sales@hurtwoodinnhotel.com
Dir: off A25 at Gomshall opposite Jet Filling Station towards Peaslake. After 2.5m turn right at village shop, hotel in village centre

PETS: Bedrooms (unattended) Public areas Exercise area (surrounding woods)

With its tranquil location this hotel makes an ideal base for exploring the attractions of the area. The brightly decorated bedrooms are well appointed, and some have views over the gardens. Recently refurbished public areas include a new restaurant, a private dining room and a bar/bistro where drinks by the open fire can be enjoyed. 'Oscars' is the setting to enjoy award-winning meals.
ROOMS: 15 en suite 6 annexe en suite (6 fmly) (6 GF) No smoking in 5 bedrooms s £65; d £75-£85 **PARKING:** 22 **NOTES:** No smoking in restaurant **CARDS:** 🖃 🖃 🖃 🖃 🖃 🖃

ALFRISTON Map 05 TQ50

★★★ 70% Deans Place Best Western
Seaford Rd BN26 5TW
☎ 01323 870248 🖷 01323 870918
e-mail: mail@deansplacehotel.co.uk
Dir: off A27 signed Alfriston & Drusillas Zoo Park. S through village

PETS: Bedrooms (unattended) £5 Public areas (except restaurant and function rooms) Food and bowls provided by prior arrangement

Situated on the southern fringe of the village, this friendly hotel is set in attractive gardens. Bedrooms vary in size and are well appointed with good facilities. A wide range of food is offered including an extensive bar menu and a fine dining option in Harcourt's Restaurant.
ROOMS: 36 en suite (2 fmly) (8 GF) No smoking in 16 bedrooms s £60-£100; d £100-£138 (incl. bkfst) **LB** **FACILITIES:** Spa STV Outdoor swimming (H) Croquet lawn Putting green Boules Xmas **PARKING:** 100 **NOTES:** No smoking in restaurant **CARDS:** 🖃 🖃 🖃 🖃 🖃 🖃

BATTLE Map 05 TQ71

★★★ 73% ⊛ 🌶🌶 Powder Mills
Powdermill Ln TN33 0SP
☎ 01424 775511 🖷 01424 774540
e-mail: powdc@aol.com
Dir: pass Abbey on A2100. 1st right, hotel 1m on right

PETS: Bedrooms (unattended) Public areas (except restaurant) Exercise area RESIDENT PETS: Jessica, Holly & Jenny (Springer Spaniels)

A delightful 18th-century country house hotel set amidst 150 acres of landscaped grounds with lakes and woodland. The individually

continued on p206

England

BATTLE continued

decorated bedrooms are tastefully furnished and thoughtfully equipped, some rooms have sun terraces with lovely views over the lake. Public rooms include a cosy lounge bar, music room, drawing room, library, restaurant and conservatory.
ROOMS: 30 en suite 10 annexe en suite (3 GF) s £90-£140; d £120-£190 (incl. bkfst) **LB FACILITIES:** STV Outdoor swimming Fishing Jogging trails & woodland walks entertainment Xmas **PARKING:** 101
NOTES: No smoking in restaurant
CARDS: 🔲 🔲 🔲 🔲 🔲 🔲 🔲

✦✦✦✦ ❤ Fox Hole Farm
Kane Hythe Rd TN33 9QU
☎ 01424 772053 📠 01424 772053
e-mail: foxholefarm@amserve.com
Dir: off A271 onto B2096, farm 0.75m from junct on right

> **PETS:** Bedrooms Public areas (except dining room) Exercise area

A delightful 18th-century woodcutter's cottage set amidst 40 acres of grounds a short drive from the historic town of Battle. The spacious bedrooms are individually decorated, tastefully furnished and thoughtfully equipped. Breakfast is served in the charming dining room and the cosy sitting room has exposed beams and an inglenook fireplace.
FACILITIES: 3 en suite No smoking TVB tea/coffee Cen ht 40 acres ducks sheep chickens **PRICES:** d £53-£63✽ **PARKING:** 6
NOTES: Closed Dec-Jan **CARDS:** 🔲 🔲 🔲

BRIGHTON & HOVE   Map 04 TQ30

★★★★★ 68%
De Vere Grand Brighton
King's Rd BN1 2FW
☎ 01273 224300 📠 01273 224321
e-mail: reservations@grandbrighton.co.uk
Dir: on seafront between piers, next to Brighton Centre

DE VERE ● HOTELS

> **PETS:** Bedrooms (unattended) £5 Exercise area (20 yards)

Dating back to the mid 19th century, this landmark seafront hotel, with its eye-catching white facade and intricate balconies, is as grand as the name suggests. Bedrooms include a number of deluxe sea view rooms, some with balconies, and suites, also with sea views. The hotel is perhaps best known for its extensive

continued

---

conference and banqueting facilities; there is also a well-equipped leisure centre and an impressive conservatory adjoining the bar.
ROOMS: 200 en suite (60 fmly) s fr £170; d £250-£360 (incl. bkfst) **LB FACILITIES:** Spa STV Indoor swimming (H) Sauna Solarium Gym Jacuzzi Hairdresser, Tropicarium, beauty salon & treatment rooms entertainment Xmas **SERVICES:** Lift **PARKING:** 70
CARDS: 🔲 🔲 🔲 🔲 🔲 🔲 🔲

★★★ 67% The Granville
124 King's Rd BN1 2FA
☎ 01273 326302 📠 01273 728294
e-mail: granville@brighton.co.uk
Dir: opposite West Pier

> **PETS:** Bedrooms (unattended) Public areas (reception and bar only) Exercise area (20 yards to beach) Pet Food
> **RESIDENT PETS:** Mai-Mai (Jack Russell), Nan-Nan (West Highland Terrier)

This stylish hotel is located on Brighton's busy seafront. Bedrooms are carefully furnished and decorated with great style. A trendy cocktail bar and restaurant, 'DaDu', meaning big belly, serves a combination of Asian and British cuisine. Tasty traditional breakfasts are also available.
ROOMS: 24 en suite (2 fmly) (1 GF) No smoking in all bedrooms s £55-£105; d £75-£185 (incl. bkfst) **LB FACILITIES:** Jacuzzi ch fac
SERVICES: Lift **PARKING:** 3 **CARDS:** 🔲 🔲 🔲 🔲 🔲 🔲 🔲

✦✦✦✦ Ambassador Hotel
22-23 New Steine, Marine Pde BN2 1PD
☎ 01273 676869 📠 01273 689988
e-mail: info@ambassadorbrighton.co.uk
Dir: follow A23 to end, facing Palace Pier. Take 1st turn left, signed Rottingdean A259. Take 9th turn on left, into Garden Square, then 1st left into New Steine. Hotel on opposite side of square

> **PETS:** Bedrooms Public areas (dogs only in bar) Exercise area (adjacent)

At the heart of bustling Kemp Town, overlooking the attractive garden square adjacent the seaside, this well established property has a friendly and relaxing atmosphere. Bedrooms vary in size with the largest enjoying the best views. A small lounge with a separate bar is available.
FACILITIES: 24 en suite (9 fmly) (3 GF) No smoking in 12 bedrooms No smoking in dining room No smoking in 1 lounge TVB tea/coffee Direct dial from bedrooms Licensed Cen ht TVL **PRICES:** s £36-£65; d £60-£95✽ **CARDS:** 🔲 🔲 🔲 🔲 🔲 🔲 🔲

◆◆◆◆ Brighton Pavilions
7 Charlotte St BN2 1AG
☎ 01273 621750 📠 01273 622477
e-mail: sanchez-crespo@lineone.net
Dir: take A23 to Palace Pier, sharp left onto A259 signed Rottingdean, Charlotte St is 15th turning on left

PETS: Bedrooms Public areas (Not dining room)
Exercise area (100 metres) RESIDENT PETS: Oscar (Red Setter)

This well-run operation is located in one of the Regency streets, minutes' walk from the seafront and town centre. Bedrooms have stylish themes such as Titanic or Pompeii, and all are very smartly presented. The cosy dining room has a nautical theme and there is a small seating area and patio.
FACILITIES: 10 rms (7 en suite) (1 fmly) (1 GF) No smoking TVB tea/coffee Direct dial from bedrooms Cen ht No coaches
PRICES: s £45-£65; d £80-£144✱ **CARDS:** 〰️ 🏧 💳 📇 🔲 ⑤

◆◆◆◆ Penny Lanes
11 Charlotte St BN2 1AG
☎ 01273 603197
e-mail: welcome@pennylanes.co.uk
Dir: from Brighton pier towards Marina. After 2nd set of lights 4th left (at "The Lanes" hotel on seafront) establishment at top on right

PETS: Bedrooms (unattended) Public areas Exercise area (2 minute walk)

This small and friendly guesthouse is situated in a quiet road not far from the seafront and the centre. Bedrooms are smart in appearance and well equipped. Breakfast is served in the wooden-panelled dining and offers a good selection including vegetarian options. There is a smart bar lounge in which to relax.
FACILITIES: 12 rms (7 en suite) (1 GF) No smoking in 5 bedrooms No smoking in dining room TVB tea/coffee Licensed Cen ht TVL No coaches **PRICES:** s £25-£35; d £50-£99✱ **LB**
CARDS: 〰️ 💳 📇 🔲 ⑤

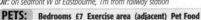

EASTBOURNE   Map 05 TV69

★★★★★ 71% ◎◎ Grand
King Edward's Pde BN21 4EQ
☎ 01323 412345 📠 01323 412233
e-mail: reservations@grandeastbourne.com
Dir: on seafront W of Eastbourne, 1m from railway station

PETS: Bedrooms £7 Exercise area (adjacent) Pet Food

This famous Victorian hotel offers high standards of service and hospitality. The extensive public rooms feature a magnificent Great Hall, with marble columns and high ceilings, where guests can relax and enjoy afternoon tea. The spacious bedrooms provide high levels of comfort and some rooms have balconies with stunning sea views. The hotel also has a choice of restaurants and bars as well as superb leisure facilities.
ROOMS: 152 en suite (20 fmly) s £135-£325; d £165-£385 (incl. bkfst)
LB FACILITIES: Spa Indoor swimming (H) Outdoor swimming (H) Snooker Sauna Solarium Gym Putting green Jacuzzi Hairdressing, Beauty therapy entertainment Xmas **SERVICES:** Lift **PARKING:** 60
NOTES: No smoking in restaurant
CARDS: 〰️ 🏧 💳 📇 🔲 ⑤

★★★ 73% Lansdowne
King Edward's Pde BN21 4EE
☎ 01323 725174 📠 01323 739721
e-mail: reception@lansdowne-hotel.co.uk
Dir: hotel at W end of seafront (B2103) facing Western Lawns

PETS: Bedrooms (unattended) £10 per dog

Enjoying an enviable position at the quieter end of the parade, this hotel overlooks the Western Lawns and Wish Tower and is just a few minutes' walk from many of the city's attractions. Public rooms include a variety of lounges, a range of meeting rooms and games rooms. Bedrooms are attractively decorated and many offer sea views.
ROOMS: 101 en suite (9 fmly) No smoking in 25 bedrooms s £47-£89; d £84-£162 (incl. bkfst) **LB FACILITIES:** STV Snooker Darts, Table tennis & Pool table ch fac Xmas **SERVICES:** Lift **PARKING:** 22
NOTES: No smoking in restaurant Closed 2-20 Jan
CARDS: 〰️ 🏧 💳 📇 🔲 ⑤

★★★ 66% Chatsworth
Grand Pde BN21 3YR
☎ 01323 411016 📠 01323 643270
e-mail: stay@chatsworth-hotel.com
Dir: M23 then A27 to Polegate. A2270 into Eastbourne, follow seafront & signs. Hotel is in centre of seafront near pier

PETS: Bedrooms £4.50 Exercise area Pet Food

Within minutes of the town centre and pier, this attractive Edwardian hotel is located on the seafront. Service is friendly and helpful throughout the public areas, which consist of the Dukes Bar, a cosy lounge and the Devonshire Restaurant. Bedrooms, many with sea views, are traditional in style and have a range of facilities.
ROOMS: 47 en suite (2 fmly) No smoking in 10 bedrooms s £55-£65; d £85-£125 (incl. bkfst) **LB FACILITIES:** STV entertainment ch fac Xmas **SERVICES:** Lift **NOTES:** No smoking in restaurant
CARDS: 〰️ 🏧 💳 📇 🔲 ⑤

> **All information was correct at the time of going to press; we recommend you confirm details on booking**

EASTBOURNE continued

★★★ 63% **Quality Hotel Langham**
Royal Pde BN22 7AH
☎ 01323 731451 🖷 01323 646623
e-mail: info@langhamhotel.co.uk
Dir: In Eastbourne, follow seafront signs. Hotel 0.5m E of pier

PETS: Bedrooms (unattended) £3 Exercise area (2 miles)

This popular hotel is situated in a prominent position with superb views of the sea and pier. Bedrooms, most of which have been refurbished, are pleasantly decorated and equipped with modern facilities. The spacious public rooms include a terrace restaurant, business lounge area and Grand Parade bar.
ROOMS: 85 en suite (5 fmly) s £55-£65; d £85-£110 (incl. bkfst) **LB**
FACILITIES: Temporary membership of Sovereign Club pools & gym Xmas
SERVICES: Lift **PARKING:** 4 **NOTES:** No smoking in restaurant
CARDS: ▭▭▭▭▭▭▭

★★ 68% **Farrar's Hotel**
Wilmington Gardens BN21 4JN
☎ 01323 723737 🖷 01323 732902
Dir: off seafront by Wish Tower, hotel opposite Congress Theatre

PETS: Bedrooms £3

Situated opposite the Congress Theatre, this hotel is just a short walk from both the seafront and Devonshire Park. Bedrooms are comfortably furnished and pleasantly decorated. Public areas are smartly appointed and include a cosy bar, a separate lounge and an attractive downstairs dining room.
ROOMS: 45 en suite (4 fmly) **FACILITIES: SERVICES:** Lift
PARKING: 35 **NOTES:** No smoking in restaurant Closed Jan
CARDS: ▭▭▭▭▭▭

♦♦♦ **Gladwyn Hotel**
16 Blackwater Rd BN21 4JD
☎ 01323 733142
e-mail: gladwynhotel@aol.com

PETS: Bedrooms (unattended) Public areas Exercise area (200 metres) **RESIDENT PETS:** Saffie & Mabel (Staffordshire Terrier crosses)

A warm welcome is guaranteed at this delightful guest house located opposite the famous tennis courts. Bedrooms each feature an individual theme and character, and all provide good levels of comfort. Freshly prepared breakfasts are served in the cosy dining room overlooking the garden, which is available for guests' use during the summer months.
FACILITIES: 10 en suite (2 fmly) No smoking TVB tea/coffee Licensed
TVL **PRICES:** s £28; d £56✳ **CARDS:** ▭▭▭▭▭▭

Please mention AA Pet Friendly Places to Stay when booking

♦♦♦ **Arden Hotel**
17 Burlington Place BN21 4AR
☎ 01323 639639 🖷 01323 417840
e-mail: mail@ardenhoteleastbourne.freeserve.co.uk
Dir: 50yds from seafront, near bandstand

PETS: Bedrooms Exercise area (100 metres)
RESIDENT PETS: William (cat)

Located close to the seafront and town centre, this friendly hotel provides guests with well appointed rooms. Public areas are tastefully decorated and include a spacious guest lounge and dining room where hearty breakfasts are served.
FACILITIES: 12 rms (10 en suite) (1 fmly) (2 GF) No smoking TVB tea/coffee Licensed Cen ht TVL No coaches **PRICES:** s £25-£28; d £50-£56✳ **PARKING:** 3 **CARDS:** ▭▭▭▭▭▭

♦♦♦ **Meridale**
91 Royal Pde BN22 7AE
☎ 01323 729686 🖷 01323 419042
e-mail: crcmeridale@aol.com
Dir: follow brown signs for sea front, Meridale is opposite car park by Redoubt Fortress

PETS: Bedrooms Exercise area (100 metres)

Located on the seafront and within easy walking distance of the town centre and the pier, this cosy guesthouse provides charming bedrooms that are well decorated and presented. In the mornings, a freshly cooked full English breakfast is served at individual tables.
FACILITIES: 5 en suite (2 fmly) No smoking in 2 bedrooms No smoking in dining room No smoking in lounges TVB tea/coffee Cen ht
No coaches **PRICES:** s £22.50-£25; d £45-£50✳
CARDS: ▭▭▭▭

♦♦♦ **Sheldon Hotel**
9-11 Burlington Place BN21 4AS
☎ 01323 724120 🖷 01323 430406
e-mail: gmeyer@sheldonhotel.fs.businesses.co.uk
Dir: 100yds from seafront, 500yds W of pier, opposite bandstand

PETS: Bedrooms (unattended) Public areas Exercise area (150 metres)

This is an impressive late Victorian house, which is situated in a quiet side road just off the seafront. The bedrooms are cheerfully decorated with co-ordinated soft furnishings and are equipped
continued

with many extra facilities. Public rooms include a smart dining room, a bar and a spacious comfortable lounge.
FACILITIES: 24 en suite (4 fmly) No smoking in bedrooms No smoking in dining room TVB tea/coffee Direct dial from bedrooms Licensed Lift Cen ht TVL Dinner Last d 7pm **PRICES:** s £29-£36; d £58-£72✱ **LB PARKING:** 15 **CARDS:**

HAILSHAM
Map 05 TQ50

★★★ 66% Boship Farm
Lower Dicker BN27 4AT
☎ 01323 844826 📠 01323 843945
e-mail: boship.farm@forestdale.com
Dir: on A22 at Boship rdbt, junct of A22, A267 and A271

Forestdale Hotels

| **PETS:** Bedrooms (unattended) £7.50 Public areas (not in restaurant) Pet Food |

Dating back to 1652, a lovely old farmhouse forms the hub of this hotel, which is set in 17 acres of well-tended grounds. Guests have the use of an all-weather tennis court, an outdoor pool and a croquet lawn. Bedrooms are smartly appointed and well-equipped; most have views across open fields and countryside.
ROOMS: 47 annexe en suite (5 fmly) (21 GF) No smoking in 17 bedrooms s fr £80; d fr £115 (incl. bkfst) **LB FACILITIES:** Outdoor swimming (H) Tennis (hard) Sauna Croquet lawn Jacuzzi Xmas **PARKING:** 100 **NOTES:** No smoking in restaurant
CARDS:

★★ 71% The Olde Forge Hotel & Restaurant
Magham Down BN27 1PN
☎ 01323 842893 📠 01323 842893
e-mail: theoldeforgehotel@tesco.net
Dir: off Boship rdbt on A271 to Bexhill & Herstmonceux. 3m on left

| **PETS:** Bedrooms £4 Exercise area (country lanes nearby) RESIDENT PETS: Poppy (Boxer) |

In the heart of the countryside, this family-run hotel offers a friendly welcome and an informal atmosphere. The bedrooms are attractively decorated with thoughtful extras. The restaurant, with its timbered beams and log fires, was a forge in the 16th century and has a good local reputation for its cuisine and service.
ROOMS: 7 en suite No smoking in 4 bedrooms s fr £48; d fr £68 (incl. bkfst) **LB PARKING:** 11 **NOTES:** No smoking in restaurant
CARDS:

All AA listed accommodation, restaurants and pubs can be found on the AA's website www.theAA.com

All abbreviations are explained on page 9

 Places with this symbol are pubs

HASTINGS & ST LEONARDS
Map 05 TQ80

★★★ 70% 🏇 Beauport Park
Battle Rd TN38 8EA
☎ 01424 851222 📠 01424 852465
e-mail: reservations@beauportprkhotel.co.uk
Dir: 3m N off A2100

| **PETS:** Bedrooms (unattended) Public areas (Not in dining areas) Exercise area (50 metres) Pet Food Country walks nearby |

Elegant Georgian manor house set in 40 acres of mature gardens on the outskirts of Hastings. The individually decorated bedrooms are tastefully furnished and thoughtfully equipped with modern facilities. Public rooms convey much of the original character and feature a large conservatory, a lounge bar, a restaurant and a further lounge, as well as conference and banqueting rooms.
ROOMS: 25 en suite (2 fmly) No smoking in 11 bedrooms s £95; d £130 (incl. bkfst) **LB FACILITIES:** STV Outdoor swimming (H) Golf 18 Tennis (hard) Riding Croquet lawn Putting green Country walks around estate entertainment ch fac Xmas **PARKING:** 60 **NOTES:** No smoking in restaurant **CARDS:**

NEWICK
Map 05 TQ42

★★★ ⍟⍟
Newick Park Hotel & Country Estate
BN8 4SB
☎ 01825 723633 📠 01825 723969
e-mail: bookings@newickpark.co.uk
Dir: S off A272 in Newick between Haywards Heath and Uckfield. Pass church, left at junct and hotel 0.25m on right

| **PETS:** Bedrooms (some rooms) Exercise area (surrounding 250 acres) Pet Food RESIDENT PETS: Ellie & Maddy - Black Labradors |

Delightful Grade II listed Georgian country house set amid 250 acres of Sussex parkland and landscaped gardens. The spacious, individually decorated bedrooms are tastefully furnished, thoughtfully equipped and have superb views of the grounds; many rooms have huge American king-size beds. The comfortable public rooms include a study, a sitting room, lounge bar and an elegant restaurant.
ROOMS: 13 en suite 3 annexe en suite (5 fmly) (1 GF) No smoking in all bedrooms s £110-£120; d £165-£285 (incl. bkfst) **LB FACILITIES:** STV Outdoor swimming (H) Tennis (hard) Fishing Croquet lawn Badminton, Tank driving, Quad biking, Clay pigeon shooting Xmas **PARKING:** 52 **NOTES:** No smoking in restaurant
CARDS:

England

★★★ 77% Flackley Ash

TN31 6YH
☎ 01797 230651 📠 01797 230510
e-mail: enquiries@flackleyashhotel.co.uk
Dir: 3m from Rye, beside A268

 Best Western

PETS: Bedrooms (unattended) £7.50 for dogs Public areas (not in restaurant) Exercise area (Surrounding area)

Five acres of beautifully kept grounds are the lovely backdrop to this elegant Georgian country house. The hotel is superbly situated for exploring the many local attractions, including the ancient Cinque Port of Rye, just a short drive away. Bedrooms are individually decorated and have a homely feel, and include added extras.
ROOMS: 45 en suite (3 fmly) s £87–£99; d £132–£156 (incl. bkfst) **LB**
FACILITIES: Spa STV Indoor swimming (H) Sauna Gym Croquet lawn Putting green Beautician aromatherapy reflexology ch fac Xmas
PARKING: 70 **NOTES:** No smoking in restaurant
CARDS: ▨▨▨▨▨▨

◆◆◆◆ Priory Court Hotel

Castle Rd BN24 5LG
☎ 01323 763150 📠 01323 769030
e-mail: info@priorycourthotel.com
Dir: at rdbt junct A27/A259 take Pevensey exit and follow main road through lights, hotel on right opposite Pevensey Castle

PETS: Bedrooms (unattended) £10 per stay Public areas (except restaurant) Exercise area (100yds) Can provide whatever is requested RESIDENT PETS: Sam - Golden Retriever, Sandy & Fluffy - cats

Retaining many original features, this 15th-century inn is situated directly opposite the Roman castle. Recently redecorated, the public rooms are cosy and inviting. Guests can choose from a wide range of imaginative dishes in the dining room. Bedrooms are mixed in size; some are suitable for families.
FACILITIES: 9 rms (7 en suite) 1 annexe en suite (2 fmly) (2 GF) No smoking in dining room TVB tea/coffee Direct dial from bedrooms Licensed Cen ht Dinner Last d 9.30pm **PRICES:** s £50–£65; d £80–£95✱
LB PARKING: 40 **CARDS:** ▨▨▨▨▨

★★★ 72% Rye Lodge

Hilder's Cliff TN31 7LD
☎ 01797 223838 📠 01797 223585
e-mail: info@ryelodge.co.uk
Dir: one-way system in Rye, follow signs for town centre, through Landgate arch, hotel 100yds on right

PETS: Bedrooms (unattended) £5 Public areas (not in restaurant) Exercise area (150yds) Pet Food

Standing in an elevated position, Rye Lodge has panoramic views across Romney Marshes and the Rother Estuary. Bedrooms come in a variety of sizes and styles; they are attractively decorated, tastefully furnished and thoughtfully equipped. Public rooms feature The Terrace Room Restaurant, where an interesting choice of home-made dishes is available, and indoor leisure facilities.
ROOMS: 18 en suite s £65–£120; d £90–£190 (incl. bkfst) **LB**
FACILITIES: Spa STV Indoor swimming (H) Sauna Aromatherapy Steam cabinet Xmas **PARKING:** 20 **NOTES:** No smoking in restaurant
CARDS: ▨▨▨▨▨▨

◆◆◆◆◆ Jeake's House

Mermaid St TN31 7ET
☎ 01797 222828 📠 01797 222623
e-mail: jeakeshouse@btinternet.com
Dir: in cobbled medieval town centre, approached either from High St or from The Strand Quay

PETS: Bedrooms £5 Public areas (except dining room) Exercise area (4 minutes' walk) RESIDENT PETS: Tonkinese cats - Yum Yum & Monty

Previously a 17th-century wool store and then a 19th-century Baptist school, this delightful house stands on an ancient cobbled street in one of the most beautiful parts of this small, bustling town. The individually decorated bedrooms combine traditional elegance and comfort with modern facilities. Breakfast is served at separate tables in the galleried dining room, and guests have the use of an oak-beamed lounge as well as a stylish book-lined bar with old chapel pews.
FACILITIES: 11 rms (10 en suite) (2 fmly) No smoking in dining room No smoking in 1 lounge TVB tea/coffee Direct dial from bedrooms Licensed Cen ht No children 12yrs No coaches **PRICES:** s £39–£79; d £86–£116✱ **PARKING:** 21 **CARDS:** ▨▨▨▨

♦♦♦ Little Saltcote

22 Military Rd TN31 7NY
☎ 01797 223210 🖷 01797 224474
e-mail: littlesaltcote.rye@virgin.net
Dir: turn off A268 onto Military Rd, signposted to Appledore. House 300mtrs on left

PETS: Bedrooms (unattended) Public areas (except dining room) Exercise area (100yds) RESIDENT PETS: Bajan - cat

This friendly, family-run guest house sits in quiet surroundings within walking distance of town. Bedrooms are pleasantly decorated and equipped with modern facilities and breakfast is served at individual tables in a smart dining room.
FACILITIES: 5 rms (3 en suite) (3 fmly) (1 GF) No smoking TVB tea/coffee Cen ht **PRICES:** s £30-£45; d £50-£70* **LB** **PARKING:** 3
CARDS:

SEAFORD — Map 05 TV49

AA Pet Friendly Guest Accommodation of the Year 2005 IAMS

♦♦♦♦ Silverdale

21 Sutton Park Rd BN25 1RH
☎ 01323 491849 🖷 01323 890854
e-mail: silverdale@mistral.co.uk
Dir: on A259 in the centre of Seaford, close to Memorial

PETS: Bedrooms Public areas (unless other guests object) Exercise area (2 minute walk) local map of dog walks and pubs that accept dogs, dog towel, bowls RESIDENT PETS: Bertie & Bessie - American Cocker Spaniels

A warm welcome is assured at this family run hotel, which is ideally situated for the town centre and seafront. Bedrooms are pleasantly decorated and equipped with many useful extras. Breakfast and dinner are served in the dining room whilst guests may also relax in the cosy well-stocked lounge bar that specialises in English wines and malt whiskies.
FACILITIES: 8 rms (6 en suite) (2 fmly) (1 GF) No smoking in 3 bedrooms No smoking in lounges TVB tea/coffee Direct dial from bedrooms Licensed Cen ht No coaches Dinner Last d 2pm
PRICES: s £28-£45; d £43-£65* **LB** **PARKING:** 6
CARDS:

UCKFIELD — Map 05 TQ42

★★★★ 74% Buxted Park Country House Hotel

HandPICKED

Buxted TN22 4AY
☎ 01825 733333 🖷 01825 732 990
e-mail: buxtedpark@handpicked.co.uk
Dir: From A26 onto A272 signed Buxted. Through lights, hotel 1 mile on right.

PETS: Bedrooms (unattended) £10 Exercise area 312-acre estate, dog bowls and baskets can be provided

An attractive Grade II listed Georgian mansion dating back to the 17th century. The property is set amidst 300 acres of beautiful countryside and landscaped gardens. The stylish, thoughtfully equipped bedrooms are split between the main house and the modern Garden Wing. An interesting choice of dishes is served in the original Victorian Orangery. Handpicked Hotels - AA Hotel Group of the Year 2004-5.
ROOMS: 44 en suite (6 fmly) (16 GF) No smoking in 22 bedrooms s £120-£370; d £140-£370 (incl. bkfst) **LB** **FACILITIES:** STV Fishing Snooker Sauna Solarium Gym Croquet lawn Putting green Beauty salon, clay pigeon shoot, archery, fishing, mountain biking, orienteering ch fac Xmas **PARKING:** 150 **NOTES:** No smoking in restaurant
CARDS:

SUSSEX, WEST

ARUNDEL — Map 04 TQ00

★★★ 67% Norfolk Arms

Forestdale Hotels

High St BN18 9AD
☎ 01903 882101 🖷 01903 884275
e-mail: norfolk.arms@forestdale.com

PETS: Bedrooms (unattended) £7.50 Public areas (not in restaurant) Pet Food

Built by the 10th Duke of Norfolk, this Georgian coaching inn enjoys a superb setting beneath the battlements of Arundel Castle. Bedrooms come in a variety of sizes and styles, all are well equipped. Public areas include two bars, a comfortable lounge, a traditional English restaurant and a range of meeting rooms.
ROOMS: 21 en suite 13 annexe en suite (4 fmly) (8 GF) No smoking in 6 bedrooms s fr £75; d fr £120 (incl. bkfst) **LB** **FACILITIES:** Xmas
PARKING: 34 **NOTES:** No smoking in restaurant
CARDS:

BOGNOR REGIS — Map 04 SZ99

★★★ 64% The Inglenook

255 Pagham Rd, Nyetimber PO21 3QB
☎ 01243 262495 & 265411 🖷 01243 262668
e-mail: reception@the-inglenook.com
Dir: A27 to Vinnetrow Rd, left at Walnut Tree, 2.5m on right

PETS: Bedrooms (unattended) Public areas (Not in restaurant - only in bar/patio areas) Exercise area RESIDENT PETS: Nicky - Parrot; Cassie & Herbie - cats

This 16th-century inn retains much of its original character,

continued on p212

England

England

including exposed beams throughout. Bedrooms are individually decorated and vary in size. There is a cosy lounge, a well-kept garden and a bar (complete with a parrot and two cats) that offers a popular evening menu and convivial atmosphere. The restaurant, overlooking the garden, also serves enjoyable cuisine.
ROOMS: 18 en suite (1 fmly) (2 GF) No smoking in all bedrooms s £50-£70; d £70-£200 (incl. bkfst) **LB FACILITIES:** STV Xmas
PARKING: 35 **NOTES:** No smoking in restaurant
CARDS: ▨▨▨▨▨▨

CHARLTON   Map 04 SU81

◆◆◆◆ Woodstock House Hotel
PO18 0HU
☎ 01243 811666 🖷 01243 811666
e-mail: info@woodstockhousehotel.co.uk
Dir: take A286 S towards Chichester, on reaching Singleton turn left and follow road for 1m to Charlton. Hotel on left.

> **PETS:** Bedrooms Exercise area (adjacent)

Peacefully located accommodation in the pleasant village of Charlton, close to a range of recommended inns and restaurants together with all the attractions of Chichester and Goodwood. Bedrooms are individually decorated and well equipped with many useful extras. Several rooms overlook the pleasant rear garden. The proprietors here offer an especially friendly welcome.
FACILITIES: 12 en suite (1 GF) No smoking in bedrooms No smoking in dining room No smoking in lounges TVB tea/coffee Direct dial from bedrooms Licensed Cen ht No coaches **PRICES:** s £50-£58; d £75-£98✳ **PARKING:** 12 **CARDS:** ▨▨▨▨▨▨

CHICHESTER   Map 04 SU80

★★★ 70% ◉
Crouchers Country Hotel & Restaurant
Birdham Rd PO20 7EH
☎ 01243 784995 🖷 01243 539797
e-mail: crouchers@btconnect.com
Dir: off A27 to A286, 1.5m from Chichester centre opp Black Horse pub

> **PETS:** Bedrooms (unattended) £10

This friendly, family run hotel is situated in open countryside and within a short drive from the harbour. The comfortable and well-equipped rooms include some in a separate barn and coachhouse
continued

and the open-plan public areas enjoy a spacious and attractive aspect.
ROOMS: 18 en suite (1 fmly) (12 GF) No smoking in 9 bedrooms
FACILITIES: STV Xmas **PARKING:** 70 **NOTES:** No smoking in restaurant
CARDS: ▨▨▨▨▨▨

◆◆◆◆ Old Chapel Forge
Lower Bognor Rd, Lagness PO20 1LR
☎ 01243 264380 🖷 01243 261649
e-mail: cfbarnes@breathemail.net
Dir: from A27 Chichester By-Pass, exit on Bognor rdbt signed Pagham/Runcton, in S direction. At rdbt turn left onto B2166 Pagham Rd, continue to Royal Oak PH on right. Left onto Lower Bognor Rd for 0.75m Old Chapel Forge on right

> **PETS:** Bedrooms Public areas Exercise area (on site)
> **RESIDENT PETS:** Eddie and Elle (geese), Jade (Labrador), Sammy (parrot)

Old Chapel Forge is located in beautiful rural surroundings and overlooks sweeping fields. The accommodation takes the form of a self-contained suite, which includes its own dining area, comfortable lounge and en suite bedroom. Breakfast is substantial and of a high quality.
FACILITIES: 1 en suite (1 fmly) (1 GF) No smoking TVB tea/coffee Cen ht TVL No coaches Croquet lawn Dinner Last d prior to stay
PRICES: s £25-£50; d £50-£80✳ **LB PARKING:** 5

CHILGROVE   Map 04 SU81

◆◆◆◆ ◉◉ 🍴 ◀🔳 The White Horse
PO18 9HX
☎ 01243 535219 🖷 01243 535301
e-mail: info@whitehorsechilgrove.co.uk
Dir: From Midhurst, take A286 then B2141 for 4m. From Petersfield, take B2146 to South Harting, then B2141 for 3m.

> **PETS:** Bedrooms (unattended) Exercise area Beanbags, bowls and leads available if forgotten **RESIDENT PETS:** Beth & Holly - working Cocker Spaniels

Dating back in parts to the seventeenth century, this homely inn still retains much of the charm of yesteryear with its wooden beams and stone floors. Food and service however are completely up to date and memorable, while the smart new bedrooms are situated in a nearby annexe and are well equipped and furnished.
FACILITIES: 8 en suite (5 GF) No smoking TVB tea/coffee Direct dial from bedrooms Cen ht No coaches Dinner Last d 10pm
PRICES: s £65-£95; d £95-£120✳ **LB PARKING:** 60 **NOTES:** Closed Sun evening & all day Mon **CARDS:** ▨▨▨▨▨▨

CLIMPING   Map 04 SU90

★★★ 78% ◉◉
Bailiffscourt Hotel & Health Spa
Climping St BN17 5RW
☎ 01903 723511 🖷 01903 718987
e-mail: bailiffscourt@hshotels.co.uk
Dir: turn off A259 at Climping following signs for Climping Beach. Hotel 0.5m on right

> **PETS:** Bedrooms (unattended) Public areas

Dating from just the 1920s, this 'medieval manor' looks like it
continued

might have been there for centuries. Bedrooms are spacious and atmospheric in parts, whilst newer rooms provide an impressive contrast of style. There is a choice of cosy lounges, warmed by log fires in the cooler months, and carefully prepared meals are served. A well-equipped spa completes the package.
ROOMS: 9 en suite 30 annexe en suite (25 fmly) (16 GF) s £165-£270; d £185-£450 (incl. bkfst) **LB FACILITIES:** Spa STV Indoor swimming (H) Outdoor swimming (H) Tennis (hard) Sauna Gym Croquet lawn Jacuzzi ch fac Xmas **PARKING:** 100 **NOTES:** No smoking in restaurant **CARDS:**

CUCKFIELD
Map 04 TQ32

★★★ ◎◎◎ Ockenden Manor
Ockenden Ln RH17 5LD
☎ 01444 416111 📠 01444 415549
e-mail: ockenden@hshotels.co.uk
Dir: from N, at end of M23 continue on A23 towards Brighton. 4.5m S of end of motorway turn left onto B2115 towards Haywards Heath. 3m on and hotel at end of Ockendon Lane (off High Street)

PETS: Bedrooms (4 rooms available to guests with pets) (unattended) £10 Public areas (except restaurant) Exercise area

This charming 16th-century hotel enjoys fine views of the South Downs. Bedrooms offer high standards of accommodation, some with historic features. Public rooms, retaining much of the original character, include an elegant sitting room with all the elements for a relaxing afternoon in front of the fire. Cuisine is impressive and a highlight to any stay.
ROOMS: 22 en suite (4 fmly) (4 GF) s £99-£175; d £155-£325 (incl. bkfst) **LB FACILITIES:** STV Xmas **PARKING:** 43 **NOTES:** No smoking in restaurant **CARDS:**

GATWICK AIRPORT (LONDON)
Map 04 TQ24

◆◆◆◆ The Lawn
30 Massetts Rd RH6 7DF
☎ 01293 775751 📠 01293 821803
e-mail: info@lawnguesthouse.co.uk
Dir: M23 junct 9, follow signs to A23 (Redhill), at rdbt by Esso garage take 3rd exit, Massetts Rd 300yds on right

PETS: Bedrooms Exercise area (0.5 mile)

Ideally situated for Gatwick Airport, this fine detached Victorian house offers comfortable bedrooms, equipped with many thoughtful extras. The atmosphere is relaxed, the welcome friendly and there is even an Internet facility available to guests. A choice of breakfast is served in an attractive dining room.
FACILITIES: 12 en suite (4 fmly) No smoking TVB tea/coffee Direct dial from bedrooms Cen ht No coaches **PRICES:** s £40-£45; d £55-£60✽
PARKING: 15 **CARDS:**

> **Please mention AA Pet Friendly Places to Stay when booking**

◆◆◆◆ Rosemead
19 Church Rd RH6 7EY
☎ 01293 784965 📠 01293 430547
e-mail: info@rosemeadguesthouse.co.uk
Dir: exit M23 junct 9, follow A23 Redhill signs, through 3 rdbts, Church Rd is 4th on right, premises 3rd house on right

PETS: Telephone for details

This large Edwardian guest house is ideally located for the airport and is within walking distance of the town centre. All bedrooms are en suite, individually furnished and decorated with co-ordinated and attractive decor. Secure parking is a bonus.
FACILITIES: 6 en suite (2 fmly) No smoking STV TVB tea/coffee Cen ht No coaches **PARKING:** 40 **CARDS:**

◆◆◆◆ Vulcan Lodge
27 Massetts Rd RH6 7DQ
☎ 01293 771522 📠 01293 786206
e-mail: reservations@vulcan-lodge.com
Dir: M23 junct 9, follow signs A23 Redhill. At 4th rdbt exit right. Take 2nd right signposted Horley Town Centre. Premises 25mtrs on right

PETS: Bedrooms (Caged animals only unattended) Public areas (except breakfast room) Exercise area (10 mins' walk) **RESIDENT PETS:** Oscar - Border Collie, Emma & Max - cats

A particularly warm and friendly welcome is offered by the hosts of this charming period house, which sits back from the main road and is convenient for Gatwick Airport. Bedrooms are all individually decorated, well equipped and feature many thoughtful extras. A choice of breakfast is offered, including vegetarian, and is served in a delightful dining room.
FACILITIES: 4 rms (3 en suite) (1 fmly) No smoking TVB tea/coffee Cen ht TVL No coaches **PRICES:** s £36-£40; d £55✽ **PARKING:** 13 **CARDS:**

HENFIELD
Map 04 TQ21

◆◆◆◆ ❤ Frylands
Wineham BN5 9BP
☎ 01403 710214 📠 01403 711449
e-mail: b&b@frylands.co.uk
Dir: A23/ A272 signed Cowfold 1.5m on, turn left at x-rds into Wineham Ln. After 2m right into Fryland Ln. Frylands 0.3m on (left).

PETS: Sep Accom (outbuilding) Exercise area (25yds) **RESIDENT PETS:** Springer Spaniel - Polly

Friendly hosts offering comfortable accommodation at this delightful half-timbered 16th-century farmhouse, set in peaceful countryside. Day rooms and bedrooms are full of character and the well-appointed dining room is a delightful setting for freshly cooked breakfasts. Ample off road parking and free car storage for travellers using Gatwick Airport is available.
FACILITIES: 3 rms (1 fmly) No smoking TVB tea/coffee No dogs (ex guide dogs) Cen ht Indoor swimming pool (heated) Outdoor swimming pool (heated) Fishing Coarse fishing 250 acres Mixed **PRICES:** s £25-£30; d £40-£45✽ **PARKING:** 6 **NOTES:** Closed 20 Dec-1 Jan

LOWER BEEDING
Map 04 TQ22

★★★★ ◎◎◎ ♨♨ South Lodge
Brighton Rd RH13 6PS
☎ 01403 891711 🖹 01403 891766
e-mail: enquiries@southlodgehotel.co.uk
Dir: on A23 left onto B2110. Turn right through Handcross to A281 junct. Turn left and hotel on right

ExclusivE
HOTELS & GOLF CLUBS

> **PETS:** Bedrooms Public areas (except food service areas) Exercise area (on site) Pet Food Food and bowls provided with prior notice

This impeccably presented 19th-century lodge is an ideal retreat for guests who wish to enjoy stunning views over the rolling South Downs. The traditional, award-winning restaurant offers memorable, seasonal dishes, and the elegant lounge is popular for afternoon teas. Bedrooms are individually designed with character and quality throughout. Leisure and conference facilities are impressive.
ROOMS: 45 en suite (4 fmly) (7 GF) **FACILITIES:** STV Golf 18 Tennis (hard) Riding Snooker Gym Croquet lawn Putting green Can organise riding, shooting, fishing & quad biking entertainment **SERVICES:** Lift **PARKING:** 100 **NOTES:** No smoking in restaurant **CARDS:** 〰️ 🔳 🔳 🔳 🔳 🔳 🔳

MIDHURST
Map 04 SU82

★★★ 73% ◎ The Angel
North St GU29 9DN
☎ 01730 812421 🖹 01730 815928
e-mail: info@theangelmidhurst.co.uk
Dir: on S side of A272 in centre of Midhurst

> **PETS:** Bedrooms £5 Public areas (except food areas) (0.5 mile) Pet Food

Dating back to the 15th century, this charming hotel offers a relaxed homely atmosphere. Bedrooms are individually decorated with some, including a room for less able guests, situated in an adjacent annexe. Public areas boast a cosy bar complete with log fire, Gabrial's, a fine-dining restaurant and Halo, a contemporary brasserie.
ROOMS: 24 en suite 4 annexe en suite (2 GF) No smoking in all bedrooms s £80; d £110 (incl. bkfst) **LB FACILITIES:** STV entertainment Xmas **PARKING:** 75 **NOTES:** No smoking in restaurant **CARDS:** 〰️ 🔳 🔳 🔳 🔳 🔳

★★★ 71% ◎
Spread Eagle Hotel and Health Spa
South St GU29 9NH
☎ 01730 816911 🖹 01730 815668
e-mail: spreadeagle@hshotels.co.uk
Dir: from M25 junct 10 follow A3 S, exit A3 at Milford and follow A286 to Midhurst. Hotel adjacent to Market Square on South Street

> **PETS:** Bedrooms (unattended) £7.50 Public areas (except restaurant) Exercise area (500yds)

Offering accommodation since 1430, this historic property has plenty of character, evident in its sloping floors and inglenook fireplaces. Individually decorated bedrooms provide modern comforts; those in
continued

the main house have oak panelling. A spa with pool, gym and beauty treatments is an attraction, as is the restaurant.
ROOMS: 35 en suite 4 annexe en suite (8 GF) No smoking in 6 bedrooms s £85-£190; d £99-£225 (incl. bkfst) **LB FACILITIES:** Spa STV Indoor swimming (H) Sauna Gym Jacuzzi Health & beauty treatment rooms Steam room Fitness trainer Xmas **PARKING:** 75 **NOTES:** No smoking in restaurant **CARDS:** 〰️ 🔳 🔳 🔳 🔳 🔳 🔳

★★ 77% ♨♨ Park House
Bepton GU29 0JB
☎ 01730 819000 🖹 01730 819099
e-mail: reservations@parkhousehotel.com
Dir: from centre of Midhurst, take B2226 to Bepton. Hotel 2m on left

> **PETS:** Bedrooms Public areas (except at certain times) Exercise area (Large gardens)

This charming country house hotel is set in attractive mature grounds in peaceful rural surroundings. Bedrooms are very comfortable and well equipped, and the smart public rooms include an elegant drawing room, honesty bar and dining room. A small team of staff provides attentive and friendly service.
ROOMS: 16 en suite (2 fmly) (1 GF) s £75-£150; d £110-£190 (incl. bkfst) **LB FACILITIES:** STV Outdoor swimming (H) Golf 9 Tennis (grass) Croquet lawn Putting green ch fac Xmas **PARKING:** 35 **NOTES:** No smoking in restaurant **CARDS:** 〰️ 🔳 🔳 🔳 🔳 🔳

◆◆◆◆ Redford Cottage
Redford GU29 0QF
☎ 01428 741242
Dir: turn off A272 1m W of Midhurst, signed Redford, Redford Cottage is 400yds past Redford village sign on left

> **PETS:** Sep Accom (boot room) £5 Exercise area (Adjacent) Large garden, paddock & walks surrounding property
> RESIDENT PETS: Patch - tabby cat

This delightful old farmhouse sits in an Area of Outstanding Natural Beauty. Bedroom styles vary, with a traditional cottage room in the main house and a garden suite of stylish Swedish design; each room has access to a private sitting room. The main house lounge opens onto the attractive mature gardens, and breakfasts are served family-style in a separate dining room.
FACILITIES: 1 en suite 2 annexe en suite (1 GF) No smoking TVB tea/coffee Cen ht TVL No coaches **PRICES:** s £50-£55; d £75-£85✻ **PARKING:** 10 **NOTES:** Closed Xmas & New Year

PULBOROUGH
Map 04 TQ01

★★ 66% Chequers
Old Rectory Ln RH20 1AD
☎ 01798 872486 🖹 01798 872715
e-mail: info@thechequershotel.com
Dir: 100mtrs N of junct of A283/A29 opposite church in Pulborough

> **PETS:** Bedrooms Public areas (except restaurant & conservatory) Exercise area (opposite) Pet Food

This Grade II listed building has been lovingly restored, offering a warm welcome and comfortable accommodation. Bedrooms vary in size and are all individually decorated; one with a four-poster
continued

bed is available. Traditionally appointed cosy lounges are adjacent to the restaurant where enjoyable meals are served.

ROOMS: 10 en suite (3 fmly) (4 GF) No smoking in all bedrooms s £55-£70; d £90-£120 (incl. bkfst) **LB FACILITIES:** Xmas **PARKING:** 20 **NOTES:** No smoking in restaurant **CARDS:** ⬚⬚⬚ 🔲 🔲 🔲 🔲 🔲

◆◆◆ Arun House
Bury RH20 1NT
☎ 01798 831736
e-mail: arunway@hotmail.com
Dir: From Pulborough, take A29 south for 5miles. Signed on right hand side after Carringdales and Turners garages.

> **PETS:** Exercise area (Field next door) **Bowl provided 2 acre garden, numerous walks** RESIDENT PETS: Labradors - Amber & Charlie, chickens, pond with fish, moorhens & ducks

Conveniently located on the A29 and ideal for Arundel, Amberley Castle and the South Downs Way, this friendly family home is popular with ramblers and cyclists and offers comfortable accommodation. Guests may sit in the conservatory or on the terrace and enjoy the views across two acres of garden, with its pond, ducks and free-range chickens.
FACILITIES: 3 rms (1 fmly) No smoking TVB tea/coffee Cen ht No coaches Last d 24hrs prior **PRICES:** s fr £28; d fr £44✳ **PARKING:** 6

RUSTINGTON   Map 04 TQ00

◆◆◆◆ Kenmore
Claigmar Rd BN16 2NL
☎ 01903 784634 📠 01903 784634
e-mail: thekenmore@amserve.net
Dir: A259 follow signs for Rustington, turn for Claigmar Rd between War Memorial & Alldays. Kenmore on right as Claigmar Rd bends

> **PETS:** Bedrooms £1 Public areas (except dining room) Exercise area (10 mins' walk)

A warm welcome is assured at this Edwardian house, located close to the sea and convenient for touring West Sussex. Spacious bedrooms, all individually decorated, are provided with many useful extras. There is a comfortable lounge in which to relax and a bright dining room where a good choice of breakfast is served.
FACILITIES: 7 rms (6 en suite) (2 fmly) (2 GF) No smoking TVB tea/coffee Cen ht No coaches **PRICES:** s £20-£26; d £52✳
PARKING: 7 **CARDS:** ⬚⬚⬚ 🔲 🔲 🔲 🔲 🔲

SELSEY   Map 04 SZ89

◆◆◆◆ St Andrews Lodge Hotel
Chichester Rd PO20 0LX
☎ 01243 606899 📠 01243 607826
e-mail: info@standrewslodge.co.uk
Dir: turn off A27 onto the B2145 for 7 miles. Hotel is on right past Police Station just before the church

> **PETS:** Bedrooms (unattended) Public areas Exercise area
> RESIDENT PETS: Pepper & Poppy - cats

Located close to the town centre, this hotel provides comfortable accommodation and a warm welcome. Bedrooms are bright and spacious and all have a range of useful extras. There are five rooms in an annexe at the back of the house, and one is adapted for guests with disabilities. Dinner is available by prior arrangement.
FACILITIES: 5 en suite 5 annexe en suite (3 fmly) (5 GF) No smoking in bedrooms No smoking in dining room TVB tea/coffee Direct dial from bedrooms Licensed Cen ht TVL No coaches **PRICES:** s £30-£50; d £60-£75✳ **LB PARKING:** 12 **NOTES:** Closed 20 Dec-1 Jan
CARDS: ⬚⬚⬚ 🔲 🔲 🔲 🔲 🔲

SLINFOLD   Map 04 TQ13

◆◆◆ 🛏 🍴 The Red Lyon
The Street RH13 0RR
☎ 01403 790339 📠 01403 791863
e-mail: enquiries@theredlyon.co.uk
Dir: Slinfold signed from A264 & A29. The Red Lyon opposite the village shop

> **PETS:** Public areas Exercise area (20 yards)

Centrally located in the village of Slinfold this delightful inn, parts of which date back to the 14th century, has a wealth of beams and a timbered panelled dining room where tasty meals are provided at lunch and dinner. Bedrooms and bathrooms are well equipped and presented.
FACILITIES: 4 rms (3 en suite) (1 fmly) No smoking in bedrooms No smoking in dining room TVB tea/coffee Cen ht TVL Dinner Last d 9.30pm **PRICES:** d £40-£50; (room only) ✳ **PARKING:** 30
CARDS: ⬚⬚⬚ 🔲 🔲 🔲 🔲 🔲

WORTHING   Map 04 TQ10

★★ 65% Cavendish   THE INDEPENDENTS
115 Marine Pde BN11 3QG
☎ 01903 236767 📠 01903 823840
e-mail: cavendishworthing@btinternet.com
Dir: Hotel is on seafront 600yds W of pier

> **PETS:** Bedrooms (unattended) Public areas (not restaurant) Exercise area (20 yards)

This popular, family-run hotel enjoys a prominent seafront location. Bedrooms are well-equipped and soundly decorated. Guests have an extensive choice of meal options, with a varied bar menu, and carte and daily menus offered in the restaurant. Limited car parking is available at the rear of the hotel.
ROOMS: 17 en suite (4 fmly) No smoking in 3 bedrooms s £39.50-£45; d £65-£80 (incl. bkfst) **LB FACILITIES:** STV **SERVICES:** air con
PARKING: 5 **CARDS:** ⬚⬚⬚ 🔲 🔲 🔲 🔲 🔲

England

WORTHING continued

◆◆◆ Beechwood Hall
Wykeham Rd BN11 4JD
☎ 01903 205049 📠 01903 238165
e-mail: reception@beechwoodhall.co.uk
Dir: From A24 follow signs for Worthing. In town centre, turn right at traffic lights onto A259 to Littlehampton

PETS: Bedrooms Public areas (Not in the restaurant)
Exercise area (Directly behind establishment)

This lively family-run hotel is located within walking distance of the seafront and the town centre. Bedrooms are attractively decorated and feature a range of extra facilities. Popular dishes are served in the restaurant, and the well-kept gardens are an attractive feature.
FACILITIES: 8 en suite (2 fmly) No smoking in bedrooms No smoking in area of dining room TVB tea/coffee Licensed Cen ht Dinner
Last d 9.15pm **PRICES:** s £25-£60; d £45-£120✳ **LB PARKING:** 40
CARDS:

◆◆◆ Manor Guest House
100 Broadwater Rd BN14 8AN
☎ 01903 236028 📠 01903 230404
e-mail: stay@manorworthing.com
Dir: At Findon on A24 continue towards Worthing town centre. At lights at St. Marys Church, Manor Guest House is 175yds on left.

PETS: Bedrooms (unattended) Public areas (not in dining room) Exercise area (1 min walk) **RESIDENT PETS:** Jack (Westie)

This attractive guest house is located within walking distance of the centre of Worthing. Bedrooms are smartly presented and include thoughtful extras as a standard. Well-cooked breakfasts are served in the bright dining room, which has separate tables. Limited parking is also available to guests.
FACILITIES: 6 rms (3 en suite) (2 fmly) (1 GF) No smoking TVB tea/coffee Licensed Cen ht landscaped gardens Dinner Last d 7pm
PRICES: s £30-£35; d £60-£80✳ **LB PARKING:** 6
CARDS:

★ **Red stars indicate the AA's Top 200 Hotels in Britain & Ireland**

NEWCASTLE UPON TYNE   Map 12 NZ26

★★★★ 78% 🏵🏵 Newcastle Marriott Hotel Gosforth Park
High Gosforth Park, Gosforth NE3 5HN
☎ 0191 236 4111 📠 0191 236 8192
Dir: onto A1056 to Killingworth and Wideopen. 3rd exit to Gosforth Park, hotel ahead

PETS: Bedrooms Sep Accom (unattended) Exercise area

Extensive conference, banqueting and leisure facilities are features of this hotel set in its own grounds and convenient for the by-pass, the racecourse and the airport. Bedrooms are well-equipped, with the executive rooms offering king-sized beds, CD players and the use of the executive lounge.
ROOMS: 178 en suite (30 fmly) No smoking in 115 bedrooms
s £99-£109; d £99-£119 **LB FACILITIES: Spa** STV Indoor swimming (H) Tennis (hard) Squash Sauna Solarium Gym Jacuzzi Trim & jogging trail in hotel grounds entertainment **SERVICES:** Lift **PARKING:** 340
NOTES: RS Xmas & New year **CARDS:**

★★★★ 76% 🏵 Vermont
Castle Garth NE1 1RQ
☎ 0191 233 1010 📠 0191 233 1234
e-mail: info@vermont-hotel.co.uk
Dir: city centre by high level bridge and Castle Keep

PETS: Bedrooms (unattended) Public areas Exercise area Pet Food

Adjacent to the castle and close to the buzzing quayside area, this imposing hotel enjoys fine views of the Tyne Bridge. Thoughtfully equipped bedrooms offer a variety of styles, including grand suites. The elegant reception lounge and adjoining bar invite relaxation, while the Bridge restaurant is the focus for dining.
ROOMS: 101 en suite (12 fmly) No smoking in 20 bedrooms
s £120-£180; d £120-£180 **LB FACILITIES:** STV Solarium Gym ch fac Xmas **SERVICES:** Lift **PARKING:** 100 **NOTES:** No smoking in restaurant
CARDS:

★★★ 77% 🏵 Malmaison
Quayside NE1 3DX
☎ 0191 245 5000 📠 0191 245 4545
e-mail: newcastle@malmaison.com
Dir: follow signs for Newcastle City Centre, then for Quayside/Law Courts. Hotel 100yds past Law Courts

PETS: Telephone for details

Overlooking the river and the new Millennium Bridge, the hotel has a prime position in the up-and-coming redeveloped quayside district. Bedrooms have striking décor, CD players, mini-bars and a number of individual, welcoming touches. Food and drink are an integral part of the operation here, with a stylish brasserie-style restaurant and café bar.
ROOMS: 116 en suite (10 fmly) s fr £129; d fr £129 **LB**
FACILITIES: STV Sauna Gym Xmas **SERVICES:** Lift air con
PARKING: 50 **CARDS:**

★★★ 63%
Quality Hotel Newcastle upon Tyne
Newgate St NE1 5SX
☎ 0191 232 5025 ▤ 0191 232 8428
e-mail: enquiries@hotels-newcastle-upon-tyne.com
Dir: A1(M) take A184 Gateshead and Newcastle centre, follow A6082. Cross Redheugh Bridge take right lane, right at 3rd set of lights, then immediate right on to Fenkle St. Car park behind Old Assembly Rooms

PETS: Bedrooms (unattended)

Benefiting from a city centre location and a secure rooftop car park, this hotel is popular with business travellers. Accommodation is provided in compact yet thoughtfully equipped bedrooms. The rooftop restaurant and lounge give fine views over the city.
ROOMS: 93 en suite (4 fmly) No smoking in 42 bedrooms s £96; d £110 **LB FACILITIES:** STV Xmas **SERVICES:** Lift **PARKING:** 120
NOTES: No smoking in restaurant
CARDS: ▤▤▤▤▤▤▤▤

★ 66% Hadrian Lodge Hotel
Hadrian Rd, Wallsend NE28 6HH
☎ 0191 262 7733 & 08081 086892 ▤ 0191 263 0714
e-mail: Claire.Stubbs@barbox.net
Dir: from Newcastle city centre follow signs for Tyne Tunnel and Wallsend. Then follow A187 to Wallsend and Newcastle. Hotel opposite Hadrian Rd Metro station

PETS: Bedrooms Exercise area

Mainly a business hotel, Hadrian Lodge lies on the north side of the River Tyne and takes its name from the nearby Roman remains. Situated only ten minutes away from Newcastle city centre, this hotel offers well-equipped and comfortable accommodation, many bedrooms being large. Home-cooked meals are served in the spacious bar and restaurant area.
ROOMS: 24 en suite (1 fmly) No smoking in 8 bedrooms s £39.50-£46; d £55 (incl. bkfst) **FACILITIES:** Xmas **PARKING:** 60 **NOTES:** No dogs (ex guide dogs) No smoking in restaurant
CARDS: ▤▤▤▤▤▤

◆◆◆ Clifton House Hotel
46 Clifton Rd, Off Grainger Park Rd NE4 6XH
☎ 0191 273 0407 ▤ 0191 273 0407
e-mail: cliftonhousehotel@hotmail.com
Dir: exit A1, Hexham A69 & City West A1856 junct, take A186 for 2m, right at General Hospital into Grainger Park Rd, left into Clifton Rd

PETS: Bedrooms

Situated west of the city in a quiet residential area, this fine period mansion has seen its public areas beautifully restored. They include a cosy residents' bar and elegant dining room. Bedrooms come in a variety of sizes and styles, the en suite rooms providing good levels of comfort.
FACILITIES: 11 rms (7 en suite) (3 fmly) No smoking in 4 bedrooms No smoking in dining room No smoking in 1 lounge TVB tea/coffee Licensed Cen ht TVL Dinner Last d 48hrs notice **PARKING:** 12
CARDS: ▤▤▤▤

WASHINGTON
Map 12 NZ35

★★★ 66%
George Washington Golf & Country Club
Stone Cellar Rd, High Usworth NE37 1PH
☎ 0191 402 9988 ▤ 0191 415 1166
e-mail: reservations@georgewashington.co.uk
Dir: turn off A1(M) junct 65 onto A194(M). Take A195 signed Washington North. Take last exit from rdbt for Washington then right at mini rdbt. Hotel 0.5m on right

PETS: Bedrooms £15 per dog per stay

Popular with business and leisure guests, this purpose-built hotel boasts two golf courses and a driving range. Bedrooms are generally spacious and comfortably equipped. Public areas include extensive conference facilities, a business centre and fitness club.
ROOMS: 103 en suite (9 fmly) (41 GF) No smoking in 44 bedrooms s £79; d £89 **LB FACILITIES:** Spa Indoor swimming (H) Golf 18 Squash Sauna Solarium Gym Putting green Jacuzzi Golf driving range, Pitch & Putt, Pool table, Beauty salon Xmas **PARKING:** 180 **NOTES:** No smoking in restaurant **CARDS:** ▤▤▤▤▤▤

WHICKHAM
Map 12 NZ26

★★★ 69% Gibside Arms
Front St NE16 4JG
☎ 0191 488 9292 ▤ 0191 488 8000
e-mail: reception@gibside-hotel.co.uk
Dir: off A1(M) towards Whickham on B6317, onto Whickham Front Street, 2m on right

PETS: Bedrooms (unattended) Exercise area (100yds) park opposite hotel

Conveniently located in the village centre, this hotel is close to the Newcastle by-pass and its elevated position affords views over the Tyne Valley. Bedrooms come in two styles, classical and contemporary. Public rooms include the Egyptian-themed Sphinx bar and a more formal restaurant. Secure garage parking is available.
ROOMS: 45 en suite (2 fmly) (13 GF) No smoking in 10 bedrooms s £45-£59.50; d £60-£71 **LB FACILITIES:** STV Golf Academy at The Beamish Park entertainment ch fac Xmas **SERVICES:** Lift **PARKING:** 28
CARDS: ▤▤▤▤▤▤

WARWICKSHIRE

ALDERMINSTER
Map 04 SP24

◆◆◆◆ 🍴 The Bell
Shipston Rd CV37 8NY
☎ 01789 450414 ▤ 01789 450998
e-mail: thebellald@aol.com
Dir: on A3400 3m S of Stratford-upon-Avon on Shipston-Oxford road

PETS: Bedrooms £10 Public areas (Only in bar and garden) Exercise area (Next door) Bowls provided, enclosed garden with some shade

A focal part of the local community, this former coaching house retains many original features enhanced by quality decor in the public areas. The inn specialises in gastronomic festivals

continued on p218

ALDERMINSTER continued

throughout the year and the thoughtfully furnished bedrooms are located in a sympathetically renovated separate house or a quality coach house conversion, accessed via the immaculate gardens.
FACILITIES: 6 annexe rms (3 en suite) (2 fmly) (2 GF) No smoking in bedrooms No smoking in dining room No smoking in lounges TVB tea/coffee Cen ht Dinner Last d 9.30pm **PRICES:** s £27-£52; d £48-£70✱ **LB PARKING:** 70 **CARDS:**

ANSTY   Map 04 SP48

★★★★ 69% Ansty Hall
Main Rd CV7 9HZ
☎ 024 7661 2222 ▪ 024 7660 2155
e-mail: ansty@macdonald-hotels.co.uk
Dir: M6 junct 2 onto B4065 signed 'Ansty'. Hotel 1.5m on left

MACDONALD HOTELS

> **PETS:** Bedrooms Exercise area (in grounds)

Dating back to 1678, this Grade II listed Georgian house is set within eight acres of attractive grounds and woodland. The hotel enjoys the best of both worlds with its central, yet tranquil location. Spacious bedrooms feature a traditional decorative style and a range of extras. Rooms are divided between the main house and the more recently built annexe.
ROOMS: 23 en suite 39 annexe en suite (4 fmly) (22 GF) No smoking in 24 bedrooms **FACILITIES: SERVICES:** Lift **PARKING:** 150
NOTES: No smoking in restaurant **CARDS:**

BRANDON   Map 04 SP47

★★★ 67% Brandon Hall
Main St CV8 3FW
☎ 0870 400 8105 ▪ 024 7654 4909
e-mail: general.brandonhall@macdonald-hotels.co.uk
Dir: A45 towards Coventry S. After Peugeot-Citroen garage on left, at island take 5th exit to M1 South/London (back onto A45). After 200yds, immediately past Texaco garage, left into Brandon Ln, hotel after 2.5m

MACDONALD HOTELS

> **PETS:** Bedrooms (unattended) £10 Public areas (except restaurant/bar) Exercise area (200 metres)

Set within 17 acred of well-tended lawns and woodland, this former shooting lodge is located within easy reach of Coventry and Rugby. Public rooms are stylishly decorated and fairly modern in style, bedrooms are more traditional. Leisure facilities include a pitch and putt course and squash courts.
ROOMS: 60 en suite (7 fmly) (20 GF) No smoking in 35 bedrooms s £85-£125; d £105-£145 (incl. bkfst) **LB FACILITIES:** STV Squash Croquet lawn Putting green Xmas **PARKING:** 100 **NOTES:** No smoking in restaurant **CARDS:**

> 🌲 **Places with this symbol are country house hotels**

> 🐾 **Places with this symbol are farms**

GREAT WOLFORD   Map 04 SP23

◆◆◆◆ 🍴 The Fox & Hounds Inn
CV36 5NQ
☎ 01608 674220 ▪ 01608 674160
e-mail: info@thefoxandhoundsinn.com
Dir: off A3400 4m S of Shipston-on-Stour towards The Wolfords, 1.5m to Great Wolford

> **PETS:** Bedrooms (unattended) £5 Public areas (if well behaved) Exercise area (adjacent) **RESIDENT PETS:** Connie (Collie/Spaniel cross), Pippi & Caffrey (cats)

Very much a focal point of the local community, this 16th-century inn retains many original features which are enhanced by the rustic furniture styles and memorabilia. The thoughtfully furnished bedrooms are located in a sympathetic conversion of outbuildings, and a warm welcome is assured.
FACILITIES: 3 annexe en suite No smoking in bedrooms No smoking in area of dining room No smoking in lounges TVB tea/coffee Cen ht No children 10yrs No coaches Dinner Last d 9pm **PARKING:** 10
CARDS:

HENLEY-IN-ARDEN   Map 07 SP16

★★ 65% Henley
Tanworth Ln B95 5RA
☎ 01564 794551 ▪ 01564 795044
e-mail: reception@henleyhotel.co.uk
Dir: Follow A3400 towards Henley-in-Arden

> **PETS:** Bedrooms (unattended) £7.50 Exercise area (250mtrs)

This popular hotel is located just outside Henley-in-Arden and is well situated for access to major road networks. Bedrooms vary in style and all are thoughtfully equipped. Parking is an asset.
ROOMS: 32 en suite (2 fmly) (14 GF) No smoking in 19 bedrooms s fr £49.50; d £59.50-£69.50 **LB FACILITIES:** STV **PARKING:** 40
NOTES: No smoking in restaurant
CARDS:

◆◆◆◆ Ashleigh House
Whitley Hill B95 5DL
☎ 01564 792315 ▪ 01564 794126
e-mail: enquiries@ashleigh-house.fsbusiness.co.uk
Dir: leave A3400 at lights on High St. Along A4189 towards Warwick, Ashleigh House, 1m from lights

> **PETS:** Bedrooms (unattended) Variable Public areas (Except dining room or lounge) Exercise area (30 yards)

Set in two acres of immaculate grounds, this impressive Edwardian house has been sympathetically upgraded, enhancing the many original features. Spacious bedrooms, some of which are located in former stable blocks, provide both practicality and comfort and ground floor areas include an elegant dining room, conservatory and a lounge with an honesty bar.
FACILITIES: 6 en suite 5 annexe en suite (2 fmly) (5 GF) No smoking in bedrooms No smoking in dining room No smoking in lounges TVB tea/coffee Direct dial from bedrooms Licensed Cen ht TVL No coaches Dinner Last d before noon **PRICES:** s £45-£55; d £55-£69.50✱ **LB PARKING:** 17 **CARDS:**

LEAMINGTON SPA (ROYAL)   Map 04 SP36

★★★ 70% Courtyard by Marriott Leamington Spa

Olympus Av, Tachbrook Park CV34 6RJ
☎ 01926 425522 ▤ 01926 881322
e-mail: reservations.leamingtonspa@whitbread.com
Dir: From M40 J13 (northbound exit) or M40 J14 (southbound exit) follow signs for Leamington A452

PETS: Bedrooms (unattended) £10 Exercise area

Just a short distance from both Warwick and Leamington Spa, this modern hotel is conveniently situated for local businesses and tourist attractions. Bedrooms are furnished and decorated to a high standard providing a comprehensive range of extras. A friendly and helpful team efficiently delivers a professional service.
ROOMS: 91 en suite (14 fmly) (13 GF) No smoking in 48 bedrooms s £52-£129; d £74-£149 (incl. bkfst) LB **FACILITIES:** STV Gym Xmas
SERVICES: Lift **PARKING:** 150 **NOTES:** No smoking in restaurant
CARDS: ▤▤▤▤▤

★★★ 66% Falstaff

16-20 Warwick New Rd CV32 5JQ
☎ 01926 312044 ▤ 01926 450574
e-mail: falstaff@meridianleisure.com
Dir: M40 junct 13 or 14 follow signs for Leamington Spa. Over 4 rdbts then under bridge. Left into Princes Drive, then right at mini rdbt

PETS: Bedrooms (unattended) £10 Exercise area (adjacent)

Bedrooms at this hotel come in a variety of sizes and styles and are well-equipped, with many thoughtful extras. Snacks can be taken within the relaxing lounge bar and an interesting selection of English and continental dishes is offered in the restaurant; 24-hour room service is also available. Conference and banqueting facilities are extensive.
ROOMS: 63 en suite (2 fmly) (16 GF) No smoking in 13 bedrooms s £70-£80; d £80-£90 (incl. bkfst) LB **FACILITIES:** Arrangement with local Health Club Xmas **PARKING:** 50 **NOTES:** No smoking in restaurant
CARDS: ▤▤▤▤▤▤

★★★ 65% The Best Western Royal Leamington Hotel

64 Upper Holly Walk CV32 4JL
☎ 01926 883777 ▤ 01926 330467
e-mail: royal@meridianleisure.com
Dir: off A46 onto A452, left onto Clarendon Ave, then right into Clarendon St, then left, hotel on left

PETS: Bedrooms £10 Exercise area (100yds)

This Victorian town house is situated near the thriving shopping centre of Leamington Spa, yet retains the relaxed and peaceful feel of yesteryear. Bedrooms are individually appointed and well equipped; public areas are full of character and include a traditional residents' lounge. Guests can dine in the atmospheric brasserie, or choose from the room service menu.
ROOMS: 32 en suite (3 GF) No smoking in 10 bedrooms s £80; d £90 (incl. cont bkfst) LB **FACILITIES:** STV Xmas **PARKING:** 20
NOTES: No smoking in restaurant
CARDS: ▤▤▤▤▤▤

★★ 73% Adams

22 Avenue Rd CV31 3PQ
☎ 01926 450742 ▤ 01926 313110
e-mail: bookings@adams-hotel.co.uk
Dir: near Library on A452

PETS: Bedrooms (unattended) £2 Exercise area Pet Food

This elegant Regency town house, originally built in 1827, is now a privately owned hotel offering high-quality accommodation, delicious home-cooked food and a relaxing setting. Public areas include a residents' bar with leather armchairs, and a pretty garden. Bedrooms are equipped with thoughtful extras, such as modem points and bathrobes.
ROOMS: 12 en suite (3 GF) **PARKING:** 14 **NOTES:** No dogs No smoking in restaurant **CARDS:** ▤▤▤▤▤▤

◆◆◆◆ Bubbenhall House

Paget's Ln CV8 3BJ
☎ 02476 302409 ▤ 02476 302409
e-mail: wharrison@bubbenhallhouse.freeserve.co.uk
Dir: approaching Bubbenhall from Leamington on A445, village on left, Pagets lane on right. 1m on single track lane (pass 4 sleeping policemen)

PETS: Bedrooms Public areas (allowed in hall only) Exercise area (surrounding area) RESIDENT PETS: Zippy - Black Labrador, Kitty - cat

Located between Leamington Spa and Coventry in extensive mature grounds with an abundance of wildlife, this impressive late Edwardian house, once the home of the Mini's designer, contains many interesting features including a fine Jacobean staircase. Thoughtful extras are provided in the comfortable bedrooms and public areas include an elegant dining room and choice of sumptuous lounges.
FACILITIES: 3 en suite No smoking in bedrooms No smoking in dining room TVB tea/coffee Cen ht TVL No coaches Tennis (hard) Croquet lawn Petanque, spa hot tub **PRICES:** s £40-£45; d £59-£65✱ LB **PARKING:** 12

NUNEATON   Map 04 SP39

★★★ 65% Weston Hall

Weston Ln, Bulkington CV12 9RU
☎ 024 7631 2989 ▤ 024 7664 0846
e-mail: info@westonhallhotel.co.uk
Dir: M6 junct 2 follow B4065 through Ansty. Left in Shilton, follow Nuneaton signs out of Bulkington, turn into Weston Ln at 30mph sign

PETS: Bedrooms (unattended) Public areas (except during meal times) Exercise area (in grounds) Pet Food RESIDENT PETS: Charlie - tabby cat, and Snowy - Burmilla cat

This Grade II listed hotel, whose origins date back to the reign of Elizabeth I, sits within seven acres of peaceful grounds. The original three-gabled building retains many original features, such as the carved wooden fireplace situated in the library. Friendly

continued on p220

NUNEATON continued

service is provided; and bedrooms, that vary in size, are thoughtfully equipped.

Weston Hall

ROOMS: 40 en suite (1 fmly) No smoking in 8 bedrooms s £70-£105; d £85-£105 (incl. bkfst) **LB FACILITIES:** Spa Fishing Sauna Gym Croquet lawn Jacuzzi Steam room **PARKING:** 300 **NOTES:** No smoking in restaurant **CARDS:** 🖃 🖃 🖃 🖃 🖃 🖃

STRATFORD-UPON-AVON   Map 04 SP25

★★★★ 65% **The Alveston Manor**
Clopton Bridge CV37 7HP
☎ 0870 400 8181 📠 01789 414095
e-mail: sales.alvestonmanor@macdonald-hotels.co.uk

MACDONALD HOTELS

Dir: S of Clopton Bridge

PETS: Bedrooms (unattended) £10 Public areas (except dining areas) Exercise area (on site)

A striking red-brick and timbered facade, well-tended grounds, and a giant cedar tree all contribute to the charm of this well-established hotel, just five minutes from Stratford. The bedrooms vary in size and character - the coachhouse conversion offers an impressive mix of full and junior suites. The superb new leisure complex offers a 20-metre swimming pool and steam sauna, a high-tech gym and a host of beauty treatments in modern surroundings.

ROOMS: 113 en suite (8 fmly) (45 GF) No smoking in 46 bedrooms s £70-£160; d £140-£230 (incl. bkfst) **FACILITIES:** STV Indoor swimming (H) Sauna Solarium Gym Leisure facilities - techno-gym etc, beauty treatments Xmas **PARKING:** 150 **NOTES:** No smoking in restaurant **CARDS:** 🖃 🖃 🖃 🖃 🖃 🖃

★★★★ 61% **The Shakespeare**
Chapel St CV37 6ER
☎ 0870 400 8182 📠 01789 415411
e-mail: shakespeare@macdonald-hotels.co.uk

MACDONALD HOTELS

Dir: M40 junct 15, take A46 then A439 into one-way system, left at rdbt opposite HSBC Bank, hotel on the left

PETS: Bedrooms (unattended) £10 Public areas (except dining areas) Exercise area (100 metres)

Dating back to the early 17th century, the Shakespeare is one of the oldest hotels in this historic town. The hotel name also represents one of the earliest exploitations of Stratford as the birthplace of one of the world's leading poets and playwrights.

continued

With exposed beams and open fires, the public rooms retain an ambience reminiscent of this romantic era.

ROOMS: 63 en suite 11 annexe en suite (3 GF) No smoking in 18 bedrooms s £65-£150; d £130-£230 (incl. bkfst) **LB FACILITIES:** STV Use of swimming pool at sister hotel Xmas **SERVICES:** Lift **PARKING:** 34 **NOTES:** No smoking in restaurant **CARDS:** 🖃 🖃 🖃 🖃 🖃 🖃

★★★ 67% **The Swan's Nest**
Bridgefoot CV37 7LT
☎ 0870 400 8183 📠 01789 414547
e-mail: swansnest@macdonald-hotels.co.uk

MACDONALD HOTELS

Dir: M40 junct 15, A46 for 2m, at 1st island turn left onto A439 towards Stratford. Follow one way system, left over river bridge, hotel on right by river.

PETS: Bedrooms (unattended) £10 Public areas (except dining areas) Exercise area (on site) Pet Food

Dating back to the 17th century, this hotel is said to be one of the earliest brick-built houses in the town. The hotel occupies a prime position on the banks of the River Avon and is ideally situated for exploring the town and the surrounding Warwickshire countryside. Bedrooms, all named after birds, have now been refurbished to a high standard.

ROOMS: 67 en suite (2 fmly) (25 GF) No smoking in 45 bedrooms s £55-£135; d £110-£175 (incl. bkfst) **LB FACILITIES:** STV Use of facilities at sister hotel Xmas **PARKING:** 80 **CARDS:** 🖃 🖃 🖃 🖃 🖃 🖃

♦♦♦ **Avon Lodge**
Ryon Hill, Warwick Rd CV37 0NZ
☎ 01789 295196

PETS: Bedrooms Exercise area (on site)
RESIDENT PETS: Jacko & Paris (German Shepherds), Ollie (cat)

Located in immaculate mature gardens on the outskirts of town, this former Victorian cottage has been tastefully modernised and extended to provide homely and cosy bedrooms. Imaginative breakfasts are taken in an attractive cottage-style dining room.
FACILITIES: 6 en suite (1 fmly) No smoking TV5B tea/coffee Cen ht No coaches **PARKING:** 7

♦♦♦ **Marlyn**
3 Chestnut Walk CV37 6HG
☎ 01789 293752 📠 01789 293752
e-mail: evansmarlynhotel@aol.com

Dir: Evesham Road A439 towards town centre, 2nd right after rdbt

PETS: Bedrooms £2-3 Public areas (not in dining room) Exercise area (300yds) **RESIDENT PETS:** BT (cat), Charlie (mongrel)

An easy walk from the old part of the town centre and theatre and with unrestricted parking opposite, Marlyn offers cheery bedrooms and a cosy dining room - the setting for breakfasts which include good vegetarian options. Aromatherapy/reflexology can be arranged, and in addition to a lounge, the pretty garden is also available for guest use.
FACILITIES: 8 rms (5 en suite) (2 fmly) (1 GF) No smoking in 6 bedrooms No smoking in dining room TVB tea/coffee Licensed Cen ht No coaches Aromatherapy & reflexology treatment Dinner Last d breakfast/midday **PRICES:** s £20-£26; d £50-£56✱ **CARDS:** 🖃 🖃

England

WARWICK
Map 04 SP26

◆◆◆◆ Croft
Haseley Knob CV35 7NL
☎ 01926 484447 🖷 01926 484447
e-mail: david@croftguesthouse.co.uk
Dir: from Warwick by-pass take A4177 towards Solihull, 4.5m turn R signed M6 Stonebridge then 0.5m turn R to Haseley Knob and follow B&B signs

PETS: Bedrooms £3 Exercise area

Set in a peaceful countryside location, convenient for Warwick and the NEC, this modern, well-proportioned detached house offers comfortable, homely accommodation. Friendly proprietors provide a real 'home from home', and spacious, well-kept gardens are overlooked from the conservative dining room where fresh eggs from home-reared chickens are used for memorable English breakfasts.
FACILITIES: 7 rms (5 en suite) 2 annexe rms (1 en suite) (2 fmly) (4 GF) No smoking TVB tea/coffee Cen ht TVL No coaches
PRICES: s £35-£40; d £52-£58✳ **PARKING:** 8 **NOTES:** Closed Xmas wk
CARDS: 💳

◆◆◆◆ Dockers Barn Farm
Oxhill Bridle Rd, Pillerton Hersey CV35 0QB
☎ 01926 640475 🖷 01926 641747
e-mail: jwhoward@onetel.net.uk
Dir: A422 Stratford-upon-Avon to Banbury, left in Pillerton Priors to Pillerton Hersey, 1st right Oxhill Bridle Rd for 0.75m. Or M40 junct 12 onto B4451 to Pillerton Hersey, after 6m left by village seat onto Oxhill Bridle Rd

PETS: Bedrooms (In downstairs suite) (dogs can stay in stables) (unattended) Exercise area (surrounding countryside)
RESIDENT PETS: Sky - Labrador/Collie cross, Lottie - Rottweiler cross, Polly & Maisie - Shetland ponies, Minty - horse, bantams

Superbly located in an Area of Outstanding Natural Beauty, this former 18th-century threshing barn retains many original features including a wealth of exposed beams and flagstone floors. The bedrooms, one of which is situated within a sympathetic conversion of a granary, are equipped with lots of thoughtful extras and the open plan ground floor areas are furnished with style and quality.
FACILITIES: 3 en suite (1 fmly) (1 GF) No smoking TVB tea/coffee Cen ht No children 8yrs No coaches Garden hot-tub with hydrotherapy jets **PRICES:** d £50-£56✳ **PARKING:** 9 **NOTES:** Closed Xmas rs Daily

◆◆◆◆ 🍴 The Hare on the Hill
37 Coventry Rd CV34 5HN
☎ 01926 491366 & 496431
e-mail: prue@thehareonthehill.co.uk
Dir: On A429 Coventry Road between railway bridge(Lakin Road) and Guys Cross Road, close to Warwick Station

PETS: Bedrooms (unattended) Public areas (if animals get on with resident dogs) Exercise area (150yds)
RESIDENT PETS: Terry - terrier, Ed - scottie dog

This well furnished and comfortable house is very convenient for the town and provides well-equipped and characterful bedrooms together with a delightful guest lounge. The use of organic produce is of great importance here and excellent breakfasts are
continued

---

served around a large table in the hall. Guests can be sure of friendly and attentive service at all times.
FACILITIES: 7 en suite (1 fmly) (1 GF) No smoking in bedrooms No smoking in dining room TVB tea/coffee Cen ht No coaches Croquet lawn Dinner Last d 9.30pm **PRICES:** s £55-£65; d £80-£90✳
PARKING: 12 **NOTES:** Closed 24 Dec-3 Jan **CARDS:** 💳

WARWICK MOTORWAY SERVICE AREA (M40) Map 04 SP35

⬆ Days Inn Stratford upon Avon
Warwick Services, M40 Northbound
junction 12-13, Banbury Rd CV35 0AA
☎ 01926 651681 🖷 01926 651634
e-mail: warwick.north.hotel@welcomebreak.co.uk
Dir: M40 northbound between junct 12 & 13

PETS: Bedrooms Public areas Exercise area (adjacent)

This modern building offers accommodation in smart, spacious and well-equipped bedrooms, suitable for families and business travellers, and all with en suite bathrooms. Continental breakfast is available and other refreshments may be taken at the nearby family restaurant. For further details see the Hotel Groups page.
ROOMS: 54 en suite

⬆ Days Inn Stratford Upon Avon
Warwick Services, M40 Southbound, Banbury Rd
CV35 0AA
☎ 01926 650168 🖷 01926 651601
Dir: M40 southbound between junct 14 & 12

PETS: Bedrooms Public areas Exercise area (adjacent)

This modern building offers accommodation in smart, spacious and well-equipped bedrooms, suitable for families and business travellers, and all with en suite bathrooms. Continental breakfast is available and other refreshments may be taken at the nearby family restaurant. For further details see the Hotel Groups page.
ROOMS: 40 en suite

WEST MIDLANDS

BIRMINGHAM
Map 07 SP08

★★★ 79% ◉
Malmaison Birmingham
1 Wharfside St, The Mailbox B1 1RD
☎ 0121 246 5000 🖷 0121 246 5002
e-mail: birmingham@malmaison.com
Dir: M6 junct 6, follow A38 towards B'ham, hotel located within The Mailbox, signed from A38

PETS: Bedrooms £10

The 'Mailbox' development of which this stylish and contemporary hotel is a part incorporates the very best in fashionable shopping, an array of restaurants and ample car parking. Air-conditioned bedrooms are stylishly decorated and feature a great range of facilities. Public rooms include a stylish bar and brasserie which are already proving a hit with guests and locals alike.
ROOMS: 189 en suite No smoking in 132 bedrooms s £99-£129; d £99-£129 **FACILITIES:** Spa STV Sauna Gym Jacuzzi **SERVICES:** Lift air con **CARDS:** 💳

BIRMINGHAM continued

★★★ 70% The Westley

80-90 Westley Rd, Acocks Green B27 7UJ
☎ 0121 706 4312 📠 0121 706 2824
e-mail: reservations@westley-hotel.co.uk
Dir: A41 signed Birmingham on Solihull by-pass, continue to Acocks Green. At rdbt, 2nd exit B4146 Westley Rd. Hotel 200yds on left

PETS: Bedrooms (unattended) Exercise area Pet Food

Set in the city suburbs and conveniently located for the N.E.C and airport, this friendly hotel provides well-equipped, smartly presented bedrooms. In addition to the main restaurant, there is also a lively bar and brasserie together with a large function room.
ROOMS: 26 en suite 11 annexe en suite (1 fmly) No smoking in 15 bedrooms s £71.50-£130; d £83.50-£180 (incl. bkfst) **LB**
FACILITIES: STV Putting green entertainment **PARKING:** 150
NOTES: No smoking in restaurant
CARDS:

★★★ 67% Novotel Birmingham Centre

70 Broad St B1 2HT
☎ 0121 643 2000 📠 0121 643 9796
e-mail: h1077@accor-hotels.com

NOVOTEL

PETS: Bedrooms £5 per pet Public areas - Guide dogs only Pet Food

This large, modern, purpose built hotel benefits from an excellent city centre location, with the bonus of secure car parking. Bedrooms are spacious, modern and well-equipped for business users. Four rooms have facilities for disabled guests. Public areas include the Garden Brasserie, function rooms and a fitness room.
ROOMS: 148 en suite (148 fmly) No smoking in 98 bedrooms
s £80-£145; d £155-£165 (incl. bkfst) **LB FACILITIES:** STV Sauna Gym Jacuzzi **SERVICES:** Lift air con **PARKING:** 53
CARDS:

★★ 72% Copperfield House

60 Upland Rd, Selly Park B29 7JS
☎ 0121 472 8344 📠 0121 415 5655
e-mail: info@copperfieldhousehotel.fsnet.co.uk
Dir: M6 junct 6/A38 through city centre. After tunnels, right at lights into Belgrave Middleway. Right at rdbt onto A441. At Selly Park Tavern, right into Upland Rd

PETS: Bedrooms £5 (0.5 mile)

A delightful Victorian hotel, situated in a leafy suburb, close to the BBC's Pebble Mill Studios and within easy reach of the centre. Accommodation is smartly presented and well-equipped; the executive rooms are particularly spacious. A tasteful lounge with honesty bar, carefully prepared, seasonally-inspired food and a well-chosen wine list add to the attractions.
ROOMS: 17 en suite (1 fmly) (2 GF) s £45-£75; d £60-£90 (incl. bkfst)
LB PARKING: 11 **NOTES:** No smoking in restaurant
Closed 24 Dec-2 Jan **CARDS:**

★★ 66% Fountain Court

339-343 Fountain Court Hotel B17 8NH
☎ 0121 429 1754 📠 0121 429 1209
e-mail: info@fountain-court.net
Dir: on A456, towards Birmingham, 3 miles from M5 junct 3

THE INDEPENDENTS

PETS: Bedrooms Exercise area (200yds)
RESIDENT PETS: 1 Jack Russell and 2 cats

This family-owned hotel is on the A456, near to the M5 and a short drive from the city centre. Hospitality is excellent, the accommodation simple, and imaginative, home-cooked food is usually available.
ROOMS: 23 en suite (4 fmly) s £45-£48.50; d £65 (incl. bkfst)
PARKING: 20 **CARDS:**

⌂ Campanile

Aston Locks, Chester St B6 4BE
☎ 0121 359 3330 📠 0121 359 1223
e-mail: birmingham@envergure.co.uk
Dir: next to rdbt at junct of A4540/A38

Campanile

PETS: Bedrooms Public areas

This modern building offers accommodation in smart, well-equipped bedrooms, all with en suite bathrooms. Refreshments may be taken at the informal Bistro. For further details consult the Hotel Groups page.
ROOMS: 109 en suite s fr £48.50; d fr £48.50

♦♦♦ Awentsbury Hotel

21 Serpentine Rd, Selly Park B29 7HU
☎ 0121 472 1258 📠 0121 472 1258
e-mail: ian@awentsbury.com
Dir: A38 from city centre, at end of dual carriageway & just after fire station, take 1st left, left again & 1st right

PETS: Bedrooms Exercise area (0.5 mile)

This large Victorian house is quietly located in a residential area, within easy walking distance of the university and local restaurants. Bedrooms are simply furnished and many have en suite showers. Breakfast is taken in a combined lounge and dining room, overlooking the garden.
FACILITIES: 16 rms (7 en suite) (1 fmly) (4 GF) No smoking TVB tea/coffee Direct dial from bedrooms Cen ht Dinner Last d 7pm
PRICES: s £40-£50; d £54-£62✱ **PARKING:** 12
CARDS:

♦♦♦ Lyndhurst Hotel

135 Kingsbury Rd, Erdington B24 8QT
☎ 0121 373 5695 📠 0121 373 5697
e-mail: info@lyndhurst-hotel.co.uk
Dir: from M6 junct 6 follow A5127, at rdbt 2nd exit (Gravelly Hill). Right fork, along Kingsbury Road, Hotel on right

PETS: Telephone for details

Convenient for the M6 and many of the city's attractions and facilities, this peaceful hotel is situated in a pleasant residential area. Bedrooms are well appointed and comfortable, with some

continued

located on the ground floor. A spacious restaurant overlooks the attractive garden and guests may relax in the bar or cosy lounge.

FACILITIES: 14 en suite (2 fmly) (5 GF) No smoking TVB tea/coffee No dogs Licensed Cen ht TVL No children No coaches Dinner Last d 8.30pm **PRICES:** s £30-£42.50; d £42.50-£49.50✱ **PARKING:** **CARDS:**

◆◆ Rollason Wood Hotel
130 Wood End Rd, Erdington B24 8BJ
☎ 0121 373 1230 🖷 0121 382 2578
e-mail: rollwood@globalnet.co.uk
Dir: M6 J6, exit Birmingham Rd. At island take A5127 to Sutton & Erdington for 1m, at island turn R onto A4040, hotel 0.25m on L

PETS: Bedrooms Exercise area

Ideally situated for major road links and the city centre, this owner-managed commercial hotel is popular with contractors. It offers a choice of three different bedroom styles, suitable for most budgets, and rates include full English breakfasts. Ground floor areas include a popular bar, cosy television lounge and dining room.
FACILITIES: 35 rms (11 en suite) (5 fmly) No smoking in 7 bedrooms No smoking in area of dining room TVB tea/coffee Licensed Cen ht TVL Pool Table Games room & darts Dinner Last d 8.30pm
PRICES: s £19.50-£39; d £34.50-£49.50✱ **BB PARKING:** 35
CARDS:

BIRMINGHAM AIRPORT Map 07 SP18

★★★ 67%
Novotel Birmingham Airport
B26 3QL
☎ 0121 782 7000 🖷 0121 782 0445
e-mail: H1158@accor-hotels.com
Dir: M42 junct 6/A45 to Birmingham, signed to airport. Hotel opposite main terminal

PETS: Bedrooms £12 Public areas (On a lead)

This large, purpose-built hotel is located opposite the main passenger terminal. Bedrooms are spacious, modern in style and well equipped, including Playstations to keep the children busy. Two rooms have facilities for less able guests. The Garden Brasserie is open from noon until midnight and a full room service is available.
ROOMS: 195 en suite (31 fmly) No smoking in 159 bedrooms s £125-£149; d £135-£159 (incl. bkfst) **FACILITIES:** STV **SERVICES:** Lift air con **CARDS:**

BIRMINGHAM Map 07 SP18
(NATIONAL EXHIBITION CENTRE)

★★★ 68%
Arden Hotel & Leisure Club
Coventry Rd, Bickenhill B92 0EH
☎ 01675 443221 🖷 01675 445604
e-mail: enquiries@ardenhotel.co.uk
Dir: M42 junct 6/A45 towards Birmingham. Hotel 0.25m on right, just off Birmingham International railway island

THE INDEPENDENTS

PETS: Bedrooms (unattended) Exercise area (Perimeter)

This smart hotel neighbouring the NEC offers modern rooms and well-equipped leisure facilities. After dinner in the formal restaurant, the place to relax is the spacious lounge area. A buffet breakfast is served in the bright and airy Meeting Place.
ROOMS: 216 en suite (6 fmly) (6 GF) No smoking in 105 bedrooms s fr £65; d fr £75 **FACILITIES:** STV Indoor swimming (H) Snooker Sauna Solarium Gym Jacuzzi Steamroom entertainment Xmas
SERVICES: Lift **PARKING:** 300 **NOTES:** No smoking in restaurant
CARDS:

★★ 67% Heath Lodge
117 Coleshill Rd, Marston Green B37 7HT
☎ 0121 779 2218 🖷 0121 779 2218
e-mail: reception@heathlodgehotel.freeserve.co.uk
Dir: M6 junct 4/A446 towards N Coleshill. After 0.5m turn left into Coleshill Heath Rd, signed to Marston Green. Hotel on right

PETS: Bedrooms £5 Public areas Exercise area (0.5 mile)

This privately-owned and personally-run hotel is ideally located for visitors to the NEC and Birmingham Airport. Hospitality and service standards are high and while some bedrooms are compact, all are well equipped and suitably comfortable. Public areas include a bar, a lounge and a dining room which overlooks the garden.
ROOMS: 17 rms (16 en suite) (1 fmly) s £49-£59; d £69-£77 (incl. bkfst)
PARKING: 22 **NOTES:** No smoking in restaurant
CARDS:

COVENTRY Map 04 SP37

⇧ Hotel Ibis Coventry South
Abbey Rd, Whitley CV3 4BJ
☎ 024 7663 9922 🖷 024 7630 6898
e-mail: H2094@accor-hotels.com
Dir: signed from A46/A423 rdbt. Take A423 towards A45. Follow signs for Esporta Health Club and Jaguar Engineering Plant

ibis

PETS: Bedrooms Public areas (except in bar/restaurant) Exercise area (adjacent)

Modern, budget hotel offering comfortable accommodation in bright and practical bedrooms. Breakfast is self-service and dinner is available in the restaurant. For further details, consult the Hotel Groups page.
ROOMS: 51 en suite s £30.95-£53.95; d £43.95-£53.95

COVENTRY continued

♦♦♦♦ Toffs Hotel

Wall Hill Rd, Corley CV7 8AD
☎ 024 7633 2030 ⓘ 024 7633 2102
e-mail: stay@toffs-hotel.co.uk
Dir: from N leave A45 at Oak Lane (signed Corley). Continue along Bridle Brook Ln. At T-junct right & Toffs 100yds on left. From S leave A45 at A4114, follow City Centre signs, left onto Coundon Wedge Rd, past Jaguar HQ, left at next rdbt. Right at White Lion pub & Toffs 1m on right

PETS: Bedrooms (unattended) Public areas (except dining room) Exercise area (on site) RESIDENT PETS: Bramble (Staffordshire Bull Terrier)

Toffs Country House, as the name suggests, is set in an attractive rural setting yet has close road links to the city. Bedrooms afford country views, and are furnished with much thought for guest comfort. Guests have a wide choice of lounges, a bar and even a games room.
FACILITIES: 10 en suite (1 GF) No smoking in 8 bedrooms No smoking in dining room No smoking in lounges TVB tea/coffee Licensed Cen ht TVL No coaches Tennis (grass) Pool Table Croquet lawn 1/2 size snooker table **PRICES:** s £49.50-£59.50; d £65-£75✳ **PARKING:** 14
CARDS: ▭▭ ▭▭ ▭ ▭ ▭ ⑤

HAMPTON-IN-ARDEN   Map 04 SP28

♦♦♦ The Cottage

Kenilworth Rd B92 0LW
☎ 01675 442323 ⓘ 01675 443323
Dir: on A452, 2m from M42, 4m from M6, 3m NEC & B'ham airport

PETS: Bedrooms Exercise area RESIDENT PETS: North and South (Longhaired German Shepherds)

A fine collection of antique memorabilia adorns the public areas of this delightful cottage, which is an ideal base from which to visit the NEC or to explore the area. A friendly atmosphere and attentive service provide a relaxing environment and many guests return. Freshly cooked traditional breakfasts are served in the cottage dining room and provide a good start to the day.
FACILITIES: 9 en suite (2 GF) No smoking in dining room TVB tea/coffee Cen ht TVL **PRICES:** s £35-£45; d £48-£58✳ **PARKING:** 14
NOTES: Closed Xmas

HOCKLEY HEATH   Map 07 SP17

★★★ ◉◉◉ ♨♦
Nuthurst Grange Country House & Restaurant

Nuthurst Grange Ln B94 5NL
☎ 01564 783972 ⓘ 01564 783919
e-mail: info@nuthurst-grange.com
Dir: off A3400, 0.5mile south of Hockley Heath. Turn at sign into Nuthurst Grange Lane

PETS: Bedrooms

The approach to this period country house is a stunning avenue drive, and the hotel benefits from several acres of well-tended gardens and mature grounds and views over rolling countryside. Public areas include restful lounges, meeting rooms and a sunny restaurant. The kitchen brigade produces highly imaginative British

continued

and French cuisine, complemented by very attentive, professional restaurant service. The spacious bedrooms and bathrooms offer considerable luxury and comfort.
ROOMS: 15 en suite (2 GF) s £129-£139; d £165-£195 (incl. bkfst) LB
FACILITIES: STV Croquet lawn Helipad **PARKING:** 86
NOTES: No smoking in restaurant Closed 1 wk Xmas
CARDS: ▭▭ ▭▭ ▭ ▭ ▭ ⑤

MERIDEN   Map 04 SP2

★★★ 70% ◉ **Manor**
Main Rd CV7 7NH
☎ 01676 522735 ⓘ 01676 522186
e-mail: reservations@manorhotelmeriden.co.uk
Dir: M42 junct 6 take A45 towards Coventry then A452, signed Leamington. At rbt join B4102, signed Meriden, for hotel on left.

PETS: Bedrooms (unattended)

A sympathetically extended Georgian manor in the heart of this sleepy village, a few minutes away from the M6, M42 and National Exhibition Centre. The Regency Restaurant offers modern dishes, while the Triumph Buttery serves lighter meals and snacks. Bedroom styles vary considerably; the Executive rooms and those in the Princess Diana wing are smart and well equipped.
ROOMS: 110 en suite (20 GF) No smoking in 54 bedrooms s £65-£145; d £80-£155 (incl. bkfst) LB **SERVICES:** Lift **PARKING:** 200
NOTES: No smoking in restaurant RS 24 Dec-2 Jan
CARDS: ▭▭ ▭▭ ▭ ▭ ▭ ⑤

WALSALL   Map 07 SP0?

★★★ 64%
Quality Hotel Birmingham North

Birmingham Rd WS5 3AB
☎ 01922 633609 ⓘ 01922 635727
e-mail: info@boundaryhotel.com
Dir: M6 junct 7, A34 to Walsall. Hotel 1.5m on left

PETS: Bedrooms (unattended) Public areas (Except food service areas) Exercise area (0.5 mile)

Bedrooms at this purpose-built hotel, including some on the ground floor, are soundly furnished and well equipped. Public areas include a pleasantly appointed main restaurant (more informal meals are served in the public bar) and a cellar bar which occasionally features live music. Hotel guests also have the use of a well-maintained tennis court.
ROOMS: 96 en suite (3 fmly) (4 GF) No smoking in 50 bedrooms s £105; d £105 LB **FACILITIES:** STV Tennis (hard) Pool table entertainment Xmas **SERVICES:** Lift **PARKING:** 250
NOTES: No smoking in restaurant
CARDS: ▭▭ ▭▭ ▭ ▭ ▭ ⑤

> **All information was correct at the time of going to press; we recommend you confirm details on booking**

WOLVERHAMPTON

Map 07 SO99

★★★ 66% **Novotel Wolverhampton**

Union St WV1 3JN
☎ 01902 871100 📠 01902 870054
e-mail: H1188@accor-hotels.com

Dir: 6m from M6 junct 10. A454 to Wolverhampton. Hotel on main ring road

PETS: Bedrooms (unattended) £5 Public areas (Bar/lounge only) Exercise area (5-minute drive)

This large, modern, purpose-built hotel stands close to the town centre and ring road. It provides spacious, smartly presented and well-equipped bedrooms, all of which contain convertible bed settees for family occupancy. In addition to the open plan lounge and bar area, there is an attractive brasserie-style restaurant, which overlooks the small outdoor swimming pool.

ROOMS: 132 en suite (10 fmly) No smoking in 88 bedrooms s £65-£105; d £75-£115 (incl. bkfst) **LB FACILITIES:** STV Outdoor swimming (H)
SERVICES: Lift **PARKING:** 120 **CARDS:**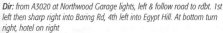

 **WIGHT, ISLE OF**

COWES

Map 04 SZ49

★★★ 68% **New Holmwood**

Queens Rd, Egypt Point PO31 8BW
☎ 01983 292508 📠 01983 295020
e-mail: nholmwdh@aol.com

Dir: from A3020 at Northwood Garage lights, left & follow road to rdbt. 1st left then sharp right into Baring Rd, 4th left into Egypt Hill. At bottom turn right, hotel on right

PETS: Bedrooms Public areas (except restaurant) Exercise area (beach 2 mins' walk)

Just metres from the Esplanade, this hotel has an enviable outlook. Bedrooms are comfortable and very well equipped. The glass-fronted restaurant serves a range of interesting meals and is light and airy restaurant and looks out to sea. The sun terrace is delightful in the summer. There is a small pool area and a conference room.

ROOMS: 26 en suite (1 fmly) (9 GF) No smoking in all bedrooms s £75-£120; d £90-£120 (incl. bkfst) **LB FACILITIES:** Spa STV Outdoor swimming (H) Xmas **PARKING:** 20 **NOTES:** No smoking in restaurant **CARDS:**

◆◆◆ **Windward House**

69 Mill Hill Rd PO31 7EQ
☎ 01983 280940 & 07771 573580 📠 01983 280940
e-mail: DavRob520@hotmail.com

Dir: A320 Cowes-Newport, halfway up Mill Hill Rd on right from floating bridge from E Cowes (Red Funnel Ferries)

PETS: Bedrooms Public areas (except dining room) Exercise area (0.25 miles) **RESIDENT PETS:** Saracen (German Shepherd)

A friendly atmosphere prevails at this comfortable Victorian house, located close to the centre of Cowes. Bedrooms are bright and neat, and downstairs there is a spacious lounge equipped with

continued

satellite TV, video and music systems. Breakfast is served in a separate dining room around a shared table.

FACILITIES: 6 rms (3 en suite) (2 fmly) (1 GF) No smoking in 1 bedrooms No smoking in dining room TVB tea/coffee Cen ht TVL No coaches Outdoor swimming pool (heated) **PRICES:** s £20-£30; d £40-£60✳ **PARKING:** 4

FRESHWATER

Map 04 SZ38

★★★ 68% ◉ **Farringford**

Bedbury Ln PO40 9TQ
☎ 01983 752500 📠 01983 756515

Dir: A3054, left to Norton Green down Pixlie Hill. Left to Freshwater Bay. At bay turn right into Bedbury Ln, hotel on left

PETS: Bedrooms (unattended) £5 Exercise area
RESIDENT PETS: Woodie (Irish Setter)

Upon seeing Farringford, Alfred Lord Tennyson is said to have remarked "we will go no further, this must be our home" and so it was for some forty years. One hundred and fifty years later, the hotel provides bedrooms ranging in style and size, from large rooms in the main house to adjoining chalet-style rooms. The atmosphere is relaxed and dinner features fresh local produce.

ROOMS: 14 en suite 4 annexe en suite (5 fmly) (4 GF) s £37-£53; d £74-£120 (incl. bkfst) **LB FACILITIES:** Outdoor swimming (H) Golf 9 Tennis (hard) Croquet lawn Putting green Bowling green entertainment ch fac Xmas **PARKING:** 55 **CARDS:**

All AA listed accommodation, restaurants and pubs can be found on the AA's website www.theAA.com

England

RYDE
Map 04 SZ59

★★ 67% Yelf's
Union St PO33 2LG
☎ 01983 564062 🖹 01983 563937
e-mail: manager@yelfshotel.com
Dir: from Ryde Esplanande, turn into Union St. Hotel on right

> **PETS:** Bedrooms Exercise area (Adjacent) Pet Food

This former coaching inn has smart public areas including a busy bar, a separate lounge and an attractive dining room. Bedrooms are comfortably furnished and well equipped and some are located in an adjoining wing. A new conservatory lounge bar and stylish terrace have been added.
ROOMS: 30 en suite (2 fmly) No smoking in 5 bedrooms s £51-£57; d £68-£72 (incl. bkfst) **LB FACILITIES:** STV ch fac **NOTES:** No smoking in restaurant **CARDS:** 🖶🖶🖶🖶🖶🖶

SANDOWN
Map 04 SZ58

★★ 68% Riviera
2 Royal St PO36 8LP
☎ 01983 402518 🖹 01983 402518
e-mail: enquiries@rivierahotel.org.uk
Dir: pass Heights Leisure Centre and church on left. Turn 2nd right (Melville St), then 2nd right again into Royal St

> **PETS:** Bedrooms Public areas Exercise area (100yds)

Regular guests return year after year to this friendly and welcoming family-run hotel. It is located near to the High Street and just a short stroll from the beach, pier and shops. Bedrooms, including several at ground floor level, are very well furnished and comfortably equipped. Enjoyable home-cooked meals are served in the spacious dining room.
ROOMS: 41 en suite (6 fmly) (10 GF) s £38-£44; d £76-£88 (incl. bkfst & dinner) **LB FACILITIES:** entertainment ch fac **PARKING:** 20
NOTES: No smoking in restaurant Closed Nov-Mar
CARDS: 🖶🖶🖶🖶🖶🖶

♦♦♦ Carisbrooke House Hotel
11 Beachfield Rd PO36 8NA
☎ 01983 402257 🖹 01983 402295
e-mail: carisbrookehotel@aol.com
Dir: follow signs through Sandown town centre and through High Street onto Beachfield Road, hotel 200yds past Post Office on right

> **PETS:** Bedrooms £5-£10 per stay Public areas (except during meal times) Exercise area (opposite) Food provided if necessary RESIDENT PETS: Tanya - Miniature Schnauzer

Located within walking distance of the town centre and seafront, this delightful family-run hotel provides guests with a warm welcome and comfortable bedrooms. There is a large dining room where full English breakfasts are served at individual tables and

continued

> 🐾 **Places with this symbol are farms**

guests have access to a well-stocked bar, which leads through to a cosy television lounge.

FACILITIES: 10 rms (8 en suite) (4 fmly) (3 GF) No smoking in bedrooms No smoking in dining room TVB tea/coffee Licensed Cen ht TVL **PRICES:** s £20-£25; d £40-£50✳ **LB**
CARDS: 🖶🖶🖶🖶

SEAVIEW
Map 04 SZ69

★★★ 77% ⊛⊛ Priory Bay
Priory Dr PO34 5BU
☎ 01983 613146 🖹 01983 616539
e-mail: enquiries@priorybay.co.uk
Dir: B3330 towards Seaview, through Nettlestone. Do not take Seaview turning, instead continue 0.5m until sign for Hotel

> **PETS:** Bedrooms (in annexes only) (unattended) £10
> Exercise area (on site) RESIDENT PETS: George - Black Labrador

This peacefully located hotel has its own stretch of beach and a range of outdoor leisure facilities. Public areas are especially comfortable, as are the well-equipped and mostly spacious bedrooms. The kitchen creates interesting and imaginative dishes, using local produce as much as possible.
ROOMS: 19 en suite 12 annexe en suite (13 fmly) (2 GF) s £65-£220; d £110-£260 (incl. bkfst) **LB FACILITIES:** STV Outdoor swimming Golf 9 Tennis (hard) Croquet lawn Private beach, 70 acres of woodland lawns and formal gardens. entertainment Xmas **PARKING:** 100
NOTES: No smoking in restaurant **CARDS:** 🖶🖶🖶🖶🖶🖶

SHANKLIN
Map 04 SZ58

★★ 65% *Cliff Hall*
16 Crescent Rd PO37 6DJ
☎ 01983 862828
Dir: From Lake to Shanklin take Ventnor Rd at traffic lights, left to esplanade

> **PETS:** Bedrooms (unattended) £5 Public areas
> Exercise area Pet Food RESIDENT PETS: 2 Labradors

A privately owned hotel situated close to the beach lift and town centre. The pleasantly decorated bedrooms are generally quite spacious and have all the usual facilities; most rooms also have stunning sea views. Public areas include a lounge, bar, restaurant, coffee shop and a superb terrace with an outdoor swimming pool.
ROOMS: 28 en suite (18 fmly) (9 GF) No smoking in all bedrooms
FACILITIES: Outdoor swimming (H) Snooker X2 Pool Table Table Tennis entertainment **PARKING:** 30 **NOTES:** No smoking in restaurant Closed Dec
CARDS: 🖶🖶🖶🖶🖶🖶

★★ 62% Melbourne Ardenlea

Queen's Rd PO37 6AP
☎ 01983 862283 ▤ 01983 862865
Dir: turn left at Fiveways crossroads, off A3055, hotel on right 150yds past church with tall spire

PETS: Bedrooms Public areas (unless other guests object) Exercise area

This quietly located hotel is within easy walking distance of the town centre and the lift down to the promenade and successfully caters for the needs of holidaymakers. Bedrooms are traditionally furnished and guests can enjoy the various spacious public areas including a welcoming bar and a large heated indoor swimming pool.
ROOMS: 50 en suite (14 fmly) (6 GF) s £34-£50; d £68-£100 (incl. bkfst & dinner) **LB FACILITIES:** Spa Indoor swimming (H) Sauna Table tennis, Pool table, Football table entertainment ch fac **SERVICES:** Lift
PARKING: 28 **NOTES:** No smoking in restaurant Closed mid Dec-mid Feb RS Nov-mid Dec & mid Feb-Mar **CARDS:** ▨ ▨ ▨ ▨ ▨ ▨ ▨

◆◆◆ Hayes Barton Hotel

7 Highfield Rd PO37 6PP
☎ 01983 867747 ▤ 01983 862104
e-mail: williams.2000@virgin.net
Dir: A3055 from Ryde or Cowes, turn off on to A3020. High St, Shanklin into Victoria Av, Highfield Rd is 3rd turning on left, hotel on right

PETS: Bedrooms (unattended) £3 Public areas (except dining room) Exercise area (200yds) RESIDENT PETS: Labrador cross - Samantha

Hayes Barton enjoys the relaxed atmosphere of a family home and also provides well-equipped bedrooms and a range of comfortable public areas. Dinner is available from a short selection of home-cooked dishes and there is a cosy bar lounge. The Old Village, beach and promenade are all within walking distance.
FACILITIES: 9 en suite (5 fmly) (2 GF) No smoking in bedrooms No smoking in dining room No smoking in lounges TVB tea/coffee Licensed Cen ht TVL No coaches Indoor swimming pool (heated) Dinner Last d noon **PARKING:** 10 **NOTES:** Closed Nov-1 Mar
CARDS: ▨ ▨ ▨ ▨ ▨

🍺 **Places with this symbol are pubs**

All abbreviations are explained on page 9

🏘 **Places with this symbol are country house hotels**

Eversley Hotel

Ventnor is renowned for its mild climate and has an almost Mediterranean feel, due to its southern aspect. The Eversley stands in an acre of grounds and boasts its own private access into Ventnor park leading on to the coastal footpaths, an ideal location for pet lovers and walkers alike having an excellent reputation for relaxing breaks in comfortable surroundings with good food.

Tel: 01983 852244
eversleyhotel@yahoo.co.uk
www.eversleyhotel.com

See entry on page 228

◆◆◆ Norfolk House Hotel

19 Esplanade PO37 6BN
☎ 01983 863023 ▤ 01983 863023
e-mail: info@norfolkhousehotel.com
Dir: A3055 Sandown-Shanklin at Arthurs Hill traffic light junct (leaving Lake) turn left onto Hope Road, signed Esplanade, Hotel on right opposite Victorian clock tower

PETS: Bedrooms (downstairs rooms only) £4 Public areas (not in dining room) Exercise area (100yds)
RESIDENT PETS: Springer Spaniel - Alfie, rabbit - Billy, guinea pig - Squeaky

A warm welcome is assured at this friendly, family-run hotel, located on the sea front with the beach across the road. Bedrooms are comfortable with many extras provided. There is also a bar, lounge and garden for guests' use. A range of drinks and cakes are served during the day.
FACILITIES: 9 en suite (2 fmly) (1 GF) No smoking in bedrooms No smoking in dining room TVB tea/coffee Licensed Cen ht TVL Beach nearby Dinner Last d 5.30pm **PRICES:** s £28-£32; d £56-£64✳ **LB**
PARKING: 8 **CARDS:** ▨ ▨ ▨ ▨

England

SHANKLIN continued

◆◆◆ The Glendene Hotel
7 Carter Av PO37 7LQ
☎ 01983 862924
e-mail: janderek@glendene48.freeserve.co.uk
Dir: Take A3056 from Newport/Sandown road. Pass Safeways on left then turn right down Whitecross Lane, approx. 1m at x-rds turn right. Glendene is 50yds on right.

PETS: Bedrooms (unattended) £2 Public areas (except dining room) Exercise area (250yds)

Located in the heart of Shanklin and within walking distance of the sandy beach, The Glendene offers comfortable accommodation within a warm and friendly environment. Breakfast is served in the attractive dining room and a delicious home cooked dinner is available by prior arrangement.
FACILITIES: 7 rms (4 en suite) (2 fmly) No smoking TVB tea/coffee TVL No coaches Dinner Last d at breakfast **PRICES:** s £18-£22; d £40-£44✶ **LB BB PARKING:** 5 **CARDS:** 🔲🔲🔲🔲🔲

VENTNOR
Map 04 SZ57

★★★ 66% Eversley
Park Av PO38 1LB
☎ 01983 852244 & 852462 📠 01983 856534
e-mail: eversleyhotel@yahoo.co.uk
Dir: on A3055 W of Ventnor, next to Ventnor Park

PETS: Bedrooms (unattended) £1.50 Public areas Exercise area (adjacent) RESIDENT PETS: Mongrel dog

Located west of Ventnor, this hotel enjoys a quiet location with some rooms offering garden and pool views. The spacious restaurant is also used for local functions and there is a bar, television room, lounge area and a card room as well as a new jacuzzi and gym. Bedrooms are generally a good size.

ROOMS: 30 en suite (8 fmly) (2 GF) s £30-£55; d £59-£99 (incl. bkfst) **LB FACILITIES:** Outdoor swimming (H) Gym Jacuzzi Childrens play equipment Pool table ch fac Xmas **PARKING:** 23 **NOTES:** No smoking in restaurant Closed 31 Nov-22 Dec & 2 Jan-8 Feb **CARDS:** 🔲🔲🔲🔲🔲

See advert on page 227

★★ 68% Hillside Hotel
Mitchell Av PO38 1DR
☎ 01983 852271 📠 01983 852271
e-mail: aa@hillside-hotel.co.uk
Dir: off A3055 onto B3327. Hotel 0.5m on right behind tennis courts

PETS: Bedrooms (unattended) Public areas (not in dining room & lounge) RESIDENT PETS: Jack - Jack Russell, Charlie - mongrel, Bob - Springer Spaniel, Jemima & Hamish - cats

Hillside Hotel dates back to the 19th Century and enjoys a superb location overlooking Ventnor and the sea beyond. Public areas consist of a traditional lounge, a cosy bar area with an adjoining conservatory and a light, airy dining room. Bedrooms have been refurbished with quality fabrics. A welcoming and homely atmosphere is assured.
ROOMS: 12 en suite (1 fmly) (1 GF) No smoking in all bedrooms s £29; d £58 (incl. bkfst) **LB FACILITIES:** Tennis (hard) **PARKING:** 12 **NOTES:** No children 5yrs No smoking in restaurant Closed Xmas **CARDS:** 🔲🔲🔲🔲🔲

◆◆◆◆ Lake Hotel
Shore Rd, Bonchurch PO38 1RF
☎ 01983 852613
e-mail: enquiries@lakehotel.co.uk
Dir: opposite Bonchurch pond in village

PETS: Bedrooms £3 - small, £5 - medium-large Exercise area (400yds)

A warm friendly welcome is assured at this family-run hotel set in two acres of attractive, well-tended gardens close to the sea. Bedrooms are comfortably appointed and equipped with modern facilities. The elegant public rooms offer a high standard of comfort. A choice of menus is offered at dinner and breakfast.
FACILITIES: 11 en suite 9 annexe en suite (7 fmly) (4 GF) No smoking in bedrooms No smoking in dining room No smoking in 1 lounge TVB tea/coffee Licensed Cen ht TVL No children 3yrs No coaches Dinner Last d 6.30pm **PRICES:** s £36-£46; d £60-£74✶ **LB PARKING:** 20 **NOTES:** Closed Nov-Feb

England

◆◆◆◆ 🏠 Fairview Cottage
Nettlecombe, Whitwell PO38 2AD
☎ 01983 730042
e-mail: info@fairview-cottage.fsnet.co.uk
Dir: take A3020 signed Shanklin from Newport. Right turn at Godshill signed Ventnor. At Whitwell turn left into Nettlecombe Lane

PETS: Sep Accom (Dog room) Public areas Exercise area (Adjacent)

Set in a rural location with panoramic views over farmland, and just a short drive away from the beach, this charming cottage offers accommodation with character and a high degree of comfort. A delicious breakfast, featuring local and home-made produce, is served either in the conservatory dining room or kitchen/diner. Dinner is available by prior arrangement. There is also a small library where guests may quietly relax.
FACILITIES: 1 en suite (1 GF) No smoking TVB tea/coffee No dogs (ex guide dogs) Cen ht No children 12yrs No coaches **PRICES:** s £40; d £70✱ **PARKING:** 1 **NOTES:** Closed Nov-Mar

WILTSHIRE

AMESBURY   Map 04 SU14

◆◆◆◆ Park House Motel
SP4 0EG
☎ 01980 629256 📠 01980 629256
Dir: at junction of A303/A338

PETS: Bedrooms Exercise area (100mtrs)
RESIDENT PETS: 2 Lhasa Apso dogs - Bernard & Max

This family-run establishment offers a warm welcome and is extremely convenient for the A303. Bedrooms are practically equipped with modern facilities and come in a variety of sizes. There is a large dining room where dinner is served during the week, and a cosy bar in which to relax.
FACILITIES: 33 rms (23 en suite) (5 fmly) (28 GF) No smoking in 5 bedrooms No smoking in dining room No smoking in lounges STV TVB tea/coffee Licensed Cen ht TVL Dinner Last d 8.30pm
PRICES: s £34-£49; d £56-£62 **PARKING:** 40 **CARDS:** 🖃🖃🖃🖃

BRADFORD-ON-AVON   Map 03 ST86

★★★ 76% ◉◉ 🏊 Woolley Grange
Woolley Green BA15 1TX
☎ 01225 864705 📠 01225 864059
e-mail: info@woolleygrange.com
Dir: Turn off A4 onto B3109. Bradford Leigh, left at crossroads, hotel 0.5m on right at Woolley Green

PETS: Bedrooms (unattended) £7 per stay Public areas (not in dining areas) Exercise area (on site) Pet Food bowls provided

This splendid Cotswold manor house is set in beautiful countryside. Children are made especially welcome; there is a trained nanny on duty in the nursery. Bedrooms and public areas are charmingly furnished and decorated in true country-house style, with many thoughtful touches and luxurious extras. The
continued

hotel offers a varied and well-balanced menu selection, including ingredients from the hotel's own garden.
ROOMS: 14 en suite 12 annexe en suite (8 fmly) s £121-£157; d £160-£395 (incl. bkfst & dinner) **LB FACILITIES:** Outdoor swimming (H) Croquet lawn Putting green Badminton, Games room, beauty treatments ch fac Xmas **PARKING:** 40 **NOTES:** No smoking in restaurant **CARDS:** 🖃🖃🖃🖃🖃

★★★ 70% Leigh Park Hotel
Leigh Park West BA15 2RA
☎ 01225 864885 📠 01225 862315
e-mail: leighparkhotel@lineone.net
Dir: A363 Bath/Frome road. Take B3105 signed Holt/Woolley Green. Hotel 0.25m on right on x-roads of B3105/B3109. N side of Bradford-on-Avon

Best Western

PETS: Bedrooms £10

Enjoying splendid views over the surrounding countryside, this relaxing Georgian hotel is set in five acres of well-tended grounds, complete with a vineyard. Combining charm and character with modern facilities, the hotel is equally well suited to business and leisure travellers. The restaurant serves dishes cooked to order, using home-grown fruit and vegetables, and wine from the vineyard.
ROOMS: 22 en suite (4 fmly) (7 GF) No smoking in 14 bedrooms s £75-£78; d £110-£130 (incl. bkfst) **LB FACILITIES:** Xmas
PARKING: 80 **NOTES:** No smoking in restaurant
CARDS: 🖃🖃🖃🖃🖃

CALNE   Map 03 ST97

★★★ 67% Lansdowne Strand
The Strand SN11 0EH
☎ 01249 812488 📠 01249 815323
e-mail: reservations@lansdownestrand.co.uk
Dir: off the A4 in the centre of Calne

Best Western

PETS: Bedrooms (unattended) Exercise area pet food and bowls provided with one day's notice

In the centre of the market town, this 16th-century, former coaching inn still retains many period features. Individually decorated bedrooms vary in size. There are two friendly bars; one offers a wide selection of ales and a cosy fireplace. An interesting menu and choice of wines is available in the brasserie-style restaurant.
ROOMS: 21 en suite 5 annexe en suite (3 fmly) No smoking in 9 bedrooms s £65-£85; d £75-£98 (incl. bkfst) **LB FACILITIES:** STV Complimentary use of nearby leisure centre ch fac Xmas **PARKING:** 21
CARDS: 🖃🖃🖃🖃🖃🖃

Please mention AA Pet Friendly Places to Stay when booking

★ Red stars indicate the AA's Top 200 Hotels in Britain & Ireland

England

CASTLE COMBE
Map 03 ST87

★★★★ ◎◎◎ ♠♣ Manor House
SN14 7HR
☎ 01249 782206 ▤ 01249 782159
e-mail: enquiries@manor-housecc.co.uk

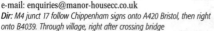
EXCLUSIVE
HOTELS & GOLF CLUBS

Dir: M4 junct 17 follow Chippenham signs onto A420 Bristol, then right onto B4039. Through village, right after crossing bridge

PETS: Bedrooms £15 Exercise area (adjacent)

This hotel is situated in a secluded valley near the village, where there have been no new buildings for 300 years. There are 365 acres of grounds to enjoy, complete with an Italian garden and 18-hole golf course. Bedrooms, some of which are in a row of stone cottages, have been superbly furnished, and public rooms include a number of cosy lounges with roaring fires. Service is a pleasing blend of professionalism and friendliness, while food focuses on top quality local produce.
ROOMS: 22 en suite 26 annexe en suite (8 fmly) (12 GF) d £180-£600 (incl. bkfst) **LB FACILITIES:** STV Outdoor swimming (H) Golf 18 Tennis (hard) Fishing Snooker Sauna Gym Croquet lawn Putting green Jogging track ch fac Xmas **PARKING:** 100 **NOTES:** No smoking in restaurant **CARDS:** ▨▨ ▨▨ ▨ ⑤

CHILMARK
Map 03 ST93

◆◆◆◆ The Dial House
SP3 5BD
☎ 01722 716353
e-mail: deacon@ukonline.co.uk

Dir: turn off A303 to Chilmark. At Black Dog pub, turn right, then left. Proceed through village on Tisbury Rd and The Dial House is on right after 30mph sign

PETS: Sep Accom (kitchen) Public areas Exercise area
RESIDENT PETS: 2 Chocolate Labradors, 1 cat, 7 rabbits, 5 guinea pigs

This elegant establishment is located in a quiet village, within easy reach of Salisbury and convenient for the City of Bath and Dorset Coast. Bedrooms provide many considerate extras and the lounge has an open fireplace for those winter nights. Breakfast, featuring home-made preserves and local produce, is served in the charming dining room and dinner is available by prior arrangement.
FACILITIES: 2 rms (1 en suite) No smoking in bedrooms TV1B tea/coffee Cen ht TVL No children 8yrs No coaches **PRICES:** s £40-£45; d £60✱ **NOTES:** Closed 15 Dec-15 Jan

DEVIZES
Map 04 SU06

★★★ 64% Bear
Market Place SN10 1HS
☎ 01380 722444 ▤ 01380 722450
e-mail: info@thebearhotel.net
Dir: town centre

PETS: Bedrooms £10 per stay Public areas (except restaurants)

Set in the market place of this small Wiltshire town, this attractive hotel has a popular local following. The individually furnished and decorated bedrooms vary in size. The attractive lounge offers a

continued

quiet area for residents to enjoy afternoon tea. Homemade cakes are available throughout the day and the restaurant serves enjoyable meals.
ROOMS: 24 en suite (5 fmly) No smoking in all bedrooms s £50; d £75 (incl. bkfst) **LB FACILITIES:** Solarium **SERVICES:** Lift
NOTES: No smoking in restaurant Closed 25-26 Dec
CARDS: ▨▨ ▨▨ ▨▨ ▨ ⑤

◆◆◆ Eastcott Manor
Easterton SN10 4PH
☎ 01380 813313
Dir: on B3098 between Urchfont & Easterton, S of Devizes between A360 Salisbury & A342 Andover

PETS: Bedrooms (unattended) £2 per dog Public areas (dependent on other guests' wishes) Exercise area (200 yards)
RESIDENT PETS: Sheba (Labrador), Dexter (Springer Spaniel), Megan (Black Labrador) and William (horse)

This 16th-century farmhouse offers comfortable accommodation in a rural setting. Bedrooms vary in size and are suitably furnished and equipped. Breakfast and evening meals are served in the delightful dining room with guests sharing one large table. A pleasant lounge and conservatory are also available to guests.
FACILITIES: 4 en suite No smoking TVB tea/coffee TVL No coaches Stabling Chair lift Dinner Last d 24hrs in advance **PRICES:** s £25-£27; d £58-£60✱ **PARKING:** 6 **NOTES:** Closed 23 Dec-1 Jan

LACOCK
Map 03 ST96

◆◆◆◆ The Old Rectory
Cantax Hill SN15 2JZ
☎ 01249 730335 ▤ 01249 730166
e-mail: sexton@oldrectorylacock.co.uk
Dir: from M4 and Chippenham take A350. Turn left at traffic lights where Lacock is straight on, The Old Rectory 1st house on right

PETS: Bedrooms Sep Accom (kennel & pen) Public areas (preferably walk through only) Exercise area (Adjacent) Spare bowls available **RESIDENT PETS:** 2 horses, 2 Labradors & 1 cockatiel

Located on the edge of the medieval village of Lacock, this imposing listed Victorian property is situated in delightful gardens with its own croquet lawn and tennis court. Bedrooms and bathrooms are comfortably furnished and equipped with a wide range of useful extra facilities. Full English breakfasts are served in the spacious dining room.
FACILITIES: 6 rms (4 en suite) (2 fmly) (1 GF) No smoking TVB tea/coffee Cen ht TVL Tennis (grass) Croquet lawn **PRICES:** s £30-£50; d £50-£70✱ **LB PARKING:** 8 **NOTES:** Closed 24-26 Dec

LOWER CHICKSGROVE
Map 03 ST92

◆◆◆◆ 🍴 🍺 Compasses Inn
SP3 6NB
☎ 01722 714318 📠 01722 714318
e-mail: thecompasses@aol.com
Dir: from Salisbury take A30 W and exit 3rd right after Fouant, signed Lower Chicksgrove. Then 1st left into Lagpond Lane down single track lane to village

PETS: Bedrooms (unattended) Public areas Exercise area (Adjacent) Bowls only provided

This charming 14th-century inn, within easy reach of the City of Bath, Salisbury, Glastonbury and the Dorset coast, offers comfortable accommodation within a peaceful setting. At dinner time guests will enjoy a warm inviting atmosphere and carefully prepared and presented dishes in the bar/restaurant area. There is a separate dining room where breakfast is served.
FACILITIES: 4 en suite (1 fmly) No smoking in bedrooms No smoking in area of dining room TVB tea/coffee Cen ht Dinner Last d 9.30pm
PRICES: s £45-£75; d £75✱ **LB PARKING:** 40 **NOTES:** Closed 25 & 26 Dec rs Mon (ex BH) & Tue after BH
CARDS: 💳 💳 💳 💳 💳 💳 💳

MALMESBURY
Map 03 ST98

★★★★ Whatley Manor
Easton Grey SN16 0RB
☎ 01666 822888 📠 01666 826120
e-mail: reservations@whatleymanor.com
Dir: M4 junct 17 to Malmesbury, left at t-junct, left at next t-junct onto B4040, hotel 2m on left

PETS: Bedrooms (2 rooms only) £15 Exercise area (on site) Pet Food

This impressive country house has been lovingly renovated to provide the highest levels of luxury. Spacious bedrooms, mostly with views over the attractive gardens, are individually decorated with splendid features. Two restaurants are available: Mazo's brasserie and the fine dining option of The Dining Room. A magnificent spa with contemporary facilities is very inviting.
ROOMS: 23 en suite (4 GF) No smoking in 6 bedrooms s £275-£850; d £275-£850 (incl. bkfst) **LB FACILITIES:** Spa STV Fishing Sauna Solarium Gym Jacuzzi Cinema, hydro pool Xmas **SERVICES:** Lift
PARKING: 100 **NOTES:** No children 12yrs No smoking in restaurant
CARDS: 💳 💳 💳 💳 💳 💳 💳

All information was correct at the time of going to press; we recommend you confirm details on booking

---

🍺 Places with this symbol are pubs

★★★ 75% ⊛⊛ Old Bell
Abbey Row SN16 0AG
☎ 01666 822344 📠 01666 825145
e-mail: info@oldbellhotel.com
Dir: M4 junct 11, follow A429 north. Left at first rdbt. Left at T-junction. Hotel next to Abbey

CLASSIC BRITISH

PETS: Bedrooms (unattended) Public areas (except restaurant) Exercise area **RESIDENT PETS:** Dave - cat

Now under new ownership. Dating back to 1220, the Old Bell is reputed to be the oldest purpose-built hotel in England. Bedrooms vary in size and style; those in the main house are traditionally furnished with antiques, while the newer bedrooms are modelled on a quasi-Japanese theme. Guests have a choice of comfortable sitting areas and dining options. Children are also well-catered for.
ROOMS: 16 en suite 15 annexe en suite (7 GF) No smoking in 12 bedrooms s fr £85; d fr £110 (incl. bkfst) **LB FACILITIES:** Spa STV Aromatherapy massages Xmas **PARKING:** 31 **NOTES:** No dogs (ex guide dogs) No smoking in restaurant
CARDS: 💳 💳 💳 💳 💳 💳 💳

MELKSHAM
Map 03 ST96

★★ 71% Shaw Country
Bath Rd, Shaw SN12 8EF
☎ 01225 702836 & 790321 📠 01225 790275
e-mail: info@shawcountryhotel.co.uk
Dir: 1m from Melksham, 9m from Bath on A365

PETS: Bedrooms Exercise area

Located within easy reach of both Bath and the M4, this hotel sits in wonderfully kept gardens. The house boasts some very well-appointed bedrooms, a comfortable lounge and bar and the Mulberry Restaurant, where a wide selection of well-cooked meals is available. A warm and friendly approach by the staff is offered throughout the stay.
ROOMS: 13 en suite (2 fmly) s £50; d £70-£90 (incl. bkfst) **LB FACILITIES:** Jacuzzi **PARKING:** 30 **NOTES:** No smoking in restaurant Closed 26-27 Dec & 1 Jan **CARDS:** 💳 💳 💳 💳 💳 💳

NETTLETON
Map 03 ST87

◆◆◆◆ 🍴 Fosse Farmhouse Country Hotel
Nettleton Shrub SN14 7NJ
☎ 01249 782286 📠 01249 783066
e-mail: caroncooper@compuserve.com
Dir: off B4039, 1.5m past Castle Combe race circuit take 1st left at Gib Village for farm 1m on right

PETS: Sep Accom (kennel) Exercise area (Adjacent) Dry food supplied, mini (car) where dogs and cats sleep

Set in the quiet Wiltshire countryside close to Castle Combe, this small hotel has well-equipped bedrooms decorated in an individual and interesting style, in keeping with its 18th-century origins. Excellent dinners are served in the farmhouse and cream teas can be enjoyed in the old stables or the delightful garden.
FACILITIES: 3 en suite (1 fmly) No smoking in 1 bedroom No smoking in dining room TVB tea/coffee Licensed Cen ht Golf 18 Dinner Last d 8.30pm **PRICES:** s £55-£68; d £85-£135✱ **LB PARKING:** 12
CARDS: 💳 💳 💳 💳

PURTON

Map 04 SU08

★★★ 78% @@
The Pear Tree at Purton
Church End SN5 4ED
☎ 01793 772100 📠 01793 772369
e-mail: stay@peartreepurton.co.uk
Dir: M4 junct 16 follow signs to Purton, at Spar shop turn right. Hotel 0.25m on left

PETS: Bedrooms Exercise area (Surrounding fields) Pet Food Welcome pack - bowl & chews; large garden, and miles of walks nearby RESIDENT PETS: Jake - Springer Spaniel

Set in attractive gardens and grounds, this 15th-century former vicarage offers a comfortable haven for guests. The resident proprietors and staff provide efficient, dedicated service and friendly hospitality. Individually styled bedrooms are spacious and feature thoughtful extra touches such as fresh flowers and sherry. Fresh ingredients feature on the menus at both lunch and dinner.

ROOMS: 17 en suite (2 fmly) (6 GF) s £115-£140; d £115-£140 (incl. bkfst) **LB FACILITIES:** Spa STV Croquet lawn ch fac **PARKING:** 60 **NOTES:** No smoking in restaurant Closed 26-30 Dec **CARDS:** 🏦

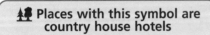
🌲 **Places with this symbol are country house hotels**

SALISBURY
Map 04 SU12

★★★ 71% **The White Hart**
St John St SP1 2SD
☎ 0870 400 8125 📠 01722 412761

MACDONALD
HOTELS

e-mail: whitehartsalisbury@macdonald-hotels.co.uk
Dir: M3 junct 7/8 take A303 to A343 for Salisbury then A30. Follow signs for City Centre on ring road, into Exeter St, leading into St. John Street. Car park at rear.

PETS: Bedrooms £10 per stay Exercise area

There has been a hotel on this site since the 16th century. Bedrooms vary between the contemporary-style, newly refurbished rooms and those decorated in more traditional style, all of which boast a comprehensive range of facilities. The bar and lounge areas are popular with guests and locals for morning coffees and afternoon teas.

ROOMS: 68 en suite (6 fmly) No smoking in 28 bedrooms s £75-£101; d £85-£111 (incl. bkfst & dinner) **LB FACILITIES:** STV Xmas **PARKING:** 90 **NOTES:** No smoking in restaurant **CARDS:** 🏦

★★★ 67% **Grasmere House**
Harnham Rd SP2 8JN
☎ 01722 338388 📠 01722 333710
e-mail: grasmerehotel@mistral.co.uk
Dir: on A3094 on S side of Salisbury next to All Saints Church in Harnham

PETS: Bedrooms (unattended) £3.50 Public areas (except restaurant) Pet Food

This popular hotel dates from 1896 and has gardens overlooking the water meadows and the cathedral. The attractive bedrooms vary in size, with the 15 added most recently offering excellent quality and comfort. Some rooms are specially equipped for less mobile guests. In summer, guests have the option of dining on the pleasant outdoor terrace.

ROOMS: 4 en suite 31 annexe en suite (16 fmly) No smoking in 30 bedrooms s £85.50-£95.50; d £115.50-£135.50 (incl. bkfst) **LB FACILITIES:** STV Fishing Croquet lawn Jacuzzi Xmas **PARKING:** 64 **CARDS:** 🏦

◆◆◆◆ Glen Lyn
6 Bellamy Ln, Milford Hill SP1 2SP
☎ 01722 327880 📠 01722 327880
e-mail: glen.lyn@btinternet.com
Dir: from A36 turn into Tollgate Rd, at lights turn right (Milford Hill). Turn sharp left at the fork with Lavestock, Shady Bower into Bellamy Lane

PETS: Bedrooms Public areas (not in dining room) Exercise area (300yds) **RESIDENT PETS:** Henry - Chocolate Labrador, Hunter - Gordon Setter

This Victorian house is tucked away in a quiet cul de sac close to the town. The proprietors have a long-standing reputation for exceptional levels of hospitality, which is well deserved. Traditionally furnished bedrooms are comfortable, some are en suite. There is a spacious lounge with books, maps and tourist information.
FACILITIES: 7 rms (4 en suite) (1 fmly) No smoking TVB tea/coffee Licensed Cen ht No coaches **PRICES:** s £37-£40; d £49.95-£80✱ **PARKING:** 5 **CARDS:**

◆◆◆ Byways House
31 Fowlers Rd SP1 2QP
☎ 01722 328364 📠 01722 322146
e-mail: byways@stonehenge-uk.com
Dir: from A30 follow A36 Southampton signs then follow 'Youth Hostel' signs to the hostel. Fowlers Rd is directly opposite

PETS: Bedrooms Exercise area (0.25 mile)

Located in a quiet street with off road parking, Byways is within walking distance of the town centre. Several bedrooms have been decorated in a Victorian style and another two have four-poster beds. All rooms offer good levels of comfort, with one adapted for less mobile guests.
FACILITIES: 23 rms (19 en suite) (5 fmly) (13 GF) No smoking in dining room No smoking in lounges STV TVB tea/coffee Licensed Cen ht **PRICES:** s £39-£65; d £60-£80✱ **PARKING:** 15 **NOTES:** Closed Xmas & New Year **CARDS:**

> ### Don't forget to let proprietors know when you book that you're bringing your pet

SWINDON | Map 04 SU18

★★★ 69% Chiseldon House
New Rd, Chiseldon SN4 0NE
☎ 01793 741010 📠 01793 741059
e-mail: chishoho@hotmail.com
Dir: M4 junct 15, onto A346 signed Marlborough, at brow of hill turn right by Esso garage onto B4005 into New Rd, hotel 200yds on right

PETS: Bedrooms £4 Exercise area (100 metres)

Best Western

Chiseldon is a traditional country house near Swindon that is ideal for a peaceful and comfortable stay. Quiet and spacious bedrooms are tastefully decorated and include a number of thoughtful extras. A varied selection of tempting dishes is offered at dinner. Guests may also enjoy the comfortable lounge and well-kept gardens.
ROOMS: 21 en suite (4 fmly) No smoking in 7 bedrooms s £85-£105; d £105-£125 (incl. bkfst) **FACILITIES:** STV Croquet lawn ch fac **PARKING:** 40 **CARDS:**

★★★ 66% Goddard Arms
High St, Old Town SN1 3EG
☎ 01793 692313 📠 01793 512984
e-mail: goddard.arms@forestdale.com
Dir: M4 junct 15, take A4259 towards Swindon, onto B4006 to Old Town follow signs to PM Hospital until reaching High St. the hotel is opposite Wood St next to Lloyds Bank

Forestdale Hotels

PETS: Bedrooms (unattended) £7.50 Public areas (not in restaurant) Exercise area Pet Food

Situated in the attractive Old Town area, this ivy-clad coaching inn offers bedrooms in either the main building or in a modern annexe to the rear of the property. Public areas are tastefully decorated in a traditional style; there is a lounge, Vaults bar and a popular restaurant. The conference rooms are extensive and the car park secure.
ROOMS: 18 en suite 47 annexe en suite (3 fmly) (24 GF) No smoking in 33 bedrooms s fr £95; d fr £120 (incl. bkfst) **LB FACILITIES:** STV **PARKING:** 90 **NOTES:** No smoking in restaurant **CARDS:**

★★★ 60% Villiers Inn
Moormead Rd, Wroughton SN4 9BY
☎ 01793 814744 📠 01793 814119
e-mail: hotels@villiersinn.co.uk
Dir: 1m S of Swindon, on A4361, hotel 100mtrs on right

PETS: Bedrooms (unattended) Exercise area (200 metres)

Conveniently situated with easy access to the motorway and Swindon, this attractive period property provides well-equipped accommodation in the main building and in a purpose built extension. Public areas include a comfortable library lounge and a spacious bar. An interesting range of dishes is offered in the restaurant. Function facilities are also available.
ROOMS: 33 en suite No smoking in 10 bedrooms s £55-£85; d £69-£99 (incl. bkfst) **LB FACILITIES:** STV ch fac Xmas **PARKING:** 60 **CARDS:**

England

SWINDON continued

⚑ Hotel Ibis Swindon

Delta Business Park, Great Western Way SN5 7XG
☎ 01793 514777 📠 01793 514570
e-mail: H1041@accor-hotels.com

Dir: A3102 to Swindon, straight over rdbt, slip road onto Delta Business Park and turn left

PETS: Bedrooms Public areas Pet Food
RESIDENT PETS: Mooshie (dog)

Modern, budget hotel offering comfortable accommodation in bright and practical bedrooms. Breakfast is self-service and dinner is available in the restaurant. For further details, consult the Hotel Groups page.
ROOMS: 120 en suite s £32-£44; d £32-£44

♦♦♦♦ Parklands Hotel & Bentleys Restaurant

High St, Ogbourne St George SN8 1SL
☎ 01672 841555 📠 01672 841533
e-mail: enquiries@parklandshoteluk.co.uk

Dir: M4 junct 15, towards Marlborough. After 4m turn left at Ogbourne Downs golf club. Right at T-junct, 1st right & hotel on right, signed by brown tourist signs

PETS: Bedrooms Public areas (with other guests' agreement) Exercise area (0.25 mile)

Located in the village of Ogbourne St George between Swindon and Marlborough, Parklands Hotel provides a peaceful and pleasant location whether visiting for business or pleasure. The dining room has plenty of character retained from the 17th-century origins and there is a pleasant adjoining bar/lounge area. A selection of freshly prepared dishes is offered on the restaurant menu and, for something less formal, the bar menu offers lighter snacks. Bedrooms are well-furnished and include a number of extra facilities.
FACILITIES: 12 en suite (2 GF) No smoking in bedrooms No smoking in dining room No smoking in 1 lounge TVB tea/coffee Direct dial from bedrooms Licensed Cen ht Dinner Last d 8.45pm
PRICES: s £50-£65; d £75-£85✱ LB **PARKING:** 11
CARDS: 🔲 🔲 🔲 🔲 🔲

♦♦♦ ⚑ The Check Inn

Woodland View, North Wroughton SN4 9AA
☎ 01793 845584 📠 01793 814640
e-mail: information@checkinn.co.uk

Dir: A361 (Swindon to Devizes), after dual carriageway bridge over M4 take the 1st right into Woodland View.

PETS: Bedrooms (unattended) Public areas Exercise area (100 metres) RESIDENT PETS: Emma (Collie/Retriever cross)

Located close to the M4, The Check Inn combines a traditional freehouse inn offering eight continually changing real ales with more modern, well-decorated and furnished bedrooms and bathrooms. A large car park is provided at the rear. A good selection of generously portioned, home-cooked meals is available.
FACILITIES: 3 en suite (1 fmly) No smoking in bedrooms No smoking in dining room No smoking in 1 lounge TVB tea/coffee Cen ht Petanque/boules terrain Dinner Last d 9pm **PRICES:** s fr £37.50; d fr £42.50; (room only) ✱ **LB PARKING:** 48
CARDS: 🔲 🔲 🔲 🔲

♦♦♦ Portquin

Broadbush, Broad Blunsdon SN26 7DH
☎ 01793 721261
e-mail: portquin@msn.com

Dir: turn off A419 at Blunsdon onto B4019 signposted Highworth, 0.5m from A419

PETS: Bedrooms Public areas Exercise area (10 metres)

Close to Swindon and with views of the Berkshire Downs, this friendly guest house offers a warm welcome. The comfortable rooms vary in shape and size - six are in the main house and three in an adjacent annexe. Full English breakfasts are taken at two large tables in the open-plan kitchen/dining area.
FACILITIES: 6 en suite 3 annexe en suite (2 fmly) (4 GF) No smoking TVB tea/coffee Direct dial from bedrooms Cen ht No coaches
PRICES: s £30-£40; d £50-£60✱ **PARKING:** 12
CARDS: 🔲 🔲 🔲 🔲 🔲 🔲

WARMINSTER   Map 03 ST84

★★★★ 74% ◉◉
Bishopstrow House

BA12 9HH
☎ 01985 212312 📠 01985 216769
e-mail: info@bishopstrow.co.uk

Dir: A303, A36, B3414, premises 2m on right

PETS: Telephone for details

This is a fine example of a Georgian country home, situated in 27 acres of grounds. Public areas are traditional in style and feature antiques and open fires. All bedrooms offer DVD players. A spa, a tennis court and several country walks ensure there is something for all guests. The restaurant serves quality contemporary cuisine.
ROOMS: 32 en suite (3 fmly) (4 GF) No smoking in 1 bedroom s fr £99; d £199-£330 (incl. bkfst) LB **FACILITIES:** Spa STV Indoor swimming (H) Outdoor swimming (H) Tennis (hard) Fishing Sauna Gym Croquet lawn Clay pigeon shooting Archery Cycling entertainment ch fac Xmas **PARKING:** 100 **NOTES:** No smoking in restaurant
CARDS: 🔲 🔲 🔲 🔲 🔲 🔲

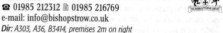

♦♦♦♦ 🛏 ⚑ The Dove Inn

Corton BA12 0SZ
☎ 01985 850109 📠 01985 851041
e-mail: info@thedove.co.uk

Dir: From A36 N of Salisbury signed to Corton & Boyton, cross railway line, turn right at x-rds. Corton approx 1m, The Dove at entrance of village

PETS: Bedrooms (unattended) - depends on the animal Public areas (except restaurant seating areas) Exercise area (across the road) Water bowls available, chocolates & dog biscuits kept behind the bar

Set in the heart of the peaceful village, this inn is the ideal location for relaxing. Courtyard rooms are well-equipped and tastefully fitted. A roaring log fire accompanies meals in the bar in cooler months and guests can enjoy the non-smoking conservatory. An imaginative menu is offered including many interesting variations.
FACILITIES: 5 annexe en suite (1 fmly) (4 GF) No smoking in 2 bedrooms No smoking in area of dining room TVB tea/coffee Cen ht Dinner Last d 9pm **PRICES:** s £45-£50; d £70-£85✱ **PARKING:** 24
CARDS: 🔲 🔲 🔲 🔲 🔲

WESTBURY
Map 03 ST85

★★ 65% The Cedar
Warminster Rd BA13 3PR
☎ 01373 822753 📠 01373 858423
e-mail: cedarwestbury@aol.com
Dir: on A350, 0.5m S of town towards Warminster

THE INDEPENDENTS

PETS: Bedrooms Public areas (allowed in bar only)
Exercise area

This 18th-century hotel offers attractive accommodation in well-equipped, individually decorated bedrooms. The hotel is an ideal base for exploring Bath and the surrounding area. An interesting selection of meals is available in both the bar lounge and conservatory; the Regency restaurant is popular for more formal dining.
ROOMS: 8 en suite 8 annexe en suite (2 fmly) (8 GF) s £50-£65;
d £60-£72 (incl. bkfst) **FACILITIES:** STV **PARKING:** 30
NOTES: No smoking in restaurant **CARDS:** 🔲 💳 VISA 🔲 🔲 🔲

WINTERBOURNE STOKE
Map 04 SU04

◆◆◆◆ Scotland Lodge Farm
SP3 4TF
☎ 01980 621199 📠 01980 621188
e-mail: william.lockwood@bigwig.net
Dir: entrance on A303, W of Winterbourne Stoke, just beyond turning to Berwick St James, immediately after Scotland Lodge on R

PETS: Bedrooms (Downstairs only) Public areas
Exercise area RESIDENT PETS: 2 West Highland terriers (sometimes on site)

Set in 46 acres of paddocks and grassland, this farm provides guests with comfortable, well-appointed rooms featuring numerous thoughtful extra touches. Full English breakfasts are served at the large farmhouse table in the conservatory/lounge overlooking the paddocks. The proprietors are keen equestrians and are happy to offer stabling. Dogs are welcome by prior arrangement.
FACILITIES: 3 en suite (1 fmly) (2 GF) No smoking TVB tea/coffee
Cen ht No coaches **PRICES:** s £30; d £50✳ **PARKING:** 5
NOTES: Closed 24-26 Dec **CARDS:** 🔲 💳 VISA 🔲 🔲

WOODFALLS
Map 04 SU12

◆◆◆◆ 🍴 Woodfalls
The Ridge SP5 2LN
☎ 01725 513222 📠 01725 513220
e-mail: woodfallsi@aol.com
Dir: M27 junct 1, then B3079 to Brook & B3078 to Fordingbridge, at Telegraph Corner take B3080 to Woodfalls. From Salisbury take A338 to Ringwood Rd, at Downton take B3080 to Woodfalls.

PETS: Bedrooms (Also have secure fields for grazing) £4.95
Public areas (except restaurant) Exercise area (Adjacent) Bowls
only provided

Centrally located in a quiet village, yet within easy reach of Salisbury and the New Forest, this attractive inn provides guests with well-furnished and comfortable bedrooms, two of which have four-poster beds. There are public and lounge bars, and a cosy
continued

restaurant area. Breakfast is served in the airy conservatory.
FACILITIES: 10 en suite (1 fmly) No smoking in bedrooms No smoking in dining room No smoking in 1 lounge TVB tea/coffee Direct dial from bedrooms Cen ht Bike hire Dinner Last d 9.30pm
PRICES: s £49.95-£52.50; d £69.90-£85.90✳ **LB PARKING:** 30
CARDS: 🔲 💳 VISA 🔲 🔲 🔲

ABBERLEY
Map 03 SO76

★★★ 73% ◎◎
Elms Hotel & Restaurant
Stockton Rd WR6 6AT
☎ 01299 896666 📠 01299 896804
e-mail: management@theelmshotel.co.uk
Dir: on A443 2m beyond Great Witley

PETS: Bedrooms (annexe bedrooms only) (unattended)
Exercise area (in grounds of hotel)

Surrounded by its own well-maintained grounds, this imposing Queen Anne mansion dates back to 1710 and offers a sophisticated and relaxed ambience throughout. The spacious public rooms and generously proportioned bedrooms exude elegance and charm, whilst the restaurant overlooks the gardens and serves imaginative and memorable dishes.
ROOMS: 16 en suite 5 annexe en suite (1 fmly) s £90-£110; d £120-£180 (incl. bkfst) **LB FACILITIES:** Tennis (grass) Croquet lawn ch fac Xmas
PARKING: 100 **NOTES:** No smoking in restaurant
CARDS: 🔲 💳 VISA 🔲 🔲 🔲

BROADWAY
Map 04 SP03

see also LAVERTON, Gloucestershire

★★★★ 76% ◎◎ The Lygon Arms
High St WR12 7DU
☎ 01386 852255 📠 01386 858611
e-mail: info@thelygonarms.co.uk
Dir: Turn off A44, signed Broadway, hotel on High Street

FURLONG

PETS: Bedrooms (unattended) £25 Exercise area Pet food
and bowls Bedding, chocolate drops, local walks' guide provided

A hotel with a wealth of historical charm and character, the Lygon Arms is situated in the heart of Broadway. It dates back to the 16th century, and offers comfortable bedrooms with modern facilities and some fine antique furniture. Public rooms include a variety of
continued on p236

BROADWAY continued

lounge areas, some with open fires, and a choice of dining options - the Great Hall or the more informal brasserie.

ROOMS: 69 rms (66 en suite) (3 fmly) (8 GF) **FACILITIES:** Spa STV Indoor swimming (H) Tennis (hard) Snooker Sauna Solarium Gym Croquet lawn Beauty treatments, Steam Room, Bike Hire, Horse riding nearby, Walking **PARKING:** 152 **NOTES:** No smoking in restaurant **CARDS:**

♦♦♦♦ ❦ Bowers Hill Farm

Bowers Hill, Willersey WR11 7HG
☎ 01386 834585 ▤ 01386 830234
e-mail: sarah@bowershillfarm.com
Dir: from A44 Broadway-Evesham, follow signs to Willersey. At Willersey, follow signs to Badsey/industrial estate from mini rdbt. Farm 2m on right by postbox

> **PETS:** Sep Accom Exercise area (surrounding)
> **RESIDENT PETS:** Indy (Lancashire Heeler), Abby (German Shepherd)

Located in immaculate gardens on a diverse farm, where point-to-point horses are also bred, this impressive Victorian house has been sympathetically renovated to provide very comfortable and homely bedrooms complimented by modern bathrooms. Breakfast is taken in the elegant dining room or magnificent conservatory and a guest lounge with open fire is also available.
FACILITIES: 3 en suite (1 fmly) No smoking in bedrooms No smoking in dining room No smoking in 1 lounge TVB tea/coffee Cen ht TVL Walking on farm. 80 acres mixed **PRICES:** s £30-£40; d £50-£60❊ **LB** **PARKING:** 5 **CARDS:** ▤▤▤

♦♦♦♦ Whiteacres

Station Rd WR12 7DE
☎ 01386 852320 ▤ 01386 852674
e-mail: whiteacres@btinternet.com
Dir: at junct of A44 and B4632

> **PETS:** Bedrooms Public areas (not in dining room)
> Exercise area (5 minute walk) **RESIDENT PETS:** Eric Cantona (Springer Spaniel)

Located a few minutes' walk from village centre, this constantly improving late Victorian villa offers a range of homely, tastefully furnished bedrooms, two of which feature four poster beds. A comprehensive breakfast is taken in an attractive dining room, overlooking the garden and a guest lounge with satellite television is also available.
FACILITIES: 5 en suite (1 fmly) No smoking TVB tea/coffee Cen ht TVL No children 5yrs No coaches Dinner **PRICES:** s £35-£40; d £50-£70❊ **PARKING:** 8

> **All AA listed accommodation, restaurants and pubs can be found on the AA's website www.theAA.com**

EVESHAM

Map 04 SP04

★★★ 75% ◉ The Evesham

Coopers Ln, Off Waterside WR11 1DA
☎ 01386 765566 & 0800 716969 (Res) ▤ 01386 765443
e-mail: reception@eveshamhotel.com
Dir: Coopers Lane is off road by River Avon

> **PETS:** Bedrooms (unattended) Exercise area

Dating from 1540 and set in large grounds, this delightful hotel has well-equipped accommodation that includes a selection of quirkily themed rooms (Alice in Wonderland, Egyptian and Aquarium with a tropical fish tank in the bathroom). A reputation for food is well-deserved, with choice particularly strong for vegetarians, and children are welcome.
ROOMS: 39 en suite 1 annexe en suite (3 fmly) (11 GF) No smoking in 20 bedrooms s £74-£87; d £118 (incl. bkfst) **LB** **FACILITIES:** Indoor swimming (H) Croquet lawn Putting green ch fac **PARKING:** 50 **NOTES:** No smoking in restaurant Closed 25 & 26 Dec **CARDS:** ▤▤▤

★★★ 70% Northwick Hotel

Waterside WR11 1BT
☎ 01386 40322 ▤ 01386 41070
e-mail: enquiries@northwickhotel.co.uk
Dir: off A46 onto A44 over traffic lights and right at next set onto B4035. Past hospital, hotel on right opposite river

Best Western

> **PETS:** Bedrooms (unattended) Exercise area (20 metres)

Standing by the River Avon, this former coaching inn is within easy walking distance of the centre of Evesham. Bedrooms are tastefully decorated and well equipped, with one specially adapted for less able guests. The refurbished public areas offer a choice of bars, meeting rooms and a restaurant.
ROOMS: 31 en suite (4 fmly) No smoking in 15 bedrooms s £65-£81; d £90-£105 (incl. bkfst) **LB** **FACILITIES:** STV **PARKING:** 85 **NOTES:** No smoking in restaurant **CARDS:** ▤▤▤

KIDDERMINSTER

Map 07 SO87

★★★ 66% Gainsborough House

Bewdley Hill DY11 6BS
☎ 01562 820041 ▤ 01562 66179
e-mail: reservations@gainsboroughhotel.co.uk
Dir: on A456. At hospital, over lights, hotel 200yds on right

> **PETS:** Bedrooms (unattended) £10 Public areas (On a lead) Exercise area (Park next door)

This listed Georgian property, situated on the edge of the town, has benefited from substantial improvements to public areas. The no-smoking bedrooms have also been extensively refurbished and are well equipped and comfortable. Additional features include a bar lounge, a restaurant with a carvery and also a carte menu, a lounge and attractive function rooms.
ROOMS: 43 en suite (8 fmly) No smoking in 12 bedrooms s £60-£75; d £80-£100 (incl. bkfst) **LB** **FACILITIES:** Solarium & beauty salon Xmas **PARKING:** 130 **NOTES:** No smoking in restaurant **CARDS:** ▤▤▤

★★★ 66% ◎ The Granary Hotel & Restaurant

Heath Ln, Shenstone DY10 4BS
☎ 01562 777535 📠 01562 777722
e-mail: info@granary-hotel.co.uk
Dir: on A450, 0.5m from junct with A448

PETS: Bedrooms (unattended) Public areas Exercise area (Adjacent)

This modern hotel offers spacious, well-equipped accommodation with many rooms enjoying views towards Great Witley and the Amberley Hills. There is an attractive modern restaurant and a carvery is available at weekends. There are also extensive conference facilities and the hotel is popular as a wedding venue.
ROOMS: 18 en suite (1 fmly) (18 GF) No smoking in 9 bedrooms s £65; d £75 (incl. bkfst) **LB PARKING:** 96 **NOTES:** No smoking in restaurant Closed 24-26 Dec **CARDS:** 🖃🖃🖃🖃🖃

MALVERN   Map 03 SO74

★★★ 75% ◎◎ Colwall Park

Walwyn Rd, Colwall WR13 6QG
☎ 01684 540000 📠 01684 540847
e-mail: hotel@colwall.com
Dir: Between Malvern & Ledbury in centre of Colwall on B4218

PETS: Bedrooms £15 per stay Public areas (except lounge/restaurant) Exercise area (100yds) Pet Food

Standing in extensive gardens, this hotel was purpose built in the early 20th century to serve the local racetrack. Today the proprietors and loyal staff provide high levels of hospitality and service, and the Seasons restaurant has a well-deserved reputation for its cuisine. Bedrooms have been tastefully refurbished and public areas help to create a fine country-house atmosphere.
ROOMS: 22 en suite (1 fmly) No smoking in 6 bedrooms s £65; d £110-£130 **LB FACILITIES:** STV Croquet lawn Boules Xmas **PARKING:** 40 **NOTES:** No smoking in restaurant **CARDS:** 🖃🖃🖃

★★★ 74% ◎◎ ♨ Cottage in the Wood

Holywell Rd, Malvern Wells WR14 4LG
☎ 01684 575859 📠 01684 560662
e-mail: proprietor@cottageinthewood.co.uk
Dir: 3m S of Great Malvern off A449, 500yds N of B4209 turning, on opposite side of road

PETS: Telephone for details

This delightful family-run hotel enjoys magnificent views across
continued

the Severn Valley. The cosy bedrooms are divided between the main house, Beech Cottage and the newly built Pinnacles. All are well equipped and have many thoughtful extras. Public rooms are elegantly appointed and feature real fires, deep-cushioned sofas and fresh flowers.

ROOMS: 8 en suite 23 annexe en suite (10 GF) No smoking in 11 bedrooms s £79-£99; d £99-£170 (incl. bkfst) **LB FACILITIES:** STV Direct access to Malvern Hills Xmas **PARKING:** 40 **NOTES:** No smoking in restaurant **CARDS:** 🖃🖃🖃🖃🖃

★★ 74% Holdfast Cottage

Marlbank Rd, Little Malvern WR13 6NA
☎ 01684 310288 📠 01684 311117
e-mail: enquiries@holdfast-cottage.co.uk
Dir: on A4104 midway between Welland and Upper Welland

PETS: Bedrooms Exercise area (200yds)
RESIDENT PETS: Jasmine & Primrose - King Charles Cavalier spaniels

This charming, wisteria-covered hotel lies in attractive grounds at the foot of the Malvern Hills. The public areas offer all the comforts of a country retreat - log fire in the lounge, a cosy bar and an elegant dining room. The bedrooms include many thoughtful touches. The regularly changing menu features fresh local produce, and ice cream and breads are made on the premises.
ROOMS: 8 en suite (1 fmly) No smoking in all bedrooms s £50-£70; d £84-£94 (incl. bkfst) **LB FACILITIES:** Croquet lawn Walking, bird watching ch fac Xmas **PARKING:** 20 **NOTES:** No smoking in restaurant **CARDS:** 🖃🖃🖃🖃

🐓 **Places with this symbol are farms**

England

MALVERN continued

♦♦♦ Four Hedges
The Rhydd, Hanley Castle WR8 0AD
☎ 01684 310405
e-mail: fredgies@aol.com
Dir: at junct of B4424/B4211, 50yds from Cliffey House School

PETS: Bedrooms (unattended) Public areas Exercise area
RESIDENT PETS: Border Collie & 2 cats

Situated in a rural location four miles from Malvern, this detached house stands in mature grounds with wild birds in abundance. Bedrooms are equipped with thoughtful extras and tasty English breakfasts, that includes free-range eggs, are taken in a cosy dining room at one table that is made from a 300-year-old elm tree.
FACILITIES: 4 rms (1 en suite) No smoking TV1B tea/coffee No coaches Fishing Croquet lawn Stair lift **PRICES:** s £18; d £40✻ **BB PARKING:** 5
NOTES: Closed Xmas

MARTLEY
Map 03 SO76

♦♦♦♦ ⬛ Admiral Rodney Inn
Berrow Green WR6 6PL
☎ 01886 821375 ▤ 01886 822048
e-mail: rodney@admiral.fslife.co.uk
Dir: A44 at Knightwick onto B4197, Inn 2m on left

PETS: Bedrooms (unattended) Public areas (not in restaurant) Exercise area (adjacent field) Water bowls, toys provided RESIDENT PETS: Penny - Alsatian/Collie cross

Located in the pretty village of Berrow Green, this 16th-century inn has been sympathetically renovated to provide high standards of comfort and facilities. Spacious, tastefully furnished bedrooms are complemented by luxurious modern bathrooms. Ground floor areas include quality bars with log fires and a unique tiered and beamed restaurant, where imaginative dishes are served.
FACILITIES: 3 en suite No smoking in area of dining room No smoking in 1 lounge TVB tea/coffee Direct dial from bedrooms Cen ht Pool Table Skittle Alley, darts & board games Dinner Last d 9pm **PRICES:** s £40-£55; d £55-£65✻ **PARKING:** 40 **CARDS:** ▤▤ ▤▤ ▤▤ ▤▤ ▤

REDDITCH
Map 07 SP06

★★★ 63% Quality Hotel Redditch
Pool Bank, Southcrest B97 4JS
☎ 01527 541511 ▤ 01527 402600
e-mail: enquiries@hotels-redditch.com
Dir: follow hotel signs, 2nd on right after B&Q. Follow Redditch signs onto A441. In Redditch follow signs for all other Redditch Districts until Southcrest signed, then take signs for hotel

PETS: Bedrooms Exercise area (on site)

Originally a manor house, this hotel enjoys a peaceful location in extensive wooded grounds. Bedrooms vary in size and style, and all are well appointed and equipped. Both the restaurant and bar/conservatory overlook the attractive, sloping gardens, with views stretching across to the Vale of Evesham.
ROOMS: 73 en suite (20 fmly) (22 GF) No smoking in 35 bedrooms s £50-£86; d £60-£99 **LB FACILITIES:** STV Xmas **PARKING:** 100
NOTES: No smoking in restaurant **CARDS:** ▤▤ ▤▤ ▤▤ ▤▤ ▤

UPTON UPON SEVERN
Map 03 SO84

★★★ 69% ◉ White Lion
21 High St WR8 0HJ
☎ 01684 592551 ▤ 01684 593333
e-mail: reservations@whitelionhotel.biz
Dir: A422, A38 towards Tewkesbury. In 8m take B4104, after 1m cross bridge, turn left to hotel, past bend on left

PETS: Bedrooms (unattended) Public areas Exercise area (Adjacent)

Famed for being the inn depicted in Henry Fielding's novel Tom Jones, this 16th-century hotel brings old England to the fore with exposed beams, wall timbers, and traditional furniture with lace table cloths and vases of fresh flowers. The White Lion has a well-deserved reputation for the quality of its food, which is complemented by friendly, attentive service.
ROOMS: 13 rms (11 en suite) (2 GF) s £67.50; d £92.50 (incl. bkfst) **LB**
PARKING: 18 **NOTES:** No smoking in restaurant Closed 1 Jan RS 25 Dec & 1 Jan **CARDS:** ▤▤ ▤▤ ▤▤ ▤▤ ▤

WORCESTER
Map 03 SO85

★★★ 64% Fownes
City Walls Rd WR1 2AP
☎ 01905 613151 ▤ 01905 23742
e-mail: reservations@fowneshotel.co.uk
Dir: M5 junct 7 take A44 for Worcester city centre. Turn right at 4th set of traffic lights into City Walls Rd

PETS: Bedrooms Pet Food

On the Birmingham canal and located close to the city centre this former Victorian glove factory has been converted into an interesting-looking, modern hotel with well proportioned bedrooms. Snacks are available in the lounge bar and the King's restaurant offers an interesting carte menu. Conference and meeting facilities are available.
ROOMS: 61 en suite (10 GF) No smoking in 28 bedrooms s £98.50; d £79-£104.50 (incl. bkfst) **LB FACILITIES:** ch fac Xmas **SERVICES:** Lift
PARKING: 82 **NOTES:** No smoking in restaurant
CARDS: ▤▤ ▤▤ ▤▤ ▤▤ ▤

YORKSHIRE, EAST RIDING OF

BEVERLEY
Map 08 TA03

★★ 74% ◉◉ Manor House
Northlands, Walkington HU17 8RT
☎ 01482 881645 ▤ 01482 866501
e-mail: info@walkingtonmanorhouse.co.uk
Dir: follow 'Walkington' signs from M62 junct 38. 4m SW off B1230. Through Walkington village, left at lights. Left at 1st x-roads. Approx 400yds hotel on left

PETS: Bedrooms

This delightful country-house hotel is set in open country amid well-tended gardens. The spacious bedrooms have been attractively decorated and thoughtfully equipped. Public rooms include a conservatory restaurant and a very inviting lounge. A

continued

good range of dishes is available from two menus, with an emphasis on fresh and local produce.

ROOMS: 6 en suite 1 annexe en suite (1 fmly) (1 GF) s £75-£80; d £90-£110 **PARKING:** 40 **NOTES:** No smoking in restaurant Closed 25 Dec-4 Jan RS Sun **CARDS:**

♦♦♦ The Eastgate
7 Eastgate HU17 0DR
☎ 01482 868464 📠 01482 871899
Dir: 100yds from Beverley Minster

PETS:	Bedrooms Exercise area (0.5 mile)
RESIDENT PETS: 1 collie, 3 cats, 3 hamsters	

This family-run hotel, situated close to The Minster, provides modern decor and well-equipped bedrooms, together with comfortable public rooms. The helpful staff, who are always on hand, provide very friendly service. Please phone in advance for details of local parking facilities.

FACILITIES: 16 rms (7 en suite) (5 fmly) (3 GF) No smoking in bedrooms No smoking in dining room TVB tea/coffee Cen ht TVL **PRICES:** s £15-£38; d £30-£53✱ **LB BB**

BRIDLINGTON   Map 08 TA16

♦♦♦♦ Marton Grange
Flamborough Rd, Marton cum Sewerby YO15 1DU
☎ 01262 602034 📠 01262 602034
e-mail: martongrange@talk21.com
Dir: on B1255, 600yds from Links golf club

PETS:	Bedrooms £5 Public areas (Conservatory only)
Exercise area (Adjacent paddock) **RESIDENT PETS:** Puss - cat & chickens	

The atmosphere of this guest house is welcoming and the bedrooms are all of high quality, offering a range of extra facilities; ground floor rooms are available. There are attractive lounges with views over the gardens. Substantial breakfasts and interesting evening meals, featuring home cooking, are served in the attractive dining rooms.

FACILITIES: 11 en suite (3 GF) No smoking TVB tea/coffee Licensed Lift Cen ht No children 12yrs No coaches Dinner Last d 10am **PRICES:** s £35-£42; d £60-£70✱ **PARKING:** 11 **NOTES:** Closed Dec-Feb rs March & Nov **CARDS:**

♦♦♦♦ Shearwater
22 Vernon Rd YO15 2HE
☎ 01262 679883
e-mail: enquiries@shearwaterhotel.co.uk
Dir: from A166 take A165 to town centre. Turn left after Tesco's onto Springfield Rd. At T junct lights, turn right and 1st left down Victoria Rd. Turn left into Trinity Rd hotel on left at beginning one way system

PETS:	Bedrooms £5 per stay Exercise area (5 mins to sea, 20 mins to park) Dog beds, clean blankets and food provided.
RESIDENT PETS: Thomas - Collie/Alsatian cross, Suzie - Black Labrador	

This well furnished house is found in a residential part of town and provides well-equipped and comfortable bedrooms. There is

continued

---

a cosy lounge and quality home cooked meals are provided in the modern dining room.

FACILITIES: 6 en suite (3 fmly) No smoking TVB tea/coffee Licensed Cen ht No coaches Dinner Last d 4pm **CARDS:**

KINGSTON UPON HULL   Map 08 TA02

★★★ 68% Portland
Paragon St HU1 3JP
☎ 01482 326462 📠 01482 213460
e-mail: info@portland-hotel.co.uk
Dir: M62 onto A63, to 1st main rdbt. Left at 2nd lights and over x-rds. Right at next junct onto Carr Ln, follow one-way system

Best Western

PETS:	Bedrooms Public areas Pet Food

A modern hotel situated in the city centre providing a good range of accommodation. Most of the public rooms are on the first floor and include the Wilberforce Restaurant and the Humber Bar and Lounge. In addition, the Bay Tree Café, at street level, is open during the day and evening. Staff are friendly and helpful and take care of car parking.

ROOMS: 126 en suite (4 fmly) No smoking in 22 bedrooms s £42-£75; d £98 **FACILITIES:** STV Complimentary use of nearby health & fitness centre Xmas **SERVICES:** Lift **PARKING:** 12 **CARDS:** (card symbols)

★★★ 67% Quality Hotel Royal Hull
170 Ferensway HU1 3UF
☎ 01482 325087 📠 01482 323172
e-mail: enquiries@hotel-hull.com
Dir: From M62 join A63 to Hull. Over flyover, left at 2nd lights signed Railway Station. Hotel on left at 2nd lights

QUALITY HOTEL
BY CHOICE HOTELS

PETS:	Bedrooms (unattended) Exercise area (1 mile)

A former Victorian railway hotel modernised in recent years. Bedrooms are well-equipped and include a number of premier rooms. A spacious lounge provides an ideal setting for light meals, drinks and relaxation. There are extensive banqueting and conference facilities, as well as an adjacent leisure club.

ROOMS: 155 en suite (6 fmly) No smoking in 85 bedrooms s £42-£98; d £50-£107 **LB** **FACILITIES:** Indoor swimming (H) Sauna Solarium Gym Jacuzzi Steamroom Xmas **SERVICES:** Lift **PARKING:** 130 **CARDS:** (card symbols)

⌂ Campanile
Beverley Rd, Freetown Way HU2 9AN
☎ 01482 325530 📠 01482 587538
e-mail: hull@envergure.co.uk
Dir: From M62 join A63 to Hull, pass Humber Bridge on right. Over flyover, follow railway station signs onto A1079. Hotel at bottom of Ferensway

Campanile

PETS:	Bedrooms (unattended)

This modern building offers accommodation in smart, well-equipped bedrooms, all with en suite bathrooms. Refreshments may be taken at the informal Bistro. For further details consult the Hotel Groups page.

ROOMS: 47 annexe en suite s fr £42.95; d fr £42.95

England

LITTLE WEIGHTON
Map 08 SE93

★★ 66% The Rowley Manor
Rowley Rd HU20 3XR
☎ 01482 848248 📠 01482 849900
e-mail: info@rowleymanor.com
Dir: leave A63 at South Cave/Market Weighton exit. Into South Cave, right into Beverley Rd at clock tower, and follow signs for Rowley

PETS: £2 **Exercise area** (1 mile)

Rowley Manor is a Georgian country house and former vicarage set in rural gardens and parkland. Bedrooms are traditionally decorated and furnished with period pieces; many rooms have panoramic views, and some are particularly spacious. The public rooms include a magnificent pine-panelled study, and the gardens feature a croquet lawn.
ROOMS: 16 en suite (2 fmly) s fr £60; d fr £80 (incl. bkfst) **LB**
FACILITIES: Croquet lawn ch fac Xmas **PARKING:** 100
NOTES: No smoking in restaurant
CARDS: ▬▬ ▬▬ ▬▬ ▬▬ ▬▬ ▬▬ 🅂

MARKET WEIGHTON
Map 08 SE84

♦♦♦ Robeanne House
Driffield Ln, Shiptonthorpe YO43 3PW
☎ 01430 873312 📠 01430 873312
e-mail: robert@robeanne.freeserve.com

PETS: **Bedrooms** **Sep Accom** (stables) (unattended) £10 horses, £3.50 dogs/cats **Public areas** (except dining room) **Exercise area** (on site) Bowls/food/hay/dogs beds on request. Large field, all weather horse exercise area, and turn out paddocks **RESIDENT PETS:** Billy - Springer Spaniel, Beatty, Josie, Jaz - horses, Moulder - cat

Conveniently located beside the A614, but set far enough back to be a quiet location, this delightful modern family home was built as a farmhouse. Access to York is easy, and the coast and Yorkshire Moors and Dales are also within easy driving distance. Bedrooms all have countryside views and include a large family room, and a charming wooden chalet is available in the garden.
FACILITIES: 2 en suite 2 annexe en suite (2 fmly) (1 GF) No smoking in 1 bedrooms No smoking in dining room No smoking in lounges TVB tea/coffee Cen ht No coaches outdoor hot-tub Dinner Last d 24hrs prior
PRICES: s £20-£30; d £45-£55✳ **LB** **PARKING:** 10
CARDS: ▬▬ ▬▬ ▬▬

NORTH FERRIBY
Map 08 SE92

★★★ 65% Elizabeth Hotel Hull
Ferriby High Rd HU14 3LG

THE INDEPENDENTS

☎ 01482 645212 📠 01482 643332
e-mail: elizabeth.hull@elizabethhotels.co.uk
Dir: M62 onto A63 to Hull. Exit for Humber Bridge. At rdbt follow Leeds signs until signs for North Ferriby. Hotel 0.5m on left

PETS: **Bedrooms** (unattended) **Public areas** **Exercise area** (hotel gardens an adjacent meadow) Pet Food Bowls only (no food) provided

A modern, purpose built hotel that enjoys spectacular views of the Humber Bridge. Bedrooms are comfortable and well equipped.

continued

Public areas are spacious and both the restaurant and lounge bar look out over the river. There is ample car parking and also a children's play area at the rear. 24-hour room service is available.
ROOMS: 95 en suite (6 fmly) (17 GF) No smoking in 77 bedrooms s £55-£75; d £65-£95 (incl. bkfst) **LB FACILITIES:** STV Nearly full size pool table Xmas **PARKING:** 140
CARDS: ▬▬ ▬▬ ▬▬ ▬▬ ▬▬ ▬▬ 🅂

SOUTH CAVE
Map 08 SE93

Rudstone Walk Country Accommodation
Brough HU15 2AH
☎ 01430 422230 📠 01430 424552
e-mail: office@rudstone-walk.co.uk
Dir: M62 junct 38, A1034 to S.Cave. Right onto B1230. 200yds on left

PETS: **Bedrooms** £10 per stay **Exercise area** (80 acres on site) **RESIDENT PETS:** Maisie - Whippet

A delightful farm conversion which offers a very comfortable lounge, a charming bar and dining room. Dinner available by prior arrangement. The old stables have been converted into comfortable and stylish bedrooms that overlook a courtyard garden. One room has facilities for less able guests.
ROOMS: 14 en suite (2 family) (10 GF) No smoking in 11 bedrooms/ dining room/lounges TVB tea/coffee Cen ht **PRICES:** s £46-£49 d £56-60 **LB PARKING:** 50 **CARDS:** ▬▬ ▬▬ ▬▬ ▬▬ ▬▬ ▬▬ 🅂

YORKSHIRE, NORTH

ASKRIGG
Map 07 SD99

♦♦♦♦ Whitfield
Helm DL8 3JF
☎ 01969 650565 📠 01969 650565
e-mail: empsall@askrigg-cottages.co.uk
Dir: off A684 at Bainbridge by Rose & Crown Hotel, signed Askrigg, over river to T-junct, turn right, 150mtrs to No Through Road sign, left up hill for 0.5m

PETS: **Bedrooms** **Public areas** **Exercise area** (adjacent) meadows nearby **RESIDENT PETS:** Meg and Sally (Border Collies)

Set high in the fells, this smart accommodation is housed in a carefully converted barn, built of Yorkshire limestone. Both bedrooms are well equipped and comfortable, and enjoy stunning views of the Wensleydale countryside. Hearty breakfasts are served around a communal table in the inviting open-plan lounge/dining room.

continued

FACILITIES: 2 en suite No smoking TVB tea/coffee Cen ht TVL.
No coaches PRICES: s fr £27; d £54✱ LB PARKING: 1
NOTES: Closed 23 Dec-2 Jan CARDS: 🔲🔲

BOLTON ABBEY
Map 07 SE05

AA *Pet Friendly Hotel*
of the Year 2005 IAMS

★★★ ◎◎◎ **Devonshire Arms**
BD23 6AJ
☎ 01756 710441 📠 01756 710564
e-mail: reservations@thedevonshirearms.co.uk
Dir: on B6160, 250yds N of junct with A59

PETS: Bedrooms (Designated rooms) (unattended)
Public areas (Not in restaurants or club) Exercise area
(Adjacent) Pet Food Water bowl in reception, feeding bowls
and food by arrangement, trails & river walks
RESIDENT PETS: Emma and Louis - Spaniels, Gizzy - Yorkshire
Terrier, Sasha - Brown Labrador

With stunning views of the Wharfedale countryside, this
beautiful hotel, owned by the Duke and Duchess of
Devonshire, dates back to the 17th century. Bedrooms are
elegantly furnished; those in the old part of the house are
particularly spacious, complete with four-posters and fine
antiques. The sitting rooms are delightfully cosy with log fires
and dedicated staff deliver service with a blend of friendliness
and professionalism. The Burlington Restaurant offers highly
accomplished dishes, while the brasserie provides a lighter
alternative.
ROOMS: 41 en suite (18 GF) No smoking in 12 bedrooms
s £160-£380; d £220-£380 (incl. bkfst) LB FACILITIES: Indoor
swimming (H) Tennis (hard) Fishing Sauna Solarium Gym
Croquet lawn Putting green Jacuzzi Laser pigeon shooting, Falconry
ch fac Xmas PARKING: 150 NOTES: No smoking in restaurant
CARDS: 🔲🔲🔲🔲🔲🔲🔲

BOROUGHBRIDGE
Map 08 SE36

♦♦♦ 🍺 **The Crown Inn**
Roecliffe YO51 9LY
☎ 01423 322578 📠 01423 324060
e-mail: crowninnroecliffe@btopenworld.com
*Dir: A1(M) junct 48 take A168 to Thirsk, at 1st rdbt turn left to Roecliffe.
Through village, inn last building on right*

PETS: Bedrooms Exercise area (50yds)
RESIDENT PETS: Socks - cat; Kira, Jemma - dogs

Situated in the centre of a picturesque village, yet just a mile from
the A1 and Boroughbridge, this old inn boasts modern, well-
appointed bedrooms that appeal to both business travellers and
tourists. Imaginative food is served in the bar and restaurant,
which are very popular with locals. A function suite is also
available.
FACILITIES: 1 en suite 6 annexe en suite (2 fmly) (3 GF) No smoking in
3 bedrooms No smoking in dining room TVB tea/coffee Direct dial
from bedrooms Cen ht Dinner Last d 9.30pm PRICES: s £39.50-£60;
d £65-£95✱ LB MEALS: Lunch £12-£20&alc Dinner £25-£30&alc✱
PARKING: 30 CARDS: 🔲🔲🔲

BUCKDEN
Map 07 SD97

★★ 69% ◎◎ **Buck Inn**
BD23 5JA
☎ 01756 760228 📠 01756 760227
e-mail: info@thebuckinn.com
*Dir: A59/B6265 to Threshfield, then B6160 to Buckden through Kettlewell &
Starbotton*

PETS: £5 Public areas (Not restaurant)

This traditional Georgian inn is privately owned, personally run
and provides warm, friendly hospitality. Fine views can be enjoyed
from many of the smartly presented bedrooms. There is a cosy
lounge area for guests and a wide range of interesting snacks and
light meals are served in the lounge bar. The Courtyard restaurant
provides a more formal menu using fresh, local, quality produce.
ROOMS: 14 en suite (2 fmly) (2 GF) s £44.50-£55; d £82-£99
(incl. bkfst) LB FACILITIES: Xmas PARKING: 30 NOTES: No smoking
in restaurant CARDS: 🔲🔲🔲🔲🔲

BURNSALL
Map 07 SE06

♦♦♦ **Burnsall Manor House Hotel**
Main St BD23 6BW
☎ 01756 720231 📠 720231
e-mail: joe@manorhouseuk.co.uk
Dir: on B6160. Village between Grassington & Bolton Abbey

PETS: Bedrooms Public areas (except restaurant)
Exercise area

A warm welcome awaits you at this 19th-century house, situated
on the River Wharfe. Bedrooms are traditionally furnished and
have delightful views. Freshly prepared meals can be enjoyed in
the spacious dining room. There is also a cosy bar, TV lounge, and
in the warmer months, the large garden provides a peaceful
setting in which to relax.
FACILITIES: 8 rms (7 en suite) No smoking tea/coffee Licensed Cen ht
TVL Fishing Croquet lawn Dinner Last d 5pm PRICES: s £24.50-£36.50;
d £49-£57✱ LB PARKING: 11 CARDS: 🔲🔲🔲🔲🔲

CARPERBY
Map 07 SE08

♦♦♦ **Wheatsheaf Hotel**
DL8 4DF
☎ 01969 663216 📠 01969 663019
e-mail: wheatsheaf@paulmit.globalnet.co.uk
*Dir: From A1 take A684 to Wensley, right turn signed Castle Bolton &
Aysgarth Falls to Carperby*

PETS: Bedrooms £5 per stay Public areas Exercise area
(400 metres) RESIDENT PETS: Elsa (Collie/Alsatian cross)

The Wheatsheaf is a typical Dales hotel and offers comfortable
accommodation. The bedrooms are pleasantly furnished and
include two with attractive four-poster beds. The comfortable
lounge features a 17th-century stone fireplace and guests can
enjoy good home cooking from extensive menus in the cosy bar
and dining room.
FACILITIES: 8 en suite (1 fmly) No smoking in 1 bedrooms No smoking
in dining room TVB tea/coffee Licensed Cen ht No coaches Fishing
Dinner Last d 9pm PRICES: s £27.50; d £58-£69✱ LB PARKING: 40
CARDS: 🔲🔲🔲🔲🔲

England

CATTERICK
Map 08 SE29

◆◆◆ Rose Cottage
26 High St DL10 7LJ
☎ 01748 811164
Dir: 5m S of Scotch Corner, take A6136 off A1 into Catterick Village. House opp newsagents

PETS: Bedrooms (unattended) Exercise area

Conveniently located for the A1 and for exploring the Dales and Moors, this small and friendly stone built guest house lies in the middle of Catterick Village. The neatly decorated bedrooms are comfortable, simply furnished and offer practical and homely extras. Breakfast is served in the cottage style dining room; dinner can be arranged during the summer months.
FACILITIES: 4 rms (2 en suite) (1 fmly) No smoking in dining room TVB tea/coffee Cen ht No coaches Dinner Last d 9.30am **PRICES:** s £27-£32; d £42-£48✱ **PARKING:** 4 **NOTES:** Closed 24-26 Dec

EAST AYTON
Map 08 SE98

★★★ 62% East Ayton Lodge
Moor Ln, Forge Valley YO13 9EW
☎ 01723 864227 🖪 01723 862680
e-mail: ealodge@cix.co.uk
Dir: 400yds off A170

PETS: Bedrooms £5 per stay

Set in three acres of grounds close to the River Derwent and discreetly situated in a quiet lane on the edge of the forest, this friendly, family-operated hotel is constructed around what was originally two cottages. Bedrooms are well-equipped and those in the courtyard are particularly spacious. A good range of food is available.
ROOMS: 10 en suite 20 annexe en suite (5 fmly) (10 GF)
FACILITIES: Xmas **PARKING:** 50 **NOTES:** No smoking in restaurant
CARDS:

FILEY
Map 08 TA18

◆◆◆◆ Gables
2A Rutland St YO14 9JB
☎ 01723 514750
e-mail: thegablesfiley@aol.com
Dir: leave A165 at Filey, right in town centre into West Ave, 2nd left into Rutland St. The Gables is on corner opp church

PETS: Bedrooms £2 Public areas (except dining room) Exercise area (opposite) RESIDENT PETS: Boots (Old English Sheepdog), Psycho & Smokey (cats)

Located in a quiet residential area, just a short stroll from the centre and promenade, this smart Edwardian house extends a warm welcome to all guests. Bedrooms are brightly decorated and well equipped and some are suitable for families. Breakfasts are substantial and a varied evening menu is available.
FACILITIES: 5 en suite (3 fmly) No smoking TVB tea/coffee Cen ht No coaches Golf 18 Dinner Last d noon **LB PARKING:** 3
CARDS:

GOATHLAND
Map 08 NZ80

◆◆◆ Fairhaven Country Hotel
The Common YO22 5AN
☎ 01947 896361 🖪 01947 896099
e-mail: thefairhaven@btconnect.com
Dir: off A169 Pickering-Whitby road, follow signs for Goathland. Hotel 0.25m from church

PETS: Bedrooms (unattended) £3 Public areas (except dining room) Exercise area (adjacent) RESIDENT PETS: Bonnie (Bull Mastiff)

This Edwardian hotel stands in the village of Goathland - the centre of 'Heartbeat Country'. All areas are furnished in a style that highlights the many retained original interior features. The spacious ground floor areas include a comfortable lounge with an open fire and a separate bar. Bedrooms are comfortable and offer stunning views of the surrounding countryside.
FACILITIES: 9 rms (8 en suite) (3 fmly) No smoking TVB tea/coffee Licensed Cen ht TVL No coaches Dinner Last d 9am
PRICES: s £29-£30; d £60✱ **PARKING:** 8
CARDS:

GREAT AYTON
Map 08 NZ51

◆◆◆ 🍴 Royal Oak Hotel
123 High St TS9 6BW
☎ 01642 722361 & 723270 🖪 01642 724047
e-mail: info@royaloak-hotel.co.uk

PETS: Bedrooms (unattended)

This 18th-century former coaching inn is very popular with locals and visitors to the village. Bedrooms are all comfortable and well-equipped. The restaurant and public bar retain many original features and offer a good selection of fine ales; an extensive range of food is available all day and is served in the bar or the dining room.
FACILITIES: 5 en suite No smoking in dining room TVB tea/coffee Direct dial from bedrooms Cen ht Dinner Last d 9.30pm
PRICES: s £30-£40; d £60✱ **CARDS:**

> ### All abbreviations are explained on page 9

GREAT BARUGH Map 08 SE77

♦♦♦♦ 🏛 Barugh House
YO17 6UZ
☎ 01653 668615
e-mail: barughhouse@amserve.net
Dir: at Amotherby turn right & follow road for 3.5m to Great Barugh. Turn left, pass Golden Lion pub on right. House 50yds downhill on right

PETS: Bedrooms £7 per animal per stay Public areas (Except dining room) Exercise area (0.25 mile) dog-sitting in hot weather RESIDENT PETS: Folly (Terrier), Ellie (Collie cross) & Daisy (cat)

This period property sits in the centre of the village, and makes a perfect base from which to explore, and a delightful place to get away from it all. The house style, one of quality and tranquillity, where everything is done to make guests feel at home and welcome. Superb home-made preserves and compotes feature on the family-style breakfast table as well as organic produce where ever possible.
FACILITIES: 2 rms No smoking TVB tea/coffee Cen ht No children 8yrs No coaches Dinner Last d midday **PRICES:** d £70✱ **PARKING:** 2
NOTES: Closed 24-26 Dec

GUISBOROUGH Map 08 NZ61

★★★★ 72% Gisborough Hall
Whitby Ln TS14 6PT
☎ 0870 400 8191 📠 01287 610844

MACDONALD HOTELS

e-mail: general.gisboroughhall@macdonald-hotels.co.uk
Dir: A171, follow signs for Whitby until Waterfall rdbt then into Whitby Lane, hotel 500yds on right

PETS: Bedrooms (unattended) Exercise area (on site)

Dating back to the mid-19th Century, this elegant hall has been carefully refurbished and extended to provide a pleasing combination of original features and modern facilities. Bedrooms, including four-poster and family rooms, are richly furnished, while there is a choice of welcoming lounges with log fires. Imaginative fare is served in Tockett's restaurant.
ROOMS: 71 en suite (2 fmly) (12 GF) No smoking in 37 bedrooms s £99-£109; d £138-£158 (incl. bkfst) **FACILITIES:** STV Sauna Revival zone-2 beauty treatment zones Xmas **SERVICES:** Lift air con
PARKING: 400 **NOTES:** No smoking in restaurant
CARDS: 🖃 🖃 💳 🖃 🖃 🖃

HARROGATE Map 08 SE35

★★★ 79% ◉◉ The Boar's Head Hotel
Ripley Castle Estate HG3 3AY
☎ 01423 771888 📠 01423 771509
e-mail: reservations@boarsheadripley.co.uk
Dir: on A61 Harrogate to Ripon road. Hotel in centre of Ripley Village

PETS: Bedrooms (unattended) £10 Public areas (Not in food service areas) Exercise area (Adjacent) Bowls, and dog biscuit treats provided

Situated in the private village of the Ripley Castle estate, this delightful and popular hotel is renowned for its warm hospitality and the restaurant, serving a mix of modern and traditional dishes. Bedrooms offer many comforts, and the luxurious day rooms feature works of art from the nearby castle.

continued

ROOMS: 19 en suite 6 annexe en suite (2 fmly) No smoking in 15 bedrooms s £105-£125; d £125-£150 (incl. bkfst) **LB**
FACILITIES: Tennis (hard) Fishing Clay pigeon shooting entertainment ch fac Xmas **PARKING:** 50 **NOTES:** No smoking in restaurant
CARDS: 🖃 🖃 💳 🖃 🖃 🖃

★★ 74% Ascot House
53 Kings Rd HG1 5HJ
☎ 01423 531005 📠 01423 503523
e-mail: admin@ascothouse.com
Dir: on entering Harrogate follow signs to town centre, Conference and Exhibition Centre into Kings Rd, hotel on left after park

PETS: Bedrooms (unattended) Exercise area (over the road)

This late-Victorian house has been tastefully transformed into a friendly and meticulously maintained hotel. Situated a short distance from the International Conference Centre, it provides comfortable and extremely well-appointed bedrooms, an inviting lounge bar and a dining room offering an interesting choice at dinner.
ROOMS: 19 en suite (2 fmly) (5 GF) No smoking in all bedrooms s £59-£71; d £87-£112 (incl. bkfst) **LB FACILITIES:** ch fac Xmas
PARKING: 14 **NOTES:** No smoking in restaurant Closed 29 Dec-4 Jan & 23 Jan-6 Feb 2005 **CARDS:** 🖃 🖃 💳 🖃 🖃 🖃

◉ 🏠 Harrogate Brasserie Hotel & Bar
28-30 Cheltenham Pde HG1 1DB
☎ 01423 505041 📠 01423 722300
e-mail: info@brasserie.co.uk
Dir: on A61 town centre behind theatre

THE INDEPENDENTS

PETS: Bedrooms (unattended)

This town centre restaurant with rooms is distinctly continental in style. The brasserie covers three cosy dining areas richly decorated and adorned with artefacts. Live jazz is featured on Wednesday, Friday and Sunday nights. The individual bedrooms feature period collectibles; many rooms have DVD players and all have lots to read.
ROOMS: 17 en suite (3 fmly) s fr £52.50; d £75-£95 (incl. bkfst) **LB**
FACILITIES: entertainment Xmas **PARKING:** 12 **NOTES:** Closed 26 & 31 Dec **CARDS:** 🖃 🖃 💳 🖃 🖃

♦♦♦♦ 🛏 Alexa House & Stable Cottages
26 Ripon Rd HG1 2JJ
☎ 01423 501988 📠 01423 504086
e-mail: alexahouse@msn.com
Dir: on A61, 0.25m from junction of A59/A61

PETS: Bedrooms (unattended) Exercise area (400 yards)

This popular hotel offers stylish, well-equipped bedrooms split between the main house and cottage rooms, all featuring practical and homely extras. Light meals are available daily and dinners are available for groups by prior arrangement. Opulent day rooms include an elegant lounge with honesty bar, and a bright dining room. Hands-on proprietors ensure high levels of customer care at every turn.
FACILITIES: 9 en suite 4 annexe en suite (2 fmly) (4 GF) No smoking in bedrooms No smoking in dining room TVB tea/coffee Direct dial from bedrooms Licensed Cen ht TVL No coaches Dinner Last d 10am
PRICES: s £45-£58; d £65-£85✱ **LB PARKING:** 10
CARDS: 🖃 🖃 💳 🖃 🖃

England

England

HARROGATE continued

◆◆◆ Princes Hotel
7 Granby Rd HG1 4ST
☎ 01423 883469 🖷 01423 881417
Dir: off A59 at Empress roundabout

PETS: Bedrooms (unattended) Public areas Exercise area (25 yards)

A tranquil and relaxing atmosphere is found at this fine Victorian house set on the edge of the town and convenient for the Yorkshire showground. The comfortable bedrooms are traditionally furnished and breakfast is taken in a lovely dining room overlooking the gardens.
FACILITIES: 6 en suite (2 fmly) No smoking in 1 bedroom No smoking in dining room TVB tea/coffee Direct dial from bedrooms Cen ht No children 3yrs No coaches **PRICES:** s £28; d £48-£59✳ **PARKING:** 1

◆◆◆ Shelbourne
78 Kings Rd HG1 5JX
☎ 01423 504390 🖷 01423 504390
e-mail: sue@shelbourne house.co.uk
Dir: on entering Harrogate follow signs for conference centre, through traffic lights by Moat House Hotel, premises on right

PETS: Bedrooms Exercise area (100 yards)
RESIDENT PETS: 2 cats - Jack and Keith

Situated opposite the conference centre and near to the town centre, this guesthouse provides bright, cheerful bedrooms of varying size and has a friendly atmosphere. There is a comfortable guests' lounge and an attractive breakfast room.
FACILITIES: 8 rms (6 en suite) (2 fmly) No smoking TVB tea/coffee Licensed Cen ht TVL No coaches **PRICES:** s £30-£35; d £45-£60✳ **LB** **PARKING:** 1 **CARDS:** 〓〓 〓

HAWES   Map 07 SD88

★★ 73% Simonstone Hall
Simonstone DL8 3LY
☎ 01969 667255 🖷 01969 667741
e-mail: hotel@simonstonehall.demon.co.uk
Dir: 1.5m N on road signed to Muker and Buttertubs

PETS: Bedrooms Sep Accom (kennels) (unattended) Public areas (except restaurant)

This former hunting lodge provides professional, friendly service and a relaxed atmosphere. There is an inviting drawing room, stylish fine dining restaurant and a bar and new conservatory. The generally spacious bedrooms are elegantly finished to reflect the style of the house, and many offer spectacular views of the surrounding countryside.
ROOMS: 18 en suite (10 fmly) (2 GF) No smoking in all bedrooms s £55-£120; d £110-£240 (incl. bkfst) **LB** **FACILITIES:** ch fac Xmas
PARKING: 40 **NOTES:** No smoking in restaurant
CARDS: 〓〓 〓〓 〓〓 〓

★★ 72% 🏨 Stone House
Sedbusk DL8 3PT
☎ 01969 667571 🖷 01969 667720
e-mail: daleshotel@aol.com
Dir: from Hawes take road signed 'Muker & The Buttertubs' to T- junct then right to Sedbusk & Askrigg. Hotel 500yds on left

PETS: Bedrooms (unattended) Public areas Exercise area (on site) Yorkshire Dales National Park nearby

Benefiting from a rural location with spectacular views of the unspoiled Wensleydale countryside, this elegant Georgian hotel is bursting with character. Bedrooms are comfortably furnished; many have luxurious bathrooms and some have their own private conservatories. Public rooms include a well-stocked library and several comfortable lounges.

ROOMS: 23 rms (22 en suite) 5 annexe en suite (1 fmly) (7 GF)
No smoking in 22 bedrooms s £45-£103; d £77-£103 (incl. bkfst) **LB**
FACILITIES: Tennis (grass) Croquet lawn Billiards table ch fac Xmas
PARKING: 30 **NOTES:** No smoking in restaurant RS Dec & Jan
CARDS: 〓〓 〓〓 〓 〓

HAWNBY   Map 08 SE58

◆◆◆◆ 🏨 🐾 Laskill Grange
Hawnby YO62 5NB
☎ 01439 798268 🖷 01439 798498
e-mail: suesmith@laskillfarm.fsnet.co.uk
Dir: 6m N of Helmsley on B1257

PETS: Telephone for details

Country lovers will enjoy this charming 19th-century farmhouse. Guests can take a walk in the surrounding countryside, fish the River Seph which runs through the grounds, or visit nearby Rievaulx. Comfortable bedrooms are in the main house or

continued

sympathetically renovated farm buildings and are well furnished and supplied with many thoughtful extras.
FACILITIES: 2 en suite 4 annexe en suite (2 GF) No smoking TVB tea/coffee Licensed Cen ht Fishing Riding 600 acres beef sheep
PARKING: 20 **NOTES:** Closed 25 Dec **CARDS:**

HELMSLEY
Map 08 SE68

★★★ 75% **Black Swan**
Market Place YO62 5BJ
☎ 0870 400 8112 🖷 01439 770174
e-mail: blackswan@macdonald-hotels.co.uk
Dir: follow A170 towards Scarborough into Helmsley. Hotel at top of market square

MACDONALD
HOTELS

> **PETS:** Bedrooms (unattended) £10 Public areas Exercise area (200yds) Pet Food

The face of this former coaching inn is a blend of Elizabethan, Georgian and Tudor and inside there are warm, welcoming interiors with candlelight, oak beams and open fireplaces. There are six guest lounges and plenty of cosy nooks for quiet conversation. The hotel also has comfortable, individually decorated bedrooms and a popular restaurant.
ROOMS: 45 en suite (4 fmly) No smoking in 13 bedrooms s £65-£85; d £80-£105 (incl. bkfst) **LB FACILITIES:** STV ch fac Xmas
PARKING: 50 **NOTES:** No smoking in restaurant
CARDS:

★★★ 71% **Pheasant**
Harome YO62 5JG
☎ 01439 771241 🖷 01439 771744
Dir: 2.5m SE, leave A170 after 0.25m. Right signed Harome for further 2m

> **PETS:** Bedrooms Exercise area (country lanes)

Guests can expect a family welcome at this hotel, which has spacious, comfortable bedrooms and enjoys a delightful setting next to the village pond. The beamed, flagstoned bar leads into the charming lounge and conservatory dining room, where very enjoyable English food is served. A separate building contains the swimming pool. The hotel offers dinner-inclusive tariffs, and has many regulars.
ROOMS: 12 en suite 2 annexe en suite s £72-£75; d £144-£150 (incl. bkfst & dinner) **LB FACILITIES:** STV Indoor swimming (H)
PARKING: 20 **NOTES:** No children 12yrs No smoking in restaurant Closed Xmas & Jan-Feb **CARDS:**

★★ 68% **Crown**
Market Square YO62 5BJ
☎ 01439 770297 🖷 01439 771595
Dir: on A170

> **PETS:** Bedrooms (unattended) Public areas (except dining room or lounge bar) Exercise area (100 yards) Pet Food
> **RESIDENT PETS:** 3 Golden Retrievers & 1 Alsatian

A 16th-century inn with plenty of character standing in the market square. It is noted for its colourful flower arrangements, excellent morning coffee and home-made scones. Bedrooms are comfortable and thoughtfully equipped. Public areas are

continued

pleasantly traditional and include cosy bars and a dining room serving wholesome dishes in generous portions.
ROOMS: 12 en suite (1 fmly) (1 GF) **FACILITIES: PARKING:** 20
CARDS:

HOVINGHAM
Map 08 SE67

★★★ 67% ◎ **Worsley Hotel Arms**
High St YO62 4LA
☎ 01653 628234 🖷 01653 628130
e-mail: worsleyarms@aol.com
Dir: from S take A64, signed York to Malton. At dual-carriageway left to Hovingham. At Slingsby left and Hovingham 2m. Hotel on main street

> **PETS:** Bedrooms £5 Public areas (except restaurant) Exercise area (adjacent) Pet Food

Overlooking the village green, this hotel has relaxing and attractive lounges with welcoming open fires. Bedrooms are also comfortable and several are contained in cottages across the green. The restaurant provides interesting quality cooking, with less formal dining in the Cricketers' Bar and Bistro to the rear.
ROOMS: 12 en suite 8 annexe en suite (2 fmly) (4 GF) No smoking in all bedrooms s £60-£90; d £75-£150 (incl. bkfst) **LB**
FACILITIES: Tennis (hard) Squash Shooting ch fac Xmas **PARKING:** 25
NOTES: No smoking in restaurant **CARDS:**

HUBY
Map 08 SE56

◆◆◆ **The New Inn Motel**
Main St YO61 1HQ
☎ 01347 810219 🖷 01347 810219
e-mail: enquiries@newinnmotel.freeserve.co.uk
Dir: Approach village from A19, L onto Main St. Motel on L. Behind the New Inn PH.

> **PETS:** Bedrooms £2 Exercise area (100yds)

Nestling behind the New Inn, this modern motel style accommodation has a quiet location in the village of Huby, nine miles north of York. Comfortable bedrooms are spacious and neatly furnished, and breakfast is served in the cosy dining room. The reception area hosts an array of tourist information and the resident owners provide a friendly and helpful service.
FACILITIES: 8 en suite (3 fmly) (8 GF) No smoking in 3 bedrooms No smoking in dining room TVB tea/coffee Cen ht No coaches
PRICES: s £30-£38; d £44-£52✳ **LB PARKING:** 8 **NOTES:** Closed part of Nov & Mar

England

HUNMANBY — Map 08 TA07

★★ 69% Wrangham House Hotel
10 Stonegate YO14 0NS
☎ 01723 891333 📠 01723 892973
e-mail: mervynpoulter@lineone.net
Dir: A64 onto A1039 to Filey. Right onto Hunmanby Rd, hotel behind All Saints Church

PETS: Bedrooms Exercise area (On site)
RESIDENT PETS: Jessie - Boxer

This former Georgian vicarage is only a few minutes' drive from lovely sandy beaches, and stands in beautiful wooded gardens next to the village church. The family-owned and well-furnished hotel features individually styled bedrooms, a comfortable sitting room and cosy bar. The spacious dining room offers a good selection of well-produced dishes.
ROOMS: 8 en suite 4 annexe en suite (1 fmly) (2 GF) No smoking in all bedrooms s £45-£50; d £75-£90 (incl. bkfst) **LB FACILITIES:** Xmas **PARKING:** 20 **NOTES:** No smoking in restaurant
CARDS: 〰️ 💳 💳 💳 🟢

KILNSEY — Map 07 SD96

◆◆◆◆◆ Kilnsey Old Hall
BD23 5PS
☎ 01756 753887
e-mail: oldhall.kilnsey@virgin.net
Dir: take B6265 Skipton to Threshfield, then B6160 to Kilnsey, immediately after Kilnsey Trout Farm left up hill, last house on right.

PETS: Bedrooms £5 Public areas (Except dining room) Exercise area (adjacent) **RESIDENT PETS:** Rupert & Hugo - Labradors

Built in 1648, this historic hall has been painstakingly restored and many of the original features blend seamlessly with the modern, stylish conversion. Bedrooms are elegantly appointed and extremely thoughtfully equipped with a host of extras, including TVs with VCRs, chocolates and mineral water. An imaginative breakfast is served round a large antique table in the central hall, which boasts an inglenook fireplace.
FACILITIES: 3 en suite No smoking TVB tea/coffee Cen ht No children 16yrs No coaches **PRICES:** s £50; d £60-£80✳ **PARKING:** 5 **NOTES:** Closed Xmas week

KIRKBYMOORSIDE — Map 08 SE68

★★ 67% George & Dragon Hotel
17 Market Place YO62 6AA
☎ 01751 433334 📠 01751 432933
e-mail: georgeatkirkby@aol.com
Dir: off A170 between Thirsk and Scarborough, in centre of market town

PETS: Bedrooms (unattended) £8 per stay Public areas (Except during dining times) Exercise area

Set in the market square, this coaching inn dates from the 1600s. With its blazing fire in the cooler months and sporting theme the pub offers a cosy, welcoming atmosphere. A wide range of hearty dishes is offered from both the menu and a blackboard. Spacious
continued

---

bedrooms are individually furnished and housed in the quiet courtyard buildings.
ROOMS: 11 en suite 7 annexe en suite (2 fmly) (2 GF) s £49; d £79-£90 (incl. bkfst) **LB FACILITIES:** Gym Xmas **PARKING:** 20 **NOTES:** No smoking in restaurant **CARDS:** 〰️ 💳 💳 💳 🟢

KNARESBOROUGH — Map 08 SE35

◆◆◆◆ Newton House
5-7 York Place HG5 0AD
☎ 01423 863539 📠 01423 869748
e-mail: newtonhouse@btinternet.com
Dir: on A59 in Knaresborough, 500yds from town centre

PETS: Bedrooms (unattended) Public areas (not in dining room) Exercise area (200yds) bowls, mats, toys & treats available. Food is available but chargeable **RESIDENT PETS:** Ben - chocolate labrador/collie cross

This delightful coaching inn is centrally located and is only two minutes from the river castle and Market Square. The hotel is entered through its own archway into a courtyard. The attractively decorated and very well equipped bedrooms include some four-posters and king-sized doubles. Guests have use of a stylish lounge whilst hearty breakfasts are served in the tasteful dining room.
FACILITIES: 9 en suite 2 annexe en suite (3 fmly) (3 GF) No smoking in bedrooms No smoking in dining room TVB tea/coffee Direct dial from bedrooms Licensed Cen ht TVL No coaches **PRICES:** s £45; d £75-£90✳ **LB PARKING:** 10 **NOTES:** Closed 1 wk at Xmas **CARDS:** 〰️ 💳 💳 💳 🟢

LEEMING BAR — Map 08 SE28

★★ 61% The White Rose
Bedale Rd DL7 9AY
☎ 01677 422707 📠 01677 425123
e-mail: john@whiterosehotel.co.uk
Dir: A1 onto A684 left towards Northallerton. Hotel 0.25m on left

PETS: Bedrooms (unattended) Public areas (except bar/restaurant) Exercise area Pet Food Bowls available

Conveniently situated just minutes from the A1, this commercial hotel boasts pleasant, well-equipped bedrooms contained in a modern block to the rear. Good-value meals are offered in either the traditional bar or attractive dining room.
ROOMS: 18 en suite (2 fmly) (1 GF) s £49; d £63 (incl. bkfst) **FACILITIES:** entertainment **PARKING:** 50 **NOTES:** No smoking in restaurant **CARDS:** 〰️ 💳 💳 💳 🟢

LEYBURN — Map 07 SE19

★ 65% Golden Lion
Market Place DL8 5AS
☎ 01969 622161 📠 01969 623836
e-mail: AnneGoldenLion@aol.com
Dir: on A684 in Market Sq

PETS: Bedrooms (unattended) Public areas Exercise area (100yds)

Dating back to 1765, this traditional inn overlooks the cobbled market square where weekly markets still take place. Bedrooms,
continued

including some family rooms, offer appropriate levels of comfort. The restaurant features murals of scenes from the Dales and offers a range of meals. Food can also be enjoyed in the cosy bar, a popular meeting place for local people.

ROOMS: 15 rms (14 en suite) (5 fmly) s £26-£34; d £52-£68 (incl. bkfst) **LB SERVICES:** Lift **NOTES:** Closed 25 & 26 Dec
CARDS: 🔲🔲🔲🔲🔲🔲🔲

♦♦♦ 🍺 The Old Horn Inn

Spennithorne DL8 5PR
☎ 01969 622370
e-mail: desmond@furlong1706.fsbusiness.co.uk
Dir: approx 1.5m from centre of Leyburn on A684 towards Bedale, right at The Pheasant pub into Harmby and follow road to end, turn right at x-roads. Inn on outskirts of village on right

PETS: Bedrooms (unattended) Public areas (allowed in bar/games room only) Exercise area (adjacent)
RESIDENT PETS: Spike - dalmation & Charlie - cat

Nestling in the quiet village of Spennithorne, this inn is full of character. The two bedrooms are comfortable and well equipped. The restaurant and public bar offer a good selection of wines and fine ales, along with an interesting selection of freshly prepared dishes. The resident owners provide caring service.

FACILITIES: 2 en suite No smoking in bedrooms No smoking in dining room TVB tea/coffee Cen ht No children 10yrs Dinner Last d 9pm **PRICES:** d £46-£50✳ **LB PARKING:** 6

MALTON   Map 08 SE77

★★★ 72% ◎ 🐾 Burythorpe House

Burythorpe YO17 9LB
☎ 01653 658200 🖷 01653 658204
e-mail: reception@burythorpehousehotel.com
Dir: 4m S of Malton, outside Burythorpe and 4m from A64 (York to Scarborough)

PETS: Bedrooms (unattended) £2 **RESIDENT PETS:** Tina (Jack Russell), Spud (German Shepherd), Saxa & Tetley (cats)

This charming house offers spacious and individually furnished bedrooms. Five rooms are situated in a rear courtyard, two of which are equipped for less able guests, and all benefiting from small kitchen areas. Comfortable, spacious lounge areas are provided along with an impressive oak-panelled dining room where interesting, freshly prepared meals are served. Leisure facilities are available.

ROOMS: 11 en suite 5 annexe en suite (2 fmly) (5 GF) No smoking in all bedrooms s fr £55; d £72-£112 (incl. bkfst) **LB FACILITIES:** Indoor swimming (H) Tennis (hard) Snooker Sauna Solarium Gym Xmas **PARKING:** 40 **NOTES:** No smoking in restaurant
CARDS: 🔲🔲🔲🔲

MARKINGTON   Map 08 SE26

★★★ 77% 🐾 Hob Green

HG3 3PJ
☎ 01423 770031 🖷 01423 771589
e-mail: info@hobgreen.com
Dir: from A61 4m N of Harrogate turn left at Wormald Green and follow hotel signs

PETS: Bedrooms (unattended) £5 Public areas Exercise area (on site) Pet Food

This hospitable country house is set in delightful gardens amidst rolling countryside midway between Harrogate and Ripon. The inviting lounges boast open fires in season and there is an elegant restaurant with a small private dining room. The individual bedrooms come with a host of thoughtful extras.

ROOMS: 12 en suite (1 fmly) No smoking in all bedrooms s £98.50-£115; d £115-£125 (incl. bkfst) **LB FACILITIES:** STV Croquet lawn ch fac Xmas **PARKING:** 40 **NOTES:** No smoking in restaurant **CARDS:** 🔲🔲🔲🔲🔲🔲🔲

MASHAM   Map 08 SE28

★★★★ ◎◎ 🐾 Swinton Park

HG4 4JH
☎ 01765 680900 🖷 01765 680901
e-mail: enquiries@swintonpark.com
Dir: A1 onto B6267 to Masham. Follow signs through town centre & turn right onto Swinton Terrace. 1m past GC over bridge, up hill. Hotel on right

PETS: Bedrooms Sep Accom (kennel) £10 Exercise area (Hotel surrounded by parkland) Pet Food Bowl, chew & dog bed provided

Extended during the Victorian and Edwardian eras, the original part of this welcoming castle dates from the 17th Century. Bedrooms are luxuriously furnished and come with a host of thoughtful extras. Samuel's restaurant (built by the current owner's great-great-great grandfather) is very elegant and serves imaginative dishes which feature local produce, much of it from the Swinton estate.

ROOMS: 30 en suite No smoking in all bedrooms s £100-£350; d £120-£350 (incl. bkfst) **LB FACILITIES:** Spa STV Golf 9 Fishing Riding Snooker Gym Croquet lawn Putting green Jacuzzi Shooting, Falconry, Pony Trekking, cookery school ch fac Xmas **SERVICES:** Lift **PARKING:** 50 **NOTES:** No smoking in restaurant
CARDS: 🔲🔲🔲🔲🔲🔲🔲

MONK FRYSTON — Map 08 SE52

★★★ 70% 🏆 **Monk Fryston Hall**
LS25 5DU
☎ 01977 682369 📠 01977 683544
e-mail: reception@monkfryston-hotel.co.uk
Dir: A1/A63 junct towards Selby. Left side in centre of Monk Fryston

PETS: Bedrooms (unattended) £5 Public areas (except restaurant) Exercise area

This delightful 16th-century mansion house enjoys a peaceful location in 30 acres of grounds, yet is only minutes' drive from the A1. Many original features have been retained and the public rooms are furnished with antique and period pieces. Bedrooms are individually styled and thoughtfully equipped for both business and leisure guests.
ROOMS: 29 en suite (2 fmly) (5 GF) No smoking in 20 bedrooms s £92-£102; d £116-£171 (incl. bkfst) **LB FACILITIES:** STV Croquet lawn ch fac Xmas **PARKING:** 80 **NOTES:** No smoking in restaurant
CARDS: ▭▭▭▭▭

NORTHALLERTON — Map 08 SE39

★★ 65% **The Golden Lion**
High St DL7 8PP

☎ 01609 777411 📠 01609 773250
Dir: A684 for 5m onto A167. Through built-up area, 3rd exit at next rdbt to town centre. 3rd rdbt left into High St

PETS: Bedrooms (unattended) Public areas (not during food service) Exercise area

This popular hotel has a convenient location in the heart of the town centre with private parking. Bedrooms and bathrooms are spacious and offer a good range of amenities. Public areas include a choice of dining options and a lively bar. The newly re-furbished drawing room and dining room are non-smoking.
ROOMS: 25 en suite (2 fmly) No smoking in 18 bedrooms s £55-£60; d £70-£85 (incl. bkfst) **FACILITIES:** ch fac **PARKING:** 100
NOTES: No smoking in restaurant **CARDS:** ▭▭▭▭▭

PICKERING — Map 08 SE78

★★ 76% ◉ **White Swan**
Market Place YO18 7AA
☎ 01751 472288 📠 01751 475554
e-mail: welcome@white-swan.co.uk
Dir: in Market Place between Church and Steam Railway Station

PETS: Bedrooms (unattended) £7.50 per stay Public areas (not restaurant) Exercise area (5 min walk)

This 16th-century coaching inn offers well-equipped, very comfortable bedrooms, including one suite. Service is friendly and attentive and the standard of cuisine high, in both the attractive restaurant and the cosy bar and lounge where log fires burn in the cooler months. A comprehensive wine list specialises in many fine vintages. A private dining room is also available.
ROOMS: 12 en suite (3 fmly) No smoking in all bedrooms s £80-£95; d £130-£180 (incl. bkfst) **LB FACILITIES:** Xmas **PARKING:** 35
NOTES: No smoking in restaurant **CARDS:** ▭▭▭▭▭

REDCAR — Map 08 NZ62

◆◆◆ **Claxton Hotel**
196 High St TS10 3AW
☎ 01642 486745 📠 01642 486522
e-mail: enquiries@claxtonhotel.co.uk
Dir: leave A174 at double rdbt signed Redcar continue across railway crossing, right at lights by St Peter's Church. Hotel rear car park on left

PETS: Bedrooms (unattended) £4 per stay Exercise area (beach nearby)

This friendly, family-owned commercial hotel overlooks the sea and is a popular venue for local functions. Bedrooms are comfortable and public areas are spacious. Hearty breakfasts are served in the attractive dining room.
FACILITIES: 28 rms (26 en suite) (2 fmly) (6 GF) No smoking in dining room No smoking in 1 lounge TVB tea/coffee Licensed Cen ht TVL Last d 9pm **PRICES:** s £27-£29.50; d £43.50✳ **PARKING:** 10
NOTES: Closed 23-27 Dec rs 27 Dec-2 Jan **CARDS:** ▭▭▭▭▭

RICHMOND — Map 07 NZ10

★★★ 66% **King's Head**
Market Place DL10 4HS
☎ 01748 850220 📠 01748 850635
e-mail: res@kingsheadrichmond.co.uk
Dir: leave A1 or A66 at Scotch Corner & take A6108 to Richmond. Follow signs to town centre

PETS: Bedrooms £5 Public areas (In front lounge only) Exercise area (0.3 mile)

Centrally located in the historic market square, this hotel is a converted coaching inn. Bedrooms are comfortable and tastefully furnished. The lounge, furnished with deep sofas, displays an interesting collection of antique clocks. Afternoon tea is served in the lounge/bar along with light meals and the stylish restaurant offers a varied choice of more formal but relaxed dining with views over the square.
ROOMS: 26 en suite 4 annexe en suite (1 fmly) No smoking in 11 bedrooms s £69; d £95 (incl. bkfst) **LB PARKING:** 25
NOTES: No smoking in restaurant
CARDS: ▭▭▭▭▭

RIPON — Map 08 SE37

★★★ 69% **Ripon Spa**
Park St HG4 2BU
☎ 01765 602172 📠 01765 690770
e-mail: spahotel@bronco.co.uk
Dir: From A61 follow signs for B6265 towards Fountains Abbey. Hotel on left after hospital

PETS: Bedrooms (unattended) Public areas (except where food is being served) Exercise area RESIDENT PETS: Black Labrador - Will

This privately owned hotel is set in extensive and attractive gardens just a short walk from the city centre. Newly refurbished bedrooms are well-equipped to meet the needs of leisure and

continue

business travellers alike, whilst the comfortable lounges are complemented by the convivial atmosphere of the Turf bar.
ROOMS: 40 en suite (5 fmly) (4 GF) No smoking in 8 bedrooms s £95-£100; d £105-£120 (incl. bkfst) **LB FACILITIES:** STV Croquet lawn Xmas **SERVICES:** Lift **PARKING:** 60 **NOTES:** No smoking in restaurant **CARDS:**

★★ 63% **Unicorn**
Market Place HG4 1BP
☎ 01765 602202 📠 01765 690734
e-mail: info@unicorn-hotel.co.uk
Dir: on SE corner of Market Place, 4m from A1 on A61

PETS: Bedrooms (unattended) £3 Exercise area (0.5 mile) Pet Food Advance notice required if pet requires food

Centrally located in Ripon's ancient market place, this traditional inn dates back 500 years to when it was a coaching house. The busy pub and attractive restaurant feature a wide selection of good-value dishes. Bedrooms are of mixed styles and all offer the expected amenities.
ROOMS: 33 en suite (4 fmly) s £53; d £75 (incl. bkfst) **LB**
FACILITIES: entertainment **PARKING:** 20 **NOTES:** No smoking in restaurant Closed 24-25 Dec **CARDS:**

ROSEDALE ABBEY
Map 08 SE79

★★★ 69% *Blacksmith's Country Inn*
Hartoft End YO18 8EN
☎ 01751 417331 📠 01751 417167
Dir: off A170 in village of Wrelton, N to Hartoft

PETS: Bedrooms (unattended) £5 one-off charge Public areas (not restaurant) Exercise area (10 metres)

Set amongst the wooded valleys and hillsides of the Yorkshire Moors, this charming hotel, now under new ownership, offers a choice of popular bars and intimate, cosy lounges, and retains the friendly atmosphere of a country inn. Food is available either in the bars or the spacious restaurant, while bedrooms vary in size and are all equipped to comfortable modern standards.
ROOMS: 19 en suite (4 GF) No smoking in all bedrooms
FACILITIES: Fishing **PARKING:** 100 **NOTES:** No smoking in restaurant RS Oct-Mar **CARDS:**

★★ 72% 🏵 **Milburn Arms**
YO18 8RA
☎ 01751 417312 📠 01751 417541
e-mail: info@milburnarms.co.uk

PETS: Bedrooms £3.50 Exercise area (Adjacent)

This attractive inn dates back to the 16th century and enjoys an idyllic, peaceful location in this scenic village. Bedrooms, some of which are located in an adjacent stone block, are spacious, comfortable and smartly appointed. Guests can enjoy carefully prepared food either in the traditional bar or in the elegant restaurant.
ROOMS: 3 en suite 8 annexe en suite (2 fmly) (4 GF) No smoking in all bedrooms **FACILITIES:** Xmas **PARKING:** 10 **NOTES:** No smoking in restaurant **CARDS:**

SALTBURN-BY-THE-SEA
Map 08 NZ62

★★★ 66% **Rushpool Hall Hotel**
Saltburn Ln TS12 1HD
☎ 01287 624111 📠 01287 625255

PETS: Bedrooms (chalets only) Public areas (dogs on a lead) Exercise area (90 acre estate & nearby beach) **RESIDENT PETS:** Horses, miniature Shetland pony - Humphrey, cat - Oscar, geese, peacocks & also lots of wildlife

A grand Victorian mansion nestling in its own grounds and woodlands. Stylish, elegant bedrooms are well-equipped and spacious; many enjoy excellent sea views. The interesting public rooms are filled with charm and character, and roaring fires welcome guests in cooler months. The hotel boasts an excellent reputation as a wedding venue thanks to its superb location and experienced event management.
ROOMS: 21 en suite s £70-£85; d £125-£150 (incl. bkfst) **LB**
FACILITIES: STV Fishing Croquet lawn Birdwatching ch fac Xmas
PARKING: 120 **NOTES:** No smoking in restaurant
CARDS:

Please mention AA Pet Friendly Places to Stay when booking

England

SCARBOROUGH Map 08 TA08

★★★ 70% Ox Pasture Hall

Lady Edith's Dr, Raincliffe Woods YO12 5TD
☎ 01723 365295 📠 01723 355156
e-mail: oxpasturehall@btconnect.com
Dir: Take Lady Edith's Drive from the Scarborough to Scalby Rd

PETS: Bedrooms (unattended) £10 per stay Public areas (bar only) Exercise area (on site) **RESIDENT PETS:** Paddy & Homee - dogs, 2 ponies

Now under new ownership this delightful family run country hotel is set in the quiet North Riding Forest Park and offers a very friendly atmosphere. Bedrooms are all individual, stylish and comfortably equipped and are split between the main house, townhouse and the delightful courtyard. Public areas include a split-level bar, quiet lounge, and attractive restaurant.
ROOMS: 17 en suite 6 annexe en suite (1 fmly) (14 GF) No smoking in 17 bedrooms s £50-£160; d £100-£160 (incl. bkfst) **LB**
FACILITIES: Fishing Croquet lawn Xmas **PARKING:** 50
NOTES: No smoking in restaurant **CARDS:** 🖼🖼🖼🖼🖼🖼🖼

★★ 60% Brooklands

Esplanade Gardens, South Cliff YO11 2AW
☎ 01723 376576 📠 01723 341093
Dir: from A64 York, left at B&Q rdbt, right at next mini-rdbt, 1st left onto Victoria Avenue, at end turn left then 2nd left

PETS: Bedrooms £5 Exercise area (10yds) Book in advance

The Brooklands is a traditional, privately-owned and run seaside hotel. It often caters for tours and offers good value for money. The hotel stands on the South Cliff overlooking Esplanade Gardens, and is within easy access of the sea. There are ample lounges to relax in and wholesome home cooking to enjoy.
ROOMS: 55 en suite (11 fmly) (1 GF) No smoking in 4 bedrooms s £25-£50; d £50-£100 (incl. bkfst) **LB FACILITIES:** entertainment Xmas
SERVICES: Lift **PARKING:** 1 **NOTES:** No smoking in restaurant
Closed Jan RS Feb **CARDS:** 🖼🖼🖼🖼🖼

SKIPTON Map 07 SD95

★★★ 73% The Coniston

Coniston Cold BD23 4EB
☎ 01756 748080 📠 01756 749487
e-mail: info@theconistonhotel.com
Dir: on A65, 6m NW of Skipton

PETS: Bedrooms (unattended) £5 per stay Public areas Exercise area (adjacent)

Privately owned and situated on a 1,200 acre estate centred around a beautiful 24-acre lake this hotel offers guests many exciting outdoor activities. The modern bedrooms are comfortable and most have king-size beds. McLeod's Bar and the main restaurant offer all-day meals and fine dining is available in the evening on both carte and fixed-price menus.
ROOMS: 40 en suite (4 fmly) (20 GF) s £82-£92; d £94-£104 (incl. bkfst) **LB FACILITIES:** STV Fishing Landrover driving, Clay pigeon shooting, Falconry, fishing ch fac Xmas **PARKING:** 120
NOTES: No smoking in restaurant
CARDS: 🖼🖼🖼🖼🖼🖼🖼🖼

★★★ 65% Hanover International

Keighley Rd BD23 2TA
☎ 01756 700100 📠 01756 700107
e-mail: hihskipton@totalise.co.uk
Dir: on A629, 1m from town

HANOVER INTERNATIONAL HOTELS & CLUBS

PETS: Bedrooms (selected rooms) (unattended) £10 Public areas (Not in food/bar areas) Exercise area (Open fields)

Located beside the canal just outside the town, the hotel has the advantage of plenty of parking and good amenities for the leisure guest. Bedrooms are well equipped and spacious, and have delightful views over the rolling countryside. Added attractions include the indoor pool and gym.
ROOMS: 75 en suite (10 fmly) (12 GF) No smoking in 14 bedrooms
FACILITIES: STV Indoor swimming (H) Squash Sauna Solarium Gym Jacuzzi Whirlpool spa, Steam room Xmas **SERVICES:** Lift **PARKING:** 150
NOTES: No smoking in restaurant Closed 25-27 Dec
CARDS: 🖼🖼🖼🖼🖼🖼🖼

◆◆◆ Craven House

56 Keighley Rd BD23 2NB
☎ 01756 794657 📠 01756 794657
e-mail: info@craven-house.co.uk
Dir: from Keighley, Craven House on A629 into Skipton just past Esso garage

PETS: Bedrooms (unattended) Exercise area (200 yards)

A warm welcome awaits guests at this conveniently located central guesthouse. The Victorian house has been sympathetically renovated to provide comfortable accommodation. Bedrooms vary in size, and feature practical and homely extras.
FACILITIES: 7 rms (3 en suite) No smoking in dining room No smoking in lounges TVB tea/coffee Cen ht **PRICES:** s £23-£32; d £44-£48✱
NOTES: Closed 25 Dec-10 Jan **CARDS:** 🖼🖼

THIRSK Map 08 SE48

★★ 73% Golden Fleece

42 Market Place YO7 1LL
☎ 01845 523108 📠 01845 523996
e-mail: goldenfleece@bestwestern.co.uk
Dir: off A19 at Thirsk turn off, to the town centre. Hotel southern edge of Market Place

Best Western

PETS: Bedrooms (unattended) Public areas (except restaurant) Exercise area (100 metres)

This delightful hotel began life as a coaching inn, and enjoys a central location in the market square. Bedrooms are comfortably furnished, extremely well equipped and individually styled with beautiful soft furnishings. Guests can eat in the attractive bar, or choose more formal dining in the smart restaurant.
ROOMS: 23 en suite (3 fmly) No smoking in 4 bedrooms s £65; d £85-£105 (incl. bkfst) **LB FACILITIES:** STV ch fac Xmas
PARKING: 35 **NOTES:** No smoking in restaurant
CARDS: 🖼🖼🖼🖼🖼🖼🖼

THORNTON WATLASS

Map 08 SE28

★ 69% **Buck Inn**
HG4 4AH
☎ 01677 422461 ▤ 01677 422447
e-mail: buckwatlass@btconnect.com
Dir: A684 towards Bedale, B6268 towards Masham, after 2m turn right at x-roads to Thornton Watlass, hotel is by cricket green

PETS: Bedrooms (unattended) Public areas (in residents' lounge only) Exercise area (300 yards) Pet Food

This traditional country inn is situated on the edge of the village green overlooking the cricket pitch. Cricket prints and old photographs are found throughout and an open fire in the bar adds to the warm and intimate atmosphere. Wholesome lunches and dinners are served in the bar or dining room from an extensive menu. Bedrooms are brightly decorated and well equipped.
ROOMS: 7 rms (5 en suite) (1 fmly) (1 GF) s £45-£50; d £60-£70 (incl. bkfst) LB **FACILITIES:** Fishing Quoits Childrens play area entertainment **PARKING:** 10 **NOTES:** No smoking in restaurant Closed 24 & 25 Dec for accommodation
CARDS: 🔲🔲🔲🔲🔲🔲🔲

WHITBY

Map 08 NZ81

★★★ 71% ◉ ♨ **Dunsley Hall**
Dunsley YO21 3TL
☎ 01947 893437 ▤ 01947 893505
e-mail: reception@dunsleyhall.com
Dir: 3m N of Whitby, signed off A171

PETS: Bedrooms (certain bedrooms only) £5 Exercise area
RESIDENT PETS: 4 peacocks

Friendly hospitality and fine cooking are strong features of this country house, situated in four acres of well-tended gardens. Oak panelling, carved fireplaces and mullion windows all add to the character of the house, which offers a well-appointed restaurant and a popular bar. Spacious bedrooms are bright, comfortable and beautifully furnished, and many have sea views.
ROOMS: 18 en suite (2 fmly) (2 GF) No smoking in all bedrooms s £80-£105; d £130-£174 (incl. bkfst) LB **FACILITIES:** Indoor swimming (H) Tennis (hard) Sauna Solarium Gym Croquet lawn Putting green Xmas **PARKING:** 60 **NOTES:** No smoking in restaurant
CARDS: 🔲🔲🔲🔲🔲

★★ 70% **Cliffemount**
Runswick Bay TS13 5HU
☎ 01947 840103 ▤ 01947 841025
e-mail: cliffemount@runswickbay.fsnet.co.uk
Dir: turn off A174 8m N of Whitby, follow road 1m to end. Hotel on clifftop

PETS: Bedrooms Public areas (on a lead, and if no objections from other guests) **RESIDENT PETS:** Black Labradors - Beau & Peg

Standing in a delightful elevated position, overlooking the pretty cliff-side village and with splendid views across the bay, a warm welcome awaits you here. The cosy bar leads to the stylish restaurant where locally caught fish features strongly on the interesting, extensive menus and special boards. The bedrooms, many with sea-view balconies, are well equipped and comfortably furnished.
ROOMS: 19 en suite (5 GF) s £31.50-£51; d £66-£100 (incl. bkfst) LB **PARKING:** 30 **NOTES:** No smoking in restaurant Closed 25-26 Dec
CARDS: 🔲🔲🔲🔲🔲

♦♦♦♦ **Chiltern**
13 Normanby Ter, West Cliff YO21 3ES
☎ 01947 604981 ▤ 01947 825604
e-mail: chilternwhitby@aol.com
Dir: from S take M1/M18 or A1 onto A64. From N take A1/A19 to A171 or A170. From W take M62 to Hull, then A63/A165 coastal route then A614

PETS: Bedrooms £2 per stay Exercise area (400 metres)
RESIDENT PETS: 2 dogs, 1 parrot and a tropical fish tank

This well-maintained Victorian terraced house is conveniently located within easy walking distance from the town centre and seafront. Bedrooms are smartly decorated and many benefit from small, modern en suites. Public areas include a bright, attractive dining room and a comfortable, elegant lounge.
FACILITIES: 9 rms (5 en suite) (3 fmly) No smoking in dining room No smoking in lounges TVB tea/coffee TVL No coaches Dinner Last d 10am **PRICES:** s £22.50; d £49✳

All AA listed accommodation, restaurants and pubs can be found on the AA's website www.theAA.com

♥ Places with this symbol are farms

All information was correct at the time of going to press; we recommend you confirm details on booking

England

WHITBY continued

♦♦♦♦ Seacliffe Hotel

North Promenade, West Cliff YO21 3JX
☎ 01947 603139 📠 01947 603139
e-mail: julie@seacliffe.fsnet.co.uk
Dir: follow signs for West Cliff & West Cliff car park, hotel on seafront

PETS: Bedrooms Public areas Exercise area (adjacent)
RESIDENT PETS: Miss Ellie (cat)

Enjoying fine sea views, this holiday hotel on the West Cliff has an attractive beamed restaurant where an extensive menu is served. Bedrooms are compact, comfortably furnished and well equipped. The residents' lounge is adjacent to the bar, which leads out onto a sunny summer patio.
FACILITIES: 19 en suite (4 fmly) No smoking in 17 bedrooms No smoking in dining room STV TVB tea/coffee Direct dial from bedrooms Licensed Cen ht TVL No coaches Pool Table Dinner Last d 8.45pm **PRICES:** d £77.90-£85.90✻ **LB PARKING:** 8
CARDS: 〓〓〓〓〓〓

♦♦♦ Sandbeck Hotel

1 & 2 Crescent Ter, West Cliff YO21 3EL
☎ 01947 604012 603349 📠 01947 606402
e-mail: dysonsandbeck@tesco.net
Dir: on West Cliff, opposite the theatre and Pavilion booking office

PETS: Bedrooms £2 Public areas (except dining room, and if no objections from other guests) Exercise area (across the road)

Enjoying spectacular views from all front rooms, this family-run hotel provides comfortable and spacious accommodation. Within strolling distance of Whitby's many attractions, the Sandbeck is quietly located on the West Cliff. An attractive lounge plus a separate bar and a pleasant dining room are provided and at breakfast, an extensive choice is offered including vegetarian and children's menus.
FACILITIES: 24 en suite (7 fmly) No smoking in 15 bedrooms No smoking in dining room No smoking in 1 lounge TVB tea/coffee Licensed Lift Cen ht TVL No coaches **PRICES:** s £30-£32.50; d £60-£70✻ **NOTES:** Closed Dec **CARDS:** 〓〓〓〓〓

YORK

Map 08 SE65

★★★★ 65% The Royal York

PRINCIPAL HOTELS

Station Rd YO24 2AA
☎ 01904 653681 📠 01904 623503
Dir: adjacent to railway station

PETS: Bedrooms Public areas Pet Food

Situated in three acres of landscaped grounds in the very heart of the city, this Victorian railway hotel has views over the city and York Minster. Contemporary bedrooms are divided between those in the main hotel and the air-conditioned garden mews. There is also a leisure complex and state-of-the-art conference centre.
ROOMS: 165 en suite (10 fmly) s £69-£130; d £90-£150 **LB**
FACILITIES: STV Indoor swimming (H) Sauna Solarium Gym Jacuzzi Steam room Xmas **SERVICES:** Lift **PARKING:** 80 **NOTES:** No smoking in restaurant **CARDS:** 〓〓〓〓〓〓

★★★ ◉◉ The Grange

1 Clifton YO30 6AA
☎ 01904 644744 📠 01904 612453
e-mail: info@grangehotel.co.uk
Dir: on A19 York/Thirsk road, approx 500yds from city centre

PETS: Bedrooms (unattended) Exercise area (local parks)

This bustling Regency town house is just a few minutes' walk from the centre of York. A professional service is efficiently delivered by caring staff in a very friendly and helpful manner. Public rooms are comfortable and have been stylishly furnished; these include two dining options, the popular and informal cellar brasserie, and The Ivy that offers fine dining in a lavishly decorated environment. The individually designed bedrooms are comfortably appointed and have been thoughtfully equipped.
ROOMS: 30 en suite (6 GF) s £110-£190; d £115-£250 (incl. bkfst) **LB**
FACILITIES: STV Discount at local health spa Xmas **PARKING:** 26
NOTES: No smoking in restaurant
CARDS: 〓〓〓〓〓〓

★★★ 70% Monkbar

Monkbar YO31 7JA
☎ 01904 638086 📠 01904 629195
e-mail: june@monkbarhotel.co.uk
Dir: From A64 take A1079 to City, turn right at city wall, take middle lane at lights. Hotel on right

Best Western

PETS: Bedrooms (unattended) £7.50 Public areas
Exercise area (50 yards) Pet Food

This smart hotel enjoys a prominent position adjacent to the city walls, minutes' walk from the cathedral. Individually styled bedrooms are well-equipped for both business and leisure guests. Spacious public areas include comfortable lounges, an American-

continued

style bar, an airy restaurant and impressive meeting and training facilities.

ROOMS: 99 en suite (3 fmly) No smoking in 45 bedrooms s £98-£108; d £140-£175 (incl. bkfst) **LB FACILITIES:** STV ch fac Xmas **SERVICES:** Lift **PARKING:** 70 **NOTES:** No smoking in restaurant **CARDS:**

★★★ 66% **Novotel York**
Fishergate YO10 4FD
☎ 01904 611660 📠 01904 610925
e-mail: H0949@accor-hotels.com
Dir: A19 north to city centre, hotel set back on left

PETS: Bedrooms £10 Public areas (except restaurant)

Set just outside the ancient city walls, this modern, family-friendly hotel is conveniently located for visitors to the city. Bedrooms feature bathrooms with separate toilet, plus excellent desk space and sofa beds. Four rooms are equipped for less able guests. The hotel's facilities include indoor and outdoor children's play areas and an indoor pool.
ROOMS: 124 en suite (124 fmly) No smoking in 91 bedrooms s fr £108; d fr £108 **LB FACILITIES:** STV Indoor swimming (H) **SERVICES:** Lift **PARKING:** 150 **CARDS:**

> All information was correct at the time of going to press; we recommend you confirm details on booking

◆◆◆◆ **Ascot House**
80 East Pde YO31 7YH
☎ 01904 426826 📠 01904 431077
e-mail: admin@ascothouseyork.com
Dir: From A1 or M1 take A64 for York. Stay on A64 ring-road to eastern side of city and take A1036 into York. After 30mph signs, take 2nd exit from rdbt signed Heworth, at traffic lights turn right into East Parade

PETS: Bedrooms (unattended) Public areas (except dining room) Exercise area (5 min walk) RESIDENT PETS: Gemma (Black Labrador)

June and Keith Wood provide friendly service at Ascot House which dates from 1869 and is 15 minutes walk from the town centre. Bedrooms are thoughtfully equipped; many with four poster or canopy beds and other period pieces of furniture.

continued

Reception rooms include a comfortable lounge also retaining original features.

FACILITIES: 15 rms (12 en suite) (3 fmly) (2 GF) No smoking in 5 bedrooms No smoking in dining room TVB tea/coffee Licensed Cen ht TVL Sauna **PRICES:** s £28-£60; d £56-£68✳ **LB PARKING:** 14 **NOTES:** Closed 21-28 Dec **CARDS:**

◆◆◆ **Greenside**
124 Clifton YO30 6BQ
☎ 01904 623631 📠 01904 623631
e-mail: greenside@amserve.com
Dir: approach city centre on A19 N, at traffic lights straight on for Greenside, on the L opp Clifton Green

PETS: Bedrooms Sep Accom (entrance halls) (unattended) Exercise area (25 yards)

Overlooking Clifton Green, this detached house is just within walking distance of the city centre. Accommodation consists of simply furnished bedrooms and there is a cosy lounge and a dining room, where dinners by arrangement and traditional breakfasts are served. It is a family home, and other families are welcome.
FACILITIES: 6 rms (3 en suite) (2 fmly) (3 GF) No smoking in dining room No smoking in lounges TVB tea/coffee Licensed Cen ht TVL Children's play area Dinner Last d 6pm **PRICES:** s fr £22; d fr £40✳ **LB PARKING:** 6 **NOTES:** Closed Xmas & New Year

◆◆◆ **The Priory Hotel**
126-128 Fulford Rd YO10 4BE
☎ 01904 625280 📠 01904 637330
e-mail: reservations@priory-hotelyork.co.uk
Dir: On S side of city, on A19 (Selby). From Leeds, take 3rd turning off A64 to York signed Fulford & Designer Centre. 2m on L

PETS: Bedrooms (unattended) Public areas (not dining rooms) Exercise area (200 yards) RESIDENT PETS: Elsa & Boo (dogs), TC & Guinness (cats)

The same family has run this well-established hotel for four generations. Reception rooms include a dining room, comfortable foyer, lounge and cosy bar, all decorated in keeping with the period of the house. Bedrooms are designed in modern style and provide a high standard of comfort. Gothic arches lead to the landscaped gardens and large car park.
FACILITIES: 16 en suite (5 fmly) TVB tea/coffee Direct dial from bedrooms Licensed Cen ht TVL **PRICES:** s £45-£60; d £60-£80✳ **LB PARKING:** 25 **NOTES:** Closed Xmas **CARDS:**

England

YORK continued

♦♦♦ St Georges House Hotel
6 St Georges Place, Tadcaster Rd YO24 1DR
☎ 01904 625056 ⓘ 01904 625009
e-mail: sixstgeorg@aol.com
Dir: A64 onto A1036, as racecourse finishes, St Georges Place on left

> **PETS:** Bedrooms Public areas (except dining areas)
> Exercise area (50yds) RESIDENT PETS: George, Ebony, Bob &
> Coral (dogs) & Kitson (cat)

Conveniently located near the racecourse, this family-run private
hotel is also within walking distance of the city. Bedrooms are
attractively decorated and are equipped with modern facilities;
some rooms have four-poster beds and others can accommodate
families. A cosy lounge is available for residents and hearty
breakfasts are served in the delightful dining room.
FACILITIES: 10 en suite (5 fmly) (1 GF) No smoking TVB tea/coffee
Licensed Cen ht No coaches Dinner Last d 11am **PRICES:** s £35-£50;
d £55-£60✱ **LB PARKING:** 7 **CARDS:** 〰️ 💳 💳 💳 💳 💳 ⑤

YORKSHIRE, SOUTH

BARNSLEY   Map 08 SE30

★★★ 73% Ardsley House
Doncaster Rd, Ardsley S71 5EH
☎ 01226 309955 ⓘ 01226 205374
e-mail: ardsley.house@forestdale.com
Dir: on A635, 0.75m from Stairfoot rdbt

Forestdale Hotels

> **PETS:** Bedrooms (unattended) £7.50 Public areas (except
> restaurant) Pet Food

Quietly situated on the Barnsley to Doncaster Road, this hotel has
many regular customers. Comfortable and well-equipped
bedrooms, very good leisure facilities including a gym and pool,
and good conference facilities are just some of the attractions.
Public rooms include a choice of bars and a busy restaurant.
Parking is plentiful.
ROOMS: 75 en suite (12 fmly) (14 GF) No smoking in 50 bedrooms
s fr £100; d fr £120 (incl. bkfst) **LB FACILITIES:** STV Indoor
swimming (H) Sauna Solarium Gym Jacuzzi Beauty Spa entertainment
Xmas **PARKING:** 200 **CARDS:** 〰️ 💳 💳 💳 💳 ⑤

DONCASTER   Map 08 SE50

★★★ 68% Regent
Regent Square DN1 2DS
☎ 01302 364180 ⓘ 01302 322331
e-mail: admin@theregenthotel.co.uk
Dir: on corner of A630 & A638, 1m from racecourse

> **PETS:** Bedrooms Exercise area (10 metres)

This town centre hotel overlooks a delightful small square. Public
rooms include a choice of bars and the restaurant, where an
interesting range of dishes is offered. Service is friendly and
attentive. Most bedrooms have been furnished in a modern style

continued

---

with contemporary colour schemes; a rolling programme of
refurbishment ensures that standards are maintained.
ROOMS: 52 en suite (6 fmly) (8 GF) s £55-£90; d £70-£105 (incl. bkfst)
LB FACILITIES: STV entertainment **SERVICES:** Lift **PARKING:** 20
NOTES: No smoking in restaurant Closed New Year's Day Xmas Day RS
Bank Hols **CARDS:** 〰️ 💳 💳 💳 💳 💳 ⑤

♦♦♦♦ East Farm
Owston Ln, Owston, Bentley DN5 0LP
☎ 01302 338300 726224 ⓘ 01302 726224
e-mail: frank@eastfarm.co.uk
*Dir: Take A19 from Doncaster towards Selby, turn left into B1220, then take
1st right & East Farm is 200yds on the right*

> **PETS:** Sep Accom (kennel) Exercise area (10 metres)
> RESIDENT PETS: 2 dogs & 2 cats

These former farm buildings have been converted into well-
appointed, comfortable bedrooms, and a spacious luxurious
lounge and sunroom. The owners provide a friendly atmosphere
and excellent breakfasts. Three golf courses are close-by, the A1 is
about five minutes, and Doncaster centre about ten minutes'
drive.
FACILITIES: 15 en suite (13 GF) No smoking in bedrooms No smoking
in dining room No smoking in 1 lounge TVB tea/coffee Cen ht TVL
No coaches **PRICES:** s £30-£35; d £45-£50✱ **PARKING:** 12
CARDS: 〰️ 💳 💳 ⑤

♦♦♦ Balmoral Hotel
129 Thorne Rd DN2 5BH
☎ 01302 364385 ⓘ 364385
e-mail: thebalmoralhotel@blueyonder.co.uk
*Dir: M18 junct 3, at Yorkshire outlet rdbt turn left, 2nd rdbt turn right to
Racecourse rdbt, go straight on, then 2nd left into Leicester Ave. Through
traffic lights onto Thorne Rd, turn left and Hotel on right*

> **PETS:** Bedrooms (pets must be caged) (unattended) £1.50
> Exercise area (200 metres) RESIDENT PETS: Coffee, Toffee,
> Sootee (cats), Asterix & Buster (dogs)

Conveniently situated on a main road and within easy walking
distance of the hospital, racecourse and the town, this well
maintained guesthouse provides a mix of bedroom styles. There is
a comfortable lounge and hearty breakfasts are served in the
attractively furnished dining room. The hotel enjoys a reputation
for hospitality.
FACILITIES: 8 rms (3 en suite) 1 annexe en suite (4 fmly) No smoking
in 6 bedrooms No smoking in dining room No smoking in 1 lounge TVB
tea/coffee Cen ht TVL Dinner Last d noon **PRICES:** s £22-£40;
d £38-£50✱ **BB PARKING:** 12 **CARDS:** 〰️ 💳 💳 💳 💳 ⑤

> **All abbreviations are**
> **explained on page 9**

> 🍺 **Places with this**
> **symbol are pubs**

ROTHERHAM Map 08 SK49

★★★ 69% Elton
Main St, Bramley S66 2SF
☎ 01709 545681 ▤ 01709 549100

e-mail: bestwestern.eltonhotel@btinternet.com
Dir: M18 junct 1 follow A631 Rotherham, turn right to Ravenfield, hotel at end of Bramley village, follow brown signs

PETS: Bedrooms Public areas Exercise area (0.25 mile) Pet Food

Within easy reach of the M18, this welcoming, stone-built hotel is set in well-tended gardens. Elton Hotel offers good modern accommodation, with larger rooms in the extension that are particularly comfortable and well equipped. A civil licence is held for wedding ceremonies and conference rooms are available.

ROOMS: 13 en suite 16 annexe en suite (4 fmly) (11 GF) No smoking in 11 bedrooms s £49-£82; d £50-£90 (incl. bkfst) **LB** **FACILITIES:** STV **PARKING:** 48 **NOTES:** No smoking in restaurant **CARDS:** ▭ ▭ ▭ ▭ ▭ ▭

SHEFFIELD Map 08 SK38

★★★★ 69%
Sheffield Marriott Hotel
Kenwood Rd S7 1NQ

☎ 0870 400 7261 ▤ 0870 400 7361
e-mail: eventorganiser.sheffield@marriotthotels.co.uk
Dir: follow A61 past Red Tape Studios on right , right at 2nd set of lights into St Marys Rd. At rdbt straight across, bear left into London Rd, right at lights, at top of hill straight across 1st and 2nd rdbt

PETS: Bedrooms (unattended) Public areas (lounge and reception areas only) Exercise area 12 acres of grounds

A smart, modern hotel peacefully located in a residential suburb a few miles from the city centre. Stylishly decorated bedrooms are spacious, quiet and very well equipped. The hotel also has an extensive range of leisure and meeting facilities. Drivers have the peace of mind of secure car parking.

ROOMS: 114 en suite (14 fmly) (27 GF) No smoking in 90 bedrooms s £64-£120; d £78-£140 (incl. bkfst) **LB** **FACILITIES:** Spa STV Indoor swimming (H) Fishing Sauna Solarium Gym Croquet lawn Jacuzzi Steam room, Health & beauty treatments **SERVICES:** Lift **PARKING:** 200 **NOTES:** No smoking in restaurant
CARDS: ▭ ▭ ▭ ▭ ▭

★★★ 67% Aston Hall
Worksop Rd, Aston S26 2EE
☎ 0114 287 2309 ▤ 0114 287 3228
e-mail: reservations@astonhallhotel.co.uk

PETS: Bedrooms (stables nearby) £5 per pet

Originally built as a manor house and set in spacious grounds with open views across the countryside to the south of the city, this hotel is well located for the M1, Meadowhall, the city or touring. Extensive conference and banqueting facilities, spacious bedrooms, and gracious service are notable features.

ROOMS: 20 en suite (4 fmly) No smoking in 10 bedrooms s £55-£70; d £65-£90 **FACILITIES:** STV **SERVICES:** air con **PARKING:** 150 **CARDS:** ▭ ▭ ▭ ▭ ▭ ▭

★★★ 67% Novotel Sheffield
50 Arundel Gate S1 2PR
☎ 0114 278 1781 ▤ 0114 278 7744
e-mail: h1348@accor-hotels.com
Dir: between Registry Office and Crucible/Lyceum Theatres, follow signs to Town Hall/Theatres & Hallam University

PETS: Bedrooms £5 per day Public areas (except restaurant)

Located in the heart of the city centre, this modern hotel is popular with both business and leisure guests. Local theatres and shopping are within easy reach, while within the hotel, facilities include an indoor heated swimming pool and a range of meeting rooms. Spacious bedrooms are suitable for family occupation and also provide an equally ideal environment for business users.

ROOMS: 144 en suite (40 fmly) No smoking in 108 bedrooms **FACILITIES:** STV Indoor swimming (H) Local gym facilities free for residents use **SERVICES:** Lift **PARKING:** 44 **NOTES:** RS 24 Dec-2 Jan **CARDS:** ▭ ▭ ▭ ▭ ▭ ▭

★★ 66% Cutlers Hotel
Theatreland George St S1 2PF
☎ 0114 273 9939 ▤ 0114 276 8332
e-mail: enquiries@cutlershotel.co.uk
Dir: In retail, commerce & academic centre, 50 metres from Crucible Theatre. Follow theatre signs.

PETS: Bedrooms (Except guide dogs) Exercise area

Situated close to the Crucible Theatre in the city centre, this boutique hotel offers accommodation in well-equipped bedrooms and extras including hairdryers, trouser presses and business facilities. Public areas include a lower ground floor bistro, and room service is available if required. Small meeting rooms are also available. Discounted overnight parking is provided in the nearby public car park.

ROOMS: 45 en suite (4 fmly) No smoking in 18 bedrooms s £45-£62; d £47.50-£72 (incl. bkfst) **LB** **FACILITIES:** Xmas **SERVICES:** Lift **PARKING:** **NOTES:** No smoking in restaurant
CARDS: ▭ ▭ ▭ ▭ ▭ ▭

◆◆◆◆ 🏠 Quarry House
Rivelin Glen Quarry, Rivelin Valley Rd S6 5SE
☎ 0114 234 0382 ▤ 0114 234 7630
e-mail: penelopeslack@aol.com
Dir: turn onto A6101 Rivelin Valley Road from Hillsborough/Malin Bridge end, in approx. 1m just after sharp bend sign turn right at end of row of old cottages. There is a lone street lamp at bottom of drive, uphill to car park

PETS: Bedrooms Public areas Exercise area (500yds)

A warm welcome is given to guests at this delightful former Quarry Master's house in the picturesque Rivelin Valley. Tasty evening meals and comprehensive breakfasts have a strong organic influence. Well-appointed bedrooms include many thoughtful extras. Public rooms include a comfortable cosy lounge and a smart dining room.

FACILITIES: 3 rms (2 en suite) (1 fmly) (1 GF) No smoking TVB tea/coffee Cen ht TVL No coaches Dinner Last d 10pm **PRICES:** s £35; d £70✱ **PARKING:** 8 **NOTES:** Closed 24 Dec-1 Jan

England

SHEFFIELD continued

◆◆◆ Parklands
113 Rustlings Rd S11 7AB
☎ 0114 267 0692
Dir: Follow A625 from Sheffield to rdbt, straight over rdbt, first on right

PETS: Bedrooms (unattended) Exercise area (park by hotel)

Situated near the Hunter's Bar area of the city and convenient for the university and hospitals, this Edwardian villa looks out over parkland at both front and rear. Friendly hospitality is provided in a home-from-home atmosphere, and a choice of breakfasts is available.
FACILITIES: 3 rms (2 en suite) (2 fmly) No smoking TVB tea/coffee Cen ht No coaches **PRICES:** s £23-£25; d £40; (room only) ✳ LB

THORNE
Map 08 SE61

★★★ 64% Belmont
Horsefair Green DN8 5EE
☎ 01405 812320 ◱ 01405 740508
e-mail: belmonthotel@aol.com
Dir: M18 junct 6 A614 signed Thorne. Hotel on right of Market Place

PETS: Bedrooms (unattended) Exercise area

This privately owned, smartly appointed hotel enjoys a prime location in the centre of town. Bedrooms vary in size and style and are all extremely well equipped for both business and leisure guests. Public areas include the popular Belmont Bar offering a good range of meals and snacks at both lunch and dinner, and the more formal restaurant and cocktail bar.
ROOMS: 23 en suite (3 fmly) (5 GF) No smoking in 5 bedrooms s £74-£77; d £85-£99 (incl. bkfst) LB **FACILITIES:** STV Putting green ch fac **PARKING:** 30 **NOTES:** Closed 24-28 Dec, 1 Jan
CARDS: ▭ ▦ ▬ ▭ ▬ ⑤

YORKSHIRE, WEST

BINGLEY
Map 07 SE13

◆◆◆◆ 🍽 Five Rise Locks
Beck Ln BD16 4DD
☎ 01274 565296 ◱ 01274 568828
e-mail: info@five-rise-locks.co.uk
Dir: in Bingley town centre turn off Main Street onto Park Rd. In 0.25m turn left into Beck Lane

PETS: Bedrooms (unattended) £5 Exercise area (0.25 mile)
RESIDENT PETS: 1 Border Collie

A warm welcome awaits you at this conveniently located and impressive Victorian hotel which has been sympathetically renovated to provide comfortable accommodation. Bedrooms are of a good size, and feature both practical and homely extras. Dinner is available in a restaurant offering imaginative, interesting dishes and the bright attractive breakfast room overlooks the surrounding countryside.
FACILITIES: 9 en suite (2 fmly) (2 GF) No smoking in bedrooms No smoking in dining room TVB tea/coffee Direct dial from bedrooms Licensed Cen ht No coaches Dinner Last d 9pm **PRICES:** s £40-£50; d £67-£70✳ **PARKING:** 20 **NOTES:** Closed 27 Dec-5 Jan
CARDS: ▭ ▬ ⑤

BRADFORD
Map 07 SE13

★★★ 68% Guide Post Hotel
Common Rd, Low Moor BD12 0ST
☎ 01274 607866 ◱ 01274 671085
e-mail: sales@guideposthotel.net
Dir: take M606, then signed

[Best Western]

PETS: Bedrooms (unattended) Public areas Exercise area

Situated south of the city, this hotel offers attractively furnished, comfortable bedrooms. The restaurant offers an extensive range of food using fresh, local produce; lighter snack meals are served in the bar. There is a choice of well-equipped meeting and function rooms.
ROOMS: 43 en suite (3 fmly) (14 GF) No smoking in 8 bedrooms s £50-£95; d £60-£105 (incl. bkfst) **FACILITIES:** STV **PARKING:** 10
NOTES: No smoking in restaurant
CARDS: ▭ ▦ ▬ ▭ ▬ ⑤

★★★ 63% Novotel Bradford
6 Roydsdale Way BD4 6SA
☎ 01274 683683 ◱ 01274 651342
e-mail: h0510@accor-hotels.com
Dir: M606 junct 2, exit to Euroway Trading Estate turn right at traffic lights at bottom of slip road, take 2nd right onto Roydsdale Way

[NOVOTEL]

PETS: Bedrooms £5 Public areas (not in restaurant, except guide dogs) Exercise area (on site)

This purpose-built hotel stands in an good location for access to the motorway. It provides spacious bedrooms that are comfortably equipped. Open-plan day rooms include a stylish bar, and a lounge that leads into the Garden Brasserie. Several function rooms are also available.
ROOMS: 119 en suite (37 fmly) (9 GF) No smoking in 69 bedrooms s £60; d £60 LB **FACILITIES:** STV Xmas **SERVICES:** Lift
PARKING: 200 **CARDS:** ▭ ▦ ▬ ▭ ▬ ⑤

🌲 **Places with this symbol are country house hotels**

★ **Red stars indicate the AA's Top 200 Hotels in Britain & Ireland**

All AA listed accommodation, restaurants and pubs can be found on the AA's website www.theAA.com

 Places with this symbol are farms

GARFORTH

Map 08 SE43

★★★ 73% ◎ Milford Hotel

A1 Great North Rd, Peckfield LS25 5LQ
☎ 01977 681800 ▤ 01977 681245
e-mail: enquiries@mlh.co.uk
Dir: On A63, 1.5m W of A1 & 4.5m E of M1 junct 46

PETS: Bedrooms (unattended) Exercise area (100 metres) Pet Food

This modern hotel provides comfortable bedrooms, which are air-conditioned, particularly spacious and have been superbly insulated against traffic noise. The contemporary-style Watermill Restaurant and Bar, which features a working waterwheel, provides creative cuisine. Staff throughout are friendly and keen to please.
ROOMS: 47 en suite (10 fmly) (14 GF) No smoking in 19 bedrooms
s £53-£63; d £53-£63 LB **FACILITIES:** STV Xmas **SERVICES:** air con
PARKING: 80 **CARDS:**

HALIFAX

Map 07 SE02

★★★ 77% ◎◎ Holdsworth House

Holdsworth HX2 9TG
☎ 01422 240024 ▤ 01422 245174
e-mail: info@holdsworthhouse.co.uk
Dir: from town centre take A629 Keighley Road. Right at garage into Shay Ln after 1.5m. Hotel on right after 1m

PETS: Bedrooms (unattended) £50 deposit Public areas (except hall and bar) Exercise area (Adjacent)

This delightful 17th-century Jacobean manor house is set in well-tended gardens and offers individually decorated, thoughtfully equipped bedrooms. Public rooms, adorned with beautiful paintings and antique pieces, include a choice of inviting lounges and superb conference and function facilities. Dinner provides the highlight of any stay and is served in the elegant restaurant, by friendly, attentive staff.
ROOMS: 40 en suite (2 fmly) No smoking in 15 bedrooms s £95-£135;
d £120-£160 (incl. cont bkfst) LB **FACILITIES:** STV **PARKING:** 60
NOTES: No smoking in restaurant
CARDS:

HUDDERSFIELD

Map 07 SE11

★★★★ 61% Cedar Court

Ainley Top HD3 3RH
☎ 01422 375431 ▤ 01422 314050
e-mail: huddersfield@cedarcourthotels.co.uk
Dir: 500yds from M62 junct 24

PETS: Bedrooms (unattended) Exercise area

Sitting adjacent to the M62, this hotel is an ideal location for business travellers or for those touring West Yorkshire. Bedrooms are spacious and comfortable and there is a busy lounge with snacks available all day as well as a modern restaurant and a fully equipped leisure centre. There are extensive meeting and banqueting facilities.
ROOMS: 114 en suite (6 fmly) (10 GF) No smoking in 70 bedrooms
s £60-£99; d £60-£99 LB **FACILITIES:** Indoor swimming (H) Sauna
Solarium Gym Steam room **SERVICES:** Lift **PARKING:** 250
CARDS:

★★ 71% ◎ Lodge

48 Birkby Lodge Rd, Birkby HD2 2BG
☎ 01484 431001 ▤ 01484 421590
e-mail: contact@birkbylodgehotel.com
Dir: M62 junct 24, exit A629 for Birkby. Left at 1st lights, right after Nuffield Hospital (Birkby Lodge Rd). Hotel 100yds on left

PETS: Bedrooms (unattended)

This family-run hotel is in a quiet residential area close to the city centre, and has a relaxed ambience. Smart public areas include two comfortable lounges and an inviting restaurant where carefully prepared meals are served. Bedrooms vary in size and style and are well equipped; one has a grand four-poster bed. Service is friendly and efficient.
ROOMS: 13 en suite (2 fmly) (3 GF) No smoking in all bedrooms
s £50-£60; d £60-£120 **PARKING:** 41 **NOTES:** No smoking in restaurant
Closed 26-27 Dec **CARDS:**

ILKLEY

Map 07 SE14

★★★ 76% ◎ Rombalds

11 West View, Wells Rd LS29 9JG
☎ 01943 603201 ▤ 01943 816586
e-mail: reception@rombalds.demon.co.uk
Dir: A65 from Leeds. Left at 3rd main lights, follow Ilkley Moor signs. Right at HSBC Bank onto Wells Rd. Hotel 600yds on left

PETS: Bedrooms Exercise area (adjacent)

This elegantly furnished Georgian townhouse is located on a peaceful terrace between the town and the moors. Delightful day rooms include a choice of comfortable lounges and an attractive restaurant which provides a relaxed venue in which to sample the skilfully prepared, imaginative meals. The bedrooms are tastefully furnished, well-equipped and include several spacious suites.
ROOMS: 18 en suite (4 fmly) No smoking in 12 bedrooms s £55-£99.50;
d £80-£119 (incl. bkfst) LB **FACILITIES:** STV Xmas **PARKING:** 28
NOTES: No smoking in restaurant Closed 28 Dec-2 Jan
CARDS:

KEIGHLEY

Map 07 SE04

★★ 67% Dalesgate

406 Skipton Rd, Utley BD20 6HP
☎ 01535 664930 ▤ 01535 611253
e-mail: stephen.e.atha@btinternet.com
Dir: In town centre follow A629 over rdbt. Right after 0.75m into St. John's Rd. 1st right into hotel car park

PETS: Bedrooms (unattended) Exercise area (500yds)
RESIDENT PETS: Max - German Shepherd cross

Originally the residence of a local chapel minister, this modern, well-established hotel has been expanded with the addition of a new wing to provide well-equipped, comfortable bedrooms. The hotel also boasts a cosy bar and pleasant restaurant, serving an imaginative range of dishes. A large car park is provided to the rear.
ROOMS: 20 en suite (2 fmly) (3 GF) s £35-£42; d £50-£60 (incl. bkfst)
LB **PARKING:** 25 **NOTES:** No smoking in restaurant RS 22 Dec-4 Jan
CARDS:

England

LEEDS
Map 08 SE33

★★★ 77% ◉ **Malmaison Hotel**
Sovereign Quay LS1 1DQ
☎ 0113 398 1000 📠 0113 398 1002
e-mail: leeds@malmaison.com
Dir: M621/M1 junct 3, follow signs to city centre. At KPMG building, right into Sovereign St. Hotel at end of street on right.

PETS: Pet baskets provided

Close to the waterfront, this stylish property offers striking bedrooms with CD players and air conditioning. The popular bar and brasserie feature vaulted ceilings, intimate lighting and offer a choice of a full three-course meal or a substantial snack. Service is both willing and friendly. A small fitness centre and impressive meeting rooms complete the package.
ROOMS: 100 en suite No smoking in 70 bedrooms s £79-£165;
d £79-£165 **LB FACILITIES:** STV Gym Xmas **SERVICES:** Lift air con
CARDS: ▨▨▨ ▨▨▨ ▨▨▨ ▨ ▨ ▨ ▨

★★★ 72% **Novotel Leeds Centre**
4 Whitehall, Whitehall Quay LS1 4HR
☎ 0113 242 6446 📠 0113 242 6445
e-mail: H3270@accor-hotels.com
Dir: exit M621 junct 3, follow signs to train station. Turn into Aire St and left at lights

PETS: Bedrooms (unattended) £5 Pet Food

With minimalist flair and style, this contemporary hotel provides a quality, value for money experience close to the city centre. Spacious, air-conditioned bedrooms reflect the modern theme of the hotel, whilst public areas offer deep leather sofas and an eye-catching water feature in reception. Light snacks are provided in the airy bar and the restaurant doubles as a bistro.
ROOMS: 195 en suite (60 fmly) No smoking in 130 bedrooms s fr £105;
d fr £105 **LB FACILITIES:** STV Sauna Gym Play station computers in rooms & play area Steam room Xmas **SERVICES:** Lift air con
PARKING: 70 **CARDS:** ▨▨▨ ▨▨▨ ▨▨▨ ▨ ▨ ▨ ▨

> ### All abbreviations are explained on page 9

> ### All information was correct at the time of going to press; we recommend you confirm details on booking

> ### Please mention AA Pet Friendly Places to Stay when booking

★★★ 70% **The Merrion**
Merrion Centre LS2 8NH
☎ 0113 243 9191 📠 0113 242 3527
e-mail: info@merrion-hotel-leeds.com
Dir: from M1, M62 and A61 onto city loop road to junct 7

PEEL HOTELS

PETS: Bedrooms (unattended) Public areas

This smart modern hotel benefits from a city centre location. Bedrooms are smartly appointed and thoughtfully equipped for both business and leisure guests. Public areas include a comfortable lounge and an airy restaurant with an adjacent bar. There is direct access to an adjacent car park via a walkway.
ROOMS: 109 en suite No smoking in 48 bedrooms s £79-£95;
d £85-£115 **LB FACILITIES:** STV Discount at local leisure club Xmas
SERVICES: Lift **CARDS:** ▨▨▨ ▨▨▨ ▨▨▨ ▨ ▨ ▨ ▨

★★★ 68% **Golden Lion**
2 Lower Briggate LS1 4AE
☎ 0113 243 6454 📠 0113 242 9327
e-mail: info@goldenlion-hotel-leeds.com
Dir: between junct 16 & junct 17

PEEL HOTELS

PETS: Bedrooms (unattended) Public areas

This smartly presented hotel is set in a Victorian building on the south side of the city. The well-equipped bedrooms offer a choice of standard or executive grades. Staff are friendly and helpful, ensuring a warm and welcoming atmosphere. Free overnight parking is provided in a 24-hour car park by the hotel.
ROOMS: 89 en suite (5 fmly) No smoking in 46 bedrooms s £95-£110;
d £110-£120 **LB FACILITIES:** STV Xmas **SERVICES:** Lift **PARKING:** 2
CARDS: ▨▨▨ ▨▨▨ ▨▨▨ ▨ ▨ ▨ ▨

OTLEY
Map 08 SE24

★★★ 69% ◉
Chevin Country Park Hotel
Yorkgate LS21 3NU
☎ 01943 467818 📠 01943 850335
e-mail: reception@chevinhotel.com
Dir: From Leeds/Bradford Airport rdbt take A658 N, towards Harrogate, for 0.75m to 1st traffic lights. Turn left, then 2nd left onto 'Yorkgate'. Hotel 0.5m on left

Best Western

PETS: Bedrooms (by prior arrangement only) £5
Exercise area (adjacent)

This hotel, peacefully situated in its own woodland yet conveniently located for major road links and the airport, offers comfortable accommodation. Rooms are split between the original main log building and chalet style accommodation situated in the extensive grounds. Public areas are spacious and well equipped. The split-level restaurant provides views over the small lake. Leisure facilities are also available.
ROOMS: 19 en suite 30 annexe en suite (7 fmly) (45 GF) No smoking in 10 bedrooms s £89-£121; d £96-£138 (incl. bkfst) **LB**
FACILITIES: STV Indoor swimming (H) Tennis (hard) Fishing Sauna Solarium Gym Jacuzzi Mountain bikes, jogging trails, CCTV surveillance on indoor pool Xmas **PARKING:** 100
CARDS: ▨▨▨ ▨▨▨ ▨▨▨ ▨ ▨ ▨ ▨

England

SHIPLEY
Map 07 SE13

⌂ Hotel Ibis Bradford
Quayside, Salts Mill Rd BD18 3ST
☎ 01274 589333 ▤ 01274 589444
e-mail: H3158@accor-hotels.com

ibis

Dir: follow tourist signs for Salts Mill. Pick up A650 signs through & out of Bradford for approx 5m to Shipley. Hotel on Salts Mill Rd

PETS: Bedrooms Public areas Exercise area

Modern, budget hotel offering comfortable accommodation in bright and practical bedrooms. Breakfast is self-service and dinner is available in the restaurant. For further details, consult the Hotel Groups page.
ROOMS: 78 en suite s £36.95-£46.95; d £36.95-£46.95

TODMORDEN
Map 07 SD92

◆◆◆ 🍺 Staff of Life
550 Burnley Rd, Knotts OL14 8JF
☎ 01706 812929 ▤ 01706 813773
e-mail: Staffoflife@btconnect.com

Dir: on A646 Halifax to Burnley rd, approx 1.5m from Todmorden centre towards Burnley, on right

PETS: Bedrooms (unattended) Public areas (except dining area) Exercise area (on site) **RESIDENT PETS:** Freyja & Zara (German Shepherds), Lizzy & Tiny (lizards), aquarium

Situated out of town on the Burnley road, this stone-built inn offers value-for-money accommodation in a friendly ambience. The comfortable bedrooms are pleasingly decorated and the bar, serving real ales, is full of character. There is also a small panelled dining room in which breakfast is served. The food is good and bar menus offer a wide choice of traditional and ethnic dishes.
FACILITIES: 3 en suite No smoking in dining room TVB tea/coffee Cen ht No coaches Dinner Last d by arrangement **PRICES:** s £30; d £42✱ **PARKING:** 26 **CARDS:** 🖃 💳 🏧 📶 ⑤

WAKEFIELD
Map 08 SE32

★★★★ 64% Cedar Court
Denby Dale Rd WF4 3QZ
☎ 01924 276310 ▤ 01924 280221
e-mail: sales@cedarcourthotels.co.uk
Dir: adjacent to M1 junct 39

PETS: Bedrooms Exercise area (in grounds)

This hotel enjoys a convenient location just off junction 39 of the M1. Traditionally styled bedrooms offer a good range of facilities while open plan public areas include a busy bar and restaurant operation. Conferences and functions are extremely well catered for and a brand new leisure club completes the picture.
ROOMS: 151 en suite (2 fmly) (74 GF) No smoking in 100 bedrooms s £65-£130; d £75-£140 **LB FACILITIES:** Spa STV Indoor swimming (H) Sauna Solarium Gym Jacuzzi Xmas **SERVICES:** Lift **PARKING:** 350
NOTES: No smoking in restaurant
CARDS: 🖃 💳 🏧 📶 ⑤

★★★ 69% Hotel St Pierre
Barnsley Rd, Newmillerdam WF2 6QG
☎ 01924 255596 ▤ 01924 252746
e-mail: sales@hotelstpierre.co.uk
THE INDEPENDENTS

Dir: M1 junct 39 take A636 to Wakefield, turn right at rdbt, on to Asdale Road to traffic lights. Right onto A61 towards Barnsley. Hotel just after lake

PETS: Bedrooms (unattended) Exercise area (200yds)

This well-furnished hotel lies south of Wakefield, close to Newmiller Dam. The interior of the modern building has comfortable and thoughtfully equipped bedrooms and smart public rooms. A good selection of conference rooms, a small gym and an intimate restaurant are all provided for guests' use.
ROOMS: 54 en suite (3 fmly) (4 GF) No smoking in 33 bedrooms s £55-£80; d £65-£90 **LB FACILITIES:** STV Gym Xmas **SERVICES:** Lift **PARKING:** 70 **CARDS:** 🖃 💳 🏧 📶 ⑤

⌂ Campanile
Monckton Rd WF2 7AL
☎ 01924 201054 ▤ 01924 201055
e-mail: wakefield@envergure.co.uk

Campanile

Dir: M1 junct 39, A636 1m towards Wakefield, left onto Monckton Rd, hotel on left

PETS: Bedrooms Public areas

This modern building offers accommodation in smart, well-equipped bedrooms, all with en suite bathrooms. Refreshments may be taken at the informal Bistro. For further details consult the Hotel Groups page.
ROOMS: 76 annexe en suite s fr £42.50; d fr £42.50

◆◆◆ Stanley View
226-230 Stanley Rd WF1 4AE
☎ 01924 376803 ▤ 01924 369123
e-mail: enquiries@stanleyviewguesthouse.co.uk

Dir: 2m off M62 junct 30 on A642 to York, close to city centre. Or 3m off M1 junct 41 on A640

PETS: Bedrooms (unattended) Exercise area (25yds)

Part of an attractive terrace this well-established guest house has private parking at the rear and is situated a short distance from the city centre. The well-equipped bedrooms are brightly and freshly decorated and there is a licensed bar and comfortable lounge. Hearty home-cooked meals are served in the attractive dining room.
FACILITIES: 17 rms (12 en suite) (6 fmly) No smoking in bedrooms No smoking in dining room STV TVB tea/coffee Direct dial from bedrooms Licensed Cen ht TVL Dinner Last d 8pm **PRICES:** s £22.32; d £31.72-£42.30✱ **BB PARKING:** 10
CARDS: 🖃 💳 🏧 📶 ⑤

🍺 Places with this symbol are pubs

England

WETHERBY
Map 08 SE44

◆◆ Prospect House
8 Caxton St LS22 6RU
☎ 01937 582428
Dir: A1 to Wetherby rdbt, turn left to Wetherby, through 1st lights, at 2nd lights turn left, continue to Kwiksave on left, house on corner

PETS: Bedrooms (unattended) Public areas (except at meal times) Exercise area (100yds)

A friendly welcome awaits at this centrally located guest house. Clean and comfortable accommodation is provided and a traditional breakfast served. Hand worked tapestries are quite a talking point in the dining room.
FACILITIES: 6 rms (4 en suite) tea/coffee Cen ht TVL No coaches
PRICES: s £25-£26; d £50-£52✱ **PARKING:** 6

CHANNEL ISLANDS

GUERNSEY

ST MARTIN
Map 16

★★★ 69% Green Acres
Les Hubits GY4 6LS
☎ 01481 235711 ▤ 01481 235978
e-mail: greenacres@guernsey.net
Dir: from airport, take road to St Martin. Turn off road leading to parish church, continue to hotel

PETS: Bedrooms (unattended) £5 Exercise area (in grounds)

Quietly located in the leafy lanes of St Martin, this pleasant hotel is ideal as a base for a relaxing break. Bedrooms are comfortable and well equipped, and staff are friendly and attentive. The public areas include a stylish lounge, which opens out onto the terrace pool area. Cuisine offers a choice of menus in different dining areas.
ROOMS: 43 en suite (3 fmly) s £30-£58; d £44-£92 (incl. bkfst) LB
FACILITIES: Outdoor swimming (H) Xmas **PARKING:** 75
NOTES: No smoking in restaurant **CARDS:** ▭▭ ▤▤ ▭▭

ISLE OF MAN

PORT ERIN
Map 06 SC16

★★ 65% Falcon's Nest
The Promenade IM9 6AF
☎ 01624 834077 ▤ 01624 835370
e-mail: falconsnest@enterprise.net
Dir: follow coastal road, S from airport or ferry. Hotel on seafront, immediately after steam railway station

PETS: Bedrooms (unattended) Public areas (not in food areas) Exercise area (50 metres)

Situated overlooking the bay and harbour, this Victorian hotel offers generally spacious bedrooms. There is a choice of bars, one of which attracts many locals, and of dining options also. Meals can be taken in the lounge bar or in the attractively decorated main restaurant.
ROOMS: 35 en suite (9 fmly) No smoking in 3 bedrooms s £43-£49; d £70-£85 (incl. bkfst) LB **FACILITIES:** STV ch fac **PARKING:** 40
CARDS: ▭▭ ▭▭ ▭▭ ▭▭ ▭▭ ▭▭ ▭

SCOTLAND

The Rest and be Thankful Pass, Argyll & Bute

Scotland

SCOTLAND

ABERDEEN CITY

ABERDEEN · Map 15 NJ90

★★★★ 78%
The Marcliffe at Pitfodels
North Deeside Rd AB15 9YA
☎ 01224 861000 📠 01224 868860
e-mail: enquiries@marcliffe.com
Dir: turn off A90 onto A93 signed Braemar. 1m on right after turn at lights

PETS: Bedrooms (unattended) Exercise area (5 miles) Pet Food **RESIDENT PETS:** Smudge (Lowchen), Drifter (cat)

Set in attractive landscaped grounds west of the city, this impressive hotel presents a blend of styles backed by caring and attentive service. A split-level conservatory restaurant, terraces and courtyards all give a sense of the Mediterranean, whilst the elegant and sophisticated cocktail lounge is classical in style. Bedrooms are well-proportioned and thoughtfully equipped.

ROOMS: 40 en suite (2 fmly) (12 GF) No smoking in 16 bedrooms s £115-£295; d £130-£295 (incl. bkfst) **LB FACILITIES:** STV Snooker Croquet lawn Putting green Xmas **SERVICES:** Lift **PARKING:** 220 **NOTES:** No smoking in restaurant **CARDS:**

Don't forget to let proprietors know when you book that you're bringing your pet

★★★★ 67% Aberdeen Patio
Beach Boulevard AB24 5EF
☎ 01224 633339 & 380000 📠 01224 638833
e-mail: patioab@globalnet.co.uk
Dir: from A90 follow signs for city centre, then for sea. On Beach Blvd, turn left at lights, hotel on right

PETS: Bedrooms (unattended) Exercise area (100yds)

Popular with both business and leisure guests, this modern, purpose-built hotel is close to the seafront and its many attractions. Bedrooms come in two different styles with the spacious Premier Club rooms particularly appealing. The conservatory style restaurant holds regular themed dining nights and there is also a striking Atrium bar.

ROOMS: 124 en suite (8 fmly) (10 GF) No smoking in 93 bedrooms s £45-£125; d £60-£135 (incl. bkfst) **LB FACILITIES:** STV Indoor swimming (H) Sauna Solarium Gym Jacuzzi Steam room, Treatment Room Xmas **SERVICES:** Lift **PARKING:** 196 **NOTES:** No smoking in restaurant **CARDS:**

★★★★ 65% ◎◎
Copthorne Hotel Aberdeen
122 Huntly St AB10 1SU

COPTHORNE

☎ 01224 630404 📠 01224 640573
e-mail: reservations.aberdeen@mill-cop.com
Dir: W of city centre, off Union Street, up Rose Street, hotel 0.25m on right on corner with Huntly Street

PETS: Bedrooms (unattended) Public areas (Not in food service areas (except guide dogs)) Exercise area (0.5 mile to park)

Set just out of the city centre, this hotel offers friendly, attentive service. The smart bedrooms are well-proportioned and guests will appreciate the added quality of the Connoisseur rooms. Mac's bar provides a relaxed atmosphere in which to enjoy a drink or to dine informally, whilst Poachers Restaurant offers a fine dining experience.

ROOMS: 89 en suite (15 fmly) No smoking in 37 bedrooms s £85-£170; d £85-£170 **LB FACILITIES:** STV **SERVICES:** Lift **PARKING:** 20 **NOTES:** RS 25-26 Dec **CARDS:**

★★★ 70% Westhill
Westhill AB32 6TT

Best Western

☎ 01224 740388 📠 01224 744354
e-mail: info@westhillhotel.co.uk
Dir: follow A944 W of city towards Alford. Hotel 6m on right

PETS: Bedrooms (unattended) Public areas (not in restaurant or lounge) Exercise area (30 yards) Pet Food

This establishment has recently changed ownership. Just a short drive from the city centre and airport, this comfortable business hotel has inviting public areas that include a choice of three contrasting bars and a smart fitness centre. Meals are available in both the lounge bar and the split-level brasserie. Bedrooms are modern in appointment and offer a good range of amenities.

ROOMS: 38 en suite (2 fmly) No smoking in 8 bedrooms s £38-£75; d £46-£95 (incl. bkfst) **LB FACILITIES:** STV Sauna Solarium Gym entertainment Xmas **SERVICES:** Lift **PARKING:** 150 **NOTES:** No smoking in restaurant **CARDS:**

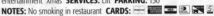

★★★ 68% ® Maryculter House Hotel
South Deeside Rd, Maryculter AB12 5GB
☎ 01224 732124 🖷 01224 733510
e-mail: info@maryculterhousehotel.com
Dir: off A90 on S side of Aberdeen, onto B9077. Hotel 8m on right, 0.5m
beyond Lower Deeside Caravan Park

PETS: Bedrooms (unattended) Exercise area (in hotel
grounds) stabling by arrangement

Set in grounds on the banks of the River Dee, this charming Scottish
mansion dates back to medieval times and is now a popular
wedding and conference venue. Exposed stonework and open fires
feature in the oldest parts, which house the cocktail bar and Priory
Restaurant. Lunch and breakfast are taken overlooking the river and
bedrooms are equipped with business travellers in mind.
ROOMS: 23 en suite (1 fmly) (12 GF) No smoking in 17 bedrooms
s £45-£75; d £70-£95 (incl. bkfst) **LB FACILITIES:** STV Fishing Clay
pigeon shooting, Archery Xmas **PARKING:** 150 **NOTES:** No smoking in
restaurant **CARDS:** 〓 〓 〓 〓 〓 🆂

◆◆◆◆ Strathisla
408 Gt Western Rd AB10 6NR
☎ 01224 321026
e-mail: elza@strathisla-guesthouse.co.uk
Dir: follow A90, over Dee Bridge, straight over rdbt, on dual-carriageway,
over 2nd rdbt to lights, then right into Great Western Rd

PETS: Bedrooms (unattended) Exercise area (0.25 mile)
RESIDENT PETS: Holly (Chocolate Labrador), Diva (cat)

A comfortable granite-built terraced house on the west side of the
city, Strathisla boasts attractive bedrooms, all individual and
inviting, with added touches such as alarm clocks and a
complimentary slice of cake with the beverage facilities. Vegetarian
options are available at breakfast.
FACILITIES: 5 en suite (1 fmly) No smoking TVB tea/coffee Cen ht
No coaches **PRICES:** s £26-£32; d £40-£44✳ **PARKING:** 1
CARDS: 〓 〓

ABERDEENSHIRE

★★★ ®®® Darroch Learg
Braemar Rd AB35 5UX
☎ 01339 755443 🖷 755252
e-mail: nigel@darrochlearg.co.uk
Dir: on A93, at western side of Ballater

PETS: Bedrooms Exercise area **RESIDENT PETS:** Holly
(Golden Labrador)

Set high above the road in extensive wooded grounds, this hotel
offers fine views over Royal Deeside. Bedrooms, some with four-
poster beds, are individually styled, bright and spacious, especially
the newly created suite. Food is a highlight of any visit, whether it
is a freshly prepared breakfast, a light lunch or the award-winning
Scottish cuisine served in the delightful conservatory restaurant.
ROOMS: 12 en suite 5 annexe en suite (1 GF) No smoking in
all bedrooms s £97.50-£135; d £155-£230 (incl. bkfst & dinner) **LB**
FACILITIES: Xmas **PARKING:** 25 **NOTES:** No smoking in restaurant
Closed Xmas & Jan (ex New Year) **CARDS:** 〓 〓 〓 〓 〓 🆂

★★ 73% ® Loch Kinord
Ballater Rd, Dinnet AB34 5JY
☎ 01339 885229 🖷 887007
e-mail: ask@kinord.com
Dir: Between Aboyne & Ballater, on A93, in village of Dinnet

THE CIRCLE
Selected Individual Hotels
GREAT BRITAIN

PETS: Bedrooms £5 Public areas (not at meal times)
Exercise area (on site)

Family-run, this roadside hotel lies between Aboyne and Ballater
and is well-located for leisure and sporting pursuits. It has lots of
character and a friendly atmosphere. There are two bars, one
outside and a cosy one inside, plus a dining room in bold, stylish
colour schemes. Food is well-promoted throughout the hotel.
ROOMS: 21 rms (19 en suite) (3 fmly) (4 GF) No smoking in
5 bedrooms s £35-£55; d £50-£85 (incl. bkfst) **LB FACILITIES:** Sauna
Jacuzzi Pool table Xmas **PARKING:** 20 **NOTES:** No smoking in
restaurant **CARDS:** 〓 〓 〓 🆂

★★★ 78% ®® Raemoir House
Raemoir AB31 4ED
☎ 01330 824884 🖷 01330 822171
e-mail: relax@raemoir.com
Dir: A93 to Banchory right onto A980, to Torphins, 2m at T-junct

PETS: Bedrooms (unattended) Public areas (only small,
quiet pets) Exercise area (in grounds) Pet Food stabling
by arrangement

This country mansion dates from the mid-18th century and retains
many period features. Individually designed bedrooms vary in size
and layout, though all are well-equipped. Gracious public rooms
include a choice of sitting rooms, a cocktail bar and a Georgian
dining room. These rooms have tapestry-covered walls, open fires,
and fine antiques.
ROOMS: 14 en suite 6 annexe en suite (1 fmly) s £60-£90; d £100-£130
(incl. bkfst) **LB FACILITIES:** Golf 9 Tennis (hard) Croquet lawn
Putting green Shooting Stalking **PARKING:** 100 **NOTES:** No smoking in
restaurant **CARDS:** 〓 〓 〓 🆂

See advert on page 265

🐾 Places with this symbol are
country house hotels

Scotland

BANCHORY continued

★★★ 78% ◎ Tor-na-Coille
AB31 4AB
☎ 01330 822242 🖷 01330 824012
e-mail: tornacoille@btinternet.com
Dir: on A93 Aberdeen/Braemar road, opposite golf course.

PETS: Bedrooms (unattended) £7 Public areas (not food service areas) Exercise area (within grounds) Pet Food

This fine granite-stone house sits in tree-studded grounds on the west side of the town. Bedrooms come in a variety of styles and sizes, many mirroring the period charm of the house. Inviting public areas include a lovely sitting room and an elegant restaurant.
ROOMS: 22 en suite (4 fmly) No smoking in 17 bedrooms s £70-£80; d £100-£130 (incl. bkfst) **LB FACILITIES:** Squash Croquet lawn entertainment ch fac **SERVICES:** Lift **PARKING:** 130
NOTES: No smoking in restaurant Closed 24-28 Dec
CARDS: ▤ ▤ ▤ ▤ ▤

★★ 70% Burnett Arms
25 High St AB31 5TD
☎ 01330 824944 🖷 01330 825553
e-mail: theburnett@totalise.co.uk
Dir: town centre on N side of A93, 18m from centre of Aberdeen

 Best Western

PETS: Bedrooms (unattended) Public areas (except dining room) Exercise area (100yds)

This popular hotel is located in the heart of the town centre and gives easy access to the many attractions of Royal Deeside. Public areas include a choice of eating and drinking options, with food served in the restaurant, bar and foyer lounge. Bedrooms are thoughtfully equipped and comfortably modern.
ROOMS: 16 en suite No smoking in 5 bedrooms s £48-£65; d £65-£90 (incl. bkfst) **LB FACILITIES:** STV ch fac Xmas **PARKING:** 40
NOTES: No smoking in restaurant
CARDS: ▤ ▤ ▤ ▤ ▤ ▤

BANFF
Map 15 NJ66

◆◆◆◆ Morayhill
Bellevue Rd AB45 1BJ
☎ 01261 815956 🖷 01261 818717
e-mail: morayhill@aol.com
Dir: A947 onto A97 towards Aberchirder, 2nd on right, 3rd house on left

PETS: Bedrooms (unattended) Public areas

A warm welcome awaits at this fine Victorian house set in mature gardens in a residential area close to the town centre. Meticulously maintained, it offers comfortable bedrooms, an inviting lounge with open fire in season, and an attractive dining room overlooking the garden. An impressive starter buffet is a feature of breakfast plus a daily-changing special hot dish.
FACILITIES: 3 rms (2 en suite) (2 fmly) No smoking in bedrooms No smoking in dining room TVB tea/coffee Cen ht TVL No coaches
PRICES: s £23; d £46✻ **LB PARKING:** 5

HUNTLY
Map 15 NJ53

★★ 63% Gordon Arms Hotel
THE INDEPENDENTS
The Square AB54 8AF
☎ 01466 792288 🖷 01466 794556
e-mail: reception@gordonarms.demon.co.uk
Dir: off A96 (Aberdeen to Inverness rd) at Huntly. Hotel immediately on left after entering town square

PETS: Bedrooms £5 Exercise area

This friendly family-run hotel is located in the town square and offers a good selection of tasty, well-portioned dishes served in the bar (or in the restaurant at weekends or midweek by appointment). Bedrooms come in a variety of sizes, and all are cheerfully decorated.
ROOMS: 13 en suite (3 fmly) s £35-£45; d £48.50-£58.50 (incl. bkfst) **LB FACILITIES:** entertainment Xmas
CARDS: ▤ ▤ ▤ ▤ ▤ ▤

INVERURIE
Map 15 NJ72

★★★ 67% Pittodrie House
Chapel of Garioch, Pitcaple AB51 5HS
☎ 01467 681444 🖷 01467 681648
e-mail: pittodrie@macdonald-hotels.co.uk
Dir: A96, Chapel of Garioch turn off

PETS: Bedrooms Sep Accom (kennel) (unattended) Public areas (not during meal service) Pet Food
RESIDENT PETS: Oscar (cat)

This house dates from the 15th century and retains many original features. Bedrooms come in two distinct styles; those in the original house are full of character and the newer wing has been refurbished to provide more modern comfort. Public areas include a striking drawing room, restaurant and a cosy bar.
ROOMS: 27 en suite (6 fmly) No smoking in 13 bedrooms s £68-£95; d £90-£140 (incl. bkfst) **LB FACILITIES:** STV Squash Snooker Croquet lawn Clay pigeon shooting Quad biking Archery etc on estate Xmas **PARKING:** 150 **NOTES:** No smoking in restaurant
CARDS: ▤ ▤ ▤ ▤ ▤ ▤

OLDMELDRUM
Map 15 NJ82

★★ 65% Meldrum Arms
The Square AB51 0DS
☎ 01651 872238 🖷 01651 872238
Dir: off the B947, in centre of village

PETS: Bedrooms Exercise area

Located in the centre of the village, the Meldrum Arms Hotel combines a cosy and welcoming atmosphere with a good range of tasty dishes available in both the bar and comfortable restaurant. Try their popular high tea - main course, tea and toast plus scones and cakes.
ROOMS: 7 en suite (1 fmly) s £39.50; d £60 (incl. bkfst)
FACILITIES: STV **PARKING:** 25 **NOTES:** No smoking in restaurant
CARDS: ▤ ▤ ▤ ▤

STONEHAVEN Map 15 NO88

◆◆◆◆ Woodside Of Glasslaw

AB39 3XQ
☎ 01569 763799 📠 01569 763799
e-mail: aileenpaton@hotmail.com
Dir: Heading N leave A90 at 1st sign for Stonehaven. At end of sweeping bend turn right, take next road on left

PETS: Bedrooms Public areas (not during breakfast) Exercise area (large garden) RESIDENT PETS: Max (Collie), Toby (cat)

A rural location amid farmland and gardens, yet close to major road links, ensures this guest house remains popular with both business and leisure guests. Bedrooms are comfortably furnished and attractively decorated. There is also a combined lounge/dining room where hearty breakfasts are served at individual tables.
FACILITIES: 6 en suite (1 fmly) (4 GF) No smoking in bedrooms No smoking in dining room TVB tea/coffee Cen ht TVL No coaches
PRICES: s £25; d fr £42✳ **PARKING:** 5

ANGUS

BRIDGEND OF LINTRATHEN Map 15 NO25

◉◉ ♔ Lochside Lodge & Roundhouse Restaurant

DD8 5JJ
☎ 01575 560340 📠 01575 560202
e-mail: enquiries@lochsidelodge.com
Dir: B951 from Kirriemuir towards Glenisla for 7m & take left turn to Lintrathen. Follow road over top of loch & into village. Hotel on left

PETS: Bedrooms Exercise area (200 yards) RESIDENT PETS: Bonnie (Spaniel/Collie cross)

This converted farmstead enjoys a rural location in the heart of Angus. The comfortable bedrooms which offer private facilities, are in the former hayloft and the original windows have been retained. Accomplished modern cuisine is served in the atmospheric Roundhouse restaurant. A spacious bar bedecked with agricultural implements and church pews features a wide range of drinks including local beers.
ROOMS: 4 en suite (1 fmly) s £45-£55; d £65-£75 (incl. bkfst)
PARKING: 40 **NOTES:** No smoking in restaurant Closed 1-24 Jan RS Sun, Mon **CARDS:** 💳

RAEMOIR HOUSE HOTEL

Wind your way up a long tree-lined drive and catch a glimpse of a Georgian mansion surrounded by 3,500 acres of parkland and forest in beautiful Royal Deeside.

Inside a fine collection of antiques and paintings, a profusion of flowers and fires blazing in our elegant reception rooms, a wonderful highland welcome. Surrounded by romantic castles such as Crathes and Dunnotter and the whole area are a treat for the imagination. Dinner is served in the

beautiful candlelit oval dining room which is acknowledged by all the guides as the finest in the area.
Do come if you can, a warm welcome awaits.

Banchory, Royal Deeside
Tel: 01330 824884 email: relax@raemoir.com

GLAMIS Map 15 NO34

★★★ ◉◉ ♠♠ Castleton House

Castleton of Eassie DD8 1SJ
☎ 01307 840340 📠 01307 840506
e-mail: hotel@castletonglamis.co.uk
Dir: on A94 midway between Forfar/Cupar Angus, 3m W of Glamis

PETS: Bedrooms (unattended) £10 Public areas (not in dining room) Exercise area Pet Food water bowls and food on request RESIDENT PETS: Greyhound, Labrador, chickens, ducks, peacock, pigs

Set in its own grounds and with a moat, this impressive Victorian house has a relaxed and friendly atmosphere. Accommodation is provided in individually designed, spacious bedrooms. Personal service from the enthusiastic proprietors is a real feature and many guests return time and again. Accomplished cooking, utilising the best local produce, is served in the conservatory restaurant.
ROOMS: 6 en suite (2 fmly) No smoking in 1 bedroom s £100-£120; d £140-£180 (incl. bkfst) **LB FACILITIES:** Croquet lawn Putting green ch fac Xmas **PARKING:** 50 **CARDS:** 💳

Scotland

GLENISLA   Map 15 NO26

◆◆◆ ♟ ⊜ **The Glenisla Hotel**
PH11 8PH
☎ 01575 582223 📠 01575 582203
e-mail: glenisla.hotel@btinternet.com
Dir: Take A926 from Blairgowrie onto B954 at Alyth; through the Glen for
10m

PETS: Telephone for details

Situated in glorious countryside, this pleasant hotel offers
comfortable, good value accommodation and delicious food.
Bedrooms vary in size and are attractive and well equipped. There
is an elegant dining room and a well-stocked beamed bar and
dining area where a log fire blazes on cooler evenings.
FACILITIES: 8 rms (6 en suite) (2 fmly) No smoking in bedrooms
No smoking in dining room tea/coffee Cen ht Fishing Pool Table Games
room Dinner Last d 9pm **PARKING:** 15 **CARDS:** 💳💳💳💳 ⑤

MONTROSE   Map 15 NO75

★★★ 73% **Links Hotel**
Mid Links DD10 8RL
☎ 01674 671000 📠 01674 672698
e-mail: reception@linkshotel.com
Dir: A935 to Montrose then right at Lochside junct, left at swimming pool
and right by tennis courts for hotel 200yds

Best
Western

PETS: Bedrooms (unattended) £5 per dog Exercise area
(opposite hotel)

This former Edwardian town house has been fully refurbished and
restored. Bedrooms offer a choice of attractive modern styles and
are extremely well equipped to cater for business guests. Public
areas have a bar, a restaurant, and a popular coffee shop
where food is available all day.
ROOMS: 25 en suite (1 GF) No smoking in 15 bedrooms s £54-£80;
d £68-£88 (incl. bkfst) **LB FACILITIES:** STV entertainment Xmas
PARKING: 45 **NOTES:** No smoking in restaurant
CARDS: 💳💳💳💳💳 ⑤

> ## All abbreviations are
> ## explained on page 9

◆◆◆ **Oaklands**
10 Rossie Island Rd DD10 9NN
☎ 01674 672018 📠 01674 672018
e-mail: oaklands1@btopenworld.com
Dir: on A92, S end of town

PETS: Bedrooms (unattended) Public areas (not dining
room)

A warm welcome and attentive service is assured at this detached
house, situated on the south side of the town. Bedrooms come in
a variety of sizes and are well-equipped. There is a guest lounge
on the ground floor adjacent to the attractive dining room, where
hearty breakfasts are served.
FACILITIES: 7 en suite (1 fmly) (1 GF) No smoking in 3 bedrooms
No smoking in dining room TVB tea/coffee Cen ht TVL No coaches
PRICES: s £25-£30; d £40-£60✱ **PARKING:** 8 **CARDS:** 💳💳

ARGYLL & BUTE

ARDUAINE   Map 10 NM71

★★★ 76% ◉◉ **Loch Melfort**
PA34 4XG
☎ 01852 200233 📠 01852 200214
e-mail: reception@lochmelfort.co.uk
Dir: on A816, midway between Oban and Lochgilphead

SCOTLAND'S HOTELS
OF DISTINCTION

PETS: Bedrooms (Cedar Wing only) (unattended)
Exercise area (on site) Pet Food Stabling by prior arrangement
RESIDENT PETS: Rosie (Beagle), Evie and Bethan (horses), Whiskers
(chinchilla)

Enjoying one of the finest locations on the West Coast, this
popular, family-run hotel has outstanding views across Asknish
Bay towards the Islands of Jura, Scarba and Shuna.
Accommodation is provided in either the balconied rooms of the
Cedar wing or the more traditional rooms in the main hotel.
Dinner can be enjoyed in both the informal Skerry Bistro and the
restaurant.
ROOMS: 7 en suite 20 annexe en suite (2 fmly) No smoking in
11 bedrooms s £49-£79; d £78-£158 (incl. bkfst) **LB FACILITIES:** ch fac
Xmas **PARKING:** 65 **NOTES:** No smoking in restaurant
CARDS: 💳💳💳💳💳 ⑤

Scotland

CAIRNDOW

Map 10 NN11

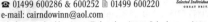

★★ 65% **Cairndow Stagecoach Inn**
PA26 8BN
☎ 01499 600286 & 600252 ▤ 01499 600220
e-mail: cairndowinn@aol.com

Dir: from North, either A82 to Tarbet, then A83 to Cairndow or A85 to Palmally, A819 to Inveraray and A83 to Cairndow.

THE CIRCLE
Selected Individual Hotels
GREAT BRITAIN

PETS: Bedrooms (unattended) Public areas Exercise area (50 yards) **RESIDENT PETS:** Rocky - Labrador

A relaxed, friendly atmosphere prevails at this 18th-century inn, overlooking the beautiful Loch Fyne. Bedrooms offer individual décor and thoughtful extras. Traditional public areas include a comfortable beamed lounge, a well-stocked bar where food is served throughout the day, and a spacious restaurant with conservatory extension.
ROOMS: 13 en suite (2 fmly) No smoking in 3 bedrooms s £35-£60; d £30-£70 (incl. bkfst) **LB FACILITIES:** Sauna Solarium Gym Xmas **PARKING:** 32 **CARDS:** 💳

CLACHAN-SEIL

Map 10 NM71

★★ 76% ◉◉ **Willowburn**
PA34 4TJ
☎ 01852 300276 ▤ 01852 300597
e-mail: willowburn.hotel@virgin.net

Dir: 0.5m from Atlantic Bridge, on left

PETS: Bedrooms (unattended) Public areas (bar only) Exercise area (0.5 mile) **RESIDENT PETS:** Sisko (Black Labrador), Laren (Border Collie), Odo (cat)

This welcoming small hotel enjoys a peaceful setting, with grounds stretching down to the shores of Clachan Sound. Friendly

continued

---

unassuming service, a relaxed atmosphere and fine food are keys to its success. Watch the wildlife from the dining room, lounge or cosy bar. Bedrooms are bright, cheerful and thoughtfully equipped.

ROOMS: 7 en suite (1 GF) No smoking in all bedrooms s £72-£74; d £144-£148 (incl. bkfst & dinner) **LB PARKING:** 20
NOTES: No children 8 yrs No smoking in restaurant Closed Dec-Feb
CARDS: 💳

CONNEL

Map 10 NM93

★★ 72% **Falls of Lora**
PA37 1PB
☎ 01631 710483 ▤ 01631 710694
Dir: hotel set back from A85 from Glasgow, 0.5 mile past Connel sign

PETS: Bedrooms Public areas (not in dining areas or lounge) Exercise area (50 yards)

Personally run and welcoming, this long-established holiday hotel enjoys fine views over Loch Etive. The pleasant public areas include a comfortable, traditional lounge and a well-stocked bar with a popular bistro and there is a separate breakfast room. Bedrooms come in a variety of styles, ranging from the standard cabin rooms to high quality, luxury rooms.
ROOMS: 30 en suite (4 fmly) (4 GF) s £39-£49; d £43-£119 (incl. bkfst)
LB FACILITIES: ch fac **PARKING:** 40 **NOTES:** Closed mid Dec & Jan
CARDS: 💳

♦♦♦♦ **Loch Etive House Hotel**
Connel Village, By Oban PA37 1PH
☎ 01631 710400 ▤ 01631 710680
e-mail: frankwop@btinternet.com
Dir: turn off A85 in Connel, 5m from Oban, 50yds from St Orons Kirk

PETS: Bedrooms Exercise area (20 metres)

Conveniently located in the centre of the village, Loch Etive House is a family run establishment where a warm friendly welcome is assured. Bedrooms are comfortably furnished and well equipped. A combined lounge/dining room is available where delicious evening meals and freshly cooked breakfasts are served at individual tables.
FACILITIES: 5 rms (3 en suite) (3 fmly) No smoking TVB tea/coffee Licensed Cen ht TVL No coaches Dinner Last d 9.30am **PARKING:** 6
CARDS: 💳

Scotland

DUNOON
Map 10 NS17

★★ 78% ⊛ **Enmore**
Marine Pde, Hunters Quay PA23 8HH
☎ 01369 702230 ▤ 01369 702148
e-mail: enmorehotel@btinternet.com
Dir: on coastal route between two ferries, 1m N of Dunoon

PETS: Bedrooms (unattended) £3.50 Public areas (except dining room) Exercise area (own beach & gardens)

This seafront hotel, built in 1875 by a Glasgow merchant, has super views over the Firth of Clyde. Elegant public areas include a peaceful lounge, a dining room that features high quality, local ingredients and two squash courts to work off the calories. Bedrooms are individual and a number have stunning bathrooms.
ROOMS: 9 en suite (1 fmly) No smoking in all bedrooms s £59-£95; d £90-£150 (incl. bkfst) **LB FACILITIES:** Squash Jacuzzi ch fac **PARKING:** 10 **NOTES:** No smoking in restaurant Closed 12 Dec-12 Feb RS Nov-Mar **CARDS:** 🖃 🔤 🔤 🔀 💆

◆◆◆◆ ☺🖥 **Dhailling Lodge**
155 Alexandra Pde PA23 8AW
☎ 01369 701253 ▤ 01369 701340
e-mail: fraser@dhaillinglodge.com
Dir: On A815 between the Ferry terminals at Dunoon and Hunter's Quay

PETS: Bedrooms (unattended) Public areas (if other guests do not object) Exercise area (adjacent)

Enjoying a seafront location overlooking the Forth of Clyde, this elegant Victorian villa is a haven of comfort, hospitality, delicious food and fine wines. Bedrooms are tastefully appointed and extremely well-equipped. One bedroom has been adapted for wheelchair users. There is a cosy lounge and an intimate dining room, where a daily changed menu featuring the best of local produce is served.
FACILITIES: 7 en suite No smoking TVB tea/coffee Licensed Lift Cen ht No coaches Dinner Last d 6pm **PRICES:** s £30-£32; d £58-£62✶ **LB PARKING:** 8 **NOTES:** Closed Nov **CARDS:** 🖃 🔤 🔤 🔀 💆

ERISKA
Map 10 NM94

★★★★ ⊛⊛⊛ ⚘ **Isle of Eriska**
Eriska, Ledaig PA37 1SD
☎ 01631 720371 ▤ 01631 720531
e-mail: office@eriska-hotel.co.uk
Dir: A85 at Connel onto A828, 4m, then follow signs from N of Benderloch

PETS: Bedrooms £10 Exercise area (300-acre grounds) Pet Food

Situated on its own private island with delightful beaches and walking trails, this hotel offers a tranquil, private setting for total relaxation. Spacious bedrooms are comfortable and boast some fine antique pieces. Local seafood, meats and game feature prominently on the award-winning menu, as do vegetables and herbs grown in the hotel's kitchen garden. Leisure facilities include an indoor swimming pool, gym, spa treatment rooms and a small golf course.
ROOMS: 17 en suite s £195; d £250 (incl. bkfst) **LB FACILITIES:** Spa Indoor swimming (H) Golf 6 Tennis (hard) Fishing Sauna Gym Croquet lawn Putting green Jacuzzi Steam room, Skeet shooting, Nature trails Xmas **PARKING:** 40 **NOTES:** No smoking in restaurant Closed Jan **CARDS:** 🖃 🔤 🔤 🔤 🔀 💆

OBAN
Map 10 NM83

★★★ 74%
The Oban Caledonian Hotel & Spa
Station Square PA34 5RT
☎ 01855 821582 ▤ 01855 821463
e-mail: reservations@freedomglen.co.uk
Dir: at head of main pier, close to rail terminal

CLASSIC BRITISH

PETS: Bedrooms (unattended) £10 Public areas (must be well behaved)

This Victorian hotel, overlooking the bay, has undergone a transformation. Public areas are modern and stylish and include a smart restaurant, spacious lounges and an informal dining option in Café Caledonian. Attractive bedrooms come in a number of different styles and grades, some with comfortable seating areas, feature bathrooms and fine sea views. Valet parking is available.
ROOMS: 59 en suite (4 fmly) No smoking in 10 bedrooms s £52.50-£100; d £52.50-£240 (incl. bkfst) **LB FACILITIES:** Discounted entry to local leisure centre entertainment Xmas **SERVICES:** Lift **PARKING:** 6 **NOTES:** No smoking in restaurant **CARDS:** 🖃 🔤 🔀 💆

★★ 61% **Lancaster**
Corran Esplanade PA34 5AD
☎ 01631 562587 ▤ 01631 562587
e-mail: john@lancasteroban.com
Dir: on seafront next to St Columba's Cathedral

PETS: Bedrooms Sep Accom (unattended) Public areas (except dining room) Exercise area (woods adjacent) Pet Food

Lovely views over the bay towards the Isle of Mull can be enjoyed from this welcoming family-run hotel on the Esplanade. Comfortable bedrooms vary in size and style and offer a good range of amenities. Public areas include a choice of contrasting lounges and bars.
ROOMS: 27 rms (24 en suite) (3 fmly) s £27.50-£33; d £60-£64 (incl. bkfst) **LB FACILITIES:** Spa STV Indoor swimming (H) Sauna Steam room **PARKING:** 20 **CARDS:** 🖃 🔤 🔀 💆

PORT APPIN
Map 14 NM94

★★★ ⊛⊛⊛ **Airds**
PA38 4DF
☎ 01631 730236 ▤ 01631 730535
e-mail: airds@airds-hotel.com
Dir: from A828, turn at Appin signed Port Appin. Hotel 2.5m on left.

PETS: Bedrooms (unattended) £10 Exercise area (adjacent)

Stunning views are to be had from this delightful small hotel on the shores of Loch Linnhe. Finely prepared meals that utilise first-rate, mostly locally sourced ingredients are served in the dining room. The bedrooms offer tasteful decor and bathrooms of a high specification. Lounges are quiet and inviting, with real fires and attractive artwork. The attentive staff can recommend many walks.
ROOMS: 12 en suite (2 fmly) (2 GF) No smoking in all bedrooms s £160-£255; d £230-£360 (incl. bkfst & dinner) **LB FACILITIES:** ch fac Xmas **PARKING:** 21 **NOTES:** No smoking in restaurant Closed 5-26 Jan RS Nov- Feb **CARDS:** 🖃 🔤 🔀 💆

Scotland

★★ 79% ® The Royal at Tighnabruaich
Shore Rd PA21 2BE
☎ 01700 811239 🖹 01700 811300
e-mail: info@royalhotel.org.uk
Dir: from Strachur on A886 turn right onto the A8003 to Tighnabruaich. Hotel is on right at the bottom of hill, at the t-junct

PETS: Bedrooms (unattended) £3 Public areas (except restaurant) Exercise area (100 metres)

This outstanding family-run hotel continues to go from strength to strength. Set just yards from the loch shore, stunning views are guaranteed from many rooms, including the elegant restaurant and informal brasserie bar where fresh seafood and game are served. The comfortable bedrooms vary in size and style.
ROOMS: 11 en suite (2 fmly) No smoking in all bedrooms d £70-£150 (incl. bkfst) **LB FACILITIES:** sailing, fishing, windsurfing, riding, walking, bird watching **PARKING:** 20 **NOTES:** No smoking in restaurant Closed 25-26 Dec **CARDS:** 🔲🔲🔲🔲🔲🔲

CITY OF EDINBURGH

★★★ 76% ® *Malmaison*
One Tower Place EH6 7DB   *Malmaison*
☎ 0131 468 5000 🖹 0131 468 5002
e-mail: edinburgh@malmaison.com
Dir: A900 from city centre towards Leith, at end of Leith Walk continue over lights through 2 more sets of lights, left into Tower St, hotel on right at the end of road

PETS: Bedrooms (unattended) £10 Exercise area (0.5 mile) Pet bowl, dog basket available

Overlooking the port of Leith, this former seamen's mission is now home to the stylish Malmaison. Bedrooms have striking décor, CD players, mini-bars and a number of individual, welcoming touches. Food and drink are equally important here, with brasserie-style dining and a café bar, both of which are popular with the local clientele.
ROOMS: 101 en suite (18 fmly) No smoking in 12 bedrooms
FACILITIES: STV Gym **SERVICES:** Lift **PARKING:** 50
CARDS: 🔲🔲🔲🔲🔲🔲

★★★ 68% Kings Manor
100 Milton Rd East EH15 2NP   [Best Western]
☎ 0131 669 0444 🖹 0131 669 6650
e-mail: info@kingsmanor.com
Dir: A720 E until Old Craighall junct, left into city, turn right at junct A1/A199 junct, hotel 200mtrs on right

PETS: Bedrooms Public areas (not in dining areas) Exercise area (on site)

Lying on the eastern side of the city and convenient for the by-pass, this hotel is popular with business guests, tour groups and for conferences. It boasts a fine leisure complex and a bright

continued

modern bistro, which complements the more traditional restaurant.
ROOMS: 67 en suite (2 fmly) (5 GF) No smoking in 31 bedrooms s £60-£83; d £90-£135 (incl. bkfst) **LB FACILITIES:** STV Indoor swimming (H) Tennis (hard) Sauna Solarium Gym Jacuzzi Health & beauty salon Xmas **SERVICES:** Lift **PARKING:** 100
CARDS: 🔲🔲🔲🔲🔲🔲

◆◆◆◆◆ 🏛 Bonnington
202 Ferry Rd EH6 4NW
☎ 0131 554 7610 🖹 0131 554 7610
e-mail: bonningtongh@btinternet.com
Dir: on A902

PETS: Bedrooms Exercise area (adjacent)

This delightful Georgian house offers individually furnished bedrooms that retain many of their original features. The homely lounge, with a grand piano for the musically gifted, is complemented by an attractive dining room, where the kilted proprietor serves a fine Scottish breakfast. The warmth of the welcome is noteworthy here.
FACILITIES: 6 rms (4 en suite) (3 fmly) No smoking in bedrooms No smoking in dining room TVB tea/coffee Cen ht TVL No coaches
PRICES: s £35-£40; d £50-£76✳ **PARKING:** 9
CARDS: 🔲🔲🔲🔲

◆◆◆ Galloway
22 Dean Park Crescent EH4 1PH
☎ 0131 332 3672 🖹 0131 332 3672
e-mail: galloway_theclarks@hotmail.com
Dir: 0.5m from Princes St (west end) on A9

PETS: Bedrooms (unattended) Public areas (not in dining room) Exercise area (5km)

Situated in a residential area near shops and bistros north of the city centre, this guest house provides smart, thoughtfully equipped bedrooms. Also a feature are breakfasts with a good choice of starters and hot dishes.
FACILITIES: 10 rms (7 en suite) (6 fmly) (1 GF) TVB tea/coffee Cen ht
PRICES: s £30-£50; d £40-£60✳ **LB CARDS:** 🔲🔲🔲🔲

◆◆◆ Kingsview Guest House
28 Gilmore Place EH3 9NQ
☎ 0131 229 8004 🖹 0131 229 8004
e-mail: kingsviewguesthouse@talk21.com
Dir: From west end of Princes St, follow Lothian Rd to the Kings Theatre. Kingsview opposite, 150yds on right in Gilmore Place.

PETS: Bedrooms Exercise area (100 yards)
RESIDENT PETS: Hamish (Westie)

Situated a short distance from the city centre and convenient for all major amenities, this friendly guest house offers comfortable good value accommodation. Bedrooms, which vary in size, are attractive and well equipped. There is a combined lounge/dining room where hearty breakfasts are served at individual tables.
FACILITIES: 8 en suite (5 fmly) (1 GF) No smoking in dining room No smoking in lounges STV TVB tea/coffee Cen ht **LB PARKING:**
CARDS: 🔲🔲🔲🔲

Scotland

CITY OF GLASGOW

CITY OF GLASGOW

GLASGOW   Map 11 NS56

★★★★ One Devonshire Gardens
1 Devonshire Gardens G12 0UX
☎ 0141 339 2001 📠 0141 337 1663
e-mail: reservations@onedevonshiregardens.com
Dir: M8 junct 17, follow signs for A82, after 1.5m turn left into Hyndland Rd, 1st right, right at mini rdbt, right at end, continue to end

PETS: Bedrooms (by prior arrangement only)   Exercise area (10 min walk)   Pet Food

This renowned townhouse occupies four houses of a Victorian terrace in a residential area. Bedrooms, including a number of suites and four-poster rooms, are stylish, individually designed and thoughtfully equipped to a high standard. Public rooms include a choice of inviting drawing rooms, meeting and conference facilities and a smart restaurant offering imaginative cooking. Personal, attentive service is a highlight.
ROOMS: 36 en suite (4 GF) s £145-£485; d £145-£485 **FACILITIES:** STV Squash Gym Tennis facilities at nearby club ch fac **NOTES:** No smoking in restaurant **CARDS:** 💳 📇 🌐 💳 📇 💳

★★★★ 69% Glasgow Moat House
Congress Rd G3 8QT
☎ 0141 306 9988 📠 0141 221 2022
e-mail: reservations.glasgow@moathousehotels.com
Dir: M8 junct 19, follow signs for SECC, hotel adjacent to Centre

PETS: Bedrooms (unattended) £20   Exercise area (5 mins walk)

This modern building, instantly recognisable from its mirrored glass exterior, has a convenient location alongside the River Clyde. A feature of the public rooms is a huge wall mural, depicting the city's history, which looks down over the informal No 1 Dockhouse restaurant and the stylish Mariners Restaurant. Bedrooms are comfortable and well-appointed and most enjoy splendid panoramic views.
ROOMS: 283 en suite (10 fmly) No smoking in 171 bedrooms s £75-£165; d £80-£165 (incl. bkfst) **LB FACILITIES:** STV Indoor swimming (H) Sauna Solarium Gym Xmas **SERVICES:** Lift air con **PARKING:** 300 **NOTES:** Closed 25-26 Dec, 1 Jan **CARDS:** 💳 📇 🌐 💳 📇 💳

★★★★ 68% Langs Hotel
2 Port Dundas Place G2 3LD
☎ 0141 333 1500 & 352 2452 📠 0141 333 5700
e-mail: reservations@langshotels.co.uk
Dir: M8 junct 16, follow signs for George Square. Hotel immediately left after Concert Square Car Park.

PETS: Bedrooms   Public areas   (not restaurants)

A contemporary-style city centre hotel offering a choice of restaurants for dinner. Oshi has an eastern slant, whilst Las Brisas has been awarded a Rosette. Bedrooms offer various designs, all with a retro style. Some feature stunning suites with a gallery bedroom above the lounge. All have Sony Play Stations and CD players.
ROOMS: 100 en suite (4 fmly) No smoking in 60 bedrooms s £90-£155; d £100-£165 (incl. bkfst) **FACILITIES:** Spa STV Sauna Gym **SERVICES:** Lift **NOTES:** No smoking in restaurant **CARDS:** 💳 📇 🌐 💳 📇 💳

★★★ 76% Malmaison
278 West George St G2 4LL
☎ 0141 572 1000 📠 0141 572 1002
e-mail: glasgow@malmaison.com
Dir: from S & E - M8 junct 18 (Charing Cross), from W & N - M8 City Centre Glasgow

 Malmaison

PETS: Pet baskets provided

Built around a former church in the historic Charing Cross area, Malmaison is a smart, contemporary hotel offering impressive levels of service and hospitality. Bedrooms are spacious and feature a host of modern facilities, such as CD players and mini bars. Dining is a treat, with French brasserie-style cuisine served in the original crypt.
ROOMS: 72 en suite (4 fmly) No smoking in 30 bedrooms s £129-£165; d £129-£165 **LB FACILITIES:** STV Gym Cardiovascular gym **SERVICES:** Lift **CARDS:** 💳 📇 🌐 💳 📇 💳

★★★ 66% Ewington
Balmoral Ter, 132 Queens Dr, Queens Park
G42 8QW
☎ 0141 423 1152 📠 0141 422 2030
e-mail: ewington.info@countryhotels.net
Dir: M8 junct 20, A77, through 8 sets of lights, left (Allison St), right (Victoria Rd) to Park Gates. Turn right, hotel 500yds on right

Best Western

PETS: Bedrooms (unattended)   Exercise area (100yds)

Quietly located on the south side of the city, this townhouse-style hotel forms part of a Victorian terrace opposite Queens Park. Public areas include a foyer lounge, restaurant and comfortable cocktail lounge. It's worth asking for one of the larger bedrooms that overlook the park.
ROOMS: 43 en suite (5 fmly) No smoking in 8 bedrooms s £50-£79; d £60-£99 **LB FACILITIES:** STV Xmas **SERVICES:** Lift **PARKING:** 10 **NOTES:** No smoking in restaurant **CARDS:** 💳 📇 🌐 💳 📇 💳

★ **Red stars indicate the AA's Top 200 Hotels in Britain & Ireland**

All AA listed accommodation, restaurants and pubs can be found on the AA's website www.theAA.com

🐓 **Places with this symbol are farms**

🍺 **Places with this symbol are pubs**

Please mention AA Pet Friendly Places to Stay when booking

Scotland

★★★ 62% Quality Hotel Glasgow

99 Gordon St G1 3SF
☎ 0141 221 9680 📠 0141 226 3948
e-mail: enquiries@quality-hotels-glasgow.com
Dir: M8 junct 19, left into Argyle St and left into Hope St

PETS: Bedrooms (unattended) Public areas (except restaurant)

A splendid Victorian railway hotel, forming part of Central Station. It retains much original charm combined with modern facilities. Public rooms are impressive and include a recently transformed bar area and a modernised reception. Bedrooms continue to be upgraded and are generally spacious and well laid out.
ROOMS: 222 en suite (8 fmly) No smoking in 70 bedrooms
FACILITIES: Spa STV Indoor swimming (H) Sauna Solarium Gym Jacuzzi Hair & beauty salon, Steam room, Sports therapist Xmas
SERVICES: Lift **NOTES:** No smoking in restaurant
CARDS: 🔲🔲🔲🔲🔲🔲

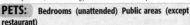

⇧ Hotel Ibis Glasgow City Centre

220 West Regent St G2 4DQ
☎ 0141 225 6000 📠 0141 225 6010
e-mail: H3139@accor-hotels.com

PETS: Bedrooms Public areas (only if house-trained)

Modern, budget hotel offering comfortable accommodation in bright and practical bedrooms. Breakfast is self-service and dinner is available in the restaurant. For further details, consult the Hotel Groups page. **ROOMS:** 141 en suite s £45.95-£55.95; d £45.95-£55.95

⇧ Tulip Inn Glasgow

80 Ballater St G5 0TW
☎ 0141 429 4233 📠 0141 429 4244
e-mail: info@tulipinnglasgow.co.uk

TULIP INN

Dir: From Glasgow Airport M8 junct 21 follow signs for East Kilbride, turn right onto A8 along Kingston St. Turn right onto South Portland St, left onto Norfolk St, straight through Gorbals St & onto Ballater St.

PETS: Bedrooms Public areas (not in restaurant)

A modern budget hotel suitable for business travellers, families and tourists. Bedrooms are bright, well-proportioned and comprehensively equipped. There is a bistro and bar.
ROOMS: 114 en suite s £45-£74.50; d £45-£74.50

♦♦♦♦ Kelvingrove Hotel

944 Sauchiehall St G3 7TH
☎ 0141 339 5011 📠 0141 339 6566
e-mail: kelvingrove.hotel@business.ntl.com
Dir: M8 junct 18 0.5m follow signed Kelvingrove Museum left

PETS: Bedrooms Exercise area (1 min walk)

This private, well-maintained and friendly hotel lies in a terrace row just west of the city centre. Bedrooms, including several rooms suitable for families, are particularly well-equipped and have smart, fully tiled en suite bathrooms. There is a bright breakfast room and a reception lounge that is open 24 hours.
FACILITIES: 22 en suite (5 fmly) (3 GF) No smoking TVB tea/coffee Direct dial from bedrooms Cen ht No coaches **PRICES:** s £40-£55; d £55-£70; (room only) ✳ LB **CARDS:** 🔲🔲🔲🔲🔲

♦♦♦ Kelvin Private Hotel

15 Buckingham Ter, Great Western Rd, Hillhead G12 8EB
☎ 0141 339 7143 📠 0141 339 5215
e-mail: enquiries@kelvinhotel.com
Dir: M8 J17, A82 Kelvinside/Dumbarton, 1m from motorway on right just before Botanic Gardens

PETS: Bedrooms Exercise area (0.25 mile)

Two substantial Victorian terraced houses on the west side of the city have been combined to create this friendly private hotel, close to the Botanical Gardens. Bedrooms are comfortably proportioned, attractive and well equipped. The dining room is situated on the first floor and is an appropriate setting for hearty traditional breakfasts, served at individual tables.
FACILITIES: 21 rms (9 en suite) (5 fmly) (2 GF) No smoking in dining room TVB tea/coffee Cen ht **PRICES:** s £24-£42; d £42-£60✳
PARKING: 5 **CARDS:** 🔲🔲🔲🔲

♦♦♦ The Merchant Lodge

52 Virginia St G1 1TY
☎ 0141 552 2424 📠 0141 552 4747
e-mail: themerchant@ukonline.co.uk
Dir: from George Square enter North Hanover Street, towards Ingram Street. Turn into Virginia Place, leads into Virginia Street

PETS: Bedrooms Public areas

Set within The Merchant City and close to Argyle Street, this former home of a tobacco lord features a cobbled courtyard and stone turnpike stair. The house, on five floors, has been fully modernised with pine floors, pine furniture and pleasant and understated décor. Breakfast is fully self-service in a bright and cheerful lower level room.
FACILITIES: 34 en suite 6 annexe en suite (8 fmly) (6 GF) TVB tea/coffee Direct dial from bedrooms Cen ht **PRICES:** s £36; d £57✳
CARDS: 🔲🔲🔲🔲🔲

CLACKMANNANSHIRE

DOLLAR

Map 11 NS99

★★ 72% Castle Campbell Hotel

11 Bridge St FK14 7DE
☎ 01259 742519 📠 01259 743742
e-mail: bookings@castle-campbell.co.uk
Dir: on A91 Stirling to St Andrews Rd, in the centre of Dollar, by bridge overlooking Dollar Burn & Clock Tower

PETS: Bedrooms £5 Public areas (not in restaurant) Exercise area (100 metres)

Set in the centre of a delightful country town, this hotel is popular with both local people and tourists. Accommodation ranges in size, though all rooms are thoughtfully equipped. Inviting public rooms feature a delightful lounge with real fire, a well-stocked whisky bar and a stylish restaurant.
ROOMS: 8 en suite (2 fmly) No smoking in all bedrooms s fr £55; d fr £80 (incl. bkfst) LB **FACILITIES:** Xmas **PARKING:** 8
NOTES: No smoking in restaurant
CARDS: 🔲🔲🔲🔲🔲🔲

Scotland

TILLICOULTRY
Map 11 NS99

◆◆◆◆ Westbourne House
10 Dollar Rd FK13 6PA
☎ 01259 750314
e-mail: odellwestbourne@aol.com
Dir: A91 to St Andrews. Establishment on left just past mini-rdbt

PETS: Bedrooms Exercise area (200 yards)
RESIDENT PETS: Brock (Border Collie)

A friendly welcome is assured at this former mill owner's home, which lies secluded in wooded gardens on the edge of the village. It is adorned with a stunning collection of memorabilia, objets d'art and items gathered by the owners during their time abroad. Breakfast is served house party style and offers an excellent choice.
FACILITIES: 3 rms (2 en suite) (1 fmly) (1 GF) No smoking TVB tea/coffee Cen ht TVL No coaches Croquet lawn **PRICES:** s £29-£31; d £48-£52✳ **PARKING:** 3 **NOTES:** Closed Xmas-New year
CARDS: [cards]

DUMFRIES & GALLOWAY

AUCHENCAIRN
Map 11 NX75

★★★ 76% ◉◉ ♨ Balcary Bay
DG7 1QZ
☎ 01556 640217 & 640311 ▤ 01556 640272
e-mail: reservations@balcary-bay-hotel.co.uk
Dir: on the A711 between Dalbeattie and Kirkcudbright, hotel on shore road, 2m from village

PETS: Bedrooms (unattended) Exercise area Pet Food

Taking its name from the bay on which it lies, this hotel has lawns running down to the shore. The larger bedrooms enjoy stunning views over the bay, whilst others overlook the gardens. Comfortable public areas invite relaxation. Imaginative dishes feature at dinner, accompanied by a good wine list.
ROOMS: 20 en suite (1 fmly) (3 GF) s £64; d £114-£138 (incl. bkfst)
LB PARKING: 50 **NOTES:** No smoking in restaurant Closed Dec-Jan
CARDS: [cards]

CANONBIE
Map 11 NY37

★★ 65% Cross Keys
DG14 0SY
☎ 01387 371205 ▤ 371878
e-mail: sg.laverack@ukonline.co.uk

PETS: Bedrooms

Located in the quiet village of Canonbie, this former 17th-century coaching inn is full of character. The hotel is family run, and guests will experience a welcoming and friendly atmosphere. Bedrooms are all individually appointed, comfortable and well equipped. The restaurant and public bar retain many original features and offer an interesting selection of freshly prepared dishes.
ROOMS: 10 rms (9 en suite) (1 fmly) s £35-£38; d £55-£58 (incl. bkfst)
PARKING: 30 **NOTES:** No smoking in restaurant
CARDS: [cards]

CASTLE DOUGLAS
Map 11 NX76

★★ 67% Imperial
35 King St DG7 1AA
☎ 01556 502086 ▤ 01556 503009
e-mail: david@thegolfhotel.co.uk
Dir: off A75 at sign for Castle Douglas, hotel opp town library.

PETS: Bedrooms (unattended) Public areas (not in restaurant) Exercise area (100 yards)

Situated in the main street, this former coaching inn, popular with golfers, offers guests well-equipped and cheerfully decorated bedrooms. There is a choice of bars and good-value meals are served either in the foyer bar or the upstairs dining room.
ROOMS: 12 en suite (1 fmly) No smoking in 6 bedrooms s £40-£50; d £62-£70 (incl. bkfst) **LB FACILITIES:** local pool and sauna/gym 75yds away ch fac **PARKING:** 29 **NOTES:** No smoking in restaurant Closed 23-26 Dec & 1-3 Jan **CARDS:** [cards]

★★ 67% King's Arms
St Andrew's St DG7 1EL
☎ 01556 502626 ▤ 01556 502097
e-mail: david@galloway-golf.co.uk
Dir: through main street, left at town clock, hotel on corner

PETS: Bedrooms (unattended) Public areas (except dining room) Exercise area (400 yards) Pet Food
RESIDENT PETS: Spider & Nola D (cats)

The King's Arms Hotel is a former coaching inn and boasts a traditional and comfortable interior. Cosy day rooms include a choice of bar areas and a restaurant overlooking an ivy clad courtyard. Creative menus are offered in both the bar and the restaurant.
ROOMS: 10 rms (9 en suite) (2 fmly) No smoking in 3 bedrooms s £40-£50; d £62-£68 (incl. bkfst) **LB PARKING:** 15
NOTES: No smoking in restaurant Closed 25-26 Dec & 1-2 Jan
CARDS: [cards]

◆◆◆◆◆ 🏠 🍽 ❤ Craigadam

Craigadam DG7 3HU
☎ 01556 650233 & 650100 📠 01556 650233
e-mail: enquiry@craigadam.com
Dir: leave Castle Douglas E on A75 to Crocketford. In Crocketford turn left on A712 for 2m, house on hill

PETS: Bedrooms Sep Accom (kennel) Exercise area (next door) A field is available **RESIDENT PETS:** Craig, Jock (Collies), Ted & Jet (Black labradors), 9 Highland cattle

Set on a working farm, this elegant country house offers gracious living in a relaxed environment. The large bedrooms, most set round a courtyard, are strikingly individual in style. Public areas include a billiard room with comprehensive honesty bar and the panelled dining room features a magnificent 15-seater table, the ideal setting for Celia Pickup's delightful meals.
FACILITIES: 8 en suite (2 fmly) (4 GF) No smoking in bedrooms No smoking in area of dining room No smoking in 1 lounge TVB tea/coffee Licensed Cen ht Fishing Snooker Croquet lawn Shooting 700 acres sheep Dinner Last d 8am **PRICES:** s £76; d £76✳
PARKING: 12 **NOTES:** Closed Xmas & New Year
CARDS: 💳

CASTLE KENNEDY   Map 10 NX15

★★ 65% The Plantings Inn

DG9 8SQ
☎ 01581 400633 📠 01581 400637
e-mail: info@plantings.com

PETS: Bedrooms £5 Exercise area (20 yards)

Convenient for Stranraer and the Irish ferries, this small hotel focuses on an pleasantly informal eating operation with a wide-ranging menu that offers hearty good-value dishes. Bedrooms are smartly furnished.
ROOMS: 5 en suite No smoking in all bedrooms s £35; d £60 (incl. bkfst) **LB FACILITIES:** Xmas **PARKING:** 30
CARDS: 💳

COLVEND   Map 11 NX85

★★ 69% Clonyard House

DG5 4QW
☎ 01556 630372 📠 01556 630422
e-mail: nickthompson@clara.net
Dir: through Dalbeattie, left onto A710 for about 4m, hotel on left

PETS: Bedrooms (unattended) 50 pence Public areas (except restaurant) Exercise area (on site) **RESIDENT PETS:** cat, 2 fish, 10 cockatiels, 30 budgies

This long-established and popular family-run hotel is set in seven acres of woodland gardens, which include a children's play area and an 'enchanted tree'. Most of the spacious, comfortable bedrooms are housed in a purpose-built extension. Creative menus are served in the bar lounge or in the restaurant.
ROOMS: 15 en suite (3 fmly) (12 GF) s £35-£45; d £55-£70 (incl. bkfst)
LB PARKING: 40 **CARDS:** 💳

★★★ 71% ◉ Cairndale Hotel & Leisure Club

English St DG1 2DF
☎ 01387 254111 📠 01387 250555
e-mail: sales@cairndale.fsnet.co.uk
Dir: from S turn off M6 onto A75 to Dumfries, left at 1st rdbt, cross railway bridge, continue to traffic lights, hotel 1st building on left

PETS: Bedrooms (by arrangement only) (unattended) Public areas Exercise area (0.25 mile)

Within walking distance of the town centre, this hotel provides a wide range of amenities, including leisure facilities and an impressive conference and entertainment centre. Bedrooms range from stylish suites to cosy singles. There's a choice of eating options in the evening. The Reivers Restaurant is smartly modern with food to match.
ROOMS: 91 en suite (22 fmly) (5 GF) No smoking in 45 bedrooms s £49-£109; d £69-£149 (incl. bkfst) **LB FACILITIES:** Spa STV Indoor swimming (H) Sauna Solarium Gym Jacuzzi Steam room, air conditioned gymnasium entertainment ch fac Xmas **SERVICES:** Lift
PARKING: 120 **NOTES:** No smoking in restaurant
CARDS: 💳

GATEHOUSE OF FLEET   Map 11 NX55

★★★ 67% Murray Arms

DG7 2HY
☎ 01557 814207 📠 01557 814370
e-mail: murrayarmshotel@ukonline.co.uk
Dir: off A75, hotel at edge of town, near clock tower

PETS: Bedrooms (unattended) Exercise area (adjacent)

A relaxed and welcoming atmosphere prevails at this family-run hotel, a former coaching inn at the north end of the main street. Public areas retain a comfortable, traditional feel and include a choice of lounges, a snug bar and an all-day restaurant. Bedrooms are comfortable and well presented.
ROOMS: 12 en suite (3 fmly) s £50-£60; d £95-£110 (incl. bkfst) **LB**
FACILITIES: Tennis (hard) Croquet lawn Xmas **PARKING:** 50
CARDS: 💳

GLENLUCE   Map 10 NX15

★★ 67% Kelvin House Hotel

53 Main St DG8 0PP
☎ 01581 300303 📠 01581 300303
e-mail: kelvinhouse@lineone.net
Dir: midway between Newton Stewart & Stranraer, just off A75

PETS: Bedrooms (unattended) Public areas (in the bar after meals, not in restaurant) Exercise area (50 yards) Pet Food **RESIDENT PETS:** Blackie (cat)

This small, privately run hotel lies in the centre of a village. The bedrooms are bright and spacious and there is a comfortable residents' lounge. Wholesome, good value meals are served either in the popular bar or separate restaurant overlooking the garden. Special golf packages are worth enquiring about.
ROOMS: 6 rms (5 en suite) (3 fmly) No smoking in 3 bedrooms s £30-£35; d £50-£60 (incl. bkfst) **LB FACILITIES:** Xmas
CARDS: 💳

GRETNA (WITH GRETNA GREEN) — Map 11 NY36

◆◆◆ Barrasgate

Millhill DG16 5HU
☎ 01461 337577 ◫ 01461 339932
e-mail: info@barrasgate.co.uk
Dir: M74 junct with A6071 signed Longtown. From S follow A6071 approx 1m, take 2nd left signed Gretna Green, establishment on left. From N follow signs for Longtown, Barrasgate House is right approx 1m from motorway

PETS: Bedrooms Exercise area (on site) dried pet food available RESIDENT PETS: Cookie (Whippet) & Megan (Greyhound cross)

This detached house lies in attractive gardens in a rural setting yet is convenient for the motorway. Bedrooms are well presented and there is a cosy lounge where breakfasts and light suppers are served round the one table.
FACILITIES: 3 en suite (1 fmly) No smoking TVB tea/coffee Cen ht TVL No coaches **LB PARKING:** 8

GRETNA SERVICE AREA (A74(M)) — Map 11 NY36

⌂ Days Inn

Welcome Break Service Area DG16 5HQ
☎ 01461 337566 ◫ 01461 337823
e-mail: gretna.hotel@welcomebreak.co.uk
Dir: between junct 21/22 on M74 - accessible from both N'bound & S'bound carriageway

 DAYS INN

PETS: Bedrooms Exercise area (adjacent)

This modern building offers accommodation in smart, spacious and well-equipped bedrooms, suitable for families and business travellers, and all with en suite bathrooms. Continental breakfast is available and other refreshments may be taken at the nearby family restaurant. For further details see the Hotel Groups page.
ROOMS: 64 en suite s £45-£55; d £45-£55

KIRKCUDBRIGHT — Map 11 NX65

★★ 66% Arden House Hotel

Tongland Rd DG6 4UU
☎ 01557 330544 ◫ 01557 330742
Dir: off A57 Euro route (Stranraer), 4m W of Castle Douglas onto A711. Signed for Kirkcudbright, crossing Telford Bridge. Hotel 400mtrs on left

PETS: Bedrooms (unattended) Public areas (not in restaurant) Exercise area (50 yards) Pet Food food and bowls on request

Set well back from the main road in extensive grounds on the north east side of town, this well-maintained hotel offers attractive bedrooms, a lounge bar and adjoining conservatory serving a range of popular dishes, which are also available in the dining room. It boasts an impressive function suite in its grounds.
ROOMS: 9 rms (8 en suite) (7 fmly) s £35; d £60 (incl. bkfst)
PARKING: 70

★★ 64% Royal

 THE INDEPENDENTS

St Cuthbert St DG6 4DY
☎ 01557 331213 ◫ 01557 331513
e-mail: reception@theroyalhotel.net
Dir: off A75 onto A711 hotel is in centre of Kirkcudbright, on the corner at crossroads

PETS: Bedrooms (unattended) Exercise area
RESIDENT PETS: Bruno (mongrel)

Lying right in the town centre this hotel has colourfully decorated bedrooms with good facilities. Good value meals are provided throughout the day and evening in either the coffee lounge, bar or dining room. Residents have an upstairs lounge.
ROOMS: 17 en suite (7 fmly) **FACILITIES:** entertainment
NOTES: No smoking in restaurant **CARDS:** 🖻 💳 ⚡ 🗒 ⑤

◆◆◆◆◆ Baytree House

110 High St DG6 4JQ
☎ 01557 330824 ◫ 01557 330824
e-mail: jackie@baytreehouse.net
Dir: from A75 take A711 into centre if Kirkcudbright, at x-rds turn right into Cuthbert S, turn left at Castle, Baytree facing at end of Castle St

PETS: £2 Exercise area (200 yards)

A beautifully restored Georgian town house, Baytree House lies just off the town centre. Bedrooms are attractively decorated, thoughtfully equipped and furnished in keeping with style of the house. A bright airy ground floor dining room overlooks the secluded garden. However, Jackie Callander's hospitality and breakfasts aside, it will be the magnificent upstairs drawing room that will leave the lasting impression.
FACILITIES: 3 en suite (1 GF) No smoking TVB tea/coffee Cen ht No children 12yrs No coaches **PRICES:** d £60-£64✱ **LB**

LOCKERBIE — Map 11 NY18

★★★ 80% ◉◉ Dryfesdale

Dryfebridge DG11 2SF
☎ 01576 202427 ◫ 01576 204187
e-mail: reception@dryfesdalehotel.co.uk
Dir: from M74 take 'Lockerbie North' junct 17, 3rd left at 1st rdbt, 1st exit left at 2nd rdbt, hotel is 200yds on left

PETS: Bedrooms (unattended) £4 Exercise area (on site) Pet Food

Conveniently situated for the M74, yet discreetly screened from it, this friendly hotel provides memorable service from a team of thoughtful, enthusiastic staff. Bedrooms, some with access to patio areas, vary in size and style, offer good levels of comfort and are well equipped. Creative, good value dinners make excellent use of local produce and are served in the airy restaurant overlooking the manicured gardens and rolling countryside. This hotel has been awarded the AA Courtesy & Care Award for Scotland 2004-5.
ROOMS: 16 en suite (2 fmly) (7 GF) No smoking in 4 bedrooms
s fr £65; d fr £75 (incl. bkfst) **LB FACILITIES:** STV Golf 9 Fishing Croquet lawn Putting green Clay pigeon shooting, Fishing entertainment Xmas **PARKING:** 40 **NOTES:** No smoking in restaurant
CARDS: 🖻 💳 💳 💳 🗒 ⑤

★★ 73% **Somerton House**

35 Carlisle Rd DG11 2DR

☎ 01576 202583 & 202384 ◻ 01576 204218

e-mail: somerton@somertonhotel.co.uk

Dir: off A74

PETS: Bedrooms (unattended) Exercise area (on site)

This friendly, family-run Victorian mansion has been sympathetically preserved and features beautiful woodwork, particularly in the dining room. Two attractive conservatories add a new dimension and are popular for bar meals and functions. The bedrooms are particularly stylish and well equipped.
ROOMS: 7 en suite 4 annexe en suite (1 fmly) No smoking in 7 bedrooms s £46; d £60-£75 (incl. bkfst) LB **FACILITIES:** Xmas
PARKING: 100 **NOTES:** No smoking in restaurant
CARDS: 🃏 🏧 💳 🅿 ⑤

★★ 65% **Ravenshill House**

12 Dumfries Rd DG11 2EF

☎ 01576 202882 ◻ 01576 202882

e-mail: aaenquiries@ravenshillhotellockerbie.co.uk

Dir: from A74(M) Lockerbie junct take A709, W of town centre. Hotel is 0.5m on right

PETS: Bedrooms (by prior arrangement) Exercise area (nature reserve nearby)

This friendly, family-run hotel is located close to the town and is set in its own tidy gardens. The bright bedrooms are very well-equipped and comfortable. Ravenshill House boasts cheerful service and features good value, home-cooked meals.
ROOMS: 8 rms (7 en suite) (2 fmly) No smoking in 5 bedrooms
s £40-£60; d £60-£70 (incl. bkfst) LB **PARKING:** 35
NOTES: No smoking in restaurant **CARDS:** 🃏 🏧 💳 🅿 ⑤

MOFFAT   Map 11 NT00

★★ 78% ❀ **Beechwood Country House**

Harthope Place DG10 9HX

☎ 01683 220210 ◻ 01683 220889

e-mail: enquiries@beechwoodcountryhousehotel.co.uk

Dir: at north end of town turn right at St Marys Church into Harthope Place and follow sign to hotel

PETS: Bedrooms Public areas (not dining room, dogs on leads) Exercise area (adjacent) Pet Food RESIDENT PETS: Olga & Anna (cats), Millie (dog)

This delightful hotel stands in landscaped gardens just a short walk from the town centre. Individually styled bedrooms are complemented by a choice of welcoming lounges, one of which has a small bar. Ever-present owners ensure prompt service in a relaxed environment.
ROOMS: 7 en suite (1 fmly) No smoking in all bedrooms s £50-£62;
d £79-£96 (incl. bkfst) LB **FACILITIES:** Croquet lawn Childrens' swings
PARKING: 15 **NOTES:** No smoking in restaurant Closed Jan-mid Feb
CARDS: 🃏 💳 🏧 ⑤

◆◆◆◆ **Hartfell House**

Hartfell Crescent DG10 9AL

☎ 01683 220153 ◻ 01683 220153

e-mail: enquiries@hartfellhouse.co.uk

Dir: off High St at War Memorial, follow Well St and Old Well Rd, Hartfell Crescent on right

PETS: Bedrooms Public areas (except dining room) Exercise area (100yds)

Built in 1850, this impressive Victorian house lies in a peaceful terrace high above the town, enjoying lovely views of the surrounding countryside. Beautifully maintained, it boasts bedrooms that offer high quality and comfort. There is an inviting first floor lounge and attractive dining room, where delicious breakfasts and evening meals are served.
FACILITIES: 8 rms (7 en suite) (2 fmly) (1 GF) No smoking TVB
tea/coffee Licensed Cen ht No coaches Gymnasium Last d 24hrs notice
PRICES: s £26; d £50✳ LB **PARKING:** 6 **CARDS:** 🃏 🏧 ⑤

◆◆◆◆ **Limetree House**

Eastgate DG10 9AE

☎ 01683 220001 ◻ 01683 221947

e-mail: limetree-house@btconnect.com

Dir: M74 junct 15, take B7076. In Moffat into Well Street, at top turn left into Eastgate, Limetree House 100yds

PETS: Bedrooms Public areas Exercise area (100yds)
RESIDENT PETS: Mike & Sully - cats

A warm welcome is assured at this well maintained guest house, quietly situated behind the main high street. Recognisable by its colourful flower baskets in season, it provides an inviting lounge and bright cheerful breakfast room. Bedrooms are smartly furnished in pine and include a large family room.
FACILITIES: 6 en suite (1 fmly) (1 GF) No smoking TVB tea/coffee
Cen ht No children 5yrs No coaches Dinner Last d 5pm
PRICES: s £27.50-£30; d £45-£60✳ LB **PARKING:** 7
CARDS: 🃏 🏧 💳 ⑤

◆◆◆ **Barnhill Springs Country**

DG10 9QS

☎ 01683 220580

Dir: leave A74(M) junct 15, Barnhill Rd 1st on right, 50mtrs from rdbt on A701 towards Moffat

PETS: Bedrooms (unattended) Public areas (except dining room) Exercise area (on site) RESIDENT PETS: Kim (Collie cross)

This former farmhouse enjoys a quiet rural location south of the town within easy reach of the M74. Bedrooms are well proportioned and although none have en suite bathrooms, one room on the ground floor has the use of its own private shower room. There is a comfortable lounge and separate dining room.
FACILITIES: 5 rms (1 en suite) (1 fmly) (1 GF) No smoking in dining room tea/coffee Cen ht TVL No coaches Dinner Last d 9am
PRICES: s £24-£26; d £48-£52✳ **PARKING:** 10

Scotland

PORTPATRICK Map 10 NW95

★★★ Knockinaam Lodge
DG9 9AD
☎ 01776 810471 📠 01776 810435
e-mail: reservations@knockinaamlodge.com
Dir: from A77 or A75 follow signs to Portpatrick through Lochans. After 2m turn left at signs for Knockinaam Lodge and watch for hotel signs

PETS: Bedrooms (unattended) £10 Exercise area (In grounds) Pet Food RESIDENT PETS: Jack and Lucy - Black Labradors

This relaxing hotel has a stunning cliff top location with views over the sea to Ireland. A warm welcome is assured from the proprietors and their committed team. Bedrooms are equipped with many extra touches, most are spacious and all have great bathrooms. Dinner in the restaurant makes use of the best quality produce and breakfasts are memorable.
ROOMS: 9 en suite No smoking in 2 bedrooms s £125-£145; d £210-£270 (incl. bkfst & dinner) LB **FACILITIES:** Fishing Croquet lawn Shooting, Walking, Sea fishing ch fac Xmas **PARKING:** 20
NOTES: No smoking in restaurant **CARDS:** 🟦🟥🟨🟩

★★★ 74% ⊛ Fernhill
Heugh Rd DG9 8TD
☎ 01776 810220 📠 01776 810596
e-mail: info@fernhillhotel.co.uk
Dir: from Stranraer A77 to Portpatrick, 100yds past Portpatrick village sign, turn right before war memorial. Hotel is 1st on left

PETS: Bedrooms

Set high above the village, this hotel looks out over the harbour and Irish Sea. A smart conservatory restaurant and some of the bedrooms take advantage of the views. A modern wing offers particularly spacious and well-appointed rooms - some have balconies.
ROOMS: 27 en suite 9 annexe en suite (3 fmly) (8 GF) No smoking in 10 bedrooms s £50-£87; d £100-£124 (incl. bkfst) LB **FACILITIES:** STV Leisure facilities available at sister hotel in Stranraer ch fac Xmas **PARKING:** 45 **NOTES:** No smoking in restaurant Closed mid-Jan - mid-Feb **CARDS:** 🟦🟥🟨🟩

SANQUHAR Map 11 NS70

★★ 66% Blackaddie House
Blackaddie Rd DG4 6JJ
☎ 01659 50270 📠 01659 50900
e-mail: enquiries@blackaddiehotel.co.uk
Dir: off A76 just N of Sanquhar at Burnside Service Station. Private road to hotel 300mtrs on right

PETS: Bedrooms (unattended) Exercise area (adjacent) Pet Food Good walking facilities by hotel RESIDENT PETS: Sam (Golden Retriever), Lisa (German Shepherd), Pandora and Tiger (cats)

This charming house, a former rectory, is quietly situated on the edge of the village beside the river. As well as an inviting lounge, public areas include a cosy bar, adorned with angling

continued

memorabilia, and a conservatory restaurant giving a very fine view over the neat garden to the River Nith.
ROOMS: 9 en suite (2 fmly) s £40; d £70 (incl. bkfst)
FACILITIES: Riding **PARKING:** 25 **NOTES:** No smoking in restaurant **CARDS:** 🟦🟥🟩

STRANRAER Map 10 NX06

★★★ 69% ⊛ 🚣 Corsewall Lighthouse Hotel
Corsewall Point, Kirkcolm DG9 0QG
☎ 01776 853220 📠 01776 854231
e-mail: lighthousehotel@btinternet.com
Dir: A718 from Stranraer to Kirkcolm (approx 8m) then follow signs to hotel for a further 4m

PETS: Bedrooms (annexe only) (unattended) £5 small dog, £10 large dog Public areas (except restaurant) Exercise area (adjacent) Pet Food

Looking for something completely different? A unique hotel converted from buildings that adjoin a listed 19th-century lighthouse set on a rocky coastline. Bedrooms come in a variety of sizes, some reached by a spiral staircase, and as with the public areas, are cosy and atmospheric. Three cottage suites in the grounds offer greater space.
ROOMS: 6 en suite 3 annexe en suite (2 fmly) (5 GF) No smoking in 6 bedrooms s £110-£260; d £130-£280 (incl. bkfst & dinner) LB
PARKING: 20 **NOTES:** No smoking in restaurant
CARDS: 🟦🟥🟨🟩

DUNDEE CITY

DUNDEE Map 11 NO43

★★★ 67% ⊛ Sandford Country House Hotel
Newton Hill, Wormit DD6 8RG
☎ 01382 541802 📠 01382 542136
e-mail: sandford.hotel@btinternet.com
Dir: off A92 at junct B946, hotel entrance 100yds from junct on left

PETS: Bedrooms Public areas (lounge only) Exercise area (on site) Pet Food RESIDENT PETS: Anthony and Cleopatra, two black Siamese cats

Built around the turn of the last century, this hotel lies in wooded grounds well off the main road. Set around a small terraced courtyard, it is a popular venue for meals, which are served in the bar or restaurant. Bedrooms come in a variety of sizes and have been refurbished in a smart modern style.
ROOMS: 16 en suite (2 fmly) No smoking in 15 bedrooms s £70-£90; d £110-£130 (incl. bkfst) LB **FACILITIES:** STV Adj to sports club, Cycle hire Xmas **PARKING:** 30 **NOTES:** No smoking in restaurant **CARDS:** 🟦🟥🟨🟩

Don't forget to let proprietors know when you book that you're bringing your pet

★★ 73% The Shaftesbury

Hyndford St DD2 1HQ
☎ 01382 669216 ▯ 01382 641598
e-mail: reservations@shaftesbury-hotel.co.uk
Dir: from Perth signed to Airport, take 1st left at circle, turn right, follow Perth Rd, turn right

THE CIRCLE
Selected Individual Hotels
GREAT BRITAIN

PETS: Bedrooms (unattended) Public areas Exercise area

A comfortable, welcoming hotel situated in the west end where the owners and their staff are friendly and willing to please. Spotlessly maintained, this impressive Victorian house has been sympathetically converted, offering inviting public areas including a cosy lounge, bar and restaurant. Bedrooms are individually decorated.

ROOMS: 12 en suite (2 fmly) s £49.50-£52; d £56-£96 (incl. bkfst & dinner) **LB NOTES:** No smoking in restaurant RS Sun-Mon
CARDS: 🟦🟦🟦🟦🟦🟦

EAST AYRSHIRE

DALRYMPLE   Map 10 NS31

◆◆◆ ⚓ Kirkton Inn Hotel

Main St KA6 6DF
☎ 01292 560241 ▯ 01292 560835
e-mail: kirkton@cqm.co.uk
Dir: between A77 and A713 approx 5m from Ayr, signed from both roads. In centre of village large black and white building with red roof

PETS: Bedrooms Public areas (only in public bar) Exercise area (30 metres)

Dating from the 1800s this friendly and historic village inn has a reputation for serving enjoyable meals, and is popular with both the locals and visitors alike. There is a separate bar, known as the Malt Room, which boasts an impressive selection of malt whiskies. Accommodation comprises three comfortable bedrooms, and self-catering units are also available. The inn is well situated for exploring Burn's country and nearby Ayr.

FACILITIES: 3 en suite No smoking in dining room TVB tea/coffee Cen ht Pool Table Dinner Last d 8.45pm **PARKING:** 40
CARDS: 🟦🟦🟦🟦

EAST LOTHIAN

GULLANE   Map 12 NT48

★★★ ◉◉ ♨ Greywalls

Muirfield EH31 2EG
☎ 01620 842144 ▯ 01620 842241
e-mail: hotel@greywalls.co.uk
Dir: A198, hotel signposted at E end of village

PETS: Bedrooms (unattended) Exercise area (on site) Pet Food

A dignified but relaxing Edwardian country house designed by Sir Edwin Lutyens; Greywalls overlooks the famous Muirfield Golf Course and is ideally placed just a half hours' drive from Edinburgh. Delightful public rooms look onto beautiful gardens

continued

and freshly prepared cuisine may be enjoyed in the restaurant. Bedrooms, whether cosy singles or spacious master rooms, are mostly furnished in period style and many command views of the course. A gatehouse lodge is ideal for golfing parties.
ROOMS: 17 en suite 5 annexe en suite (5 GF) s £130-£245; d £220-£260 (incl. bkfst) **LB FACILITIES:** STV Tennis (hard & grass) Croquet lawn Putting green Extensive gardens **PARKING:** 40
NOTES: No smoking in restaurant Closed Nov-Mar
CARDS: 🟦🟦🟦🟦🟦🟦

FALKIRK

CASTLECARY   Map 11 NS77

★★ 66% Castlecary House

Castlecary Rd G68 0HD
☎ 01324 840233 ▯ 01324 841608
e-mail: enquiries@castlecaryhotel.com
Dir: off A80 onto B816 between Glasgow and Stirling

PETS: Bedrooms (unattended) Exercise area (100yds)

Close to the Forth Clyde Canal and convenient for the M80, this popular hotel provides a versatile range of accommodation, within purpose-built units in the grounds and also in an extension to the original house. The attractive and spacious restaurant serves a short carte menu and enjoyable meals are served in the busy bars.
ROOMS: 60 rms (55 en suite) (2 fmly) s £60-£75; d £60-£75 (incl. bkfst) **SERVICES:** Lift **PARKING:** 100
CARDS: 🟦🟦🟦🟦🟦

FIFE

ABERDOUR   Map 11 NT18

★★ 65% The Aberdour Hotel

38 High St KY3 0SW
☎ 01383 860325 ▯ 01383 860808
e-mail: reception@aberdourhotel.co.uk
Dir: M90 junct 1, E on A921 for 5m. Hotel in centre of village opp post office

THE CIRCLE
Selected Individual Hotels
GREAT BRITAIN

PETS: Bedrooms (unattended) £10 Public areas (except restaurant) Exercise area (200 yards)

This small hotel has a relaxed and welcoming atmosphere. Real ales are featured in the cosy bar where good value, home-cooked meals are available, as they are in the beamed dining room. Though all are well equipped, bedrooms vary in size and style, and those in the stable block are particularly comfortable. The hotel is in easy reach of Edinburgh by train.
ROOMS: 12 en suite 4 annexe en suite (4 fmly) (2 GF) s £40-£48; d £50-£65 (incl. bkfst) **LB FACILITIES:** STV **PARKING:** 8
NOTES: No smoking in restaurant
CARDS: 🟦🟦🟦🟦🟦🟦

♨ **Places with this symbol are country house hotels**

Scotland

ANSTRUTHER Map 12 NO50

🐕 🐈

♦♦♦♦ 🏆 The Spindrift

Pittenweem Rd KY10 3DT
☎ 01333 310573 📠 01333 310573
e-mail: info@thespindrift.co.uk
Dir: from W 1st building on left on entering town.

PETS: Bedrooms (unattended) Exercise area (2 mins) blankets & beds

This immaculately maintained Victorian villa is located at the western edge of the village. The attractive bedrooms offer a wide range of extra touches. The Captain's Room, a replica of a wood-panelled cabin, is a particular feature. The inviting lounge boasts an honesty bar, whilst imaginative breakfasts and enjoyable home-cooked meals are served in the cheerful dining room, by prior arrangement.
FACILITIES: 8 rms (7 en suite) (2 fmly) No smoking TVB tea/coffee Direct dial from bedrooms Licensed Cen ht TVL No children 10yrs No coaches Dinner Last d noon **PRICES:** s £30-£40; d £53-£62✻ **LB**
PARKING: 12 **NOTES:** Closed 24-26 Dec **CARDS:** 💳 💳 💳 💳

BURNTISLAND Map 11 NT28

🐕 🐈 🐇 🐦

★★★ 63% Kingswood

Kinghorn Rd KY3 9LL
☎ 01592 872329 📠 01592 873123
e-mail: rankin@kingswoodhotel.co.uk
Dir: A921 coastal road at Burntisland, right at rdbt, left at T-junct, at bottom of hill to Kingshorn road, hotel 0.5m on left

PETS: Bedrooms Exercise area (0.5 mile)

Lying in sheltered grounds east of the town, this hotel has views across the Firth of Forth to Edinburgh. Bedrooms are housed in a modern extension on the first floor. Public areas include a recently completed function suite, lounge bar and extended restaurant where good-value meals are served.
ROOMS: 13 en suite (3 fmly) (1 GF) No smoking in 2 bedrooms s £47-£66; d £76-£105 (incl. bkfst) **LB FACILITIES:** ch fac
PARKING: 50 **NOTES:** Closed 26 Dec & 1 Jan
CARDS: 💳 💳 💳 💳 💳 💳

DUNFERMLINE Map 11 NT0

🐕 🐈 🐇 🐦

★★★ 70% Pitbauchlie House

Aberdour Rd KY11 4PB
☎ 01383 722282 📠 01383 620738
e-mail: info@pitbauchlie.com
Dir: M90 junct 2, onto A823, then B916. Hotel 0.5m on right

PETS: Bedrooms (unattended)

This family hotel is set in landscaped gardens a mile south of the town centre. A stylish foyer and cocktail lounge catch the eye; the latter overlooking the garden, as does the restaurant and separate bar/bistro. The modern bedrooms are well equipped, the deluxe rooms having CD players and videos.
ROOMS: 50 en suite (2 fmly) (19 GF) No smoking in 19 bedrooms s £85-£95; d £103-£113 (incl. bkfst) **LB FACILITIES:** STV Gym
PARKING: 80 **NOTES:** No smoking in restaurant
CARDS: 💳 💳 💳 💳 💳 💳 💳

GLENROTHES Map 11 NO2

🐕

★★ 77% ✿ Rescobie House Hotel & Restaurant

6 Valley Dr, Leslie KY6 3BQ
☎ 01592 749555 📠 01592 620231
e-mail: rescobiehotel@compuserve.com
Dir: off A92 at Glenrothes onto A911, through Leslie. End of High St follow straight ahead. Take 1st left, hotel entrance 2nd left

PETS: Bedrooms

Hospitality and guest care are second to none at this relaxing country house, which lies secluded in gardens on the fringe of Leslie. Period architecture is enhanced by a combination of contemporary and Art Deco styling, a theme carried through to the bright airy bedrooms. There is an inviting lounge and an intimate restaurant serving memorable meals.
ROOMS: 10 en suite s £49-£68; d £72-£98 (incl. bkfst) **PARKING:** 12
NOTES: No smoking in restaurant **CARDS:** 💳 💳 💳 💳 💳 💳

LADYBANK Map 11 NO3

🐕 🐈 🐇 🐦

★★★ 61% Fernie Castle

Letham KY15 7RU
☎ 01337 810381 📠 01337 810422
e-mail: mail@ferniecastle.demon.co.uk
Dir: M90 junct 8 take A91E (Tay Bridge/St Andrews) to Melville Lodges rdbt. Left onto A92 signed Tay Bridge. Hotel 1.2m on right

PETS: Bedrooms Public areas (must be on leads) Exercise area (200 yards) Pet Food RESIDENT PETS: Tigger (Great Dane), Apollo (Dalmatian), cows, chickens

This turreted castle is set amid 17 acres of wooded grounds in the heart of Fife. Bedrooms range from King and Queen rooms, to the more standard-sized Squire and Lady rooms. The elegant Auld Alliance Restaurant presents a formal setting, whilst guests can

continued

also dine in the keep bar with its impressive vaulted stone walls and ceiling.

ROOMS: 20 en suite (2 fmly) No smoking in 15 bedrooms s £70-£99; d £70-£99 (incl. bkfst & dinner) **LB** **FACILITIES:** Croquet lawn ch fac Xmas **PARKING:** 80 **NOTES:** No smoking in restaurant **CARDS:**

LUNDIN LINKS   Map 12 NO40

★★★ 78% @@ **Old Manor**
Leven Rd KY8 6AJ
☎ 01333 320368 🖷 01333 320911
e-mail: enquiries@oldmanorhotel.co.uk
Dir: 1m E of Leven on A915 Kirkaldy-St Andrews Rd for hotel on right

PETS: Bedrooms Exercise area (grounds & beach 400 yards)

This long-established hotel lies on the edge of the village and overlooks the golf course to the Firth of Forth. Enthusiastically run, high standards are maintained throughout. Bedrooms come in a variety of styles and there is a choice of restaurants - the new conservatory Terrace Brasserie and Grill with outstanding views or the more informal Coachman's Bistro within the well-tended grounds.
ROOMS: 24 en suite (2 fmly) (8 GF) No smoking in 4 bedrooms s £75-£100; d £67.50-£135 (incl. bkfst) **LB** **FACILITIES:** Complimentary membership of Lundin Sports Club ch fac Xmas **PARKING:** 100 **NOTES:** No smoking in restaurant **CARDS:**

PEAT INN   Map 12 NO40

★★ @@@ **Peat Inn**
KY15 5LH
☎ 01334 840206 🖷 01334 840530
e-mail: reception@thepeatinn.co.uk
Dir: 6m SW of St Andrews at junct B940/B941

PETS: Bedrooms (unattended) Exercise area (50 yards) Pet Food

This 300-year-old former coaching inn enjoys a rural location yet is close to St Andrews. Accommodation, luxuriously appointed, is provided in an adjacent building and comprises split-level suites with a comfortable lounge upstairs. Food is a highlight of any visit
continued

---

with high quality, local produce utilised by David Wilson and his talented kitchen team.

ROOMS: 8 en suite (2 fmly) s £80-£95; d £165-£175 (incl. bkfst) **LB** **PARKING:** 24 **NOTES:** No smoking in restaurant Closed Sun, Mon, 25 Dec & 1 Jan **CARDS:**

ST ANDREWS   Map 12 NO51

★★★★★ @@
The Old Course Hotel, Golf Resort & Spa
KY16 9SP
☎ 01334 474371 🖷 01334 477668
e-mail: reservations@oldcoursehotel.co.uk
Dir: close to A91 on outskirts of the city

PETS: Bedrooms (unattended) £10 per animal Exercise area (adjacent) Pet Food

A haven for golfers, this internationally renowned hotel sits adjacent to the 17th hole of the championship course. Bedrooms vary in size and range from the traditional to the contemporary and stylish fairway rooms, complete with course facing balconies. Day rooms include intimate lounges, a bright conservatory, a well-equipped spa and a range of golf shops. The fine dining 'Grill', the seafood bar 'Sands' or the informal Jigger Inn pub prove popular eating venues.
ROOMS: 134 en suite (6 fmly) No smoking in 118 bedrooms s £230-£580; d £295-£595 (incl. bkfst) **LB** **FACILITIES:** Spa STV Indoor swimming (H) Golf 18 Sauna Solarium Gym Putting green Jacuzzi Health spa Steam room ch fac Xmas **SERVICES:** Lift **PARKING:** 150 **NOTES:** No smoking in restaurant Closed 24-28 Dec **CARDS:**

Scotland

ST ANDREWS continued

★★★★ 74% ◉◉ Rusacks
Pilmour Links KY16 9JQ
☎ 0870 400 8128 ▤ 01334 477896
e-mail: rusacks@macdonald-hotels.co.uk
Dir: from W on A91 past golf course, through an old viaduct, hotel 200mtrs on left before rdbt

MACDONALD HOTELS

PETS: Bedrooms (unattended) £10 Exercise area

This long-established hotel enjoys an almost unrivalled location with superb views across the famous golf course. Bedrooms are generally spacious and all are comfortably appointed and well equipped. Public rooms include a smart restaurant - the perfect place to watch golfers - plus a choice of bars and roomy lounges.
ROOMS: 68 en suite **FACILITIES:** STV Sauna Golf Mgr to organise golf **SERVICES:** Lift **PARKING:** 21 **NOTES:** No smoking in restaurant **CARDS:** ▨▨▨▨▨▨

★★★ ◉◉ St Andrews Golf
40 The Scores KY16 9AS
☎ 01334 472611 ▤ 01334 472188
e-mail: reception@standrews-golf.co.uk
Dir: follow signs 'Golf Course' into Golf Place and in 200yds turn right into The Scores

PETS: Bedrooms £10 per stay Exercise area (100yds)

A genuinely warm approach to guest care is found at this delightful, family-run hotel. In a stunning location the views of the beach, golf links and coastline can be enjoyed from the inviting day rooms. There is a choice of bars and an informal atmosphere in Ma Bell's. Bedrooms come in two distinct styles with those on the higher floors offering stylish, modern design and comfort.
ROOMS: 21 en suite (9 fmly) s £115-£170; d £170-£215 (incl. bkfst) **LB**
FACILITIES: STV ch fac Xmas **SERVICES:** Lift **PARKING:** 6
NOTES: No smoking in restaurant
CARDS: ▨▨▨▨▨

★★ 74% ◉◉ The Inn at Lathones THE INDEPENDENTS
Largoward KY9 1JE
☎ 01334 840494 ▤ 01334 840694
e-mail: lathones@theinn.co.uk
Dir: 5m S of St Andrews on A915, 0.5m before village of Largoward on left just after hidden dip

PETS: Bedrooms (unattended) £10 per stay Exercise area (2 miles)

A lovely country inn, full of character and individuality, parts of which date back 400 years. The friendly staff help to create a relaxed atmosphere. Smart contemporary bedrooms are in two separate wings, both accessed from outside. The colourful, cosy restaurant is the main focus, the menu adding a modern style to Scottish and European dishes.
ROOMS: 13 annexe en suite (2 fmly) (11 GF) s £100-£130; d £140-£200 (incl. bkfst) **LB FACILITIES:** STV ch fac **PARKING:** 35
NOTES: No smoking in restaurant Closed 25-26 Dec & 3-23 Jan RS 24 Dec **CARDS:** ▨▨▨▨▨

Ⓤ St Andrews Bay Golf Resort & Spa
KY16 8PN
☎ 01334 837000 ▤ 01334 471115
e-mail: info@standrewsbay.com

PETS: Bedrooms (unattended) £20 Public areas (on leash and not in dining areas) Exercise area (adjacent) Pet bowls provided but no food

At the time of going to press, the star classification for this hotel was not confirmed. Please refer to the AA internet site www.theAA.com for current information.
ROOMS: 209 en suite 8 annexe en suite (86 fmly) (57 GF) No smoking in 195 bedrooms s £120-£270; d £120-£270 (incl. bkfst & dinner) **LB**
FACILITIES: Spa STV Indoor swimming (H) Golf 36 Sauna Gym Putting green Jacuzzi Clay pigeon shooting etc can be organised Xmas
SERVICES: Lift air con **NOTES:** No smoking in restaurant
CARDS: ▨▨▨▨▨

HIGHLAND

BALLACHULISH
Map 14 NN05

★★★ 71% Ballachulish Hotel
PH49 4JY
☎ 0871 222 3415 ▤ 0871 222 3416
e-mail: reservations@freedomglen.co.uk
Dir: on A828, Fort William-Oban road, 3m N of Glencoe

PETS: Bedrooms (unattended) £10 Public areas Exercise area (200 yards) Pet Food

A relaxed atmosphere prevails at this long-established hotel, which boasts stunning views over Loch Linnhe. Bedrooms vary in size and in style and all are comfortably appointed with many rooms providing super lochside views. Inviting public areas include a spacious and comfortable lounge, the informal Ferry Bar and a cocktail bar adjacent to the bold and attractive restaurant.
ROOMS: 54 en suite (4 fmly) s £52.50-£150; d £110-£280 (incl. bkfst & dinner) **LB FACILITIES:** Complimentary Membership of Leisure Club at nearby sister hotel entertainment ch fac Xmas **PARKING:** 50
NOTES: No smoking in restaurant Closed 9-23 Dec & 5-27 Jan
CARDS: ▨▨▨▨

◆◆◆◆ Lyn-Leven
West Laroch PH49 4JP
☎ 01855 811392 ▤ 01855 811600
Dir: off A82 signed on left West Lorroch

PETS: Bedrooms Exercise area

Genuine Highland hospitality and high standards are part of the appeal of this comfortable guest house. The attractive bedrooms vary in size, are well equipped, offering many thoughtful extra touches. There is a spacious lounge and a smart dining room where delicious home-cooked evening meals and breakfasts are served at individual tables.
FACILITIES: 8 en suite 4 annexe en suite (1 fmly) (12 GF) No smoking in 1 bedroom TVB tea/coffee Licensed Cen ht TVL Dinner Last d 7pm
PRICES: s £24-£30; d £48-£54✱ **LB PARKING:** 12
NOTES: Closed Xmas **CARDS:** ▨▨▨▨

BOAT OF GARTEN

Map 14 NH91

★★★ 72% ◉◉ Boat

THE CIRCLE
Selected Individual Hotels
GREAT BRITAIN

PH24 3BH
☎ 01479 831258 📠 01479 831414
e-mail: info@boathotel.co.uk
Dir: off A9 N of Aviemore onto A95, follow signs to Boat of Garten

PETS: Bedrooms (unattended) £5 Exercise area (in grounds) Pet Food

In the heart of the Spey valley, this Victorian station hotel is adjacent to the Strathspey Steam Railway. Bedrooms, all individually decorated, have been tastefully upgraded and comfortably appointed. The Capercaillie Restaurant offers classic cuisine with a Scottish twist, whilst the warm cocktail bar has a selection of meals and specialises in a wide range of malt whisky.
ROOMS: 28 en suite (2 fmly) No smoking in 22 bedrooms
s £69.50-£155; d £109-£155 (incl. bkfst) **LB FACILITIES:** Snooker Golf course adjacent Xmas **PARKING:** 36 **NOTES:** No smoking in restaurant RS 3 wks Jan **CARDS:**

CARRBRIDGE

Map 14 NH92

★★★ 68% Dalrachney Lodge
PH23 3AT
☎ 01479 841252 📠 01479 841383
e-mail: dalrachney@aol.com
Dir: follow Carrbridge signs off A9. At the N end of the village on A938

PETS: Bedrooms £5 Exercise area (on site) Pet Food

A traditional Highland lodge, Dalrachney lies in grounds by the River Dulnain on the edge of the village. Spotlessly maintained public areas include a comfortable and relaxing sitting room and a cosy well-stocked bar, which has a popular menu providing an alternative to the dining room. Bedrooms are generally spacious and furnished in period style.
ROOMS: 11 en suite (3 fmly) No smoking in 7 bedrooms s £50-£75;
d £90-£150 (incl. bkfst) **LB FACILITIES:** STV Fishing Xmas
PARKING: 40 **NOTES:** No smoking in restaurant
CARDS:

◆◆◆ Pines Country House
Duthil PH23 3ND
☎ 01479 841220 📠 01479 841220 *51
e-mail: Lynn@thepines-duthil.fsnet.co.uk
Dir: A9 to Carrbridge, turn onto A938 Grantown-on-Spey road, 2m to Duthil. 5th house on left

PETS: Bedrooms (unattended) Exercise area (on site)
RESIDENT PETS: Corrie (English Springer Spaniel)

A warm and friendly welcome is assured at this comfortable home which enjoys a delightful rural setting. The bright bedrooms are comfortable, traditionally furnished and offer the expected amenities. Enjoyable home cooked fare is served around a communal table. There is a bright conservatory lounge where guests can watch squirrels feed in the nearby wood.
FACILITIES: 4 en suite (1 fmly) (1 GF) No smoking STV TVB tea/coffee Cen ht No coaches Dinner Last d 4pm **PRICES:** s £30; d £45✳ **LB**
PARKING: 5 **CARDS:**

CONTIN

Map 14 NH45

★★★ 71% ♨ Coul House

SCOTLAND'S HOTELS OF DISTINCTION

IV14 9ES
☎ 01997 421487 📠 01997 421945
e-mail: coulhouse@bestloved.com
Dir: Turn off A9 north onto A835 Ullapool road. Hotel drive on right in Contin just past filling station

PETS: Bedrooms (unattended) Public areas (reception area only) Exercise area (in grounds)

This imposing mansion house is set back from the road in extensive grounds. A number of the generally spacious bedrooms have superb views of the distant mountains and all are thoughtfully equipped. There is a choice of dining options available, with international cuisine served in both the elegant dining room and the less formal bistro.
ROOMS: 20 en suite (3 fmly) (4 GF) No smoking in 7 bedrooms
s £55-£75; d £78-£163 (incl. bkfst) **LB FACILITIES:** STV Putting green 9 hole pitch & putt Xmas **PARKING:** 36 **NOTES:** No smoking in restaurant **CARDS:**

DRUMNADROCHIT

Map 14 NH53

★★★ 68% ♨ Polmaily House Hotel
IV63 6XT
☎ 01456 450343 📠 01456 450813
e-mail: polmaily@btinternet.com
Dir: in Drumnadrochit, next to the Monster exhibition, turn onto A831(signed Cannich), hotel 2m on right. 1.5m from Loch Ness

PETS: Bedrooms (unattended) £5-10 Exercise area (on site) Pet Food **RESIDENT PETS:** Puddles (Cavalier King Charles), Oscar (Golden Retriever), Spider, Max & Dennis (cats)

Run by a family, this relaxing country house is geared for children, with a pets corner and well-stocked play areas. The 18 acres of lawns and woods also include good leisure facilities, such as a swimming pool, horse riding and tennis. Good home-cooked dinners are also on offer.
ROOMS: 10 en suite (6 fmly) (1 GF) No smoking in all bedrooms
s £40-£72; d £80-£144 (incl. bkfst) **LB FACILITIES:** Indoor swimming (H) Tennis (hard) Fishing Riding Solarium Croquet lawn Indoor/outdoor childs play area, Boating, Pony rides, Beauty massage, bicycles ch fac Xmas **PARKING:** 20 **NOTES:** No smoking in restaurant
CARDS:

◆◆◆◆ Clunebeg Lodge
Clunebeg Estate IV63 6US
☎ 01456 450387 📠 01456 450152
e-mail: info@clunebeg.com
Dir: On A82 S of Drumnadrochit, take turn off signed to Bunloit. After 100yds take next right up a private track to Clunebeg Estate.

PETS: Bedrooms Public areas (not at meal times) Exercise area (27 acres of grounds)

A warm welcome awaits at this establishment sitting in the unspoilt beauty of Glen Urquhart, ideal for walkers and cyclists as the Great Glen Way is on the doorstep. The ground-floor bedrooms are attractive and very well equipped. There is a spacious combined dining room/lounge with Internet access,

continued on p282

Scotland

Scotland

DRUMNADROCHIT continued

wide-screen TV, DVD, and video. A luxury flat situated in the main house has recently been completed and is beautifully furnished and equipped. A full breakfast, snacks, packed lunches, and by prior arrangement, evening meals are served. Two patio areas are available for guests' use.

FACILITIES: 6 en suite (6 GF) No smoking in bedrooms TVB tea/coffee Licensed Cen ht TVL No coaches Fishing Dinner Last d 7.30pm **PRICES:** s £37.50-£45; d £50-£60✱ **LB PARKING:** 6 **CARDS:** 🔲🔲🔲🔲🔲🔲

FORT WILLIAM
Map 14 NN17

★★★ 75% ◉ Moorings
Banavie PH33 7LY
☎ 01397 772797 ▤ 01397 772441
e-mail: reservations@moorings-fortwilliam.co.uk
Dir: 3m N, off A830. Take A830 for 1m, cross Caledonian Canal, 1st right

PETS: Bedrooms (unattended) £5 (not during busy service) Exercise area (100 yards)

Located on the Caledonian Canal next to a series of locks known as Neptune's Staircase, and close to Thomas Telford's house, this hotel offers friendly service from a dedicated, young team. Accommodation comes in two distinct styles with the newer rooms particularly appealing. Meals can be taken in a choice of bars and the spacious dining room.

ROOMS: 28 en suite (1 fmly) (1 GF) No smoking in 9 bedrooms s £62-£66; d £82-£110 (incl. bkfst) **LB FACILITIES:** STV Xmas **PARKING:** 60 **NOTES:** No smoking in restaurant **CARDS:** 🔲🔲🔲🔲🔲🔲

◆◆◆◆ 🍴 Distillery House
Nevis Bridge, North Rd PH33 6LR
☎ 01397 700103 ▤ 01397 702980
e-mail: disthouse@aol.com
Dir: from S, A82 through Fort William towards Inverness. On left after Glen Nevis rdbt (3rd coming through Fort William). From N, A82 towards Fort William, right at sign after 2nd lights

PETS: Bedrooms Exercise area **RESIDENT PETS:** Corrie (dog)

Situated in the grounds of the former Glenlochy Distillery, this friendly guesthouse was once the distillery manager's home. Bedrooms are attractively decorated, comfortably furnished and very well equipped. There is a relaxing lounge, which features a superb range of games, and a bright airy dining room where traditional Scottish breakfasts are served at individual tables.
FACILITIES: 8 en suite (1 fmly) (1 GF) No smoking TVB tea/coffee Cen ht No coaches Fishing **LB PARKING:** 20 **CARDS:** 🔲🔲🔲🔲🔲🔲

> **Don't forget to let proprietors know when you book that you're bringing your pet**

◆◆◆◆ Seangan Croft
Seangan Bridge, Banavie PH33 7PB
☎ 01397 773114 & 01397 772228
e-mail: seangan-chalets@fortwilliam59.freeserve.co.uk
Dir: take A82 2m N of Fort William at traffic lights and turn left onto A830. After 1m turn right onto B8004 (Gairlochy), House 2m further than Moorings Hotel opposite An Crann Restaurant.

PETS: Exercise area (on site)

This modern bungalow situated on the north side of the Caledonian Canal offers stunning views of Ben Nevis and the ski slopes of Aonach Mor. The bedrooms are contemporary in style and guests have use of a spacious and comfortable lounge. Full breakfasts are served in the neat dining room and if dinner is required guests can eat at the An Crann (The Plough) restaurant across the road, also run by Sinè Ross.
FACILITIES: 3 en suite No smoking TVB tea/coffee Licensed Cen ht TVL ch fac No coaches Last d 9pm **PRICES:** s £25-£35; d £40-£46✱ **LB PARKING:** 6 **NOTES:** Closed Dec-Feb **CARDS:** 🔲🔲🔲🔲

GAIRLOCH
Map 14 NG87

★★ 69% Myrtle Bank
Low Rd IV21 2BS
☎ 01445 712004 ▤ 01445 712214
e-mail: myrtlebank@msn.com
Dir: turn onto A832 to Gairloch. Straight through village, at Mace store turn left at T junction. Hotel 2nd on Left

PETS: Bedrooms Public areas (not in restaurant or lounge bar) Exercise area (25 yards)

A seafront location and views to the Isle of Skye are key features at this friendly, family-run hotel. The spacious bedrooms are comfortably equipped. The public areas include a smart conservatory lounge, a well-stocked bar and the sea-facing restaurant, where guests can enjoy the breathtaking sunsets of Wester Ross.
ROOMS: 12 en suite (2 fmly) s £36-£44; d £72-£88 (incl. bkfst) **PARKING:** 20 **NOTES:** No smoking in restaurant **CARDS:** 🔲🔲🔲🔲🔲

◆◆◆◆ The Old Inn
Flowerdale Glen IV21 2BD
☎ 01445 712006 ▤ 01445 712445
e-mail: nomadscot@lineone.net
Dir: from Inverness take A9 N over Kessock Bridge, at Tore rdbt take A835 to Garve. N of Garve A835 to Achnasheen, continue on A832 at Achnasheen rdbt to Gairloch. Establishment on right side of A832, opposite Gairloch harbour

PETS: Telephone for details

Situated close to the harbour, this well established and lively inn has an idyllic location overlooking the burn and the old bridge. A good range of meals, featuring many seafood dishes, are served in the bars and dining areas, and at picnic tables outside on the finer

continued

days. Live music is also a feature several evenings a week. Bedrooms are well equipped and attractively decorated.

FACILITIES: 14 en suite (3 fmly) (2 GF) No smoking in bedrooms No smoking in dining room STV TVB tea/coffee Direct dial from bedrooms Cen ht No coaches Pool Table Dinner Last d 9.30pm **PRICES:** s £35-£47; d £50-£84✱ **LB PARKING:** 40 **CARDS:** 🖃 💳 ▨ 🔳 💳

GLENFINNAN   Map 14 NM98

★★ 75% ☻ **The Prince's House**
PH37 4LT
☎ 01397 722246 📠 01397 722323
e-mail: princeshouse@glenfinnan.co.uk
Dir: on A830, 0.5m on right past Glenfinnan Monument.

PETS: Bedrooms £5 per stay Public areas (except restaurant) Exercise area (100 metres) Pet food if pre-ordered

This delightful hotel enjoys a well-deserved reputation for fine food and excellent hospitality. The hotel sits close to the site where 'Bonnie' Prince Charlie raised the Jacobite standard, and enjoys inspiring views of mountains and forests. Comfortably appointed bedrooms offer pleasing décor and bathrooms and have now been upgraded. Local game and seafood can be enjoyed in either Flora's restaurant or the spacious bar.
ROOMS: 9 en suite (1 fmly) No smoking in all bedrooms s £42-£48; d £70-£80 (incl. bkfst) **LB FACILITIES:** Fishing Xmas **PARKING:** 18 **NOTES:** No smoking in restaurant Closed Christmas & Jan-early Feb **CARDS:** 🖃 💳 ▨ 🔳 💳

INVERNESS   Map 14 NH64

★★★ 74% ☻☻ 🍴 **Bunchrew House**
Bunchrew IV3 8TA
☎ 01463 234917 📠 01463 710620
e-mail: welcome@bunchrew-inverness.co.uk
Dir: W on A862. Hotel on right 2m after canal

PETS: Bedrooms £10 Exercise area (adjacent)

Overlooking the Beauly Firth this impressive mansion house dates from the 17th century and retains much original character. Individually styled bedrooms are spacious and tastefully furnished. A wood-panelled restaurant is the setting for artfully constructed cooking and there is a choice of comfortable lounges complete with real fires.
ROOMS: 14 en suite (3 fmly) s £90-£127.50; d £130-£155 (incl. bkfst) **LB FACILITIES:** Fishing **PARKING:** 40 **NOTES:** No smoking in restaurant Closed 24 Dec-27 Dec **CARDS:** 🖃 💳 ▨ 🔳 💳

★★★ 68% **Royal Highland**
Station Square, Academy St IV1 1LG
☎ 01463 231926 📠 01463 710705
e-mail: info@royalhighlandhotel.co.uk

PETS: Bedrooms

Built in 1858, this hotel has the typically grand foyer of the Victorian era with comfortable seating. Adjacent to this is the new ASH brasserie and bar, which offers a refreshing style for both eating and drinking throughout the day. The generally spacious bedrooms are comfortably equipped for the business traveller, with the railway station nearby.
ROOMS: 70 en suite (12 fmly) No smoking in 40 bedrooms s £39.95-£79.95; d £59.95-£119.95 (incl. bkfst) **LB FACILITIES:** STV Putting green Jacuzzi Xmas **SERVICES:** Lift **PARKING:** 8 **NOTES:** No smoking in restaurant **CARDS:** 🖃 💳 ▨ 🔳 💳

★★ 70% **The Maple Court**
12 Ness Walk IV3 5SQ
☎ 01463 230330 📠 01463 237700
e-mail: maplecourt@macleodhotels.co.uk
Dir: off A9 into city centre, follow one-way system. Over Tomnachurich St Bridge, 1st right onto Ness Walk

PETS: Bedrooms (unattended) Public areas (not in restaurant) Exercise area

Set in gardens on the banks of the River Ness and close to the Eden Court Theatre, this hotel is within a short stroll of the city centre. It has been substantially upgraded and provides smart ground-floor bedrooms and a restaurant serving good-value meals. The friendliness of staff leaves a lasting impression.
ROOMS: 9 en suite (2 fmly) (9 GF) No smoking in 5 bedrooms s £60-£65; d £80-£90 (incl. bkfst) **LB FACILITIES:** entertainment ch fac Xmas **PARKING:** 32 **NOTES:** No smoking in restaurant **CARDS:** 🖃 💳 ▨ 🔳 💳

◆◆◆◆◆ **Moyness House**
6 Bruce Gardens IV3 5EN
☎ 01463 233836 📠 01463 233836
e-mail: stay@moyness.co.uk
Dir: off A82 Fort William road, almost opposite Highland Regional Council headquarters

PETS: Bedrooms (unattended) Exercise area (nearby)

Situated in a quiet residential area just a short distance from the city centre, this elegant Victorian villa dates back to 1880 and offers beautifully decorated, comfortable bedrooms and well-appointed bathrooms. There is an attractive sitting room and an inviting dining room, where traditional Scottish breakfasts are served. Guests are welcome to use the secluded and well-maintained back garden.
FACILITIES: 7 en suite (1 fmly) (2 GF) No smoking TVB tea/coffee Cen ht No coaches **PRICES:** s £35-£38; d £70-£76✱ **LB PARKING:** 10 **CARDS:** 🖃 💳 ▨ 🔳 💳

🐓 Places with this symbol are farms

Scotland

INVERNESS continued

◆◆◆ Fraser House
49 Huntly St IV3 5HS
☎ 01463 716488 ▤ 01463 716488
e-mail: fraserlea@btopenworld.com
Dir: city centre on W of River Ness approx 100mtrs from Friars Bridge

PETS: Bedrooms Exercise area (50 metres)

Situated on the west bank of the River Ness, Fraser House enjoys a commanding location overlooking the city, and is within easy walking distance of all the central amenities. Bedrooms, all of which have en suite facilities, vary in size and are comfortably furnished and well equipped. The ground-floor dining room is the setting for freshly cooked Scottish breakfasts.
FACILITIES: 5 en suite (2 fmly) No smoking TVB tea/coffee Cen ht
PRICES: s £20-£35; d £40-£50✱ LB

KINGUSSIE
Map 14 NH70

★★ 71% The Scot House
Newtonmore Rd PH21 1HE
☎ 01540 661351 ▤ 01540 661111
e-mail: enquiries@scothouse.com
Dir: A9, take Kingussie exit, hotel approx 0.5m at S end of Main St

PETS: (Pets by prior arrangement only) Bedrooms £5
Exercise area Pet Food

This long established hotel offers comfortable accommodation in thoughtfully equipped, generally spacious rooms. The young enthusiastic team provides warm hospitality. A popular bar and restaurant are the setting for a wide range of carefully prepared meals and an excellent range of malt whiskies.
ROOMS: 9 en suite (1 fmly) No smoking in all bedrooms s £42-£50; d £68-£84 (incl. bkfst) LB **FACILITIES:** Xmas **PARKING:** 50
NOTES: No smoking in restaurant Closed 10-31 Jan
CARDS:

LETTERFINLAY
Map 14 NN29

★★ 67% Letterfinlay Lodge
PH34 4DZ
☎ 01397 712622
e-mail: info@letterfinlaylodgehotel.com
Dir: 7m N of Spean Bridge, on A82 beside Loch Lochy

PETS: Bedrooms (unattended) £2 per night (dogs & cats)
Public areas (not in dining room) Exercise area (in grounds)
Pet Food

This comfortable, family-run hotel stands in grounds beside the A82, overlooking Loch Lochy. There is a cosy bar, a choice of lounges - one of which has stunning lochside views - and is popular for its bar food - and an attractive dining room. Bedrooms come in a variety of sizes, some being particularly spacious.
ROOMS: 13 rms (11 en suite) (5 fmly) s £30-£45; d £60-£80 (incl. bkfst)
LB **FACILITIES:** Fishing **PARKING:** 100 **NOTES:** No smoking in restaurant Closed Nov-Feb **CARDS:**

LOCHINVER
Map 14 NC0

★★★ ◉ Inver Lodge
IV27 4LU
☎ 01571 844496 ▤ 01571 844395
e-mail: stay@inverlodge.com
Dir: A835 to Lochinver through village and turn left after village hall, follow private road for 0.5m

CLASSIC BRITISH

PETS: Bedrooms (unattended) Public areas (front foyer only)

Genuine hospitality is a real feature at this delightful, modern hotel. Set high on the hillside above the village all bedrooms and public rooms enjoy stunning views. Public areas include a choice of lounges, a well stocked bar and a restaurant where skilful chefs make use of the abundant local produce. Accommodation is spacious, stylish and of high quality.
ROOMS: 20 en suite s fr £80; d fr £150 (incl. bkfst) LB
FACILITIES: STV Fishing Snooker Sauna Solarium **PARKING:** 30
NOTES: No smoking in restaurant Closed Nov-Etr
CARDS:

MALLAIG
Map 13 NM6

★★ 67% West Highland
PH41 4QZ
☎ 01687 462210 ▤ 01687 462130
e-mail: westhighland.hotel@virgin.net
Dir: from Fort William turn right at rdbt then 1st right up hill, from ferry left at rdbt then 1st right uphill

PETS: Bedrooms (unattended) Exercise area (adjacent)
Pet Food

Originally the town's station hotel the original building was destroyed by fire and the current hotel built on the same site in the early 20th century. Fine views over to Skye are a real feature of the public rooms, whilst bedrooms are thoughtfully equipped and generally spacious.
ROOMS: 34 en suite (6 fmly) No smoking in 6 bedrooms s £35-£40; d £70-£74 (incl. bkfst) LB **FACILITIES:** entertainment **PARKING:** 40
NOTES: No smoking in restaurant Closed 16 Oct-15 Mar RS 16 Mar-1 Apr
CARDS:

MUIR OF ORD
Map 14 NH55

★★ 67% ♨ Ord House
IV6 7UH
☎ 01463 870492 ▤ 01463 870492
e-mail: eliza@ord-house.com
Dir: off A9 at Tore rdbt onto A832. Follow for 5m into Muir of Ord. Turn left outside Muir of Ord, to Ullapool still on A832. Hotel 0.5m on left

THE CIRCLE
Selected Individual Hotels
GREAT BRITAIN

PETS: Bedrooms Sep Accom (kennel) (unattended)
Public areas (not in restaurant) Exercise area (surrounding gardens) Pet Food

Dating back to 1637, this country-house hotel is situated peacefully in wooded grounds and offers brightly furnished and well-proportioned accommodation. Comfortable day rooms reflect the character and charm of the house, with inviting lounges, a cosy

continued

snug bar and an elegant dining room where wide-ranging, creative menus are offered.

ROOMS: 11 en suite (2 GF) s fr £50; d fr £100 (incl. bkfst)
FACILITIES: no TV in bdrms Croquet lawn Putting green Clay pigeon shooting **PARKING:** 30 **NOTES:** No smoking in restaurant Closed Nov-Apr **CARDS:** 💳 💳 💳

★ ◉◉ The Dower House
Highfield IV6 7XN
☎ 01463 870090 📠 01463 870090
e-mail: aa@thedowerhouse.co.uk
Dir: on Dingwall rd A862, 1m from Muir of Ord, on left

PETS: Bedrooms (unattended) £3.50 Exercise area Pet Food

This enchanting house enjoys a secluded location on the northern edge of the village. The relaxed, friendly atmosphere and attentive service are key features of the hotel and guests are made to feel that this is a real home from home. The cosy sitting room is full of books, whilst the dining room has quiet elegance and antique furniture. The charming bedrooms come in various sizes; one has its own sitting room.
ROOMS: 5 en suite 2 annexe en suite (1 fmly) (5 GF) No smoking in all bedrooms s £65-£105; d £110-£150 (incl. bkfst) **LB**
FACILITIES: Croquet lawn Bird watching ch fac **PARKING:** 20
NOTES: No smoking in restaurant Closed 25 Dec & 2wks Nov
CARDS: 💳 💳 💳 💳

NAIRN   Map 14 NH85

★★★★ 71% ◉ Golf View
The Seafront IV12 4HD
☎ 01667 452301 📠 01667 455267
e-mail: golfview@morton-hotels.com
Dir: off A96 into Seabank Rd, follow road to end, hotel on right

PETS: Telephone for details

Adjacent to both the beach and Nairn Golf Club, this hotel has benefited from recent investment. Thoughtfully equipped bedrooms are spacious and include a number of lovely suites. Public areas include an attractive leisure club. Freshly prepared meals can be enjoyed in both the informal conservatory and restaurant.
ROOMS: 42 en suite (7 fmly) No smoking in 7 bedrooms s £92-£113; d £139-£236 (incl. bkfst) **LB FACILITIES:** STV Indoor swimming (H) Tennis (hard) Sauna Solarium Gym Putting green Jacuzzi Cycle hire, Swimming pool supervised ch fac Xmas **SERVICES:** Lift **PARKING:** 65
NOTES: No smoking in restaurant **CARDS:** 💳 💳 💳 💳 💳

★★★★ 70% ◉ Newton
Inverness Rd IV12 4RX
☎ 01667 453144 📠 01667 454026
e-mail: info@morton-hotels.com
Dir: 15m from Inverness on A96, turn left into tree lined driveway

PETS: Telephone for details

The original part of this hotel dates from 1650, while a stylish, modern extension houses a large conference centre and some super bedrooms. Public rooms include spacious lounges, a well-stocked, recently refurbished bar and an elegant restaurant, where much use is made of the abundant local produce.
ROOMS: 56 en suite (2 fmly) No smoking in 15 bedrooms s £92-£113; d £114-£196 (incl. bkfst) **LB FACILITIES:** STV Tennis (hard) Fishing Use of leisure club at sister hotel ch fac Xmas **SERVICES:** Lift **PARKING:** 200
NOTES: No smoking in restaurant Closed 23-27 Dec
CARDS: 💳 💳 💳 💳 💳 💳

ONICH   Map 14 NN06

★★★ 76% ◉◉ Onich
PH33 6RY
☎ 01855 821214 📠 01855 821484
e-mail: enquiries@onich-fortwilliam.co.uk
Dir: beside A82, 2m N of Ballachulish Bridge

PETS: Bedrooms (unattended) £5 per stay Public areas (not during peak service times) Exercise area (beach 50 yards)

Genuine hospitality is part of the appeal of this hotel, which has gardens extending to the shore of picturesque Loch Linnhe. Nicely presented public areas include a choice of inviting lounges and contrasting bars, and views of the loch can be enjoyed from the attractive restaurant. Bedrooms, with pleasing colour schemes, are comfortably modern in appointment.
ROOMS: 25 en suite (6 fmly) No smoking in 6 bedrooms d £82-£125 (incl. bkfst) **LB FACILITIES:** STV Jacuzzi Games room Xmas
PARKING: 50 **NOTES:** No smoking in restaurant
CARDS: 💳 💳 💳 💳 💳

★★★ 72% ◉◉ Lodge on the Loch
PH33 6RY
☎ 0871 222 3462 📠 0871 222 3416
e-mail: reservations@freedomglen.co.uk
Dir: beside A82 - 5m N of Glencoe, 10m S of Fort William

PETS: Bedrooms £10 Public areas (lounge only) Exercise area (100 yards) Pet Food

Warm, Highland hospitality is a real feature of this stunningly located, holiday hotel. Fine views over Loch Linnhe can be enjoyed from the public areas and many of the individually styled bedrooms. A real fire warms the cosy lounge in the cooler months and accomplished cooking features on the dinner menus.
ROOMS: 16 en suite (1 GF) No smoking in all bedrooms s £80-£300; d £160-£300 (incl. bkfst & dinner) **LB FACILITIES:** Free use of leisure facilities at sister hotel Xmas **PARKING:** 25 **NOTES:** No children 16yrs No smoking in restaurant Closed Jan-14 Feb & Nov-23 Dec RS 14 Feb-4 April **CARDS:** 💳 💳 💳 💳

Scotland

PORTNANCON — Map 14 NC46

♦♦♦♦ 🏛 🍽 Port-Na-Con House

Loch Eriboll IV27 4UN
☎ 01971 511367 📠 01971 511367
e-mail: portnacon70@hotmail.com
Dir: 0.25m off A838, on shore of loch, 6m SE of Durness

PETS: Bedrooms (unattended) Exercise area (on site)
RESIDENT PETS: Heather (Boxer)

Although it might take nearly a day to reach this secluded guest house on the shores of Loch Eriboll, few journeys can be better rewarded - the tranquillity and picture-book loch and mountain scenery will provide an unforgettable memory. Genuine hospitality and attentive service are offered. Bedrooms are comfortable, breakfasts are substantial and at dinner wide-ranging menus are served.

FACILITIES: 3 rms (1 en suite) (1 fmly) No smoking tea/coffee Licensed Cen ht No coaches local golf & fishing Dinner Last d 5pm
PRICES: d £40-£42✱ **PARKING:** 6 **CARDS:** 〰 ▨ 💳 ▨ S

ROY BRIDGE — Map 14 NN28

★★★ 71% Glenspean Lodge Hotel

PH31 4AW
☎ 01397 712223 📠 01397 712660
e-mail: reservations@glenspeanlodge.co.uk
Dir: 2m E of Roy Bridge, right off A82 at Spean Bridge onto A86

[Best Western logo]

PETS: Bedrooms Exercise area (100 yards)

Originally a Victorian hunting lodge, this hotel has been impressively extended and enjoys stunning views from its elevated position in the Spean Valley. Accommodation is provided in well laid out bedrooms, some suitable for families. Meals can be enjoyed in either the smart restaurant or less formal bar area.

ROOMS: 15 en suite (3 fmly) No smoking in 10 bedrooms s £45-£95; d £90-£200 (incl. bkfst) **LB FACILITIES:** STV Sauna Gym Jacuzzi snooker room, small children's play room Xmas **PARKING:** 50
NOTES: No smoking in restaurant **CARDS:** 〰 ▨ 💳 ▨ S

SCOURIE — Map 14 NC14

★★ 70% Scourie

IV27 4SX
☎ 01971 502396 📠 01971 502423
e-mail: patrick@scourie-hotel.co.uk
Dir: on A894

PETS: Bedrooms (unattended) Public areas (except dining areas) Exercise area (0.25 mile) **RESIDENT PETS:** Molly (Springer Spaniel), Jessie & Clemmie (cats)

This well-established hotel is an angler's paradise with extensive fishing rights available on a 25,000-acre estate. Public areas include a choice of comfortable lounges, a cosy bar and a smart dining room offering wholesome fare. The bedrooms are comfortable and generally spacious and the resident proprietors and their staff create a relaxed and friendly atmosphere.

ROOMS: 18 rms (17 en suite) 2 annexe en suite (2 fmly) (5 GF) No smoking in all bedrooms s £35-£46; d £60-£80 (incl. bkfst) **LB**
FACILITIES: no TV in bdrms Fishing Trout and Salmon fishing, Hill walking, Sea fishing **PARKING:** 30 **NOTES:** No smoking in restaurant Closed mid Oct-end Mar **CARDS:** 〰 ▨ 💳 S

SPEAN BRIDGE — Map 14 NN28

♦♦♦♦ Distant Hills

PH34 4EU
☎ 01397 712452 📠 01397 712452
e-mail: enquiry@distanthills.com
Dir: turn off A82 from Fort William to Inverness onto A86 at junct in village of Spean Bridge. Establishment 0.5m on right

PETS: Bedrooms (unattended) Public areas (not dining room) Exercise area (100yds) **RESIDENT PETS:** Shadow (Black Labrador), Mitzy (Miniature Poodle), Nevin (Lurcher) & Garraul (Labrador cross)

A warm and friendly welcome is assured at this family-run guesthouse set in its own well-tended garden. Bedrooms are maintained to a high standard with tasteful modern appointments. There is a spacious split-level lounge, with access to the large garden. Enjoyable home cooked evening meals (by prior arrangement) and hearty Scottish breakfasts are served at individual tables in the peaceful dining room.

FACILITIES: 7 en suite No smoking in bedrooms No smoking in dining room TVB tea/coffee Cen ht TVL No coaches Dinner Last d 2pm
PRICES: s £30-£50; d £42-£50✱ **PARKING:** 10 **NOTES:** Closed Xmas rs Nov-Jan **CARDS:** 〰 ▨ 💳 ▨ S

♦♦♦♦ The Smiddy House

Roy Bridge Rd PH34 4EU
☎ 01397 712335 📠 01397 712043
e-mail: enquiry@smiddyhouse.com
Dir: on A82 Fort William to Inverness road, through Spean Bridge. Turn right for Roy Bridge on A86. On corner at this junction

PETS: Bedrooms £3 Exercise area (0.5 mile)
RESIDENT PETS: Cara (King Charles Cavalier)

Enjoying a prominent village location next to the old village blacksmith, Smiddy House offers guests a warm and friendly welcome. Bedrooms, all of which are named after Scottish Islands, are attractively decorated, comfortably furnished in pine and well equipped. Delicious evening meals and breakfasts are served in Russell's Bistro, where the best of local produce is used to good effect.

FACILITIES: 4 en suite (1 fmly) No smoking TVB tea/coffee Licensed Dinner Last d 9.30pm **PRICES:** s £25-£40; d £45-£55✱ **PARKING:** 15
NOTES: Closed Nov **CARDS:** 〰 ▨ 💳 ▨ S

STRATHPEFFER — Map 14 NH45

♦♦♦ Inver Lodge

IV14 9DL
☎ 01997 421392
e-mail: derbyshire@inverlg.fsnet.co.uk
Dir: from A834 through Strathpeffer centre, turn beside Spa Pavilion signed Bowling Green. Inver Lodge on right

PETS: Exercise area

Guests are assured of a warm welcome at this Victorian lodge, situated within easy walking distance of the town centre. Bedrooms are comfortable and well equipped. Imaginative

continued

breakfasts, and by prior arrangement, enjoyable home-cooked evening meals, are served at a communal table.
FACILITIES: 2 rms (1 fmly) No smoking TVB tea/coffee Cen ht No coaches Fishing and riding can be arranged Dinner Last d 4pm
PRICES: s £25-£28; d £34✱ **LB BB PARKING:** 2
NOTES: Closed mid Dec-Feb **CARDS:** 🖃 🖃 🖃

STRONTIAN   Map 14 NM86

★★ ◎◎ Kilcamb Lodge
PH36 4HY
☎ 01967 402257 📠 01967 402041
e-mail: enquiries@kilcamblodge.co.uk
Dir: off A861, via Corran Ferry

PETS: Bedrooms **£3.50 Exercise area (21 acre grounds)**
Pet Food RESIDENT PETS: Suzie (Westie)

This historic house on the shores of Loch Sunart was one of the first stone buildings in the area and was used as military barracks around the time of the Jacobite uprising. Accommodation is provided in tastefully decorated rooms with high quality fabrics. Accomplished cooking, utilising much local produce, can be enjoyed in the stylish dining room. Warm hospitality is assured.
ROOMS: 11 en suite No smoking in all bedrooms s £75; d £110-£170 (incl. bkfst) **LB FACILITIES:** Fishing Boating Xmas **PARKING:** 18
NOTES: No children 12yrs No smoking in restaurant Closed 2 Jan-11 Feb
CARDS: 🖃 🖃 🖃 🖃 🖃 🖃

◆◆◆ Creag Ard House
5 Longrigg Rd PH36 4HY
☎ 01967 402012 📠 01967 402012
e-mail: lynnejenkins@btinternet.com
Dir: in village approx 25m W of Fort William and via Corran Ferry

PETS: Bedrooms Public areas (not in dining room and kitchen) Exercise area **RESIDENT PETS:** Rio (Golden Retriever), Scooby (Cocker Spaniel), P.F. and Scooty (cats)

Situated in an elevated location, Creag Ard House enjoys stunning views of the surrounding hills and countryside to Loch Sunart beyond. Bedrooms in this friendly family run house are very well equipped, comfortably proportioned and attractive. There is a spacious lounge; a snooker room with full size table and for the more energetic washing and drying facilities are available.
FACILITIES: 3 rms (3 GF) No smoking in dining room STV TVB tea/coffee Cen ht TVL No children 5yr No coaches Snooker
PARKING: 5

TAIN   Map 14 NH88

★★★ 74% ◎ Morangie House
Morangie Rd IV19 1PY
☎ 01862 892281 📠 01862 892872
e-mail: wynne@morangiehotel.com
Dir: turn right off A9 northwards

PETS: Bedrooms (unattended) Exercise area Pet Food

This welcoming family-run hotel has fine views of the Dornoch Firth. Spacious bedrooms in the newer wing are comfortable and modern, and those in the main house are more traditional; all are
continued

well equipped with useful accessories. A wide range of dishes is available in the smart Garden Restaurant.
ROOMS: 26 en suite (1 fmly) (6 GF) No smoking in 6 bedrooms s £65-£75; d £100-£130 (incl. bkfst) **LB FACILITIES:** STV **PARKING:** 40
CARDS: 🖃 🖃 🖃 🖃 🖃

★★ ◎◎ ♨ Glenmorangie Highland Home at Cadboll
Cadboll, Fearn IV20 1XP
☎ 01862 871671 📠 01862 871625
e-mail: relax@glenmorangieplc.co.uk
Dir: from A9 turn onto B9175 towards Nigg and follow tourist board signs

PETS: Bedrooms (Cottage suites only) (unattended) Exercise area (0.25 mile) Pet Food **RESIDENT PETS:** Tot (Black Labrador) and Toffee and Misty (cats)

A warm welcome is assured at this historic house that has been converted into a very individual hotel by the famous whisky distillers. Stylish accommodation is provided in both the main house and a row of converted cottages. A relaxed atmosphere prevails with dinner taken house-party style in the impressive dining room. Enjoy a walk on the nearby beach before tucking in to a hearty local breakfast.
ROOMS: 6 en suite 3 annexe en suite (4 fmly) (3 GF) No smoking in all bedrooms s £140-£185; d £280-£370 (incl. bkfst & dinner) **LB FACILITIES:** STV Fishing Croquet lawn Putting green Falconry, Clay pigeon shooting, Beauty treatments, Husky Sledding, Archery entertainment Xmas **PARKING:** 20 **NOTES:** No children 14yrs No smoking in restaurant Closed 3-31 Jan RS Feb&Mar
CARDS: 🖃 🖃 🖃 🖃 🖃 🖃

TONGUE   Map 14 NC55

★★ 71% ◎ Ben Loyal
Main St IV27 4XE
☎ 01847 611216 📠 01847 611336
e-mail: benloyalhotel@btinternet.com
Dir: at A838/A836 junct. Hotel in centre of village, next to Royal Bank of Scotland

PETS: Bedrooms (unattended) Public areas (not restaurant or bar during meal times) Exercise area (adjacent) **RESIDENT PETS:** Jasper (Cocker Spaniel), Beanie and Danny (cats)

Enjoying a super location close to Ben Loyal and with views of the Kyle of Tongue, a welcoming atmosphere is a hallmark of this family run hotel. Bedrooms are thoughtfully equipped and brightly decorated. Five-course dinners are available in the restaurant and a wide-ranging menu is provided in the bar.
ROOMS: 11 en suite No smoking in all bedrooms s £32; d £50-£64 (incl. bkfst) **LB FACILITIES:** Fishing Fly fishing tuition and equipment
PARKING: 20 **NOTES:** No smoking in restaurant RS Nov-Mar
CARDS: 🖃 🖃 🖃 🖃

All abbreviations are explained on page 9

Scotland

WHITEBRIDGE — Map 14 NH41

★★ 66% **Whitebridge**

IV2 6UN
☎ 01456 486226 & 486272 📠 01456 486413
e-mail: info@whitebridgehotel.co.uk
Dir: off A9 onto B851, follow signs to Fort Augustus. Off A82 onto B862 at Fort Augustus.

PETS: Bedrooms (unattended) Public areas (except restaurant) Exercise area (adjacent)

Close to Loch Ness and set amid rugged mountain and moorland scenery this hotel is popular with tourists, fishermen and deer stalkers. The cosy bar is the hub of the village and the ideal place to enjoy a chat with local people. Bedrooms are appropriately equipped and simply furnished.
ROOMS: 12 rms (11 en suite) (3 fmly) s £35-£38; d £50-£58 (incl. bkfst)
LB FACILITIES: Fishing **PARKING:** 32 **NOTES:** No smoking in restaurant Closed 21 Dec-Feb **CARDS:** 〰️ 🔲 VISA 🔲 🔲 🔲 🔲

MIDLOTHIAN

ROSLIN — Map 11 NT26

◆◆◆ 🏠 **Olde Original Rosslyn**

4 Main St EH25 9LE
☎ 0131 440 2384 📠 0131 4402514
Dir: off city bypass at Straiton for A703. Inn is close to Roslin Chapel

PETS: Bedrooms

This delightful village inn offers well-equipped and comfortable bedrooms, four of which have four-poster beds, and recently upgraded en suite facilities. A variety of eating options are available: in addition to the attractive Victorian restaurant, both the lounge and conservatory provide a comprehensive selection of bar meals.
FACILITIES: 6 en suite (2 fmly) No smoking in area of dining room No smoking in 1 lounge STV TVB tea/coffee Cen ht Dinner Last d 9.30pm **PRICES:** s £55; d £75✳ **LB PARKING:** 14
CARDS: 〰️ 🔲 🔲 🔲 🔲 🔲 🔲

MORAY

ARCHIESTOWN — Map 15 NJ24

★★ 78% 🌸 **Archiestown**

AB38 7QL
☎ 01340 810218 📠 01340 810239
e-mail: rml@archiestownhotel.co.uk
Dir: from A95 Grantown to Elgin road, at Craigellachie onto B9102. Archiestown is 4m from main road, hotel in village square

PETS: Bedrooms (unattended) Public areas (only in sitting room if quiet) Exercise area Pet Food Bowls for dogs
RESIDENT PETS: Thomas (Springer Spaniel), Basil (Miniature Dachshund)

This small, smart hotel is set in the heart of this attractive Speyside village, and is very popular with anglers. The owners are now

continued

---

promoting its charm and character to a broader market, with particular emphasis on food. The newly refurbished bedrooms and bathrooms are comfortable and well equipped.
ROOMS: 11 en suite s £30-£49; d £60-£98 (incl. bkfst) **LB**
PARKING: 18 **NOTES:** No smoking in restaurant Closed 24-27 Dec, 3 wks in Jan **CARDS:** 〰️ 🔲 🔲 🔲 🔲

BALLINDALLOCH — Map 15 NJ13

◆◆◆◆ **Craighead**

Glenlivet AB37 9DR
☎ 01807 590442
e-mail: karenlock@craighead-glenlivet.co.uk
Dir: Off A95 onto B9008 in approx 5m turn left onto B9009 Dufftown Road. Craighead approx 2m on left

PETS: Bedrooms Public areas Exercise area (surrounding countryside) **RESIDENT PETS:** Poppy (Collie cross), Jammie & Petie (rabbits), Jakey (hamster), Trix & Jessie (rats)

A warm welcome is assured at this friendly, family-run house, situated in the heart of Glen Livet and conveniently located for fishing, skiing and other outdoor pursuits. The spacious bedroom is attractively decorated and comfortably furnished in pine. Tasty breakfasts are taken in the cosy dining room, with the comfortable lounge situated nearby.
FACILITIES: 1 en suite (1 fmly) No smoking TVB tea/coffee Cen ht TVL No coaches **PRICES:** s £19; d £38✳ **BB PARKING:** 12
NOTES: Closed 24-25 Dec

CRAIGELLACHIE — Map 15 NJ24

★★★ 78% 🌸🌸 **Craigellachie**

AB38 9SR
☎ 01340 881204 📠 01340 881253
e-mail: info@craigellachie.com
Dir: on A95 in Craigellachie, 300yds from A95/A941 junct

PETS: Bedrooms (unattended) Exercise area (adjacent)

This impressive hotel is located in the heart of Speyside, so it is no surprise that malt whisky is a real feature. The Quaich bar boasts one of the largest collections of malts in the world and the enthusiasm for them is infectious! Bedrooms come in a various sizes, all are tastefully decorated and bathrooms are of a high specification.
ROOMS: 25 en suite No smoking in all bedrooms s £100-£135; d £125-£160 (incl. bkfst) **LB FACILITIES:** STV Gym Xmas
PARKING: 50 **NOTES:** No smoking in restaurant
CARDS: 〰️ 🔲 🔲 🔲 🔲

CULLEN — Map 15 NJ56

★★★ 65% **The Seafield Hotel**

Seafield St AB56 4SG
☎ 01542 840791 📠 01542 840736
e-mail: accom@theseafieldhotel.com
Dir: in centre of town on A950

PETS: Bedrooms (unattended) £5 Exercise area (2 minutes)

Originally built by the Earl of Seafield as a coaching inn, this hotel was modernised to provide individually designed, comfortable

continued

bedrooms and is now gradually being refurbished. One of the features here is a lovely, carved wooden fireplace in the spacious lounge bar. Service is friendly and attentive with good-value and enjoyable meals served in the restaurant.

ROOMS: 19 en suite (2 fmly) s £45-£60; d £75-£85 (incl. bkfst) **LB**
FACILITIES: STV Tennis (hard) Snooker Clay pigeon shooting, Cycling, Quads, 4x4 driving, Archery ch fac Xmas **PARKING:** 28
NOTES: No smoking in restaurant **CARDS:**

NORTH AYRSHIRE

KILWINNING — Map 10 NS34

★★★ 72%
Montgreenan Mansion House
Montgreenan Estate KA13 7QZ

Best Western

☎ 01294 557733 🖷 01294 850397
e-mail: enquiries@montgreenhotel.com
Dir: signs for hotel 4m north of Irvine on A736 and from Kilwinning on A737

> **PETS:** Bedrooms (unattended) £5 Exercise area (20 metres)

In a peaceful setting of 48 acres of parkland and woods, this 19th-century mansion retains many of its original features. Public areas include a splendid drawing room, a library, a club-style bar and a restaurant. Accommodation ranges from compact modern rooms to the well-proportioned classical rooms of the original house. Service is friendly and attentive.

ROOMS: 21 en suite (1 fmly) No smoking in 16 bedrooms s £79.50-£139.50; d £159-£219 (incl. bkfst & dinner) **LB FACILITIES:** STV Golf 5 Tennis (hard) Snooker Croquet lawn Putting green Jacuzzi in honeymoon suite, woodland walks ch fac Xmas **PARKING:** 50
NOTES: No smoking in restaurant
CARDS:

LARGS — Map 10 NS25

★★ 69% **Willowbank**
96 Greenock Rd KA30 8PG
☎ 01475 672311 & 675435 🖷 01475 689027
e-mail: iaincsmith@btconnect.com
Dir: on A78

> **PETS:** Bedrooms (unattended) Exercise area (200 metres)

A relaxed, friendly atmosphere prevails at this well-maintained hotel. The well-decorated bedrooms tend to be spacious and offer comfortable modern appointments, while public areas include a large, well-stocked bar, a lounge and a dining room. Attractive hanging baskets are a feature in the summer.

ROOMS: 30 en suite (4 fmly) **FACILITIES:** entertainment Xmas
PARKING: 40 **NOTES:** No smoking in restaurant
CARDS:

All AA listed accommodation, restaurants and pubs can be found on the AA's website www.theAA.com

---

NORTH LANARKSHIRE

CUMBERNAULD — Map 11 NS77

★★★★ 69% **Westerwood Hotel Golf & Country Club**
1 St Andrews Dr, Westerwood G68 0EW
☎ 01236 457171 🖷 01236 738478
e-mail: westerwood@morton-hotels.com
Dir: A80 exit after passing Oki factory signed Wardpark/Castlecary, 2nd left at Old Inns rdbt and right at mini rdbt

> **PETS:** Bedrooms (unattended) Exercise area (on site) Pet Food

This stylish, contemporary hotel enjoys an elevated position within 400 acres at the foot of the Campsie Hills. Accommodation is provided in spacious, bright bedrooms, many with super bathrooms, and day rooms include sumptuous lounges, an airy restaurant and extensive golf, fitness and conference facilities.

ROOMS: 100 en suite (13 fmly) No smoking in 51 bedrooms s £95-£118; d £110-£133 (incl. bkfst) **LB FACILITIES:** Spa STV Indoor swimming (H) Golf 18 Tennis (hard) Sauna Solarium Gym Putting green Jacuzzi Beauty salon Hairdresser Xmas **SERVICES:** Lift air con **PARKING:** 204 **NOTES:** No smoking in restaurant
CARDS:

PERTH & KINROSS

AUCHTERARDER — Map 11 NN91

★★★★★ ◉◉◉◉ **The Gleneagles**
PH3 1NF
☎ 01764 662231 🖷 01764 662134
e-mail: resort.sales@gleneagles.com
Dir: off A9 at exit for A823 follow signs for Gleneagles Hotel

> **PETS:** Bedrooms (unattended) £15 per night for dogs Exercise area (adjacent) Pet Food Dog beds and bowls included in price

With its international reputation for high standards, this grand hotel provides something for everyone. Set in a delightful location, Gleneagles offers a peaceful retreat, as well as many sporting activities, including the famous championship golf courses. Afternoon tea is a feature, and cocktails are prepared with flair and skill at the bar. Amongst the dining options is Strathearn, with two AA rosettes, as well as some inspired cooking at Andrew Fairlie at Gleneagles, a restaurant with four rosettes. Service is

continued on p290

Scotland

AUCHTERARDER continued

always professional, staff are friendly and nothing is too much trouble.
ROOMS: 270 en suite (115 fmly) (11 GF) No smoking in 149 bedrooms d £330-£465 (incl. bkfst) **LB FACILITIES: Spa** STV Indoor swimming (H) Outdoor swimming (H) Golf 18 Tennis (hard & grass) Fishing Squash Riding Snooker Sauna Solarium Gym Croquet lawn Putting green Jacuzzi Falconry, Equestrian, Off roading, Golf range, Archery, Clay target shooting entertainment ch fac Xmas **SERVICES:** Lift **PARKING:** 200 **CARDS:**

BLAIR ATHOLL   Map 14 NN86

★★ 63% **Bridge of Tilt**
Bridge of Tilt PH18 5SU
☎ 01796 481333 ▤ 01796 481335
e-mail: hotels@theholidaygroup.com
Dir: turn off A9 onto B8079, hotel 0.75m on left with wishing well in front

PETS: Exercise area

Frequented by tour groups, this friendly hotel is situated close to Blair Castle. Bedrooms come in a variety of styles, with the chalet rooms being particularly popular. Public areas include a lounge, dining areas and a bar which offers live entertainment three times a week in season.
ROOMS: 20 en suite 7 annexe en suite (7 fmly) (7 GF) s £30-£35; d £40-£80 (incl. bkfst) **LB FACILITIES:** Jacuzzi entertainment Xmas **PARKING:** 40 **NOTES:** No smoking in restaurant Closed Jan-Feb **CARDS:**

CRIEFF   Map 11 NN82

◆◆◆◆ **Comely Bank**
32 Burrell St PH7 4DT
☎ 01764 653409
e-mail: kathleen@comelybank.demon.co.uk
Dir: from A9, take A822 at Braco

PETS: Bedrooms Exercise area (0.5 mile)
RESIDENT PETS: Sam (Cocker Spaniel)

The proprietors extend a warm and friendly welcome to guests visiting their comfortable home. Bedrooms are bright and airy with attractive soft furnishings; one room on the ground floor is suitable for less mobile guests. The lounge invites relaxation and carefully prepared breakfasts are served in the dining room.
FACILITIES: 5 rms (3 en suite) (2 fmly) (1 GF) No smoking in bedrooms No smoking in dining room TVB tea/coffee Cen ht TVL No coaches **PRICES:** s £18-£20; d £36-£44✻ **BB**

> All information was correct at the time of going to press; we recommend you confirm details on booking

KENMORE   Map 14 NN74

★★★ 67% **Kenmore Hotel**
The Square PH15 2NU
☎ 01887 830205 ▤ 01887 830262
e-mail: reception@kenmorehotel.co.uk
Dir: off A9 at Ballinluig onto A827, through Aberfeldy to Kenmore for hotel in village centre

PETS: Bedrooms (Annexe only) Public areas (except restaurant) Exercise area (100 metres)

Dating back to 1572, this riverside hotel is Scotland's oldest inn and has a rich and interesting history. Bedrooms have been upgraded and modernised, with tasteful decor. Dinner can be enjoyed in the restaurant with its panoramic views of the River Tay. The choice of bars includes one with real fires.
ROOMS: 27 en suite 13 annexe en suite (4 fmly) (7 GF) s £43-£66; d £70-£102 (incl. bkfst) **LB FACILITIES:** STV Tennis (hard) Fishing Jacuzzi Discounted salmon fishing on River Tay Xmas **SERVICES:** Lift **PARKING:** 30 **NOTES:** No smoking in restaurant **CARDS:**

KINCLAVEN   Map 11 NO13

★★★ ⊚⊚ ♣♠ **Ballathie House**
PH1 4QN
☎ 01250 883268 ▤ 01250 883396
e-mail: email@ballathiehousehotel.com
Dir: from A9 2m N of Perth, B9099 through Stanley & signed or off A93 at Beech Hedge follow signs for Ballathie 2.5m

PETS: Bedrooms Exercise area (in grounds)
RESIDENT PETS: Sam (Cocker Spaniel)

Set in delightful grounds, this splendid Scottish mansion house combines classical grandeur with modern comfort. Bedrooms range from well-proportioned master rooms to modern standard rooms and many boast antique furniture and art deco bathrooms. For the ultimate in quality, request one of the Riverside Rooms, a purpose-built development right on the banks of the river, complete with balconies and terraces. The elegant restaurant has views over the River Tay.
ROOMS: 26 en suite 16 annexe en suite (2 fmly) s £79-£110; d £158-£220 (incl. bkfst) **LB FACILITIES:** STV Fishing Croquet lawn Putting green Xmas **SERVICES:** Lift **PARKING:** 50 **NOTES:** No smoking in restaurant **CARDS:**

KINROSS   Map 11 NO10   PERTH   Map 11 NO12

★★★ 75% Green
2 The Muirs KY13 8AS
☎ 01577 863467 📠 01577 863180
e-mail: reservations@green-hotel.com
Dir: M90 junct 6 follow signs for Kinross, turn onto A922

PETS: Bedrooms Public areas (not in restaurant)
Exercise area (on site) Pet Food RESIDENT PETS: Samantha &
Shuna (Cocker Spaniels)

A long-established hotel offering a wide range of indoor and
outdoor activities. Public areas include a classical restaurant, a
choice of bars and a well-stocked gift shop. The comfortable, well-
equipped bedrooms, most of which are generously proportioned,
boast attractive colour schemes and smart modern furnishings.
ROOMS: 46 en suite (4 fmly) (14 GF) No smoking in 12 bedrooms
s £85-£105; d £150-£170 (incl. bkfst) **LB FACILITIES:** STV Indoor
swimming (H) Golf 36 Fishing Squash Sauna Solarium Gym
Croquet lawn Putting green Curling in season, Petanque (French boules)
ch fac Xmas **PARKING:** 60 **NOTES:** No smoking in restaurant
Closed 23-28 Dec excluding Xmas day RS 25 Dec
CARDS: 💳💳💳💳💳💳

**All abbreviations are
explained on page 9**

**All AA listed accommodation,
restaurants and pubs can be
found on the AA's website
www.theAA.com**

The Hotel Guide 2005
Britain's best-selling
hotel guide for all
your leisure needs.

Just AAsk.

www.theAA.com

★★★ 74% ◉ Huntingtower
Crieff Rd PH1 3JT
☎ 01738 583771 📠 01738 583777
e-mail: reservations@huntingtowerhotel.co.uk
Dir: 3m W off A85

PETS: Bedrooms (unattended) Public areas (Not in food
areas) Exercise area (on site)

Enjoying an idyllic country setting, this Edwardian house has been
extended to offer smart, comfortable public areas and a high
standard of accommodation. Comfortable lounges lead to a
conservatory where lunches are served, whilst the elegant Oak
Room restaurant offers skilfully prepared dinners. Bedrooms are
generally spacious and provide a host of modern facilities.
ROOMS: 31 en suite 3 annexe en suite (2 fmly) (8 GF) s £70-£110;
d £100-£160 (incl. bkfst) **LB FACILITIES:** STV ch fac Xmas
SERVICES: Lift **PARKING:** 150 **NOTES:** No smoking in restaurant
CARDS: 💳💳💳💳💳

**★★★ 74% ◉◉ Murrayshall Country House
Hotel & Golf Course**
New Scone PH2 7PH
☎ 01738 551171 📠 01738 552595
e-mail: lin.murrayshall@virgin.net
*Dir: from Perth take A94 (Coupar Angus), 1m from Perth, right to
Murrayshall just before New Scone*

PETS: Telephone for details

This imposing country house is set in 350 acres of grounds, which
include two golf courses, one of which is of championship
standard. Bedrooms come in two distinct styles: modern suites in
a purpose-built building contrast with more traditional rooms in
the main building. The Clubhouse bar serves a range of meals all
day, whilst more accomplished cooking can be enjoyed in the Old
Masters Restaurant.
ROOMS: 27 en suite 14 annexe en suite (17 fmly) (4 GF) No smoking in
1 bedroom s £80-£110; d £110-£150 (incl. bkfst & dinner) **LB**
FACILITIES: Spa STV Golf 36 Tennis (hard) Sauna Gym Putting green
Jacuzzi Driving range ch fac Xmas **PARKING:** 80 **NOTES:** No smoking
in restaurant **CARDS:** 💳💳💳💳💳

**Please mention AA Pet Friendly
Places to Stay when booking**

Scotland

PERTH continued

🐕 🐈 🐇 🐦

♦♦♦♦ Westview

49 Dunkeld Rd PH1 5RP
☎ 01738 627787 📠 01738 447790
e-mail: angiewestview@aol.com
Dir: 2nd exit at Inveralmond rdbt off A9. House 1m on left opp Royal Bank of Scotland

PETS: **Bedrooms Exercise area (5 mins walk)**
RESIDENT PETS: William Wallace & Flora McDonald (Yorkshire Terriers)

Enthusiastic owner Angie Livingstone assures guests of a warm welcome. Angie is a Victoriana fan, and her house is a time warp of that period, one feature being the teddies on the stairs. Best use has been made of available space in the bedrooms, which are full of character. Public areas include an inviting lounge and a separate dining room.
FACILITIES: 5 rms (3 en suite) (1 fmly) (1 GF) No smoking in 3 bedrooms No smoking in dining room No smoking in lounges STV TVB tea/coffee Cen ht TVL No coaches Dinner Last d 12.30pm
PRICES: s £22-£25; d £46-£52* **LB** **PARKING:** 4

🐕

♦♦♦ Clunie

12 Pitcullen Crescent PH2 7HT
☎ 01738 623625 📠 01738 623238
e-mail: ann@clunieguesthouse.co.uk
Dir: on A94 opposite side of river from town

PETS: **Telephone for details**

Lying on the east side of town on the A94, this family run guest house offers a warm and friendly welcome. The comfortable bedrooms, which vary in size, are attractively decorated and well equipped. Dinner, by prior arrangement, and breakfast are served at individual tables in the elegant ground-floor dining room.
FACILITIES: 7 en suite (2 fmly) No smoking in 5 bedrooms No smoking in dining room No smoking in lounges TVB tea/coffee Cen ht No coaches Dinner Last d by arrangement **PRICES:** s £22-£28; d £44-£50* **LB** **PARKING:** 8 **CARDS:**

Please mention AA Pet Friendly Places to Stay when booking

PITLOCHRY Map 14 NN95

🐕 🐈

★★★ 76% 🏵 🌲 Green Park

Clunie Bridge Rd PH16 5JY
☎ 01796 473248 📠 01796 473520
e-mail: bookings@thegreenpark.co.uk
Dir: turn off A9 at Pitlochry, follow signs 0.25m through town, hotel on banks of Loch Faskally

PETS: **Bedrooms (unattended) Exercise area (50 yards)**

Benefiting from a stunning setting on the shores of Loch Faskally, this lovely hotel has lovely landscaped gardens, complete with interesting works of art. Thoughtfully designed bedrooms, many with fine views, are spacious and offer bright decor. Dinner utilises fresh produce, much of it grown in the kitchen garden.
ROOMS: 39 en suite (10 GF) No smoking in all bedrooms s £49-£79; d £98-£142 (incl. bkfst & dinner) **LB** **FACILITIES:** Putting green Xmas
PARKING: 45 **NOTES:** No smoking in restaurant **CARDS:**

🐕

★★★ 72% Pine Trees

Strathview Ter PH16 5QR
☎ 01796 472121 📠 01796 472460
e-mail: info@pinetreeshotel.co.uk
Dir: on main street (Atholl Rd) into Larchwood Rd, follow hotel signs

PETS: **Bedrooms (unattended) £5 Public areas (lounge only) Exercise area (0.5 mile)**

Set in ten acres of tree-studded grounds high above the town, this fine Victorian mansion retains many fine features including wood panelling, ornate ceilings and a wonderful marble staircase. The atmosphere is refined and relaxing, with public rooms looking onto the lawns. Bedrooms come in a variety of sizes and many are well proportioned.
ROOMS: 20 en suite (3 fmly) No smoking in all bedrooms s £62-£86; d £108-£152 (incl. bkfst & dinner) **LB** **FACILITIES:** ch fac Xmas
PARKING: 20 **NOTES:** No smoking in restaurant
CARDS:

🐕 🐇 🐦

★★ 72% 🏵 🌲 Donavourd House

PH16 5JS
☎ 01796 472100 📠 01796 474455
e-mail: reservations@donavourdhousehotel.co.uk
Dir: from A9 slip road take immediate right under railway, continue 0.5m, then left up hill. At junct take left for hotel 0.5m on left

PETS: **Bedrooms Public areas (in reception & lounge only) Exercise area (approx 30yds)**

This attractive country house sits in its own gardens in a quiet, elevated location overlooking Strathtummel. Bedrooms are spacious and well appointed with attractive colour schemes. The public areas are in period style where the dining room has crisp linen and fine glassware that complements the sound cooking skills of chef-patron Nicole McKechnie.
ROOMS: 9 en suite (1 fmly) (1 GF) No smoking in all bedrooms s £65-£75; d £130-£150 (incl. bkfst & dinner) **LB** **FACILITIES:** Xmas
PARKING: 15 **NOTES:** No smoking in restaurant Closed 25 Dec, 5 Jan-Feb **CARDS:**

★★ 70% **Balrobin**
Higher Oakfield PH16 5HT
☎ 01796 472901 📠 01796 474200
e-mail: info@balrobin.co.uk

THE CIRCLE
Selected Individual Hotels
GREAT BRITAIN

Dir: leave A9 at Pitlochry junct, continue to town centre and follow brown tourists signs to hotel

PETS: Bedrooms Exercise area (200 yards)

A welcoming atmosphere prevails at this family-run hotel which, from its position above the town, enjoys delightful countryside views. Public rooms include a relaxing lounge, a well-stocked bar and an attractive restaurant offering traditional home-cooked fare. The bedrooms are comfortable and many enjoy the fine views.
ROOMS: 14 en suite (2 fmly) No smoking in all bedrooms s £38-£49.50; d £61-£86 (incl. bkfst) **LB PARKING:** 15 **NOTES:** No children 5yrs No smoking in restaurant Closed Nov-Feb **CARDS:** 💳

◆◆◆◆ **The Well House**
11 Toberargan Rd PH16 5HG
☎ 01796 472239 📠 01796 472239
e-mail: enquiries@wellhouseandarrochar.co.uk
Dir: close to town centre on road running parallel to main street

PETS: Bedrooms Public areas (Except dining room) Exercise area (100 yards)

Pretty flowering baskets and colourful tubs adorn the exterior of this delightful family home. Bedrooms are comfortably furnished, attractively decorated and well equipped with video recorders and an extensive video library. There is a spacious, tastefully appointed lounge - the ideal setting in which to relax - and an inviting dining room where enjoyable home-cooked fare is served.
FACILITIES: 6 en suite (1 fmly) No smoking in bedrooms No smoking in dining room TVB tea/coffee Licensed Cen ht No coaches Dinner Last d 5.30pm **PRICES:** d £40-£52✱ **PARKING:** 6
NOTES: Closed Dec-Feb **CARDS:** 💳

◆◆◆◆ **Wellwood House**
13 West Moulin Rd PH16 5EA
☎ 01796 474288 📠 01796 474299
e-mail: wellwoodhouse@aol.com
Dir: from A9 follow signs for Pitlochry, then follow signs for Braemar & Town Hall. Wellwood directly opposite Town Hall

PETS: Bedrooms Exercise area (in grounds)

Set in lovely grounds in an elevated position overlooking the town, Wellwood House enjoys stunning views of the Vale of Atholl and the surrounding countryside. The house has recently been sympathetically refurbished and bedrooms are comfortably proportioned, attractively decorated and well equipped. There is an elegant lounge with an honesty bar and a fire for cooler evenings, and the spacious dining room is the setting for hearty breakfasts served at individual tables.
FACILITIES: 10 rms (7 en suite) (1 fmly) No smoking in bedrooms No smoking in dining room No smoking in 1 lounge TVB tea/coffee Licensed Cen ht TVL No coaches **PRICES:** d £48-£66✱ **PARKING:** 20
NOTES: Closed 22-29 Dec **CARDS:** 💳

ST FILLANS
Map 11 NN62

★★★ 68% 🌸🌸 **The Four Seasons Hotel**
Loch Earn PH6 2NF
☎ 01764 685333 📠 01764 685444
e-mail: info@thefourseasonshotel.co.uk
Dir: on A85, towards W of village facing Loch

PETS: Bedrooms (unattended) Exercise area (on site) Pet Food Dog menu **RESIDENT PETS:** Munsterlander

Set on the edge of Loch Earn, this welcoming hotel and many of its bedrooms benefit from fine views. There is a choice of lounges, including a library, warmed by log fires during winter. Local produce is used to good effect in both the Meall Reamhar restaurant and the more informal Tarken Room.
ROOMS: 12 en suite 6 annexe en suite (7 fmly) No smoking in 3 bedrooms s £40-£78; d £80-£106 (incl. bkfst) **LB FACILITIES:** ch fac Xmas **PARKING:** 40 **NOTES:** No smoking in restaurant Closed 5 Jan-end of Feb RS Nov, Dec, Mar **CARDS:** 💳

★★ 72% **Achray House**
PH6 2NF
☎ 01764 685231 📠 01764 685320
e-mail: info@achray-house.co.uk
Dir: follow A85 towards Crainlarich, from Stirling follow A9 then B822 at Braco, B827 to Comrie. Turn left onto A85 to St Fillians

PETS: Bedrooms (unattended) Public areas (not in eating areas) Exercise area (20 yards)

A friendly holiday hotel set in gardens overlooking picturesque Loch Earn, Achray House offers smart, attractive and well-equipped bedrooms. An interesting range of freshly prepared dishes is served both in the conservatory and in the adjoining dining rooms.
ROOMS: 9 rms (8 en suite) 1 annexe en suite (2 fmly) (3 GF) No smoking in 5 bedrooms s £50-£55; d £70-£80 (incl. bkfst) **LB FACILITIES:** Xmas **PARKING:** 30 **NOTES:** No smoking in restaurant **CARDS:** 💳

🌲 **Places with this symbol are country house hotels**

Scotland

LOCHWINNOCH   Map 10 NS35

♦♦♦♦♦ ☎ 🚲 East Lochhead
Largs Rd PA12 4DX
☎ 01505 842610 📠 01505 842610
e-mail: admin@eastlochhead.co.uk
Dir: from Glasgow take M8 junct 28a for A737 Irvine. At Roadhead rdbt turn right on A760. Premises 2m on left, follow brown tourist sign

> **PETS:** Bedrooms £5 Public areas **(Only if well behaved and under control)** Exercise area **(Adjacent)** RESIDENT PETS: Peggy and Maggie (dogs), Millie (cat)

A relaxed country-house atmosphere prevails at this former farmhouse, which dates back to the 1800s. Sitting in colourful and immaculately maintained grounds, the house boasts magnificent views over Barr Loch. The stylishly furnished bedrooms are attractive and superbly equipped. There is a combined lounge/dining room where delicious evening meals and breakfasts are served. A barn has been tastefully converted into five self-contained units with their own private entrances, and a separate barn hosts a function room.
FACILITIES: 3 en suite (1 fmly) (1 GF) No smoking TVB tea/coffee Licensed Cen ht TVL No coaches Cycle hire Dinner Last d 10am
PRICES: s £45-£55; d £70-£80✱ **LB PARKING:** 24
CARDS: 💳

SCOTTISH BORDERS

BROUGHTON   Map 11 NT13

♦♦♦♦ Glenholm Centre
ML12 6JF
☎ 01899 830408 📠 01899 830408
e-mail: glenholm@dircon.co.uk
Dir: A701, 1m S of Broughton, turn right signposted Glenholm. Follow road for 1m, centre on right near road, before cattlegrid

> **PETS:** Bedrooms (unattended) Exercise area (adjacent) Areas of farm available for dog walking RESIDENT PETS: Dill (Border Collie), Tarry (Bearded Collie)

Surrounded by peaceful farmland, this former schoolhouse has a distinct African theme. The home-cooked meals and baking have received much praise and are served in the spacious open-plan dining room/lounge. The bright airy bedrooms are thoughtfully
continued

equipped. Service is friendly and attentive. Computer courses are available.
FACILITIES: 4 en suite (1 fmly) (1 GF) No smoking TVB tea/coffee Direct dial from bedrooms Licensed Cen ht TVL No coaches Dinner Last d 6pm **PARKING:** 14 **NOTES:** Closed Jan
CARDS: 💳

CHIRNSIDE   Map 12 NT85

★★★ 68% 🐾 Chirnside Hall
TD11 3LD
☎ 01890 818219 📠 01890 818231
e-mail: chirnsidehall@globalnet.co.uk
Dir: on A6105 Berwick on Tweed/Duns road approx 3m after village Foulden hotel sign on right

> **PETS:** Bedrooms £10 Exercise area (adjacent) Pet Food RESIDENT PETS: Jill, Roefus, Baltazar, Tim (dogs in kennels)

At the end of a tree-lined drive this hotel is ideal for guests wishing to get away from the hustle and bustle of city life. Bedrooms are spacious, many with views of the rolling Borders countryside. Real fires warm the elegantly styled lounges and fresh local produce features on the restaurant menus.
ROOMS: 10 en suite (2 fmly) s £85-£140; d £140-£155 (incl. bkfst) **LB**
FACILITIES: Fishing Snooker Gym Croquet lawn Putting green Shooting ch fac Xmas **PARKING:** 20 **NOTES:** No smoking in restaurant
CARDS: 💳

CRAILING   Map 12 NT62

♦♦♦♦ ☎ 🚲 Crailing Old School B&B
TD8 6TL
☎ 01835 850382 📠 01835 850382
e-mail: jean.player@virgin.net
Dir: off A698 Jedburgh to Kelso road on B6400 signposted Nisbet, Harestanes visitor centre.Crailing Old School also signed

> **PETS:** Sep Accom (kennel with run) £2 Exercise area **(0.2 miles)** RESIDENT PETS: Reiver (Lurcher)

A delightful rural retreat, built in 1887 as the village school, and imaginatively renovated to combine Victorian architectural features with modern comforts. The spacious bedroom are beautifully maintained and decorated, and filled with homely extras. The lodge annexe located 10 metres from the house offers alternative ground-floor/disabled access and suite accommodation. The best of local produce can be sampled in the tasty breakfasts, served in the stylish lounge/dining room, with evening meals by arrangement.
FACILITIES: 3 rms (1 en suite) 1 annexe en suite (1 GF) No smoking TVB tea/coffee Cen ht TVL No children 9yrs Dinner Last d 7.30pm
PRICES: s £25-£30; d £50-£60✱ **LB PARKING:** 7
NOTES: Closed 24-27 Dec & 2 wks Feb and Nov **CARDS:** 💳

> **All AA listed accommodation, restaurants and pubs can be found on the AA's website www.theAA.com**

GALASHIELS
Map 12 NT43

★★★ 66% Kingsknowes
Selkirk Rd TD1 3HY
☎ 01896 758375 📠 01896 750377
e-mail: enq@kingsknowes.co.uk
Dir: off A7 at Galashiels/Selkirk rdbt

PETS: Bedrooms (unattended) Public areas (not during meals) Exercise area (on site)

An imposing turreted mansion, this hotel lies in attractive gardens on the outskirts of town close to the River Tweed. It boasts elegant public areas and many spacious bedrooms, some with excellent views. There is a choice of bars, one with a popular menu to supplement the restaurant.

ROOMS: 12 en suite (2 fmly) s fr £59; d fr £89 (incl. bkfst) **LB**
FACILITIES: STV **PARKING:** 50 **NOTES:** No smoking in restaurant
CARDS: 💳

♦♦♦ 🐾 Over Langshaw
Langshaw TD1 2PE
☎ 01896 860244 📠 01896 860244
e-mail: bergius@overlangshaw.fsnet.co.uk
Dir: From A7 turn right after Langshaw sign 1m N of Galashiels. 2m to T-junct and turn right again. In Langshaw turn left at Earlston sign. Over Langshaw is 1m, signed at farm road

PETS: Bedrooms Exercise area

An organic farm, Over Langshaw provides fine panoramic views from its hillside position three miles north of Galashiels. It offers two comfortable and spacious bedrooms, one with en suite on the ground floor and one upstairs right next to its own private bathroom. Hearty breakfasts are provided at individual tables set up in the lounge.

FACILITIES: 2 en suite (1 fmly) (1 GF) No smoking tea/coffee Cen ht 500 acres dairy/sheep/organic Dinner Last d at breakfast
PRICES: d fr £48✳ **PARKING:** 4

JEDBURGH
Map 12 NT62

♦♦♦♦ Glenfriars House
The Friars TD8 6BN
☎ 01835 862000 📠 01835 862112
e-mail: glenfriars@edenroad.demon.co.uk
Dir: from A68 follow signs for Abbey, follow to T-junct right then immediate left between the Wishing Well shop and hairdresser. In 100yds, hard right into Friarsgate. House 0.25 mile on left

PETS: Bedrooms (unattended) Exercise area (0.25 mile)
RESIDENT PETS: Kilroy & Hamish - cats

A substantial and interesting period house, Glenfriars lies secluded in its own gardens overlooking the town, yet only a short walk from the centre. The house is currently being restored to its former glory. Bedrooms are comfortable, most being well proportioned.

FACILITIES: 6 en suite (3 fmly) No smoking TVB tea/coffee Cen ht TVL No coaches Country sports can be arranged Dinner Last d by arrangement **PRICES:** s fr £30; d fr £50✳ **LB PARKING:** 6
NOTES: Closed 22 Dec-7 Jan **CARDS:** 💳

♦♦♦ 🍔 Ferniehirst Mill Lodge
TD8 6PQ
☎ 01835 863279 📠 863279
e-mail: ferniehirstmill@aol.com
Dir: 2.5m S on A68, at end of private track directly off A68

PETS: Bedrooms (unattended) Exercise area (On site)
RESIDENT PETS: Arctic - maremma (Sheepdog), Flight - Whippet & Joe - Jack Russell

Reached by a rough farm track and a rustic bridge, this chalet-style lodge enjoys a secluded setting by the River Jed where wildlife abounds. Bedrooms are small and functional but there is a comfortable lounge in which to relax. Excellent home-cooked dinners and hearty breakfasts are served in the cosy dining room.
FACILITIES: 7 en suite (1 GF) No smoking tea/coffee Direct dial from bedrooms Licensed Cen ht TVL No coaches Fishing Riding Dinner Last d 5pm **PRICES:** s £20-£25; d £40-£50✳ **PARKING:** 10
CARDS: 💳

KELSO
Map 12 NT73

★★★ 76% ◎◎ 🏌 The Roxburghe Hotel & Golf Course
Heiton TD5 8JZ
☎ 01573 450331 📠 01573 450611
e-mail: hotel@roxburghe.net
Dir: from A68 Jedburgh join A698 to Heiton, 3m SW of Kelso

PETS: Bedrooms (courtyard bedrooms only) Sep Accom (Kennels)

Outdoor sporting pursuits are popular at this impressive Jacobean mansion owned by the Duke of Roxburghe and set in 500 acres of woods and parkland. Gracious public areas are the perfect settings for afternoon teas and carefully prepared meals. Bedrooms are individually designed, with some of the superior rooms having their own fires.

ROOMS: 16 en suite 6 annexe en suite (3 fmly) (3 GF) No smoking in 1 bedroom s £125-£225; d £140-£280 (incl. bkfst) **LB FACILITIES:** STV Golf 18 Tennis (hard) Fishing Croquet lawn Putting green Clay shooting Health & Beauty Salon Mountain bike hire, riding stables nearby ch fac Xmas **PARKING:** 150 **NOTES:** No smoking in restaurant
CARDS: 💳

PEEBLES
Map 11 NT24

★★★ 80% ◎◎ 🏌 Cringletie House
Edinburgh Rd EH45 8PL
☎ 01721 725750 📠 01721 725751
e-mail: enquiries@cringletie.com
Dir: 2m N on A703

PETS: Bedrooms (unattended) £10 Exercise area (own grounds) Pet Food

This long-established and now refurbished hotel is a romantic baronial mansion set in 28 acres of gardens and woodland with stunning views from all rooms. Delightful public rooms include a cocktail lounge with adjoining conservatory, whilst the first-floor restaurant is graced by a magnificent hand-painted ceiling.

continued on p296

PEEBLES continued

Bedrooms come in a variety of sizes, and all areas have wheelchair access.
ROOMS: 14 en suite (2 GF) No smoking in all bedrooms s £95-£120; d £115-£160 (incl. bkfst) **LB FACILITIES:** STV Croquet lawn Putting green Xmas **SERVICES:** Lift **PARKING:** 30 **NOTES:** No smoking in restaurant Closed Early Jan-Early Feb
CARDS:

★★★ 73% ◉◉ ♨ Castle Venlaw
Edinburgh Rd EH45 8QG
☎ 01721 720384 ▨ 01721 724066
e-mail: stay@venlaw.co.uk
Dir: off A703 Peebles/Edinburgh road, 0.75m from Peebles

PETS: Bedrooms (unattended) £4.50 Exercise area (on site)

This 18th-century castle is set in four acres of landscaped gardens, set high above the town. Bedrooms, many with delightful views, are named after malt whiskies and include three with adjoining turrets. Well-prepared meals are served in the formal restaurant, while light meals are served in the wood-panelled library bar.
ROOMS: 13 en suite (3 fmly) No smoking in 12 bedrooms s £72-£92; d £120-£170 (incl. bkfst) **LB FACILITIES:** STV Xmas **PARKING:** 30
NOTES: No smoking in restaurant **CARDS:** ▨▨▨

★★★ 71% Park
Innerleithen Rd EH45 8BA
☎ 01721 720451 ▨ 01721 723510
e-mail: reserve@parkpeebles.co.uk
Dir: in centre of Peebles opposite filling station

Best Western

PETS: Bedrooms (unattended) Public areas (not when food is served) Exercise area (on site)

The Park Hotel offers pleasant, well-equipped bedrooms of various sizes; those in the original house are particularly spacious. Public areas enjoy views of the gardens and include a tartan-clad bar, a relaxing lounge and a spacious wood-panelled restaurant. Guests can use the extensive leisure facilities on offer at the sister hotel, The Hydro.
ROOMS: 24 en suite No smoking in 6 bedrooms s £75-£89; d £136-£195 (incl. bkfst & dinner) **LB FACILITIES:** Putting green Use of facilities of Peebles Hotel Hydro entertainment Xmas **SERVICES:** Lift **PARKING:** 50
CARDS: ▨▨▨

ST BOSWELLS
Map 12 NT53

★★ 71% Buccleuch Arms
The Green TD6 0EW
☎ 01835 822243 ▨ 01835 823965
e-mail: bucchotel@aol.com
Dir: on A68, 8m N of Jedburgh

PETS: Bedrooms (unattended) £5 Public areas (not in bar/restaurant) Exercise area (on site) Pet Food
RESIDENT PETS: Jasper (Black Labrador) and Kelly (Springer)

Formerly a coaching inn, this long-established hotel stands opposite the village green. The lounge bar is a popular eating venue and complements the restaurant. Morning coffees and afternoon teas are served in the attractive lounge with its open fire. The well-equipped bedrooms come in a variety of sizes.
ROOMS: 19 en suite (2 fmly) No smoking in all bedrooms s £46-£49; d £77-£82 (incl. bkfst) **LB FACILITIES:** Putting green Xmas
PARKING: 50 **NOTES:** No smoking in restaurant Closed 25 Dec
CARDS: ▨▨▨

SWINTON
Map 12 NT84

◉◉ 🏠 The Wheatsheaf
Main St TD11 3JJ
☎ 01890 860257 ▨ 01890 860688
e-mail: reception@wheatsheaf-swinton.co.uk
Dir: from Edinburgh turn off A697 onto B6461. From East Lothian, turn off A1 onto B6461

PETS: Bedrooms Exercise area (200 yards) Pet Food
RESIDENT PETS: Basher (cat)

Overlooking the village green, The Wheatsheaf has a country pub atmosphere. It's the food that is the main focus however, served in a bright pine-furnished sun lounge, and when times are busy also in the cosy traditional dining room. Bedrooms offer a mix of sizes, but all are well equipped, the larger ones having luxury bathrooms.
ROOMS: 7 en suite No smoking in all bedrooms s £62-£90; d £95-£120 (incl. bkfst) **LB FACILITIES:** Xmas **PARKING:** 7 **NOTES:** No smoking in restaurant Closed 24-26 Dec RS 1 Dec-31 Jan **CARDS:** ▨▨▨

SOUTH AYRSHIRE

AYR
Map 10 NS3

★★★ 72% Savoy Park
16 Racecourse Rd KA7 2UT
☎ 01292 266112 ▨ 01292 611488
e-mail: mail@savoypark.com
Dir: from A77 follow Holmston road (A70) for 2m, through Parkhouse Street, turn left into Beresford Terrace, 1st right into Bellevue Rd

THE INDEPENDENT

PETS: Bedrooms Exercise area (adjacent) Pet Food

This well-established hotel retains many of its traditional values. Public rooms feature impressive panelled walls, ornate ceilings and open fires. The restaurant is reminiscent of a Highland shooting lodge and offers a good value menu to suit all tastes. Th

continue

large superior bedrooms retain a classical elegance while others are smart and modern; all have lovely bathrooms.
ROOMS: 15 en suite (3 fmly) No smoking in all bedrooms s £75-£85; d £95-£115 (incl. bkfst) **LB FACILITIES:** STV ch fac Xmas
PARKING: 60 **NOTES:** No smoking in restaurant
CARDS:

◆◆◆◆ Daviot House
12 Queens Ter KA7 1DU
☎ 01292 269678 📠 01292 880567
e-mail: thedaviot@aol.com
Dir: into Ayr by A71(N) or A77(S). Follow town centre signs, left at Esso petrol station, right at traffic lights. Next left, right at next lights, 2nd left and 2nd right

PETS: Bedrooms Exercise area (20 yards)

This well-maintained Victorian house sits in a peaceful location close to the beach and town centre. Bedrooms are attractive, modern in style and well-equipped. Public areas include a comfortable lounge and dining room, where enjoyable home-cooked evening meals and hearty breakfasts are served. A member of Golf South Ayrshire Hoteliers golf booking service for residents on local municipal courses.
FACILITIES: 5 en suite (3 fmly) No smoking TVB tea/coffee Cen ht TVL No coaches Dinner Last d 5pm **PRICES:** s £28-£32; d £44-£52✱
LB PARKING: 2

◆◆◆ Belmont
15 Park Circus KA7 2DJ
☎ 01292 265588 📠 01292 290303
e-mail: belmontguesthouse@btinternet.com
Dir: off A77 onto A70 Holmston road. At double rdbt follow Town Centre signs. Over railway bridge and left at traffic lights. After next lights turn right into Bellevue St. At end of street right into park circus establishment on right

PETS: Bedrooms Exercise area (250 yards)

Belmont Guesthouse is a pleasant terraced house in an attractive tree-lined conservation area, close to the town centre. Well-equipped, spacious bedrooms come with many thoughtful extras. Public areas include a lounge with a vast array of books and an elegant dining room. The hosts demonstrate a genuine concern for conservation and environmental issues.
FACILITIES: 5 en suite (3 fmly) (2 GF) TVB tea/coffee Cen ht TVL No coaches **PRICES:** s £26; d £46✱ **PARKING:** 5 **NOTES:** Closed Xmas & New Year **CARDS:**

◆◆◆ Windsor Hotel
6 Alloway Place KA7 2AA
☎ 01292 264689
e-mail: windsorhotel.ayr@ukonline.co.uk
Dir: from centre of Ayr, take A19 through Wellington Square. Hotel 1st on right.

PETS: Bedrooms Public areas (except dining room) Exercise area (adjacent)

This friendly private hotel is situated between the seafront and town centre. Bedrooms are well presented, with several on the ground floor and some suitable for families. The upstairs lounge

continued

looks towards the sea, whilst tasty breakfasts are served in the ground floor dining room.
FACILITIES: 10 rms (7 en suite) (4 fmly) (3 GF) No smoking in 1 bedrooms No smoking in dining room TVB tea/coffee Cen ht TVL No coaches **PRICES:** s fr £25; d fr £50✱ **LB**
NOTES: Closed mid Dec-mid Jan **CARDS:**

BALLANTRAE   Map 10 NX08

★★★ ◉◉◉ Glenapp Castle
KA26 0NZ
☎ 01465 831212 📠 831000
e-mail: enquiries@glenappcastle.com
Dir: 1m from A77 near Ballantrae village

RELAIS & CHATEAUX.

PETS: Bedrooms (ground floor only) Exercise area (in gardens) Pet Food RESIDENT PETS: Maggie (Springer Spaniel)

This stunning Victorian castle is set in extensive, private grounds to the south of the village. The all-inclusive price covers a skilfully prepared five-course dinner with carefully selected wines, afternoon tea, and aperitifs and liqueurs. Impeccably furnished bedrooms are graced with antiques and period pieces and there are a number of spacious, luxurious suites. Breathtaking views of Arran and Ailsa Craig can be enjoyed from the bedrooms and the delightful day rooms.
ROOMS: 17 en suite (2 fmly) (7 GF) No smoking in all bedrooms s £255-£395; d £365-£515 (incl. bkfst & dinner)
FACILITIES: Tennis (hard) Croquet lawn 30 acres of beautifully tended gardens ch fac Xmas **SERVICES:** Lift **PARKING:** 20
NOTES: No smoking in restaurant Closed Nov-Mar (Open New Year)
CARDS:

TURNBERRY   Map 10 NS20

★★★★★ ◉◉
Westin Turnberry Resort
KA26 9LT
☎ 01655 331000 📠 01655 331706
e-mail: turnberry@westin.com
Dir: from Glasgow take A77/M77 S towards Stranraer, 2m past Kirkoswald, follow signs for A719/Turnberry, hotel 500mtrs on right

WESTIN
HOTELS & RESORTS®

PETS: Bedrooms Public areas (foyer only) Exercise area (500yds)

This famous hotel enjoys magnificent views over to Arran, Ailsa Craig and the Mull of Kintyre. Facilities include a world-renowned golf course, the excellent Colin Montgomerie Golf Academy, a luxurious spa and a host of outdoor and country pursuits. Elegant bedrooms and suites are located in the main hotel, while adjacent lodges provide spacious, well-equipped accommodation. The Ailsa lounge is a very welcoming area since its refurbishment. As well as the elegant main restaurant for dining, there is a Mediterranean Terrace Brasserie, or the relaxed Clubhouse.
ROOMS: 132 en suite 89 annexe en suite (9 fmly) No smoking in 28 bedrooms s £115-£735; d £149-£790 (incl. bkfst) **LB**
FACILITIES: Spa STV Indoor swimming (H) Golf 36 Tennis (hard) Fishing Riding Snooker Sauna Gym Putting green Jacuzzi Health Spa & Leisure Club, Outdoor activity centre, Colin Montgomerie Golf Academy entertainment Xmas **SERVICES:** Lift **PARKING:** 200
NOTES: No smoking in restaurant Closed 12-27Dec
CARDS:

SOUTH LANARKSHIRE

BIGGAR
Map 11 NT03

★★★ 73% ◉◉ ♨ **Shieldhill Castle**
Quothquan ML12 6NA
☎ 01899 220035 ▤ 01899 221092
e-mail: enquiries@shieldhill.co.uk
Dir: off A702 onto B7016, 2m left. Hotel 1.5m on right

PETS: Bedrooms Public areas (Not in dining areas)
Exercise area (100 yards) Pet Food RESIDENT PETS: Ozzy,
Mutley, Gunner and Archie (dogs)

This imposing castle is set in rolling countryside and dates back
almost 800 years. Public areas are atmospheric and include the
high ceilinged Chancellor's restaurant and oak-panelled lounge.
Bedrooms, many with oversized baths, are spacious. A friendly
welcome is assured from both the enthusiastic staff and even the
proprietor's dogs! Food is a highlight of any stay.
ROOMS: 16 en suite No smoking in all bedrooms s £95-£248;
d £118-£190 (incl. bkfst) **LB FACILITIES:** Croquet lawn Jacuzzi Cycling,
Clay shoot, Hot air ballooning, laser shooting Xmas **PARKING:** 50
NOTES: No smoking in restaurant **CARDS:** ▤▤▤▤▤

KIRKMUIRHILL
Map 11 NS74

♦♦♦ ✿ **Dykecroft**
ML11 0JQ
☎ 01555 892226 ▤ 01555 892226
*Dir: from S M74 junct 10 (from N junct 9), take B7078 for 2m, then B7086
to Strathaven for 1.5m, past Boghead, 1st bungalow on left*

PETS: Bedrooms £1 Public areas Exercise area (nearby)
RESIDENT PETS: dogs

A warm and friendly welcome is assured at this modern
bungalow, situated in an open rural location on the road to
Strathaven. The bedrooms are traditionally furnished and
comfortable. There is a bright airy lounge/dining room that enjoys
lovely views of the surrounding countryside.
FACILITIES: 3 rms (3 GF) No smoking tea/coffee Cen ht TVL
60 acres sheep **PRICES:** s £23; d £42✶ **PARKING:** 4

NEW LANARK
Map 11 NS84

★★★ 72% **New Lanark Mill Hotel**
Mill One, New Lanark Mills ML11 9DB
☎ 01555 667200 ▤ 01555 667222
e-mail: hotel@newlanark.org
Dir: signed from all major roads, M74 junct 7 also signed from M8

PETS: Bedrooms (unattended) £10 Exercise area (adjacent)

Originally a cotton mill in the 18th-century, this hotel forms part of
a fully restored village, now a World Heritage Site. There's a bright
modern style throughout which contrasts nicely with features from
the original mill. There is a comfortable foyer-lounge with a
galleried restaurant above.
ROOMS: 38 en suite (2 fmly) No smoking in 28 bedrooms s £64.50; d £99
(incl. bkfst) **LB FACILITIES:** Fishing Xmas **SERVICES:** Lift **PARKING:** 75
NOTES: No smoking in restaurant **CARDS:** ▤▤▤▤▤▤▤

STIRLING

CALLANDER
Map 11 NN60

♦♦♦♦ ♨ **The Priory Country Guest House**
Bracklinn Rd FK17 8EH
☎ 01877 330001 ▤ 01877 339200
e-mail: judith@bracklinnroad.fsnet.co.uk
*Dir: M9 to Stirling, take A84 signed to Crianlarich/Callander. 7m through
Doune, then 6m to Callander. Right into Bracklinn Rd, house on right*

PETS: Bedrooms Exercise area (on site)
RESIDENT PETS: Hannah & Meg (Labradors), Gladstone (tortoise),
Whisky & Tipsy (cats)

Warm, genuine hospitality can be found at this delightful house,
set in a peaceful location within easy walking distance of the town
centre. The stylish bedrooms are tastefully decorated and
thoughtfully equipped; one has a four-poster. There is an elegant
lounge adjacent to the conservatory dining room, where delicious
breakfasts featuring local produce are served.
FACILITIES: 9 rms (8 en suite) (1 fmly) (1 GF) No smoking TV8B
tea/coffee Cen ht TVL No coaches Golf 18 Golf discount available at
local golf club **PRICES:** s fr £45; d fr £80✶ **PARKING:** 9
CARDS: ▤▤▤▤

DUNBLANE
Map 11 NN70

★★★ ◉◉ ♨ **Cromlix House**
Kinbuck FK15 9JT
☎ 01786 822125 ▤ 01786 825450
e-mail: reservations@cromlixhouse.com
*Dir: off A9 N of Dunblane. Exit B8033 to Kinbuck Village then after village
cross narrow bridge drive 200yds on left*

PETS: Bedrooms (unattended) Exercise area (set in
2000 acres) RESIDENT PETS: Dachshund

Situated in sweeping gardens and surrounded by a 2000-acre
estate, Cromlix House is an imposing Victorian mansion, boasting
gracious and inviting public areas. Well-appointed bedrooms, the
majority of which are suites, are spacious and elegant. The two
dining rooms offer contrasting décor but both ideal in which to
enjoy the skilfully prepared food.
ROOMS: 14 en suite s £140-£210; d £235-£385 (incl. bkfst) **LB**
FACILITIES: Tennis (hard) Fishing Croquet lawn Clay pigeon shooting,
Falconry, Archery ch fac Xmas **PARKING:** 51 **NOTES:** No smoking in
restaurant Closed 2-29 Jan RS Oct-Apr
CARDS: ▤▤▤▤▤▤

Scotland

LOCHEARNHEAD
Map 11 NN52

♦♦♦♦ Mansewood Country House
FK19 8NS

☎ 01567 830213 & 830485 📠 01567 830485

e-mail: katiestalker@aol.com

Dir: turn onto A84 at Stirling. Through Callender and Strathyre to Lochearnhead. 1st building on the left

PETS: Telephone for details

This charming 250-year-old former manse is set in its own well-tended grounds on the south side of the village. Bedrooms have been attractively decorated to offer high standards of comfort. Drinks can be enjoyed in the cosy bar or the elegant and comfortable lounge, and meals prepared with flair are served in the attractive restaurant.

FACILITIES: 6 en suite (1 GF) No smoking in bedrooms No smoking in dining room No smoking in lounges TVB tea/coffee Licensed Cen ht No coaches Dinner Last d 5pm **PARKING:** 10

CARDS: 🖃 🖃 VISA 🖃 🔟

PORT OF MENTEITH
Map 11 NN50

★★ 70% ◎ Lake
FK8 3RA

☎ 01877 385258 📠 01877 385671

e-mail: enquiries@lake-of-menteith-hotel.com

Dir: M9 junct 10, take either A84/A873/A81 to Port of Menteith. Hotel located beside village church

PETS: Bedrooms (unattended) Exercise area Pet Food

Art deco styling and a stunning setting on the shores of Scotland's only lake make this hotel unique. The conservatory style restaurant has fantastic views over the lake and there is a spacious lounge and bar. Individually styled bedrooms come in a range of sizes and offer co-ordinated decor.

ROOMS: 16 en suite (5 GF) No smoking in all bedrooms s £60-£88; d £120-£156 (incl. bkfst & dinner) **LB** **FACILITIES:** Fishing Xmas **PARKING:** 50 **NOTES:** No children 8yrs No smoking in restaurant Closed 1 Jan RS Jan & Feb **CARDS:** 🖃 🖃 🖃 🖃 🔟

All information was correct at the time of going to press; we recommend you confirm details on booking

STRATHYRE
Map 11 NN51

★ ◎◎ Creagan House
FK18 8ND

☎ 01877 384638 📠 01877 384319

e-mail: eatandstay@creaganhouse.co.uk

Dir: 0.25m N of Strathyre on A84

PETS: Bedrooms Sep Accom (Kennel) (unattended) Exercise area (park nearby) Pet Food

This delightful property dates back to the 17th century and has been sympathetically restored and upgraded to provide comfortable accommodation. Attractive bedrooms are thoughtfully equipped with CD players, mineral water and bathrobes, and TVs and videos are available on request. The baronial style dining room provides a wonderful backdrop for imaginative cooking. Warm hospitality and attentive service are the highlight of any stay.

ROOMS: 5 en suite (1 fmly) (1 GF) No smoking in all bedrooms s £60; d £100 (incl. bkfst) **LB** **FACILITIES:** Xmas **PARKING:** 26 **NOTES:** No smoking in restaurant Closed 23 Jan-5 Mar, 6-25 Nov RS Thurs **CARDS:** 🖃 🖃 VISA 🔟

WEST DUNBARTONSHIRE

BALLOCH
Map 10 NS38

♦♦♦ Sunnyside
35 Main St G83 9JX

☎ 01389 750282

e-mail: sunnyside@i12.com

Dir: from Glasgow on A82 to Barloan rdbt. Take 3rd exit (A813) over 2 rdbts to lights. Straight through lights for Sunnyside 0.2m on right

PETS: Bedrooms (unattended) £3 Exercise area (0.25 mile)

Set in its own grounds well back from the road by Loch Lomond, Sunnyside is an attractive, traditional detached house, parts of which date back to the 1830s. Bedrooms are attractively decorated and provide comfortable modern accommodation. The dining room is located on the ground floor, and is an appropriate setting for hearty Scottish breakfasts.

FACILITIES: 3 en suite (1 fmly) No smoking TVB tea/coffee Cen ht No coaches **PRICES:** s £15-£28; d £40-£50✱ **BB** **PARKING:** 8

WEST LOTHIAN

LINLITHGOW
Map 11 NS97

♦♦♦♦ ❦ Bomains Farm
by Bo'Ness EH49 7RQ

☎ 01506 822188 & 822861 📠 01506 824433

e-mail: bomains.farmhouse@euphony.net

Dir: M9 junct 3, left to Linlithgow, take A706 for Boness, 1.5m to golf course x-roads, turn left, first farm on right

PETS: Bedrooms (by arrangement) (unattended) £2 Exercise area (adjacent) **RESIDENT PETS:** Laddie (Jack Russell) & Zana (German Shepherd)

From its elevated position this friendly farmhouse enjoys delightful

continued on p300

Scotland

LINLITHGOW continued

views across the Firth of Forth. There is an elegant and stylish combined lounge and dining room where delicious home-cooked fare is served. Bedrooms vary in size and the smart, modern fitted-furniture makes excellent use of space and is enhanced by quality fabrics.

FACILITIES: 3 en suite No smoking STV TVB tea/coffee Cen ht TVL 180 acres Arable Dinner Last d 5.30pm **PRICES:** s £30-£35; d £50-£60✳
PARKING: 8

SCOTTISH ISLANDS

ARRAN, ISLE OF

BRODICK   Map 10 NS03

★★ ◎◎ ♨♨ Kilmichael Country House
Glen Cloy KA27 8BY
☎ 01770 302219 📠 01770 302068
e-mail: enquiries@kilmichael.com
Dir: from Brodick ferry terminal follow N'bound (Lochranza) road for 1m. Left at golf course, inland between sports field & church, follow signs

PETS: Bedrooms (unattended) Exercise area (adjacent) dogs must be on a lead in garden RESIDENT PETS: Puccini (Dalmatian), Jehan & Aurangzeb (peacocks), chickens & ducks

Reputed to be the oldest on the island, this lovely house lies in attractive gardens in a quiet glen less than five minutes' drive from the ferry terminal. It has been lovingly restored to create a stylish, elegant country house, adorned with ornaments from around the world. There are two inviting drawing rooms and a bright dining room, serving award-winning contemporary cuisine. The delightful bedrooms are furnished in classical style; some are contained in a pretty courtyard conversion.

ROOMS: 4 en suite 3 annexe en suite (6 GF) No smoking in all bedrooms s fr £85; d £150-£190 (incl. bkfst) **LB FACILITIES:** STV Jacuzzi **PARKING:** 12 **NOTES:** No children 12yrs No smoking in restaurant Closed Nov-Feb (ex for prior bookings)
CARDS: 💳 💳 💳 💳 💳

♦♦♦♦ Dunvegan House
Dunvegan Shore Rd KA27 8AJ
☎ 01770 302811 📠 01770 302811
e-mail: dunveganhouse1@hotmail.com
Dir: turn right from ferry terminal, 500yds along Shore Road

PETS: Sep Accom

Dunvegan is a delightful detached home overlooking the bay towards Brodick Castle with Goat Fell beyond. The comfortable lounge and attractive dining room, as well as the pine-furnished bedrooms, enjoy the views. A daily-changing dinner menu and an interesting wine list encourage guests to dine in.

FACILITIES: 9 en suite (1 fmly) (3 GF) No smoking in 2 bedrooms No smoking in dining room TVB tea/coffee Licensed Cen ht TVL No coaches Dinner Last d 4pm **PRICES:** s fr £35; d fr £60✳
PARKING: 10 **NOTES:** Closed Xmas & New Year

BARRA, ISLE OF

TANGASDALE   Map 13 NF60

★★ 68% Isle of Barra
Tangasdale Beach HS9 5XW
☎ 01871 810383 📠 01871 810385
e-mail: barrahotel@aol.com
Dir: left after leaving ferry terminal onto A888, hotel 2m on left

PETS: Bedrooms (unattended) Exercise area (adjacent)
RESIDENT PETS: Velvet (cat)

Overlooking the white sands of Halaman Bay and the Atlantic Ocean beyond, this modern hotel enjoys a stunning location. Public areas, including a comfortable lounge and light and airy restaurant, make the most of the views, as do most of the bedrooms. The restaurant features superb local shellfish. Service is both friendly and attentive.

ROOMS: 30 en suite (2 fmly) (7 GF) s £42-£49; d £68-£84 (incl. bkfst)
LB FACILITIES: STV Beach ch fac **PARKING:** 50 **NOTES:** No smoking in restaurant Closed mid Oct-Mar **CARDS:** 💳 💳 💳 💳

HARRIS, ISLE OF

SCARISTA   Map 13 NG09

◎◎ 🏠 Scarista House
HS3 3HX
☎ 01859 550238 📠 01859 550277
e-mail: timandpatricia@scaristahouse.com
Dir: on A859, 15 miles south of Tarbert

PETS: Bedrooms (unattended) Public areas Exercise area (200yds) Pet Food RESIDENT PETS: Max and Misty (cats), Molly (Cavalier King Charles Spaniel), 2 rabbits & guinea pig

A former manse, Scarista lies in an idyllic position with a panoramic view of the Atlantic and just a short walk to miles of sandy beach. The house is run in a relaxed country house manner by the friendly hosts. Expect wellies in the hall and masses of books and CDs in one of two lounges. Bedrooms are cosy and delicious set dinners and memorable breakfasts are provided.

ROOMS: 3 en suite 2 annexe en suite (2 GF) No smoking in all bedrooms s £83-£88; d £130-£140 (incl. bkfst) **LB FACILITIES:** no TV in bdrms **PARKING:** 12 **NOTES:** No smoking in restaurant Closed Xmas RS Nov-Mar **CARDS:** 💳 💳

ISLAY, ISLE OF

PORT ASKAIG   Map 10 NR46

★★ 63% Port Askaig
PA46 7RD
☎ 01496 840245 📠 01496 840295
e-mail: hotel@portaskaig.co.uk
Dir: at Ferry Terminal

PETS: Bedrooms (unattended) Public areas (public bar & beer garden only) Exercise area Pet Food

This family-run hotel, set in an 18th-century building, offers

continued

comfortable bedrooms. The lounge provides fine views over to nearby Jura and there is a choice of bars, popular with locals. Traditional dinners are served in the bright restaurant and a full range of bar snacks and meals is also available.

ROOMS: 8 rms (6 en suite) (1 fmly) s £35-£55; d £60-£78 (incl. bkfst)
LB PARKING: 21 **NOTES:** No children 5yrs No smoking in restaurant
CARDS: 🔲 💳 🔛 🔳 💲

MULL, ISLE OF

DERVAIG Map 13 NM45

★★ 78% ◎◎ ♨ Druimard Country House
PA75 6QW
☎ 01688 400345 & 400291 📠 01688 400345
e-mail: druimard.hotel@virgin.net
Dir: from Craignure ferry terminal turn right towards Tobermory, through Salen Village, after 1.5m turn left to Dervaig, hotel on right

PETS: Bedrooms (unattended) Exercise area (0.25 mile)
Pet Food **RESIDENT PETS:** Beech, Jo, Cassie, Boswell, Kes and Dickson (Labradors), Kizzy (cat)

A charming Victorian country house, on the edge of the village beside the Mull Little Theatre. Attractive colour schemes feature in the bedrooms, which are comfortably furnished and thoughtfully equipped. There is a relaxing lounge and conservatory bar, but the focal point is the newly refurbished dining room, where tempting five-course dinners attract much praise.

ROOMS: 5 en suite 2 annexe en suite (2 fmly) (2 GF) s £90-£110; d £130-£170 (incl. bkfst & dinner) **LB FACILITIES:** Mull Little Theatre within grounds **PARKING:** 20 **NOTES:** No smoking in restaurant Closed Nov-Mar **CARDS:** 🔲 💳 🔛 🔳 💲

TOBERMORY Map 13 NM55

★★★ 73% Western Isles
PA75 6PR
☎ 01688 302012 📠 01688 302297
e-mail: wihotel@aol.com
Dir: from ferry follow signs to Tobermory. Over 1st mini-rdbt in Tobermory then over small bridge and immediate right & follow road to T-junct. Right again then keep left and take 1st left for hotel at top of hill on right

PETS: Bedrooms £5 Public areas (not dining areas)
Exercise area Pet Food **RESIDENT PETS:** Sam (Black Labrador), Smokey (cat)

Built in 1883 and standing high above the village, this hotel enjoys spectacular views over Tobermory harbour and the Sound of Mull. Public rooms range from the classical drawing room and restaurant to the bright modern conservatory bar/bistro. Bedrooms come in a variety of styles; the impressive superior rooms include a suite complete with its own piano.

ROOMS: 28 en suite s £45-£114; d £99-£124 (incl. bkfst) **LB**
FACILITIES: ch fac Xmas **PARKING:** 28 **NOTES:** No smoking in restaurant Closed 17-27 Dec **CARDS:** 🔲 💳 🔛 🔳 💲

All abbreviations are explained on page 9

★★ ◎◎ Highland Cottage
Breadalbane St PA75 6PD
☎ 01688 302030
e-mail: davidandjo@highlandcottage.co.uk
Dir: A848 Craignure/Fishnish ferry terminal, pass Tobermory signs, mini rdbt across narrow bridge, turn right. Hotel on right opp Fire Station

PETS: Bedrooms (unattended) Exercise area (park 5 mins walk) Pet Food **RESIDENT PETS:** Charlie (tortoise shell cat)

Providing the highest level of natural and unassuming hospitality, this delightful little gem lies high above the island's capital. There are two inviting lounges in which to relax, one with an honesty bar and both adorned with books and magazines. The cosy dining room offers memorable dinners and splendid breakfasts. Bedrooms are all individual; some have four-posters and all are comprehensively equipped to include video TVs and music centres.

ROOMS: 6 en suite (1 GF) No smoking in all bedrooms s £95-£120; d £120-£150 (incl. bkfst) **LB FACILITIES:** STV **PARKING:** 6
NOTES: No children 10yrs No smoking in restaurant Closed 4 wks mid Oct/mid Nov RS 6 Jan-6 Mar **CARDS:** 🔲 💳 🔛 🔳 💲

★★ 69% ◎ Tobermory
53 Main St PA75 6NT
☎ 01688 302091 📠 01688 302254
e-mail: tobhotel@tinyworld.co.uk
Dir: on waterfront, overlooking Tobermory Bay

PETS: Bedrooms Exercise area (300 yards)

This friendly hotel, with its pretty pink frontage, sits on the seafront amid other brightly coloured buildings. There is a comfortable lounge where drinks are served (there is no bar) prior to dining in the cosy restaurant. Bedrooms, in a variety of sizes, are bright and vibrant; the superior rooms have video TVs.

ROOMS: 16 rms (15 en suite) (3 fmly) (2 GF) No smoking in all bedrooms s £41-£102; d £82-£102 (incl. bkfst) **LB FACILITIES:** ch fac Xmas **NOTES:** No smoking in restaurant Closed Xmas
CARDS: 🔲 💳 🔛 🔳 💲

SHETLAND

BRAE Map 16 HU36

★★★ 69% ♨ Busta House
ZE2 9QN
☎ 01806 522506 📠 01806 522588
e-mail: reservations@bustahouse.com
Dir: take A970 north through village, at north end follow signs to Busta House 0.5m

THE CIRCLE
Selected Individual Hotels
GREAT BRITAIN

PETS: Bedrooms (unattended) Exercise area (on site)
Pet Food

Dating back to 1724, this popular hotel boasts the reputation of being Britain's most northerly country-house hotel. Bedrooms vary in size and style but are well equipped, comfortable, and many have excellent sea views. Day rooms include the comfortable "long room" lounge; and wide-ranging menus are to be found in

continued on p302

Scotland

BRAE continued

the Pitcairn restaurant and popular, traditional bar. The staff are friendly and keen to please.

ROOMS: 20 en suite (1 fmly) No smoking in 6 bedrooms s £75; d £100-£140 (incl. bkfst) **LB PARKING:** 40 **NOTES:** No smoking in restaurant Closed 23 Dec-5 Jan **CARDS:** 〰️ 🟦 💳 🟦 💳 🔳 Ⓢ

LERWICK   Map 16 HU44

◆◆◆◆ Glen Orchy House
20 Knab Rd ZE1 0AX
☎ 01595 692031 📠 01595 692031
e-mail: glenorchy.house@virgin.net
Dir: adjacent to coastguard station

> **PETS:** Bedrooms (unattended) Exercise area (20 yards)

This welcoming and well-presented hotel lies above the town with views over the Knab, and is within easy walking distance of the town centre. Bedrooms are modern in design and there is a choice of lounges with books and board games, one with an honesty bar. Breakfasts are as substantial as dinner, chosen from the daily-changing menu.

FACILITIES: 22 en suite (5 fmly) No smoking in 7 bedrooms No smoking in dining room No smoking in 1 lounge STV TVB tea/coffee Licensed Cen ht No coaches Dinner Last d 2pm **PARKING:** 10
CARDS: 〰️ 🟦 🔳

> ★ **Red stars indicate the AA's Top 200 Hotels in Britain & Ireland**

> **Don't forget to let proprietors know when you book that you're bringing your pet**

PORTREE   Map 13 NG44

★★★ 75% ◉◉ Bosville
Bosville Ter IV51 9DG
☎ 01478 612846 📠 01478 613434
e-mail: bosville@macleodhotels.co.uk
Dir: A87 signed Portree, then A855 into town for the Bosville

> **PETS:** Bedrooms £5 Exercise area (500mtrs)

This stylish, popular hotel has been recently extended and enjoys fine views over the harbour. Bedrooms are furnished to a high specification and have a fresh, contemporary feel. Public areas include a smart new bar, bistro and the Chandlery restaurant where fantastic local produce is treated with respect and refreshing restraint.

ROOMS: 25 en suite (2 fmly) No smoking in 10 bedrooms s £65-£75; d £80-£150 (incl. bkfst) **LB FACILITIES:** Use of nearby leisure club Xmas
PARKING: 10 **NOTES:** No smoking in restaurant
CARDS: 〰️ 🟦 💳 🟦 💳 🔳 Ⓢ

★★ 73% ◉ Rosedale
Beaumont Crescent IV51 9DB
☎ 01478 613131 📠 01478 612531
e-mail: rosedalehotelsky@aol.com
Dir: follow the directions to the village centre & harbour, hotel on waterfront of Harbourside

> **PETS:** Bedrooms (By arrangement) (unattended) Public areas

The atmosphere is wonderfully warm at this delightful family-run waterfront hotel. A labyrinth of stairs and corridors connects the comfortable lounges, bar and charming restaurant, which are set on different levels. The restaurant offers fine views of the bay. Modern bedrooms offer a good range of amenities.

ROOMS: 18 en suite (1 fmly) No smoking in all bedrooms s £35-£50; d £60-£116 (incl. bkfst) **LB PARKING:** 2 **NOTES:** No smoking in restaurant Closed mid Nov- Mar **CARDS:** 〰️ 🟦 🔳 Ⓢ

WALES

Roman road, near Pen-y-fan Mountain, Powys

WALES

ANGLESEY, ISLE OF

AMLWCH
Map 06 SH49

★★ 70% **Lastra Farm**
Penrhyd LL68 9TF
☎ 01407 830906 ▤ 01407 832522
e-mail: booking@lastra-hotel.com
Dir: after 'Welcome to Amlwch' sign turn left. Straight across main road, left at T-junct on to Rhosgoch Rd

PETS: Bedrooms (unattended) Public areas Exercise area (200 yards) Pet Food

This 17th-century farmhouse offers pine-furnished, colourfully decorated bedrooms. There is also a comfortable lounge and a cosy bar. A wide range of good-value food is available either in the restaurant or Granary's Bistro. The hotel can cater for functions in a separate purpose built suite.

ROOMS: 5 en suite 3 annexe en suite (1 fmly) s £39.50-£44.50; d £60-£68 (incl. bkfst) **LB PARKING:** 40 **NOTES:** No smoking in restaurant **CARDS:** ▤▤▤▤▤

BEAUMARIS
Map 06 SH67

★★★ 64% **The Bulkeley Hotel**
Castle St LL58 8AW
☎ 01248 810415 ▤ 01248 810146
e-mail: bulkeley@bestwestern.co.uk
Dir: from M56 & M6 take A5 or A55 coast road

PETS: Bedrooms (unattended) £5 Public areas (except restaurant & bistro) Exercise area Pet Food

A Grade I listed hotel built in 1831, the Bulkeley has fine views from many rooms. Well-equipped bedrooms are generally spacious, with pretty fabrics and wallpapers. There is a choice of bars, an all-day coffee lounge and a health club. Regular jazz evenings, a resident pianist and a friendly staff create a relaxed atmosphere.

ROOMS: 43 en suite (6 fmly) No smoking in 10 bedrooms s fr £74.50; d fr £107 (incl. bkfst) **LB FACILITIES:** Spa Sauna Solarium Gym Jacuzzi Hair & Beauty Salon Xmas **SERVICES:** Lift **PARKING:** 30 **NOTES:** No smoking in restaurant **CARDS:** ▤▤▤▤▤▤

HOLYHEAD
Map 06 SH28

★★ 66% **Boathouse**
Newry Promenade, Newry Beach LL65 1YF
☎ 01407 762094 ▤ 01407 764898
e-mail: boathousehotel@supanet.com
Dir: follow expressway into Holyhead continue through yellow box & follow signs for Marina. From ferry terminal turn right at 1st lights and right at 2nd set and follow signs for Marina. Hotel at bottom of hill on seafront

PETS: Bedrooms (unattended) £5 Public areas (Bar only) Exercise area (100 yards)

Situated in a prominent position overlooking the harbour, this hotel makes an ideal stop for ferry travellers. Bedrooms are attractively decorated to a high standard and are well equipped. The attractive lounge bar offers a wide range of home-cooked food; there is also a separate dining room.

ROOMS: 17 en suite (1 fmly) (5 GF) No smoking in 15 bedrooms s £40-£55; d £70-£80 (incl. bkfst) **LB FACILITIES:** Painting & sketching guidance available **PARKING:** 40 **NOTES:** No smoking in restaurant **CARDS:** ▤▤▤▤▤

◆◆◆ **Wavecrest**
93 Newry St LL65 1HU
☎ 01407 763637 ▤ 01407 764862
e-mail: cwavecrest@aol.com
Dir: at end of A55 turn left. After 600yds turn by railings, premises 100yds up hill on right

PETS: Bedrooms Exercise area

Conveniently located for the Irish ferry terminals and within easy walking distance of the town centre, the Wavecrest is proving to be a popular overnight stop-off. Pretty bedrooms are equipped with satellite television and other modern facilities. There is a comfortable lounge and evening meals may be booked in advance.

FACILITIES: 4 rms (2 en suite) (3 fmly) No smoking STV TVB tea/coffee Cen ht TVL No coaches Dinner Last d 3pm **PARKING:** 1 **NOTES:** Closed 24-31 Dec

MENAI BRIDGE
Map 06 SH57

★★ 63% **Victoria Hotel**
Telford Rd LL59 5DR
☎ 01248 712309 ▤ 01248 716774
e-mail: vicmenai@barbox.net
Dir: over Menai Suspension Bridge, take 2nd exit from rdbt on Anglesey side, continue 100yds, hotel on right

PETS: Bedrooms (unattended) Public areas Exercise area (100 yards)

This family-run hotel is situated in Menai Bridge and has panoramic views of the Menai Straits and Britannia Bridge. Many bedrooms have their own balconies. There are two character bars where meals are available, and also a more formal conservatory dining room. The hotel holds a civil wedding licence.

ROOMS: 14 en suite 3 annexe en suite (4 fmly) (1 GF) s fr £39; d fr £49.50 (incl. bkfst) **LB FACILITIES:** Childrens playground Xmas **PARKING:** 40 **NOTES:** No smoking in restaurant RS 25 Dec **CARDS:** ▤▤▤▤▤▤

BRIDGEND

CARDIFF

BRIDGEND
Map 03 SS97

★★★ 69% Heronston
Ewenny Rd CF35 5AW
☎ 01656 668811 📠 01656 767391
e-mail: reservations@heronston-hotel.demon.co.uk
Dir: M4 junct 35, follow signs for Porthcawl, at 4th rdbt turn left towards Ogmore-by-Sea (B4265), hotel 200yds on left

PETS: Bedrooms (unattended) Public areas (not in restaurant) Exercise area (on grounds) Pet Food

Situated within easy reach of the town centre and the M4, this large modern hotel offers spacious well-equipped accommodation, including no-smoking bedrooms and ground floor rooms. Public areas include an open plan lounge/bar, attractive restaurant and a smart leisure & fitness club. The hotel also has a choice of function/conference rooms.
ROOMS: 69 en suite 6 annexe en suite (4 fmly) (37 GF) No smoking in 21 bedrooms s fr £39.50; d fr £59 (incl. bkfst) LB **FACILITIES:** STV Indoor swimming (H) Outdoor swimming (H) Sauna Solarium Gym Jacuzzi Steamroom ch fac Xmas **SERVICES:** Lift **PARKING:** 250
NOTES: No smoking in restaurant **CARDS:** 💳💳💳💳💳💳

PENCOED
Map 03 SS98

★★★ 73%
St Mary's Hotel & Country Club
St Marys Golf Club CF35 5EA
☎ 01656 861100 & 860280 📠 01656 863400
e-mail: stmarysgolfhotel@btinternet.com
Dir: M4 junct 35, on A473

PETS: (kennel) Exercise area Pet Food

This charming 16th-century farmhouse has been converted and extended into a modern and restful hotel, surrounded by its own two golf courses. Bedrooms are generously appointed, well-equipped and most feature whirlpool baths. Guests are offered a choice of bars, which are popular with club members, and may dine in the Rafters Restaurant.
ROOMS: 24 en suite (19 fmly) **FACILITIES:** STV Golf 18 Putting green Floodlit driving range Xmas **PARKING:** 140
CARDS: 💳💳💳💳💳💳

SARN PARK MOTORWAY SERVICE AREA (M4)
Map 03 SS98

⇧ **Welcome Lodge**
Sarn Park Services CF32 9RW
☎ 01656 659218 📠 01656 768665
e-mail: sarnpark.hotel@welcomebreak.co.uk
Dir: M4 junct 36

PETS: Bedrooms (unattended) Public areas Exercise area (adjacent)

This modern building offers accommodation in smart, spacious and well-equipped bedrooms, suitable for families and business travellers, and all with en suite bathrooms. Refreshments may be taken at the nearby family restaurant. For further details consult the Hotel Groups page.
ROOMS: 40 en suite s £35-£55; d £35-£55

CARDIFF
Map 03 ST17

★★★★ 70% 🏅
Copthorne Hotel Cardiff-Caerdydd
Copthorne Way, Culverhouse Cross CF5 6DH
☎ 029 2059 9100 📠 029 2059 9080
e-mail: sales.cardiff@mill-cop.com
Dir: M4 junct 33, take A4232 for 2.5m towards Cardiff West and then A48 W to Cowbridge

COPTHORNE

PETS: Bedrooms (unattended) £5 Exercise area

A comfortable, popular and modern hotel, conveniently located for the airport and city. Bedrooms are a good size and some have a private lounge. Public areas are smartly presented with features including a gym, pool, meeting rooms and a restaurant which overlooks the lake.
ROOMS: 135 en suite (14 fmly) (27 GF) No smoking in 97 bedrooms s £85-£195; d £95-£205 (incl. bkfst) LB **FACILITIES:** STV Indoor swimming (H) Sauna Gym Jacuzzi Steam room ch fac Xmas **SERVICES:** Lift **PARKING:** 225
CARDS: 💳💳💳💳💳💳

★★★ 72%
St Mellons Hotel & Country Club
Castleton CF3 2XR
☎ 01633 680355 📠 01633 680399
e-mail: stmellons@bestwestern.co.uk
Dir: M4 junct 28 follow signs into Castleton. Through village, then sharp left at brow of hill following hotel sign into driveway

PETS: Bedrooms (unattended) £4 Exercise area

This former Regency mansion has been tastefully converted into an elegant hotel and has an adjoining leisure complex with a strong local following. Bedrooms are spacious and smart; some are in purpose-built wings. The public areas retain their pleasing former proportions and include relaxing lounges and a restaurant.
ROOMS: 21 en suite 20 annexe en suite (9 fmly) No smoking in 18 bedrooms s £105-£115; d £115-£125 (incl. bkfst) LB **FACILITIES:** STV Indoor swimming (H) Tennis (hard) Squash Sauna Solarium Gym Jacuzzi Beauty salon Xmas **PARKING:** 90 **NOTES:** No smoking in restaurant **CARDS:** 💳💳💳💳💳💳

⇧ **Hotel Ibis Cardiff**
Churchill Way CF10 2HA
☎ 029 2064 9250 📠 029 2920 9260
e-mail: H2936@accor-hotels.com
Dir: M4, then A48 2nd exit A4232. Follow signs to City Centre on Newport Rd, left after railway bridge, left after Queen St station.

ibis

PETS: Bedrooms Public areas

Modern, budget hotel offering comfortable accommodation in bright and practical bedrooms. Breakfast is self-service and dinner is available in the restaurant. For further details, consult the Hotel Groups page.
ROOMS: 102 en suite s fr £47; d £47-£52

Wales

CARDIFF continued

⌂ **Hotel Ibis Cardiff Gate**

Malthouse Av, Cardiff Gate Business Park,
Pontprennau CF23 8RA
☎ 029 2073 3222 🗎 029 2073 4222
e-mail: H3159@accor-hotels.com
Dir: M4 junct 30, take slip rd signed Cardiff Service Station. Hotel on left.

PETS: Bedrooms

Modern, budget hotel offering comfortable accommodation in bright and practical bedrooms. Breakfast is self-service and dinner is available in the restaurant. For further details, consult the Hotel Groups page.
ROOMS: 78 en suite s £38.95-£43.95; d £38.95-£43.95

◆◆◆◆ **Big Sleep Hotel**

Bute Ter CF10 2FE
☎ 029 2063 6363 🗎 029 2063 6364
e-mail: bookings.cardiff@thebigsleephotel.com
Dir: opposite Cardiff International Arena

PETS: Bedrooms (unattended) Exercise area (10 minute walk)

Part of Cardiff's skyline, this city centre hotel offers well-equipped bedrooms ranging from standard to penthouse, with spectacular views over the city towards the bay. There is a bar on the ground floor and secure parking. Continental breakfast is served or 'Breakfast to go' is an alternative for the traveller wishing to make an early start.
FACILITIES: 81 en suite (6 fmly) No smoking in 40 bedrooms
No smoking in area of dining room STV TVB tea/coffee Direct dial from bedrooms Licensed Lift Cen ht **PRICES:** d £45-£135✱ LB
PARKING: 30 **CARDS:** 🌑 💳 💳 💳 🌑 💳 🔄

CARMARTHENSHIRE

CWMDUAD

Map 02 SN33

◆◆◆◆ **Neuadd-Wen**

SA33 6XJ
☎ 01267 281438 🗎 01267 281438
e-mail: goodbourn@neuaddwen.plus.com
Dir: on A484, 9m N of Carmarthen

PETS: Bedrooms (unattended) Public areas (not in dining room) Exercise area (field adjacent)

Excellent customer care is assured at this combined post office and house situated in pretty gardens in an unspoilt village. Bedrooms are filled with thoughtful extras and there is a choice of guest lounges. One bedroom is contained in a tastefully renovated, early-Victorian toll cottage across the road. There is an attractive dining room that serves imaginative dinners utilising fresh local produce.
FACILITIES: 8 rms (6 en suite) (2 fmly) (2 GF) No smoking in dining room No smoking in 1 lounge TVB tea/coffee Direct dial from bedrooms Licensed Cen ht TVL No coaches Dinner Last d 6pm
PRICES: s £19.50-£23.50; d £39-£47✱ LB **PARKING:** 12
CARDS: 🌑 💳 💳 🌑 💳

LLANDOVERY

Map 03 SN73

★★★ 63% **Castle**

King's Rd SA20 0AP
☎ 01550 720343 🗎 01550 720673
e-mail: castlehotelllandovery@hotmail.com
Dir: on the A40 in town centre, between Brecon & Carmarthen

PETS: Bedrooms (unattended) Exercise area (Back gardens) Pet Food RESIDENT PETS: Meg (chocolate Labrador), Annie (Mountain dog)

Overlooked by the original Norman keep, the Castle Hotel is in the heart of this market town. There is a warm atmosphere, enhanced by the roaring log fires lit in the winter. There is a wide variety of bedroom styles and sizes and many have benefited from refurbishment, including rooms once occupied by George Borrow and Lord Nelson.
ROOMS: 23 en suite (4 fmly) No smoking in 21 bedrooms s £35-£45; d £60-£75 (incl. bkfst) **FACILITIES:** STV Fishing Xmas **PARKING:** 30
NOTES: No smoking in restaurant **CARDS:** 🌑 💳 💳 💳 🌑 💳 🔄

◆◆◆◆◆ **Cwm Rhuddan Mansion**

SA20 0DX
☎ 01550 721414 🗎 01550 721414
e-mail: cwmrhuddan@hotmail.com
Dir: Travelling from Brecon turn left off A40, in Llandovery, on to A4069. After 1m turn left and immediately left into drive to House.

PETS: Bedrooms (unattended) Public areas (not in dining room) Exercise area (in grounds) RESIDENT PETS: Oscar (Great Dane)

This French château-style mansion was built in 1871 and stands in extensive grounds and gardens. In recent years, it has been extensively and painstakingly restored to provide spacious, comfortable and tastefully appointed accommodation, including a four-poster room. There is a choice of lounges, where welcoming log fires are lit during cold weather. Separate tables are provided in the elegant breakfast room. The owner has an impressive collection of motoring memorabilia including two vintage Austins, which guests are welcome to view.
FACILITIES: 3 en suite (2 fmly) No smoking in bedrooms No smoking in dining room No smoking in 1 lounge TVB tea/coffee Cen ht TVL
No coaches Games lounge, table tennis table LB **PARKING:** 14

LLANELLI

Map 02 SN50

★★★ 67% **Diplomat Hotel**

Felinfoel SA15 3PJ
☎ 01554 756156 🗎 01554 751649
e-mail: enquiries@diplomat-hotel-wales.com
Dir: M4 junct 48 onto A4138 then B4303 hotel in 0.75m on right

PETS: Bedrooms £5 Public areas (except restaurant, lounge or hallway) Exercise area (Adjacent) Pet Food

This former Victorian mansion, set in mature grounds, has been extended over the years to provide a comfortable and relaxing hotel. The well-appointed bedrooms are located in the main house and the nearby coach house. Public areas include

continued

Wales

Trubshaw's restaurant, a large function suite and a modern leisure centre.
ROOMS: 23 en suite 8 annexe en suite (2 fmly) No smoking in 6 bedrooms s £65-£75; d £85-£95 (incl. bkfst) **LB FACILITIES: Spa** Indoor swimming (H) Sauna Solarium Gym Jacuzzi entertainment Xmas **SERVICES:** Lift **PARKING:** 250
CARDS: ▨▨▨▨▨▨▨

See advert on this page

RHANDIRMWYN Map 03 SN74

♦♦♦ 🍺 The Royal Oak
SA20 0NY
☎ 01550 760201 🖷 01550 760332
e-mail: royaloak@rhandirmwyn.com
Dir: follow signs to Rhandirmwyn from A40 at Llandovery

PETS: Bedrooms Public areas Exercise area (10 yards)

Located north of Llandovery in an Area of Outstanding Natural Beauty, this 17th-century former hunting lodge for the Cawdor Estate offers a wealth of character within its public areas. There are a wide range of real ales and imaginative food served. Comfortable bedrooms are equipped with both practical and homely extras.
FACILITIES: 5 rms (3 en suite) (1 fmly) TV3B tea/coffee Pool table Clay pigeon wknds Last d 9.30pm **PARKING:** 20
CARDS: ▨▨▨▨▨

CEREDIGION

ABERPORTH Map 02 SN25

♦♦♦ Ffynonwen
SA43 2HT
☎ 01239 810312 🖷 01239 814910
e-mail: ffynon.wen@tesco.net
Dir: Follow A487 N from Cardigan then 2nd left signed for Aberporth on B4333. Continue for 0.5m and Ffynonwen is signed to left. Follow lane for 0.5m and Ffynonwen is on right.

PETS: Bedrooms Public areas (except dining areas) **Exercise area** (surrounding farmland) **RESIDENT PETS:** Trusty and Elly (dogs), four cats, chickens and peacocks

Quietly located in twenty acres of grounds one mile from the sea, this 17th-century former farmhouse provides comfortable, traditionally furnished accommodation. The bedrooms are homely and include a two-bedroom family suite, as well as a ground-floor
continued

Wales

room. The spacious public areas include a dining room, a separate bar where welcoming log fires burn in cold weather, and a guest lounge.

FACILITIES: 5 rms (3 en suite) (1 fmly) (1 GF) No smoking in bedrooms No smoking in dining room No smoking in lounges TVB tea/coffee Licensed Cen ht No coaches Fishing Dinner Last d 8.30pm
PRICES: s £25; d £50✱ **PARKING:** 10 **CARDS:** ▨▨▨▨

Please mention AA Pet Friendly Places to Stay when booking

🍺 **Places with this symbol are pubs**

ABERYSTWYTH

Map 06 SN58

★★ 65% **Marine Hotel**
The Promenade SY23 2BX
☎ 01970 612444 📠 01970 617435
e-mail: marinehotel1@btconnect.com
Dir: from W on A44. From N or S Wales on A487. On seafront west of pier

PETS: Bedrooms (unattended) £5 Exercise area (beach)

The Marine is a privately owned hotel situated on the promenade overlooking Cardigan Bay. Bedrooms have been tastefully decorated, some have four-poster beds and many have sea views. The refurbished reception rooms are comfortable and relaxing, and meals are served in the elegant dining room or the bar.
ROOMS: 44 rms (43 en suite) (7 fmly) No smoking in 1 bedroom
s £45-£60; d £60-£95 (incl. bkfst) **LB FACILITIES:** Spa Sauna Solarium Gym Jacuzzi ch fac Xmas **SERVICES:** Lift **PARKING:** 15
NOTES: No smoking in restaurant
CARDS: 💳

★★ 64% **Harry's**
40-46 North Pde SY23 2NF
☎ 01970 612647 📠 01970 627068
e-mail: info@harrysaberystwyth.com
Dir: N on A487, in town centre

PETS: Bedrooms Sep Accom (Boarding kennels £8 per night) (unattended) small dogs £5, large dogs £8 Public areas (except restaurant) Exercise area (400 yards) Pet Food **RESIDENT PETS:** Earl & Duke (Chocolate Labradors)

Conveniently located for the shopping area and seafront, this is a friendly and popular hotel. The main attraction is the popular Harry's restaurant with its wide selection of dishes and specialising in local produce. Bedrooms are well equipped with modern facilities.
ROOMS: 24 en suite (2 fmly) No smoking in 6 bedrooms s fr £45; d fr £70 (incl. bkfst) **LB PARKING:** 6 **NOTES:** Closed 25-26 Dec
CARDS: 💳

> **All abbreviations are explained on page 9**

> **Places with this symbol are farms**

◆◆◆ **Queensbridge Hotel**
Promenade, Victoria Ter SY23 2DH
☎ 01970 612343 📠 01970 617452
Dir: N end of promenade, near Constitution Hill

PETS: Bedrooms £5

A friendly private hotel on the promenade. The bedrooms, some suitable for families, are well equipped with modern facilities and many have fine sea views. Facilities include a comfortable lounge and bar, where snacks are available and a lift serves all floors.
FACILITIES: 15 en suite (2 fmly) No smoking in 6 bedrooms
No smoking in dining room No smoking in 1 lounge TVB tea/coffee Direct dial from bedrooms Licensed Lift Cen ht TVL Golf Di **LB**
PARKING: 6 **CARDS:** 💳

CARDIGAN

Map 02 SN14

◆◆◆ **Webley Hotel**
Poppit Sands, St Dogmaels SA43 3LN
☎ 01239 612085
Dir: from St Dogmaels follow signs to Poppit. Hotel by side of Teifi estuary, 0.5m from Poppit Beach

PETS: Bedrooms Public areas (during certain hours) Exercise area (0.5 mile) **RESIDENT PETS:** 1 dog

This friendly riverside inn overlooks the Teifi Estuary near Poppit Sands on the south bank. There are lovely views from many of the bedrooms, which are smart and modern with good facilities. The bar is popular locally and good-value meals are usually on offer. There is a small cosy lounge for residents and separate tables are provided in the traditionally furnished dining room.
FACILITIES: 8 rms (5 en suite) No smoking in bedrooms No smoking in dining room No smoking in lounges TV5B tea/coffee Cen ht TVL Dinner Last d 9pm **PRICES:** s £25-£35; d £40-£60✳ **LB PARKING:** 53
CARDS: 💳

EGLWYSFACH

Map 06 SN69

★★★ **Ynyshir Hall**
SY20 8TA
☎ 01654 781209 📠 01654 781366
e-mail: info@ynyshir-hall.co.uk
Dir: off A487, 5.5m S of Machynlleth, signposted from the main road

RELAIS & CHATEAUX

PETS: Bedrooms (some rooms) (unattended) £3 Exercise area (adjacent) **RESIDENT PETS:** Oscar (Bernese Mountain Dog)

continued

Set in beautifully landscaped grounds and surrounded by an RSBP reserve, Ynyshir Hall is a haven of calm and a no-smoking hotel. Lavishly styled bedrooms, each individually themed around a great painter, provide high standards of luxury and comfort. Lounge and bar have different moods, and both feature abundant fresh flowers; and the dining room offers outstanding cooking using best ingredients with modern style. The Reens really put their individual stamp on the hotel, Rob with his bold paintings, and Joan with her charming and caring hospitality.

ROOMS: 7 en suite 2 annexe en suite No smoking in all bedrooms
s £95-£220; d £180-£250 (incl. bkfst) **LB FACILITIES:** Croquet lawn
Xmas **PARKING:** 20 **NOTES:** No children 9yrs No smoking in restaurant
Closed 5-29 Jan **CARDS:**

GWBERT-ON-SEA　　　　　　　　　　Map 02 SN15

★★★ 67% **Cliff**
SA43 1PP
☎ 01239 613241 📠 01239 615391
e-mail: reservations@cliffhotel.com
Dir: off A487 into Cardigan, follow signs to Gwbert, in 3m straight to hotel

> **PETS:** **Bedrooms Sep Accom (Kennels) Public areas
> Exercise area (20 yards) Pet Food**

Set in 30 acres of grounds that include a 9-hole golf course, and enjoying a cliff-top location overlooking Cardigan Bay, this hotel offers superb sea views. Bedrooms come in a variety of sizes, with some overlooking the bay. Public areas are spacious and offer a choice of bars.

ROOMS: 72 en suite (5 fmly) No smoking in 10 bedrooms
FACILITIES: STV Outdoor swimming (H) Golf 9 Fishing Snooker Sauna
Gym Putting green entertainment **SERVICES:** Lift **PARKING:** 95
NOTES: No smoking in restaurant
CARDS:

LAMPETER　　　　　　　　　　　　Map 02 SN54

★★★ 71% **Falcondale Mansion**

Best Western

SA48 7RX
☎ 01570 422910 📠 01570 423559
e-mail: info@falcondalehotel.com
Dir: 800yds W of High St A475 or 1.5m NW of Lampeter A482

> **PETS:** **Bedrooms (unattended) Public areas (except
> restaurants) Exercise area (14 acres on site) Pet food by
> arrangement RESIDENT PETS:** Chloe & Truffles (cats), Major &
> Pudgeley (Cocker Spaniels)

Built in the Italianate style, this charming Victorian property is set in extensive grounds and beautiful parkland. Bedrooms are generally spacious, well-equipped and, following a recent refurbishment programme, are individually and tastefully decorated. Bars and lounges are similarly well-appointed with additional facilities including a conservatory and function room.

ROOMS: 20 en suite (2 fmly) No smoking in 8 bedrooms s £80-£150;
d £120-£180 (incl. bkfst) **LB FACILITIES:** Tennis (hard) Croquet lawn
Xmas **SERVICES:** Lift **PARKING:** 60 **NOTES:** No smoking in restaurant
CARDS:

> 🌲 **Places with this symbol are
> country house hotels**

◆◆◆ **Haulfan**
6 Station Ter SA48 7HH
☎ 01570 422718
e-mail: haulfanguesthouse@lampeter.freeserve.co.uk
*Dir: from N A485/A482, towards Lampeter, left at 1st x-rds near university.
From S, M4/A485, through town centre, right by fountain, right*

> **PETS:** **Bedrooms Sep Accom (ground-floor bedroom)
> Exercise area**

Very popular with visitors to the nearby university, this Victorian town house provides modern furnished and equipped bedrooms. Facilities here include a homely, comfortable lounge and generous breakfasts are served in the cosy dining room, where separate tables are provided. A warm welcome is assured from proprietors, who have an excellent knowledge of the area.

FACILITIES: 3 rms (2 en suite) (1 fmly) No smoking STV TVB
tea/coffee Cen ht TVL No coaches **PRICES:** s £22-£27; d £40-£44✳ **LB**
NOTES: Closed 20 Dec-mid Jan

LLANDYSUL　　　　　　　　　　　Map 02 SN44

◆◆◆◆ **Plas Cerdin**
Ffostrasol SA44 4TA
☎ 01239 851329
*Dir: from Llandysul take A486 to New Quay through Bwlch-y-Groes. R into
private rd*

> **PETS:** **Bedrooms Exercise area (paddock adjacent)**

Located north of the town in an elevated position that offers stunning views of the Cerdin Valley and Cambrian mountains, this very well maintained modern house stands in lovely gardens and provides homely and thoughtfully furnished bedrooms, one of which is ideal for family use. A comfortable lounge is also available.

FACILITIES: 3 en suite (1 fmly) (1 GF) No smoking in bedrooms
No smoking in dining room TVB tea/coffee Cen ht TVL No children 3yrs
No coaches Dinner Last d 24hrs prior **PRICES:** s £25-£30; d £45-£50✳
PARKING: 4 **NOTES:** Closed Dec & Jan

CONWY

BETWS-Y-COED　　　　　　　　　　Map 06 SH75

★★★ 70%
Craig-y-Dderwen Riverside Hotel

THE INDEPENDENTS

LL24 0AS
☎ 01690 710293 📠 01690 710362
e-mail: craig-y-dderwen@betws-y-coed.co.uk
Dir: A5 to town, cross Waterloo Bridge and take 1st left

> **PETS:** **Bedrooms (unattended) £5 per night Public areas (not
> in restaurant or conservatory) Exercise area (on site) Pet Food**

This Victorian country-house hotel is set in well-maintained grounds alongside the River Conwy, at the end of a tree-lined drive. Very pleasant views can be enjoyed from many rooms, and two of the bedrooms have four-poster beds. There are comfortable lounges and the atmosphere is tranquil and relaxing.

ROOMS: 16 en suite (2 fmly) (1 GF) s £60-£100; d £70-£110
(incl. bkfst) **LB FACILITIES:** Spa Croquet lawn Badminton, Volleyball
ch fac **PARKING:** 50 **NOTES:** No smoking in restaurant
Closed 23-26 Dec & 30 Dec-1 Feb **CARDS:**

BETWS-Y-COED continued

★★★ 68% Best Western Waterloo

LL24 0AR
☎ 01690 710411 📠 01690 710666
e-mail: reservations@waterloo-hotel.info
Dir: A5 London-Holyhead near Waterloo Bridge

PETS: Bedrooms (cottage style rooms) £3.50 per day
Exercise area (woodland walks nearby)

This long-established hotel, named after the nearby Waterloo Bridge, is ideally located for Snowdonia. Accommodation is split between rooms in the main hotel and modern, cottage-style rooms located in buildings to the rear. The attractive Garden Room Restaurant serves traditional Welsh specialities, and the Wellington Bar offers light meals and snacks.
ROOMS: 10 en suite 30 annexe en suite (2 fmly) (30 GF) No smoking in 14 bedrooms s £55-£70; d £90-£120 (incl. bkfst) **LB FACILITIES:** Spa Indoor swimming (H) Sauna Solarium Gym Jacuzzi Steam room ch fac **PARKING:** 180 **NOTES:** No smoking in restaurant Closed 25 Dec
CARDS: 💳💳💳💳💳

COLWYN BAY   Map 06 SH87

★★ 64% Lyndale

410 Abergele Rd, Old Colwyn LL29 9AB
☎ 01492 515429 📠 01492 518805
e-mail: lyndale@tinyworld.co.uk
Dir: junct 22 A55 Old Colwyn, turn left. At rdbt through village continue for 1m on A547

PETS: Bedrooms Exercise area (adjacent)

A range of accommodation is available at this friendly, family-run hotel, including suites that are suitable for family use and a four-poster bedroom. There is a cosy bar and a comfortable foyer lounge, and weddings and other functions can be catered for.
ROOMS: 14 en suite (3 fmly) No smoking in 3 bedrooms s £25-£39; d £45-£59 (incl. bkfst) **LB FACILITIES:** ch fac **PARKING:** 20
CARDS: 💳💳💳💳

Don't forget to let proprietors know when you book that you're bringing your pet

---

★★ 64% Marine

West Promenade LL28 4BP
☎ 01492 530295 📠 0870 168 9400
e-mail: reservations@marinehotel.co.uk
Dir: off A55 at Old Colwyn to seafront. Turn left, after pier left before lights, car park on corner

PETS: Bedrooms (unattended) Charge for damage/laundry
Public areas (not in restaurant) Exercise area (25 yards)

This privately owned and personally run hotel stands on the promenade, overlooking the sea. The accommodation is soundly maintained and equipped to suit both commercial visitors and holidaymakers. Facilities include a small bar and a lounge.
ROOMS: 14 rms (12 en suite) (4 fmly) No smoking in 9 bedrooms s £27-£32; d fr £54 (incl. bkfst) **LB PARKING:** 11 **NOTES:** No smoking in restaurant Closed mid Oct-Apr **CARDS:** 💳💳💳💳💳

♦♦♦♦ Whitehall Hotel

51 Caley Promenade, Rhos-on-Sea LL28 4EP
☎ 01492 547296
e-mail: mossd.cymru@virgin.net
Dir: From A55 E or W Old Colwyn exit. At T-junct turn into Promenade. Left at Promenade and W for 1.9m to Rhos on Sea. Left at Puppet Theatre. Hotel 5th on right

PETS: Bedrooms (Allowed in one bedroom only)
Exercise area (10yds)

Overlooking Rhos-on-Sea promenade, this popular, family-run hotel is convenient for shopping and local amenities. Pretty bedrooms include several family rooms and all benefit from an excellent range of facilities such as video and CD players. A bar and separate lounge cater for residents and the menu offers hearty, home-cooked meals in addition to bar snacks.
FACILITIES: 12 rms (10 en suite) (4 fmly) No smoking STV TVB tea/coffee Direct dial from bedrooms Licensed Cen ht TVL VCR/DVDs in rooms Dinner Last d 4.30pm **PRICES:** s fr £26.75; d £53.50-£59.50✳
LB PARKING: 5 **CARDS:** 💳💳💳💳

♦♦♦ Northwood Hotel

47 Rhos Rd, Rhos-on-Sea LL28 4RS
☎ 01492 549931
e-mail: welcome@northwoodhotel.co.uk
Dir: exit A55 at Rhos-on-Sea, follow signs for Promenade. Left at seafront, after 200yds, turn left (opp building with clock), hotel 150yds on left

PETS: Bedrooms (unattended) £2-4 Public areas (Not dining room or lounge) Exercise area (200 yards)
RESIDENT PETS: Two love birds

A short walk from the seafront and shops, Northwood Hotel has a warm and friendly atmosphere and welcomes back many regular guests. Bedrooms are furnished in modern style and freshly prepared meals can be enjoyed in the spacious dining room/bar while light refreshments are offered in the lounge.
FACILITIES: 12 rms (10 en suite) (3 fmly) (2 GF) No smoking in 3 bedrooms No smoking in dining room No smoking in lounges TVB tea/coffee Licensed TVL No children 10yrs No coaches Dinner Last d 7pm **PRICES:** s £25-£28; d £56-£66 **LB PARKING:** 12
CARDS: 💳💳💳💳

Wales

◆◆◆ Cabin Hill Private Hotel
College Av, Rhos-on-Sea LL28 4NT
☎ 01492 544568
Dir: exit A55 at Rhos-on-Sea, signed to promenade, through Rhos, L at Rhos Fynach pub. 3rd R (College Ave).

PETS: Bedrooms (unattended) Public areas (except dining room) Exercise area (5 mins walk)

Cabin Hill lies in a quiet residential area within walking distance of the seafront and local shops. Bedrooms are neatly decorated and thoughtfully furnished and equipped. Ground floor areas include a spacious and attractive dining room and a comfortable guest lounge.
FACILITIES: 9 rms (7 en suite) (2 fmly) No smoking in dining room TVB tea/coffee Cen ht TVL Dinner Last d 4.30pm **LB PARKING:** 2

CONWY Map 06 SH77

★★★ 73% ◉ Groes Inn
Tyn-y-Groes LL32 8TN
☎ 01492 650545 📠 01492 650855
Dir: A55, cross Old Conwy Bridge, 1st left through Castle Walls on B5106 (Trefriw rd), hotel 2m on right.

PETS: Bedrooms (One bedroom available) (unattended) £5 Exercise area (Adjacent)

This inn dates back in part to the 16th century and has charming features. It offers a choice of bars and has a beautifully appointed restaurant, with a conservatory extension opening on to the lovely rear garden. The comfortable, well-equipped bedrooms are contained in a separate building; some have balconies or private terraces.
ROOMS: 14 en suite (1 fmly) (4 GF) No smoking in 6 bedrooms
PARKING: 100 **NOTES:** No smoking in restaurant Closed Xmas
CARDS: 🔲🔲🔲🔲 🔲

★★★ 71% ◉ Castle Hotel Conwy
High St LL32 8DB
☎ 01492 582800 📠 01492 582300
e-mail: mail@castlewales.co.uk
Dir: A55 junct 18, follow signs for town centre and cross estuary with castle on left. Right then left at mini rdbts onto one-way system. Right at Town Wall Gate, right onto Berry St then along High St on left

PETS: Bedrooms £5 Exercise area (100 metres)

This family-run, 16th-century hotel is one of Conwy's most distinguished buildings and offers a relaxed and friendly atmosphere. Bedrooms have been extensively refurbished to an impressive standard including a stunning new suite. Public areas have also been upgraded and include a popular modern bar and the award-winning Shakespeare's restaurant.
ROOMS: 28 en suite (2 fmly) No smoking in 20 bedrooms s £60-£79; d £90-£250 (incl. bkfst) **LB FACILITIES:** ch fac Xmas **PARKING:** 34
NOTES: No smoking in restaurant **CARDS:** 🔲🔲🔲🔲 🔲

★★ ◉◉◉ ♨ The Old Rectory Country House
Llanrwst Rd, Llansanffraid Glan Conwy LL28 5LF
☎ 01492 580611 📠 01492 584555
e-mail: info@oldrectorycountryhouse.co.uk
Dir: 0.5m S from A470/A55 junct on left side, by 30mph sign

PETS: Bedrooms (Pets allowed in Coach House only) (unattended) Exercise area (adjacent)

This friendly and welcoming hotel enjoys elevated views of the Conwy Estuary and Snowdonia. Traditionally-styled day rooms are luxurious and elegant and home-baked afternoon teas can be taken in the elegant lounge. Dinner is the highlight of any stay and the daily changing set menu makes excellent use of fresh and seasonal local produce. Bedrooms make the most of the views and are furnished with thought and care. Super hospitality sustains a real 'home-from-home' ambience.
ROOMS: 4 en suite 2 annexe en suite No smoking in all bedrooms
PARKING: 10 **NOTES:** No children 5yrs No smoking in restaurant
Closed 14 Dec-15 Jan **CARDS:** 🔲🔲🔲🔲 🔲

◆◆◆◆◆ ⊜ Sychnant Pass House
Sychnant Pass Rd LL32 8BJ
☎ 01492 596868 📠 01492 596868
e-mail: bresykes@sychnant-pass-house.co.uk
Dir: follow signs to Conwy Town Centre. Past visitor centre then 2nd left into Uppergate St. Continue out of town for 1.75m on right near top of hill

PETS: Bedrooms (unattended) Public areas (not in restaurant) Exercise area (Snowdonia Park opposite) pets must be well behaved **RESIDENT PETS:** Morris (cat) and two dogs

Fine views can be had from this Edwardian house set in its own landscaped grounds. Bedrooms, including suites and four poster rooms, are individually furnished and equipped with a range of thoughtful extras. Lounges, warmed by open fires in the chillier months, are comfortable and inviting, and imaginative dinners and suppers are served in the attractive dining room.
FACILITIES: 10 en suite (6 fmly) (3 GF) No smoking in bedrooms
No smoking in dining room No smoking in 1 lounge TVB tea/coffee
Licensed Cen ht TVL No coaches Riding Croquet lawn All rooms with video, films & CDs available Dinner Last d 8.30pm **PRICES:** s £60-£120; d £80-£140✱ **LB PARKING:** 30 **CARDS:** 🔲🔲🔲🔲 🔲

Wales

LLANDUDNO Map 06 SH78

🐕

★★★ 64% St George's

The Promenade LL30 2LG
☎ 01492 877544 📠 01492 877788
e-mail: stgeorges@countrytown-hotels.co.uk
Dir: A55-A470, follow road to the promenade, 0.25m, hotel on corner

PETS: Bedrooms Sep Accom (pen) Public areas Exercise area (20 yards) Pet Food

This popular and friendly seafront hotel was the first to be built in the town. Its many Victorian features include the splendid, ornate Wedgwood Room. The main lounges overlook the bay, are comfortable, and hot and cold snacks are available all day. Several bedrooms have views over the sea, and some have balconies.
ROOMS: 86 en suite (6 fmly) No smoking in 12 bedrooms s £72-£112; d £110-£150 (incl. bkfst) **LB FACILITIES:** STV Sauna Solarium Jacuzzi Hairdressing Health & beauty salon ch fac Xmas **SERVICES:** Lift **PARKING:** 50 **NOTES:** No smoking in restaurant
CARDS: MasterCard American Express Visa Diners Barclays Connect Delta Switch

🐕 🐹 🐦

★★ 72% Sunnymede

West Pde LL30 2BD
☎ 01492 877130 📠 01492 871824
Dir: from A55 follow signs for Llandudno & Deganwy. At 1st rdbt after Deganwy take 1st exit towards the sea. At corner turn left & follow road for 400yds

PETS: Bedrooms (unattended) Public areas (except restaurant/library) Exercise area (10 yards) Pet Food
RESIDENT PETS: Sassy, Tommy and Candy (crossbreed dogs)

Sunnymede is a friendly family-run hotel located on Llandudno's West Shore. Many rooms have views over the Conwy Estuary and Snowdonia. Modern bedrooms are attractively decorated and well equipped. Bar and lounge areas are particularly comfortable and attractive. All areas of the hotel have benefited from recent refurbishment.
ROOMS: 15 en suite (3 fmly) (4 GF) No smoking in all bedrooms s £43-£86; d £86-£98 (incl. bkfst & dinner) **LB FACILITIES:** Xmas **PARKING:** 18 **NOTES:** No children 3yrs No smoking in restaurant Closed Jan-Feb & Nov RS Xmas period **CARDS:** MasterCard Visa Barclays Connect Delta Switch

🐕

★★ 70% Epperstone

15 Abbey Rd LL30 2EE
☎ 01492 878746 📠 01492 871223
e-mail: epperstonehotel@btconnect.com
Dir: A55-A470 to Mostyn Street. Left at rdbt, 4th right into York Rd. Hotel on junct of York Rd & Abbey Rd

PETS: Bedrooms £3 Exercise area

This delightful hotel is located in wonderful gardens in a residential part of town, within easy walking distance of the seafront and shopping area. Bedrooms are attractively decorated and thoughtfully equipped. Two lounges, a comfortable non-smoking room and a Victorian-style conservatory are available. A daily changing menu is offered in the bright dining room.
ROOMS: 8 en suite (5 fmly) (1 GF) No smoking in all bedrooms s £25-£33; d £50-£66 (incl. bkfst) **LB FACILITIES:** STV Xmas **PARKING:** 8 **NOTES:** No children 5yrs No smoking in restaurant
CARDS: MasterCard Visa Delta Switch

🐕

★★ 68% Somerset

St Georges Crescent, Promenade LL30 2LF
☎ 01492 876540 📠 01492 863700
e-mail: somerset@favroy.freeserve.co.uk
Dir: on the Promenade

PETS: Bedrooms (unattended) £3 per night (except dining areas) Exercise area (10 yards)

With its sister hotel, The Wavecrest, this cheerful holiday hotel occupies an ideal location on the central promenade and affords superb views over the bay from many rooms. Regular entertainment is provided as well as a range of bar and lounge areas. Bedrooms are well decorated and modern facilities are provided.
ROOMS: 37 en suite (4 fmly) **FACILITIES:** Games room entertainment Xmas **SERVICES:** Lift **PARKING:** 20 **NOTES:** No smoking in restaurant Closed Jan-Feb **CARDS:** MasterCard Visa Barclays Connect Delta Switch

🐕 🐈

★★ 68% Wavecrest

St Georges Crescent, Central Promenade LL30 2LF
☎ 01492 860615 📠 01492 863700
e-mail: somerset@favroy.freeserve.co.uk
Dir: on promenade behind Marks & Spencer

PETS: Telephone for details

The Wavecrest is the sister hotel of the adjoining Somerset, and public areas are shared. It lies on the central promenade and most bedrooms have lovely sea views. Lounge and bar areas are comfortably furnished and a games room is available. Staff are friendly and regular entertainment is staged.
ROOMS: 41 en suite (7 fmly) **FACILITIES:** Games room, Patio garden entertainment Xmas **SERVICES:** Lift **PARKING:** 12 **NOTES:** No smoking in restaurant Closed Jan-Feb **CARDS:** MasterCard Visa Barclays Connect Delta Switch

🐕

♦♦♦ Quinton Hotel

36 Church Walks LL30 2HN
☎ 01492 876879 📠 01492 876879
Dir: exit A55 at Conwy and follow road through Deganwy to west shores

PETS: Bedrooms Public areas Exercise area

The Quinton Hotel is conveniently located for the town centre and both beaches. Personally run by the same owners for over 25 years, it provides warm and friendly hospitality and value for money. Bedrooms are well equipped and include one on the ground floor.
FACILITIES: 9 en suite (3 fmly) (1 GF) No smoking in dining room TVB tea/coffee Direct dial from bedrooms Licensed Cen ht TVL No children 12yrs Pool Table Dinner Last d 7pm **PRICES:** s £18.50-£20; d £37-£40✳ **LB BB PARKING:** 12

All information was correct at the time of going to press; we recommend you confirm details on booking

Wales

◆◆◆ Tudno Lodge
66 Church Walks LL30 2HG
☎ 01492 876174 & 0800 6525274
e-mail: tudnolodge@supanet.com
Dir: turn off A55 at Llandudno Junction towards Llandudno, 4m. To top of Mostyn Street, with Empire Hotel opposite, turn left and Lodge is on right

PETS: Bedrooms (unattended)

Peacefully located a few minutes' walk from pier, beach and shops, this Victorian villa retains many features and sympathetic improvements have resulted in homely and thoughtfully equipped bedrooms, some with fine sea views. Breakfasts and dinners are served in an attractive front-facing dining room and a first floor lounge with an open fire is also available.

FACILITIES: 7 rms (4 en suite) (3 fmly) No smoking in bedrooms
No smoking in dining room TVB tea/coffee TVL No coaches Dinner
Last d 4pm **PRICES:** s £19-£22; d £38-£44✳ **LB BB**
NOTES: Closed Dec-Jan **CARDS:** ▭ ▥ ▨ ▩ ▧

◆◆◆ Vine House
23 Church Walks LL30 2HG
☎ 01492 876493
e-mail: barryharris@bigfoot.com
Dir: by Great Orme tram station

PETS: Bedrooms Exercise area (200mtrs)

Vine House is a friendly family run house located a short walk from the seafront and pier, opposite the historic tram station. Bedrooms vary in size and style and include some spacious, stylish refurbished rooms with separate sitting areas and modern bathrooms. All rooms have views of the sea or the Orme.

FACILITIES: 5 rms (3 en suite) (1 fmly) No smoking TVB tea/coffee
Cen ht **PRICES:** s £17-£20; d £34-£40✳ **LB BB**
NOTES: Closed Dec-Feb **CARDS:** ▭ ▥ ▨ ▩ ▧ ▧

LLANRWST
Map 06 SH86

★★★ 66% Maenan Abbey
Maenan LL26 0UL
☎ 01492 660247 ▤ 01492 660734
e-mail: reservations@manab.co.uk
Dir: 3m N on A470

PETS: Bedrooms £5 Exercise area (surrounding countryside)

This traditionally run private hotel was built as an abbey in 1850 on the site of a 13th-century monastery. It is now a popular venue for weddings and the grounds and magnificent galleried staircase make an ideal backdrop for photographs. Bedrooms include a large suite and are equipped with modern facilities. Meals are served in the bar and restaurant.

ROOMS: 14 en suite (2 fmly) s £45; d £80 (incl. bkfst) **LB**
FACILITIES: Fishing guided mountain walks Xmas **PARKING:** 60
NOTES: No smoking in restaurant **CARDS:** ▭ ▥ ▨ ▩ ▧

 🔌 **Places with this symbol are pubs**

★★ 73% Hafod Country Hotel
LL27 0RQ
☎ 01492 640029 ▤ 01492 641351
e-mail: hafod@breathemail.net
Dir: on B5106 between A5 at Betws-y-Coed & A55 at Conwy. 2nd entrance on right entering Trefriw from S

PETS: Bedrooms (unattended) £5 Public areas (Bar only)
Exercise area (200 yards) **RESIDENT PETS:** Gizzmo (cat)

This former farmhouse is a personally run and friendly hotel with a wealth of charm and character. The tasteful bedrooms feature period furnishings and thoughtful extras such as fresh fruit. There is a comfortable sitting room and a cosy bar. The fixed-price menu is imaginative and makes good use of fresh, local produce while the breakfast menu offers a wide choice.

ROOMS: 6 en suite No smoking in all bedrooms s £35-£43; d £60-£75 (incl. bkfst) **LB FACILITIES:** Xmas **PARKING:** 14
NOTES: No children 11yrs No smoking in restaurant
Closed early Jan-mid Feb **CARDS:** ▭ ▥ ▨ ▩ ▧

◆◆◆◆◆ 🔌 Bron-y-Graig
LL21 0DR
☎ 01490 413007 ▤ 01490 413007
e-mail: business@north-wales-hotel.co.uk
Dir: on A5 eastern edge of Corwen

PETS: Bedrooms Public areas (not in restaurant)
Exercise area (30 yards) **RESIDENT PETS:** Jodie (Labrador),
Eleanor and Tiptoes (cats)

Located within a few minutes' walk from town centre, this impressive Victorian house retains many original features including fireplaces, stained glass and a tiled floor in the entrance hall. Bedrooms, complemented by luxurious bathrooms, are thoughtfully furnished and two are located in a sympathetically renovated coach house. Ground floor areas include a traditionally furnished dining room and comfortable guest lounge. A warm welcome, attentive service and imaginative food is assured.

FACILITIES: 8 en suite 2 annexe en suite (3 fmly) No smoking in bedrooms No smoking in dining room STV TVB tea/coffee Direct dial from bedrooms Licensed Cen ht ch fac Fishing Dinner Last d 9.30pm
PRICES: s £35-£45; d £49✳ **LB PARKING:** 15
CARDS: ▭ ▥ ▨ ▩ ▧

Wales

CORWEN continued

◆◆◆◆ Powys Country House
Holyhead Rd, Bonwm LL21 9EG
☎ 01490 412367
e-mail: info@powyscountryhouse.co.uk
Dir: on A5 Corwen to Llangollen road, premises approx 1m on left after leaving Corwen

PETS: Bedrooms (some) £5 max Exercise area (100 metres) **RESIDENT PETS:** Alfie (Dachshund), Twix and Shadow (cats)

This delightful country house is peacefully located in three acres of gardens and woodland. The impressive entrance hall is wood-panelled, and a spacious dining room is the setting for imaginative breakfasts. Bedrooms are equipped with modern facilities and include one with a four-poster bed. Hospitality is warm and welcoming; self-catering cottages are also available.
FACILITIES: 5 en suite (1 fmly) (2 GF) No smoking in bedrooms No smoking in dining room TVB tea/coffee Licensed Cen ht **PRICES:** s £25-£32.50; d £36-£50✱ **LB BB PARKING:** 12

All AA listed accommodation, restaurants and pubs can be found on the AA's website www.theAA.com

★ Red stars indicate the AA's Top 200 Hotels in Britain & Ireland

🌲 Places with this symbol are country house hotels

RUTHIN
Map 06 SJ15

◆◆◆◆ Eyarth Station
Llanfair Dyffryn Clwyd LL15 2EE
☎ 01824 703643 📠 01824 707464
e-mail: stay@eyarthstation.com
Dir: off A525, 1 m S Ruthin. Take lane on right - 600 metres to Eyarth Station

PETS: Bedrooms £5 Public areas (except dining room & lounge) Exercise area (on site)

Until 1964 and the Beeching cuts, this was a sleepy country station. A comfortable lounge and outdoor swimming pool occupy the space once taken up by the railway and platforms. Bedrooms are tastefully decorated and full of thoughtful extras. Family rooms are available, and two rooms are in the old stationmaster's house adjoining the main building.
FACILITIES: 6 en suite 1 annexe en suite (2 fmly) (4 GF) No smoking in bedrooms No smoking in dining room No smoking in 1 lounge TV1B tea/coffee Licensed Cen ht TVL No coaches Outdoor swimming pool (heated) Dinner Last d 7pm **PRICES:** s £37; d £56✱ **LB PARKING:** 6 **NOTES:** Closed Feb & 2 wks in Nov **CARDS:** 🖃 🖃 💳

FLINTSHIRE

MOLD
Map 07 SJ26

★★★ 67% Beaufort Park Hotel
Alltami Rd, New Brighton CH7 6RQ
☎ 01352 758646 📠 01352 757132
e-mail: bph@beaufortparkhotel.co.uk
Dir: A55/A494. Through Alltami lights, over mini rdbt by petrol station towards Mold, A5119. Hotel 100yds on right

PETS: Bedrooms £10 per dog per night

This large, modern hotel is conveniently located a short drive from the North Wales Expressway and offers various styles of spacious accommodation. There are extensive public areas, and several meeting and function rooms are available. There is a wide choice of meals in the formal restaurant and in the popular Arches bar.
ROOMS: 106 en suite (4 fmly) (33 GF) No smoking in 25 bedrooms s £70-£95; d £120 (incl. bkfst) **LB FACILITIES:** Squash Jacuzzi Games Room, Darts entertainment ch fac Xmas **PARKING:** 200
CARDS: 🖃 🖃 🖃 🖃 💳 🖃 💳

GWYNEDD

ABERDYFI
Map 06 SN69

★★ 74% 🌲 Penhelig Arms Hotel & Restaurant
LL35 0LT
☎ 01654 767215 📠 01654 767690
e-mail: info@penheligarms.com
Dir: take A493 coastal road, hotel faces Penhelig harbour

PETS: Bedrooms (unattended) £3 Public areas Exercise area (25 yards)

Situated opposite the old harbour, this delightful 18th-century hotel overlooks the Dyfi Estuary. The well-maintained bedrooms have good quality furnishings and modern facilities. The character public bar is much loved by locals who enjoy the real ale selections and the food with its emphasis on seafood. AA Seafish Pub of the Year for Wales 2004-5.
ROOMS: 10 en suite 5 annexe en suite (4 fmly) No smoking in all bedrooms s fr £45; d £78-£98 (incl. bkfst) **LB FACILITIES:** ch fac **PARKING:** 14 **NOTES:** No smoking in restaurant Closed 25 & 26 Dec **CARDS:** 🖃 🖃 🖃 💳 🖃 💳

◆◆◆◆ Cartref
LL35 0NR
☎ 01654 767273 📠 01654 767000
e-mail: enquiries@cartref-guesthouse.com
Dir: on A493. At W end of village opp road to railway stn

PETS: Bedrooms £4 Public areas Exercise area (2 mins walk) **RESIDENT PETS:** Bibi (Black Labrador)

Situated on the edge of the village, close to both the golf course and bowling green, this detached Edwardian-style villa is an easy walk from the sandy beach. Bedrooms are quite spacious and well-equipped and family accommodation is available. There is also a comfortable well-furnished lounge.
FACILITIES: 4 rms (3 en suite) (1 fmly) No smoking TVB tea/coffee Cen ht TVL No coaches **PRICES:** d £50-£56✱ **LB PARKING:** 4 **NOTES:** Closed Xmas & New Year **CARDS:** 🖃 🖃 🖃 💳 🖃 💳

ABERSOCH

Map 06 SH32

★★ 66% **Deucoch**

LL53 7LD

☎ 01758 712680 ▤ 01758 712670

e-mail: deucoch@supanet.com

Dir: through Abersoch village following signs for Sarn Bach. At cross roads in Sarn Bach (approx 1m from village centre) turn right, hotel on top of hill on left

PETS: Bedrooms (unattended) (except eating and drinking areas) Exercise area (30 metres)

This hotel sits in an elevated position above the village and enjoys lovely views. There is a choice of bars and food options; the regular carvery is excellent value and has a large following, so booking is essential. Pretty bedrooms are equipped with modern amenities and the hotel specialises in golfing packages.

ROOMS: 10 rms (9 en suite) (2 fmly) s £35-£39; d £70-£78 (incl. bkfst)
LB FACILITIES: Xmas **PARKING:** 30 **NOTES:** No smoking in restaurant
CARDS: 🌐 💳 💳 💳 💳

BARMOUTH

Map 06 SH61

★★ 70% ◉ **Ty'r Graig Castle Hotel**

Llanaber Rd LL42 1YN

☎ 01341 280470 ▤ 01341 281260

e-mail: reservations@tyr-graig-castle.co.uk

Dir: 0.75m from Barmouth on the Harlech rd, seaward side

PETS: Bedrooms (unattended) £5 Public areas (not restaurant) Exercise area (0.5 miles to beach)

This impressive and unusual house was designed and built by the famous Birmingham gunsmith WW Greener. Victorian and gothic charm are combined and original features include some magnificent stained glass windows and wood panelling. Bedrooms are well-equipped and many have views of Cardigan Bay. Dishes range from the truly Welsh to the very eclectic.

ROOMS: 11 en suite No smoking in all bedrooms s £55; d £88 (incl. bkfst) **LB PARKING:** 15 **NOTES:** No smoking in restaurant
Closed 25 Dec-6 Feb **CARDS:** 💳 💳 💳 💳 💳 💳

◆◆◆◆ 🍴 ❧ **Llwyndu Farmhouse**

Llanaber LL42 1RR

☎ 01341 280144 ▤ 01341 281236

e-mail: Intouch@llwyndu-farmhouse.co.uk

Dir: A496 towards Harlech. Where street lights end, on outskirts of Barmouth, take next R

PETS: Bedrooms (unattended) Exercise area
RESIDENT PETS: Juke (Jack Russell), Lampshade & Suzy (cats), Holly & Melody (horses)

This converted 16th-century farmhouse retains many original features including inglenook fireplaces, exposed beams and timbers. There is a cosy lounge for residents and meals can be enjoyed at individual tables in the character dining room.

continued

Bedrooms are modern and well equipped; some have four-poster beds. Four rooms are in nearby buildings.

FACILITIES: 3 en suite 4 annexe en suite (2 fmly) No smoking TVB tea/coffee Licensed Cen ht TVL 4 acres non-working Dinner
Last d 6.30pm **PARKING:** 10 **NOTES:** Closed 25-26 Dec rs Sundays
CARDS: 💳 💳 💳 💳 💳

BEDDGELERT

Map 06 SH54

★★★ 67% **The Royal Goat**

LL55 4YE

☎ 01766 890224 ▤ 01766 890422

e-mail: info@royalgoathotel.co.uk

Dir: On A498 at Beddgelert

THE CIRCLE
Selected Individual Hotels
GREAT BRITAIN

PETS: Bedrooms £5 Exercise area (100yds)

An impressive building steeped in history, the Royal Goat provides well-equipped accommodation. Public areas include a choice of bars and restaurants, a residents' lounge and function rooms.

ROOMS: 32 en suite (3 fmly) No smoking in 10 bedrooms s £50-£64; d £86-£116 (incl. bkfst) **LB FACILITIES:** STV Fishing Xmas
SERVICES: Lift **PARKING:** 100 **NOTES:** No smoking in restaurant
Closed 1 Jan-1 Mar **CARDS:** 💳 💳 💳 💳 💳 💳

◆◆◆◆ 🍴 **Sygun Fawr Country House**

LL55 4NE

☎ 01766 890258 ▤ 01766 890258

e-mail: sygunfawr@aol.com

Dir: Follow brown signs from A498 on Capel Curig side of village, turn off road over river at sign and the lane leads to hotel

PETS: Bedrooms £3 for dogs Public areas (bar only) Exercise area (30 metres)

Sygun Fawr is set in a spectacular location within the Snowdonia National Park, where the surrounding countryside and immaculate gardens are a mass of colour in the spring. Bedrooms are neat and pretty and many have superb views. Stone walls and exposed timbers abound and a cosy bar is provided in addition to several comfortable sitting rooms.

FACILITIES: 12 en suite (1 GF) No smoking in bedrooms No smoking in dining room No smoking in 1 lounge tea/coffee Licensed Cen ht TVL
Dinner Last d 8pm **PRICES:** d £68-£79✳ **LB PARKING:** 20
NOTES: Closed Jan **CARDS:** 💳 💳 💳 💳 💳

Wales

CRICCIETH — Map 06 SH43

◆◆◆◆ Abereistedd Hotel
West Pde LL52 0EN
☎ 01766 522710 ▤ 01766 523526
e-mail: info@abereistedd.co.uk
Dir: take A487 through Criccieth towards Pwllheli. 400yds after petrol station, turn left following signs for beach. On left at seafront

PETS: Bedrooms (some rooms) (unattended) Public areas (not dining room) Exercise area (20 yards) RESIDENT PETS: Jess (Border Collie Cross)

An extremely warm welcome is asssured at this Victorian hotel which offers uninterrupted mountain and coastal views. The attractive bedrooms are all very well equipped with thoughtful extras to enhance guest comfort. Ground floor areas include a comfortable lounge with a bar extension and a bright, attractive dining room overlooking the seafront.
FACILITIES: 12 en suite (3 fmly) No smoking in bedrooms No smoking in dining room No smoking in lounges TVB tea/coffee Direct dial from bedrooms Licensed Cen ht No coaches Dinner Last d 7pm
PRICES: s £30; d £52-£62✳ **LB PARKING:** 9 **NOTES:** Closed Nov-Mar
CARDS: ▭▭ ▭▭ ▭▭ ▭▭ ⑤

DOLGELLAU — Map 06 SH71

★★★ 80% ◉◉ Penmaenuchaf Hall
Penmaenpool LL40 1YB
☎ 01341 422129 ▤ 01341 422787
e-mail: relax@penhall.co.uk
Dir: off A470 onto A493 to Tywyn. Hotel approx 1m on left

PETS: Bedrooms (One bedroom only) £5 Public areas (some) Exercise area (21 acres on site)

Built in 1860, this impressive hall stands in 20 acres of formal gardens, grounds and woodland and enjoys magnificent views across the River Mawddach. Careful restoration has created a comfortable and welcoming hotel. Fresh produce cooked in modern British style is served in the panelled restaurant.
ROOMS: 14 en suite (2 fmly) (1 GF) No smoking in 5 bedrooms s £75-£135; d £120-£180 (incl. bkfst) **LB FACILITIES:** Fishing Snooker Croquet lawn Complimentary salmon & trout fishing ch fac Xmas
PARKING: 30 **NOTES:** No children 6yrs No smoking in restaurant
CARDS: ▭▭ ▭▭ ▭▭ ▭▭ ▭▭ ⑤

★★★ 74% Plas Dolmelynllyn
Ganllwyd LL40 2HP
☎ 01341 440273 ▤ 01341 440640
e-mail: info@dolly-hotel.co.uk
Dir: 5m N of Dolgellau on A470

PETS: Bedrooms (Only some rooms) £10 plus deposit (2 rooms with outside stairs - pets must use) Exercise area (100 yards) RESIDENT PETS: Misty & McCavity - cats

Surrounded by three acres of mature gardens and National Trust land, this fine house dates back to the 16th century. Spacious bedrooms are attractive and offer many thoughtful extras.

continued

Carefully prepared meals are served in the comfortable dining room, adjacent to the conservatory bar.
ROOMS: 10 en suite (2 fmly) No smoking in all bedrooms
FACILITIES: STV Fishing Mountain walking Mountain Bike riding Xmas
PARKING: 16 **NOTES:** No smoking in restaurant Closed Jan
CARDS: ▭▭ ▭▭ ▭▭ ▭▭ ⑤

★★ 67% Fronoleu Country Hotel
Tabor LL40 2PS
☎ 01341 422361 & 422197 ▤ 01341 422023
e-mail: fronoleu@fronoleu.co.uk
Dir: A487/A470 junct, towards Tabor opposite Cross Foxes & continue for 1.25m. From Dolgellau take road for hospital & continue 1.25m up the hill

PETS: Bedrooms (unattended) Public areas Exercise area (on site) Pet Food

This 16th-century farmhouse lies in the shadow of Cader Idris. Carefully extended, it retains many original features. The bar and lounge are located in the old building where there are exposed timbers and open fires. Most of the bedrooms are in a modern extension. The restaurant attracts a large local following.
ROOMS: 11 en suite (3 fmly) No smoking in 6 bedrooms s £36.50-£39; d £63-£68 (incl. bkfst) **LB FACILITIES:** Fishing Pool table, Childrens play area entertainment ch fac **PARKING:** 60 **NOTES:** No smoking in restaurant **CARDS:** ▭▭ ▭▭ ▭▭ ⑤

◆◆◆◆ Dolgun Uchaf Guesthouse
Dolgun Uchaf LL40 2AB
☎ 01341 422269
e-mail: dolgunuchaf@guesthousessnowdonia.com
Dir: turn off A470 onto unclassified road at the Little Chef Service Station just S of Dolgellau. Dulgun Uchaf is 1st property on right

PETS: Bedrooms Public areas Exercise area (200 metres)

Located in a peaceful area with stunning views of the surrounding countryside, this 500-year-old late medieval hall house retains many original features, including exposed beams and open fireplaces. Bedrooms are equipped with thoughtful extras and a comfortable guest lounge is also available.
FACILITIES: 3 en suite 1 annexe en suite (1 GF) No smoking TVB tea/coffee Cen ht TVL No children 5yrs Dinner Last d 24hrs prior
PARKING: 6 **CARDS:** ▭▭ ▭▭ ▭▭ ▭▭ ⑤

FFESTINIOG
Map 06 SH74

◆◆◆ Ty Clwb
The Square LL41 4LS
☎ 01766 762658 📠 01766 762658
e-mail: tyclwb@talk21.com
Dir: on B4391 in centre of Ffestiniog, opp church, 100mtrs from A470

PETS: Bedrooms (unattended) Public areas (not dining room) Exercise area (100 metres)

Located opposite the historic church this elegant period town house has been sympathetically modernised and is immaculately maintained throughout. Bedrooms are thoughtfully furnished and in addition to an attractive dining room, a spacious lounge with sun patio provides stunning views of the mountains.
FACILITIES: 3 en suite No smoking tea/coffee Cen ht TVL No coaches
PRICES: d £40-£50✳ **CARDS:** 🔳🔳 VISA 🔲

◆◆◆ Morannedd
Blaenau Rd LL41 4LG
☎ 01766 762525 & 762734
e-mail: morannedd@talk21.com
Dir: at edge of village on A470 towards Blaenau Ffestiniog

PETS: Bedrooms Public areas (not dining room)
RESIDENT PETS: Ida (Burmese Mountain Dog)

This guest house is set in the Snowdonia National Park and is ideally located for touring North Wales. A warm and friendly welcome is offered and the atmosphere is relaxed and informal. Bedrooms are smart and modern with a cosy lounge available for residents. Hearty home cooking can be enjoyed here.
FACILITIES: 4 en suite No smoking TVB tea/coffee Cen ht No coaches
PRICES: s £20-£21; d £40-£46✳ **LB NOTES:** Closed Xmas

HARLECH
Map 06 SH63

★★ ◉◉ ♠♠
Maes y Neuadd Country House
LL47 6YA
☎ 01766 780200 📠 01766 780211
e-mail: maes@neuadd.com
Dir: 3m NE of Harlech, signposted on an unclassed road off B4573

PETS: Bedrooms £5

This 14th-century hotel enjoys fine views over the mountains and across the bay to the Lleyn Peninsula. The team here is committed to highlighting and restoring some of the hidden features of the house. Bedrooms, some in an adjacent coach house, are individually furnished and many boast fine antique pieces. Public areas display a similar welcoming charm, including the restaurant, which serves locally-sourced and many home-grown ingredients.
ROOMS: 16 en suite (3 GF) No smoking in all bedrooms s £75-£95; d £179-£270 (incl. bkfst & dinner) **LB FACILITIES:** Croquet lawn clay pigeon, cooking tuition Xmas **PARKING:** 50 **NOTES:** No smoking in restaurant **CARDS:** 🔳🔳🔳🔳🔳🔲

★★ 67% Estuary Motel
Stryd Fawr, Talsarnau LL47 6TA
☎ 01766 771155 📠 01766 771393
e-mail: enquiries@the-estuary.fsnet.co.uk
Dir: from Barmouth take A496 to Porthmadog. Talsarnau is approximately 4m N of Harlech. Motel on right

PETS: Bedrooms Exercise area (20 metres)
RESIDENT PETS: Patience & Berkeley (cats)

This single storey, purpose built small hotel is conveniently located for visiting Snowdonia, Harlech Castle and the many coastal attractions of the area. Privately owned and personally run, it provides friendly hospitality and well equipped, motel style accommodation.
ROOMS: 10 annexe en suite (3 fmly) (10 GF) No smoking in 9 bedrooms s £35-£41; d £50-£62 (incl. bkfst) **LB PARKING:** 20
NOTES: No smoking in restaurant **CARDS:** 🔳🔳🔳🔳🔳🔲

LLANBEDR
Map 06 SH52

★★ 64% Ty Mawr
LL45 2NH
☎ 01341 241440 📠 01341 241440
e-mail: tymawrhotel@onetel.com
Dir: from Barmouth A496 Harlech road and at Llanbedr turn right after bridge in the village, hotel 50yds on left, brown tourist signs on junct

PETS: Bedrooms (unattended) Public areas (except dining room) Exercise area (100 yards) Pet Food
RESIDENT PETS: Cano & Tara (Welsh Sheepdogs), Lucy (Springer Spaniel/Sheepdog), Chelly (Border Collie)

Located in a picturesque village, this family-run hotel has a relaxed, friendly atmosphere. The pleasant grounds opposite the River Artro are a popular beer garden during fine weather. The attractive, cane-furnished bar offers a blackboard selection and a good choice of real ales. A more formal menu is available in the restaurant. Bedrooms are smart and brightly decorated.
ROOMS: 10 en suite (2 fmly) No smoking in all bedrooms s £40-£45; d £60-£70 (incl. bkfst) **LB FACILITIES:** STV ch fac **PARKING:** 30
NOTES: No smoking in restaurant Closed 24-26 Dec
CARDS: 🔳🔳🔳🔳🔳🔲

◆◆◆◆ Bryn Artro Country House
LL45 2LE
☎ 01341 241619
e-mail: julie@llanbedr-brynartro.com
Dir: on A496 3m S of Harlech & 7m N of Barmouth in Llanbedr, opposite Maes Artro Tourist Attraction

PETS: Bedrooms (only on ground floor) £5 Exercise area (3 min walk)

Located in mature grounds which include a water garden, this Victorian house faced in local slate has many interesting features, including tiled floors and stained glass windows. Bedrooms are thoughtfully equipped with homely extras, and comprehensive Welsh breakfasts are provided in a spacious dining room, that overlooks the pretty rear gardens.
FACILITIES: 7 rms (4 en suite) (3 fmly) (1 GF) No smoking in bedrooms No smoking in dining room TVB tea/coffee Licensed Cen ht TVL Bike hire available Dinner Last d 11am **PRICES:** s £25-£33.50; d £50-£59✳
LB PARKING: 9 **CARDS:** 🔲

Wales

LLANBEDR continued

♦♦♦♦ Pensarn Hall Country Guest House
Pensarn LL45 2HS
☎ 01341 241236
e-mail: welcome@pensarn-hall.co.uk
Dir: S on A496 past Harlech. After 1.75m, Pensarn Hall on left

PETS: Bedrooms Exercise area (1 mile)

This lovely Victorian country house stands in its own spacious gardens, overlooking the Artro Estuary and Shell Island. The house has an interesting history, including connections with David Lloyd-George. It provides warm and friendly hospitality as well as thoughtfully equipped accommodation, including a room with a four-poster bed.

FACILITIES: 7 en suite (1 fmly) No smoking TVB tea/coffee Licensed Cen ht TVL No children 2yrs No coaches Large garden **PRICES:** s £35-£40; d £50-£80✳ **LB** **PARKING:** 8 **CARDS:** 💳

PENYGROES   Map 06 SH45

♦♦♦ 🐓 Llwyndu Mawr
Carmel Rd LL54 6PU
☎ 01286 880419 📠 01286 880845
Dir: A487 to Penygroes, in village turn onto B4418. After 500yds L for Carmel, 500yds up hill after cemetery, 1st L

PETS: Bedrooms (some rooms) Sep Accom (kennel & hutch) Public areas (not in dining room) Exercise area (adjacent) **RESIDENT PETS:** Monty (African Grey Parrot), dogs, cats, ducks & geese

This hillside farmhouse dates back to the 19th century. Home from home hospitality is provided and guests are welcome to take part in the life of this working sheep farm. Prettily decorated bedrooms offer views over the Menai Straits and toward Snowdonia. A choice of smoking and non-smoking lounges is available.

FACILITIES: 3 rms (2 en suite) (1 fmly) (1 GF) No smoking in bedrooms No smoking in dining room No smoking in 1 lounge TV1B tea/coffee Cen ht TVL 98 acres sheep Dinner Last d 4pm **PRICES:** s fr £20; d £36-£40✳ **LB** **BB** **PARKING:** 7 **NOTES:** Closed 20 Dec-6 Jan

---

PORTHMADOG   Map 06 SH53

★★ 69% Royal Sportsman
131 High St LL49 9HB
☎ 01766 512015 📠 01766 512490
e-mail: enquiries@royalsportsman.co.uk
Dir: On High Street by rdbt, at A497-A487 junct

PETS: Bedrooms (unattended) £2 Public areas (except dining room) Exercise area (200 yards) **RESIDENT PETS:** Collie dog

Ideally located in the centre of Porthmadog, this former Victorian coaching inn dates from 1862 and has been restored into a friendly, family-run hotel. Rooms are tastefully decorated and well equipped. Some are in an annexe close to the hotel. There is a large comfortable lounge and a wide range of meals is served in the bar or restaurant.

ROOMS: 19 en suite 9 annexe en suite (7 fmly) (9 GF) No smoking in all bedrooms s £42; d £65-£75 (incl. bkfst) **LB**
FACILITIES: entertainment Xmas **PARKING:** 18 **NOTES:** No smoking in restaurant **CARDS:** 💳

♦♦♦♦♦ 🐓 Tyddyn-Du Farm Holidays
Gellilydan, Ffestiniog LL41 4RB
☎ 01766 590281 📠 01766 590281
e-mail: paula@snowdonia-farm.com
Dir: 1st farmhouse on L after junct of A487/A470 near village of Gellilydan

PETS: Telephone for details

Superbly located in an elevated position with stunning views of the surrounding countryside, this constantly improving 400-year-old stone-built property provides a range of spacious, beautifully furnished and equipped bedrooms, sympathetically renovated from former stables and barns. Superb breakfasts are taken in a cosy pine-furnished dining room, and a guest lounge with log fire is available. Pets and families are especially welcome.

FACILITIES: 4 en suite (4 fmly) (4 GF) No smoking TVB tea/coffee Cen ht TVL Tennis (grass) Large garden, duck pond & chickens 150 acres organic/sheep Dinner Last d 5pm **PARKING:** 10

TYWYN   Map 06 SH50

♦♦♦♦ 🐓 Eisteddfa
Eisteddfa, Abergynolwyn LL36 9UP
☎ 01654 782385 📠 01654 782228
Dir: on B4405 between Abergynolwyn and Dolgoch Falls

PETS: Bedrooms (unattended) Public areas Exercise area (on site)

Eisteddfa is a modern, stone-built bungalow situated less than a mile from Abergynolwyn, and is an ideal spot for walking or for visiting the local railway. Rooms are comfortable and well equipped, and the lounge and dining room have views over the valley. Evening meals are by arrangement and coeliac diets are catered for.

FACILITIES: 3 rms (2 en suite) (3 GF) STV TVB tea/coffee Cen ht TVL 1200 acres mixed **PRICES:** s £25-£30; d £44-£50✳ **LB** **NOTES:** Closed Dec-Feb

---

🐓 **Places with this symbol are farms**

Don't forget to let proprietors know when you book that you're bringing your pet

ABERGAVENNY
Map 03 SO21

★★★ 70% ◉◉ **Llansantffraed Court**
Llanvihangel Gobion NP7 9BA
☎ 01873 840678 🖷 01873 840674
e-mail: reception@llch.co.uk
Dir: at A465/A40 Abergavenny intersection take B4598 signposted to Usk (do not join A40). Continue towards Raglan and hotel on left after 4.5m

PETS: Bedrooms Sep Accom (heated kennels) (unattended) £20 Public areas (not in dining areas) Exercise area (on site) Pet food Dog walking

In a commanding position and in its own grounds this red brick country hotel has enviable views of the Brecon Beacons. Extensive public areas are complemented by a spacious restaurant, where imaginative and enjoyable dishes are served. Bedrooms are comfortably furnished and have modern facilities.
ROOMS: 21 en suite (3 fmly) No smoking in 7 bedrooms s £86-£110; d £110-£160 (incl. bkfst) LB **FACILITIES:** STV Tennis (grass) Fishing Croquet lawn Putting green Ornamental trout lake, Salmon fishing on River Usk ch fac **SERVICES:** Lift **PARKING:** 250 **NOTES:** No smoking in restaurant **CARDS:** 🖸🖸🖸🖸🖸🖸

★★★ 67% ◉ **Angel**
15 Cross St NP7 5EN
☎ 01873 857121 🖷 01873 858059
e-mail: mail@angelhotelabergavenny.com
Dir: follow town centre signs from the rdbt, south of Abergavenny, past railway and bus stations. Turn left by hotel

PETS: Bedrooms £10 Public areas (except restaurant) Exercise area (20 yards) Pet Food

The Angel Hotel has long been a popular venue for both local people and visitors to the area. Two traditional function rooms and a ballroom are in regular use. However, those not having called for a while may be surprised to note the recent changes with a major refurbishment programme now well underway, resulting in a comfortable lounge, relaxed bar and award-winning restaurant.
ROOMS: 29 en suite (1 fmly) No smoking in 14 bedrooms s fr £60; d fr £85 (incl. bkfst) **FACILITIES:** STV entertainment ch fac Xmas **PARKING:** 30 **NOTES:** No smoking in restaurant Closed 25 Dec RS 24-26 Dec **CARDS:** 🖸🖸🖸🖸🖸🖸

◆◆◆◆ ✿ **Hardwick Farm**
NP7 9BT
☎ 01873 853513 & 01873 854238 🖷 01873 854238
e-mail: carol.hardwickfarm@virgin.net
Dir: 1m from Abergavenny, off A4042, farm sign on R

PETS: Bedrooms (unattended) £5 Public areas Exercise area (On site)

Pleasantly and quietly located in Usk Valley with wonderful views, this large old farmhouse is family run and provides warm and friendly hospitality. The spacious bedrooms are comfortably furnished, well equipped and include two that are suitable for

continued

families. Traditional farmhouse breakfasts are served at separate tables, in the traditionally furnished dining room.

FACILITIES: 2 en suite (1 fmly) No smoking TVB tea/coffee Cen ht 230 acres dairy mixed **PRICES:** s £27-£30; d £45-£50✳ LB **PARKING:** 2 **NOTES:** Closed Xmas

CHEPSTOW
Map 03 ST59

★★ 66% **Beaufort**
Beaufort Square NP16 5EP
☎ 01291 622497 🖷 01291 627389
e-mail: info@thebeauforthotel.co.uk
Dir: off A48, at St Mary's church turn left and left again at end of public car park (Nelson St). Hotel car park 100yds on right

PETS: Bedrooms Sep Accom Exercise area Pet food and bowls provided by prior arrangement

Privately owned and personally run, this 16th-century coaching inn is centrally located in town. The bedrooms vary in style and size and include two rooms on ground-floor level with direct access from the car park. The inviting and popular public areas have plenty of charm and character. They include a friendly bar and a pleasant restaurant where well-prepared meals are served. There is also a large meeting and function room available.
ROOMS: 22 en suite (2 fmly) s £35-£46; d £59 LB **FACILITIES:** STV ch fac **PARKING:** 14 **NOTES:** No smoking in restaurant **CARDS:** 🖸🖸🖸🖸🖸🖸

MONMOUTH
Map 03 SO51

★★ 65% **Riverside**
Cinderhill St NP25 5EY
☎ 01600 715577 & 713236 🖷 01600 712668
e-mail: info@riversidehotelmonmouth.co.uk
Dir: leave A40 signed Rockfield & Monmouth hotel on left beyond garage & before rdbt

PETS: Bedrooms (unattended) Public areas (except restaurant) Exercise area (20 metres)

This establishment has recently changed ownership. Just a short walk from the famous 13th-century bridge, this hotel offers accommodation in a relaxed and informal atmosphere. Bedrooms are well-equipped and soundly decorated. Public areas include a separate restaurant, a popular bar and a conservatory lounge at the rear of the property.
ROOMS: 17 en suite (2 fmly) No smoking in 2 bedrooms s £43-£49.95; d £50-£59.95 LB **FACILITIES:** STV ch fac Xmas **PARKING:** 30 **NOTES:** No smoking in restaurant **CARDS:** 🖸🖸🖸🖸🖸

Wales

MONMOUTH continued

◆◆◆◆◆ 🍽 🐾 Hendre Farm House
Hendre, Wonastow NP25 4DJ
☎ 01600 740484 📠 01600 740177
e-mail: thehendrefarmhouse@hotmail.com
Dir: From Monmouth Town take B4233 to Rockfield, onto Hendre Village. Roels Golf Course on left, take immediate left. Farm on right after 1.5m.

PETS: Bedrooms £2 Public areas (not dining room and lounges) Exercise area RESIDENT PETS: Tommy Baker (Sheepdog), Kitty Blueit (cat)

A warm welcome is assured at this relaxing farmhouse where the present owner's family have lived since 1885. Peacefully located overlooking the surrounding meadows and hills, the farmhouse is an ideal base from which to explore. The bedrooms and guest lounge combine old world charm with modern comforts. Delicious home-cooked meals are a highlight, available by prior arrangement.
FACILITIES: 3 en suite (1 fmly) No smoking STV TVB tea/coffee Cen ht TVL Fishing 73 acres Mixed Dinner Last d 24hrs before **PRICES:** s £34; d £58✱ **PARKING:** 20

SKENFRITH   Map 03 SO42

◉◉◉ 🏛 The Bell at Skenfrith
NP7 8UH
☎ 01600 750235 📠 01600 750525
e-mail: enquiries@skenfrith.co.uk
Dir: A40/ A466 N towards Hereford. 4m left onto B4521, hotel 2m on left

PETS: Bedrooms £5 Public areas (not during dining times) Exercise area (adjacent)

The Bell is a beautifully restored, 17th-century former coaching inn which still retains much of its charm and character. Natural materials have been used throughout, while the bedrooms, which include full suites and rooms with four-poster beds, are stylish, luxurious and equipped with DVDs.
ROOMS: 8 en suite No smoking in all bedrooms s £85-£120; d £100-£165 (incl. bkfst) **FACILITIES:** Xmas **PARKING:** 36
NOTES: No smoking in restaurant RS end Oct-Etr
CARDS: 💳 💳 💳 💳 🔜 ⑤

TINTERN PARVA   Map 03 SO50

★★★ 68% The Abbey Hotel   THE INDEPENDENTS
NP16 6SF
☎ 01291 689777 📠 01291 689727
e-mail: info@theabbeyhoteltintern.com
Dir: M48 junct 2/A466, hotel opposite the abbey ruins

PETS: Bedrooms £3.50 Public areas (not in restaurant) Exercise area (within grounds) RESIDENT PETS: 3 Jack Russells

Now refurbished to a high standard and possessing stunning views of nearby Tintern Abbey, this friendly hotel provides modern bedrooms, including a family suite. Diners are spoilt for choice between the brasserie with its daytime carvery, the formal
continued

carte service for dinner, and the pleasant hotel bar where lighter meal options are on offer.
ROOMS: 23 en suite No smoking in 7 bedrooms s £70-£75; d £99-£140 (incl. bkfst) **LB FACILITIES:** Spa STV Fishing Jacuzzi entertainment ch fac Xmas **PARKING:** 60 **NOTES:** No smoking in restaurant
CARDS: 💳 💳 💳 💳 🔜 ⑤

★★ 73% ◉ Parva Farmhouse Hotel & Restaurant   THE CIRCLE
NP16 6SQ   *Selected Individual Hotels*
☎ 01291 689411 & 689511 📠 01291 689557   *GREAT BRITAIN*
e-mail: parva_hotelintern@hotmail.com
Dir: From S leave M48 junct 2, N edge of village on A466. From N, 10m S of Monmouth town & M50

PETS: Bedrooms £3.50 Public areas (not in restaurant) Exercise area

This relaxed and friendly hotel is situated on a sweep of the River Wye with far reaching views of the valley. Originally a farmhouse dating from the 17th century, many of the original features have been retained to provide a lounge full of character, which has a fire in colder months, and an atmospheric restaurant with a popular local following. Bedrooms are tastefully decorated and thoughtfully equipped.
ROOMS: 9 en suite (3 fmly) (1 GF) s £55-£76; d £76-£80 (incl. bkfst)
LB FACILITIES: Cycle hire ch fac **PARKING:** 10 **NOTES:** No smoking in restaurant **CARDS:** 💳 💳 💳 💳 🔜 ⑤

◆◆◆ 🍽 Fountain Inn
Trellech Grange NP16 6QW
☎ 01291 689303 📠 01291 689303
e-mail: dmaachi@aol.com
Dir: A466 turn left just before Royal George Hotel, signed Raglan, continue bearing right for approx 2m. Inn at top of hill on left hand side

PETS: Bedrooms (unattended) Public areas Exercise area (surrounding fields) RESIDENT PETS: Peggy (cat)

Located in a peaceful valley north of Tintern, this 17th-century inn retains many original features highlighted by rustic-style furniture. Bedrooms are compact, cosy and homely with thoughtful extras. A range of imaginative dishes is available in the various bar areas, and the proprietors provide a transport service for guests visiting Chepstow Racecourse.
FACILITIES: 5 rms (2 en suite) No smoking in bedrooms No smoking in dining room TVB tea/coffee Cen ht Dinner Last d 10pm **PRICES:** s £32; d £42-£48✱ **PARKING:** 30 **CARDS:** 💳 💳 💳 🔜 ⑤

All AA listed accommodation, restaurants and pubs can be found on the AA's website www.theAA.com

All abbreviations are explained on page 9

NEATH PORT TALBOT

PORT TALBOT Map 03 SS79

★★★ 68% **Aberavon Beach**
SA12 6QP

☎ 01639 884949 🖷 01639 897885
e-mail: sales@aberavonbeach.com
Dir: M4 junct 41/A48 & follow signs for Aberavon Beach & Hollywood Park

PETS: Bedrooms (unattended) Exercise area (100yds to beach)

This friendly, purpose-built hotel enjoys a prominent position on the seafront overlooking Swansea Bay. Bedrooms, many of which have sea views, are comfortably appointed and thoughtfully equipped. Public areas include a leisure suite, open-plan bar and restaurant and a selection of function rooms.
ROOMS: 52 en suite (6 fmly) No smoking in 26 bedrooms s £74-£79; d £84-£89 (incl. bkfst) **LB FACILITIES:** Indoor swimming (H) Sauna Jacuzzi All weather leisure centre entertainment ch fac Xmas
SERVICES: Lift **PARKING:** 150 **NOTES:** No smoking in restaurant
CARDS:

NEWPORT

NEWPORT Map 03 ST38

◆◆◆◆◆ ⓢ ⌂ ⬛ **The Inn at the Elm Tree**
St Brides Wentlooge NP10 8SQ
☎ 01633 680225 🖷 01633 681035
e-mail: inn@the-elm-tree.co.uk
Dir: From M4 J28, A48 to Cardiff, take 1st left across 2 rdbts ASDA on left, 1st right along Morgan Way to T Junct, turn right on B4239 for 2m, on left in village St Brides

PETS: Bedrooms £10 Public areas (bar only) Exercise area (adjacent field) food by arrangement

A stylish barn conversion in a tranquil setting on Wentlooge Flats. Individually decorated bedrooms combine the traditional and the contemporary - hand-made brass beds, beamed ceilings and sumptuous fabrics, together with minimalist bathrooms - some with spa/jacuzzi - ISDN lines and business services. The restaurant offers an extensive choice including seafood and game in season, with the emphasis firmly on top quality ingredients.
FACILITIES: 13 en suite (3 fmly) (2 GF) No smoking in 4 bedrooms No smoking in dining room TVB tea/coffee Direct dial from bedrooms Cen ht No children 12yrs No coaches Croquet lawn Dinner Last d 10pm
PRICES: s £75-£90; d £80-£110✳ **LB PARKING:** 30
CARDS:

All information was correct at the time of going to press; we recommend you confirm details on booking

PEMBROKESHIRE

HAVERFORDWEST Map 02 SM91

★★ 68% **Hotel Mariners**
Mariners Square SA61 2DU
☎ 01437 763353 🖷 01437 764258
Dir: follow town centre signs, over bridge, up High St, 1st right, hotel at end

PETS: Bedrooms Exercise area (1 mile)

Located just out of the town centre, this privately owned and friendly hotel is reputed to date back to 1625. The bedrooms are equipped with modern facilities and are soundly maintained. A good range of food is offered in the popular bar, which is a focus for the town. The restaurant offers a more formal dining option.
ROOMS: 28 en suite (5 fmly) No smoking in 11 bedrooms s £56.50-£65.50; d £75.50-£85 (incl. bkfst) **LB FACILITIES:** STV Short mat bowls **PARKING:** 50 **NOTES:** Closed 25-27 Dec & 1 Jan
CARDS:

◆◆◆◆ **College**
93 Hill St, St Thomas Green SA61 1QL
☎ 01437 763710
e-mail: colinlarby@aol.com
Dir: towards town centre, follow signs for St Thomas Green car park

PETS: Bedrooms (unattended) Public areas Exercise area
RESIDENT PETS: Zag and Alfie (cats)

Located in a mainly residential area within easy walking distance of central attractions, this impressive Georgian town house has been upgraded to offer good levels of comfort and facilities. A range of practically equipped bedrooms is provided and public areas include a spacious lounge (with internet access) and an attractive dining room, the setting for comprehensive breakfasts.
FACILITIES: 8 en suite (3 fmly) No smoking in bedrooms No smoking in dining room TVB tea/coffee Cen ht TVL Dinner Last d by prior arrangement **PRICES:** s £27-£30; d £45-£50✳ **PARKING:** 2
CARDS:

MANORBIER Map 02 SS09

★★ 67% **Castle Mead**
SA70 7TA
☎ 01834 871358 🖷 01834 871358
e-mail: castlemeadhotel@aol.com
Dir: A4139 towards Pembroke, turn onto B4585 into village & follow signs to beach & castle. Hotel on left above beach

PETS: Bedrooms (unattended) Exercise area (100 yards to beach) RESIDENT PETS: Rosie (Border Collie), Max (cat)

Benefiting from a superb location with spectacular views of the bay, the Norman church and Manorbier Castle, this family-run establishment is friendly and welcoming. Bedrooms are generally quite spacious and offer modern facilities throughout. Public areas include a sea view restaurant, bar and residents' lounge.
ROOMS: 5 en suite 3 annexe en suite (2 fmly) (3 GF) No smoking in 2 bedrooms s fr £40; d fr £78 (incl. bkfst) **LB PARKING:** 20
NOTES: No smoking in restaurant Closed Jan-Feb RS Nov/Dec/Feb
CARDS:

Wales

PEMBROKE DOCK Map 02 SM90

★★★ 67% **Cleddau Bridge**
Essex Rd SA72 6EG
☎ 01646 685961 📠 01646 685746
e-mail: information@cleddaubridgehotel.co.uk
Dir: M4/A40 to St Clears, A477 to Pembroke Dock, at rdbt 2nd exit for Haverfordwest via toll bridge, take left before the toll bridge

PETS: Bedrooms £5 Exercise area (200yds)

Now under new ownership this modern, purpose-built hotel is sited adjacent to the Cleddau Bridge and overlooks the river. The well-equipped bedrooms are all on the ground floor, while the comfortable public areas consist of an attractive bar and restaurant, both with impressive views.
ROOMS: 24 en suite (2 fmly) No smoking in 12 bedrooms
FACILITIES: STV Xmas **PARKING:** 140 **NOTES:** No smoking in restaurant Closed 25-26 Dec RS Xmas Eve and New Years Day
CARDS: 🖃 🖼 🖼 🖂 📇 🔄 💲

ST DAVID'S Map 02 SM72

★★★ 77% ◉◉ **Warpool Court**
SA62 6BN
☎ 01437 720300 📠 01437 720676
e-mail: warpool@enterprise.net
Dir: At Cross Square bear left beside Cartref Restaurant (Goat St). Pass Farmers Arms Pub, 400mtrs left follow hotel signs, entrance on right

PETS: Bedrooms (unattended) £6 Exercise area (adjacent)

Originally the cathedral choir school, Warpool Court Hotel is set in landscaped gardens looking out to sea and is within easy walking distance of the Pembrokeshire coastal path. The lounges are spacious and comfortable and bedrooms are well furnished and equipped with modern facilities. The restaurant offers delightful, award-winning cuisine.
ROOMS: 25 en suite (3 fmly) s £65-£100; d £130-£200 (incl. bkfst) **LB**
FACILITIES: Indoor swimming (H) Tennis (hard) Gym Croquet lawn ch fac Xmas **PARKING:** 100 **NOTES:** No smoking in restaurant
Closed Jan **CARDS:** 🖃 🖼 🖼 🖂 📇 🔄 💲

🍺 Places with this symbol are pubs

★★ 69% **Old Cross**
Cross Square SA62 6SP
☎ 01437 720387 📠 01437 720394
e-mail: enquiries@oldcrosshotel.co.uk
Dir: in centre of St David's facing Cross Square

PETS: Bedrooms (unattended) £5 Public areas (guide dogs only in restaurant) Exercise area (country walks within 500 metres) **RESIDENT PETS:** Mickey (Pomeranian)

This friendly and comfortable hotel is situated in the centre of the town, just a short walk from the famous cathedral. Bedrooms are generally spacious and have a good range of facilities with some being suitable for families. Public areas include comfortable lounges, a popular bar and an airy restaurant where good wholesome food is offered.
ROOMS: 17 rms (16 en suite) 1 annexe en suite (2 fmly) No smoking in 8 bedrooms s £38-£75; d £68-£100 (incl. bkfst) **PARKING:** 17
NOTES: No smoking in restaurant Closed end Dec-last week Jan
CARDS: 🖃 🖂 💲

SAUNDERSFOOT Map 02 SN10

★★★ 67% **St Brides**
St Brides Hill SA69 9NH
☎ 01834 812304 📠 01834 811766
e-mail: reservations@stbrideshotel.com
Dir: Exit A478 at Twycross rdbt, signed Saundersfoot. Hotel at bottom of hill on right.

PETS: Bedrooms £4 Exercise area (0.25 mile)

This privately owned hotel is situated above the village and has stunning views of the harbour and coastline. The refurbished public areas are spacious and tastefully decorated, and feature exhibitions of Welsh artists' work. Bedrooms, many of which have sea views, vary in size and style.
ROOMS: 43 en suite (2 fmly) (5 GF) No smoking in 6 bedrooms s £65-£95; d £80-£140 (incl. bkfst) **LB FACILITIES:** Art gallery exhibiting Welsh modern art Xmas **PARKING:** 70 **NOTES:** No smoking in restaurant **CARDS:** 🖃 🖼 🖼 🖂 🔄 💲

♦♦♦♦ **Vine Cottage**
The Ridgeway SA69 9LA
☎ 01834 814422
e-mail: enquiries@vinecottageguesthouse.co.uk
Dir: at Kilgetty rdbt on A477 take exit A478 Saundersfoot/Tenby, in Pentlepoir left opp Fountain Head Inn. B4316 signed Saundersfoot continue 0.5m under railway bridge turn right signed Saundersfoot (Ridgeway). Cottage on left 100mtrs

PETS: Bedrooms Public areas (except dining room) Exercise area (paddock on site)

This 200-year-old former farmhouse has a convenient roadside location and is set in its own extensive, mature, award-winning gardens, on the outskirts of the village. Bedrooms which include a ground floor room, are modern and well equipped. Some are suitable for families. Guests can relax in the comfortable and airy lounge, whilst breakfast and dinner are taken in the dining room.
FACILITIES: 5 en suite (2 fmly) (1 GF) No smoking TVB tea/coffee Cen ht TVL No children 6yrs No coaches Dinner Last d 10am
PRICES: s £25-£50; d £46-£60✱ **LB PARKING:** 10

SOLVA   Map 02 SM82

◆◆◆◆◆ ❦ Lochmeyler Farmhouse
Llandeloy SA62 6LL
☎ 01348 837724 📠 01348 837622
e-mail: stay@lochmeyler.co.uk
Dir: from Haverfordwest A487 St Davids Rd to Penycwm, turn R, follow road to village of Llandeloy.

PETS: Bedrooms Sep Accom (kennels) Exercise area
RESIDENT PETS: George (Labrador), Patch (Collie), Juno (Springer Spaniel)

Located on a 220-acre dairy farm in an Area of Outstanding Natural Beauty, this constantly improving farmhouse provides high levels of comfort and excellent facilities. The spacious bedrooms, some are located in sympathetically renovated former outbuildings, are equipped with a wealth of thoughtful extras and four have private sitting rooms. Comprehensive breakfasts are served in the dining room and two sumptuous lounges are also available.
FACILITIES: 15 en suite (15 fmly) (7 GF) No smoking in bedrooms No smoking in dining room No smoking in 1 lounge TVB tea/coffee Direct dial from bedrooms Licensed Cen ht TVL 220 acres dairy Dinner Last d 2pm **PRICES:** s £25-£40; d £50-£60✳ **LB PARKING:** 15
NOTES: Closed Xmas & New Year **CARDS:** 🔲 🔲 🔲 🔲 🔲

TENBY   Map 02 SN10

★★★ 69% Fourcroft
North Beach SA70 8AP
☎ 01834 842886 📠 01834 842888
e-mail: staying@fourcroft-hotel.co.uk
Dir: A478, after "Welcome to Tenby" sign left towards North Beach & walled town. At seafront turn sharp left. Hotel on left

PETS: Bedrooms (unattended) £10 Exercise area (100 metres) Pet Food

This friendly, family-run hotel offers a beachfront location, together with a number of extra facilities that make it particularly suitable for families with children. Guests have direct access to the beach through the hotel's clifftop gardens. Bedrooms are of a good size, with modern facilities.
ROOMS: 40 en suite (12 fmly) No smoking in 10 bedrooms s £39-£59; d £78-£118 (incl. bkfst) **LB FACILITIES:** STV Outdoor swimming (H) Sauna Jacuzzi Table tennis Giant chess Human Gyroscope Snooker Pool Xmas **SERVICES:** Lift **PARKING:** 12 **NOTES:** No smoking in restaurant
CARDS: 🔲 🔲 🔲 🔲 🔲 🔲

◆◆◆ Brambles Lodge
Penally SA70 7QE
☎ 01834 842393 📠 01834 849183
e-mail: sparksemail@tiscali.co.uk
Dir: from Tenby take A4139 signed Penally and Pembroke. Take 2nd turning into Penally (approx 1m from Tenby) 200yds on right after Penally train station establishment on left, by 30mph sign

PETS: Bedrooms (one room only) Exercise area

A quietly located property just a short drive away from Tenby. A number of pleasant walks are available from here or guests may just wish to relax in the garden or lounge. Bedrooms differ in size but feature several welcome extras. A good choice is available at breakfast including an American-style option with crispy bacon and maple syrup.
FACILITIES: 8 rms (5 en suite) (1 fmly) No smoking TVB tea/coffee Licensed Cen ht TVL No children 5yrs No coaches Dinner Last d 9am
PRICES: s £23-£25; d £46-£52✳ **LB PARKING:** 8

WOLF'S CASTLE   Map 02 SM92

★★ 73% 🏵 Wolfscastle Country Hotel
SA62 5LZ
☎ 01437 741688 & 741225 📠 01437 741383
e-mail: enquiries@wolfscastle.com
Dir: on A40 in the village of Wolf's Castle, at top of hill on left, 6m N of Haverfordwest

PETS: Bedrooms (unattended) £5 Exercise area (10yds)

This large stone house dates back to the mid-19th century and has stunning views of the village. Now a friendly, privately owned and personally run hotel, it provides modern, well-maintained and equipped bedrooms. There is a pleasant bar and an attractive restaurant, which has a well-deserved, high reputation for its food.
ROOMS: 20 en suite 4 annexe en suite (2 fmly) No smoking in 21 bedrooms s £55-£75; d £79-£107 (incl. bkfst) **LB FACILITIES:** STV
PARKING: 60 **NOTES:** No smoking in restaurant Closed 24-26 Dec RS Sun nights **CARDS:** 🔲 🔲 🔲 🔲 🔲

BRECON   Map 03 SO02

★★ 70% Lansdowne Hotel & Restaurant
The Watton LD3 7EG
☎ 01874 623321 📠 01874 610438
e-mail: reception@lansdownehotel.co.uk
Dir: off A40/A470 onto the B4601, hotel in town centre

PETS: Bedrooms £2.50 Exercise area (2 minutes' walk)
RESIDENT PETS: Scoot (Mongrel)

Now a privately owned and personally run hotel, this Georgian house is conveniently located close to the town centre. The accommodation is well equipped and includes family rooms and a bedroom on ground floor level. There is a comfortable lounge and an attractive split level dining room containing a bar.
ROOMS: 9 en suite (2 fmly) (1 GF) s £30-£35; d £50-£55 (incl. bkfst)
LB NOTES: No children 5yrs No smoking in restaurant
CARDS: 🔲 🔲 🔲 🔲 🔲 🔲

Wales

BRECON continued

◆◆◆ Borderers
47 The Watton LD3 7EG
☎ 01874 623559
e-mail: ian@borderers.com
Dir: E on B4601, on right 200mtrs past pedestrian crossing opp church. From W on A40 200mtrs past mini rdbt on left

PETS: Bedrooms (unattended) Exercise area (300mtrs)
RESIDENT PETS: Heather and Tessa (Black Labradors)

This 17th-century guest house was originally a drover's inn. The courtyard, now a car park, is surrounded by many of the bedrooms. Appropriately a former winner of the 'Brecon in Bloom' competition, pretty hanging baskets are seen everywhere. The non-smoking bedrooms are attractively decorated with rich floral fabrics. A room suitable for guests with disabilities is available.

FACILITIES: 4 rms (3 en suite) 5 annexe en suite (2 fmly) (4 GF) No smoking TVB tea/coffee Cen ht No coaches **PRICES:** s £30-£35; d £46-£50✱ **PARKING:** 6 **CARDS:** ▨ ▨ ▨ ▨ ▨

BUILTH WELLS
Map 03 SO05

Caer Beris Manor
LD2 3NP
☎ 01982 552601 ▤ 01982 552586
e-mail: caerberismanor@btinternet.com
Dir: from town centre follow signs for A483 Llandovery. Hotel on left

★★★ 70% ◉ ♨

THE INDEPENDENTS

PETS: Bedrooms (unattended) £5 Public areas Exercise area 30 acres of parkland. Separate paddock and stable for horses RESIDENT PETS: May (dog)

With extensive landscaped grounds, guests can expect a relaxing stay at this friendly and privately owned hotel. Bedrooms are individually decorated and furnished and retain a feel of a bygone era. A spacious and comfortable lounge and a lounge bar enhance this atmosphere together with the elegant restaurant, complete with 16th-century panelling.

ROOMS: 23 en suite (1 fmly) (3 GF) s £57.50-£67.50; d £95-£105 (incl. bkfst) **LB FACILITIES:** STV Fishing Riding Sauna Gym Clay pigeon shooting ch fac Xmas **PARKING:** 32 **NOTES:** No smoking in restaurant **CARDS:** ▨ ▨ ▨ ▨ ▨

See advert on opposite page

CRICKHOWELL
Map 03 SO21

★★★ 71% ◉ Bear
NP8 1BW
☎ 01873 810408 ▤ 01873 811696
e-mail: bearhotel@aol.com
Dir: on A40 between Abergavenny and Breen

PETS: Bedrooms (unattended) Public areas (not in restaurant) Exercise area (5 minutes' walk) Cooked chicken as a treat RESIDENT PETS: Magic - cat, Max - Labrador

A favourite with locals as well as visitors, the character and friendliness of this 15th-century coaching inn are renowned. The bar and restaurant areas are furnished in keeping with the style and character of the building and provide a comfortable area in which to enjoy some of the finest locally-sourced ingredients. The hotel has very popular and extensive bar food.

ROOMS: 13 en suite 13 annexe en suite (6 fmly) s £59-£110; d £78-£145 (incl. bkfst) **PARKING:** 45 **CARDS:** ▨ ▨ ▨ ▨ ▨

★★★ 68% ◉ Manor Hotel
Brecon Rd NP8 1SE
☎ 01873 810212 ▤ 01873 811938
e-mail: info@manorhotel.co.uk
Dir: on A40, Crickhowell/Brecon, 0.5m from Crickhowell

PETS: Bedrooms (unattended) £40 refundable deposit Public areas (except dining room) RESIDENT PETS: Honey (Golden Retriever)

This impressive manor house set in a stunning location was the birthplace of Sir George Everest. The bedrooms and public areas are elegant, and there are extensive leisure facilities. The restaurant has panoramic views and is the setting for exciting modern cooking. Guests can also dine informally at the nearby Nantyffin Cider Mill, a sister operation of the hotel.

ROOMS: 22 en suite (1 fmly) No smoking in 8 bedrooms s £45-£65; d £70-£95 (incl. bkfst) **LB FACILITIES:** STV Indoor swimming (H) Sauna Solarium Gym Jacuzzi Fitness assessment Sunbed ch fac Xmas **PARKING:** 200 **NOTES:** No smoking in restaurant **CARDS:** ▨ ▨ ▨ ▨ ▨ ▨

> ♨ **Places with this symbol are country house hotels**

★★ 74% ☺ Ty Croeso
The Dardy, Llangattock NP8 1PU
☎ 01873 810573 🗎 01873 810573
e-mail: info@ty-croeso.co.uk
Dir: A40 at Shell garage take opposite road, down hill over river bridge. Turn right, after 0.5m turn left, up hill over canal, hotel signed

PETS: Bedrooms (unattended) £5 Public areas (except restaurant) Exercise area (100 metres) **RESIDENT PETS:** Jemima & Schubert (cats)

Ty Croeso, meaning 'House of Welcome' lives up to its name. The restaurant has an interesting carte and set-price menu. Glamorgan sausages and laverbread are available at breakfast. Public areas are comfortable and feature log fires. Bedrooms are decorated with pretty fabrics and all have good facilities.
ROOMS: 8 en suite (1 fmly) No smoking in 4 bedrooms **PARKING:** 20
NOTES: No smoking in restaurant RS 24-26 Dec
CARDS: 〰〰〰

CRIGGION   Map 07 SJ21

◆◆◆◆ ❦ Brimford House
SY5 9AU
☎ 01938 570235 🗎 01938 570235
e-mail: info@brimford.co.uk
Dir: At Shrewsbury take A458 (Welshpool), through Ford, right on B4393. Left after Crew Green for Criggion, on left after pub

PETS: Bedrooms Public areas Exercise area (surrounding fields) **RESIDENT PETS:** Emma & Jo (Black Labradors)

This elegant Georgian house lies in lovely open countryside and is a convenient base for touring Mid Wales and the Marches. Bedrooms are spacious, tastefully furnished and thoughtful extras enhance guest comfort. A relaxing lounge is available for residents and a cheery log fire burns here during colder weather. Hospitality is warm and friendly and the atmosphere throughout is peaceful and relaxing.
FACILITIES: 3 en suite No smoking TVB tea/coffee Cen ht TVL Fishing 250 acres Arable, beef **PRICES:** d £50-£60✳ **LB PARKING:** 4

ERWOOD   Map 03 SO04

◆◆◆◆ Hafod-Y-Garreg
LD2 3TQ
☎ 01982 560400
Dir: turn off A470 into Trericket Mill, turn immediately right into track as it opens out (with cream painted farmhouse on right) straight ahead towards pine forest on hill, through gate with AA sign

PETS: Bedrooms (unattended) Public areas Exercise area (Adjacent) **RESIDENT PETS:** Two cats, Rosie - goat

This quietly located Grade II* listed medieval farmhouse is one of the oldest houses in Wales. It has a wealth of charm, having been furnished and decorated throughout in a style befitting its age and character, but the bedrooms also have modern facilities and equipment. There is a cosy dining room with a fireplace, a comfortable lounge, and a small conservatory breakfast room.

continued

CAER BERIS MANOR
HOTEL & RESTAURANT
🅰🅰 ★★★ ☺ 72%

Builth Wells, Powys, Wales LD2 3NP
Tel: 01982 552601
Email: caerberismanor@btinternet.com

Set in 27 acres of parkland surrounded by the River Irfon, Caer Beris is the former home of Lord Swansea. The current owners, Peter and Katharine Smith, have spent the last 15 years restoring and converting the Manor into a welcoming family run three star country house hotel.

The individually furnished bedrooms, comfortable lounges overlooking the gardens, historic panelled restaurant and well stocked bar all help to create a relaxing hideaway in the very Heart of Wales.

Friendly hospitality from John and Annie McKay is undoubtedly the major strength here.
FACILITIES: 2 en suite (1 fmly) No smoking in dining room TVB tea/coffee Cen ht Dinner Last d Day before **PRICES:** d £48✳
PARKING: 6 **NOTES:** Closed Xmas

HAY-ON-WYE   Map 03 SO24

★★★ 70% The Swan-at-Hay
Church St HR3 5DQ
☎ 01497 821188 🗎 01497 821424
e-mail: info@swanathay.co.uk
Dir: Hay-on-Wye on B4350 from Brecon, hotel on left. From any other route follow signs for Brecon & just before leaving town hotel on right

PETS: Bedrooms £5 Public areas (public bar only) Exercise area (100 yards) Pet food by arrangement

This former coaching inn dates back to the 1800s and is only a short walk from the town centre. Bedrooms are well equipped and some are located in converted cottages across the courtyard. Spacious, relaxing public areas include a comfortable lounge, a choice of bars and a more formal restaurant. There is also a large function room and a smaller meeting room.
ROOMS: 15 en suite 4 annexe en suite (1 fmly) s £65-£115; d £85-£125 (incl. bkfst) **LB FACILITIES:** Fishing Xmas **PARKING:** 18
NOTES: No smoking in restaurant
CARDS: 〰〰〰

Wales

★★ 69% Baskerville Arms

Clyro HR3 5RZ
☎ 01497 820670 📠 01497 821609
e-mail: lyn@baskervillearms.co.uk
Dir: from Hereford follow Brecon A438 into Clyro. Hotel signed

PETS: Bedrooms £2 (£17 per week) Public areas
Exercise area Pet Food RESIDENT PETS: Rocky (dog)

Situated near Hay-on-Wye in the peaceful village of Clyro, this
former Georgian coaching inn is personally run by its friendly and
enthusiastic owners. Bedrooms are well equipped with comfort in
mind, while public areas include a bar with a village inn
atmosphere, a separate restaurant and a comfortable residents'
lounge. There is also a large function room, plus a meeting room.
ROOMS: 12 rms (10 en suite) (1 fmly) No smoking in 4 bedrooms
s £35-£45; d £60-£80 (incl. bkfst) LB **FACILITIES:** Fishing ch fac
PARKING: 12 **NOTES:** No smoking in restaurant
CARDS: 🖾 💳 💳 💳 💳 💳

★★ 67% Kilverts Hotel

The Bull Ring HR3 5AG
☎ 01497 821042 📠 01497 821580
e-mail: info@kilverts.co.uk
*Dir: from Brecon on B4350, on entering Hay-on-Wye take 1st right after
Cinema Bookshop. Then 1st left and hotel is on right after 40yds*

PETS: Bedrooms (unattended) £5.50 per stay Public areas
(not back garden or restaurant) Exercise area (400 yards)
Pet Food RESIDENT PETS: Ted (cat)

Situated in the centre of this fascinating town, Kilverts is a
genuinely friendly and welcoming hotel. The committed staff
provide attentive hospitality within a convivial atmosphere. Well-
equipped bedrooms are cosy, with plenty of character. Food has
an international influence, available in either the bar or stylish
restaurant. The extensive gardens are ideal in summer.
ROOMS: 11 en suite (1 fmly) s fr £50; d £70-£90 (incl. bkfst) LB
PARKING: 13 **NOTES:** No smoking in restaurant Closed 25 Dec
CARDS: 🖾 💳 💳 💳 💳 💳

◆◆◆◆ York House

Hardwick Rd, Cusop HR3 5QX
☎ 01497 820705 📠 01497 820705
e-mail: roberts@yorkhouse59.fsnet.co.uk
Dir: on B4348 0.5m from main car park in Hay-on-Wye

PETS: Bedrooms £6 per visit Public areas (except dining
room) Exercise area (100 yards) Pet food with advance notice
RESIDENT PETS: Sybil (cat)

This fine Victorian house is set in its own lovely and extensive
gardens, just half a mile from Hay town centre. The proprietors
offer a friendly welcome to their guests and the bedrooms are
attractively decorated and well equipped with modern facilities.
Separate tables are provided in the traditionally furnished dining
room and there is also a comfortable lounge.
FACILITIES: 4 en suite (1 fmly) No smoking TVB tea/coffee Cen ht
No children 8yrs No coaches **PRICES:** s £28-£38; d £56-£60✱ LB
PARKING: 8 **NOTES:** Closed 24-26 Dec
CARDS: 🖾 💳 💳 💳 💳 💳

★★★ ◉◉ ♨ Lake Country House

LD4 4BS
☎ 01591 620202 & 620474 📠 01591 620457
e-mail: info@lakecountryhouse.co.uk
*Dir: W from Builth Wells on A483 to Garth (approx 6m). Left for
Llangammarch Wells, follow hotel signs*

PETS: Bedrooms (unattended) £6.00 Pet Food
RESIDENT PETS: Belle - Labrador, Cassie - Collie/Labrador

Expect good old fashioned values of service and hospitality at this
Victorian country house hotel, which comes complete with a
9-hole, par 3 golf course, 50 acres of wooded grounds and a river.
Bedrooms, including many suites, are individually decorated and
have many extra comforts as standard. Traditional afternoon teas
are served in the lounge in front of a log fire, and award-winning
cuisine is provided in the spacious and elegant restaurant.
ROOMS: 19 en suite (2 GF) No smoking in 6 bedrooms s £105-£170;
d £140-£240 (incl. bkfst) LB **FACILITIES:** Golf 9 Tennis (hard) Fishing
Snooker Croquet lawn Putting green Clay pigeon shooting, horse riding,
mountain biking, quad biking, archery Xmas **PARKING:** 72
NOTES: No smoking in restaurant
CARDS: 🖾 💳 💳 💳 💳 💳 💳

◆◆◆◆ Old Vicarage

SY18 6RN
☎ 01686 440280 📠 01686 440280
e-mail: theoldvicarage@llangurig.fslife.co.uk
*Dir: 5m from Llanidloes towards Aberystwyth. At rdbt take A44 into
Llangurig; take 1st R, Old Vicarage is 100yds on L*

PETS: Bedrooms £1 Public areas (except dining areas)
Exercise area (nearby) food by arrangement
RESIDENT PETS: Polly and Jason (Red Chows)

Quietly set in the heart of Llangurig, the Old Vicarage offers
attractively furnished, well equipped bedrooms. Downstairs, a
small bar serves the dining room and both lounges, where there
are wonderful collections of porcelain and antiques. Evening
meals and afternoon teas make good use of local produce.
FACILITIES: 4 en suite (1 fmly) No smoking in bedrooms No smoking in
dining room No smoking in 1 lounge TVB tea/coffee Licensed Cen ht
TVL No coaches Dinner Last d 5pm **PRICES:** s £28-£40; d £44-£50✱
LB **PARKING:** 5

★★★ 73% ◉◉ ♨ Lake Vyrnwy

Lake Vyrnwy SY10 0LY
☎ 01691 870692 📠 01691 870259
e-mail: res@lakevyrnwy.com
Dir: on A4393, 200yds past dam

PETS: Bedrooms Sep Accom (heated kennels) £10
Pet Food Free kennels for dogs RESIDENT PETS: Rastus, Leroy &
Luke (Black Labradors)

This fine country house hotel lies in 26,000 acres of woodland above
Lake Vyrnwy. It provides a wide range of bedrooms, most with superb

continued

views and many with four-poster beds and balconies. The extensive public rooms are elegantly furnished and include a terrace, a choice of bars serving meals and the more formal dining in the restaurant.
ROOMS: 35 en suite (4 fmly) s £90-£135; d £120-£190 (incl. bkfst) **LB**
FACILITIES: STV Tennis (hard) Fishing Riding Game/Clay shooting, Sailing, Cycling, Archery, Quad trekking, Fly fishing ch fac Xmas
PARKING: 70 **NOTES:** No smoking in restaurant
CARDS:

LLANWRTYD WELLS   Map 03 SN84

◎◎◎ ⋔ Carlton House
Dolycoed Rd LD5 4RA
☎ 01591 610248 📠 01591 610242
e-mail: info@carltonrestaurant.co.uk
Dir: centre of town

PETS: Bedrooms (unattended) Exercise area (100 metres)

Guests are made to feel like one of the family at this characterful home, set amidst stunning countryside in what is reputedly the smallest rural town in Britain. Carlton House offers award-winning cuisine, complemented by a well-chosen wine list and served in an atmospheric restaurant. The themed bedrooms, like the public areas, have period furniture and are decorated in warm colours.
ROOMS: 6 rms (5 en suite) (2 fmly) s £45; d £60-£80 (incl. bkfst) **LB**
FACILITIES: Pony trekking Mountain biking **NOTES:** No smoking in restaurant Closed 15-30 Dec RS All year **CARDS:** 💳

LLYSWEN   Map 03 SO13

★★★★ 74% ◎◎ ⚓ Llangoed Hall
LD3 0YP
☎ 01874 754525 📠 01874 754545
e-mail: enquiries@llangoedhall.com
Dir: A470 through village for 2m. Hotel drive on right

PETS: Sep Accom (heated kennels)

Set against the stunning backdrop of the Black Mountains and the Wye Valley, this imposing country house is a haven of peace and quiet. The interior is no less impressive, with a noteworthy art collection complementing the many antiques featured in day rooms and bedrooms. Comfortable, spacious bedrooms and suites are matched by equally inviting lounges.
ROOMS: 23 en suite s £140-£320; d £180-£360 (incl. bkfst) **LB**
FACILITIES: STV Tennis (hard) Fishing Snooker Croquet lawn Maze, Clay pigeon shooting Xmas **PARKING:** 80 **NOTES:** No children 8yrs No smoking in restaurant **CARDS:** 💳

MACHYNLLETH   Map 06 SH70

★★ 67% ◎ Wynnstay
Maengwyn St SY20 8AE
☎ 01654 702941 📠 01654 703884
e-mail: info@wynnstay-hotel.com
Dir: at junct of A487/A489, in the town centre, 25yds from the clock tower

PETS: Bedrooms Sep Accom (kennels) (unattended) £5 Public areas (except restaurant) Exercise area (50yds)

Long established, this former posting house lies in the centre of historic Machynlleth. Bedrooms, which include no-smoking rooms
continued

and family bedded rooms, have modern facilities. The bars are popular with locals and a good range of food is available. The restaurant offers more formal dining and guests can choose from a fixed-price menu.

ROOMS: 23 en suite (3 fmly) No smoking in all bedrooms s £50-£65; d £80-£100 (incl. bkfst) **LB FACILITIES:** STV Fishing Clay shooting, Game shooting, Mountain biking Xmas **PARKING:** 40
NOTES: No smoking in restaurant RS New Years Day
CARDS: 💳

◆◆◆◆ Dyfiguest
20 Ffordd Mynydd Griffiths SY20 8DD
☎ 01654 702562 & 07790 715256
e-mail: dyfiguest@yahoo.co.uk
Dir: from town centre take A487 to Dolgellau. Turn right for railway station and stay right to top of hill. Establishment last but one bungalow on right

PETS: Sep Accom (large garage) Exercise area (300 yards)

Located in a peaceful residential area within easy walking distance of town centre, a warm welcome is assured at this modern bungalow that has stunning countryside views. Wholesome breakfasts, which include excellent vegetarian options, are served in a cosy dining room, and a spacious lounge is also available.
FACILITIES: 1 en suite (1 GF) No smoking tea/coffee Cen ht TVL No children No coaches Dinner Last d 2pm **PRICES:** s £30; d £52✱
LB PARKING: 3

MONTGOMERY   Map 07 SO29

★★ 71% ◎ Dragon Hotel
SY15 6PA
☎ 01686 668359 📠 01686 668287
e-mail: reception@dragonhotel.com
Dir: behind the Town Hall

THE INDEPENDENTS

PETS: Bedrooms (unattended) Public areas (except in dining areas) Exercise area (countryside)

This fine 17th-century coaching inn stands in the centre of Montgomery. Beams and timbers from the nearby castle, which was destroyed by Cromwell, are visible in the lounge and bar. A wide choice of soundly prepared, wholesome food is available in both the restaurant and bar. Bedrooms are well equipped and family rooms are available.
ROOMS: 20 en suite (6 fmly) No smoking in 16 bedrooms s £47-£57; d £79.50 (incl. bkfst) **LB FACILITIES:** Indoor swimming (H) Sauna entertainment ch fac Xmas **PARKING:** 21 **NOTES:** No smoking in restaurant **CARDS:** 💳

Wales

RHONDDA CYNON TAFF

MISKIN
Map 03 ST08

★★★★ 69% 🏵
Miskin Manor Hotel & Health Club
Groes Faen, Pontyclun CF72 8ND
☎ 01443 224204 📠 01443 237606
e-mail: info@miskin-manor.co.uk
Dir: M4 junct 34, exit onto A4119, signed Llantrisant, hotel is 300yds on left

Best Western

PETS: Bedrooms (unattended) £10 Public areas (except restaurant) Exercise area (On site) RESIDENT PETS: Rosie & Lucy - Boxers

This manor house is set in 20 acres of grounds, only minutes away from the M4. Bedrooms are furnished to a high standard and include some located in converted stables and cottages. Public areas are spacious and comfortable and include a variety of function rooms. Frederick's health club has leisure facilities and a bar/bistro.

ROOMS: 34 en suite 9 annexe en suite (6 fmly) (6 GF) No smoking in 11 bedrooms s £80-£94; d £100-£126 (incl. bkfst) **LB FACILITIES:** STV Indoor swimming (H) Squash Sauna Solarium Gym Croquet lawn Jacuzzi ch fac Xmas **PARKING:** 200 **NOTES:** No smoking in restaurant **CARDS:** 💳💳💳💳💳💳

PONTYPRIDD
Map 03 ST08

★★★ 70% **Llechwen Hall**
Llanfabon CF37 4HP
☎ 01443 742050 & 743020 📠 01443 742189
e-mail: llechwen@aol.com
Dir: A470 N towards Merthyr Tydfil, then A472, then onto A4054 for Cilfynydd. After 0.25m, turn left at hotel sign & follow to top of hill

PETS: Bedrooms (unattended) Exercise area (on site)

Set on top of a hill with a stunning approach, this hotel has served a variety of uses in its 200-year history, including as a private school and as a magistrates' court. Bedrooms are individually decorated and well equipped and some are situated in the comfortable coach house nearby. The Victorian-style public areas are attractively appointed and the hotel is a popular venue for weddings.

ROOMS: 12 en suite 8 annexe en suite (11 fmly) (4 GF) No smoking in 8 bedrooms s £54.50-£65.45; d £70-£106.90 (incl. bkfst) **LB**
FACILITIES: ch fac Xmas **PARKING:** 100 **NOTES:** No smoking in restaurant Closed 25-28 Dec **CARDS:** 💳💳💳💳💳💳

SWANSEA

LLANRHIDIAN
Map 02 SS49

★★ 66% *North Gower*
SA3 1EE
☎ 01792 390042 📠 01792 391401
e-mail: enquiries@northgowerhotel.co.uk
Dir: on B4295, turn left at Llanrhidian Esso Service Station

PETS: Telephone for details

Situated on the Gower Peninsula with delightful views over the sea, this family-owned hotel offers guests a relaxing and comfortable stay. Bedrooms are spacious and airy, whilst public areas consist of a bar full of character, a pleasant restaurant and a choice of meeting and function rooms.
ROOMS: 18 en suite (10 fmly) (7 GF) No smoking in 8 bedrooms
FACILITIES: PARKING: 100 **NOTES:** No smoking in restaurant
CARDS: 💳💳💳💳💳💳

SWANSEA
Map 03 SS69

★★ 71% 🏵 *Windsor Lodge*
Mount Pleasant SA1 6EG
☎ 01792 642158 & 652744 📠 01792 648996
e-mail: reservations@windsor-lodge.co.uk
Dir: M4 junct 42, A483, right at lights past Sainsburys, left at station, right immediately after 2nd set of lights

PETS: Bedrooms (unattended)

This privately owned and personally run, smart and stylish hotel is just a short walk from the city centre. Bedrooms vary in size, but

continued

all are similarly well equipped. There is a choice of lounge areas and a deservedly popular restaurant.

ROOMS: 19 en suite (2 fmly) s £50-£65; d £65-£75 (incl. bkfst) **LB**
PARKING: 25 **NOTES:** No smoking in restaurant Closed 25-26 Dec RS Sun & BH's **CARDS:** ▱▱▱ ▱▱ ▱ ▱ ▱▱ ▱

VALE OF GLAMORGAN

BARRY   Map 03 ST16

★★★ 73% ◉ ♨ **Egerton Grey Country House**
Porthkerry CF62 3BZ
☎ 01446 711666 ▤ 01446 711690
e-mail: info@egertongrey.co.uk
Dir: M4 junct 33 follow signs for airport, left at rdbt for Porthkerry, after 500yds turn left down lane between thatched cottages

PETS: Bedrooms (unattended) £10 Public areas (Quiet public rooms only) Exercise area (100yds) Pet Food

This former rectory enjoys a peaceful setting and views over delightful countryside with distant glimpses of the sea. The non-smoking bedrooms are spacious and individually furnished. Public areas offer charm and elegance, and include an airy lounge and restaurant, which has been sympathetically converted from the billiards room.

ROOMS: 10 en suite (4 fmly) s £89.50-£95; d £100-£130 (incl. bkfst) **LB FACILITIES:** STV Croquet lawn Putting green 9 hole golf course 200yds away. ch fac Xmas **PARKING:** 41 **NOTES:** No smoking in restaurant **CARDS:** ▱▱▱ ▱▱ ▱▱ ▱ ▱▱ ▱

★★★ 69% **Mount Sorrel**
Porthkerry Rd CF62 7XY
☎ 01446 740069 ▤ 01446 746600
e-mail: reservations@mountsorrel.co.uk
Dir: M4 J33 on A4232. Follow signs for A4050 through Barry. Upon reaching mini rdbt (with church opp) turn L, hotel 300mtrs on L.

Best Western

PETS: Bedrooms Exercise area (200 metres)

Situated in an elevated position above the town centre, this extended Victorian property is ideally placed for exploring the nearby coast and Cardiff, and offers comfortable accommodation. The public areas include a choice of conference rooms, a restaurant and a bar, together with leisure facilities.

ROOMS: 42 en suite (3 fmly) (5 GF) No smoking in 8 bedrooms s £65-£130; d £90-£130 (incl. bkfst) **LB FACILITIES:** STV Indoor swimming (H) Sauna Gym Xmas **PARKING:** 17 **NOTES:** No smoking in restaurant **CARDS:** ▱▱▱ ▱▱ ▱ ▱▱ ▱

WREXHAM

GLYN CEIRIOG   Map 07 SJ23

★★★ 66% **Golden Pheasant**
LL20 7BB
☎ 01691 718281 ▤ 01691 718479
e-mail: goldenpheasant@micro-plus-web.net
Dir: A5/B4500 at Chirk, continue for 5m, to Pontfadog & follow signs for hotel, 1st left after Cheshire Home, follow road to top of small hill & hotel

PETS: Bedrooms (unattended) £5 pets, £10 horses Public areas (not restaurant and lounge) Exercise area (200 yards) **RESIDENT PETS:** Fred and Ted (Labradors)

This 18th-century hostelry is quietly situated in open countryside surrounded by rolling hills. The bedrooms include four-poster and family rooms and there is a choice of bars, as well as a lounge and a restaurant. To the rear is an attractive courtyard with shrubs and flowerbeds.

ROOMS: 19 en suite (5 fmly) s £40-£88; d £80-£100 (incl. bkfst) **LB FACILITIES:** Xmas **PARKING:** 45 **NOTES:** No smoking in restaurant RS Closed 25 Dec pm **CARDS:** ▱▱▱ ▱▱ ▱▱ ▱ ▱

LLANARMON DYFFRYN CEIRIOG   Map 07 SJ13

★★ 74% ◉ **West Arms**
LL20 7LD
☎ 01691 600665 & 600612 ▤ 01691 600622
e-mail: gowestarms@aol.com
Dir: off A483/A5 at Chirk, take B4500 to Ceiriog Valley, Llanarmon 11m at end of B4500

PETS: Bedrooms Sep Accom (kennel) (unattended) £6 Public areas (not in restaurant) Exercise area (large garden and country lanes) Pet Food **RESIDENT PETS:** Sam (King Charles Spaniel)

Set in the beautiful Ceiriog Valley, this delightful hotel has a wealth of charm and character. There is a comfortable lounge, a room for private dining and two bars, as well as a pleasant restaurant offering a fixed-price menu of freshly cooked dishes. The attractive bedrooms have a mixture of modern and period furnishings.

ROOMS: 15 en suite (2 fmly) (3 GF) s £52.50-£94; d £85-£174 (incl. bkfst) **LB FACILITIES:** Fishing ch fac Xmas **PARKING:** 22 **NOTES:** No smoking in restaurant **CARDS:** ▱▱▱ ▱▱ ▱

Wales

IRELAND

Beach in County Donegal

NORTHERN IRELAND

CO DOWN

HOLYWOOD Map 01 D5

◆◆◆◆◆ 🏆 GH Beech Hill
23 Ballymoney Rd, Craigantlet BT23 4TG
☎ 028 9042 5892 🖷 028 9042 5892
e-mail: info@beech-hill.net
Dir: leave Belfast on A2 (Bangor) bypassing Holywood, 1.5m from bridge at Ulster Folk Museum, right along Ballymoney Rd. House 1.75m on left

PETS: Bedrooms Sep Accom (kennel) (unattended) Public areas Exercise area (adjacent) Dog & cat food available RESIDENT PETS: Mistle - Deer Hound Lurcher, Dipper - mongrel, Pippet - Whippet, Bandit & Bigsy - cats

Situated high in the rolling Holywood Hills, this delightful Georgian-style house enjoys panoramic views of the surrounding countryside. The classically styled bedrooms, all on the ground floor, include many useful extras and a host of homely touches. Public areas include a large conservatory, a comfortable lounge and a dining room where a generous breakfast is served.
FACILITIES: 3 en suite (3 GF) No smoking in bedrooms No smoking in dining room No smoking in lounges TVB tea/coffee Direct dial from bedrooms Cen ht TVL No children 10yrs No coaches Croquet lawn boules **PRICES:** s £45-£50; d £65-£70✱ **PARKING:** 6
CARDS: 🔲🔲

Please mention AA Pet Friendly Places to Stay when booking

CO LONDONDERRY

AGHADOWEY Map 01 C6

★★ 70% Brown Trout Golf & Country Inn
209 Agivey Rd BT51 4AD
☎ 028 7086 8209 🖷 028 7086 8878
e-mail: bill@browntroutinn.com
Dir: on junction of A54/B66 on road to Coleraine

PETS: Bedrooms (unattended) Public areas Exercise area (Golf course on site) RESIDENT PETS: Muffin (Chocolate Labrador)

Set alongside the Agivey River and featuring its own 9-hole golf course, this welcoming inn offers a choice of spacious accommodation. Comfortable and attractively furnished bedrooms are situated around a courtyard area whilst the cottage suites also have lounge areas. Home-cooked meals are served in the restaurant; lighter fare is available in the charming lounge bar.
ROOMS: 15 en suite (11 fmly) **FACILITIES:** Golf 9 Fishing Gym Putting green Game fishing entertainment Xmas **PARKING:** 80
NOTES: No smoking in restaurant **CARDS:**

CO TYRONE

AUGHNACLOY Map 01 C5

◆◆◆◆ GH Rehaghy Lodge
35 Rehaghy Rd BT69 6EW
☎ 028 8555 7693 🖷 028 8555 7693
e-mail: sandra.ligget@btopenworld.com
Dir: turn off M1 Dungannon bypass onto B35 for Aughnacloy. 0.25m from Aughnacloy at local primary school turn right (signed) for Benburb approx 2m, also signed for Rehaghy Lodge

PETS: Sep Accom (kennel & pen) Public areas Exercise area bowls, possibly food RESIDENT PETS: 2 Irish Wolfhounds, 2 Yorkshire Terriers, 2 cats

Sandra and Mervyn Ligget provide a hospitable welcome to guests at their country home. Neat gardens, with beehives, doves and family pets all help to create the home from home atmosphere. The pleasant bedrooms, one on the ground floor, have all of the expected facilities as well as a host of extras. There are two comfortable lounges and a cosy breakfast room. Evening meals can be served by arrangement.
FACILITIES: 3 en suite (1 fmly) (1 GF) No smoking in 1 bedroom No smoking in dining room No smoking in 1 lounge STV TVB tea/coffee Cen ht TVL No coaches Dinner Last d 9pm **PRICES:** s £20-£25; d £40✱ **LB PARKING:** 6

Ireland

REPUBLIC OF IRELAND

CO CLARE

BALLYVAUGHAN
Map 01 B3

◆◆◆◆◆ GH Drumcreehy
☎ 065 7077377 ▤ 065 7077379
e-mail: info@drumcreehyhouse.com
Dir: At Hyland's Hotel in the village of Ballyvaughan, turn onto N67 in direction of Galway. House on right approx 1m outside village

PETS: Bedrooms £5 **Public areas** (lounge only if other guests agree) **Exercise area** (0.5 mile)

A detached house surrounded by attractive gardens, situated in the famous Burren area of County Clare and enjoying wonderful sea views over Galway Bay. Facilities include comfortable sitting and dining rooms, where evening meals are served by arrangement. Home-baking is a feature, and the hosts are friendly and attentive. There are village pubs and restaurants nearby, as well as golf and hill walking.
FACILITIES: 10 en suite (2 fmly) (2 GF) No smoking STV TVB Direct dial from bedrooms Licensed Cen ht Dinner Last d noon
PRICES: s €48-€58; d €64-€84✻ **PARKING:** 12 **CARDS:** 💳 💳

◆◆◆◆ GH Cappabhaile House
Newtown
☎ 065 7077260 ▤ 065 7077300
e-mail: cappabhaile@oceanfree.net
Dir: 1km outside Ballyvaughan towards Aillwee Cave

PETS: Sep Accom (pens) **Exercise area** (on site)

A new property built using local stone and natural materials, on a 12-acre site on the outskirts of the village in the heart of The Burren. The hosts are happy to assist guests with planning walks and hill climbs, or with archaeological or botanical information. The spacious bedrooms are suitable for families and are very well appointed. Guests can relax in the comfortable lounge or enjoy a game of pool in the games room. An 18-hole pitch-and-putt course surrounds the house. An extensive breakfast menu is on offer, with home baking a speciality.
FACILITIES: 8 en suite (4 fmly) No smoking TVB tea/coffee Direct dial from bedrooms Cen ht No coaches Pool Table 18 hole pitch & putt
PARKING: 20 **NOTES:** Closed Nov-Feb **CARDS:** 💳 💳

> **Places with this symbol are farms**

> ★ **Red stars indicate the AA's Top 200 Hotels in Britain & Ireland**

CO CORK

BANDON
Map 01 B2

◆◆◆◆ T&C Glebe Country House
Ballinadee
☎ 021 4778294 ▤ 021 4778456
e-mail: glebehse@indigo.ie
Dir: exit N71 at Innishannon Bridge signed Ballinadee, 8km along river bank, left after village sign

PETS: Bedrooms **Exercise area** (on site) **Large garden**
RESIDENT PETS: Tarka (Dalmatian)

This lovely old guest house stands in well kept gardens, and is run with great attention to detail. Antique furnishings predominate throughout this comfortable house, which has a guest lounge and an elegant dining room. An interesting breakfast menu offers unusual options, and a country-house style dinner is available by reservation.
FACILITIES: 4 en suite (2 fmly) No smoking tea/coffee Direct dial from bedrooms Cen ht TVL outdoor badminton Dinner Last d noon
PRICES: s €52-€57; d €80-€90✻ **LB PARKING:** 30
NOTES: Closed 21 Dec-3 Jan **CARDS:** 💳 💳 💳

CLONAKILTY
Map 01 B2

◆◆ 🐓 Desert House
Coast Rd
☎ 023 33331 ▤ 023 33048
e-mail: deserthouse@eircom.net
Dir: signposted on N71, 1km E of Clonakilty, at 1st rdbt. Guest House is 500mtrs on left overlooking bay.

PETS: Bedrooms (unattended) **Exercise area** (adjacent)
RESIDENT PETS: Holly & Sophie (golden cocker), Tess (sheepdog)

This Georgian farmhouse, overlooking Clonakilty Bay, is an ideal centre for touring West Cork and Kerry.
FACILITIES: 5 rms (4 en suite) No smoking in dining room No smoking in lounges TVB tea/coffee Cen ht 100 acres dairy mixed **PRICES:** s €39; d €54-€66✻ **PARKING:** 10 **CARDS:** 💳 💳 💳

Ireland

CO GALWAY

ATHENRY
Map 01 B4

◆◆◆◆ GH Caheroyan House and Farm
☎ 091 844858
e-mail: caheroyanhouseandfarm@eircom.net
Dir: N6 (westbound) to Craughwell, 2nd right to Athenry Town. In Athenry take 1st right alongside castle. At t-junct turn right, continue for 0.5m until signposts on right for Caheroyn House & Farm

PETS: £15 Public areas (on leash) Exercise area (on site) bowls provided but no food RESIDENT PETS: 1 dog, 2 cats, 1 goat, 2 donkeys, 1 horse

FACILITIES: 4 en suite (3 fmly) No smoking in 1 bedroom No smoking in dining room No smoking in 1 lounge TVB tea/coffee Lift Cen ht TVL Tennis (hard & grass) Fishing jacuzzi/spa **PRICES:** s €40-€60; d €70-€100✱ LB **PARKING:** 30 **NOTES:** Closed 23 Dec-2 Jan

CLIFDEN
Map 01 A4

★★★ 73% ◎◎◎ Ardagh
Ballyconneely Rd
☎ 095 21384 ▤ 095 21314
e-mail: ardaghhotel@eircom.net
Dir: N59 Galway to Clifden, signposted for Ballyconneely

IRISH COUNTRY HOTELS

PETS: Bedrooms Public areas (except bar and restaurant) Exercise area (on site)

Situated at the head of Ardbear Bay, this family-run hotel makes full use of the spectacular scenery in the area. The restaurant is renowned for its cuisine, which is complemented by friendly and knowledgeable service. Bedrooms have large picture windows and plenty of comfort.
ROOMS: 19 en suite (2 fmly) No smoking in all bedrooms s €105-€118; d €150-€196 (incl. bkfst) LB **FACILITIES:** Pool room entertainment **PARKING:** 35 **NOTES:** No smoking in restaurant Closed Nov-Mar **CARDS:** ▨▨ ▨▨ ▨▨ ▨▨ ▨

GALWAY
Map 01 B3

◆◆◆◆ T&C Atlantic Heights
2 Cashelmara, Knocknacarra Cross, Salthill
☎ 091 529466 & 528830 ▤ 091 529529
e-mail: atlanticheights@galway.iol.ie
Dir: 1km from Salthill Promenade in upper Salthill on R336. 0.25m on right after Spinnaker House Hotel, before t-junct

PETS: Bedrooms (unattended) Exercise area (on site)

This fine balconied house overlooks Galway Bay, where enthusiastic hosts, Robbie and Madeline Mitchell, take great pride in their home. All bedrooms have TV, tea and coffee making facilities, telephone, hairdryer and many thoughtful extras. An extensive breakfast menu, served late if required, features home baking. Laundry service available.
FACILITIES: 6 en suite (3 fmly) No smoking STV TVB tea/coffee Direct dial from bedrooms Cen ht **PRICES:** s €40-€60; d €70-€95✱ LB **PARKING:** 6 **NOTES:** Closed Nov-Mar **CARDS:** ▨▨ ▨▨

RECESS
Map 01 A4

★★★ 77% ◎◎ ♣♠
Lough Inagh Lodge
Inagh Valley
☎ 095 34706 & 34694 ▤ 095 34708
e-mail: inagh@iol.ie
Dir: after Recess take R344 towards Kylemore through Inagh Valley, hotel in middle of valley

MANOR HOUSE

PETS: Sep Accom (kennels)

This 19th-century former fishing lodge is a relaxing, comfortable hotel. The setting is superb, nestling in woodland, fronted by a good fishing lake with beautiful mountain views. A choice of lounge areas is matched by very spacious well appointed bedrooms.
ROOMS: 12 en suite (4 GF) **FACILITIES:** STV Fishing Hill walking, Fly fishing, Cycling **SERVICES:** air con **PARKING:** 16 **NOTES:** No smoking in restaurant Closed mid Dec-mid Mar **CARDS:** ▨▨ ▨▨ ▨▨ ▨▨

CO KERRY

CASTLEGREGORY
Map 01 A2

◆◆◆ T&C Griffin's Palm Beach Country House
Goulane, Conor Pass Rd
☎ 066 7139147 ▤ 066 7139073
e-mail: griffinspalmbeach@eircom.net
Dir: 1m from Stradbally village

PETS: Exercise area (field in front of house, & 0.25 mile to beach) RESIDENT PETS: Sheepdog - Rose

Situated only a short distance from a golf club and a Blue Flag beach, one of the many unspoilt beaches along the coastline of the Dingle Peninsula. Mrs Griffin believes in a warm welcome, good beds and home baking to keep her guests happy. The dining room offers a panorama of Tralee Bay.
FACILITIES: 8 rms (6 en suite) (3 fmly) (1 GF) No smoking tea/coffee Cen ht TVL **PRICES:** s €32-€35; d €64-€70✱ **PARKING:** 10 **NOTES:** Closed Dec-Feb **CARDS:** ▨▨ ▨▨

> 🍺 **Places with this symbol are pubs**

Ireland

CO MAYO

ACHILL ISLAND
Map 01 A4

◆◆◆◆ GH Gray's
Dugort
☎ 098 43244 & 43315
Dir: towards Castlebar, Newport, Mulrany, Achill Sound and then Dugort

PETS: Bedrooms Exercise area RESIDENT PETS: Cuddles (Corgi), Huggy Bear & Phoebe (cats)

This welcoming guest house is in Dugort, on the northern shore of the island, at the foot of the Slievemore Mountains. There is a smart conservatory and various lounges. Dinner is served nightly in the cheerful dining room, and the cosy bedrooms all have orthopaedic beds. A self-contained villa, ideal for families, is also available.
FACILITIES: 5 en suite 10 annexe en suite (4 fmly) (2 GF) No smoking TVB tea/coffee Licensed Cen ht TVL Pool Table Croquet lawn Table tennis Dinner Last d 6pm **PRICES:** s fr €61; d fr €110✱ **PARKING:** 30
NOTES: Closed 25 Dec-1 Jan

CO SLIGO

TOBERCURRY
Map 01 B4

◆◆◆ T&C Cruckawn House
Ballymote/Boyle Rd
☎ 071 918 5188 📠 071 918 5188
e-mail: cruckawn@esatclear.ie
Dir: 300mtrs off N17 on R294, on right, overlooking golf course

PETS: Sep Accom (kennel) Public areas Exercise area (adjacent) RESIDENT PETS: Lady (Cavalier King Charles Spaniel)

Overlooking the golf course, just a few minutes walk from the town centre, Cruckawn House offers friendly hospitality. The dining room adjoins the comfortable sun lounge, and there is also a TV lounge. Salmon and coarse fishing, riding and mountain climbing are all available nearby and the area is renowned for traditional Irish music.
FACILITIES: 5 en suite (2 fmly) No smoking in bedrooms No smoking in dining room No smoking in 1 lounge TVB Cen ht TVL Golf 9 Gymnasium Pool Table Putting green Game & coarse fishing, bike hire Dinner Last d 6pm **PRICES:** s €40-€45; d €60-€65✱ **LB**
PARKING: 8 **NOTES:** Closed Nov-Feb **CARDS:** 💳💳

CO WATERFORD

DUNGARVAN
Map 01 C2

◆◆◆◆◆ ♥ Castle Country House
Millstreet, Cappagh
☎ 058 68049 📠 058 68099
e-mail: castlefm@iol.ie
Dir: N72, take R671 for 3.5m, right at Millstreet, house 200yds on right

PETS: Bedrooms (unattended) Exercise area (adjacent)

This delightful house is to be found in the west wing of a 15th century castle. Guests are spoilt by host Joan Nugent who loves to cook and hunt out antiques for her visitors to enjoy. She is helped by her husband Emmett who enjoys showing off his high-tech dairy farm and is a fount of local knowledge. Bedrooms are spacious and enjoy lovely views. There is a river walk and a beautiful garden to relax in.
FACILITIES: 5 en suite (1 fmly) No smoking TVB tea/coffee Licensed Cen ht Fishing Farm tour 200 acres dairy & beef Dinner Last d 5pm **PRICES:** s €50-€60; d €80-€90✱ **LB PARKING:** 11
NOTES: Closed Dec-Feb **CARDS:** 💳💳💳

CO WEXFORD

CAMPILE
Map 01 C2

◆◆◆◆◆ T&C Kilmokea Country Manor & Gardens
Great Island
☎ 051 388109 📠 051 388776
e-mail: kilmokea@indigo.ie
Dir: from New Ross take R733 S towards Campile, before village turn right for Great Island and Kilmokea Gardens. 12km from New Ross

PETS: Bedrooms (unattended) Exercise area (on site) RESIDENT PETS: Breezy & Jasmine (Black Labradors), Jackie & Martha (horses), chickens, peacocks

KILMOKEA
COUNTRY MANOR & GARDENS
Great Island, Campile, Co. Wexford, Ireland

A gracious 18th-century, stone-built rectory, recently restored. Nestling in wooded gardens (open to the public), where peacocks wander and trout fishing is available on the lake. Comfortable bedrooms and public rooms are richly furnished, and a 'country house' style dinner is served nightly (booking essential). Take

continued

breakfast in the conservatory and tea overlooking the beautiful gardens.
FACILITIES: 4 en suite 2 annexe en suite (1 fmly) (2 GF) No smoking tea/coffee Direct dial from bedrooms Licensed Cen ht Indoor swimming pool (heated) Tennis (hard) Fishing Sauna Gymnasium Croquet lawn Dinner Last d 6pm **PRICES:** s €105-€130; d € 160-€260✳ **LB**
PARKING: 12 **NOTES:** Closed 6 Nov-Feb **CARDS:** 🔲 🔲

KILMORE QUAY
Map 01 D2

◆◆◆◆ GH Quay House Guest House
☎ 053 29988 🖹 053 29808
e-mail: quayhome@eircom.net
Dir: turn off N25 onto R739 following sign to Kilmore Quay, house on left past Hotel Saltees

PETS: Exercise area (50 metres)

Situated on the main street in this fishing village that is only 15 minutes from Rosslare Harbour. Comfortable accommodation is provided by the friendly and hospitable owners. Local attractions include fishing, bird-watching and island cruises. Private parking available.
FACILITIES: 8 en suite (6 fmly) (2 GF) No smoking TVB tea/coffee Cen ht No coaches Angling and diving facilities **PRICES:** s €45; d €80✳ **LB PARKING:** 16 **CARDS:** 🔲 🔲 🔲

> **All abbreviations are explained on page 9**

> **Don't forget to let proprietors know when you book that you're bringing your pet**

DUNLAVIN
Map 01 C3

◆◆◆◆ ❧ Tynte House
☎ 045 401561 🖹 045 401586
e-mail: info@tyntehouse.com
Dir: N81 at Hollywood Cross, right at Dunlavin, follow finger signs for Tynte House, past market house in centre of town

PETS: Bedrooms Public areas (not in dining room) Exercise area

A gracious 19th-century farmhouse standing in the square of this quiet country village. The friendly hosts have carried out a lot of restoration and facilities now include bedrooms, self-catering apartments in an adjoining courtyard, a laundry, tennis courts, children's play area and indoor games room.
FACILITIES: 7 en suite (2 fmly) No smoking in 2 bedrooms No smoking in dining room No smoking in lounges TVB tea/coffee Direct dial from bedrooms Cen ht TVL Golf 18 Tennis (hard) Pool Table Playground games room with table tennis 200 acres arable beef Dinner Last d Noon **PRICES:** s fr €44; d fr €70✳ **LB PARKING:** 16
NOTES: Closed 23 Dec-2 Jan **CARDS:** 🔲 🔲 🔲

Ireland

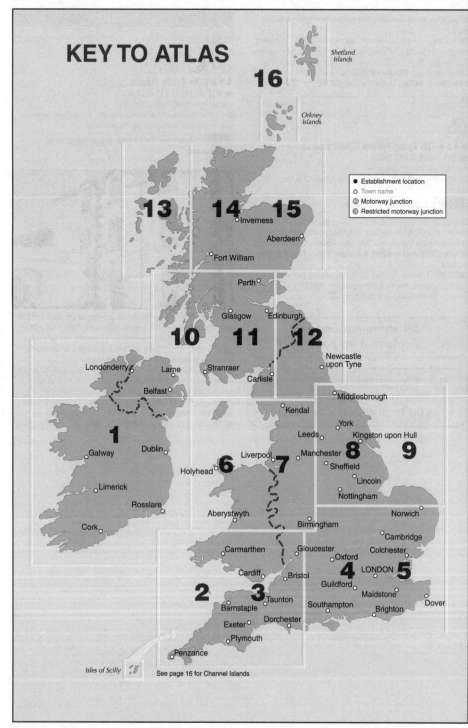

KEY TO ATLAS

- • Establishment location
- ○ Town name
- ⊚ Motorway junction
- ⊚ Restricted motorway junction

Shetland Islands

16

Orkney Islands

13   **14**   **15**

Inverness

Aberdeen

Fort William

Perth

10   **11**   **12**

Glasgow   Edinburgh

Newcastle upon Tyne

Londonderry   Larne   Stranraer

Belfast   Carlisle

Middlesbrough

Kendal

1   York

Dublin   Leeds   Kingston upon Hull

Galway   Liverpool   **7**   Manchester   **8**   **9**

Holyhead   **6**   Sheffield

Limerick   Lincoln

Rosslare   Nottingham

Cork   Aberystwyth   Norwich

Birmingham   Cambridge

Carmarthen   Gloucester   Colchester

Cardiff   Oxford

2   **3**   Bristol   **4**   LONDON   **5**

Taunton   Guildford

Barnstaple   Southampton   Maidstone   Dover

Exeter   Dorchester   Brighton

Plymouth

Isles of Scilly   Penzance

See page 16 for Channel Islands

© Automobile Association Developments Limited 2004

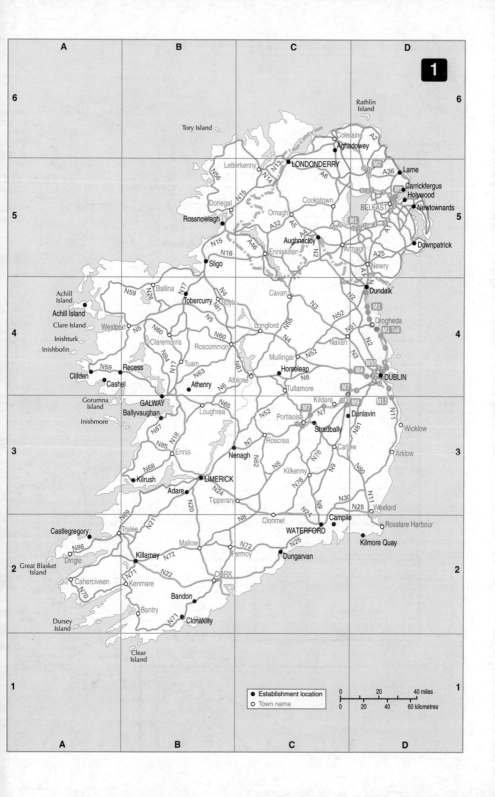

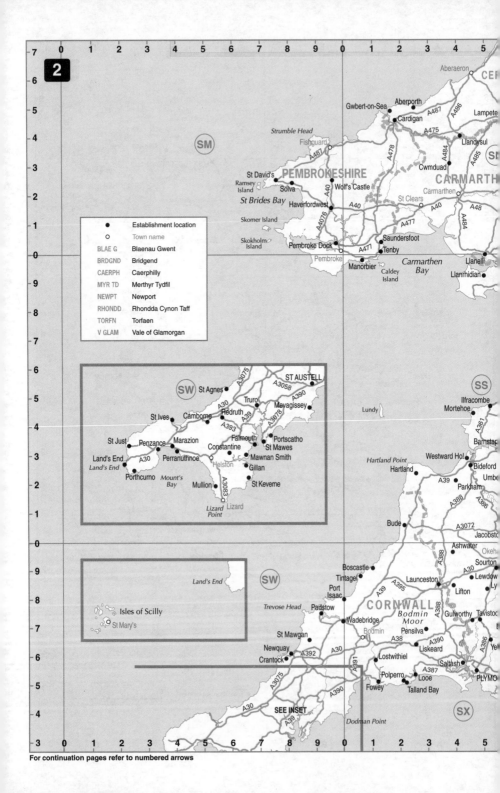

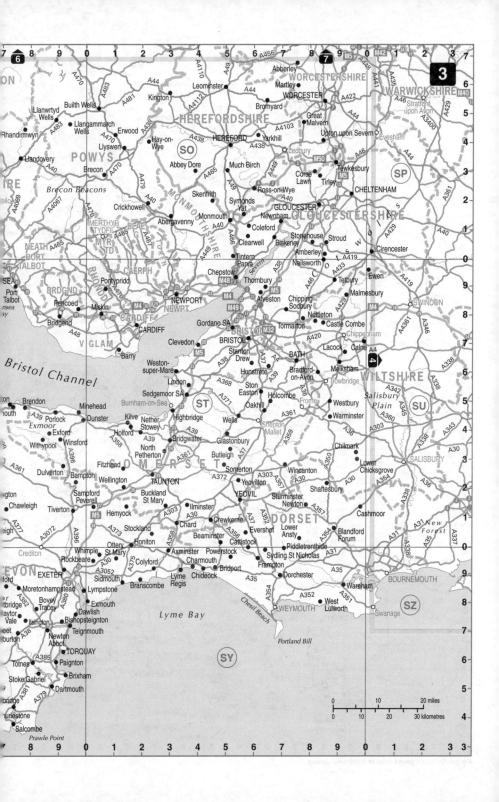

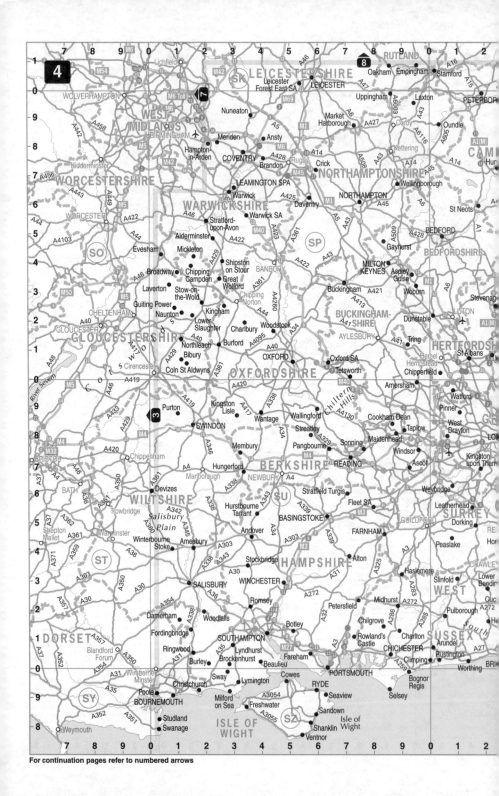

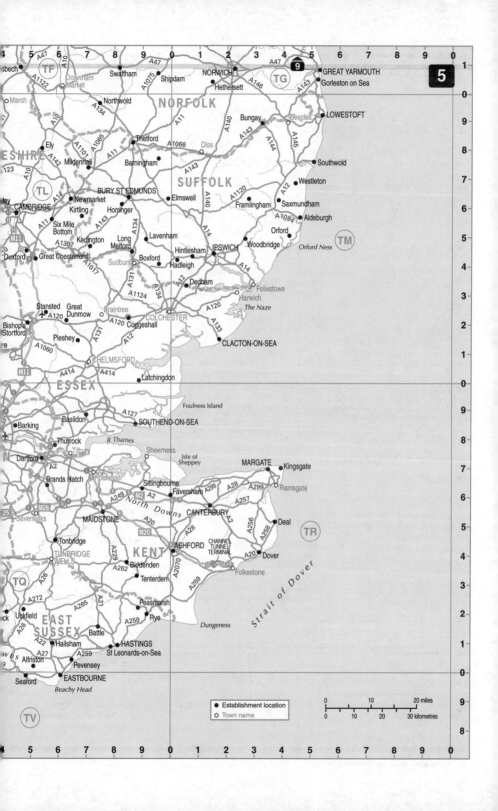

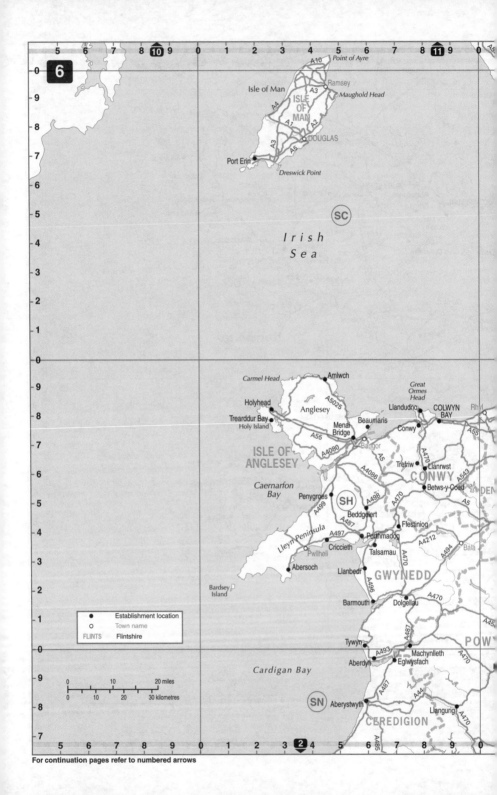

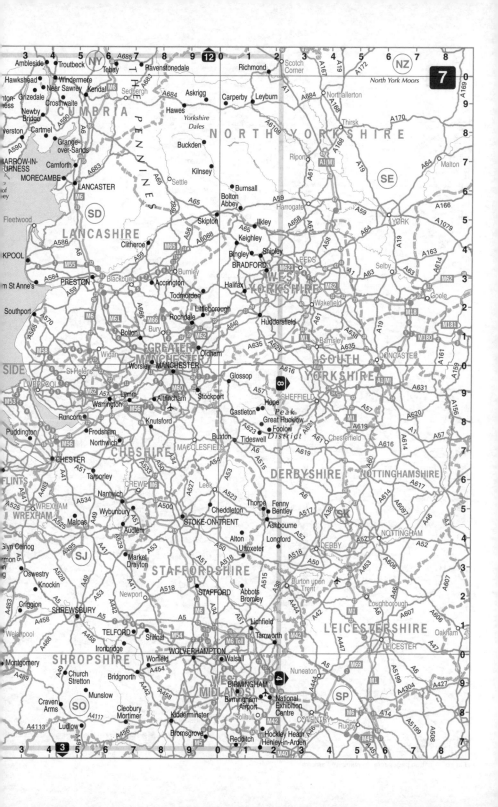

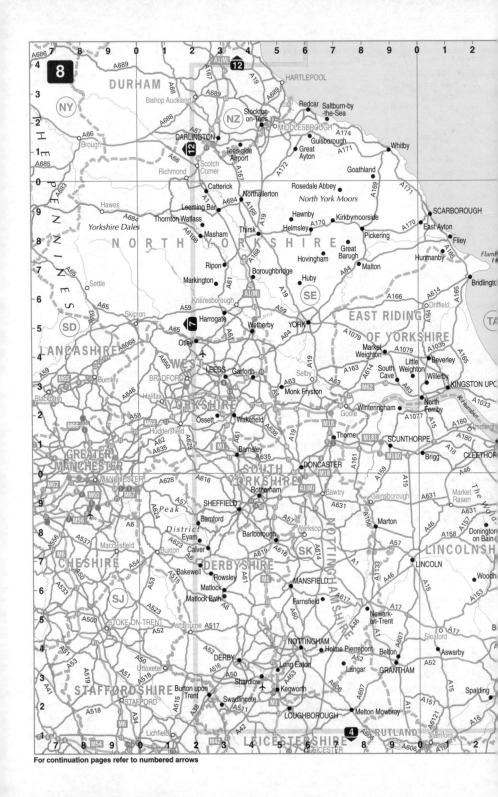

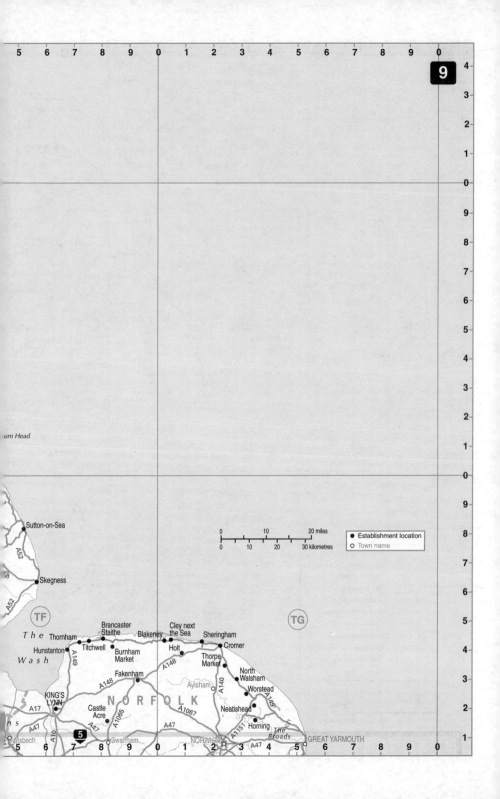

| 5 | 6 | 7 | 8 | 9 | 0 | 1 | 2 | 3 | 4 | 5 | 6 | 7 | 8 | 9 | 0 |

4
3
2
1
0
9
8
7
6
5
4
3
2
1
0
9
8
7
6
5
4
3
2
1

urn Head

Sutton-on-Sea

A52

58

Skegness

A52

TF

TG

The   Thornham   Brancaster   Cley next   Sheringham
Wash   Staithe   Blakeney   the Sea   Cromer
         Hunstanton Titchwell   Burnham   Holt   Thorpe
                                        Market   Market
                     A149   North
                           A148   Walsham
                     A148   Fakenham   A140   Worstead
                                                    Aylsham
         KING'S   NORFOLK   A149
         LYNN   Neatishead
    A17   Castle   A1067
                        Acre   A1065   A47   Horning   The
    A47   A1151   Broads
ns   A47   A47
   Wisbech   Swaffham   NORWICH   GREAT YARMOUTH

5

| 0 | 10 | 20 miles |
| 0 | 10 | 20 | 30 kilometres |

● Establishment location
○ Town name

| 5 | 6 | 7 | 8 | 9 | 0 | 1 | 2 | 3 | 4 | 5 | 6 | 7 | 8 | 9 | 0 |

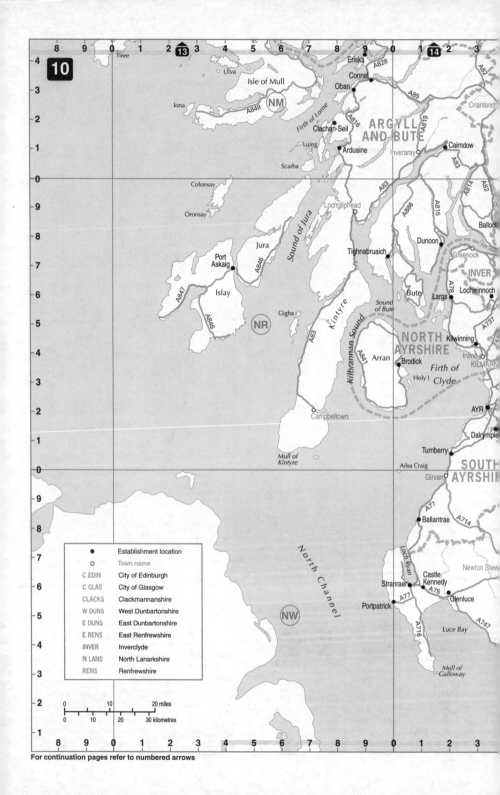

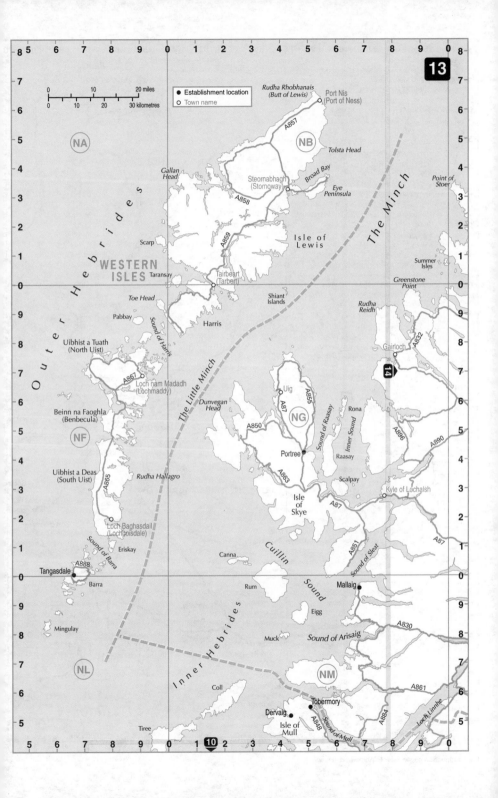

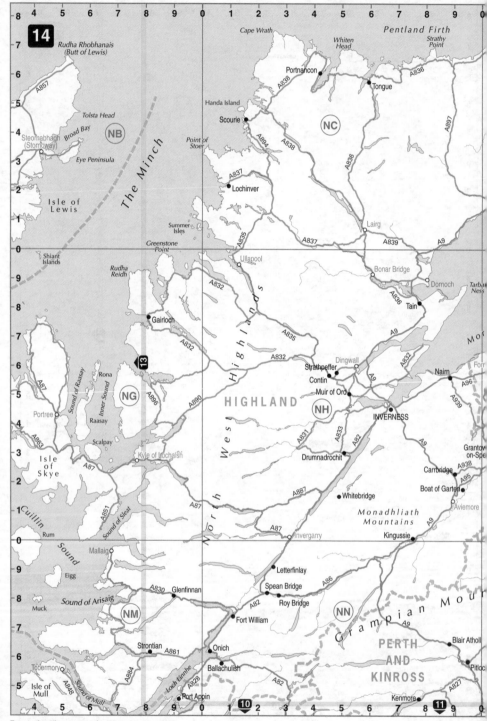

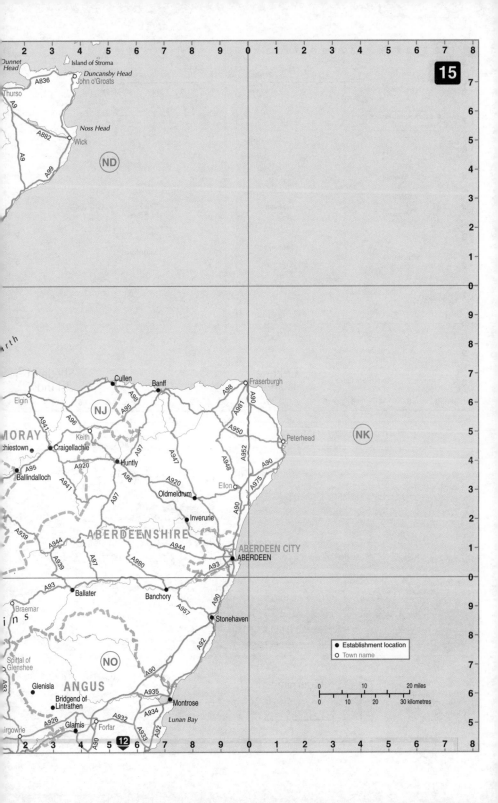

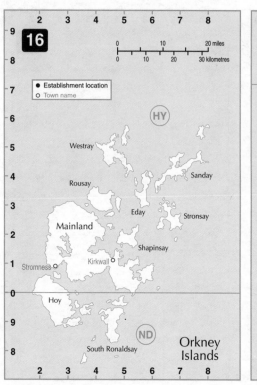

Orkney Islands

16

● Establishment location
○ Town name

HY

Westray

Rousay

Sanday

Eday

Stronsay

Mainland

Shapinsay

Stromness ○   ○ Kirkwall

Hoy

ND

South Ronaldsay

Shetland Islands

HP

Unst

Yell

Fetlar

Whalsay

● Brae

Mainland

Lerwick ○

Bressay

HU

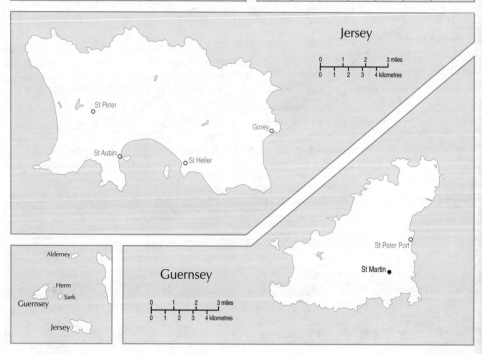

Jersey

St Peter ○

Gorey ○

St Aubin ○   ○ St Helier

Guernsey

St Peter Port ○

St Martin ●

Alderney

Herm

Guernsey   Sark

Jersey

ifestyle Collection

Index

A

ABBERLEY
Elms Hotel & Restaurant 235
ABBEY DORE
Tan House Farm 137
ABBOTS BROMLEY
Marsh Farm 197
ABERDEEN
Aberdeen Patio 262
Copthorne Hotel Aberdeen 262
The Marcliffe at Pitfodels 262
Maryculter House Hotel 263
Strathisla 263
Westhill 262
ABERDOUR
The Aberdour Hotel 277
ABERDYFI
Cartref 314
Penhelig Arms Hotel &
  Restaurant 314
ABERGAVENNY
Angel 319
Hardwick Farm 319
Llansantffraed Court 319
ABERPORTH
Ffynonwen 307
ABERSOCH
Deucoch 315
ABERYSTWYTH
Harry's 308
Marine Hotel 308
Queensbridge Hotel 308
ACCRINGTON
Sparth House Hotel 147
ACHILL ISLAND
GH Gray's 334
AGHADOWEY
Brown Trout Golf
  & Country Inn 331
ALDEBURGH
The Brudenell 199
Wentworth 199
White Lion 199
ALDERMINSTER
The Bell 217-8
ALFRISTON
Deans Place 205
ALTON (Hants)
Alton Grange 129
ALTON (Staffs)
Chained Oak Farm 197
ALTRINCHAM
Cresta Court Hotel 127
Quality Hotel Altrincham 127
ALVESTON
Alveston House 115
AMBERLEY
The Amberley Inn 115

AMBLESIDE
Brathay Lodge 58
Regent 58
Skelwith Bridge 58
Wanslea 58
AMERSHAM
The Crown 34
AMESBURY
Park House Motel 229
AMLWCH
Lastra Farm 304
ANDOVER
Esseborne Manor 129
ANSTRUTHER
The Spindrift 278
ANSTY
Ansty Hall 218
APPLEBY-IN-WESTMORLAND
Appleby Manor
  Country House 58-9
ARCHIESTOWN
Archiestown 288
ARDUAINE
Loch Melfort 266
ARUNDEL
Norfolk Arms 211
ASCOT
The Berystede 30
ASHBOURNE
The Dog & Partridge 73
Mercaston Hall 73
Stone Cottage 73
ASHBURTON
Holne Chase 80-1
The Rising Sun 81
ASHFORD
Ashford International 143
Croft Hotel 143
Eastwell Manor 143
ASHWATER
Blagdon Manor Hotel &
  Restaurant 81
ASKRIGG
Whitfield 240-1
ASPLEY GUISE
Moore Place Hotel 30
ASWARBY
Tally Ho 151
ATHENRY
GH Caheroyan
  House and Farm 333
AUCHENCAIRN
Balcary Bay 272
AUCHTERARDER
The Gleneagles 289-90
AUDLEM
Little Heath Farm 39
AUGHNACLOY
GH Rehaghy Lodge 331
AXMINSTER
Fairwater Head 81
Lea Hill 81-2
Sellers Wood Farmhouse 82

AYR
Belmont 297
Daviot House 297
Savoy Park 296-7
Windsor Hotel 297

B

BAKEWELL
Croft Cottages 74
Monsal Head Hotel 74
Rutland Arms Hotel 74
BALLACHULISH
Ballachulish Hotel 280
Lyn-Leven 280
BALLANTRAE
Glenapp Castle 297
BALLATER
Darroch Learg 263
Loch Kinord 263
BALLINDALLOCH
Craighead 288
BALLOCH
Sunnyside 299
BALLYVAUGHAN
GH Cappabhaile House 332
GH Drumcreehy 332
BAMBURGH
The Lord Crewe 171
Waren House 171
BAMFORD
Yorkshire Bridge Inn 74
BAMPTON
Exeter Inn 82
BANCHORY
Burnett Arms 264
Raemoir House 263
Tor-na-Coille 264
BANDON
T&C Glebe Country House 332
BANFF
Morayhill 264
BARKING
Hotel Ibis 126
BARLBOROUGH
Hotel Ibis Sheffield South 74
BARMOUTH
Llwyndu Farmhouse 315
Ty'r Graig Castle Hotel 315
BARNARD CASTLE
The Morritt Arms Hotel &
  Restaurant 111
BARNINGHAM
College House Farm 199
BARNSLEY
Ardsley House 254
BARNSTAPLE
Cresta 82
Halmpstone Manor 82
BARROW-IN-FURNESS
Lisdoonie 59
BARRY
Egerton Grey
  Country House 329
Mount Sorrel 329
BASILDON
Campanile 114

BASINGSTOKE
Hanover International
  Hotel & Club — 129
Hatchings — 129
BASSENTHWAITE
Armathwaite Hall — 59
The Pheasant — 59
BATH
The Abbey Hotel — 186
The Bath Spa — 185
Cliffe — 185
Eagle House — 186
The Francis — 185
Marlborough House — 186
Pratts — 186
BATTLE
Fox Hole Farm — 206
Powder Mills — 205-6
BEAMINSTER
Bridge House — 102
BEAULIEU
Beaulieu — 130
BEAUMARIS
The Bulkeley Hotel — 304
BEDDGELERT
The Royal Goat — 315
Sygun Fawr Country House — 315
BEDFORD
Knife & Cleaver Inn — 30
BELFORD
Market Cross — 171
BELTON
De Vere Belton Woods — 152
BERWICK-UPON-TWEED
Dervaig Guest House — 172
King's Arms — 172
Marshall Meadows
  Country House — 171
BETWS-Y-COED
Best Western Waterloo — 310
Craig-y-Dderwen
  Riverside Hotel — 309
BEVERLEY
The Eastgate — 239
Manor House — 238-9
BIBURY
Bibury Court — 116
BIDDENDEN
Heron Cottage — 143
BIDEFORD
The Pines at Eastleigh — 83
Yeoldon Country House — 82
BIGGAR
Shieldhill Castle — 298
BINGLEY
Five Rise Locks — 256
**BIRCHANGER GREEN MOTOR-
  WAY SERVICE AREA [M11]**
Days Inn Stansted — 114
BIRMINGHAM
Awentsbury Hotel — 222
Campanile — 222
Copperfield House — 222
Fountain Court — 222
Lyndhurst Hotel — 222-3

Malmaison Birmingham — 221
Novotel Birmingham Centre — 222
Rollason Wood Hotel — 223
The Westley — 222
**BIRMINGHAM [NATIONAL
  EXHIBITION CENTRE]**
Arden Hotel & Leisure Club — 223
Heath Lodge — 223
BIRMINGHAM AIRPORT
Novotel Birmingham Airport — 223
BISHOP'S STORTFORD
Broadleaf Guest House — 141
Harewood — 141
BISHOPSTEIGNTON
Cockhaven Manor Hotel — 83
BLACKPOOL
Brabyns — 147
Briar Dene Hotel — 147
Burlees Hotel — 147
Windsor Park Hotel — 147-8
BLAIR ATHOLL
Bridge of Tilt — 290
BLAKENEY (Norfolk)
Morston Hall — 163
The Pheasant Hotel — 163
BLAKENEY (Gloucs)
Old Nibley Farmhouse — 116
BLANCHLAND
Lord Crewe Arms — 172
BLANDFORD FORUM
The Anvil Inn — 103
Whiteways Farm — 103
BOAT OF GARTEN
Boat — 281
BOGNOR REGIS
The Inglenook — 211-2
BOLTON
Broomfield Hotel — 127
BOLTON ABBEY
Devonshire Arms — 241
BOROUGHBRIDGE
The Crown Inn — 241
BORROWDALE
Borrowdale — 59
Royal Oak — 59-60
BOSCASTLE
Old Coach House — 42
Tolcarne House Hotel — 43
BOSTON
Boston Lodge — 152
BOTLEY
Botley Park Hotel
  & Country Club — 130
BOURNEMOUTH
Alum Grange Hotel — 105
Bay View Court — 104
Bournemouth Sands — 105
Burley Court — 104
Carrington House — 103-4
The Connaught — 103
East Cliff Cottage Hotel — 105
Fircroft — 105
Heathlands Hotel — 104
Langtry Manor -
  Lovenest of a King — 103

Ocean View Hotel — 104
Wessex — 103
Whitehall — 104
BOVEY TRACEY
Coombe Cross — 83
BRADFORD
Guide Post Hotel — 256
Novotel Bradford — 256
BRADFORD-ON-AVON
Leigh Park Hotel — 229
Woolley Grange — 229
BRAE
Busta House — 301-2
BRAMPTON
Farlam Hall — 60
BRANCASTER STAITHE
White Horse — 163
BRANDON
Brandon Hall — 218
BRANDS HATCH
Brandshatch Place — 144
BRANSCOMBE
The Masons Arms — 83
BRECON
Borderers — 324
Lansdowne Hotel
  & Restaurant — 323
BRENDON
Leeford Cottage — 83
BRIDGEND
Heronston — 305
BRIDGEND OF LINTRATHEN
Lochside Lodge & Roundhouse
  Restaurant — 265
BRIDGNORTH
Oldfield Cottage — 179
BRIDGWATER
Model Farm — 186
BRIDLINGTON
Marton Grange — 239
Shearwater — 239
BRIDPORT
Bridge House — 105
Britmead House — 105
BRIGG
The Red Lion Hotel — 152
BRIGHTON
Ambassador Hotel — 206
Brighton Pavilions — 207
De Vere Grand Brighton — 206
The Granville — 206
Penny Lanes — 207
BRISTOL
Arno's Manor Hotel — 33
The Avon Gorge — 33
Berkeley Square Hotel — 33
The Bowl Inn — 34
Henbury Lodge Hotel — 34
Washington Hotel — 34
BRIXHAM
Berryhead — 84
BROADWAY
Bowers Hill Farm — 236
The Lygon Arms — 235-6
Whiteacres — 236

BROCKENHURST
Bridge House 130-1
Forest Park 130
New Park Manor 130
Seraya 131
Thatched Cottage
Hotel & Restaurant 130
BRODICK
Dunvegan House 300
Kilmichael Country House 300
BROMYARD
Little Hegdon Farm House 137
BROUGHTON
Glenholm Centre 294
BROUGHTON-IN-FURNESS
The Black Cock Inn 60
BUCKDEN
Buck Inn 241
BUCKINGHAM
Buckingham Beales Best
Western Hotel 34
BUCKLAND ST MARY
Hillside 187
BUDE
Cliff Hotel 43
Fairway House 43
Penarvor 43
BUILTH WELLS
Caer Beris Manor 324
BUNGAY
Earsham Park Farm 199
BURFORD
The Inn For All Seasons 176
The Lamb Inn 176
BURLEY
Burley Manor 131
BURNHAM MARKET
Hoste Arms 163
BURNSALL
Burnsall Manor
House Hotel 241
BURNTISLAND
Kingswood 278
**BURRINGTON [NEAR
PORTSMOUTH
ARMS STATION]**
Northcote Manor 84
BURTON UPON TRENT
Riverside 197
BURY ST EDMUNDS
The Fox & Hounds 200
Ravenwood Hall 200
BUTLEIGH
Court Lodge 187
BUTTERMERE
Bridge 60
BUXTON
Best Western Lee
Wood Hotel 75
Buckingham Hotel 75
Hawthorn Farm 75
Wellhead Farm 75

C

CAIRNDOW
Cairndow Stagecoach Inn 267
CALLANDER
The Priory Country
Guest House 298
CALNE
Lansdowne Strand 229
CALVER
Valley View 75
CAMBORNE
Tyacks 43
CAMBRIDGE
De Vere University Arms 36
Gonville 36
Hotel Felix 36
Lynwood House 37
Royal Cambridge 36
CAMPILE
T&C Kilmokea Country Manor &
Gardens 334-5
CANONBIE
Cross Keys 272
CANTERBURY
Cathedral Gate Hotel 144
The County 144
Ebury 144
Upper Ansdore 145
Yorke Lodge Hotel 144
CARDIFF
Big Sleep Hotel 306
Copthorne Hotel Cardiff-
Caerdydd 305
Hotel Ibis Cardiff 305
Hotel Ibis Cardiff Gate 306
St Mellons Hotel
& Country Club 305
CARDIGAN
Webley Hotel 308
CARLISLE
Angus Hotel
& Almonds Bistro 61
Cherry Grove 61
Lakes Court 61
The Crown & Mitre 61
CARNFORTH
New Capernwray Farm 148
Royal Station Hotel 148
CARPERBY
Wheatsheaf Hotel 241
CARRBRIDGE
Dalrachney Lodge 281
Pines Country House 281
CARTMEL
Uplands Hotel 61
CASHMOOR
Cashmoor House 106
CASTLE ACRE
Lodge Farm 163
CASTLE COMBE
Manor House 230
CASTLE DOUGLAS
Craigadam 273
Imperial 272
King's Arms 272

CASTLE KENNEDY
The Plantings Inn 273
CASTLECARY
Castlecary House 277
CASTLEGREGORY
T&C Griffin's Palm Beach
Country House 333
CASTLETON
The Rising Sun Hotel 76
CATTERICK
Rose Cottage 242
CATTISTOCK
Fox & Hounds Inn 106
CHAGFORD
Gidleigh Park 84
Mill End 84
Three Crowns Hotel 84
CHARD
Lordleaze 187
Watermead 187
CHARLBURY
The Bell 176
CHARLTON
Woodstock House Hotel 212
CHARMOUTH
White House 106
**CHARNOCK RICHARD MOTOR-
WAY SERVICE AREA [M6]**
Welcome Lodge 148
CHAWLEIGH
The Barn-Rodgemonts 85
CHEDDLETON
Prospect House 197
CHELTENHAM
Butlers Hotel 117
Carlton 117
Charlton Kings 116
Cotswold Grange 117
The Greenway 116
Hope Orchard 117
The Queen's 116
White House 117
White Lodge 117
CHEPSTOW
Beaufort 319
CHESTER
Blossoms 39
Grosvenor Pulford 39
The Mount 39-40
CHICHESTER
Crouchers Country Hotel &
Restaurant 212
Old Chapel Forge 212
CHIDEOCK
Chideock House 106
Rose Cottage 106
CHILGROVE
The White Horse 212
CHILMARK
The Dial House 230
CHIPPERFIELD
The Two Brewers 141-2
CHIPPING CAMPDEN
Cotswold House 118
The Kings Arms Hotel 118

Manor Farm 118
CHIPPING SODBURY
The Moda Hotel 118
CHIRNSIDE
Chirnside Hall 294
CHRISTCHURCH
Stour Villa 107
CHURCH STRETTON
Mynd House 180
North Hill Farm 180
Stretton Hall Hotel 179
CIRENCESTER
The Crown Of Crucis 118-9
Fleece Hotel 119
Stratton House 118
CLACHAN-SEIL
Willowburn 267
CLACTON-ON-SEA
Sandrock Hotel 114
CLEARWELL
The Wyndham Arms 119
Tudor Farmhouse Hotel &
Restaurant 119
CLEETHORPES
Tudor Terrace 152
CLEOBURY MORTIMER
Old Bake House 180
CLEVEDON
Walton Park 187
CLEY NEXT THE SEA
The George Hotel 164
CLIFDEN
Ardagh 333
CLIMPING
Bailiffscourt Hotel
& Health Spa 212-3
CLITHEROE
Shireburn Arms 148
CLONAKILTY
Desert House 332
COCKERMOUTH
Highside Farmhouse 62
Rose Cottage 62
Shepherds Hotel 62
The Trout 61
COGGESHALL
White Hart 114
COLEFORD
Cor Unum 120
The Speech House 119-20
COLN ST ALDWYNS
The New Inn At Coln 120
COLVEND
Clonyard House 273
COLWYN BAY
Cabin Hill Private Hotel 311
Lyndale 310
Marine 310
Northwood Hotel 310
Whitehall Hotel 310
COLYFORD
Lower Orchard 85
CONNEL
Falls of Lora 267
Loch Etive House Hotel 267

CONSETT
Derwent Manor 112
CONSTANTINE
Trengily Wartha Inn 43
CONTIN
Coul House 281
CONWY
Castle Hotel Conwy 311
The Groes Inn 311
The Old Rectory
Country House 311
Sychnant Pass House 311
COOKHAM DEAN
The Inn on the Green Garry
Hollihead 31
CORNHILL-ON-TWEED
Ivy Cottage 172
Tillmouth Park
Country House 172
CORSE LAWN
Corse Lawn House 120
CORWEN
Bron-y-Graig 313
Powys Country House 314
COVENTRY
Hotel Ibis Coventry South 223
Toffs Hotel 224
COWES
New Holmwood 225
Windward House 225
CRAIGELLACHIE
Craigellachie 288
CRAILING
Crailing Old School B&B 294
CRANTOCK
Crantock Bay 44
CRAVEN ARMS
Castle View 180
CREWKERNE
Greenways 187
Manor Farm 188
CRICCIETH
Abereistedd Hotel 316
CRICK
Hotel Ibis Rugby East 170
CRICKHOWELL
Bear 324
Manor Hotel 324
Ty Croeso 325
CRIEFF
Comely Bank 290
CRIGGION
Brimford House 325
CROMER
The Cliftonville 164
Sandcliff Private Hotel 164
CROSTHWAITE
Crosthwaite House 63
Damson Dene 62
CUCKFIELD
Ockenden Manor 213
CULLEN
The Seafield Hotel 288-9

CUMBERNAULD
The Westerwood Hotel Golf &
Country Club 289
CWMDUAD
Neuadd-Wen 306

D

DALRYMPLE
Kirkton Inn Hotel 277
DAMERHAM
The Compasses 131
DARLINGTON
Kings Head 112
Walworth Castle Hotel 112
DARTFORD
Campanile 145
DARTMEET
Brimpts Farm 85
DARTMOUTH
Cherub's Nest 85
Warfleet Lodge 85
DAVENTRY
Fawsley Hall 170
DAWLISH
Langstone Cliff 86
DEAL
Sutherland House Hotel 145
DEDHAM
The Sun Inn 114
DERBY
Aston Court Hotel
& Conference Centre 76
Days Hotel Derby 76
International 76
DERBY SERVICE AREA [A50]
Days Inn 76
DERVAIG
Druimard Country House 301
DEVIZES
Bear 230
Eastcott Manor 230
DOLGELLAU
Dolgun Uchaf Guesthouse 316
Fronoleu Country Hotel 316
Penmaenuchaf Hall 316
Plas Dolmelynllyn 316
DOLLAR
Castle Campbell Hotel 271
DONCASTER
Balmoral Hotel 254
East Farm 254
Regent 254
DONINGTON ON BAIN
The Black Horse Inn 152
DORCHESTER
Long Barn House 107
Yalbury Cottage 107
DORKING
The White Horse 204
DOVER
Castle House 145
Hubert House 145
DRUMNADROCHIT
Clunebeg Lodge 281-2
Polmaily House Hotel 281

DULVERTON
Highercombe 188
Lion 188
Threadneedle 188
DUMFRIES
Cairndale Hotel
& Leisure Club 273
DUNBLANE
Cromlix House 298
DUNDEE
Sandford Country
House Hotel 276
The Shaftesbury 277
DUNFERMLINE
Pitbauchlie House 278
DUNGARVAN
Castle Country House 334
DUNLAVIN
Tynte House 335
DUNOON
Dhailling Lodge 268
Enmore 268
DUNSTABLE
Hanover International Hotel 30
DUNSTER
Higher Orchard 189
The Luttrell Arms Hotel 188-9
DURHAM
Bowburn Hall 112
Durham Marriott Hotel,
Royal County 112
The Gables 113
Kings Lodge Hotel
& Restaurant 112
DUXFORD
Duxford Lodge 37

E
EAST AYTON
East Ayton Lodge 242
EASTBOURNE
Arden Hotel 208
Chatsworth 207
Farrar's Hotel 208
Gladwyn Hotel 208
Grand 207
Lansdowne 207
Meridale 208
Quality Hotel Langham 208
Sheldon Hotel 208-9
EDINBURGH
Malmaison 269
Bonnington 269
Galloway 269
Kings Manor 269
Kingsview Guest House 269
EGLWYSFACH
Ynyshir Hall 308-9
ELMSWELL
Kiln Farm 200
ELY
Castle Lodge Hotel 37
Chapel Cottage 37
Lamb 37
EMBLETON
Dunstanburgh Castle Hotel 173

EMPINGHAM
The White Horse Inn 178
ERISKA
Isle of Eriska 268
ERWOOD
Hafod-Y-Garreg 325
EVERSHOT
Summer Lodge 107
EVESHAM
The Evesham 236
Northwick Hotel 236
EWEN
Wild Duck Inn 120
EXETER
Culm Vale Country House 87
The Edwardian 87
Gissons Arms 87
Hotel Barcelona 86
Lord Haldon Country House 86
Queens Court 86
Rydon 87
St Olaves Hotel & Restaurant 86
EXFORD
Crown 189
EXMOUTH
Royal Beacon 87
EYAM
Miners Arms 76

F
FAKENHAM
Abbott Farm 164
FALMOUTH
Falmouth 44
Falmouth Beach Resort Hotel 44
Green Lawns 44
Penmorvah Manor 44
Prospect House 45
Rosemary Private Hotel 45
FAREHAM
Travelrest -
Avenue House Hotel 131
FARNHAM
Sleepy Hollow 205
FARNSFIELD
Grange Cottage 174
FAVERSHAM
Eastling Holiday Centre 145
FENNY BENTLEY
Bentley Brook Inn 77
FFESTINIOG
Morannedd 317
Ty Clwb 317
FILEY
Gables 242
FIR TREE
Helme Park Hall Hotel 113
FITZHEAD
Fitzhead Inn 189
**FLEET MOTORWAY SERVICE
AREA [M3]**
Days Inn 132
FOOLOW
The Bulls Head Inn 77
FORDINGBRIDGE
Ashburn Hotel & Restaurant 132

FORT WILLIAM
Distillery House 282
Moorings 282
Seangan Croft 282
FOWEY
Carnethic House 45
Fowey Hall 45
Marina 45
Trevanion 45
FRAMLINGHAM
Church Farm 200
FRAMPTON
Frampton House 108
FRESHWATER
Farringford 225
FRODSHAM
Forest Hill Hotel
& Leisure Complex 40

G
GAIRLOCH
Myrtle Bank 282
The Old Inn 282-3
GALASHIELS
Kingsknowes 295
Over Langshaw 295
GALWAY
T&C Atlantic Heights 333
GARFORTH
Milford Hotel 257
GATEHOUSE OF FLEET
Murray Arms 273
GATWICK AIRPORT [LONDON]
The Lawn 213
Rosemead 213
Vulcan Lodge 213
GAYHURST
Mill Farm 34
GILLAN
Tregildry 46
GLAMIS
Castleton House 265
GLASGOW
Malmaison 270
Ewington 270
Glasgow Moat House 270
Hotel Ibis Glasgow
City Centre 271
Kelvin Private Hotel 271
Kelvingrove Hotel 271
Langs Hotel 270
The Merchant Lodge 271
One Devonshire Gardens 270
Quality Hotel Glasgow 271
Tulip Inn Glasgow 271
GLASTONBURY
Hedgehog House B & B 189
GLENFINNAN
The Prince's House 283
GLENISLA
The Glenisla Hotel 266
GLENLUCE
Kelvin House Hotel 273
GLENRIDDING
Glenridding 63
The Inn on the Lake 63

GLENROTHES
Rescobie House Hotel &
  Restaurant 278
GLOSSOP
Brentwood 77
Kings Clough Head Farm 77
GLOUCESTER
Hatherley Manor 121
GLYN CEIRIOG
Golden Pheasant 329
GOATHLAND
Fairhaven Country Hotel 242
GORDANO SERVICE AREA [M5]
Days Inn 190
GORLESTON ON SEA
Avalon Private Hotel 164
GRANGE-OVER-SANDS
Elton Hotel 63
Netherwood 63
GRANTHAM
Kings 152-3
GRASMERE
Grasmere 64
Oak Bank 64
The Swan 64
Thistle Grasmere 64
GREAT AYTON
Royal Oak Hotel 242
GREAT BARUGH
Barugh House 243
GREAT CHESTERFORD
The Crown House 114-5
GREAT DUNMOW
Starr Restaurant with Rooms 115
GREAT HUCKLOW
The Queen Anne 77
GREAT WOLFORD
The Fox & Hounds Inn 218
GREAT YARMOUTH
Barnard House 165
Imperial 165
Regency Dolphin 165
**GRETNA [WITH GRETNA
GREEN]**
Barrasgate 274
**GRETNA SERVICE AREA
[A74(M)]**
Days Inn 274
GRIMSBY
Elizabeth 153
GRIZEDALE
Grizedale Lodge The Hotel in
  the Forest 64
GUISBOROUGH
Gisborough Hall 243
GUITING POWER
Guiting Guest House 121
Hollow Bottom 121
GULLANE
Greywalls 277
GULWORTHY
Horn of Plenty 87
GWBERT-ON-SEA
Cliff 309

H

HADLEIGH
Edgehall Hotel 200
HAILSHAM
Boship Farm 209
The Olde Forge Hotel &
  Restaurant 209
HALIFAX
Holdsworth House 257
HAMPTON-IN-ARDEN
The Cottage 224
HARLECH
Estuary Motel 317
Maes y Neuadd
  Country House 317
HARROGATE
Alexa House
  & Stable Cottages 243
Ascot House 243
The Boar's Head Hotel 243
The Harrogate Brasserie
  Hotel & Bar 243
Princes Hotel 244
Shelbourne 244
HARTLAND
Fosfelle 88
HASLEMERE
Wheatsheaf 205
HASTINGS & ST LEONARDS
Beauport Park 209
HATFIELD
Quality Hotel Hatfield 142
HAVERFORDWEST
College 321
Hotel Mariners 321
HAWES
Simonstone Hall 244
Stone House 244
HAWKSHEAD
Kings Arms Hotel 65
HAWNBY
Laskill Grange 244-5
HAY-ON-WYE
Baskerville Arms Hotel 326
Kilverts Hotel 326
The Swan-at-Hay 325
York House 326
HAYTOR VALE
Rock Inn 88
**HEATHROW AIRPORT
[LONDON]**
Novotel London Heathrow 126
Harmondsworth Hall 126
HELMSLEY
Black Swan 245
Crown 245
Pheasant 245
HELTON
Beckfoot Country House 65
HENFIELD
Frylands 213
HENLEY-IN-ARDEN
Ashleigh House 218
Henley 218

HEREFORD
Sink Green 138
HEXHAM
De Vere Slaley Hall 173
Rye Hill 173
HIGHBRIDGE
Sundowner 190
HINTLESHAM
Hintlesham Hall 201
HOCKLEY HEATH
Nuthurst Grange Country House
  & Restaurant 224
HOLCOMBE
The Ring O' Roses 190
HOLFORD
Combe House 190
Winsors Farm B & B 190
HOLME PIERREPONT
Holme Grange Cottage 174
HOLYHEAD
Boathouse 304
Wavecrest 304
HOLYWOOD
GH Beech Hill 331
HONITON
Atwell's at Wellington Farm 89
Combe House Hotel &
  Restaurant 88
The Crest 89
Home Farm 88
Ridgeway Farm 89
HOOK
Oaklea 132
HOPE
Stoney Ridge 78
Round Meadow Barn 78
Underleigh House 77
HORNING
Petersfield House 165
HORRINGER
The Ickworth 201
HOVINGHAM
Worsley Arms Hotel 245
**HOWTOWN [NEAR POOLEY
BRIDGE]**
Sharrow Bay Country House 65
HUBY
The New Inn Motel 245
HUDDERSFIELD
Cedar Court 257
Lodge 257
HUNGERFORD
Beacon House 31
Crown & Garter 31
HUNMANBY
Wrangham House Hotel 246
HUNSTANTON
Claremont 165
The Lodge Hotel
  & Restaurant 165
HUNSTRETE
Hunstrete House 191
HUNTINGDON
Huntingdon Marriott Hotel 37

HUNTLY
Gordon Arms Hotel 264

I

ILFRACOMBE
Norbury House Hotel 89
Strathmore Hotel 89
ILKLEY
Rombalds 257
ILMINSTER
Shrubbery 191
ILSINGTON
The Ilsington Country House 90
INVERNESS
Bunchrew House 283
Fraser House 284
The Maple Court 283
Moyness House 283
Royal Highland 283
INVERURIE
Pittodrie House 264
IPSWICH
Novotel Ipswich 201
IRONBRIDGE
Broseley House 180
Woodlands Farm
Guest House 180

J

JACOBSTOWE
Higher Cadham 90
JEDBURGH
Ferniehirst Mill Lodge 295
Glenfriars House 295

K

KEDINGTON
The White House 201
KEIGHLEY
Dalesgate 257
KELSO
The Roxburghe Hotel
& Golf Course 295
KENDAL
Gilpin Bridge 65
KENMORE
Kenmore Hotel 290
KESWICK
Craglands 66
Cragside 67
Derwentwater 65-6
Hall Garth 66
Hazeldene Hotel 66
Hazelmere 66
Heatherlea 67
Howe Keld Lakeland Hotel 66
Keswick Park Hotel 66-7
Rickerby Grange Hotel 67
KIDDERMINSTER
Gainsborough House 236
The Granary Hotel
& Restaurant 237
KILMORE QUAY
GH Quay House
Guest House 335
KILNSEY
Kilnsey Old Hall 246

KILVE
Hood Arms Hotel 191
KILWINNING
Montgreenan
Mansion House 289
KINCLAVEN
Ballathie House 290
KINGHAM
Mill House Hotel
& Restaurant 176-7
KING'S LYNN
Maranatha Guest House 166
KINGSBRIDGE
Buckland-Tout-Saints 90
KINGSGATE
The Fayreness 146
KINGSTON LISLE
The Blowing Stone Inn 177
KINGSTON UPON HULL
Campanile 239
Portland 239
Quality Hotel Royal Hull 239
KINGSTON UPON THAMES
Chase Lodge Hotel 126
KINGTON
Burton 138
KINGUSSIE
The Scot House 284
KINROSS
Green 291
KIRKBY STEPHEN
Brownber Hall
Country House 67
Southview Farm 67
KIRKBYMOORSIDE
George & Dragon Hotel 246
KIRKCUDBRIGHT
Arden House Hotel 274
Baytree House 274
Royal 274
KIRKMUIRHILL
Dykecroft 298
KIRTLING
Hill Farm Guest House 38
KNARESBOROUGH
Newton House 246
KNOCKIN
Top Farm House 181
KNUTSFORD
The Longview Hotel &
Restaurant 40

L

LACOCK
The Old Rectory 230
LADYBANK
Fernie Castle 278-9
LAMPETER
Falcondale Mansion 309
Haulfan 309
LANCASTER
Lancaster House 148
LAND'S END
The Land's End Hotel 46
LANGAR
Langar Hall 174

LARGS
Willowbank 289
LAUNCESTON
Eagle House 46
LAVENHAM
Lavenham Great
House Hotel 201
LAVERTON
Leasow House 121
LEAMINGTON SPA (ROYAL)
Adams 219
The Best Western Royal
Leamington Hotel 219
Bubbenhall House 219
Courtyard by Marriott
Leamington Spa 219
Falstaff 219
LEATHERHEAD
Bookham Grange 205
LEEDS
Golden Lion 258
Malmaison Hotel 258
The Merrion 258
Novotel Leeds Centre 258
LEEMING BAR
The White Rose 246
LEICESTER
Stoneycroft Hotel 150
**LEICESTER FOREST EAST
MOTORWAY SERVICE AREA
[M1]**
Days Inn 150
LEOMINSTER
Ford Abbey 138
Woonton Court Farm 138
LERWICK
Glen Orchy House 302
LETTERFINLAY
Letterfinlay Lodge 284
LEWDOWN
Lewtrenchard Manor 90
LEYBURN
Golden Lion 246-7
The Old Horn Inn 247
LICHFIELD
The George 197
LIFTON
Arundell Arms 91
LINCOLN
Castle 153
Eagles 153
Edward King House 154
Hillcrest 153
Jaymar 154
Newport 153
Tower Hotel 153
LINLITHGOW
Bomains Farm 299-300
LISKEARD
Well House 46
LITTLE WEIGHTON
The Rowley Manor 240
LITTLEBOROUGH
Hollingworth Lake Bed &
Breakfast 127

LLANARMON
DYFFRYN CEIRIOG
West Arms 329
LLANBEDR
Bryn Artro Country House 317
Pensarn Hall Country
Guest House 318
Ty Mawr 317
LLANDOVERY
Castle 306
Cwm Rhuddan Mansion 306
LLANDUDNO
Epperstone 312
Quinton Hotel 312
St George's 312
Somerset 312
Sunnymede 312
Tudno Lodge 313
Vine House 313
Wavecrest 312
LLANDYSUL
Plas Cerdin 309
LLANELLI
Diplomat Hotel 306-7
LLANGAMMARCH WELLS
Lake Country House 326
LLANGURIG
Old Vicarage 326
LLANRHIDIAN
North Gower 328
LLANRWST
Maenan Abbey 313
LLANWDDYN
Lake Vyrnwy 326-7
LLANWRTYD WELLS
Carlton House 327
LLYSWEN
Llangoed Hall 327
LOCHEARNHEAD
Mansewood Country House 299
LOCHINVER
Inver Lodge 284
LOCHWINNOCH
East Lochhead 294
LOCKERBIE
Dryfesdale 274
Ravenshill House 275
Somerton House 275
LONDON E14
Hotel Ibis London Docklands 156
LONDON EC1
Malmaison
Charterhouse Square 156
LONDON EC3
Novotel London
Tower Bridge 156
LONDON N4
Parkside Hotel 157
LONDON NW3
Quality Hotel Hampstead 157
LONDON SE1
Mercure London
City Bankside 157
Novotel London City South 157

LONDON SE3
Clarendon 157
LONDON SE10
Hamilton House 158
LONDON SW1
No 41 158
The Rubens at the Palace 158
Sofitel St James London 158
22 Jermyn Street 158
LONDON SW3
The Draycott 158-9
LONDON SW5
Maranton House Hotel 159
LONDON SW7
The Bentley 159
LONDON SW10
Conrad London 159
LONDON SW15
The Lodge Hotel 160
LONDON W1
Athenaeum 160
The Chesterfield 160
Four Seasons Hotel London 160
The Washington
Mayfair Hotel 160
LONDON W2
Comfort Inn Bayswater 161
Pembridge Court 160-1
LONDON W6
Vencourt 161
LONDON W8
Milestone Hotel
& Apartments 161
LONDON WC1
The Montague on
the Gardens 161
LONDON GATEWAY MOTOR-
WAY SERVICE AREA [M1]
Days Hotel 162
LONG MELFORD
The Black Lion Hotel 202
LONGFORD
Russets 78
LONGHORSLEY
Linden Hall 173
LOOE
Fieldhead 47
Gulls Hotel 47
Hannafore Point 46
LOSTWITHIEL
Restormel Hotel 47
LOUGHBOROUGH
Garendon Park Hotel 150
The Quality Hotel & Suites
Loughborough 150
LOUTH
Beaumont 154
Kenwick Park 154
LOWER ANSTY
The Fox Inn 108
LOWER BEEDING
South Lodge 214
LOWER CHICKSGROVE
Compasses Inn 231

LOWER SLAUGHTER
Washbourne Court 121
LOWESTOFT
Albany Hotel 202
Fairways 203
Ivy House Country Hotel 202
Somerton House 202
LOWESWATER
Grange Country House 68
LOXTON
Webbington 191
LUDLOW
Bromley Court B & B 181
Charlton Arms 182
Church Inn 182
Cliffe 181
Dinham Hall 181
The Hoopits 181
Moor Hall 182
Overton Grange
Country House 181
Timberstone
Bed & Breakfast 182
LUNDIN LINKS
Old Manor 279
LYDFORD
Moor View House 91
LYME REGIS
Alexandra Hotel 108
Victoria Hotel 108
The White House 108
LYMINGTON
1 Honeysuckle Gardens 133
Efford Cottage 132
Gorse Meadow 133
Harts Lodge 132
Jevington 133
Passford Farm 133
Stanwell House 132
LYMM
Lymm Hotel 40
LYMPSTONE
Varnes 91
LYNDHURST
Knightwood Lodge 133-4
Lyndhurst Park 133
LYNMOUTH
Bath 91
Countisbury Lodge Hotel 92
The Heatherville 92
Tors 91
LYNTON
Lynton Cottage Hotel 92
Seawood Hotel 92
LYTHAM ST ANNES
Lindum 149

M

MACHYNLLETH
Dyfiguest 327
Wynnstay 327
MADINGLEY
Beck Brook Farm 38
MAIDENHEAD
Elva Lodge Hotel 31

MAIDSTONE
Wits End 146
MALLAIG
West Highland 284
MALMESBURY
Old Bell Hotel 231
Whatley Manor 231
MALPAS
Millmoor Farm 40
MALTON
Burythorpe House 247
MALVERN
Colwall Park 237
Cottage in the Wood 237
Four Hedges 238
Holdfast Cottage Hotel 237
MANCHESTER
Hotel Ibis Manchester
  City Centre 128
Malmaison 128
Old Rectory Hotel 128
MANORBIER
Castle Mead 321
MANSFIELD
Portland Hall 174-5
MARAZION
Godolphin Arms 47
MARGATE
Elonville Hotel 146
The Greswolde Hotel 146
MARKET DRAYTON
Haywood Farm B & B 182
MARKET HARBOROUGH
Three Swans 150
MARKET WEIGHTON
Robeanne House 240
MARKINGTON
Hob Green 247
MARTLEY
Admiral Rodney Inn 238
MARTON [VILLAGE]
Black Swan Guest House 154
MASHAM
Swinton Park 247
MATLOCK
New Bath 79
Farley 79
Hearthstone Farm 79
Hodgkinsons Hotel 79
Riber Hall 78
MAWNAN SMITH
Meudon Hotel 48
MELKSHAM
Shaw Country 231
MELTON MOWBRAY
Bryn Barn 151
Noels Arms 151
Stapleford Park 150-1
Sysonby Knoll 151
MEMBURY
Days Inn 32
MENAI BRIDGE
Victoria Hotel 304
MERIDEN
Manor 224

MEVAGISSEY
Spa Hotel 48
MICKLETON
Three Ways 122
MIDHURST
Park House 214
Redford Cottage 214
Spread Eagle Hotel
  and Health Spa 214
The Angel 214
MILDENHALL
Riverside 203
MILFORD ON SEA
Westover Hall 134
MILTON KEYNES
Campanile 35
Novotel Milton Keynes 35
Parkside 35
Swan Revived Hotel 35
Welcome Lodge 35
MINEHEAD
The Old Ship Aground 191
MISKIN
Miskin Manor Hotel
  & Health Club 328
MOFFAT
Barnhill Springs Country 275
Beechwood Country House 275
Hartfell House 275
Limetree House 275
MOLD
Beaufort Park Hotel 314
MONK FRYSTON
Monk Fryston Hall 248
MONMOUTH
Hendre Farm House 320
Riverside 319
MONTGOMERY
Dragon Hotel 327
MONTROSE
Links Hotel 266
Oaklands 266
MORECAMBE
Clarendon 149
Elms 149
Hotel Prospect 149
MORETONHAMPSTEAD
Bovey Castle 93
MORTEHOE
Lundy House Hotel 93
MUCH BIRCH
Pilgrim 138
MUIR OF ORD
The Dower House 285
Ord House 284-5
MULLION
Polurrian 48
MUNGRISDALE
The Mill 68
MUNSLOW
Crown Country Inn 182-3

N
NAILSWORTH
Aaron Farm 122
NAIRN
Golf View 285
Newton 285
NANTWICH
Crown 41
Rookery Hall 40-1
NAUNTON
Mill View 122
NEAR SAWREY
Ees Wyke Country House 68
NEATISHEAD
Regency 166
NETHER STOWEY
Castle of Comfort 192
NETTLETON
Fosse Farmhouse
  Country Hotel 231
NEW LANARK
New Lanark Mill Hotel 298
NEWARK-ON-TRENT
Willow Tree Inn 175
NEWBY BRIDGE
Lakes End 68
NEWCASTLE UPON TYNE
Clifton House Hotel 217
Hadrian Lodge Hotel 217
Malmaison 216
Newcastle Marriott Hotel
  Gosforth Park 216
Quality Hotel
  Newcastle upon Tyne 217
Vermont 216
NEWICK
Newick Park Hotel &
  Country Estate 209
NEWMARKET
Heath Court 203
NEWNHAM
Swan House Country
  Guest House 122
NEWPORT
The Inn at the Elm Tree 321
NEWQUAY
Barrowfield 49
Corisande Manor Hotel 49
Esplanade Hotel 49
Headland 48
Hotel Bristol 49
Kellsboro Hotel 50
Philema 49
Whipsiderry 49
NEWTON ABBOT
Bulleigh Park Farm 93
NORTH FERRIBY
Elizabeth Hotel Hull 240
NORTH WALSHAM
Beechwood 166
Green Ridges 166
NORTHALLERTON
The Golden Lion 248
NORTHAMPTON
Northampton Marriott Hotel 170

NORTHLEACH
The Puesdown Inn 122
The Wheatsheaf Inn 123
NORTHWICH
The Floatel 41
NORTHWOLD
Comfort Inn Thetford 166
NORWICH
Edmar Lodge 167
The Georgian House 167
The Larches 167
The Old Rectory 167
Stower Grange 167
NOTTINGHAM
Bestwood Lodge 175
Fairhaven Private Hotel 175
Hart's 175
Lace Market 175
NOTTINGHAM EAST MIDLANDS AIRPORT
Best Western Yew Lodge Hotel 151
NUNEATON
Weston Hall 219-20

O

OAKHAM
Barnsdale Lodge 178-9
Hambleton Hall 179
OAKHILL
Oakhill Lodge 192
OBAN
Lancaster 268
The Oban Caledonian Hotel & Spa 268
OLDHAM
La Pergola 128
OLDMELDRUM
Meldrum Arms 264
ONICH
Lodge On The Loch 285
Onich 285
ORFORD
Crown & Castle Inn 203
OSWESTRY
Pen-y-Dyffryn Country Hotel 183
Wynnstay 183
OTLEY
Chevin Country Park Hotel 258
OTTERBURN
The Otterburn Tower Hotel 173-4
OTTERY ST MARY
Fluxton Farm 93
OUNDLE
Ship 170
OXFORD
Fallowfields Country House Hotel 177

P

PADSTOW
The Metropole 50
The Newlands Hotel 50
The Old Ship Hotel 50
Rick Stein's Cafe 51

St Petroc's Hotel and Bistro 50
The Seafood Restaurant 50
PAIGNTON
Bay Cottage Hotel 94
Park Hotel 94
PANGBOURNE
The Copper Inn Hotel & Restaurant 32
PARKHAM
Penhaven Country House 94
PEASLAKE
Hurtwood Inn Hotel 205
PEASMARSH
Flackley Ash 210
PEAT INN
Peat Inn 279
PEEBLES
Castle Venlaw 296
Cringletie House 295-6
Park 296
PEMBROKE DOCK
Cleddau Bridge 322
PENCOED
St Mary's Hotel & Country Club 305
PENRITH
Glendale 68
Queen's Head Inn 68-9
PENSILVA
Wheal Tor Country Hotel 51
PENYGROES
Llwyndu Mawr 318
PENZANCE
Mount Prospect 51
Penmorvah Hotel 52
Queen's 51
Woodstock 51
PERTH
Clunie 292
Huntingtower 291
Murrayshall Country House Hotel & Golf Course 291
Westview 292
PETERBOROUGH
Bull 38
Orton Hall 38
PETERLEE
Hardwicke Hall Manor 113
PETERSFIELD
Langrish House 134
PEVENSEY
Priory Court Hotel 210
PICKERING
White Swan 248
PIDDLETRENTHIDE
The Poachers 109
PINNER
Tudor Lodge Hotel 126
PITLOCHRY
Balrobin 293
Donavourd House 292
Green Park 292
Pine Trees 292
The Well House 293
Wellwood House 293

PLYMOUTH
Camelot 94
Cranbourne 95
Four Seasons 95
Hotel Ibis 95
The Lamplighter Hotel 95
The Moorland 94
Novotel Plymouth 94
POLPERRO
Higher Polgassic 52
Penryn House Hotel 52
Talland Bay Hotel 52
PONTYPRIDD
Llechwen Hall 328
POOLE
Arndale Court 109
Norfolk Lodge 109
Salterns Harbourside 109
PORLOCK
Andrews on the Weir 192
PORT APPIN
Airds 268
PORT ASKAIG
Port Askaig 300-1
PORT ERIN
Falcon's Nest 260
PORT ISAAC
The Corn Mill 52-3
PORT OF MENTEITH
Lake 299
PORT TALBOT
Aberavon Beach 321
PORTHCURNO
The Porthcurno Hotel 52
PORTHMADOG
Royal Sportsman Hotel 318
Tyddyn Du Farm Holidays 318
PORTNANCON
Port-Na-Con House 286
PORTPATRICK
Fernhill 276
Knockinaam Lodge 276
PORTREE
Bosville 302
Rosedale 302
PORTSCATHO
Rosevine 53
PORTSMOUTH
Portsmouth Marriott Hotel 134
Royal Beach Hotel 134
Seacrest Hotel 134
POSTBRIDGE
Lydgate House 95
POWERSTOCK
Three Horseshoes Inn 109
PRESTON
Novotel Preston 149
Withy Trees 149
PUDDINGTON
Craxton Wood 41
PULBOROUGH
Arun House 215
Chequers 214-5
PURTON
The Pear Tree at Purton 232

R

RAVENSTONEDALE
The Fat Lamb 69
READING
Courtyard by
Marriott Reading 32
Millennium Madejski Hotel
Reading 32
RECESS
Lough Inagh Lodge 333
REDCAR
Claxton Hotel 248
REDDITCH
Quality Hotel Redditch 238
REDRUTH
Crossroads Lodge 53
RHANDIRMWYN
The Royal Oak 307
RICHMOND
King's Head 248
RINGWOOD
Little Forest Lodge 135
Lochend 135
RIPON
Ripon Spa 248-9
Unicorn 249
ROCHDALE
Norton Grange 128
ROCKBEARE
Lower Allercombe Farm 95
ROMSEY
The White Horse 135
ROSEDALE ABBEY
Blacksmith's Country Inn 249
Milburn Arms 249
ROSLIN
Olde Original Rosslyn 288
ROSS-ON-WYE
Brookfield House 140
Brynheulog 140
Castle Lodge Hotel 139
Chasedale 139
King's Head 139
Lea House 140
Lumleys 140
Pencraig Court 139
Pengethley Manor 138-9
The Royal 139
Thatch Close 140
Wilton Court Hotel 139
ROTHERHAM
Elton 255
ROWLANDS CASTLE
The Fountain Inn 135
ROWSLEY
The Peacock at Rowsley 79
ROY BRIDGE
Glenspean Lodge Hotel 286
RUNCORN
Campanile 41
RUSTINGTON
Kenmore 215
RUTHIN
Eyarth Station 314

RYDE
Yelf's 226
RYE
Jeake's House 210
Little Saltcote 211
Rye Lodge 210

S

ST AGNES
The Beacon Country House
Hotel 53
Driftwood Spars Hotel 54
Rose in Vale Country House 53
ST ALBANS
Apples Hotel 142
Sopwell House Hotel, Country
Club & Spa 142
ST ANDREWS
The Inn at Lathones 280
The Old Course Hotel,
Golf Resort & Spa 279
Rusacks 280
St Andrews Bay Golf
Resort & Spa 280
St Andrews Golf 280
ST AUSTELL
The Lodge at Carlyon Bay 54
Sunnycroft 54
White Hart 54
ST BOSWELLS
Buccleuch Arms 296
ST DAVID'S
Old Cross 322
Warpool Court 322
ST FILLANS
Achray House 293
The Four Seasons Hotel 293
ST IVES
Chy Roma 55
The Old Vicarage Hotel 55
Slepe Hall 38
ST JUST [NEAR LAND'S END]
Wellington Hotel 55
ST KEVERNE
Gallen-Treath Guest House 55
White Hart Hotel 55
ST MARTIN
Green Acres 260
ST MAWES
Idle Rocks 55
ST MAWGAN
The Falcon 56
ST NEOTS
Abbotsley Golf Hotel 38
ST TEATH
Tregarthen Bed & Breakfast 56
SALCOMBE
Soar Mill Cove 96
Tides Reach 96
SALISBURY
Byways House 233
Glen Lyn 233
Grasmere House 232
The White Hart 232
SALTASH
The Crooked Inn 56

SALTBURN-BY-THE-SEA
Rushpool Hall Hotel 249
SAMPFORD PEVERELL
Parkway House
Country Hotel 96
SANDOWN
Carisbrooke House Hotel 226
Riviera 226
SANQUHAR
Blackaddie House 276
**SARN PARK MOTORWAY
SERVICE AREA [M4]**
Welcome Lodge 305
SAUNDERSFOOT
St Brides 322
Vine Cottage 322
SAXMUNDHAM
Sandpit Farm 203
SCARBOROUGH
Brooklands 250
Ox Pasture Hall 250
SCARISTA
Scarista House 300
SCOURIE
Scourie 286
SCUNTHORPE
Wortley House 154-5
SEAFORD
Silverdale 211
SEAHOUSES
Bamburgh Castle 174
SEAVIEW
Priory Bay 226
**SEDGEMOOR MOTORWAY
SERVICE AREA [M5]**
Days Inn 192
SELSEY
St Andrews Lodge Hotel 215
SHAFTESBURY
Royal Chase 110
SHANKLIN
Cliff Hall 226
Hayes Barton Hotel 227
Melbourne Ardenlea 227
Norfolk House Hotel 227
The Glendene Hotel 228
SHEFFIELD
Aston Hall 255
Cutlers Hotel 255
Novotel Sheffield 255
Parklands 256
Quarry House 255
Sheffield Marriot Hotel 255
SHERINGHAM
Highfield 168
SHIFNAL
Park House 183
SHIPDHAM
Pound Green Hotel 168
SHIPLEY
Hotel Ibis Bradford 259
SHREWSBURY
Albright Hussey 183
Albrighton Hall 183
Lion & Pheasant 184

Lythwood Hall
  Bed & Breakfast 184
Mytton & Mermaid 184
SIDMOUTH
Kingswood 96
The Salty Monk 96-7
Sid Valley Country House 96
SILLOTH
The Skinburness 69
SITTINGBOURNE
Hempstead House
  Country Hotel 146
SIX MILE BOTTOM
Swynford Paddocks 39
SKEGNESS
Vine 155
SKENFRITH
The Bell at Skenfrith 320
SKIPTON
The Coniston 250
Craven House 250
Hanover International 250
SLINFOLD
The Red Lyon 215
SOLVA
Lochmeyler Farmhouse 323
SOMERTON
Stowford House 192
SONNING
The Great House at Sonning 32
SOURTON
Collaven Manor 97
SOUTH CAVE
Rudstone Walk Country
  Accommodation 240
SOUTHAMPTON
The Elizabeth House 136
Hotel Ibis 136
Hunters Lodge Hotel 136
Southampton Park 136
The Woodlands Lodge 135
SOUTHEND-ON-SEA
Balmoral 115
Terrace Hotel 115
SOUTHPORT
Edendale Hotel 162
Metropole Hotel 162
Whitworth Falls Hotel 162
SOUTHWOLD
No 21 204
The Blyth Hotel 203-4
SPALDING
Cley Hall 155
SPEAN BRIDGE
Distant Hills 286
The Smiddy House 286
STAFFORD
Yew Tree Inn & Restaurant 198
STAMFORD
Garden House 155
STANTON DREW
Greenlands 192-3
STEVENAGE
Novotel Stevenage 142

STOCKBRIDGE
York Lodge 136
STOCKLAND
The Kings Arms Inn 97
STOCKPORT
Henry's 129
STOCKTON-ON-TEES
The Parkwood Hotel 113
STOKE GABRIEL
Gabriel Court 97
STOKE-ON-TRENT
Haydon House 198
STON EASTON
Ston Easton Park 193
STONEHAVEN
Woodside Of Glasslaw 265
STONEHOUSE
Stonehouse Court 123
STOW-ON-THE-WOLD
Limes 123-4
Old Stocks 123
The Unicorn Hotel 123
Wyck Hill House Hotel 123
STRANRAER
Corsewall Lighthouse Hotel 276
STRATFIELD TURGIS
Wellington Arms 136
STRATFORD-UPON-AVON
The Alveston Manor 220
Avon Lodge 220
Marlyn 220
The Shakespeare 220
The Swan's Nest 220
STRATHPEFFER
Inver Lodge 286-7
STRATHYRE
Creagan House 299
STREATLEY
The Swan at Streatley 32
STRONTIAN
Creag Ard House 287
Kilcamb Lodge 287
STROUD
The Bell 124
Hyde Crest 124
STUDLAND
Manor House 110
STURMINSTER NEWTON
Honeysuckle House 110
Plumber Manor 110
SUTTON-ON-SEA
Athelstone Lodge Hotel 155
SWADLINCOTE
Overseale House 79
SWAFFHAM
George 168
SWANAGE
The Pines 111
SWANSEA
Windsor Lodge 328-9
SWAY
Acorn Shetland Pony Stud 137
Sway Manor
  Restaurant & Hotel 137

SWINDON
The Check Inn 234
Chiseldon House 233
The Goddard Arms 233
Hotel Ibis Swindon 234
Parklands Hotel & Bentleys
  Restaurant 234
Portquin 234
Villiers Inn 233
SWINTON
The Wheatsheaf 296
SYDLING ST NICHOLAS
Greyhound Inn 111
SYMONDS YAT [WEST]
Norton House 141

T

TAIN
The Glenmorangie Highland
  Home at Cadboll 287
Morangie House 287
TAMWORTH
Oak Tree Farm 198
The Old Rectory 198
TANGASDALE
Isle of Barra Hotel 300
TAPLOW
Cliveden 35
TARPORLEY
Hill House Farm 41-2
Willington Hall 41
TAUNTON
Blorenge House 193
Castle 193
Farthings Hotel
  and Restaurant 193
Gatchells 194
Meryan House Hotel 194
Rumwell Manor 193
TAVISTOCK
Bedford 97
Coach House 98
Sampford Manor 97-8
TEBAY
Cross Keys 69
Westmorland Hotel &
  Bretherdale Restaurant 69
TEES-SIDE AIRPORT
The St George 113
TEIGNMOUTH
Potters Mooring 98
TELFORD
Avenue Farm 184
Church Farm 184
Clarion Hotel Madeley Court 184
TELFORD SERVICE AREA [M54]
Days Inn Telford 185
TENBY
Brambles Lodge 323
Fourcroft 323
TENTERDEN
White Lion 146
TETBURY
Hare & Hounds 124
Tavern House 124

TETSWORTH
Little Acre Bed & Breakfast   177
TEWKESBURY
Royal Hop Pole   125
THETFORD
The Thomas Paine Hotel   168
THIRSK
Golden Fleece   250
THORNBURY
Thornbury Castle   125
THORNE
Belmont   256
THORNHAM
Lifeboat Inn   168-9
THORNTON WATLASS
Buck Inn   251
THORPE [DOVEDALE]
Izaak Walton Hotel   80
The Peveril of the Peak   80
THORPE MARKET
Elderton Lodge Hotel & Langtry
   Restaurant   169
Green Farm
   Restaurant & Hotel   169
THURLESTONE
Thurlestone   98
THURROCK
Hotel Ibis London Thurrock   115
TIDESWELL
Greystones   80
Jaret House   80
Poppies   80
TIGHNABRUAICH
The Royal at Tighnabruaich   269
TILLICOULTRY
Westbourne House   272
TINTAGEL
Bossiney House   56
Port William Inn   57
TINTERN PARVA
The Abbey Hotel   320
Fountain Inn   320
Parva Farmhouse Hotel &
   Restaurant   320
TIRLEY
Town Street Farm   125
TITCHWELL
Titchwell Manor   169
TIVERTON
Rhode Farm House   98-9
TIVERTON
Tiverton   98
TOBERCURRY
T&C Cruckawn House   334
TOBERMORY
Highland Cottage   301
Tobermory   301
Western Isles   301
TODMORDEN
Staff of Life   259
TONBRIDGE
The Langley   147
TONGUE
Ben Loyal Hotel   287

TORMARTON
Compass Inn   125
TORQUAY
Albaston House Hotel   99
Anchorage Hotel   100
Ansteys Lea   99
Belgrave   99
Hotel Blue Conifer   100
Ingoldsby Hotel   100
Manor Farm   100
Orestone Manor Hotel &
   Restaurant   99
The Palms Hotel   100
Rainbow International   99
Red House   100
Stover Lodge Hotel   101
Tyndale   101
TOTNES
Royal Seven Stars   101
TRING
Pendley Manor   142
**TROUTBECK
   [NEAR WINDERMERE]**
Mortal Man   69
TRURO
Alverton Manor   57
TURNBERRY
Westin Turnberry Resort   297
TWO BRIDGES
Prince Hall Hotel   101
Two Bridges Hotel   101
TYWYN
Eisteddfa   318

U

UCKFIELD
Buxted Park Country
   House Hotel   211
ULVERSTON
Church Walk House   70
Lonsdale House Hotel   70
UMBERLEIGH
Eastacott Barton   101
UPPINGHAM
Falcon   179
UPTON UPON SEVERN
White Lion   238
UTTOXETER
Oldroyd Guest
   House & Motel   198

V

VENTNOR
Eversley   228
Fairview Cottage   229
Hillside Hotel   228
Lake Hotel   228

W

WADEBRIDGE
Molesworth Arms   57
WAKEFIELD
Campanile   259
Cedar Court   259
Hotel St Pierre   259
Stanley View   259

WALLINGFORD
Shillingford Bridge   177
Springs Hotel & Golf Club   177
WALSALL
Quality Hotel
   Birmingham North   224
WANTAGE
Down Barn Farm   177
WARE
Roebuck   143
WAREHAM
Worgret Manor   111
WARMINSTER
Bishopstrow House   234
The Dove Inn   234
WARRINGTON
De Vere Daresbury Park   42
Fir Grove   42
Paddington House   42
WARWICK
Croft   221
Dockers Barn Farm   221
The Hare on the Hill   221
**WARWICK MOTORWAY SER-
   VICE AREA**
Days Inn
   Stratford Upon Avon   221
WASHINGTON
George Washington Golf &
   Country Club   217
WATERMILLOCK
Brackenrigg Inn   70
Leeming House   70
WELLINGBOROUGH
The Hind   170
Hotel Ibis Wellingborough   170
WELLINGTON
Bindon Country House
   Hotel & Restaurant   194
The Cleve Hotel
   & Country Club   194
WELLS
Ancient Gate House   195
Crown at Wells   195
Infield House   195
White Hart   194
WEST AUCKLAND
The Manor House Hotel &
   Country Club   113
WEST LULWORTH
Cromwell House   111
WESTBURY
The Cedar   235
WESTLETON
Westleton Crown   204
WESTON-SUPER-MARE
Braeside   195
Madeira Cove Hotel   195
WESTWARD HO!
Culloden House Hotel   102
WETHERBY
Prospect House   260
WHICKHAM
Gibside Arms   217

WHIMPLE
Larkbeare Farmhouse 102
WHITBY
Chiltern 251
Cliffemount 251
Dunsley Hall 251
Sandbeck Hotel 252
Seacliffe Hotel 252
WHITEBRIDGE
Whitebridge 288
WINCANTON
Holbrook House 196
WINCHESTER
Lainston House Hotel 137
The Wessex 137
WINDERMERE
Cedar Manor
  Country Lodge 72-3
The Coppice 73
Hideaway 72
Holbeck Ghyll
  Country House 70-1
Langdale Chase 72
Linthwaite House Hotel 71
Low Wood 70
The Old England 72
Storrs Hall 71
WINDSOR
The Castle 33
Clarence Hotel 33
Royal Adelaide 33
WINKLEIGH
The Old Parsonage 102

WINSFORD
Karslake House 196
WINTERBOURNE STOKE
Scotland Lodge Farm 235
WINTERINGHAM
Winteringham Fields 155
WISBECH
Elme Hall 39
WITHYPOOL
Royal Oak Inn 196
WOBURN
The Inn at Woburn 30
WOLF'S CASTLE
Wolfscastle Country Hotel 323
WOLVERHAMPTON
Novotel Wolverhampton 225
WOODBRIDGE
Best Western Ufford Park Hotel
  Golf & Leisure 204
Seckford Hall 204
WOODFALLS
Woodfalls 235
WOODHALL SPA
Claremont 156
Golf Hotel 156
Petwood 156
WOODSTOCK
Feathers 178
The Townhouse 178
WORCESTER
Fownes 238
WORFIELD
Old Vicarage 185

WORKINGTON
Hunday Manor
  Country House Hotel 73
WORSLEY
Novotel Manchester West 129
WORSTEAD
The Ollands 169
WORTHING
Beechwood Hall 216
Cavendish 215
Manor Guest House 216
WYBUNBURY
Lea Farm 42

Y

YARKHILL
Garford Farm 141
YELVERTON
Moorland Links 102
YEOVIL
Preston Hotel 196
YEOVILTON
Cary Fitzpaine Farm 196-7
YORK
Ascot House 253
The Grange 252
Greenside 253
Monkbar 252-3
Novotel York 253
The Priory Hotel 253
The Royal York 252
St Georges House Hotel 254

The Automobile Association wishes to thank the following photographers and agencies for their assistance in the preparation of this title:

Willow, Collaven Manor Hotel, Devon 18bl; Teddy and Harry, Ees Wyke Country House, Nr Sawrey 27t; McCoy, Knife and Clover Inn, Bedford 27b; Clover and Saffron, North Hill Farm, Church Street 26; Elma, The Old Rectory, Wiltshire 27b; Archie, Stonycroft Hotel, Leicester 18br; Aku, Thatch Close, Ross on Wye 15; K Trew 8, 19; Amber, Tyacks Hotel, Cornwall 27t; Lucy and Tara, Tymawr Hotel, Gwynedd 18t; Jessica, Wrangham House Hotel, North Yorkshire 17;

The remaining images are held in the Association's own library (AA WORLD TRAVEL LIBRARY) with contributions from the following:

Chris Coe 3; Ian Dawson 330; Colin and Andrew Molyneaux 303; Ken Paterson 261; Tony Souter 4; Wyn Voysey 29